B_1, thiamin, mg (1–1.4 mg)	B_2, riboflavin, mg (1.2–1.6 mg)	Niacin, mg (13–18 mg)	C, mg (60 mg)	A, IU (4000–5000 IU)	D, μg (10 μg)	E, mg (8–10 mg)	K, μg (70–140 μg)	Ca, mg (800–1200 mg)	Fe, mg (10–18 mg)
0.04	0.02	0.1	8	75	0	1.1		8	0.4
0.26	4.2	16.5	27	53,000	0.85	1.4	200	10	8
0.06	0.04	0.5	Trace	Trace	Trace	0.1		16	0.6
0	Trace	Trace	0	230‡	0.16	0.17		1	0
0.06	0.05	0.6	8	12,000	0	0.5		39	0.8
0.05	0.15	Trace	0	265	0.5	0.6		219	0.3
0.05	0.16	7.4	0	25	NA	0.2		8	1.4
0.01	0.03	0.2	0	8	NA	NA		11	1
0	0	0	0	0	0	0	0	3	0.18
0	0	0	0	0	0.03	12		0	0
0.04	0.34	0.2	Trace	342	NA	—		212	0.7
0.04	0.14	Trace	0	260	31	0.8		27	1.1
0.09	0.11	0.6	16	675	NA	NA		62	0.8
0.04	0.2	4	0	25	0	0.1		9	3
0.05	0.33	0.1	1	740	0.1	0.1		175	0.1
0.23	0.14	1.9	0	0	0	—		14	1.4
Trace	Trace	0	0	230‡	NA	4.6	0	1	0
0.08	0.42	0.1	2	350	2.5‡	0.3	2	288	0.1
0.12	0.05	0.5	75	240	0	0.4		49	0.2
0.21	0.03	0.8	112	200	0	NA		22	0.2
0.02	0.02	2.4	0	0	0	NA		11	0.3
0.63	0.18	3.8	0	0	0	0.7		8	2.2
0.1	0.04	1.7	20	Trace	NA	0.06	20	9	0.5
0.1	0.06	0.5	2	8	NA	NA		50	3
0.19	0.1	1.6	0	0	0	0.4		17	1.5
0.12	0.26	1	50	14,600	0	2.4	600	167	4
0	0	0	0	0	0	0	0	0	0
0.13	0.07	1.8	39	1,000	0	2		17	2
0.04	0.1	10.1	0	70	6	0.5		7	1.6
0.09	0.43	0.2	2	150	NA	NA		295	0.1

†Only selected values listed for vitamin K.
‡Vitamins added to fortify these foods.

Introduction to
GENERAL, ORGANIC, AND BIOLOGICAL CHEMISTRY

Introduction to

GENERAL, ORGANIC, AND BIOLOGICAL CHEMISTRY

Sally Solomon

Drexel University

McGRAW-HILL
BOOK COMPANY

New York • St. Louis • San Francisco • Auckland • Bogotá • Hamburg • Johannesburg • London • Madrid • Mexico • Milan • Montreal • New Delhi • Panama • Paris • São Paulo • Singapore • Sydney • Tokyo • Toronto

INTRODUCTION TO GENERAL, ORGANIC, AND BIOLOGICAL CHEMISTRY

1 2 3 4 5 6 7 8 9 0 VNHVNH 8 9 8 7

ISBN 0-07-059661-1

This book was set in Sabon by General Graphic Services, Inc.
The editors were Karen S. Misler, Randi B. Kashan, and J. W. Maisel;
the designer was Jo Jones;
the production supervisor was Joe Campanella.
Von Hoffmann Press, Inc., was printer and binder.

Cover by Paul Jenkins, "Phenomena Tibetan Light Bridge," © 1983. Courtesy Gimpel Weitzenhoffer Gallery.

Solomon, Sally.
Introduction to general, organic,
and biological chemistry.

Includes index.
1. Chemistry. I. Title. (DNLM I. Chemistry.
QD 31.2 S689i)
QD 31.2.S645 1987 540 86-20815
ISBN 0-07-059661-1

TO

My young children Jennifer and Gregory Shahade; my friend Evelyn Ringold, whose writing skills I tried to emulate; and my friend Frederick R. Longo, a colleague whose constant encouragement helped me finish this project

CONTENTS

CHAPTER 5 THE MOLE AND CHEMICAL CALCULATIONS 119

CHAPTER 6 NUCLEAR CHEMISTRY 147

CHAPTER 7 GASES AND THE ATMOSPHERE 185

CHAPTER 8 LIQUIDS AND SOLIDS 219

CHAPTER 9 SOLUTIONS 243

CHAPTER 10 CHEMICAL REACTIONS 279

PREFACE

Introduction to General, Organic, and Biological Chemistry will appeal particularly to anyone planning to enter one of the allied health fields such as nursing, medical technology, physical therapy, or nutrition. No previous chemistry course is needed to understand the material.

As suggested by the title of the book, the topics covered belong to three main areas:

General Chemistry: Chapters 1 through 11 discuss the fundamental principles of chemistry. The behavior of matter is understood in terms of atoms and molecules.
Organic chemisty: Chapters 12 through 20 cover the chemistry of carbon-containing compounds.
Biochemistry: Chapters 21 through 28 are devoted to the structures and functions of biomolecules.

Throughout this text the excitement and usefulness of chemistry are conveyed by making clear connections between chemical principles, the surrounding world and the human body. Practical applications are presented along with their underlying chemical principles. For instance, acid-base properties of blood are found in the acid-base chapter, fat-soluble vitamins are discussed in a chapter on lipids, and sickle-cell anemia is covered in the nucleic acids chapter, where the disease's molecular basis is best explained. The practical applications of chemistry are not isolated by setting them aside from the rest of the material, rather they are integrated into the text to emphasize the close correlation between chemical theory and its biological application.

An important feature of this text is the great number of learning aids intended to make chemistry more accessible and enjoyable.

Sample exercises: Every chapter contains sample exercises that are solved in detail.
Exercises: Accompanying each sample exercise is an unsolved exercise. The answers to all the unsolved in-chapter exercises are given at the end of the book along with the answers to the odd-numbered end-of-chapter questions.
Margin comments: The wide margins of this text include comments that summarize ideas or supply interesting information about the topic in the adjacent paragraph.
Highlighted margin comments: Marginal comments printed in color are set next to paragraphs that discuss medical and biological applications. These notes can be used to quickly locate material that is of special interest to students of the allied health sciences.
Keywords: New terms are shown in boldface. At the end of every chapter these are listed as keywords, all of which are defined in the glossary found at the end of the text.

Summary: Each chapter is accompanied by a concise summary.
Appendexes: For students who need extra help in mathematical skills, there are appendexes that cover exponentials, significant figures, and algebraic expressions. Like the chapters that precede them, each appendix has both sample exercises and unsolved exercises.
Color photographs: In the middle of the text you will find a section of color photographs, most of which were taken by Paul Winkfield, a photographer with incredible patience who welcomed the challenge of bringing chemical experiments to life on film. The color plates are not restricted to simply pretty pictures of colorful compounds but are designed to demonstrate chemical principles discussed throughout the text. Most of the experiments that we photographed can be performed in the classroom, laboratory, or lecture hall using instructions found in the *Instructor's Manual* for this text.

There are a great many people without whom this book could never have been produced. I wish to thank the following reviewers for their constructive comments and for the many positive remarks that helped provide me with the inspiration that I needed to finish this project.

R.G. Bass	Virginia Commonwealth University
Thomas Berke	Brookdale Community College
Dennis Berzansky	Westmoreland Community College
John Bumpus	Lake Superior State College
Michael Carlo	Angelo State University
David A. Darnall	Shelby State Community College
Stanley C. Grenda	University of Nevada, Las Vegas
Opey D. Jeanes	Mount Olive College
Joseph Landesberg	Adelphi University
Elva Mae Nicholson	Eastern Michigan State University
John Searle	College of San Mateo
Donald Titus	Temple University
David Tuleen	Vanderbilt University
Catherine Hickey-Williams	Western Connecticut State University
Vern Wolfmeyer	Jefferson College
Seymour Yolles	University of Delaware

The people at McGraw-Hill were patient and helpful. I was continually amazed by the ability of Randi Kashan, editor, to make the right suggestion about whatever it was we were trying to do, to spot my mistakes, and to keep me on schedule (almost). The efforts of Jack Maisel, editing supervisor, who coordinated the production process, seem to me just short of miraculous. Jo Jones, the designer, intuitively understood what inside and cover design would best lend itself to my writing and teaching style. Finally, the enthusiastic response from my students at Drexel University to my chemistry courses encouraged me to create my own textbook.

Sally Solomon

1. MEASUREMENT

1.1 INTRODUCTION

To the untrained eye it may seem that chemists are able to do magic in the laboratory, producing something where once there was nothing. From simple chemicals the modern chemist can synthesize a drug with the ideal structural features to treat a particular disease or create a remarkable plastic with just the right properties to replace a worn body part. Very rarely does a sudden, almost magical, discovery lead the way to this sort of success. In most cases careful, occasionally tedious, experimentation must come first.

Performing experiments in chemistry and interpreting their results is what chemists do. It is with the devices used to produce measured quantities, the units in which they are expressed, and the techniques used to do calculations upon them that the study of chemistry begins.

1.2 EXPERIMENTS

A formal term for the experimental approach to the solution of problems is the **scientific method**. The scientific method can be defined as an approach by which scientists combine an idea, or *hypothesis,* with experimental observations to arrive at *theories,* which not only explain the experiments but can also be used to predict the results of future experiments. The scientific method is applied by combining experimental observation with new ideas until it is possible to predict what will happen with no exceptions. Let us put the scientific method into practice in a clinical situation. Suppose you notice that a certain patient becomes violently ill after taking aspirin. Your hypothesis is that the person is allergic to aspirin. Future experiments seem to support this hypothesis. Every time aspirin is administered in any of its forms, the individual exhibits the same hypersensitivity. Then one day you notice the identical allergic reaction when the same patient drinks a glass of root beer. Because of this new experimental observation you must modify the original hypothesis to state that similar substances present in aspirin tablets and in root beer are causing the allergic reaction. You design a series of experiments to prove that the patient is allergic to aspirin, root beer, or anything containing a chemical known as a *salicylate*. All substances that you test are in agreement with the modified hypothesis and so it stands as theory. All theories survive until new observations no longer can support them. It is probable that 100 years from now, certain theories presented in this text will have to be modified or discarded to explain events that have yet to be observed.

Experiments fall into one of two broad categories. In **qualitative** experiments the presence or absence of some physical quantity is noted. When the physical quantity is measured to see just how much of it there is, the experiment becomes **quantitative**. For example, suppose the experiment is to test for glucose in urine. The observation that the urine sample contains glucose is qualitative; the observation that the urine sample contains 10 mg of glucose is quantitative.

1.3 UNITS AND THE SI SYSTEM

Measured quantities such as 10 mg include a numerical value (10) and a unit (mg). The unit describes the physical quantity that is being measured, which in this case is a unit of mass, the milligram (mg). A practical and useful set of units must be internationally accepted and must include units that are unambiguously defined. Three sets of units in use are the English system, the metric system, and the latter's close relative, the International System of Units, called the **SI system**. The English system, with units such as foot and pound, is rarely if ever mentioned in scientific studies, although it is still used in the United States for other purposes. The metric system, which includes the meter and kilogram units, has been widely adopted, as most countries in the world have "gone metric" or are "going metric." The International System of Units was created in 1969 to clear up any possible confusion about which units should be included in the modern metric system. The **SI system** includes the SI base units, the SI derived units, and the SI prefixes.

SI Units

There are seven **base units** in the SI system: the meter, kilogram, kelvin, second, mole, ampere, and candela. Their names and abbreviations appear in Table 1.1.

TABLE 1.1 **SI BASE UNITS**

Physical quantity	Name of base unit	Abbreviation
Length	meter	m
Mass	kilogram	kg
Time	second	s
Amount of substance	mole	mol
Temperature	kelvin	K
Electric current	ampere	A
Luminous intensity	candela	cd

TABLE 1.2 SI PREFIXES

Prefix	Abbreviation	Meaning*
pico	p	10^{-12} ($1/10^{12}$ or one-trillionth)
nano	n	10^{-9} ($1/10^{9}$ or one-billionth)
micro	μ	10^{-6} ($1/10^{6}$ or one-millionth)
milli	m	10^{-3} ($1/10^{3}$ or one-thousandth)
centi	c	10^{-2} ($1/10^{2}$ or one-hundredth)
deci	d	10^{-1} (1/10 or one-tenth)
kilo	k	10^{3} (1000 or one thousand times)
mega	M	10^{6} (1,000,000 or one million times)

*See Appendix A for coverage of scientific notation.

Two of them, the ampere and the candela, will not be discussed further, since they will not be encountered again in this text. By some combination of the base units, it is possible to express the unit for any other measured quantity.

The slash sign (/) means "per" or "divided by."

The **SI derived units** are those which are formed by multiplication or division of the SI base units. One example of a derived unit is the unit for speed, which is meters divided by seconds or meters per second, m/s. We will introduce more derived units as they appear in the topics to come.

SI Prefixes

Many SI units are formed from a prefix and a base unit.

The SI prefixes are used to form multiples or fractions of SI units. Many quantities are conveniently expressed in terms of a prefix plus a base unit. For example, the quantity 1000 m may also be written as 1 kilometer (1 km), since the prefix kilo means 1000. The prefixes most often added to base units are listed in Table 1.2. That one of the base units, the kilogram, already has a prefix is a peculiar feature of the SI system, which is explained in the discussion about mass in Section 1.5. Multiples and fractions of the kilogram are formed by attaching an SI prefix not to kilogram (kg) but to gram (g).

SAMPLE EXERCISE 1.1

Using Tables 1.1 and 1.2 express the following quantities in terms of a prefix plus a base unit:

(**a**) 0.01 meter

(**b**) One-millionth of a second

Solution:

(**a**) 0.01 = 1/100

(**b**) One-millionth = $1/10^{6} = 10^{-6}$

Prefix: centi (c)
Base unit: meter (m)
Complete unit: centimeter (cm)

Prefix: micro (μ)
Base unit: second (s)
Complete unit: microsecond (μs)

EXERCISE 1.1

The mean cell hemoglobin (MCH) refers to the average mass of hemoglobin per red blood cell. The normal MCH is 27 to 31 pg. Would the value 3×10^{-11} g fall within this range?

Definitions of SI Units

To measure a physical quantity we must compare it with some other well-defined physical quantity. For example, suppose we wished to measure the length of a room. One way would be to walk across the room, carefully placing one foot in front of the other. The length of the room could then be measured in terms of some number of "person-feet." But whose feet? Person-feet are very poorly defined and could be acceptable only in the crudest measurements. What makes the SI base units excellent references for measuring quantities is that they are clearly and unambiguously defined. In the next two sections we will take a careful look at the definitions for two of the SI *standard* units, the meter and the kilogram. Standard units such as these must be unchanging and reproducible.

1.4 LENGTH

The meter is the base unit of length.

Until the year 1960 the **meter** was defined as the distance between two scratch marks engraved on a metal bar made of the metals platinum and iridium, which are especially resistant to corrosion. This bar is still carefully housed in Sèvres, France at the International Bureau of Weights and Measures. Meter sticks were made by comparison with this standard or with copies of it.

Wavelengths of light are discussed in section 2.11.

A better method for defining the meter divides the meter distance into a number of very small divisions equal to the wavelength of the red light which comes from glowing krypton gas, which glows in the same way that the neon in neon lights does. The number of red wavelengths which spans the distance between the scratches on the standard meter bar is 1,650,763.73, a number which can be accurately reproduced anywhere in the world. This new definition did not change the length of the meter but considerably improved the accuracy with which it could be measured. Another advantage is that objects, even those made of relatively unreactive metals, can change with time, but a number of wavelengths always stays the same.

Some important SI length units and the distances to which they correspond can be illustrated by viewing an ordinary street scene in ever-increasing detail. This is shown in Figure 1.1. Useful relationships involving both SI and non-SI length units are given in Table 1.3.

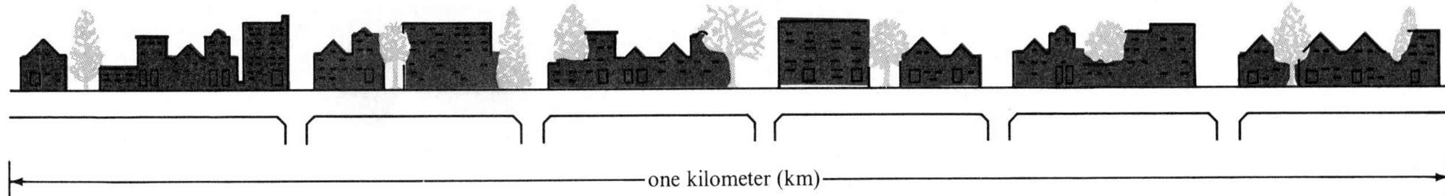

(*a*) One **kilometer (km)** corresponds to about six city blocks.

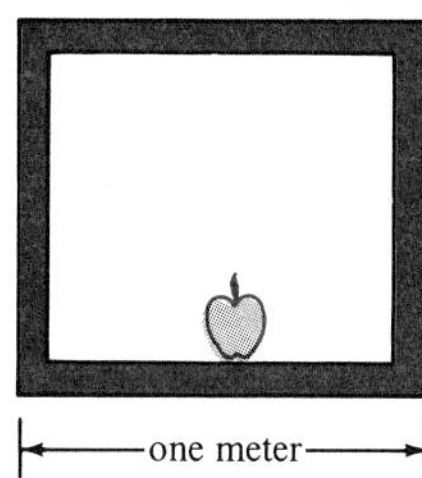

(*b*) One window of one house is about one **meter (m)** wide.

(*c*) On the windowsill is an apple which is about 1 **decimeter (dm)** wide.

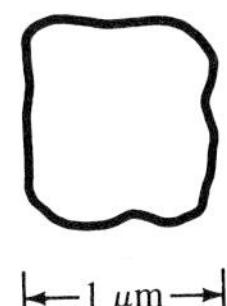

(*d*) Taking a microscopic look into the apple reveals a single plant cell which is about one **micrometer** (**μm**) on a side.

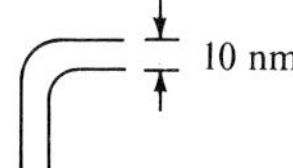

(*e*) Surrounding the plant cell is a cell wall about 10 **nanometers (nm)** thick.

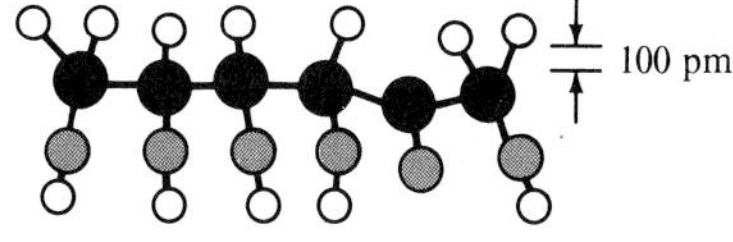

(*f*) Inside the cell is a sugar molecule, fructose, which includes 24 atoms which are roughly 100 **picometers** (pm) thick.

FIGURE 1.1
Length units.

TABLE 1.3 USEFUL RELATIONSHIPS AMONG LENGTH UNITS

Unit	Equivalent
SI	
1 kilometer (km)	10^3 m
1 decimeter (dm)	10^{-1} m
1 centimeter (cm)	10^{-2} m
1 millimeter (mm)	10^{-3} m
1 micrometer (μm)	10^{-6} m
1 nanometer (nm)	10^{-9} m
1 picometer (pm)	10^{-12} m
1 meter (m)	10^3 km
	10 dm
	10^2 cm
	10^3 mm
	10^6 μm
	10^9 nm
	10^{12} pm
Non-SI	
1 inch (in)	2.54 cm
1 angstrom (Å)	10^{-10} m
1 mile (mi)	1.61 km
1 yard (yd)	0.914 m

1.5 MASS

The kilogram is the base unit of mass.

The only unit which is still defined by a physical object is the **kilogram**, which is the mass of a platinum-iridium object stored at the International Bureau of Standards. Originally the standard chosen was the gram, but a platinum-iridium object used to represent a gram was so small (about half the size of a dime) that it could not be accurately copied. Mass measurements are made by comparison with the standard kilogram and its copies.

Mass may be defined as a measure of the *inertia* of an object, which is the tendency of the object to remain at constant speed. The greater the inertia, the greater the mass. For example, the inertia of two objects, a real car and a toy car, can be contrasted by comparing the difficulty with which each one could be put into motion starting from a standstill. Pushing the real car to get it moving would require considerably more effort than getting the toy car into motion. That means that the real car has a greater inertia and thus a greater mass than the toy car.

The weight of a body is the gravitational force exerted on it. The force of gravity differs from place to place. On the moon the force of gravity is one-sixth of that on earth, so an object on the moon weighs just one-sixth of what that object weighs on earth. But the mass of the object does not change, no matter what the force of gravity. The weight of an object is related to its mass by the equation below in which g is the acceleration of gravity:

$$\text{Weight} = \text{mass} \times g$$

We tend to use the terms *weight* and *mass* as though they mean the same thing.

The mass of an object is measured by comparing it with a standard mass on a balance, where the value of g is constant. Thus, since the two objects are "weighed" in the same place, we need not consider the gravity factor. Some scientists tend to use the terms *weight* and *mass* interchangeably, knowing that the two quantities do not mean the same thing. A person who "weighs" 60 kg (132 lb) has a mass which is the same as that of sixty 1-kg standard masses. The actual weight corresponding to the mass of 60 kg has a different unit (called the *newton*) and a different numerical value (about 590 on earth) and depends on the gravitational force at the place of measurement.

The simplest type of balance used for weighing is constructed by attaching two pans to a balance beam, which is supported on a vertical column. The object to be weighed is placed on one pan and an object or objects of known mass on the other pan. The mass of the object weighed is equal to that of the standard objects needed to balance the beam (see Figure 1.2). Weighings can be done much more rapidly by using single-pan balances, in which there is a pan on one end

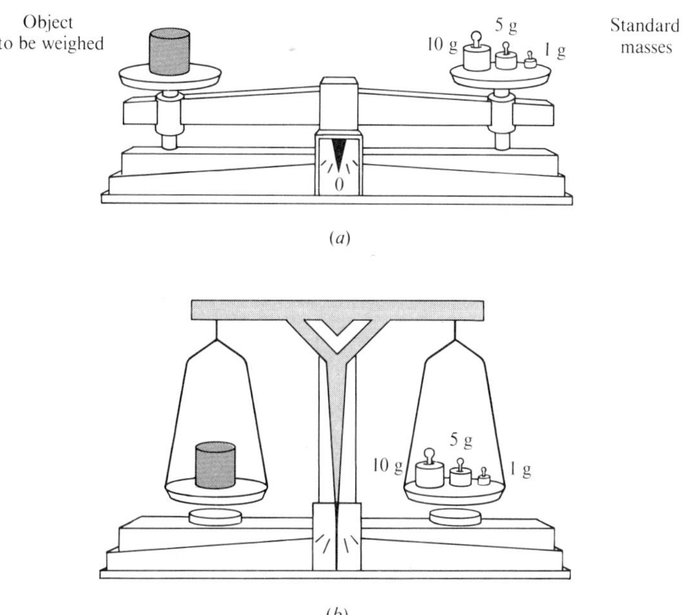

FIGURE 1.2
Double-pan balances. When the pointer reads zero, the masses are balanced. In both *a* and *b*, the weighed object has a mass of 16.0 g.

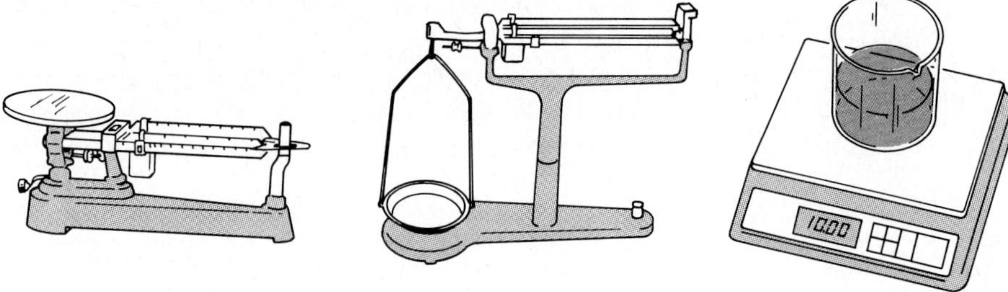

FIGURE 1.3
Single-pan balances.

of the beam and a variable standard mass on the other. To weigh an object the standard mass in increased or decreased by turning dials or by moving standard masses attached to the beam until balance is achieved (see Figure 1.3). With modern electronic single-pan balances accurate weighings can be made in less than 1 min.

Some SI mass units, along with the quantities of table salt which approximate their amounts, are shown in Figure 1.4. Non-SI units such as the pound or the ounce hardly ever are used in scientific measurements. Table 1.4 lists some useful relationships among SI and non-SI mass units.

One kilogram (1 kg) of salt is contained in about 1 1/3 boxes of salt.

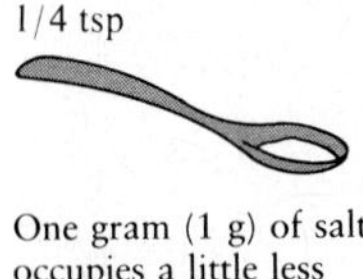

One gram (1 g) of salt occupies a little less than 1/8 of a teaspoon.

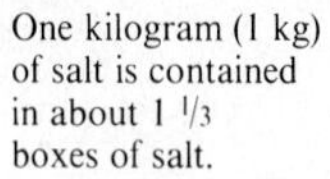

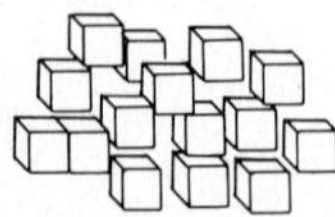

One milligram (1 mg) of salt includes about 15 "grains" of salt.

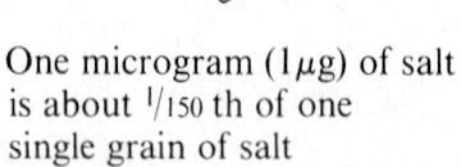

One microgram (1 μg) of salt is about 1/150 th of one single grain of salt

FIGURE 1.4
Mass units.

TABLE 1.4 USEFUL RELATIONSHIPS AMONG MASS UNITS

Unit	Equivalent
	SI
1 kilogram (kg)	10^{3} g
1 decigram (dg)	10^{-1} g
1 centigram (cg)	10^{-2} g
1 milligram (mg)	10^{-3} g
1 microgram (μg)	10^{-6} g
1 nanogram (ng)	10^{-9} g
1 picogram (pg)	10^{-12} g
1 gram (g)	10^{-3} kg
	10 dg
	10^{2} cg
	10^{3} mg
	10^{6} μg
	10^{9} ng
	10^{12} pg
	Non-SI
1 pound (lb)	454 g (2.20 lb = 1000 g = 1 kg)
1 ounce (oz)	28.3 g
1 grain*	0.0648 g
	64.8 mg

*The unit grain should be spelled out, not abbreviated. However, in pharmacological references the abbreviation gr is often used for grain.

1.6 TEMPERATURE

High temperatures bring to mind hot summer afternoons and pots of boiling water, while low temperatures suggest frosty winter nights and ice cubes. More quantitative temperature measurements are done with a variety of different types of thermometers, which take advantage of the fact that many properties of substances change with temperature in a known way. For instance, the standard thermometer at the International Bureau of Weights and Measures depends upon the expansion of hydrogen gas with increasing temperature. Ordinary laboratory and fever thermometers made of glass rely upon the expansion of liquid mercury. Thermoelectric fever thermometers used in many hospitals respond to changing temperatures because the flow of electricity depends upon temperature. A quick response and the absence of a glass tube make the electronic fever thermometers especially convenient and safe to use.

The symbol K for kelvins has no degree sign.

The SI units for degrees of temperature are kelvins, given the symbol K. On this scale water freezes at 273.15 K and boils at 373.15 K (see Figure 1.5). There are 100 equal degrees between the boiling and freezing points of water:

$$373.15 \text{ K} - 273.15 \text{ K} = 100 \text{ K}$$

The lowest temperature possible is zero kelvin (0 K), and this point is called **absolute zero.** It is for this reason that the kelvin scale is often referred to as the *absolute temperature scale.*

Because the kelvin scale defines absolute zero as zero kelvin, it is considered to be the most fundamental temperature scale. However, the **Celsius scale** (formerly called the centigrade scale) is still more commonly used in chemistry, biology, and medicine. In the Celsius scale water freezes at zero degrees Celsius (0°C) and boils at 100°C (see Figure 1.5). Thus there are 100 equal degrees between the freezing and boiling points of water, as there are in the kelvin scale:

$$373.15 \text{ K} - 273.15 \text{ K} = 100 \text{ K} \qquad \text{and} \qquad 100°\text{C} - 0°\text{C} = 100°\text{C}$$

Although the size of each kelvin is equal to that of each Celsius degree, the numbers assigned to various temperatures differ by 273.15, so that 273.15 K equals 0°C, 373.15 K equals 100°C, and so on. From this we can write the relationship between a kelvin temperature and the corresponding Celsius temperature:

$$\text{K} = °\text{C} + 273.15$$

The number 273.15 is usually rounded off to 273, so that

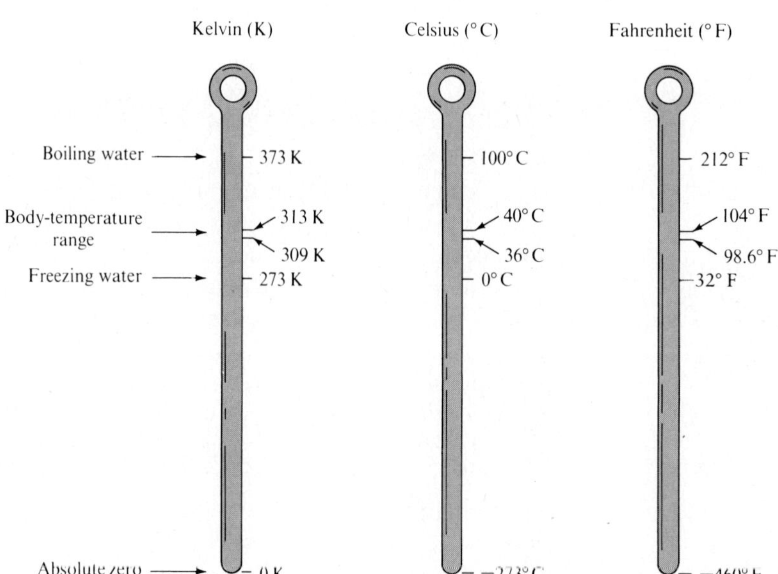

FIGURE 1.5
Comparison of temperature scales.

$$K = °C + 273$$

The Fahrenheit scale, the one with which many of us are familiar, is hardly ever used for scientific measurements. In the Fahrenheit scale water freezes at 32 degrees (32°F) and boils at 212°F. There are 180 equal degrees between these two temperatures:

$$212°F - 32°F = 180°F$$

This means that each Fahrenheit degree is only 100/180 or 5/9 times as large as a kelvin or a Celsius degree. Occasionally it may be necessary to convert from °F to °C or from °C to °F by using one of the relationships

$$°C = 5/9(°F - 32) \qquad °F = 9/5°C + 32$$

Normal body temperature is about 37°C.

Figure 1.5 compares some temperatures, including those of absolute zero, freezing water, normal body temperature, and boiling water in the kelvin, Celsius, and Fahrenheit scales.

1.7 VOLUME

Volume units are derived units formed by multiplying length units by length units by length units, that is, by cubing length units:

$$\text{Volume unit} = (\text{length unit})^3$$

For example, the volume of a rectangular solid is measured by multiplying the lengths of its three sides.

$$\text{Volume} = \text{length} \times \text{width} \times \text{height}$$

When the solid is a cube, in which all sides are equal, the volume is found by cubing any one side. For instance, one commonly used SI volume unit is the cubic centimeter (cm^3), which is the volume of a cube that measures 1 centimeter (1 cm) on each side (Figure 1.6*a*). The cubic centimeter is sometimes called the *cc,* from *c*ubic *c*entimeter. The request for 10 cc's of a dextrose injection solution refers to a volume that measures 10 cm^3. Another frequently used SI volume is the cubic decimeter (dm^3), which is also drawn to scale in Figure 1.6*b*.

Both these important volume units, the cubic centimeter and the cubic decimeter, have special commonly used names. The milliliter (ml) is exactly equal to the cubic centimeter and the liter (L) to the cubic decimeter.

$$1\ cm^3 = 1\ ml$$

$$1\ dm^3 = 1\ L = 1000\ ml = 1000\ cm^3$$

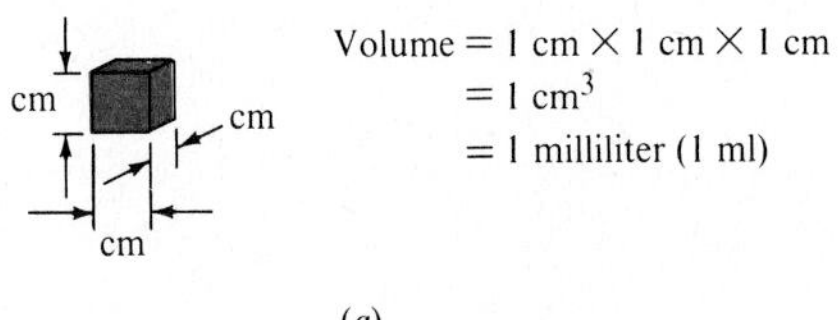

(*a*)

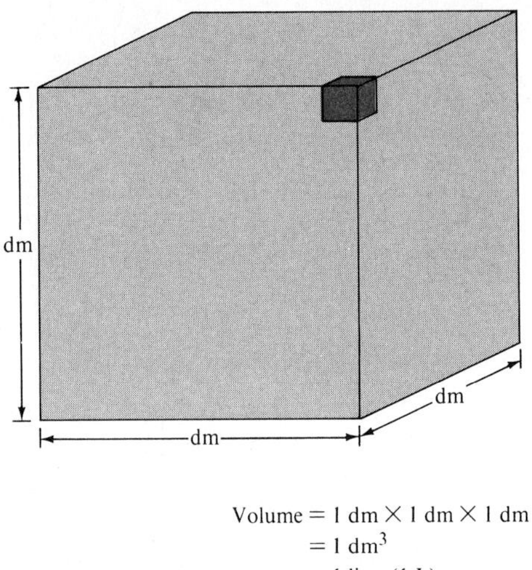

Volume = 1 dm × 1 dm × 1 dm
= 1 dm^3
= 1 liter (1 L)

(*b*)

FIGURE 1.6
Cubic centimeter and cubic decimeter.

The use of the capital L for liter helps to distinguish the abbreviation from the numeral 1 and will be used throughout the test. The non-SI unit *quart* is never used in scientific measurements. If conversion from quarts to liters happens to be necessary,

$$1 \text{ U.S. liquid quart} = 0.9463 \text{ L}$$

There are a number of containers in which liquid volumes can be determined with varying degrees of accuracy. Among them are the beaker, graduated cylinder, buret, pipet, volumetric flask, and syringe, all of which are pictured in Figure 1.7.

As you can see from Figure 1.6, the volume of a solid with a regular geometric shape is easily measured by using known dimensions. For example, the volume of a cube which is 2 cm on a side is 8 cm^3 (2 cm × 2 cm × 2 cm), or 8 ml. One way to measure the volume of an object is to place it in water (this method works only for objects which do not float or dissolve in water) and measure the amount of water displaced by the solid. This measured volume is equal to the volume of the immersed object, as shown in Figure 1.8.

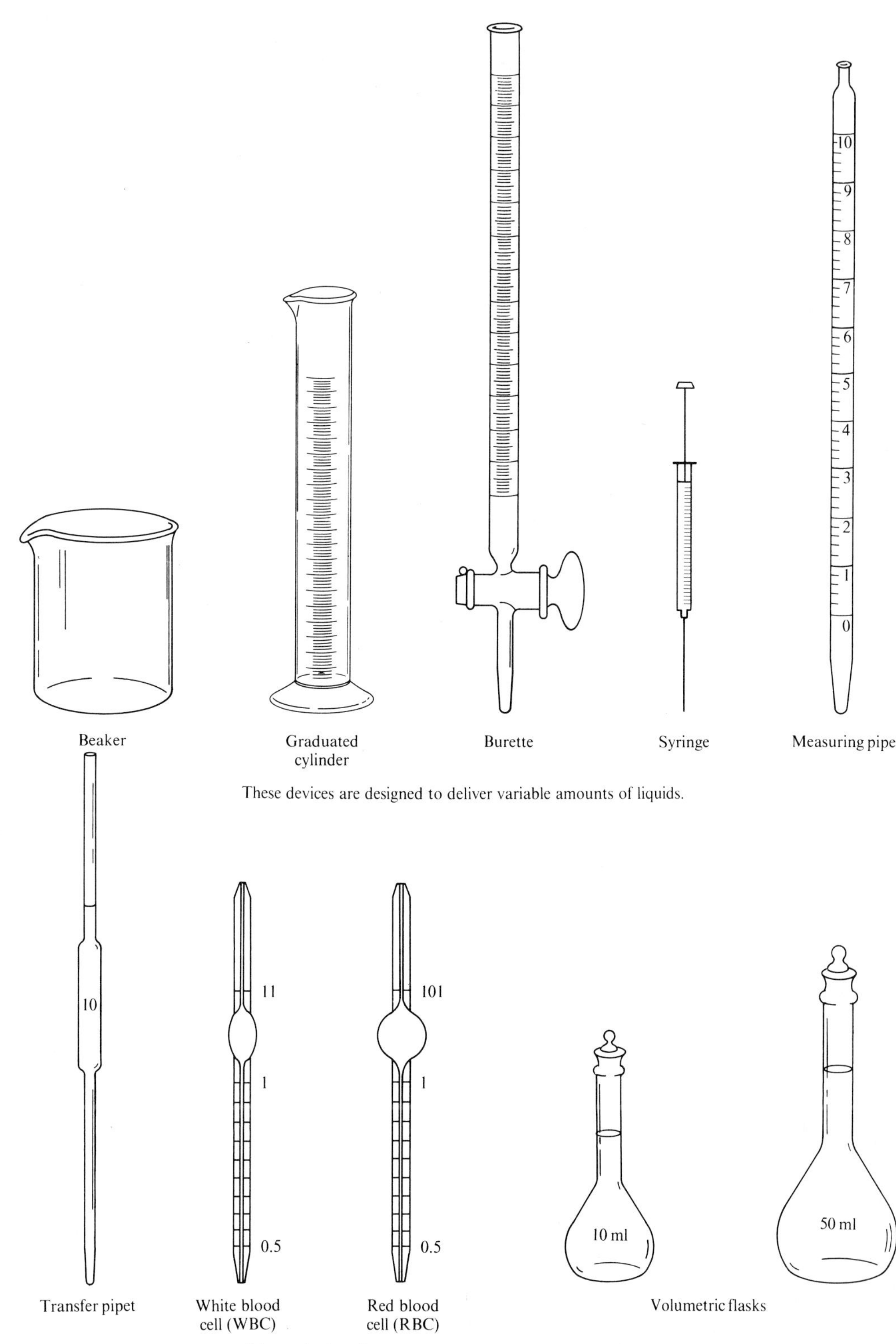

10
9
8
7
6
5
4
3
2
1
0
Beaker
Graduated cylinder
Burette
Syringe
Measuring pipet
These devices are designed to deliver variable amounts of liquids.
10
11
1
0.5
101
1
0.5
10 ml
50 ml
Transfer pipet
White blood cell (WBC)
Red blood cell (RBC)
Blood-dilution pipets
Volumetric flasks
This glassware is designed to deliver specific volumes. The graduations on the blood-dilution pipets are for frequently used dilutions.

FIGURE 1.7
Containers used to measure volume.

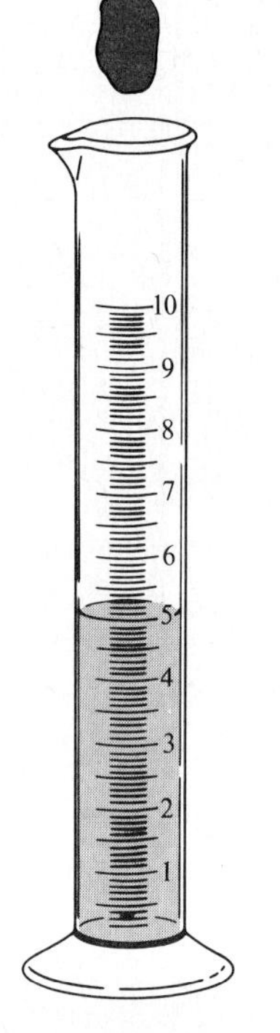

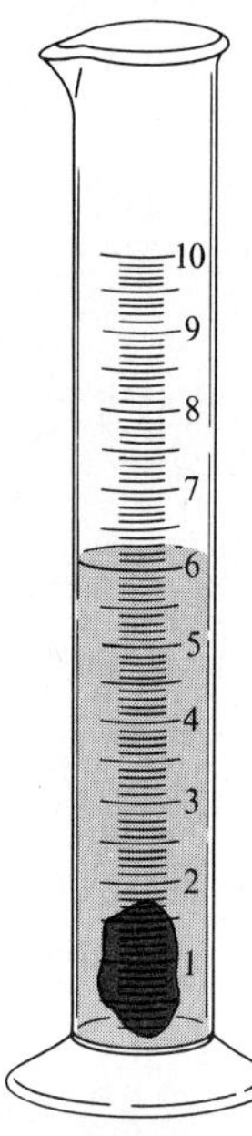

FIGURE 1.8
Determination of the volume of a solid by water displacement. Since the volume of water displaced by the irregularly shaped object is 1 cm^3, the volume of the object must also be 1 cm^3.

1.8 DENSITY

Density is also a derived unit, which is created by dividing mass by volume:

$$\text{Density} = \frac{\text{mass}}{\text{volume}}$$

Density, unlike mass or volume, does not vary with the amount of material. The density of a 1-g piece of pure gold is the same as that of a 1-kg bar of pure gold. The density of 1 ml of water is the same as that of 1 L of water. For this reason, measuring the density of a substance can help to identify it.

One way to measure the density of a material is to weigh a known volume of it. For example, a 1-cm^3 volume of water weighs 1 g, which means that the density of water is 1 g/cm^3 or 1 g/ml. A 1-cm^3 sample of gold weighs 19.3 g, so the density of metallic gold is 19.3 g/cm^3 (19.3 g/ml). The densities of some common substances are given in Table 1.5. Note that most of the densities listed, except for those of the metals, are not very far from 1 g/ml, the density of water.

Gas densities are considerably lower than those of liquids or solids. A 1-cm^3 sample of air weighs just 0.00121 g, making its density 0.00121 g/cm^3. A more convenient numerical value is obtained if we measure the densities of gases in grams per decimeter instead of grams per centimeter. Since 1 dm^3 of air weighs 1.21 g, that makes the density of air 1.21 g/dm^3, or 1.21 g/L. Most of the gas densities listed in Table 1.5 are fairly close to 1 g/L. Two of them with unusually low densities, hydrogen (0.09 g/L) and helium (0.16 g/L), are used to keep balloons

TABLE 1.5 **DENSITIES OF SELECTED LIQUIDS, SOLIDS, AND GASES**

Substance	Density,* 20°C and sea level
Liquids	
Ethyl ether	0.71
Acetone	0.79
Isopropyl alcohol (rubbing alcohol)	0.79
Corn oil	0.92
Water	1.00
Vinegar	1.01
Glucose solution 5%	1.02
Glycerol	1.26
Chloroform	1.49
Mercury	13.6
Solids	
Cork	0.3
Mahogany	0.7–0.8
Cholesterol	1.07
Urea	1.32
Starch	1.53
Sucrose	1.59
Vitamin C	1.65
Salt	2.17
Aluminum	2.70
Diamond	3.0–3.5
Nickel	8.90
Copper	8.96
Silver	10.5
Lead	11.4
Gold	19.3
Plutonium	19.8
Platinum	21.5
Gases	
Hydrogen	0.09
Helium	0.16
Nitrogen	1.16
Air	1.21
Oxygen	1.3
Nitrous oxide	1.8
Carbon dioxide	1.8
Sulfur dioxide	2.9
Xenon	5.5

*Density units for liquids and solids are grams per cubic centimeter or grams per milliliter and those for gases are grams per cubic decimeter or grams per liter.

and dirigibles afloat in air because, in general, a lower-density substance will float in a higher-density substance.

Tables of densities must specify the temperatures at which densities are measured, since substances expand or contract with changing temperatures. As the volumes change, so do the densities. Gas volumes and thus gas densities are especially sensitive to temperature changes. Notice that the data listed in Table 1.5 was obtained at 20°C.

SAMPLE EXERCISE 1.2

Calculate the density of a cube of ice which is 4 cm on a side and has a mass of 58.9 g.

Solution:

$$\text{Density} = \frac{\text{mass}}{\text{volume}}$$

$$\text{Mass} = 58.9 \text{ g}$$

$$\text{Volume} = 4 \text{ cm} \times 4 \text{ cm} \times 4 \text{ cm} = 64 \text{ cm}^3$$

$$\text{Density} = \frac{58.9 \text{ g}}{64 \text{ cm}^3}$$

$$= 0.92 \text{ g/cm}^3 \text{ (or } 0.92 \text{ g/ml)}$$

The fact that ice has a density lower than that of water agrees with the everyday observation that ice floats on water. Whenever possible, it is a good idea to think about whether or not an answer to a problem makes practical sense.

EXERCISE 1.2

A metal statuette which you find in your attic looks like silver. When placed in water, it sinks and displaces 10 cm^3 of water and weighs 80 g. Is it silver?

Measuring density also has another practical use. Sometimes the weight of a substance is more easily determined by measuring its volume and using its known density. This is especially true for liquids, whose volumes are easily measured since they can be poured from one of the containers pictured in Figure 1.8. For instance, suppose a deodorant solution for a hospital room is to be prepared by using 79 g of isopropyl alcohol as one ingredient. Each milliliter of the alcohol weighs 0.79 g, according to its density listed in Table 1.5. That means that 100 ml of isopropyl alcohol contains 79 g. Instead of weighing out the 79 g, 100 ml of the isopropyl alcohol can be poured from a graduated cylinder.

The specific gravity of a substance compares its density with the density of water at some specified temperature. A useful working definition for the **specific gravity** of a substance is the density of the substance divided by the density of

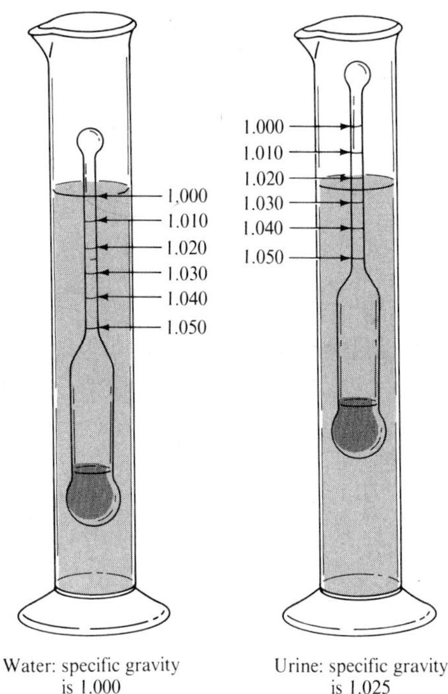

FIGURE 1.9
Urinometer. A special hydrometer used to measure specific gravity of urine samples. The colored area represents the substance used to weight the glass tube.

water in the same units. For example, the density of isopropyl alcohol is 0.79 g/ml. To find its specific gravity:

$$\text{Specific gravity} = \frac{0.79\text{ g/ml}}{1\text{ g/ml}} = 0.79$$

Since the unit grams per milliliter appears both in the numerator and in the denominator of the specific-gravity expression, it cancels out, leaving no unit at all. Thus specific gravity is a dimensionless (unitless) quantity. As long as densities are expressed in grams per milliliter, the numerical value of the specific gravity and density of a substance will be identical, since the density of water is 1 g/ml.

Urine specific-gravity tests reflect the ability of the kidneys to concentrate or dilute urine.

In clinical work the term *specific gravity* is often used instead of density. The hydrometer, a weighted glass tube which floats in liquids, is used to measure the specific gravity of liquids. The reading on the graduated stem of the hydrometer where the liquid surface meets the tube is the specific gravity. A special type of hydrometer called a *urinometer* is pictured in Figure 1.9. The urinometer is used to measure the specific gravity of urine samples, which should fall between 1.015 and 1.025 with normal fluid intake.

1.9 SIGNIFICANT FIGURES

Measured quantities are never perfect. Every physical measurement is accompanied by uncertainty, due primarily to the sensitivity of the measuring device. The **uncertainty** of a particular device is the smallest division which can be registered on it. For example, suppose a single-pan analytical balance such as the electronic one pictured in Figure 1.3 is sensitive to 0.01 g. This means that the smallest division on the most sensitive of its scales registers 0.01 g. It would be ridiculous to try to weigh a 1-mg sample on such a balance, because 1 mg is equal to 0.001 g, which is less than the uncertainty of the balance. The balance is not sensitive enough to weigh this small quantity accurately. The pointer used to indicate when balance is achieved would not even deflect!

However, for a 1-g sample the balance shown in Figure 1.3 would be acceptable, because the uncertainty would be just 0.01 g out of 1.00 g. The sample could weigh as much as 1.01 g or as little as 0.99 g. The second zero digit in the $1.0\underline{0}$ g measurement is called the *uncertain* digit and is sometimes indicated by underlining. The uncertain digit and the ones which come before it are all said to be **significant figures**, which means that the quantity 1.00 g weighed on a balance with an uncertainty of 0.01 g has three significant figures. A fourth added digit would have no significance, since when this balance is used, there is no way to estimate what it is. More on how to count significant figures in measured quantities is given in Appendix B.

Significant figures are the meaningful digits in a measured quantity.

It is very important to design experiments in which the number of significant figures in the measured result is enough to allow some conclusion to be drawn. For example, suppose a laboratory test used to find the amount of glucose in a 100-ml blood sample produces a result to the nearest 0.1 g. The normal range is 0.08 to 0.10 g glucose per 100 ml blood. A measurement of 0.1 g glucose per 100 ml sample *cannot* ensure a normal level. The actual amount may be as much as 0.13 or 0.14 g or as little as 0.06 or 0.07 g, all of which are outside the normal range. A measurement which provides just one significant figure is simply not good enough to perform this test.

1.10 UNIT CONVERSIONS

Even though the SI system is preferred, the English system is encountered often enough that converting from one system of units to another is frequently necessary. There is a standard method for doing this which makes use of unit conversion factors, such as the ones listed in Tables 1.3 and 1.4. A **conversion factor** is an equation that relates two different units for a particular physical quantity. For instance, the conversion factor which relates the centimeter and the inch is

$$1 \text{ in} = 2.54 \text{ cm}$$

One method by which conversion factors can be used to change from one unit to another can be summarized in several steps:

1. Decide what units are given and what units are desired.
2. Choose the necessary conversion factor(s).
3. Rewrite the conversion factor as a fraction. Note that this fraction will be equal to unity, since the conversion factor relates two equivalent quantities.
4. Multiply given quantity by the conversion factor(s) to arrive at the desired unit.

To see how this conversion system is applied, let us tackle a simple problem. Suppose we wish to find out how much a 150-lb person weighs in kilograms.

1. Decide what units are given and what units are desired. We are given pounds and wish to convert to kilograms.

$$150 \text{ lb} = ? \text{ kg}$$

2. Choose the necessary conversion factor.

$$1 \text{ kg} = 2.20 \text{ lb (see Table 1.4)}$$

3. Rewrite the conversion factor to make it equal to unity. To do this divide both sides of the conversion factor, first by 1 kg:

$$\frac{1 \text{ kg}}{1 \text{ kg}} = \frac{2.20 \text{ lb}}{1 \text{ kg}} \quad \text{to give} \quad 1 = \frac{2.20 \text{ lb}}{1 \text{ kg}}$$

Then divide both sides of the conversion factor by 2.20 lb:

$$\frac{1 \text{ kg}}{2.20 \text{ lb}} = \frac{2.20 \text{ lb}}{2.20 \text{ lb}} \quad \text{to give} \quad \frac{1 \text{ kg}}{2.20 \text{ lb}} = 1$$

These manipulations, which more often than not are done mentally, produce two new forms of the conversion factor 1 kg = 2.20 lb:

$$1 = \frac{2.20 \text{ lb}}{1 \text{ kg}} \quad \text{and} \quad 1 = \frac{1 \text{ kg}}{2.20 \text{ lb}}$$

Since multiplying something by unity does not change its value, conversion factors in this form can be used as multipliers.

4. Multiply the given quantity (150 lb) by a conversion factor to arrive at the desired unit (kg). Choose the form of the conversion factor above which forces the unit lb to cancel, leaving kg. The one which works is $1 = \dfrac{1 \text{ kg}}{2.20 \text{ lb}}$:

$$150 \cancel{\text{lb}} \times \frac{1 \text{ kg}}{2.20 \cancel{\text{lb}}} = 68.2 \text{ kg}$$

Arithmetic must be performed on both numbers *and* units.

Whatever arithmetic is performed on the numerical part of a quantity must also be performed on the units. In this example, the unit lb cancels.

It is always important to make sure that the calculated unit makes sense. For instance, if the wrong conversion factor is chosen in the problem above, the unit lb does not cancel. Furthermore, the calculated unit is not sensible:

$$150 \text{ lb} \times \frac{2.20 \text{ lb}}{1 \text{ kg}} = 330 \frac{\text{lb}^2}{\text{kg}} \qquad ?????$$

The unit lb^2/kg is a nonsense unit, which should give warning to the problem solver that the numerical part of the problem is also nonsense!

SAMPLE EXERCISE 1.3

A headache tablet contains 5.75 grains of aspirin. How many grams of aspirin is this?

Solution:

1. 5.75 grain = ? g
2. 1 grain = 0.0648 g (see Table 1.4)
3. $\dfrac{1 \text{ grain}}{0.0648 \text{ g}} = 1 \quad \text{or} \quad \dfrac{0.0648 \text{ g}}{1 \text{ grain}} = 1$
4. $5.75 \cancel{\text{grain}} \times \dfrac{0.0648 \text{ g}}{1 \cancel{\text{grain}}} = 0.373 \text{ g}$

The tablet contains 0.373 *grams* of aspirin or 5.75 *grains* of aspirin. In pharmacological references the abbreviation *gr* means grain (*not* gram).

EXERCISE 1.3

The adult male kidney weighs about 160 g. How many pounds does it weigh?

Sometimes more than one conversion factor must be used to solve a problem. For example, suppose we wish to know the height of a 5.00-ft person in centimeters.

1. Decide what units are given and what units are desired.

$$5.00 \text{ ft} = ? \text{ cm}$$

2. Choose necessary conversion factors. This time we will need a "strategy" to get from the given quantity to the desired quantity, because we have no single conversion factor that converts feet to centimeters. However, we do have one that converts feet to inches and another that converts inches to centimeters. Our strategy is

$$5.00 \text{ ft} \rightarrow ? \text{ in} \rightarrow ? \text{ cm}$$

The conversion factors are

$$1 \text{ ft} = 12 \text{ in} \qquad \text{and} \qquad 1 \text{ in} = 2.54 \text{ cm}$$

3. Rewrite the conversion factors to make them equal to unity:

$$\frac{12 \text{ in}}{1 \text{ ft}} = 1 \quad \text{or} \quad \frac{1 \text{ ft}}{12 \text{ in}} = 1$$

and

$$\frac{2.54 \text{ cm}}{1 \text{ in}} = 1 \quad \text{or} \quad \frac{1 \text{ in}}{2.54 \text{ cm}} = 1$$

4. Multiply the given quantity (5.00 ft) by conversion factors to arrive at the desired unit (cm). First pick out the one that cancels the unit feet (ft) and then continue with the factor that cancels the unit inches (in):

$$5.00 \not{\text{ft}} \times \frac{12 \not{\text{in}}}{1 \not{\text{ft}}} \times \frac{2.54 \text{ cm}}{1 \not{\text{in}}} = 152 \text{ cm}$$

SAMPLE EXERCISE 1.4

The recommended daily allowance (RDA) of vitamin C for an adult is 0.00212 oz (2.12×10^{-3} oz). What is the RDA for vitamin C in milligrams? Retain just two significant figures in your answer.

Solution:

1. 2.12×10^{-3} oz = ? mg
2. Strategy: 2.12×10^{-3} oz → ? g → ? mg

$$1 \text{ oz} = 28.3 \text{ g} \quad \text{and} \quad 1 \text{ g} = 10^3 \text{ mg}$$

3. $\dfrac{1 \text{ oz}}{28.3 \text{ g}} = 1 \quad \text{or} \quad \dfrac{28.3 \text{ g}}{1 \text{ oz}} = 1 \quad \text{and} \quad \dfrac{1 \text{ g}}{10^3 \text{ mg}} = 1 \quad \text{or} \quad \dfrac{10^3 \text{ mg}}{1 \text{ g}} = 1$

4. $2.12 \times 10^{-3} \not{\text{oz}} \times \dfrac{28.3 \not{\text{g}}}{1 \not{\text{oz}}} \times \dfrac{10^3 \text{ mg}}{1 \not{\text{g}}} = 60.0 \text{ mg}$

Keeping two significant figures, the RDA of vitamin C is 60 mg.

EXERCISE 1.4

The potentially toxic dose of the local anesthetic lidocaine is over 6.00×10^3 ng per milliliter of blood. What is the toxic dose of lidocaine in micrograms per milliliter of blood?

In Section 1.7 you saw that volume units are expressed in terms of the cube of some length unit. To convert one volume unit to another it is therefore necessary to cube the conversion factor. For example, suppose the problem is to find out how many cubic centimeters are in 20.0 in^3.

1. Decide what units are given and what units are desired.

$$20.0 \text{ in}^3 = ? \text{ cm}^3$$

2. Choose the necessary conversion factor.

$$\text{Start with } 1 \text{ in} = 2.54 \text{ cm}$$

Both sides of an equation can be squared or cubed.

To introduce cubic inches and cubic centimeters, this factor must be cubed by cubing both sides of the equation above. (For a review of this and other important algebraic manipulations, see Appendix C.)

$$(1 \text{ in})^3 = (2.54 \text{ cm})^3 \qquad \text{or} \qquad 1^3 \text{ in}^3 = 2.54^3 \text{ cm}^3$$

and

$$1 \text{ in}^3 = 16.4 \text{ cm}^3$$

3. Rewrite the conversion factor to make it equal to unity:

$$\frac{1 \text{ in}^3}{16.4 \text{ cm}^3} = 1 \qquad \text{or} \qquad \frac{16.4 \text{ cm}^3}{1 \text{ in}^3} = 1$$

4. Multiply by the appropriate conversion factor:

$$20.0 \not{\text{in}^3} \times \frac{16.4 \text{ cm}^3}{1 \not{\text{in}^3}} = 328 \text{ cm}^3$$

SAMPLE EXERCISE 1.5

A normal value for the number of red blood cells (RBCs) in blood is about 5,000,000 (5×10^6) per cubic millimeter. How many RBCs would be present in 1 cm^3 of blood?

Solution:

1. $\dfrac{5 \times 10^6 \text{ RBCs}}{\text{mm}^3} = \dfrac{?}{\text{cm}^3}$
2. 10 mm = 1 cm
   By cubing both sides of this factor
   $10^3 \text{ mm}^3 = 1 \text{ cm}^3$
3. $\dfrac{10^3 \text{ mm}^3}{1 \text{ cm}^3} = 1 \qquad \text{or} \qquad \dfrac{1 \text{ cm}^3}{10^3 \text{ mm}^3} = 1$

4. $\frac{5 \times 10^6 \text{ RBC}}{\cancel{\text{mm}^3}} \times \frac{10^3 \cancel{\text{mm}^3}}{1 \text{ cm}^3} = \frac{5 \times 10^9 \text{ RBCs}}{\text{cm}^3}$

One cubic centimeter of blood contains 5×10^9 RBCs.

EXERCISE 1.5

Suppose the body surface area (BSA) of a child is 8×10^3 cm^2. What is the child's BSA in square meters?

Using this same four-step method to convert from unit to unit permits relatively easy solution of multiple-step problems such as the ones in the next exercises.

SAMPLE EXERCISE 1.6

The density of bone is 110 lb/ft^3. Convert this to grams per milliliter.

Solution:

1. 110 lb/ft^3 = ? g/ml
2. 1 lb = 454 g
   $(1 \text{ ft})^3 = (12 \text{ in})^3$ or $1 \text{ ft}^3 = 1728 \text{ in}^3$
   $(1 \text{ in})^3 = (2.54 \text{ cm})^3$ or $1 \text{ in}^3 = 16.4 \text{ cm}^3$
3. This time try rewriting each conversion factor in your mind.
4. $\frac{110 \cancel{\text{lb}}}{1 \cancel{\text{ft}^3}} \times \frac{454 \text{ g}}{1 \cancel{\text{lb}}} \times \frac{1 \cancel{\text{ft}^3}}{1728 \cancel{\text{in}^3}} \times \frac{1 \cancel{\text{in}^3}}{16.4 \cancel{\text{cm}^3}} \times \frac{1 \cancel{\text{cm}^3}}{1 \text{ ml}} = 1.76 \text{ g/ml}$

The density of 1.76 g/ml for bone is a seemingly sensible answer, since bones are indeed denser than water.

EXERCISE 1.6

The density of a gemstone is measured to be 0.75 oz/in^3. Could the gem be a diamond? (See Table 1.5.)

SAMPLE EXERCISE 1.7

What is the mass in grams of a 500-ml volume of glycerol?

Solution:

1. 500 mL = ? g

Densities can be used as conversion factors.

2. We can use the density as a conversion factor to go from milliliters to grams. Density = 1.26 g/ml (Table 1.5); thus 1 ml glycerol has a mass of 1.26 g. Conversion factor: 1 ml = 1.26 g
3. Rewrite the conversion factor in your mind.
4. $500 \cancel{\text{ml}} \times \frac{1.26 \text{ g}}{1 \cancel{\text{ml}}} = 630 \text{ g}$

A 500-ml sample of glycerol weighs 630 g.

EXERCISE 1.7

Suppose you wish to measure out 950 g of 5% glucose solution using a volumetric device. How many milliliters would you need?

The conversion-factor approach to problem solving can do much more than convert quantities from one system of units to another. Conversion factors involving chemical quantities will be introduced in upcoming chapters. In general, carrying units through calculations helps to avoid errors and may replace the need to memorize many equations. The habit of incorporating units in *all* calculations, even in very simple ones, is a good habit to develop in preparation for the study of any experimental science.

SUMMARY

Scientists apply the scientific method by doing experiments to develop theories. The measured quantities which come from quantitative experiments include both a numerical part and a unit. In scientific studies the most important units belong to the SI system, which includes SI base units, SI derived units, and SI prefixes. Base units are carefully defined by some standard object or by the application of some physical method. Of the seven base units, the five which appear most often in chemical discussions include the meter (length), kilogram (mass), second (time), kelvin (temperature), and mole (amount of substance). Volume (length^3) and density (mass/volume) are two examples of derived units. Volume may be expressed in terms of the milliliter (ml) or the liter (L) instead of the equivalent cubic centimeter (cm^3) or cubic decimeter (dm^3). Densities of liquids and solids usually approach 1 g/ml and those of gases are close to 1 g/L. Experiments must be designed to provide enough significant figures, or meaningful digits, that a valid conclusion can be drawn.

It is often necessary to convert from one system of units to another. The most effective method to use applies conversion factors in such a way that units cancel in a calculation, leaving the desired unit only. This method tends to prevent errors in doing calculations and helps to organize thinking in the solution of all scientific problems.

KEY WORDS

scientific method
qualitative
quantitative
SI system of units
SI base units
SI derived units
meter
kilogram
mass
weight
kelvin scale
absolute zero
Celsius scale
milliliter
liter
density
specific gravity
hydrometer
uncertainty
significant figures
conversion factor

EXERCISES

1.8 Decide whether the following observations are qualitative or quantitative:
(a) Blood cholesterol levels tend to increase with age.
(b) A 1200-ml sample of urine was found to contain 1.0 g of ammonia.
(c) The level of glucose in the blood of a diabetic patient was abnormally high.
(d) When the temperature of a patient suffering from an infection was measured, it was found to be 2°F above normal.

1.9 Give the abbreviation for an SI unit which could substitute for (a) One-thousandth of a meter; (b) 1/1,000,000 g; (c) one-hundredth of a mole; (d) 0.1 g (e) 10^{-9} s.

1.10 How is the modern meter defined? Why is this better than using the distance between two marks on a standard metal bar?

1.11 Why is the kilogram used as the base unit for mass instead of the gram?

1.12 What is the difference between the terms *weight* and *mass?* What do we mean when we say that someone *weighs* 50 kg?

1.13 Can the angstrom be expressed in terms of an SI prefix plus base unit? (See Table 1.3.)

1.14 Write the name that corresponds to each of the following unit abbreviations: (a) pg; (b) μmol; (c) ns.

1.15 An attogram (ag) is 1/1,000,000,000,000,000,000 g. What is the meaning of the prefix *atto?*

1.16 A femtogram (fg) is 0.000000000000001 g. Using scientific notation, state how many femtometers there are in 1 m.

1.17 At one time the unit *micron* (abbreviated μ) was used to mean one-millionth of a meter. What is the modern SI symbol for 1 μ? Another unit commonly used was the millimicron (mμ). What is the SI unit that corresponds to 1 mμ?

1.18 Which of the following temperatures corresponds to absolute zero: (a) 0°C; (b) 0°F; (c) 0 K; (d) any of these?

1.19 Convert the following temperatures to degrees Celsius:
(a) A room temperature of 298 K
(b) The temperature of a patient with a fever of 103°F
(c) The temperature of a bitter cold day when the thermometer reads −40°F. (What is interesting about this temperature?)

1.20 Which of these temperatures is the highest: (a) 98°F; (b) 40°C; (c) 310 K?

1.21 Find both the density and the specific gravity of each of the following substances:
(a) A material that is 10 times as dense as water
(b) A sugar cube that is 1 cm on a side and has a mass of 1.59 g
(c) A metal object that has a mass of 24 g and displaces 3 cm^3 of water

1.22 Of the following quantites, which are identical to 1 L: (a) 1000 m^3; (b) 1 dm^3; (c) 1000 cm^3; (d) 100 ml; (e) 1 quart?

1.23 The unit *microliter* (μl) is sometimes used to express very small volumes. How many cubic centimeters are there in 1 μl?

1.24 The volume of blood in a person is 4 to 6 L and accounts for about 7 to 9 percent of body weight. In what unit must body weight be expressed for this to be true?

1.25 Suppose a bar of metal weighing 290 g measures 5.0 cm by 3.0 cm by 1.0 cm. Could it be pure gold?

1.26 A 130.0-ml sample of cerebrospinal fluid has a mass of 130.7 g. If the normal range of specific gravity for this fluid is 1.003 to 1.008, is this a normal sample?

1.27 A brilliant red gemstone that you find in a box of trinkets purchased at an auction looks like a ruby, a mineral which has a specific gravity of 4.0. Suppose the stone displaces 0.50 cm^3 of water and weighs 1.00 g. Could it be a ruby?

1.28 What volume of water in cubic centimeters would be required to fill each of the following containers: (a) A 120-ml teacup; (b) a quart bottle; (c) a 0.750-L bottle?

1.29 How does a urinometer work?

1.30 A sample of urine weighing 1 kg occupies a volume of 995.0 ml. Does the specific gravity of this urine fall within the normal range? (See Section 1.8.)

1.31 The following ingredients are mixed with water to make a disinfectant spray:

60 ml pine oil
60 ml formaldehyde solution
72 g acetone
250 g isopropyl alcohol

Using the densities listed in Table 1.5, calculate the volume (in milliliters) of acetone and isopropyl alcohol that must be put into this mixture.

1.32 A metal cube measures 3 cm on a side. If the cube weighs 72.9 g, which of the metals listed in Table 1.5 is it?

1.33 Suppose you determine the density of a metallic object with a mass of 10.75 g found by weighing it on a balance that weighs to the nearest centigram. Using the method of water displacement, you find that the volume of the object is 1.2 ml as measured with a graduated cylinder that can be read to the nearest 0.1 ml. The metal is one of those listed in Table 1.5. Can you specify with certainty which one it is?

1.34 How many grams of air are present in a balloon which has a volume of 2 L (at 20°C)? How many grams of helium would be required to fill the balloon to 2 L?

1.35 Which of the following quantities could be measured *accurately* using the balance shown in Figure 1.3: (a) 25.6 g; (b) 256 mg; (c) 2.56 mg; (d) 25 cg; (e) 25.60 cg?

1.36 Convert the following to length in meters:
(a) The height of a 5-ft 5-in person
(b) The distance covered in a 100-yd race
(c) The length of a newborn baby measuring 22 in
(d) A bond length of 1.5 Å

1.37 Express the quantities below in kilograms:
(a) The weight of a 115-lb person
(b) 1 ton (2000 lb)
(c) The weight of a 7-lb 8-oz newborn baby

1.38 The fate of inhaled particulates in polluted air is summarized in the table below:

Size	Fate of particulate
10 μm	Filtered by nose
2–10 μm	Settles on walls of trachea bronchi and bronchioles
0.3–2 μm	Reaches alveoli of lungs
0.3 μm	Taken up by blood or exhaled

Decide what happens to particulates of the following sizes when they are inhaled: (a) 10^{-6} m; (b) 0.004 mm; (c) 5×10^{-5} cm?

1.39 If the unit 1 dram is equal to 60 grains, how many grams correspond to 1 dram?

1.40 Suppose 40 grains of aspirin is administered daily for relief of muscle and joint pain and inflammation. If each pain relief tablet contains 340 mg aspirin, how many tablets must be taken each day?

1.41 One (metric) carat is equal to 200 mg.
(a) What is the mass in ounces of a 15-carat diamond?
(b) What is the approximate volume (in milliters) of the diamond? (See Table 1.5.)

1.42 A *carat* of gold refers to the number of grams of gold present in 24 g of a mixture containing gold, which means that 100 percent gold is 24 carats. How would you describe a 1-g "gold" sample in carats, if it contains 583 mg of pure gold?

1.43 Calculate the density of a sample of salted water if 69 lb of the salt water occupies 1 ft^3. Does your answer seem reasonable? Why?

1.44 The cell-wall thickness shown in Fig. 1.1*e* is 10 nm. Express this in: (a) m; (b) pm; (c) μm.

1.45 What is the meaning of the unit deciliter (dl)? Compare this unit *qualitatively* with the milliliter and the liter.

1.46 Levels of blood glucose higher than 400 mg/dl or lower than 40 mg/dl are life-threatening and are sometimes called "panic values." Are any of the laboratory glucose levels shown below panic values? If so, state whether they are too low or too high.
(a) 50,000 μg/dl
(b) 300 μg/ml
(c) 0.03 g/L

1.47 The labels have fallen off three identical glass bottles each containing the same volume of one of the following liquids: glycerol, corn oil, and chloroform. What simple method could you use to replace the labels?

1.48 A normal level for blood platelets, small cells which play an important role in the clotting mechanism, is 200,000 to 400,000 per cubic millimeter. Are the levels below within this range?
(a) 4,000,000 per cubic inch
(b) 3×10^8 per cubic centimeter

1.49 The following formula is sometimes used to estimate drug doses for children:

$$\text{Child dose} = \frac{\text{body surface area (m}^2) \times \text{adult dose}}{1.7\ \text{m}^2}$$

If the adult dose of aspirin is 250 mg, what is the dose appropriate for a young child with a body surface area of 9 ft^2?

1.50 The normal range of maximum breathing capacity for a male is about 100 to 150 L/min. If the maximum breathing capacity of a particular male is 4 m^3/h, does this fall within the normal range?

1.51 Burn victims must be fed intravenously with a solution, containing dextrose (a form of glucose) and other nutrients to help replace body fluids continuously lost by damaged skin. For every square meter of body surface area (BSA) that is burned a volume of 1500 ml of this solution must be administered daily. What daily volume of solution should be given to a body with a BSA of 1200 in^2 that has suffered burns over 40 percent of the body?

***1.52** A quantity of gold weighing 28 g can be pounded out so that it covers an area of 300 ft^2. If a perfect rectangular solid is formed, how many micrometers thick is the gold foil produced in this way?

1.53 Calculate the mass of one measuring cup of corn oil if one cup has a volume of about 240 ml.

1.54 Suppose the price of silver is $10 per ounce. How much is a 1-kg bar of silver worth?

1.55 What is unusual about the density of mercury compared with the densities of other liquids? If you wished to measure out 125 g of mercury, what volume would you pour?

1.56 What should happen to a balloon filled with: (**a**) Hydrogen gas; (**b**) xenon gas?

1.57 Would a 1-lb sample of glycerol fit into a 1-pint bottle? (1 quart = 2 pints)

1.58 A patient is suffering from severe renal disease, resulting in the inability of the kidneys to concentrate the urine. The specific gravity of this patient's urine is most likely to be which of the following: (**a**) 1.030; (**b**) 1.010; (**c**) 0.995; (**d**) 1.020?

2 . . MATTER AND ENERGY

2.1 INTRODUCTION

Matter is anything that has mass and occupies space. It may be extraordinarily complex, as it is when it takes the form of the human body, or relatively simple, as in a drink of water or a chunk of metal or a breath of air. Chemists study matter from one particular point of view. They explain the behavior of matter in terms of the invisible building blocks of which it is made. These incredibly tiny particles, too small to be observed even with the most powerful of microscopes, are called atoms and molecules. **Atoms** are the indivisible, discrete particles of which all matter is composed. **Molecules** are collections of two or more atoms which are held together by links called *chemical bonds.* Molecules can include a small number of atoms or they can be much more complex. The deoxyribonucleic acid (DNA) molecule, for instance, which determines all of an organism's characteristics, is an enormous molecule containing millions of atoms. Atoms and molecules are the subjects of all the remaining chapters of this text.

Since atoms and molecules *cannot* be seen, the chemist must learn about their behavior by looking at the characteristics of matter which *can* be seen. These characteristics are called **properties,** and by studying them we begin our journey into the science of chemistry.

2.2 CHEMICAL PROPERTIES OF MATTER

Chemical changes involve bond breaking.

A **chemical property** describes the ability of a substance to undergo a chemical change. A **chemical change** occurs when the atoms of a substance rearrange by bond breaking and bond formation to produce a new substance that is chemically different from the original one. When such chemical changes occur, a **chemical reaction** is said to have taken place. The original substances are called **reactants** and the new ones are called **products.** Chemists describe chemical reactions by using an arrow pointing from the reactants to the products:

$$\text{Reactants} \rightarrow \text{products}$$

The tendency to burn is one example of a chemical property. When a piece of paper is set on fire, the ashes that remain after it burns are different chemically from the paper. A chemical change has taken place—the molecules of the paper are not the same as those of the ashes. Corrosion is another chemical change; the rust that forms when an iron object is exposed to air is not the same chemical substance as the iron.

Many standard medical tests detect the presence or absence of some chemical by causing a chemical reaction to take place on addition of a testing substance, called a *reagent*. For instance, Benedict's reagent, used to test for glucose in urine, works by combining with the glucose in the urine to form a color easily visible to the tester (see Color Plate 1). In this test the glucose and the test reagent undergo chemical changes.

2.3 PHYSICAL PROPERTIES OF MATTER

Physical changes do not involve bond breaking.

When a substance undergoes a **physical change**, no chemical bonds are formed or broken and no chemical reaction takes place. The molecules and atoms of the original substance are the same before *and* after the physical change. Some important physical properties which can be used to describe a substance are color, density, boiling point, and freezing point. The **physical properties** of a substance can be observed without changing the molecules of the substance or without causing it to undergo a chemical change. Thus, when liquid water freezes to become solid water (ice), the same molecules are present in both the liquid water and the ice. Liquid water is the same chemical substance as ice.

Since measuring the physical properties of something does not change the identity of its atoms or molecules, properties of this type are especially useful in analyzing unknown materials. Identifying characteristics, such as color, density, and boiling and melting points are often listed in handbooks and tables. (See Figure 2.1, which reproduces a portion of the handbook most often used by chemists.) One physical property which is readily observed is the **physical state**, that is, whether something is a solid, a liquid, or a gas (at a given temperature and pressure).

2.4 STATES OF MATTER

There are three states of matter, namely, gas, liquid, and solid. They can be compared in terms of the shapes and volumes they attain when placed in a container. A **gas** assumes the same shape as its container and will expand or compress to fill it exactly. A 25-ml volume of gas expands to 100 ml when placed in a 100-ml vessel, as shown in Figure 2.2*a*. The same 25 ml of gas can also be compressed to fill a 15-ml flask. In other words, a gas has no definite shape and no definite volume. Like gases, **liquids** have no definite shape but they do have definite volume. A liquid will adopt the shape of its container but its volume will not change. A 25-ml sample of liquid will still be 25 ml when placed in a 100-

PHYSICAL CONSTANTS OF INORGANIC COMPOUNDS (*Continued*)

Name	Synonyms and Formulae	Mol. wt.	Crystalline form, properties and index of refraction	Density or specific gravity	Melting point, °C	Boiling point, °C	Solubility, in grams per 100 cc		
							Cold water	Hot water	Other solvents
Sodium									
Bromoplatinate	$Na_2PtBr_6.6H_2O$	828.62	dk red, tricl	3.323	d 150		v s	v s	v s al
Cacodylate	$Na[(CH_3)_2AsO_2].3H_2O$	214.03	wh		*ca* 60	$-H_2O$, 120	200^{15-20}		40^{25} al; 100^{15-20} 90% al
Calcium sulfate	$Na_2Ca(SO_4)_2.2H_2O$	314.21	col, monocl need	2.64	$-2H_2O$, 80		d	d	
d-Camphorate	$Na_2C_{10}H_{14}O_4.3H_2O$	298.25	wh need, hygr		$-3H_2O$, 100		122^{14}		s al
Carbide	Na_2C_2	70.00	wh powd	1.575^{15}	*ca* 700		d	d	s a; d al
Carbonate	Na_2CO_3	105.99	wh powd, hygr, 1.535	2.532	851	d	7.1^{0}	45.5^{100}	sl s abs al; i acet
Carbonate, deca-hydrate	Washing soda, $Na_2CO_3.10H_2O$	286.14	wh, monocl, 1.405, 1.425 1.440	1.44^{15}	32.5–34.5	$-H_2O$, 33.5	21.52^{0}	421^{104}	i al
Carbonate, hepta-hydrate	$Na_2CO_3.7H_2O$	232.10	rhomb bipyr, effl	1.51	$-H_2O$, 32		16.90	33.9^{35}	
Carbonate, mono-hydrate	Crystal carbonate, thermonatrite, $Na_2CO_3.H_2O$	124.00	col, rhomb, deliq, 1.506, 1.509	2.25	$-H_2O$, 100		33	52.08	14^{25} glyc; i al, eth
Carbonate, sesqui-	$Na_2CO_3.NaHCO_32H_2O$	226.03	col, monocl, 1.5073	2.112	d		13^{0}	42^{100}	
Carbonate hydrogen	$NaHCO_3$	84.00	wh, monocl pr, 1.500	2.159	$-CO_2$, 270		6.9^{0}	16.4^{60}	sl s al
Chlorate	$NaClO_3$	106.44	col, cub or trig, 1.513	2.490^{15}	248–261	d	79^{0}	230^{100}	s al, liq NH_3, glyc
Perchlorate	$NaClO_4$	122.44	wh, rhomb, deliq, 1.4606, 1.4617, 1.4731		d 482	d	s	v s	s al
Perchlorate, hydrate	$NaClO_4.H_2O$	140.46	col rhbdr, deliq	2.02	130	d 482	209^{15}	284^{50}	s al
Chloride	Common salt, nat. halite, NaCl	58.44	col, cub, 1.5442	2.165^{25}	801	1413	35.7^{0}	39.12^{100}	sl s al, liq, NH_3; s glyc; i HCl

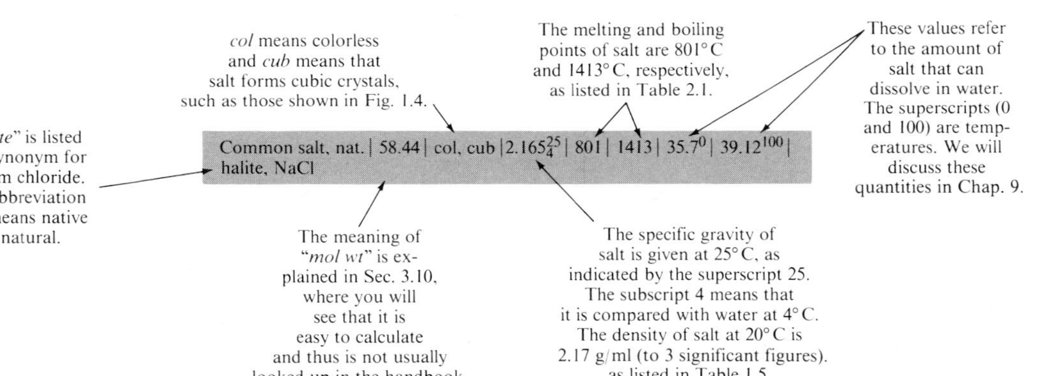

col means colorless and *cub* means that salt forms cubic crystals, such as those shown in Fig. 1.4.
The melting and boiling points of salt are 801°C and 1413°C, respectively, as listed in Table 2.1.
These values refer to the amount of salt that can dissolve in water. The superscripts (0 and 100) are temperatures. We will discuss these quantities in Chap. 9.
"*Halite*" is listed as a synonym for sodium chloride. The abbreviation *nat.* means native or natural.
Common salt, nat. | 58.44 | col, cub | 2.165^{25}_{4} | 801 | 1413 | 35.7^{0} | 39.12^{100} |
halite, NaCl
The meaning of "*mol wt*" is explained in Sec. 3.10, where you will see that it is easy to calculate and thus is not usually looked up in the handbook.
The specific gravity of salt is given at 25°C, as indicated by the superscript 25. The subscript 4 means that it is compared with water at 4°C. The density of salt at 20°C is 2.17 g/ml (to 3 significant figures), as listed in Table 1.5.

FIGURE 2.1
Segment of a page in the *Handbook of Chemistry and Physics.*

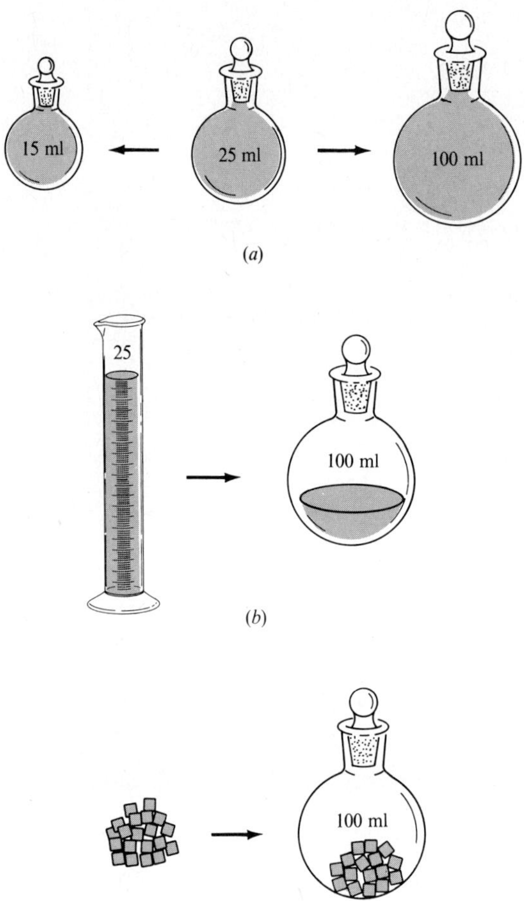

FIGURE 2.2
Comparing shape and volume of a gas, liquid, and solid. (*a*) 25 ml of gas expands to fill a 100-ml flask and contracts to fill a 15-ml flask. Gases are without shape or definite volume. (*b*) 25 ml of liquid conforms to the shape of the 100-ml flask but fills it only one-quarter full. Liquids do not have defined shapes but do have definite volume. (*c*) 25 ml of solid does not conform to the shape of the flask. Solids have definite shape and definite volume.

ml flask and will overflow a 15-ml container (see Figure 2.2*b*). A **solid** has both a definite shape and a definite volume. The shape and volume of a solid, such as the one pictured in Figure 2.2*c*, are not affected by its container.

As mentioned previously, heating or cooling can cause a material to change from one physical state to another without altering its chemical composition. The temperatures at which such changes occur are important physical properties because they are characteristic of a given substance and thus help to define it.

Melting and Freezing

When a solid is transformed into a liquid by applying heat to it, the process is called **melting**, and the temperature at which the solid becomes a liquid is the **melting point**. In the reverse process, *freezing*, heat is removed from liquids by cooling them until they are converted to solids. The temperature at which the conversion from liquid to solid occurs is the *freezing point*. Freezing and melting points are the same and the term chosen depends upon the point of view.

Table 2.1 gives the melting points of some selected substances. The melting point of a substance can be used to determine whether or not it is a solid at some

TABLE 2.1 BOILING POINTS AND MELTING POINTS

Name of substance	Boiling point, °C*	Melting point, °C*	Physical state at 25°C*
Oxygen	−183	−218	Gas
Carbon monoxide	−191	−205	Gas
Ammonia	−33.3	−77.7	Gas
Butane (fuel)	−0.5	−138	Gas
Nitrous oxide (laughing gas)	−88.5	−90.8	Gas
Water	100	0	Liquid
Benzene	80.1	5.5	Liquid
Diethyl ether (ether)	34.5	−116	Liquid
Sulfur trioxide	44.8	16.8	Liquid
Cyclohexane	80.7	6.6	Liquid
Acetic acid (in vinegar)	118	16.6	Liquid
Triolein (unsaturated fat)	†	−5	Liquid
Mercury	357	−39	Liquid
Acetone	56.2	−95.4	Liquid
Methanol (wood alcohol)	65	−94	Liquid
Ethylene glycol (antifreeze)	197.6	−13	Liquid
Sodium chloride (salt)	1413	801	Solid
Vanillin (flavoring ingredient)	285	78	Solid
Lead metal	1744	327	Solid
Cholesterol	360	148.5	Solid
Tristearin (saturated fat)	†	71	Solid
Acetylsalicylic acid (aspirin)	†	135	Solid
Testosterone (male sex hormone)	†	155	Solid

*All the entries in the table apply at sea-level pressure.
†These compounds would decompose before boiling at sea-level pressure.

given temperature. Any substance that is a solid at a room temperature of 25°C (77°F) must have a melting point higher than 25°C. This means that cholesterol (mp 148.5°C) is a solid at room temperature and benzene (mp 5.5°C) is not.

Vaporization

When a liquid is converted into a gas by heating, the process is called **vaporization** and the temperature at which gaseous bubbles form within the liquid is called the **boiling point.** Boiling points, much more than melting points, are very sensitive to the atmospheric pressure in the environment of the liquid. Tables which include boiling points, such as Table 2.1, must always specify the pressure at which they are measured. In many cases the pressures are close to sea-level pressure.

Substances that have boiling points below ordinary room temperature must be gases. For example, in Table 2.1, ammonia (bp = −33.3°C) and butane (bp = -0.5°C) are gases. Anything with a boiling point higher than a given room temperature must be a solid or a liquid at that particular temperature (and sea-level pressure).

SAMPLE EXERCISE 2.1

What is the physical state of the general anesthetic called *diethyl ether* (or simply *ether*) at a room temperature of 25°C and sea-level pressure?

Solution:

To find out, look up the melting and boiling points in Table 2.1:

$$\text{bp} = 34.5°\text{C} \qquad \text{mp} = -116°\text{C}$$

Since its boiling point is higher than 25°C, ether must be a liquid or a solid but not a gas. Since its melting point is less than 25°C, diethyl ether is a liquid.

EXERCISE 2.1

What is the physical state of acetic acid (the substance that is mixed with water to make vinegar) when it is stored at a temperature of 50°F?

2.5 TYPES OF MATTER

Some very general classifications can be used to sort different types of matter. The term **substance** is usually loosely used to mean a particular kind of matter. But the expression *pure substance* is reserved for matter containing just one kind of atom, known as an *element*, or matter containing one kind of molecule, known as a *compound*. All other substances are mixtures. Whether matter should be classified as a compound or element or mixture is determined by examining its properties.

Elements

Elements contain one kind of atom.

An **element** is a pure substance which consists of just one kind of atom. The 106 different elements on earth are listed in the **periodic table** of elements, which appears on the inside cover of this text. No chemical reactions or physical changes can break an element down into more than one substance. For example, diamond is one form of the element carbon and contains carbon atoms only. Pure oxygen gas is also an element and includes just one kind of atom, oxygen. Diamond and oxygen gas cannot be broken down into simpler substances by any chemical or physical means.

Compounds

Compounds contain more than one kind of atom.

A **compound** is a pure substance which contains just one kind of molecule. Each molecule must include at least two different kinds of atoms. For example, water, a pure substance, is a compound which contains only molecules of water. Each water molecule includes two atoms of the element hydrogen and one atom of the element oxygen. For a compound to break down into its constituent elements, a chemical reaction must take place. When the compound water breaks down into the elements hydrogen and oxygen, the bonds which hold the hydrogen atoms to oxygen atoms in water molecules must break.

Breaking a compound down into its constituent elements can be relatively easy or very difficult depending upon the nature of the compound. For example, heating is enough to break down a few compounds. One dramatic example of a compound which can be decomposed into its elements by heating was observed by the alchemists, who were mystified by the behavior of a reddish orange powder, which they called "red precipitate." Simply heating this material caused a startling chemical change in which two new substances formed, one a silvery liquid and the other a colorless gas (see Figure 2.3). Today red precipitate is known to be a compound, mercury(II) oxide, which consists of two elements, mercury and oxygen.

Heating, however, is rarely enough to generate the constituent elements of a compound. Heating water, for instance, causes the water to boil but does not liberate hydrogen or oxygen. A direct electric current must be passed through water to decompose it into its constituent elements. Thus we see that heating can cause a physical change (in water) or a chemical change (in mercury oxide).

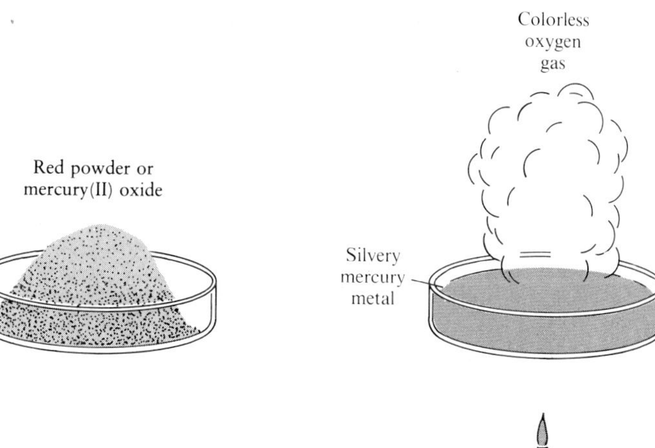

FIGURE 2.3
Breakdown of mercury(II) oxide. Compound separates as a result of a chemical change.

Mixtures

Mixtures can be separated by physical means.

Mixtures include more than one pure substance, which can be separated from each other without a chemical reaction. The components of a mixture are not joined to each other by any chemical bonds and can be separated by making use of a physical property. Saline solution, which appears to be a single uniform substance, is really a mixture of two compounds, salt and water. The salt and water are not joined to each other by chemical bonds. One way to separate the salt from the water in saline solution is to take advantage of the difference in their boiling points. Heating the saline solution causes the water to boil away, but leaves the salt behind.

A difference in magnetic properties can be used to separate a mixture of the elements iron and sulfur. The iron atoms and the sulfur atoms in the mixture are not linked by any chemical bonds. Passing a magnet over the powdery mixture of the two elements attracts the iron powder and leaves the sulfur behind (see Figure 2.4). Iron(II) sulfide is a blackish brown solid compound which also contains the elements iron and sulfur. Not only does this compound look different from a mixture of iron and sulfur but it is also very different chemically. The iron atoms in iron(II) sulfide are joined to sulfur atoms by chemical bonds, unlike those atoms in the iron and sulfur mixture. A magnet cannot be used to remove the iron from this or any other iron compound.

The first chromatography experiment separated plant pigments into colored bands; hence the name was derived from *chroma,* the Greek word for "color."

In principle, any mixture can be separated into its components by utilizing a physical property which differs for each constituent substance. Often the separations are difficult. One powerful technique which can succeed in separating even the most stubborn of mixtures is **chromatography.** In very general terms, separations by chromotography depend upon differences in the ability of each component of a mixture to "adhere" to a given material. For instance, many chromatographic devices make use of a solid packed into a vertical cylindrical tube called a *column,* such as the one pictured in Figure 2.5. The sample of mixture to be separated is introduced as a thin layer at the top of the column. In the device in Figure 2.5 a liquid is added at the top of the column, and as it flows through the column, it carries the sample with it. The separation occurs

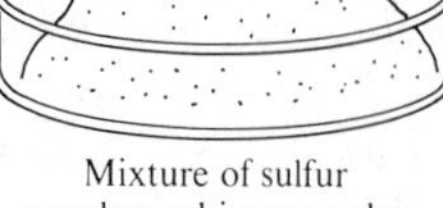

Mixture of sulfur powder and iron powder
Magnet picks up iron and leaves sulfur behind

FIGURE 2.4
Separation of sulfur and iron. Mixture separates physically.

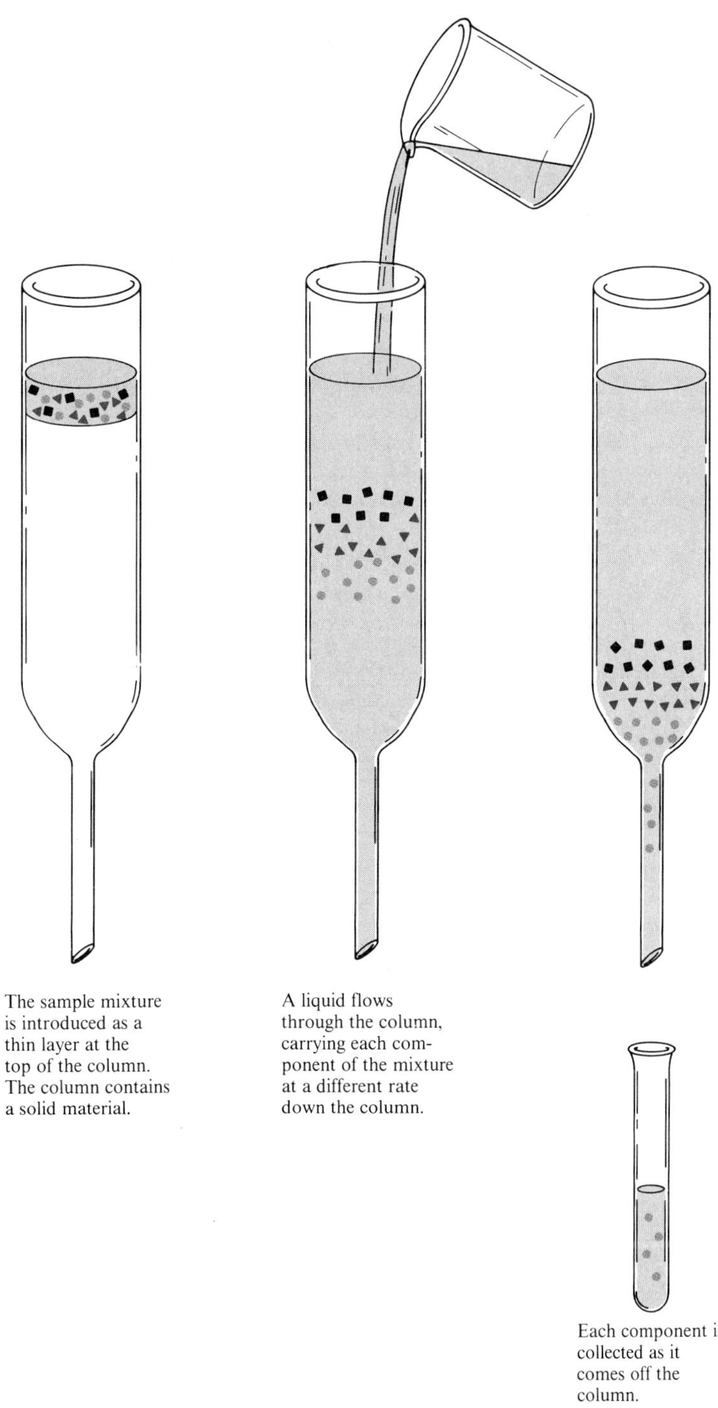

The sample mixture
is introduced as a
thin layer at the
top of the column.
The column contains
a solid material.
A liquid flows
through the column,
carrying each com-
ponent of the mixture
at a different rate
down the column.
Each component is
collected as it
comes off the
column.

FIGURE 2.5
Chromatography column.

because some components of the mixture adhere more tightly to the solid and thus move more slowly down the column. Color Plate 2 shows the separation of a sample of "dark blue" dye into its three colored components—one orange, one blue, and one violet.

Modern chromatography techniques can separate from a mixture a component that is present in only trace amounts, as little as one part in a trillion. One important step in the preparation of compounds that are to be used as drugs or food additives is to make sure that they are not mixed with even very small amounts of other substances that could produce toxic side effects. Chromatography techniques can help to ensure that a substance believed to be a single compound is not really a mixture.

SAMPLE EXERCISE 2.2

Nitrogen dioxide is a toxic, brown, gaseous compound that contains 30.4 percent nitrogen and 69.6 percent oxygen. A mixture that contains 30.4 percent nitrogen and 69.6 percent oxygen is a colorless gas that supports life. How do you explain the difference in the properties of these two substances even though they contain the same amounts of the same two elements?

Solution:

The compound contains nitrogen dioxide molecules in which nitrogen atoms are joined to oxygen atoms by chemical bonds. In the mixture there are no chemical bonds joining nitrogen and oxygen atoms.

EXERCISE 2.2

Would it be possible to separate water into hydrogen and oxygen by passing it through a chromatography column?

2.6 LAW OF CONSERVATION OF MATTER

You have seen that it is possible for matter to be changed in form as a result of a physical or chemical change. Chemical changes produce particularly dramatic changes in matter in that the resulting substances are chemically different from the original substance. However, regardless of what chemical reaction takes place, careful weighings show that the mass of the reactants is always *exactly* the same as the mass of products. Thus, matter cannot be created or destroyed, a principle known as the **law of conservation of matter.**

One scientist whose early quantitative work helped to establish the law of conservation of matter was Joseph Black (1728–1799), who was studying the effects of chalk on stomach acidity, a project to be used for his doctoral thesis. Upon heating the chalk, he discovered that two new substances formed, one a white solid (lime) and the other a gas (carbon dioxide). If the mass of the original chalk was 1.00 g, the mass of the new substances was also 1.00 g:

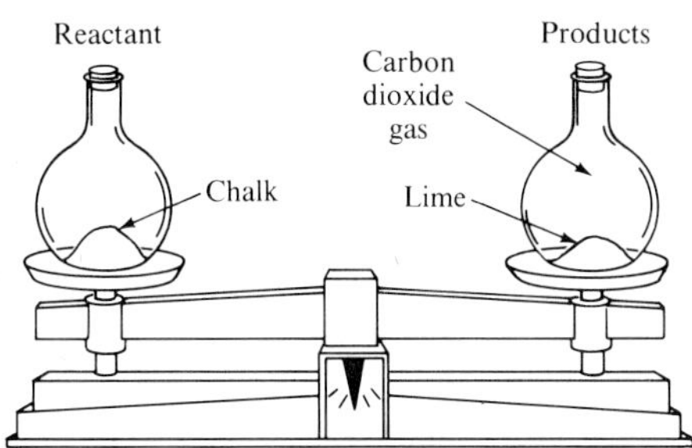

FIGURE 2.6
Law of conservation of matter. When the chalk decomposes by being heated, the mass of the chalk is the same as that of the products--carbon dioxide and lime.

In a chemical reaction the mass of the reactants equals the mass of the products.

$$1.00 \text{ g (chalk)} = 0.56 \text{ g (white solid)} + 0.44 \text{ g (gas)}$$

Whatever the mass of the original chalk, it was always the same as the sum of the masses of the white solid and the gas which formed (see Figure 2.6).

SAMPLE EXERCISE 2.3

If 216.6 g of mercury(II) oxide is completely decomposed by heating to produce 16.0 g of oxygen gas, how much mercury metal is also produced?

Solution:

$$\begin{aligned} \text{Mass of mercury(II) oxide} &= \text{mass of oxygen} + \text{mass of mercury} \\ 216.6 \text{ g} &= 16.0 \text{ g} + \text{mass of mercury} \\ \text{Mass of mercury} &= 216.6 \text{ g} - 16.0 \text{ g} \\ &= 200.6 \text{ g of mercury} \end{aligned}$$

EXERCISE 2.3

Heating of a sample of chalk weighing 0.50 g produces 0.28 g of lime. What is the other product and how much of it forms?

2.7 ENERGY

What do scientists mean by energy? The word itself suggests motion. Whirling tornadoes, rushing streams, and moving people are all sources of energy. What the tornadoes, streams, and people all have in common is the ability to cause motion, that is, to do what scientists call *work*. Tornadoes can lift roofs from houses, rushing streams can move wheels to operate generators, and people can perform tasks as they move about. **Energy** is defined as the ability to do work.

The energy that involves objects in motion, as in the examples cited, is called **kinetic energy**. However, the water behind a dam, an arched bow, and a slice of bread are also sources of energy even though they are not in motion. Stored energy is called **potential energy**. Energy comes in many different forms. Some familiar kinds of energy are mechanical motion, electrical energy, sound, light, and heat. We will be particularly interested in the energy changes that accompany chemical reactions, or **chemical energy**.

All forms of energy are interconvertible. For instance, chemical energy is converted to heat energy when natural gas or oil is burned to warm houses. As food is digested in human beings via chemical reactions, the molecules in the food compounds break down to release energy, some of which is heat used to maintain body temperature. Light energy is converted to chemical energy when plants use energy from the sun to convert carbon dioxide and water to sugar in a process called *photosynthesis*. When energy is converted from one form to another, it is changed but is never used up. In scientific terms it is said that the energy is conserved, just as matter is conserved. The **law of conservation of energy** states that energy is neither created nor destroyed but may be changed in form.

2.8 UNITS OF ENERGY

The SI energy unit is the joule, abbreviated J, a derived unit which is a combination of the kilogram, meter, and second:

$$1\ \text{J} = \frac{1\ \text{kg}\cdot\text{m}^2}{\text{s}^2}$$

Chemists and biochemists sometimes substitute the non-SI energy unit calorie (cal). One calorie is a little more than 4 J:

$$1\ \text{cal} = 4.184\ \text{J}$$

Since the calorie and the joule represent relatively small amounts of energy, the units kilocalorie (kcal) and kilojoule (kJ) are often used:

$$1\ \text{kJ} = 1000\ \text{J} \qquad 1\ \text{kcal} = 1000\ \text{cal} \qquad 1\ \text{kcal} = 4.184\ \text{kJ}$$

1 food calorie = 1 kcal.

Although food calories are called "calories," they are really kilocalories and may be referred to as "big calories." To distinguish food calories from ordinary calories, the food calorie abbreviation starts with a capital C:

$$1\ \text{food calorie} = 1\ \text{kcal} = 1\ \text{Cal}$$

SAMPLE EXERCISE 2.4

If there are about 4 Cal in 1 g of protein, how many grams of protein are needed to provide 100 kJ?

Solution:

$$4 \text{ Cal} = 4 \text{ food calories} = 4 \text{ kcal}$$

We wish to convert kilocalories to kilojoules by using the conversion factor

$$1 \text{ kcal} = 4.184 \text{ kJ}$$

$$\frac{1 \text{ g}}{4 \cancel{\text{kcal}}} \times \frac{1 \cancel{\text{kcal}}}{4.184 \cancel{\text{kJ}}} \times 100 \cancel{\text{kJ}} = 5.98 \text{ g}$$

About 6 g of protein will provide 100 kJ.

EXERCISE 2.4

One gram of fat provides about 37,600 J. How many calories is this?

2.9 HEAT ENERGY

Heat is the energy which is transferred to or from an object when that object changes its temperature. For example, water gains heat when its temperature is raised and loses heat when its temperature is lowered. Some substances heat up or cool down more readily than others. The **specific heat** of a substance is the amount of heat required to raise the temperature of one gram of it by one Celsius degree. The specific heat of water is 4.18 J (or 1.00 cal) per gram (g) of water for a 1°C temperature change (t):

$$\text{Specific heat of water} = 4.18 \frac{\text{J}}{\text{g} \times t\ (^\circ\text{C})}$$

or

$$\text{Specific heat of water} = 1.00 \frac{\text{cal}}{\text{g} \times t\ (^\circ\text{C})}$$

The fact that the specific heat of water in calories per gram per degree Celsius happens to be 1.00 is no accident, since the original definition of the calorie was the heat needed to raise the temperature of one gram of water by one degree

TABLE 2.2 **SPECIFIC HEATS OF SOME COMMON SUBSTANCES**

Substance	Specific heat cal/(g)(°C)	Specific heat J/(g)(°C)
Water	1.00	4.18
Alcohol	0.60	2.5
Wood	0.42	1.8
Aluminum	0.21	0.88
Iron	0.12	0.50
Copper	0.093	0.39
Silver	0.056	0.23

Celsius. Table 2.2 lists the specific heats of a variety of common substances. Note that the specific heat for wood is much higher than that listed for metals such as copper or iron. That is why a metal spoon immersed in hot foods heats up much more rapidly than a wooden spoon does. The specific heat of water is much higher than any of the others listed in Table 2.2 and is in fact much higher than that of nearly all substances. For this reason water makes an excellent cooling agent, for example, in the cooling systems of automobiles. A hot-water bottle filled with water remains warm much longer than it would if filled with any other liquid, because it takes more heat to warm water than it would to warm the same amount of a different liquid by the same number of degrees.

Specific heats can be used to calculate the amount of heat energy needed to accomplish temperature changes for given substances. In general, the heat gained or lost depends upon the specific heat, the mass of the substance, and the temperature change:

$$\text{Heat transferred} = \text{specific heat} \times \text{mass} \times \text{temperature change}$$

For example, we can calculate the heat needed to raise the temperature of 20 g of water by 10°C, given the specific heat of water:

$$\text{Specific heat} = 1.00\ \text{cal/(g)(°C)}$$

$$\text{Mass} = 20\ \text{g}$$

$$\text{Temperature change} = 10°\text{C}$$

$$\text{Heat} = \frac{1.00\ \text{cal}}{(\cancel{\text{g}})(°\cancel{\text{C}})} \times 20\ \cancel{\text{g}} \times 10°\cancel{\text{C}} = 200\ \text{cal}$$

SAMPLE EXERCISE 2.5

Calculate the amount of heat needed to raise the temperature of 5.0 g of copper metal from 20°C to the boiling point of water.

Solution:

$$\text{Mass of copper} = 5.0 \text{ g}$$

$$\text{Specific heat of copper} = 0.093 \text{ cal/(g)(°C)}$$

$$\text{Temperature change} = 100°\text{C} - 20°\text{C} = 80°\text{C}$$

$$\text{Heat} = \frac{0.093 \text{ cal}}{(\cancel{\text{g}})(\cancel{°\text{C}})} \times 5.0 \cancel{\text{g}} \times 80\cancel{°\text{C}} = 37 \text{ cal}$$

EXERCISE 2.5

Suppose you wished to line the bottom of a cooking pot with a metal that requires the least amount of heat to raise its temperature. Which two metals listed in Table 2.2 would be best suited for this?

2.10 ENERGY REQUIREMENTS FOR HUMANS

Basal, derived from the word *base*, is used to mean "minimal" or "resting."

As we have seen, humans derive energy from the breakdown of food molecules via chemical reactions. (**Metabolism**, which has to do with the chemical reactions in living systems, is covered in detail in the final four chapters of this text.) Different individuals need different amounts of energy, and thus of food, depending upon their age, weight, activities, and other factors. For a person at rest (physically and emotionally) but awake, the amount of energy which must be expended just to maintain the body is known as the **basal metabolic rate**, or BMR.

The BMR can be roughly estimated by assuming that 101 kJ (24 kcal) is necessary for each kilogram of body weight per day to satisfy the basal (basic) body needs:

$$\text{BMR (estimated)} = \frac{101 \text{ kJ}}{\text{kg}} \times \text{weight (in kg)}$$

By starting with the BMR, total energy needs can be estimated for sedentary persons, those with a moderate level of activity, and very active individuals:

$$\text{Energy for sedentary person} = \text{BMR} + (0.30 \times \text{BMR})$$

$$\text{Energy for moderately active person} = \text{BMR} + (0.40 \times \text{BMR})$$

$$\text{Energy for very active person} = \text{BMR} + (0.50 \times \text{BMR})$$

For example, to estimate the total energy requirements needed for a moderately active person weighing about 55 kg (121 lb), we have

$$\text{BMR} = 101 \frac{\text{kJ}}{\cancel{\text{kg}}} \times 55 \cancel{\text{kg}} = 5555 \text{ kJ (1330 kcal)}$$

$$\text{Total energy required} = 5555 \text{ kJ} + (0.40 \times 5555 \text{ kJ})$$

$$= 7780 \text{ kJ (1860 kcal)}$$

Thus, this person would need to consume enough food to provide 1860 kcal of energy.

SAMPLE EXERCISE 2.6

Make a rough estimate of the total energy required for a 155-lb person who spends a great deal of time studying chemistry and watching television.

Solution:

$$\text{BMR} = \frac{101 \text{ kJ}}{\text{kg}} \times \text{weight (kg)}$$

$$2.2 \text{ lb} = 1 \text{ kg}$$

$$155 \cancel{\text{lb}} \times \frac{1 \text{ kg}}{2.2 \cancel{\text{lb}}} = 70.4 \text{ kg}$$

$$\text{BMR} = \frac{101 \text{ kJ}}{\cancel{\text{kg}}} \times 70.4 \cancel{\text{kg}} = 7110 \text{ kJ (1700 kcal)}$$

$$\text{Total energy} = 7110 \text{ kJ} + (0.30 \times 7110 \text{ kJ})$$
$$= 9240 \text{ kJ (2210 kcal)}$$

This person requires about 2210 Cal.

EXERCISE 2.6

Calculate the total energy requirement for a 155-lb person who plays on the basketball team and runs daily to keep in shape.

The amount of energy which can be derived from various foodstuffs has been determined. The table on the inside back cover lists the caloric content of given portions of some common foods. By using the energy values in the table, you can plan a diet to suit a particular individual.

2.11 LIGHT ENERGY

Photon comes from the Greek *phot-* "light."

The energy associated with light is determined by combining two different views of the nature of light. Light can be thought of as wave motion or as a stream of "particles," which are really energy packets called **photons.**

Properties of Light

The light which comes from some light source such as the sun or an electric light bulb produces waves as it travels. The shape of a typical wave is pictured in Figure 2.7. Another term for light is *electromagnetic radiation,* since the wave is produced as a result of traveling electric and magnetic field disturbances.

All electromagnetic radiation, or light, travels at the same speed, called the *speed of light,* which is given the symbol c:

$$c = 3.00 \times 10^8 \text{ m/s}$$

The distance between any two equivalent points on a wave such as the one in Figure 2.7 is called the *wavelength,* an important identifying feature of light which is symbolized by the Greek letter lambda, λ. The units of a wavelength are the units of length. The number of waves which pass a particular point in one second is the *frequency* ν (Greek nu) and has the unit of 1/s or s^{-1}, often called the hertz (Hz). To summarize these three characteristics of light:

$$c = \text{speed of light } (3.00 \times 10^8 \text{ m/s})$$

$$\lambda = \text{wavelength (length units)}$$

$$\nu = \text{frequency (1/s or Hz)}$$

The speed of light is always equal to the wavelength multiplied by the frequency:

$$c = \lambda \times \nu$$

This means that the shorter the wavelength, the higher the frequency, and the longer the wavelength, the lower the frequency.

Electromagnetic radiation ranges in wavelength from small fractions of a nanometer (cosmic rays) to many meters (radio waves). Figure 2.8 shows the entire range of wavelengths, called the *electromagnetic radiation spectrum,* and gives an approximate wavelength for each of the different kinds of radiation. Note that the visible light that humans can detect is but a tiny sliver of the entire spectrum, which ranges from 390 nm on the violet end to about 760 nm on the red end. The colors in the visible region of the spectrum are shown in Color Plate 3*a*.

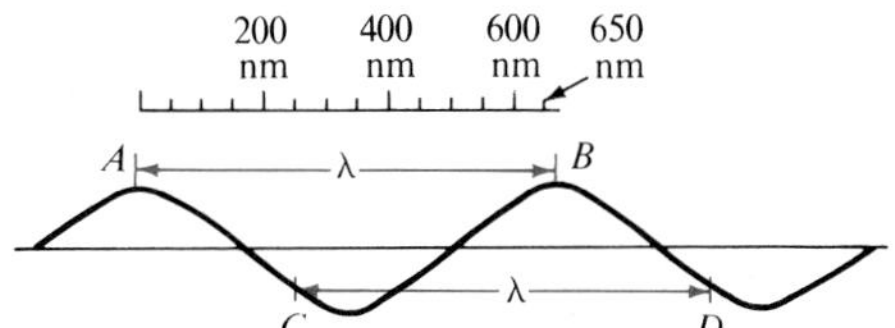
This wave has a wavelength of 650 nm, which is in the red region of the visible spectrum.
200 nm
400 nm
600 nm
650 nm
A
λ
B
λ
C
D

FIGURE 2.7
Light wave and wavelength. Point *A* is equivalent to point *B* on the wave shown. Point *C* corresponds to point *D*. The distance between *A* and *B* and between *C* and *D* are identical and equal to the wavelength lambda, or λ.

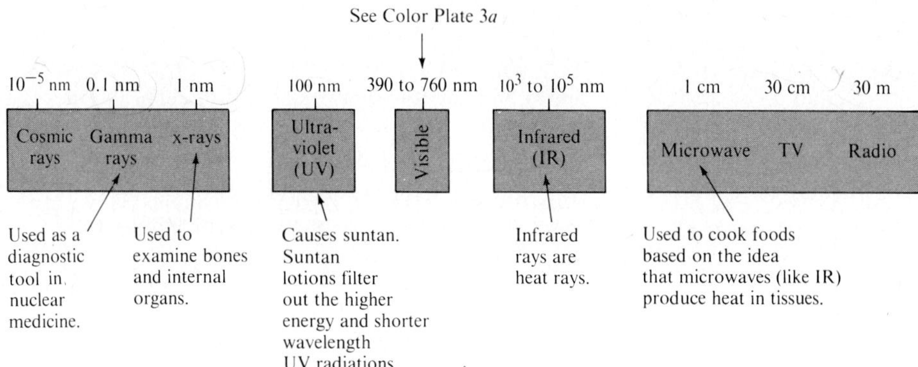

FIGURE 2.8
Electromagnetic radiation spectrum.

Some of the properties of light are best described if we think of light as a stream of energy packets (photons). The energy of each photon is related to its frequency according to the relationship below:

$$\text{Energy of photon} = h \times \nu$$

The *h* in the equation is a constant called Planck's constant, named after Max Planck, the physicist who first proposed this theory around 1900. Because *h* never changes, the energy of a photon depends upon its frequency. From the equation given we see that the higher the frequency of a light photon, the higher its energy. Since high frequencies mean short wavelengths, it can also be said that the lower the wavelength, the higher the photon's energy. Radiation of very low wavelength, such as cosmic rays, gamma rays, x-rays, and even ultraviolet rays, are all highly energetic.

High-energy short wavelength radiations are damaging to living things.

High-energy photons are especially effective in interactions with matter such as body tissues. In some cases they can cause serious biological damage in living things by changing atoms and molecules within their tissues. X-ray photons, for example, can harm genes and chromosomes that are responsible for reproduction. When this happens, offspring from the exposed organism can be born with serious defects. Exposure to any high-energy radiation sources, some of which are used as diagnostic tools in medicine, must be carefully controlled.

SAMPLE EXERCISE 2.7

Which is more energetic, one photon of violet light or one photon of red light?

Solution:

From Color Plate 3*a* we find the following wavelengths:

Violet is about 400 nm
Red is about 700 nm

The wavelength of violet light is shorter than that of red light and so its frequency must be higher. The higher the frequency of light, the higher the energy.

Thus the violet photon has more energy.

EXERCISE 2.7

One photon of which type of radiation below is the most energetic?

(**a**) X-ray (**b**) Ultraviolet (**c**) Microwave (**d**) Yellow light

2.12 LASER LIGHT ENERGY IN SURGERY

Lasers are light sources with special characteristics. Figure 2.9 shows the difference between light that comes from an ordinary light source, such as the sun or a light bulb, and that which comes from a laser. Light energy from a laser travels in a narrow beam, which means that lasers can serve as concentrated sources of light energy (Figure 2.9*a*). Furthermore, the light which comes from a laser is said to be *monochromatic* because it includes only a very narrow band of wavelengths (Figure 2.9*b*). For surgical uses the wavelength of a laser is one of its most important features. Some wavelengths of radiation are more readily absorbed by tissues than others. High-energy, short-wavelength radiation must be avoided because of its potential to cause dangerous chemical alterations in tissues. The lasers used in medicine emit light in the visible and infrared portions of the spectrum, radiation that causes heat production in tissues rather than chemical changes.

One important laser used in surgery, called the carbon dioxide laser, emits radiations with wavelength of about 10,600 nm. Looking at Figure 2.8 we see that this is invisible, infrared radiation. So that the surgeon can see the beam of light used, a red helium neon laser (λ = 633 nm) must also be included.

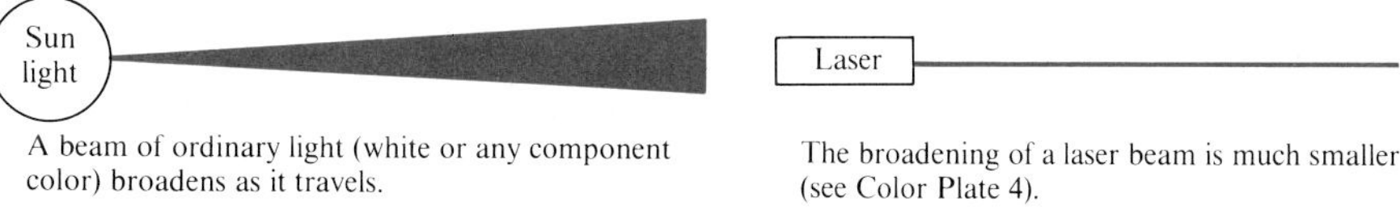

A beam of ordinary light (white or any component color) broadens as it travels.

The broadening of a laser beam is much smaller (see Color Plate 4).

(*a*)

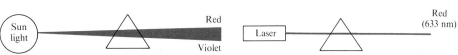

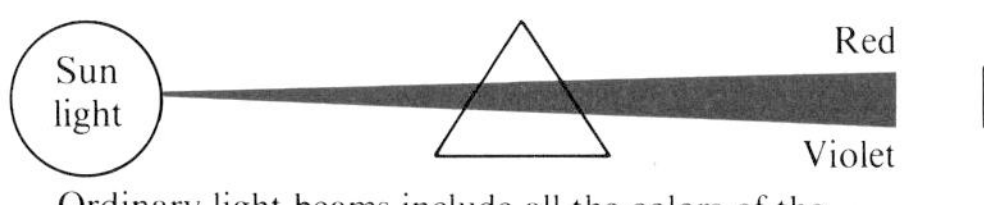

Ordinary light beams include all the colors of the visible spectrum.

Laser

Red (633 nm)

The light from this laser, a helium-neon laser, is monochromatic, 633 nm (red).

(*b*)

FIGURE 2.9
Laser light compared with ordinary light.

In laser surgery light energy can be used instead of the scalpel to cut tissues. One advantage that the laser has over conventional cutting methods is that it causes little bleeding, since coagulation occurs in the blood vessels before bleeding can start. This happens because the laser light energy produces heat in the tissue cells, which modifies the cell protein and produces a physical block to the passage of blood. In ophthalmology lasers are often used to coagulate tissue protein, a process known as *photocoagulation.* Color Plate 4 shows the blue-green beam from an argon laser being used to produce coagulation and obliterate excess blood vessels on the retina of a diabetic patient. Lasers are particularly useful in the area of microsurgery because they can be precisely aimed at even very small targets.

Laser light is used to cut and to coagulate tissues.

The blood vessels are about 30 to 50 μm in size.

SUMMARY

Chemists study the behavior of matter in terms of its microscopic invisible building blocks called atoms, which are discrete particles, and molecules, which are collections of atoms joined by chemical bonds.

Matter can be investigated by examining its properties. Chemical properties describe the ability of a substance to undergo a chemical change. A chemical reaction occurs in which the original substance, the reactant, is converted into a chemically different substance, the product. According to the law of conservation of matter, which states that matter cannot be created or destroyed, the mass of the reactants is always the same as the mass of products. When physical properties are observed, only physical changes occur in which no chemical reaction takes place.

Elements and compounds are pure substances. Elements contain just one kind of atom and cannot be decomposed into simpler substances. Compounds include one kind of molecule in which there are two or more different kinds of atoms joined by chemical bonds. To break down into their constituent elements, compounds must undergo chemical changes. Mixtures are made up of more than one substance. The components of a mixture can be separated from each other by making use of some physical change. Chromatography is an extremely powerful separation method for mixtures.

Chemists also learn a great deal about the nature of matter by studying the energy changes which it undergoes. Energy is the capacity to do work. The SI unit for energy is the joule (J), although the calorie (cal) is sometimes used by chemists and biochemists. Chemical energy (the energy which accompanies chemical reactions), heat energy, mechanical energy, and light energy are some of the various forms of energy. The law of conservation of energy is analogous to the law of conservation of matter and states that like matter, energy may be changed in form but cannot be created or destroyed.

Heat is the energy which is transferred as a body changes its temperature. Specific heat measures the energy needed to raise the temperature of 1 g of a substance by 1°C. Water has an unusually high specific heat and is relatively difficult to heat or cool as compared with most other materials.

Chemical energy is converted to heat energy when heat is evolved in chemical reactions. In humans heat energy is one form of energy produced as a result of the chemical reactions involved in the digestion of food. The energy needed to maintain humans at rest is called the basal metabolic rate (BMR).

Light energy is evaluated by considering both the wave and the particle properties of light. Light has a wavelength λ, frequency ν, and speed c, related by $c = \lambda \times \nu$. Energy packets of light called photons have energies (E) given by the Planck equation, $E = h \times \nu$, in which the h is a constant. Low wavelength, high-frequency photons have high energies. Light energy in the form of a laser can substitute for the scalpel in certain surgical procedures.

KEY WORDS

matter	product	melting point	chemical energy
atoms	physical change	boiling point	law of conservation of matter
molecules	physical property	element	law of conservation of energy
chemical property	physical state	compound	specific heat
chemical change	gas	mixture	basal metabolic rate
chemical reaction	liquid	chromatography	photon
reactant	solid	energy	laser

EXERCISES

2.8 How do physical changes differ from chemical changes?

2.9 For the substances below, which descriptions include physical properties only, chemical properties only, or both chemical and physical properties?
(a) *Glucose* is a white solid.
(b) *Ethanol* boils at 80°C.
(c) *Ether* is highly flammable.
(d) *Sodium* is a soft low-melting solid.
(e) *Nitric acid,* a colorless liquid, discolors skin.

2.10 What physical and chemical properties are included in the following description of the compound called halothane, which is used as a general anesthetic? Halothane is a colorless nonflammable liquid, which is metabolized to the extent of 10 to 20 percent in the human body.

2.11 Which separation below could be accomplished by physical means?
(a) Pure water into hydrogen and oxygen
(b) Salt water into salt and pure water

2.12 If the substances listed in Table 2.1 were all stored at 14°F, which ones would be in physical states different from the ones in the table?

2.13 Deduce the identity of the following two substances, which are among those listed in Table 2.1:
(a) A substance that is a solid at body temperature and liquid at 165°F
(b) A gas that could be liquefied if cooled to 10° below the freezing point of water. (Will your answer depend upon whether the temperature is measured in Celsius or Fahrenheit degrees?)

2.14 Each of the following samples of matter has undergone some transformation. In which cases do you think a chemical reaction has taken place?
(a) Torn paper (b) Melted snow
(c) Tarnished silver (d) Soured milk

2.15 Rust consists of a compound called iron oxide. Is it possible to remove the iron from rust by using a magnet? Why?

2.16 Give a brief description of chromatographic separations.

2.17 One way in which two liquids can be separated is by taking advantage of differences in their boiling points. Two substances in Table 2.1 are practically impossible to separate this way. Which ones are they most likely to be? Can you suggest some other method which could be used to separate them?

2.18 A commercially prepared drug compound was found to cause occasional liver damage. The same drug compound when carefully prepared in a research laboratory produced no toxic side effects. Can you think of a reason for this and an experimental method which could be used to test your theory?

2.19 Mixtures are often not homogeneous, that is, uniform throughout, in appearance. Can you think of a sample of some pure compound which is not homogeneous? (*Hint:* Remember that compounds may exist in more than one physical state.)

2.20 How does the law of conservation of matter apply to chemical reactions?

2.21 A sample of water was decomposed into its elements, producing 2.000 g hydrogen gas and 16.000 g oxygen gas. What was the mass of the original water sample? What law of nature allows this calculation to be made?

2.22 Copper metal reacts with oxygen gas to produce a compound known as an oxide of copper. A sample of copper metal weighing 5.00 g is heated in an open container over which a stream of oxygen gas is passed until the copper has entirely reacted. What experimental measurement would allow you to calculate the mass of oxygen gas used up?

2.23 Of the substances listed below only one is a compound. Which is it: (**a**) Blood; (**b**) urine; (**c**) insulin; (**d**) air; (**e**) sea water?

2.24 What is the difference between the terms *kinetic energy* and *potential energy?* Give examples of each.

2.25 Using the table on the inside back cover, find the number of calories, kilocalories, and joules in 1 tablespoon of sugar.

2.26 What is meant by the term *basal metabolic rate?*

2.27 If running requires an approximate energy expenditure of 3000 kJ/h, what is the "cost" in calories of a 2-h run?

2.28 Calculate the total energy needs in kilojoules and kilocalories for a construction worker weighing 185 lb.

2.29 How much heat in joules and in calories is needed to raise the temperature of a 10-g piece of silver from 25 to 50°C?

2.30 A sample of water gains 250 cal of heat energy in changing from a temperature of 15 to 30°C. What was the mass of the water?

2.31 A 5.0-g piece of wire made of one of the metals in Table 2.2 requires 10.5 cal to raise its temperature by 10°C. Which one is it?

2.32 Why would a "hot alcohol bottle" be less effective than a hot-water bottle?

2.33 Glass has a specific heat of 0.15 cal/(g)(°C). What is the specific heat of glass in joules per gram per degree Celsius? Would it take more heat to raise the temperature from 25 to 35°C for a 100-g sample of glass or a 100-g sample of wood?

2.34 What is meant by the term *photon?*

2.35 How is the energy of a photon related to its: (**a**) Frequency; (**b**) wavelength?

2.36 Of the following radiation types, which one consists of the highest-energy photons: (**a**) Green light; (**b**) ultraviolet; (**c**) infrared (**d**) blue light?

2.37 Why would lasers emitting ultraviolet light be poor choices for use in laser surgery?

2.38 Why is it necessary to include a red helium-neon laser along with a carbon dioxide laser used for surgery?

*2.39 Basal metabolic rates are actually measured in terms of energy per body surface area per hour. The experimental device used measures a volume of oxygen gas consumed in a given time on the assumption that 4.8 cal of heat is generated by the body per liter of oxygen consumed.

A woman weighing 55 kg (121 lb) has a body surface area of 1.6 m^2 and is observed to consume 2000 L of oxygen gas over a 10-min period.

(**a**) Calculate the BMR for this woman in kilocalories per square meter per hour. (Pay very careful attention to units in your calculation.)

(**b**) Calculate her BMR in kilocalories per day and in kilojoules per day.

(**c**) How does the calculated value for (**b**) compare with the estimated daily BMR arrived at by using the equation in Section 2.10?

3 . . . ATOMS

3.1 INTRODUCTION

In Greek *atomos* means "indivisible."

The idea that all matter is composed of atoms was not widely accepted in the scientific community until 1800. Before then there were two conflicting views about the invisible microscopic nature of matter. One hypothesis was that a sample of matter could be divided into smaller and smaller and smaller pieces indefinitely without ever reaching ultimate indivisible particles. The other idea was that if the matter were divided a sufficient number of times, it could eventually be reduced to the indivisible, indestructible particles called **atoms**. It is this theory, the *atomic theory,* which fits the experimental evidence. In the words of Michael Faraday (1794–1867) and J. B. Dumas (1800–1884), two early supporters of the atomic theory, "whether matter be atomic or not, this much is certain, that granting it to be atomic, it would appear as it now does." By this they meant that everything they observed about the behavior of matter was consistent with the idea that it was composed of atoms. Thus, we accept the atomic theory even though we cannot *see* atoms.

3.2 DALTON'S ATOMIC THEORY

The British chemist John Dalton (1766–1844) produced one of the greatest advances in the history of chemistry when he presented his atomic theory in the early 1800s. We will first review the main points of his theory and then show how the theory meshed with the experimental evidence of the time.

Dalton's atomic theory can be summarized to include the following main points:

1. The ultimate particles of elements are atoms.
2. Atoms are indestructible.
3. Elements consist of only one kind of atom.
4. Atoms of different elements differ in mass and in other properties.

5. Compounds consist of molecules (which Dalton called "compound atoms"), which form from *simple* and *fixed* combinations of different kinds of atoms. (By *simple* combinations he meant whole number ratios of atoms.)

We will discover that some of the points of Dalton's theory (2 and 3) do not agree with modern experimental evidence because atoms can be broken down and atoms of one particular element can differ in mass. However, the theory did agree with several important laws of nature known in the early 1800s. For instance, the law of conservation of matter, which says that matter can neither be created nor destroyed (Section 2.6), agrees with Dalton's idea of indestructible atoms. According to Dalton, creating or destroying atoms is as unlikely as trying to introduce new planets into the solar system or to annihilate ones already in existence.

The **law of constant composition** states that chemical compounds always break down in a constant, predictable way. For instance, a 100.00-g sample of water always produces 88.89 g of the element oxygen and 11.11 g of the element hydrogen. This is true no matter whether the water comes from the ocean, from a sample of urine, or from any other source. This is consistent with Dalton's point that compounds consist of molecules that form from *fixed* combinations of atoms.

It is possible for two elements A and B to form more than one compound. According to the **law of multiple proportions,** the weight of A relative to that of B in each of the compounds must be multiples of each other. We can use two compounds containing the elements N and O, N_2O (nitrous oxide) and NO (nitric oxide), to illustrate this. In N_2O a 100.0-g sample contains 63.6 g N and 36.4 g O, that is, 63.6/36.4, or *1.75* times as much N as O. A 100.0-g sample of NO always produces 46.7 g N and 53.3 g O, that is, 46.7/53.3, or *0.877* times as much N as O. Thus we see that in N_2O the weight of N relative to the weight of O is very close to twice (1.75/0.877) the weight of N relative to O in NO. That the law of multiple proportions holds agrees with point 5 in Dalton's theory, which says that atoms must unite in *simple* combinations.

3.3 ELEMENT SYMBOLS

With the discovery of atoms came the chemical alphabet of element symbols. Dalton chose the circle as the symbol for oxygen and represented all other elements by variations of the circle. These early primitive symbols evolved into the modern system of using one or two letters of the English alphabet. The first letter is always a capital and the second, if there is one, a lowercase letter. The symbols are often formed from the first letter of the element name or from the first letter along with one other. For example, B stands for the element **b**oron, Ba for **ba**rium, Be for **be**ryllium, and Bk for **b**er**k**elium.

For some of the 106 elements it is not possible to guess the symbol by examining the English name. For instance, the symbol for the element iron is Fe (not I or Ir). Iron, along with copper, silver, gold, sodium, potassium, lead, tin, antimony, and tungsten have symbols that are derived from one or two letters of their Latin or German names (see Table 3.1).

TABLE 3.1 ELEMENTS WITH SYMBOLS BASED UPON NON-ENGLISH NAMES

Element name	Latin or German name	Symbol
Iron	Ferrum	Fe
Tungsten	Wolfram	W
Copper	Cuprum	Cu
Gold	Aurum	Au
Silver	Argentum	Ag
Sodium	Natrium	Na
Potassium	Kalium	K
Mercury	Hydrargyrum	Hg
Lead	Plumbum	Pb
Tin	Stannum	Sn
Antimony	Stibium	Sb

The symbols and names for all the elements are listed in alphabetical order on the inside cover of the text. Table 3.2 gives the 11 elements that constitute the bulk of living matter and the 11 most abundant elements in the earth's crust. Note that the most abundant elements in nature, namely, O, Si, Al, and Fe, are different from those in the human body, namely, H, O, C, and N. We will see that C has special chemical properties that make it particularly suitable to serve as one of the fundamental elements of life.

TABLE 3.2 ABUNDANCE OF ELEMENTS IN THE EARTH AND IN THE HUMAN BODY

Human body		Earth	
H	63*	O	47
O	25.5	Si	28
C	9.5	Al	7.9
N	1.4	Fe	4.5
Ca	0.31	Ca	3.5
P	0.22	Na	2.5
Cl	0.08	K	2.5
K	0.06	Mg	2.2
S	0.05	Ti	0.46
Na	0.03	H	0.22
Mg	0.01	C	0.19

*For each element the numbers listed represent the percentage of total atoms of that element in the body or on the earth.

3.4 FORMULAS

Element symbols are the "letters" of the chemical alphabet. In formulas they are combined to spell out the "words" of the language of chemistry. The **formulas** used to represent compounds and elements include element symbols and subscripts. The element symbols identify the kinds of atoms present and the subscripts give the number of each kind of atom. The subscripts must always be whole numbers. The compound water, for instance, contains water molecules in which there are two hydrogen atoms joined to one oxygen atom, which means that the chemical formula for water is written H_2O:

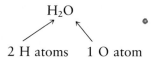

H_2O

2 H atoms → 1 O atom

Note that the presence of one atom of oxygen is understood so that we do not include a subscript 1. The compound diethyl ether contains three elements, carbon, hydrogen, and oxygen. In each diethyl ether molecule there are two atoms of carbon, six atoms of hydrogen, and one atom of oxygen, so the chemical formula is C_2H_6O.

A group of elements such as PO_4 is sometimes called a *radical.*

In some formulas parentheses are used to indicate that an entire group of atoms appears more than once. For example, the formula for a major constituent of bones and teeth is $Ca_3(PO_4)_2$, a compound called calcium phosphate. The subscript outside the parentheses applies to all the atoms in the parentheses. Thus each molecule of calcium phosphate contains three calcium atoms, two phosphorus atoms, and eight oxygen atoms.

$Ca_3(PO_4)_2$

3 Ca atoms 2 PO_4 containing 2 P atoms and 8 O atoms

The formulas for most elements are the same as the element symbol; for example, the formula for iron is Fe and the formula for carbon is C. However, some elements consist of two or more atoms connected to each other by chemical bonds to form molecules. They are still elements because they contain just one *kind* of atom. For example, the element oxygen, present in air, is actually composed of oxygen molecules. In each molecule two oxygen atoms are joined by a chemical bond. This form of elemental oxygen is represented by the formula O_2. The subscript 2 means that there are two oxygen atoms per oxygen molecule. The element oxygen also exists in another form, O_3, called *ozone,* in which there are three O atoms per molecule. Both O_2 and O_3 are element formulas because they include oxygen atoms only. Other examples of elements in which atoms are connected by chemical bonds to form molecules include: hydrogen, H_2; phosphorus, P_4; sulfur, S_8; nitrogen, N_2; and chlorine, Cl_2.

The terms *mon*atomic, *di*atomic, *tri*atomic, *tetra*tomic, and so on, are used to indicate the number of atoms per molecule. Thus C and Fe are monatomic; O_2, H_2, N_2, and Cl_2 are all diatomic; O_3 is triatomic; P_4 is tetratomic; and S_8 is octatomic.

SAMPLE EXERCISE 3.1

For each of the formulas below, give the name and number of each kind of atom present.

(a) Hg_2O (b) C_6H_6 (c) $Al_2(SO_4)_3$

Solution:

(a) 2 mercury atoms
1 oxygen atom
(The subscript 1 is understood for O).

(b) 6 carbon atoms
6 hydrogen atoms

(c) 2 aluminum atoms
3 sulfur atoms
12 oxygen atoms
The subscript 3 means that there are 3 SO_4 groups

EXERCISE 3.1

One ingredient of tincture of iodine is elemental iodine, which contains diatomic molecules. What is its formula?

3.5 SUBATOMIC PARTICLES

Dalton's atomic theory was wrong about the indestructible atom (main point 2 of theory).

In order to understand how atoms combine to form molecules, it is necessary to take a closer look at the atom. It *is* true that ordinary chemical and physical processes cannot break down atoms. However, it is *not* true that atoms are indestructible. Atoms can be broken down via nuclear processes (which are discussed in Chapter 6 on nuclear chemistry). Particles smaller than even the smallest atoms are called **subatomic particles.**

The first subatomic particle to be observed was the **electron** (1870s), which was followed by the **proton** (later 1800s) and then the **neutron** (1930s). To date about 30 subatomic particles have been identified, including positrons, quarks, neutrinos, and mesons. Protons, neutrons, and electrons are the particles of greatest interest to chemists.

The protons and neutrons account for nearly all the mass of an atom. The mass of a proton is just slightly less than that of a neutron:

$$\text{Proton mass} = 1.673 \times 10^{-24}\ \text{g}$$

$$\text{Neutron mass} = 1.675 \times 10^{-24}\ \text{g}$$

The mass of an electron is considerably less than that of either a proton or a neutron:

$$\text{Electron mass} = 9.110 \times 10^{-28}\ \text{g}$$

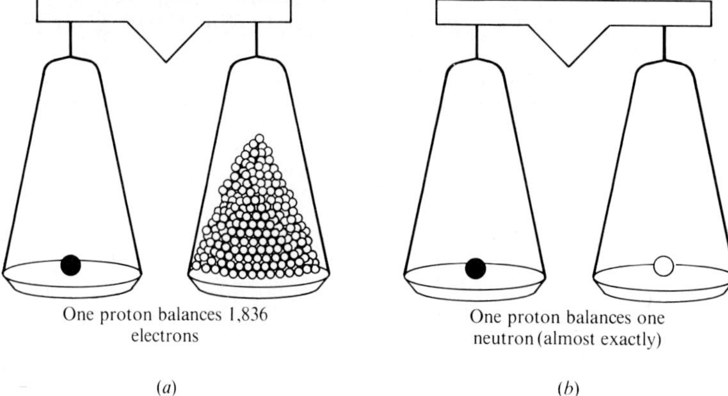
One proton balances 1,836 electrons
(a)
One proton balances one neutron (almost exactly)
(b)

FIGURE 3.1
Comparing the masses of protons, neutrons, and electrons.

Comparing the masses of the proton and electron, we see that protons are nearly 2000 times as massive as electrons:

$$\frac{\text{Proton mass}}{\text{Electron mass}} = \frac{1.673 \times 10^{-24}\ \cancel{\text{g}}}{9.110 \times 10^{-28}\ \cancel{\text{g}}} = 1836$$

Figure 3.1 shows an imaginary weighing experiment which illustrates the relative masses of protons, electrons, and neutrons. (Protons, neutrons, and electrons are much too small to be actually weighed on any balance constructed by humans, the most sensitive of which can weigh things only to the nearest 10^{-6} g.)

It is difficult to comprehend how incredibly small are the masses of subatomic particles. Even a particle of the finest dust weighs about 10^{-14} g. A single proton or neutron has a mass only one six-trillionth of the mass of the tiniest speck of dust! The masses of subatomic particles are so small that quoting them in grams is awkward. A convenient unit to use is the **atomic mass unit,** abbreviated **amu:**

$$1 \text{ amu} = 1.66057 \times 10^{-24} \text{ g}$$

The masses of the proton and the neutron are close to 1 amu and the mass of the electron is 1/1836 amu.

Electric charge is another important identifying feature of subatomic particles. There are two kinds of charge, positive (+) and negative (−). Like charges repel each other and opposite charges attract. When hair is vigorously combed on a dry day, it becomes positively charged and is attracted by the comb, which becomes negatively charged (see Figure 3.2). The SI unit for charge is the coulomb (C). One coulomb is an enormous charge. Shuffling across a thick rug on a dry winter day produces a charge of about one-millionth of a coulomb, or 10^{-6} C.

The charges on the proton and the electron are the same in magnitude but opposite in sign—protons are positive and electrons are negative. Neutrons have no charge.

$$\text{Proton charge} = +1.60 \times 10^{-19} \text{ C}$$

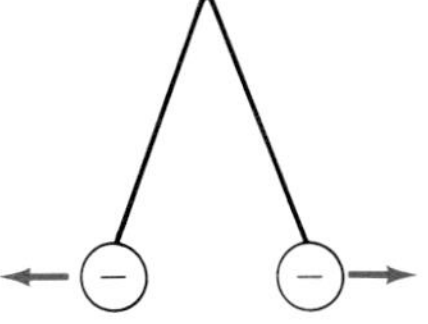

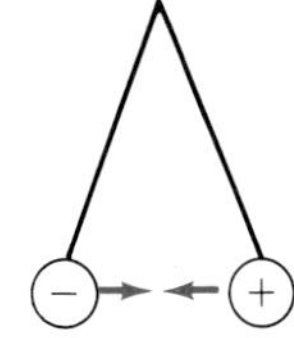

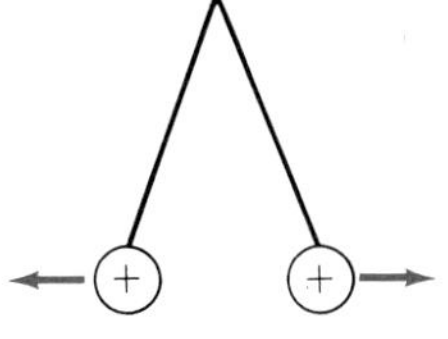
Like charges repel

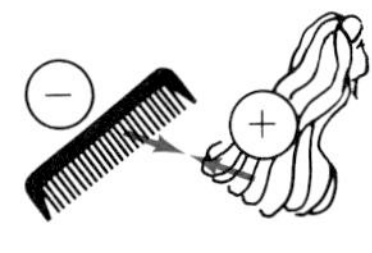
Opposite charges attract

FIGURE 3.2
+ and − charges.

$$\text{Electron charge} = -1.60 \times 10^{-19}\ \text{C}$$
$$\text{Neutron charge} = 0$$

Electric charges are often expressed in terms of multiples of 1.60×10^{-19} C, the charge on the proton. According to this system, the proton charge is simply +1, while that of the electron becomes −1.

$$\text{Proton charge} = +1$$
$$\text{Electron charge} = -1$$
$$\text{Neutron charge} = 0$$

A charge of +2 is 2 times 1.60×10^{-19} C or 3.20×10^{-19} C, a charge of −2 is -3.20×10^{-19} C, and so on.

The symbols p (or p^+), e (or e^-), and n can be used to represent protons, electrons, and neutrons. Table 3.3 summarizes the masses and charges of the proton, electron, and neutron.

TABLE 3.3 **MASSES AND CHARGES OF THE PROTON, NEUTRON, AND ELECTRON**

Particle	Symbol	Mass	Charge
Proton	p (or p^+)	1.673×10^{-24} g or ≈ 1 amu	1.60×10^{-19} C or +1
Neutron	n	1.675×10^{-24} g or ≈ 1 amu	0
Electron	e (or e^-)	9.110×10^{-28} g or 1/1836 amu	-1.60×10^{-19} C or −1

3.6 THE "EMPTY" ATOM

At least 99.95 percent of the mass of an atom is located in a tiny volume with a radius that is only one ten-thousandth that of the whole atom. This is the **nucleus** of the atom, where the protons and neutrons reside. The much less massive electrons occupy nearly the entire atomic volume (see Figure 3.3). To give you an idea of just how empty this is, imagine that a lowercase "o" on a page of this text represents the nucleus of a carbon atom. The electrons in this atom would occupy a volume with a radius of about 50 ft!

Atoms are mostly empty space.

That all matter is mostly empty space was discovered by Lord Rutherford (1871–1937), a physicist who was studying the element radium, Ra. Radium is one example of a **radioactive element**. The atoms of radioactive elements have unstable nuclei and so spontaneously disintegrate, with the emission of smaller particles. The nuclei of radium atoms emit particles called **alpha (α) particles,** which have a mass of 4 amu and a charge of +2. Rutherford was interested in the ability of these alpha particles to penetrate solid matter. Would they, for example, penetrate a section of gold foil with a thickness of about 1000 atoms? This is what he observed when he tried this experiment:

1. Of about 100,000 alpha particles shot at the gold foil, 99,999 went through as if there were nothing in the way. From this, Rutherford concluded that *most of the atom must be empty space.*
2. One out of every 100,000 particles was deflected. Of the deflected alphas, some were actually rejected by this foil. These, he believed, must have made direct hits with a *positively charged nucleus,* which repelled the positively charged alpha particles. Because so few particles do this, *the nucleus must occupy only a very small part of the atomic volume.*

From this important experiment, done in 1911, the modern picture of the atom

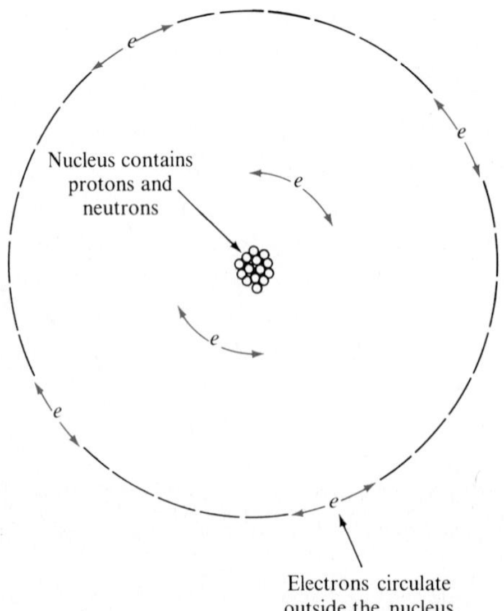
Nucleus contains protons and neutrons
e
e
e
e
e
e
Electrons circulate outside the nucleus.

FIGURE 3.3
Empty atom. The diagram is not drawn to scale. The nucleus, with a diameter of 1/10,000th that of the entire atom would be too small to see.

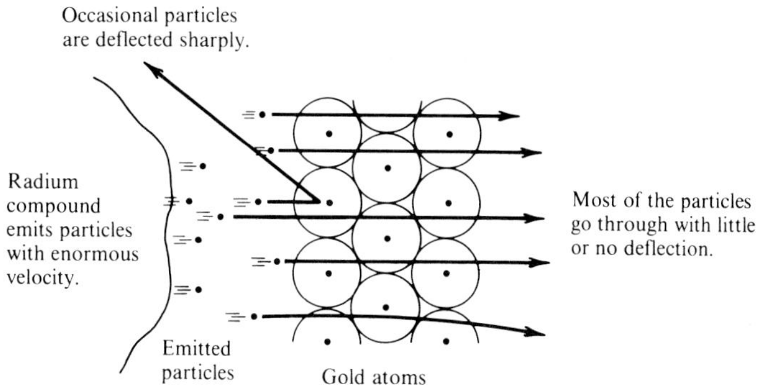

FIGURE 3.4
Rutherford's experiment with gold.

Occasional particles are deflected sharply.
Radium compound emits particles with enormous velocity.
Most of the particles go through with little or no deflection.
Emitted particles
Gold atoms

began to develop. A simplified diagram of Rutherford's experiment is shown in Figure 3.4, in which only 3 of the 1000 gold atoms are included.

3.7 ATOMIC NUMBER Z

The identity of an element depends upon the number of protons in the nuclei of its atoms. The number of protons in the nucleus of an atom is called the **atomic number** of the atom, labeled Z. All atoms of the same element *must* have the same number of protons.

The atomic number of an element is the same as the ordering number of that element in the periodic table of elements, pictured on the inside cover of this text. The atomic number Z is the whole number printed in the upper part of each element box. For instance, carbon is the sixth element in the periodic table and has an atomic number of 6:

The atomic number identifies an element.

6
C

That is, *all* carbon atoms have six protons in their nuclei. Furthermore, any atom which has six protons in its nucleus *has* to be a carbon atom.

In an uncharged atom the number of electrons is equal to the number of protons. All uncharged or neutral atoms must have a net charge of zero. The number of positively charged protons and the number of negatively charged electrons in an atom must be the same. For example, all neutral carbon atoms contain six electrons. There is no special symbol for the number of electrons in an atom.

SAMPLE EXERCISE 3.2

How many protons and electrons are there in one gold atom?

Solution:

The symbol for gold is Au. Au is the seventy-ninth element in the periodic table.

$$\text{Atomic number} = 79 \qquad \boxed{\begin{array}{c}79\\ \text{Au}\end{array}}$$

$$Z = 79$$

One gold atom contains 79 protons and 79 electrons.

EXERCISE 3.2

An atom of an element has 19 protons in its nucleus. Give the symbol and name of the element.

3.8 ISOTOPES AND MASS NUMBERS

The sum of the number of protons and the number of neutrons in the nucleus of an atom is the **mass number.** If we choose the label A for mass number and N for the number of neutrons, then

$$A = N + Z$$

The existence of isotopes violates main point 3 of Dalton's atomic theory.

Atoms of the same element must have the same number of protons, that is, the same value of Z. However, they *can* have a different number of neutrons in their nuclei. **Isotopes** are atoms of the same element which contain a different number of neutrons and thus have different mass numbers. For instance, there are three oxygen isotopes in nature. They all have 8 protons in their nuclei (otherwise they would not be oxygen), but one has 8, one 9, and the third 10 neutrons. Table 3.4 lists the natural abundance of oxygen and chlorine isotopes. No matter where on earth oxygen is found, its isotopes will be present in the same relative amounts. We can interpret the numbers to mean that for every 10,000 atoms of oxygen

TABLE 3.4 **ISOTOPES OF OXYGEN AND CHLORINE**

Isotope	p	n	e	Natural abundance, %
^{16}O, or O-16	8	8	8	99.76
^{17}O, or O-17	8	9	8	0.04
^{18}O, or O-18	8	10	8	0.20
^{35}Cl, or Cl-35	17	18	17	75.53
^{37}Cl, or Cl-37	17	20	17	24.47

TABLE 3.5

^{16}O	^{17}O	^{18}O
$Z = 8$	$Z = 8$	$Z = 8$
$N = 8$	$N = 9$	$N = 10$
$A = N + Z$	$A = N + Z$	$A = N + Z$
$A = 8 + 8 = 16$	$A = 9 + 8 = 17$	$A = 10 + 8 = 18$

we breathe, 9976 atoms will have 8 neutrons, 20 atoms will have 10 neutrons, and 4 atoms will have 9 neutrons.

The mass number A of a particular isotope is indicated by placing a superscript on the left of the element symbol. The atomic number Z is the subscript on the left of the symbol. For an isotope of the element E the symbol is written

$$^{A}_{Z}\mathrm{E}$$

Thus the symbols for the three isotopes of oxygen are as given in Table 3.5.

Because the element symbol automatically fixes the atomic number of an element, the Z is often omitted from the symbol. The isotopes of oxygen could then be written

$$^{16}\mathrm{O} \qquad ^{17}\mathrm{O} \qquad ^{18}\mathrm{O}$$

A third way to indicate a particular isotope is to write its element symbol followed by the mass number: E-A, as in O-18.

The symbols in the periodic table refer to an average atom of an element.

If you examine the element boxes in the periodic table, you will not find the number which corresponds to the mass number A. That is because the element symbols in the periodic table do not represent any particular isotope. Rather the symbol O refers to the mixture of oxygen isotopes in nature, that is, to an *average* oxygen atom, not to any one particular oxygen isotope.

Many elements have, like oxygen, one highly predominant isotope, but there are some exceptions. About 75 percent of all chlorine atoms have 18 neutrons and a mass number of 35, while the other 25 percent have 20 neutrons and a mass number of 37 (see Table 3.4). Some elements, sodium and fluorine, for instance, do not have any isotopes in nature. All natural sodium is Na-23 and all fluorine is F-19.

SAMPLE EXERCISE 3.3

An isotope of cobalt containing 33 neutrons is used in the treatment of cancer. Write the symbol for this isotope.

Solution:

The symbol for cobalt is Co.
Co is element number 27.
In this Co isotope there are 33 n and 27 p.
To find A:
$A = Z + N$
$N = 33$
$Z = 27$
$A = 27 + 33 = 60$

The isotope symbol is written $^{60}_{27}Co$, ^{60}Co, or Co-60.

EXERCISE 3.3

How many protons, neutrons, and electrons are present in U-235 and U-238, two isotopes of the element uranium?

3.9 ATOMIC WEIGHT

Dalton recognized the hopelessness of ascertaining the *absolute weights* of atoms because atoms are much too small to be weighed. However, he realized that it was possible to determine the *relative weights* of different kinds of atoms, that is, it is possible to compare the weights of a large number of atoms of element A with that of the same number of atoms of element B. Using relative atomic weights, Dalton hoped to be able to determine formulas for compounds by measuring the weights of the elements needed to make the compound.

To see why we need relative atomic weights to do this, let's try to interpret the results of an experiment without them. Suppose we find that mixing 2 g of hydrogen with 16 g of oxygen gives 18 g of water with nothing left over. By itself, these data cannot provide the chemical formula for water. All we can say is that the mass of the element oxygen in water is eight times that of the element hydrogen. To find the formula for water we must first know how much heavier oxygen atoms are than hydrogen atoms, that is, their relative atomic weights.

The atomic weights of the elements in the periodic table are the decimal numbers under the element symbols. **Atomic weights** for elements are determined by comparing a very large number of the atoms of the element with the same number of atoms of C-12, which in 1961 was the isotope chosen to be the reference standard. By definition the atomic weight of C-12 is exactly 12:

$$\text{Atomic weight of C-12} = 12 \text{ (exactly)}$$

1
H
1.008

The atomic weight of H, for instance, is 1.008, meaning that H atoms are about one-twelfth as heavy as C-12 atoms. Figure 3.5 shows an imaginary weighing experiment in which we see that 12 H atoms are required to balance one C-12 atom. One reason that the number 12 was chosen for the atomic weight of C-

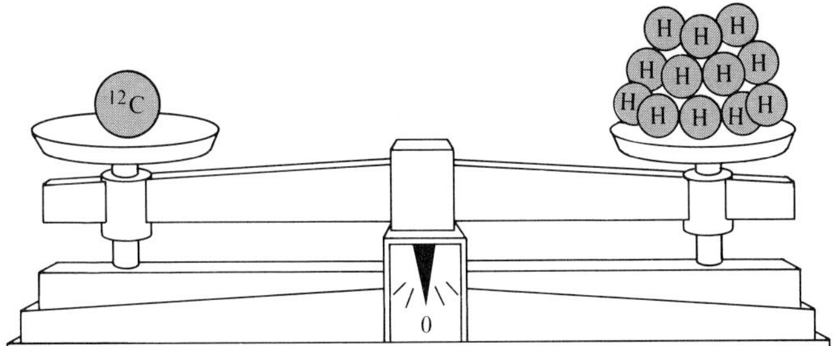

FIGURE 3.5
The atomic weight of hydrogen compared with carbon-12. The atomic weight of hydrogen is 1.0, meaning that it would require 12 hydrogen atoms to balance a single carbon-12 atom. This experiment, however, is impossible to do.

12 is that it fixes the atomic weight of H close to 1, a convenient value for the lightest known element.

For doing most calculations it is acceptable to retain just one digit to the right of the decimal place in an atomic weight. Thus, the atomic weight for H can be rounded off to 1.0. The atomic weight for 0 is 15.999, which is rounded to 16.0.

SAMPLE EXERCISE 3.4

If the atoms of an element are about nine times as heavy as C-12 atoms, what is the element?

Solution:

The element must have an atomic weight of about 9 × 12, or 108. The element with an atomic weight closest to 108 is silver, Ag.

47
Ag
107.89

EXERCISE 3.4

Atoms of C-12 are about three times as heavy as atoms of what other element?

The atomic weight of an element is the weighted average of the atomic weights of all its natural isotopes and can be calculated if the atomic weights and relative abundances of the isotopes are given. Thus, to determine the weighted average, the fraction of each isotope is multiplied by its atomic weight. This is similar to the method used to calculate a course grade. For instance, suppose that your chemistry grade is to be computed from a midterm which is 40 percent of your grade and a final which is 60 percent. If you get a grade of 90 in the midterm and an 80 in the final, your grade is determined by taking a weighted average:

$$\text{Grade} = (0.40 \times 90) + (0.60 \times 80) = 84$$

There are two naturally occurring chlorine isotopes, Cl-35 and Cl-37. Their atomic weights and relative abundances (retaining just three significant figures) are

Cl-35	Atomic weight = 35.0	75.5%
Cl-37	Atomic weight = 37.0	24.5%

To calculate the atomic weight of Cl, a weighted average is used:

$$\text{Atomic weight Cl} = (0.755 \times 35.0) + (0.245 \times 37.0)$$

$$\text{Atomic weight Cl} = 35.5$$

SAMPLE EXERCISE 3.5

From the atomic weights and natural abundances given for the three isotopes of magnesium, calculate the atomic weight of Mg.

Mg-24	Atomic weight = 24.0	78.7%
Mg-25	Atomic weight = 25.0	10.1%
Mg-26	Atomic weight = 26.0	11.2%

Solution:

Calculate a weighted average:

$$\text{Atomic weight Mg} = (24.0 \times 0.787) + (25.0 \times 0.101) + (26.0 \times 0.112)$$

The atomic weight of Mg is 24.3.

EXERCISE 3.5

Natural copper is 69.1 percent Cu-63 (atomic weight = 62.9) and 30.9 percent Cu-65 (atomic weight = 64.9). Calculate the atomic weight of copper.

3.10 FORMULA WEIGHT

The **formula weight** of an element or compound is calculated by adding the atomic weights of all the atoms in its formula. For example, the formula weight of Na, the formula for monatomic sodium, is the same as the atomic weight of Na:

$$\text{Formula weight of Na} = 23.0$$

The term molecular weight is often used instead of formula weight.

The formula weight of O_2 is twice the atomic weight of O:

$$\text{Formula weight of } O_2 = 2 \times 16.0 = 32.0$$

The formula weight of water, H_2O, is the sum of the atomic weights of two H atoms and one O atom:

$$\text{Formula weight of } H_2O = (2 \times 1.0) + (1 \times 16.0) = 18.0$$

SAMPLE EXERCISE 3.6

Calculate the formula weight of the compound barium nitrate, $Ba(NO_3)_2$.

Solution:

First, look up the atomic weights:

Atomic weight of Ba = 137.3
Atomic weight of N = 14.0
Atomic weight of O = 16.0

In the formula $Ba(NO_3)_2$ there are

One Ba atom
Two N atoms
Six O atoms

$$\text{Formula weight} = (1 \times 137.3) + (2 \times 14.0) + (6 \times 16.0)$$

The formula weight of $Ba(NO_3)_2$ = 261.3.

EXERCISE 3.6

Find the formula weight of iron(II) sulfate, $FeSO_4$, a compound that is used to treat iron deficiency anemia.

In Chapter 5 we will use measured atomic weights and formula weights to calculate the amounts of materials that are consumed or produced in chemical reactions.

3.11 ELECTRONS IN ATOMS

Although electrons hardly contribute to the mass of atoms, it is the electrons that are responsible for the chemical properties of atoms. Electrons form the bonds that connect atoms to one another to form molecules. Since chemical reactions involve the making and breaking of bonds, chemists are particularly interested in electrons in atoms. The way in which the electrons are distributed in an atom is called the *electronic structure* of the atom. The Rutherford empty atom, with its small, heavy positive nucleus surrounded by circulating electrons, was able to give a general picture of all atoms but could not provide a detailed electronic structure for any atom. Modern atomic theory describes electronic structures well enough to explain and to predict a great deal of the chemical behavior of atoms.

This modern theory is based upon complex mathematics, so here we will present only a general picture of the electronic structure that it provides. Included in the electronic structure are the energies of electrons and the regions of space occupied by the electrons.

3.12 ELECTRONIC CONFIGURATIONS

Each electron in an atom possesses a total energy (kinetic plus potential). The lowest-energy electrons are those closest to the nucleus of the atom and are the most difficult to remove from the atom. The highest-energy electrons are those farthest from the nucleus and are the ones most easily removed, because the electrostatic attraction between the negatively charged electrons and positively charged nucleus is greater, the closer they are to each other. High-energy electrons are the ones which are especially important in the formation of chemical bonds.

The positions of electrons in atoms, that is, their distances from the nucleus, cannot be determined exactly. There is a fundamental reason for this, which depends upon the fact that there is always some uncertainty in measuring the positions of microscopic particles, because any physical method used to measure the position of an electron actually moves the electron! Modern atomic theory describes the positions of electrons in atoms by giving probabilities that they are at some given distance from the nucleus.

Niels Bohr (1885–1962), a Danish physicist, first introduced the idea of *electronic energy levels*. He made use of two ideas which we have already introduced. One cornerstone of his atomic model was the Rutherford picture of the atom, in which the positively charged nucleus occupies a tiny volume and the electrons circulate outside. The other was the quantum theory of energy, which we applied to light energy in Chapter 2.

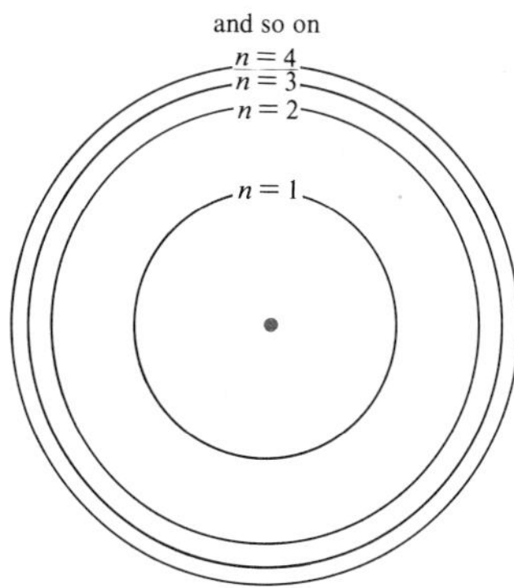

FIGURE 3.6
Bohr energy levels. The first four energy levels in Bohr's model of the hydrogen atom. The colored dot represents the nucleus of the atom.

According to Bohr, the energy levels in atoms can be pictured as orbits in which electrons travel at definite distances from the nucleus (see Figure 3.6). These he called "quantized energy levels," also known as *principal energy levels*, each of which was labeled with an integer number *n* called a **principal quantum number**. According to Bohr, these, and *only* these, energy levels could be occupied by electrons.

Bohr's original theory laid the groundwork for modern atomic theory. In 1926 Erwin Schrödinger (1887–1961) proposed the modern picture of the atom, which is used today. This theory is based upon a complicated mathematical approach. Without presenting the details of this approach, we can give the results.

In the Schrödinger atom, the principal energy levels used by Bohr are divided into *sublevels*. The sublevels are designated by a principal quantum number and a lowercase letter (*s*, *p*, *d*, and *f*). The higher the energy level, the more sublevels there are. Thus, the first principal energy level has only one sublevel, *s* (called 1*s*); the second principal energy level has two sublevels, *s* and *p* (designated 2*s* and 2*p*); the third principal energy level has three sublevels, *s*, *p*, and *d* (designated 3*s*, 3*p*, and 3*d*). The *p* energy sublevels come in groups of three, all of which are at the same energy. The *d* sublevels appear in groups of five, and the *f* sublevels in groups of seven. (We will not encounter *f* sublevels in our discussions.) The Schrödinger energy sublevels which correspond to the first few Bohr levels are

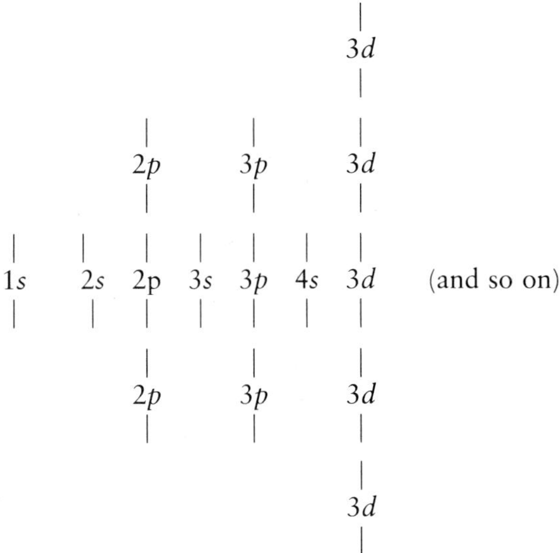

You will notice that there is a peculiarity in this ordering of energy levels. According to the Schrödinger model, the 4*s* level has a lower energy than the 3*d* levels. Similar anomalies in the ordering of energy levels appear as the principal quantum number increases. Figure 3.7 provides a memory device which is useful in remembering the ordering of energy levels in atoms.

The electronic energy levels (1*s*, 2*s*, 2*p*, and so on) are also called **orbitals**. We can think of these orbitals as three-dimensional "probability" shapes. Their surfaces represent points at which there is an equal probability of finding the electron. The shapes are different for *s*, *p*, *d*, and *f* orbitals; the *s* orbitals are spherical (see Figure 3.8*a*) and the *p* orbitals are dumbbell-shaped. The three *p*

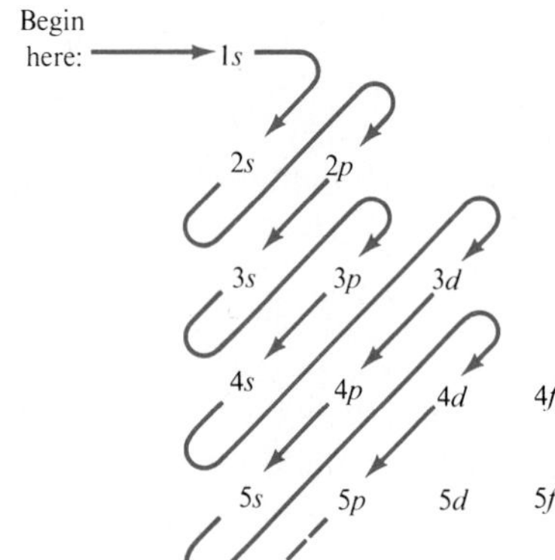

FIGURE 3.7
Energies of atomic orbitals. To help you remember this ordering, you can follow the diagram, noting that the orbital belonging to energy level 1 is written in row 1 and those belonging to level 2, in row 2; and so on.

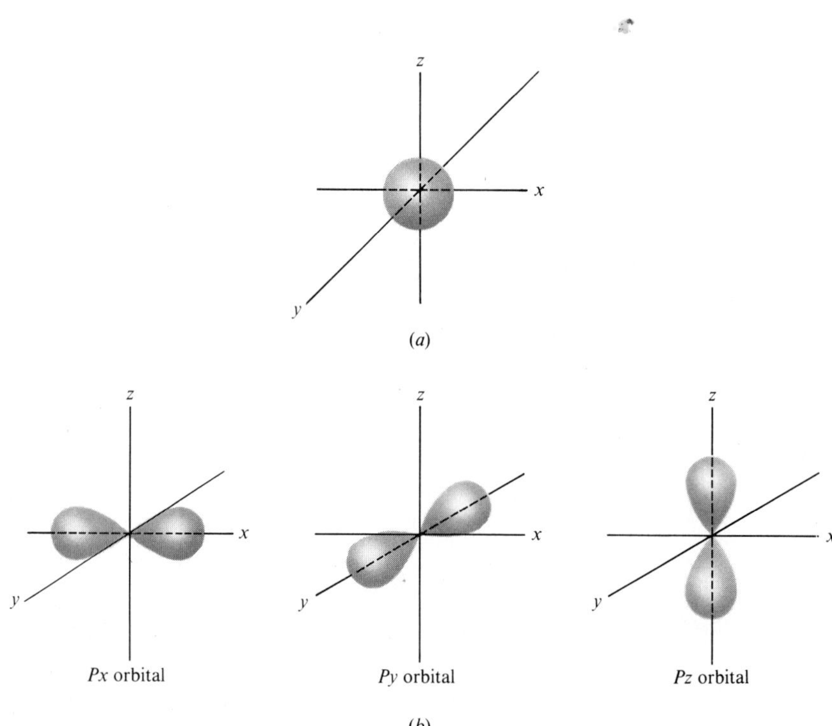

FIGURE 3.8
(*a*) *s*- and (*b*) *p*-orbital shapes.

orbitals are oriented perpendicular to each other, as shown in Figure 3.8*b*. We can say, for instance, that an electron is in a 1*s* orbital, a 3*p* orbital, or a 4*s* orbital, and so on. The Schrödinger model also makes it possible to calculate the most probable distance from the nucleus for an electron in an atom. However, there is a probability that the electron may be closer or farther away than this calculated distance. Figure 3.9 uses dots to represent the probability of finding an electron at some point in a 1*s* orbital of hydrogen; where the density of dots is highest, the probability of finding the electron is highest. Note that the density

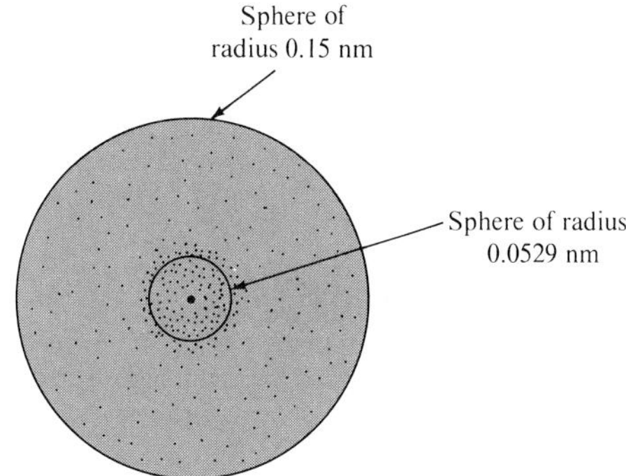

FIGURE 3.9
Hydrogen 1*s* orbital (cloud picture). The density of dots is highest where the probability of finding the electron is highest.

of dots is very great at a radius of 0.0529 nm. Thus, the electron in a 1*s* orbital of a hydrogen atom has a very high probability of being 0.0529 nm from the nucleus. The low density of dots beyond a radius of 0.15 nm means that the probability of finding the electron there is also very low.

Each orbital can hold no more than *two* electrons. The two electrons in a particular orbital differ in one way, namely, they have different *spins*. (The concept of a spinning electron is part of the modern atomic model.) Electrons can "spin" in one of two directions, which we indicate by using arrows, one pointing upward and one pointing downward:

$\uparrow \; \downarrow$ The two possible spins

From knowing that each orbital can accommodate two electrons, we can now figure out how many electrons can be found in any principal energy level.

The first principal energy level contains just one orbital, the *s* orbital, and so it can accommodate two electrons. Two ways in which we can illustrate a 1*s* orbital containing two electrons are drawn below:

$$1s\ \underline{\uparrow\downarrow} \qquad \text{or} \qquad 1s^2$$

In the second principal energy level there are four orbitals, a 2*s* orbital and three 2*p* orbitals. The *p* orbitals are labeled p_x, p_y, and p_z according to their orientations in space, as shown in Figure 3.8*b*. If every one of these orbitals is filled with two electrons, the second energy level can contain a total of eight electrons:

$$\begin{matrix} 2p_x\ \underline{\uparrow\downarrow}\ 2p_y\ \underline{\uparrow\downarrow}\ 2p_z\ \underline{\uparrow\downarrow} \\ 2s\ \underline{\uparrow\downarrow} \end{matrix} \qquad \text{or} \qquad \begin{matrix} 2p_x^2\ 2p_y^2\ 2p_z^2 \\ 2s^2 \end{matrix}$$

There are a total of nine orbitals in the third energy level: one 3*s* (can hold two electrons), three 3*p*'s (can hold six electrons), and five 3*d*'s (can hold ten electrons). Thus, the third energy level can house a total of 9 × 2, or 18 electrons. There are five different labels used to distinguish the five 3*d* orbitals (*xy*, *xz*, *yz*,

x^2y^2, and z^2). Because they are cumbersome and difficult to remember, we will replace them with the numbers 1 through 5.

$$3d_1 \underline{\uparrow\downarrow}\ 3d_2 \underline{\uparrow\downarrow}\ 3d_3 \underline{\uparrow\downarrow}\ 3d_4 \underline{\uparrow\downarrow}\ 3d_5 \underline{\uparrow\downarrow} \quad \text{or} \quad 3d_1^2\, 3d_2^2\, 3d_3^2\, 3d_4^2\, 3d_5^2$$
$$3p_x \underline{\uparrow\downarrow}\ 3p_y \underline{\uparrow\downarrow}\ 3p_z \underline{\uparrow\downarrow} \qquad 3p_x^2\, 3p_y^2\, 3p_z^2$$
$$3s \underline{\uparrow\downarrow} \qquad 3s^2$$

There is a useful expression which can be used to recall the maximum number of electrons that can occupy any principal energy level, n:

$$\text{Number of electrons} = 2n^2$$

For $n = 1$, $2n^2 = 2$; for $n = 2$ the answer is 8; and for $n = 3$ it is 18.

3.13 WRITING ELECTRONIC CONFIGURATIONS FOR ATOMS

The *electronic configuration for an atom* is written by listing the orbitals occupied by the electrons in the atom along with the number of electrons in each orbital. Three rules which must be followed in writing electronic configurations are

In German *Aufbau* means "building up."

1. *Pauli principle:* Each orbital may contain two electrons. It is possible for an orbital to contain no electrons or just one electron but no more than two electrons. A 1s orbital containing one electron is written $1s^1$.
2. *Aufbau principle:* Orbitals are filled by starting with the lowest-energy orbital first (see Figure 3.7). For example, 1s orbitals are filled before 2s orbitals, which in turn are filled before 2p orbitals.
3. *Hund's rule:* When orbitals of equal energy, such as the three p orbitals, are being filled, electrons tend to have the *same* spin. The electrons occupy different orbitals so as to remain as far apart as possible. This is reasonable, since electrons have like charges and tend to repel each other. The electrons do not pair up until there is at least one electron in each of the equal-energy orbitals.

For instance, if there are four electrons to "feed" into three 2p orbitals, one electron will enter each 2p orbital before the fourth electron pairs with one of them, in accordance with Hund's rule. This is illustrated in Figure 3.10.

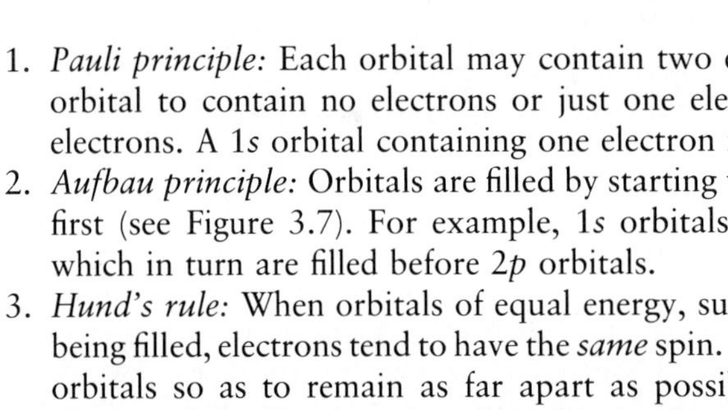

FIGURE 3.10
Hund's rule illustrated.

To write the electronic configuration for a particular atom, we must first find its atomic number to see how many electrons must be distributed. We then place the electrons into orbitals according to the three rules above. You can refer to the diagram in Figure 3.7 for the energy ordering of the orbitals. To demonstrate how this works, let us write electronic configurations for the first 10 elements in the periodic table:

Hydrogen Z = 1

An H atom has just one electron, which occupies the lowest energy level, 1*s*. The electronic configuration for H is written

H) $1s^1$ or $1s\ \underline{\uparrow\ \ }$

Helium Z = 2

Each He atom contains two electrons. Both go into the 1*s* orbital:

He) $1s^2$ or $1s\ \underline{\uparrow\downarrow}$

Lithium Z = 3

In the lithium atom there are three electrons to distribute among energy levels. The first two enter the 1*s* orbital and the third the 2*s* orbital:

Li) $1s^2\,2s^1$ or

$2s\ \underline{\uparrow\ \ }$
$1s\ \underline{\uparrow\downarrow}$

Beryllium Z = 4

Two of the four beryllium electrons go into the 1*s* orbital and the other two into the 2*s* orbital:

Be) $1s^22s^2$ or

$2s\ \underline{\uparrow\downarrow}$
$1s\ \underline{\uparrow\downarrow}$

Boron Z = 5

There are five electrons in a boron atom. The fifth must be placed in a 2*p* orbital. (Although any 2*p* orbital could be used, we often pick out the $2p_x$ orbital when writing the electronic configuration.)

B) $1s^22s^22p_x^1$ or

$2p_x\ \underline{\uparrow\ \ }\ 2p_y\ \underline{\ \ \ \ }\ 2p_z\ \underline{\ \ \ \ }$
$2s\ \underline{\uparrow\downarrow}$
$1s\ \underline{\uparrow\downarrow}$

Sometimes the labels which distinguish the different p or d orbitals are left out of the electronic configuration. Using this shorthand notation, we can write this configuration for boron:

B) $1s^2 2s^2 2p^1$

Carbon Z = 6

Of the six electrons in a carbon atom, four are placed in the 1s or 2s orbitals. The fifth electron enters one of the 2p orbitals and the sixth electron enters another, according to Hund's rule. The electronic configuration for carbon is

C) $1s^2 2s^2 2p_x^1 2p_y^1$ or $1s^2 2s^2 2p^2$

$2p_x$ ↑ $2p_y$ ↑ $2p_z$ ___
2s ↑↓
1s ↑↓

Nitrogen Z = 7

Using Hund's rule to write the electronic configuration for nitrogen, we see that each of the three p orbitals must contain one electron:

N) $1s^2 2s^2 2p_x^1 2p_y^1 2p_z^1$ or $1s^2 2s^2 2p^3$

$2p_x$ ↑ $2p_y$ ↑ $2p_z$ ↑
2s ↑↓
1s ↑↓

Oxygen Z = 8

The eighth electron in oxygen can pair up with the electron in the $2p_x$ orbital to produce this configuration:

O) $1s^2 2s^2 2p_x^2 2p_y^1 2p_z^1$ or $1s^2 2s^2 2p^4$

$2p_x$ ↑↓ $2p_y$ ↑ $2p_z$ ↑
2s ↑↓
1s ↑↓

Fluorine Z = 9

In the electronic configuration of fluorine there are two electrons in each of the $2p_x$ and $2p_y$ orbitals but only one electron in the $2p_z$ orbital:

F) $1s^2 2s^2 2p_x^2 2p_y^2 2p_z^1$ or $1s^2 2s^2 2p^5$

$2p_x$ ↑↓ $2p_y$ ↑↓ $2p_z$ ↑
2s ↑↓
1s ↑↓

TABLE 3.6 **ELECTRONIC CONFIGURATIONS OF ELEMENTS 1 THROUGH 20**

Atomic number	Element	Electronic configuration			
		Level 1	Level 2	Level 3	Level 4
1	H	$1s^1$			
2	He	$1s^2$			
3	Li	$1s^2$	$2s^1$		
4	Be	$1s^2$	$2s^2$		
5	B	$1s^2$	$2s^22p^1$		
6	C	$1s^2$	$2s^22p^2$		
7	N	$1s^2$	$2s^22p^3$		
8	O	$1s^2$	$2s^22p^4$		
9	F	$1s^2$	$2s^22p^5$		
10	Ne	$1s^2$	$2s^22p^6$		
11	Na	$1s^2$	$2s^22p^6$	$3s^1$	
12	Mg	$1s^2$	$2s^22p^6$	$3s^2$	
13	Al	$1s^2$	$2s^22p^6$	$3s^23p^1$	
14	Si	$1s^2$	$2s^22p^6$	$3s^23p^2$	
15	P	$1s^2$	$2s^22p^6$	$3s^23p^3$	
16	S	$1s^2$	$2s^22p^6$	$3s^23p^4$	
17	Cl	$1s^2$	$2s^22p^6$	$3s^23p^5$	
18	Ar	$1s^2$	$2s^22p^6$	$3s^23p^6$	
19	K	$1s^2$	$2s^22p^6$	$3s^23p^6$	$4s^1$
20	Ca	$1s^2$	$2s^22p^6$	$3s^23p^6$	$4s^2$

Neon Z = 10

The 10 electrons in the neon atom are distributed to fill all the available first- and second-energy-level orbitals:

Ne) $1s^22s^22p_x^22p_y^22p_z^2$ or $1s^22s^22p^6$

$2p_x$ $\underline{\uparrow\downarrow}$ $2p_y$ $\underline{\uparrow\downarrow}$ $2p_z$ $\underline{\uparrow\downarrow}$
$2s$ $\underline{\uparrow\downarrow}$
$1s$ $\underline{\uparrow\downarrow}$

The electronic configurations of the first 20 elements are summarized in Table 3.6. As we mentioned previously, electronic configurations of atoms give clues about the chemical behavior of the atom. Highest-energy-level electrons are the ones that are most important in forming chemical bonds.

SAMPLE EXERCISE 3.7

Write the electronic configuration for sodium.

Solution:

Sodium is Na, the eleventh element; $Z = 11$

The first 10 electrons fill up the first two principal energy levels. The eleventh electron is in a $3s$ orbital.

Answer: Na) $1s^2 2s^2 2p_x^2 2p_y^2 2p_z^2 3s^1$ or $1s^2 2s^2 2p^6 3s^1$

or

$3s \ \underline{\uparrow\ \ }$

$2p_x \ \underline{\uparrow\downarrow}\ 2p_y \ \underline{\uparrow\downarrow}\ 2p_z \ \underline{\uparrow\downarrow}$

$2s \ \underline{\uparrow\downarrow}$

$1s \ \underline{\uparrow\downarrow}$

• •

EXERCISE 3.7

Write the electronic configuration for potassium. (Try first without Table 3.6.)

3.14 PERIODIC TABLE AND ELECTRONIC CONFIGURATIONS

The highest-energy s and p orbitals are shown in color in Figure 3.12.

In Figure 3.12 the outermost d orbitals are in gray.

The periodic table is arranged according to increasing atomic number. Let us take a closer look at the periodic table, using the diagram in Figure 3.11. The vertical columns of the table are called **groups**, or **families**, and are labeled with Roman numerals and capital letters A or B. Elements in the A groups, called **representative elements** have their highest-energy electrons in s or p orbitals. See Figure 3.12, where the outermost electronic configurations are included for elements in a segment of the periodic table. Elements in the B groups have their highest-energy electrons in d orbitals and are known as **transition elements.** Note from Figure 3.12 that the elements with atomic numbers 21 to 30 (scandium to zinc) are all transition elements and all have their outermost electrons in d orbitals. The elements in group 0 (He, Ne, Ar, Kr, Xe, and Rn), the **noble gases,** have their highest-energy-level s and p orbitals completely filled. The horizontal rows of the periodic table are called **periods** and are labeled from 1 to 7. Two segments of the periodic table are isolated at the bottom of the table (see Figure 3.11). These include the 14 elements which follow lanthanum ($Z = 57$), called the *lanthanide series,* and the 14 elements which follow actinium ($Z = 89$), called the *actinide series.* Lanthanide and actinide elements all have their highest-energy electrons in f orbitals. That is why the lanthanide and actinide elements are similar to each other (unlike other horizontal rows of the periodic table).

The periodic table is especially useful to chemists because it is arranged in such a way that the groups of elements, especially the representative elements, all have similar properties.

Elements from any one group undergo similar chemical reactions and form similar chemical compounds.

This is explained by the fact that elements in the same group all have closely related electronic configurations.

Elements in a given A group of the periodic table have similar chemical properties.

In general, the number of outermost electrons for representative elements is the same as their group number. For instance, the elements in group IA, called the **alkali metals,** have electronic configurations in which there is *one* electron in

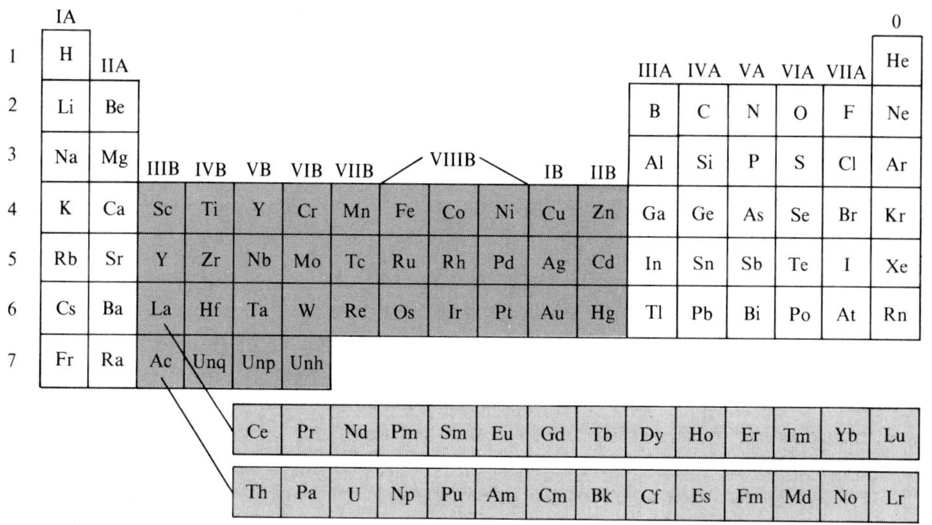

FIGURE 3.11 *(Left)* Features of the periodic table. The families, or groups, labeled with roman numerals and letters (A or B) are the vertical columns. The periods, labeled with numbers (1 to 7) are the horizontal rows.

Outermost electron in *s* or *p* orbital — Representative elements

Outermost electron in *d* orbital — Transition elements

Outermost electron in *f* orbital — Lanthanides and actinides

IA	IIA											IIIA	IVA	VA	VIA	VIIA	0
H $1s^1$																	**He** $1s^2$
Li $1s^2$ $2s^1$	**Be** $1s^2$ $2s^1$											**B** $1s^2$ $2s^2 2p^1$	**C** $1s^2$ $2s^2 2p^2$	**N** $1s^2$ $2s^2 2p^3$	**O** $1s^2$ $2s^2 2p^4$	**F** $1s^2$ $2s^2 2p^5$	**Ne** $1s^2$ $2s^2 2p^6$
Na $1s^2$ ${}^2 2p^6$ $3s^1$	**Mg** $1s^2$ $2s^2 2p^6$ $3s^2$											**Al** $1s^2$ $2s^2 2p^6$ $3s^2 3p^1$	**Si** $1s^2$ $2s^2 2p^6$ $3s^2 3p^2$	**P** $1s^2$ $2s^2 2p^6$ $3s^2 3p^3$	**S** $1s^2$ $2s^2 2p^6$ $3s^2 3p^4$	**Cl** $1s^2$ $2s^2 2p^6$ $3s^2 3p^5$	**Ar** $1s^2$ $2s^2 2p^6$ $3s^2 3p^6$
K $1s^2$ ${}^2 2p^6$ ${}^2 3p^6$ $4s^1$	**Ca** $1s^2$ $2s^2 2p^6$ $3s^2 3p^6$ $4s^2$	**Sc** $1s^2$ $2s^2 2p^6$ $3s^2 3p^6$ $4s^2\ 3d^1$	**Ti** $1s^2$ $2s^2 2p^6$ $3s^2 3p^6$ $4s^2\ 3d^2$	**Y** $1s^2$ $2s^2 2p^6$ $3s^2 3p^6$ $4s^2\ 3d^3$	**Cr** $1s^2$ $2s^2 2p^6$ $3s^2 3p^6$ $4s^1\ 3d^5$	**Mn** $1s^2$ $2s^2 2p^6$ $3s^2 3p^6$ $4s^2\ 3d^5$	**Fe** $1s^2$ $2s^2 2p^6$ $3s^2 3p^6$ $4s^2\ 3d^6$	**Co** $1s^2$ $2s^2 2p^6$ $3s^2 3p^6$ $4s^2\ 3d^7$	**Ni** $1s^2$ $2s^2 2p^6$ $3s^2 3p^6$ $4s^2\ 3d^8$	**Cu** $1s^2$ $2s^2 2p^6$ $3s^2 3p^6$ $4s^1\ 3d^{10}$	**Zn** $1s^2$ $2s^2 2p^6$ $3s^2 3p^6$ $4s^2\ 3d^{10}$	**Ga** $1s^2$ $2s^2 2p^6$ $3s^2 3p^6$ $4s^2 4p^1$	**Ge** $1s^2$ $2s^2 2p^6$ $3s^2 3p^6$ $4s^2 4p^2$	**As** $1s^2$ $2s^2 2p^6$ $3s^2 3p^6$ $4s^2 4p^3$	**Se** $1s^2$ $2s^2 2p^6$ $3s^2 3p^6$ $4s^2 4p^4$	**Br** $1s^2$ $2s^2 2p^6$ $3s^2 3p^6$ $4s^2 4p^5$	**Kr** $1s^2$ $2s^2 2p^6$ $3s^2 3p^6$ $4s^2 4p^6$

FIGURE 3.12
Electronic configurations of elements 1 to 36 in the periodic table. Chromium and copper have electronic configurations that do not correspond to the Aufbau ordering. Their structures include only one electron in the 4*s* orbital. That is so that their *d* orbitals can all be half filled (Cr) or completely filled (Cu). Those configurations are unusually stable, a rule about building up electronic configurations that we did not list.

their highest-energy s orbital. The electronic configurations of these elements can thus be written as ns^1, where n gives the period in which the element is found. From Figure 3.12 we see that the outermost electrons of Li, Na, and K are in the $2s$, $3s$, and $4s$ orbitals. (The element H does not belong to group IA, since it has vastly different properties from the other elements in it.) The alkali metals all combine with water in a vigorous, sometimes explosive, reaction (See Color Plate 5) and also react with chlorine to form compounds with the formula MCl, where M is the group IA representative element. This closeness in chemical behavior for group IA elements is explained by their parallel electronic configurations. Similar trends exist for the other A groups of the periodic table. This correlation between the chemical properties of elements and their electronic configurations gives excellent support to the theory of electrons in atoms that we have been using.

The repetition of chemical properties of elements with regular variation in atomic number is called *periodicity*. We can observe one simple repeating pattern by examining the second two periods of the periodic table, containing elements 3 to 18. Each element is chemically similar to a corresponding element which is eight atomic number units away. Thus, element 3 (Li) is like element 11 (Na), element 4 (Be) is like element 12(Mg), and element 8 (O) is like element 16 (S).

SAMPLE EXERCISE 3.8

Write the general electronic configurations for elements of group VIIA.

Solution:

Elements in group VIIA have seven electrons in their outermost levels. For each element, two of these electrons are in an s orbital and the other five are in p orbitals. Elements in group VIIA all have the configurations $ns^2np_x^2np_y^2np_z^1$, or simply ns^2np^5.

EXERCISE 3.8

Give the general electronic configuration for group IIA elements known as the **alkaline earth** elements.

3.15 ATOMIC EMISSION SPECTRA

It is possible for electrons in the atoms of an element to be elevated to higher unoccupied energy levels by subjecting the vapor (gaseous form) of the element to high voltages or intense heat. Once elevated, the electrons return to lower

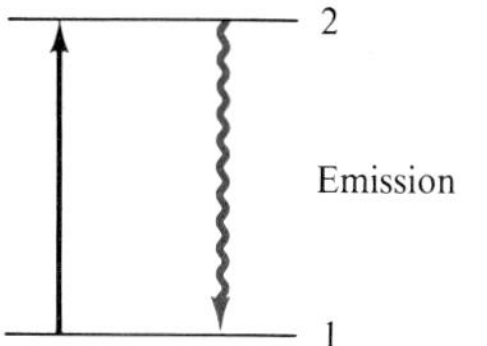

FIGURE 3.13
Emission (simple energy-level diagram) of light. An electron can be elevated from a lower energy level (1) to a higher energy level (2). When the electron returns to the lower level, electromagnetic radiation is emitted, as indicated by the wavy colored line.

energy levels; when this happens, light is *emitted* and the element glows. Figure 3.13 shows how an electron in an atom is first elevated and then falls to a lower electronic level. This is the source of the glow of a neon light or a mercury light bulb. The red color of the fireworks and the flame shown in Color Plate 6 is derived from the characteristic red glow of the element strontium, Sr.

The wavelengths of light emitted by atoms of an element can be measured accurately with a device called an *atomic spectrometer,* such as the one shown in Figure 3.14. The recording of the wavelengths of light is called an **atomic spectrum.** The atomic spectra for neon and the other elements shown do not include all the colors of the visible portion of the spectrum (see Color Plate 3*b*). In general, light emitted because of electronic transitions among levels in atoms includes only certain specific wavelengths. In fact, the wavelengths of emitted light correspond exactly to the energy differences between each pair of electronic energy levels. Recall that photon energies (E) are related to wavelengths (λ) by Planck's equation (h and c are constants):

$$E = \frac{hc}{\lambda}$$

As you can see by looking at Color Plate 3*b*, light emitted from element vapor appears as many lines of color, different for each element shown. For each of the 106 elements there is a different set of electronic energy levels and hence a unique pattern of wavelengths of emitted light. Thus, an atomic spectrum can serve as a sort of fingerprint for an element, which distinguishes it from any other element.

Atomic spectra can be used to detect heavy metal poisoning.

There are many practical uses for atomic spectra. They can be used to identify new elements. Unambiguous proof that the gas argon, Ar, was a new element was provided when its atomic spectrum turned out to be different from that of any element known. Atomic spectroscopy can also be used as a method to analyze for the presence of particular elements, whether they are uncombined or present in compound form. For example, in cases in which lead poisoning is suspected it is possible to measure the amount of lead in a sample of the patient's blood or urine by use of atomic spectroscopy. Normal lead levels and elevated lead

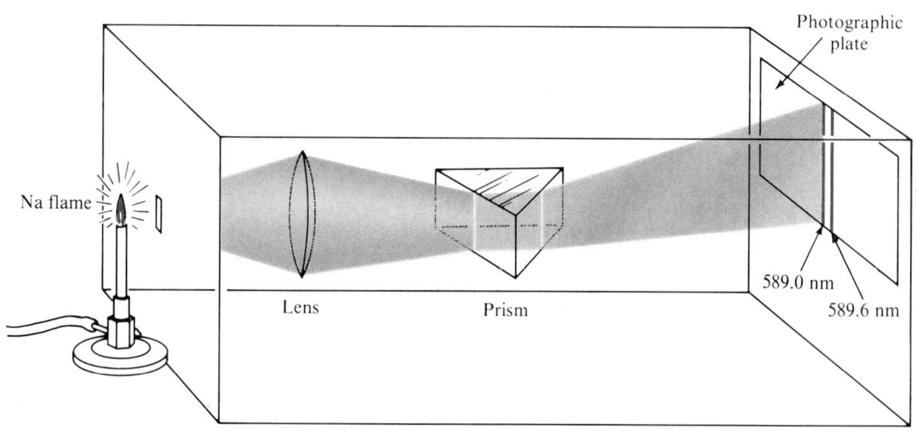

FIGURE 3.14
Atomic spectrometer.
If we replaced the Na flame with a sodium lamp (Color Plate 6) the spectrum would be the same.

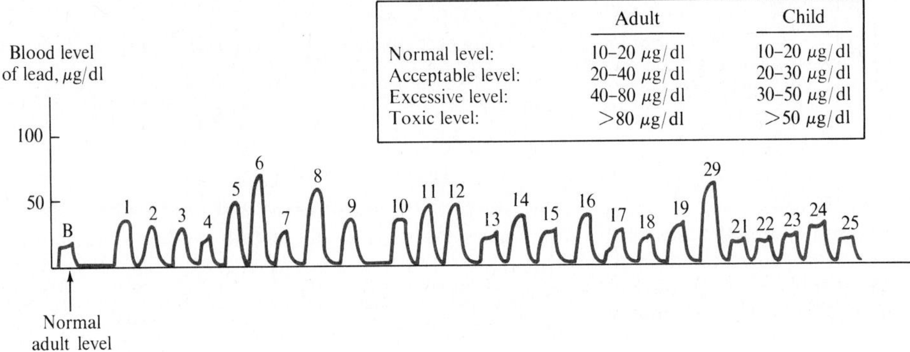

	Adult	Child
Normal level:	10–20 μg/dl	10–20 μg/dl
Acceptable level:	20–40 μg/dl	20–30 μg/dl
Excessive level:	40–80 μg/dl	30–50 μg/dl
Toxic level:	>80 μg/dl	>50 μg/dl

FIGURE 3.15
Blood levels of lead in 25 patients. Patients 6, 8, and 20 have levels higher than 50 μg/dl and will exhibit toxicity symptoms, particularly if they are children. (Data provided by the Public Health Laboratory, Philadelphia, PA.)

The Pb line used for analysis is at 283 nm, in the ultraviolet part of the spectrum.

levels are pictured in Figure 3.15. The measurements are made by looking for the height (on a chart recording) of a line in the lead spectrum. The line heights are then converted to concentrations of lead. Even a blood sample as small as 10 μl (10^{-2} cm^3, or one-hundredth of 1 cm^3) is sufficient to reveal the presence of abnormally high lead concentrations in the blood.

SUMMARY

The early atomic theories grew out of experimental evidence that could be explained only by assuming that all matter is composed of atoms. Each element is assigned a symbol that represents one of its atoms.

Atoms can be subdivided into even smaller particles. Protons (p) have a charge of +1 unit (1.60×10^{-19} C) and a mass of about one atomic mass unit (1.66×10^{-24} g), abbreviated 1 amu. Neutrons have a charge of 0 and a mass slightly more than the mass of protons. Electrons have a charge of −1 and a mass of 9.11×10^{-28} g, which is only 1/1836 of the mass of the proton or neutron. Atoms are mostly empty space, with the massive particles (protons and neutrons) in a tiny volume called the nucleus and the electrons circulating outside.

The number of protons in the nucleus of an atom is called the atomic number (Z) of the atom. The atomic number is the same as the ordering number of the element in the periodic table and identifies the element. The mass number (A) is the total of the protons and the neutrons in a nucleus ($A = N + Z$). Atoms of the same element may have different values of A and are called isotopes; the symbol for an isotope of an element E is written as ^{A}E or E-A. Most elements have more than one naturally occuring isotope. The element symbols in the periodic table refer to an average atom of an element.

The relative weight of the atoms of a element compared with the same number of atoms of C-12 is called the atomic weight of the element. The atomic weight of a given element in the periodic table is written below the element symbol and corresponds to the weighted average of all isotopes of that element present in nature.

Formulas are written by using element symbol and subscripts that indicate how many atoms of each element are present. Formula weights are determined by adding up the atomic weights for all atoms in the formula.

It is the electrons in atoms that are responsible for their chemical properties. The electrons in a particular atom are arranged in discrete, quantized energy levels. Some of the energy levels possible, in order of increasing energies, are $1s$, $2s$, $2p$ ($2p_x$, $2p_y$, or $2p_z$), $3s$, $3p$ ($3p_x$, $3p_y$, or $3p_z$), $4s$, $3d$ ($3d_1$, $3d_2$, $3d_3$, $3d_4$, or $3d_5$). To write the electronic configuration for an atom, all its electrons are fed into orbitals, starting with the lowest and putting no more than two electrons in any one orbital. When orbitals of equal energy (such as a set of p orbitals) are to be filled, a single electron is fed into each one before any electrons are paired.

The periodic table of elements is arranged in order of increasing atomic numbers. Elements in the A groups are representative elements. Within a given group, representative elements have the same general electronic configurations and thus exhibit similar chemical properties. The repeating trend of properties of the elements is known as periodicity. Elements in the B families are called transition elements and all have their outermost electrons in *d* orbitals.

By imparting high voltages or heat to the gaseous form of an element, its electrons can be elevated in energy. When they return to lower levels, the elements glow with a light composed of certain specific wavelengths. The display of wavelengths, called a spectrum, is different for every element and can thus be used to make positive identification of elements.

KEY WORDS

atom
Dalton's atomic theory
law of constant composition
law of multiple proportions
formula
subatomic particle
proton
neutron
electron
atomic mass unit
nucleus
atomic number
mass number
isotope
atomic weight
formula weight
electronic configuration
principal quantum number
atomic orbital
group
family
representative element
transition element
period
periodic table
atomic spectrum

EXERCISES

3.9 Match the laws below with corresponding experimental evidence:
(a) Law of conservation of matter
(b) Law of multiple proportions
(c) Law of constant composition
(1) A 100-g sample of H_2O_2 always contains 5.9 g H and 94.1 g O.
(2) A 100-g sample of H_2O_2 always decomposes to form 52.9 g H_2O and 47.1 g O_2.
(3) The ratio of O to H is 16 in H_2O_2 and 8 in H_2O.

3.10 Show that the following data are consistent with the law of multiple proportions:
(a) A 100-g sample of carbon monoxide (CO) contains 42.9 g C and 57.1 g O.
(b) A 100-g sample of carbon dioxide (CO_2) contains 27.3 g C and 72.7 g O.

3.11 Name the elements that correspond to the following symbols: (a) Fe; (b) Na; (c) S; (d) C; (e) K; (f) Tc; (g) Pb.

3.12 Give the symbols for the following elements: (a) Tin; (b) cobalt; (c) magnesium; (d) manganese; (e) nitrogen; (f) copper; (g) mercury.

3.13 Give the name and atomic number of each kind of atom in the following formulas: (a) Li_2S; (b) $Ba_3(PO_4)_2$; (c) NH_4NO_2; (d) CH_3COOH; (e) $NaUO_2(C_2H_3O_2)_3$, (f) Ca_3As_2; (g) $Ni(IO_3)_2$.

3.14 Compare the masses and charges of electrons, protons, and neutrons.

3.15 What do we mean when we talk about a charge of +3?

3.16 If a Ping-Pong ball with a diameter of 1.5 in represents the nucleus of an atom, calculate the approximate diameter of the atom in: (a) inches; (b) feet; (c) miles (5280 ft = 1 mi).

3.17 How many protons and electrons does one atom of each of the following elements contain: (a) Carbon; (b) aluminum; (c) lead; (d) uranium; (e) potassium?

3.18 The radioactive (unstable) isotopes iodine-131 and radium-226 are used in cancer radiation treatments. How many protons, neutrons, and electrons are present in an atom of each isotope?

3.19 How many protons, neutrons, and electrons are present in an atom of each of the following isotopes: (a) He-4; (b) Na-22; (c) Sr-90; (d) C-14; (e)Pb-206?

3.20 Write symbols for the following isotopes: (a) Tin with 70 neutrons; (b) sodium with 13 neutrons; (c) carbon with 8 neutrons; (d) plutonium with 148 neutrons.

3.21 Is it possible for isotopes of an element to have different (a) atomic numbers; (b) atomic weights; (c) mass numbers?

3.22 The atoms of a certain element are about four times as heavy as the atoms of C-12. What is the element?

3.23 Why is the atomic weight of carbon equal to 12.01 instead of 12 exactly?

3.24 Give the atomic numbers and atomic weights of the following elements: (a) Chlorine; (b) zinc; (c) phosphorus; (d) neon.

3.25 Of the carbon in nature, 98.89 percent is C-12 and the rest is C-13. From this calculate the atomic weight of the element carbon.

3.26 An element consists of isotopes with the following atomic weights and relative abundances:

Atomic weight	**Percent natural abundance**
27.98	92.21
28.98	4.70
29.97	3.09

Identify the element and calculate its average atomic weight.

3.27 If the atomic weight of C-12 had been assigned a value of 100, what would the atomic weight of H be? Why is the choice of C-12 = 12 a convenient standard to use?

3.28 There are three isotopes of oxygen in nature. Which one is represented by the symbol O in the periodic table box?

3.29 Calculate the formula weights of the following elements: (a) I_2; (b) O_3; (c) S_8.

3.30 Calculate the formula weights of the following compounds: (a) H_2O_2; (b) $NaHCO_3$; (c) $Al(OH)_3$; (d) CH_3NH_2; (e) $(NH_4)_2S$; (f) $Ba_3(PO_4)_2$.

3.31 Using the shorthand notation in which all p orbitals (p_x, p_y, and p_z) are designated by the symbol p, write the electronic configurations for the first 20 elements of the periodic table. Do this without looking at Table 3.6. Check your answers.

3.32 Using the notation in which p orbitals are labeled p_x, p_y, or p_z, write the electronic configuration for: (a) Carbon; (b) oxygen; (c) nitrogen; (d) sulfur.

3.33 Count the number of unpaired electrons, that is, orbitals containing a single electron, in (a) carbon; (b) beryllium; (c) sodium.

3.34 What is wrong with the following electronic configurations?

(a) Li) $1s^3$
(b) C) $1s^2 2s^2 2p_x^2$
(c) K) $1s^2 2s^2 2p^6 3s^2 3p^6 4d^1$

3.35 Make a sketch of an s orbital and a p orbital.

3.36 What is meant by the statement: A hydrogen electron is in a $2p$ orbital.

3.37 Give the general electronic configurations for elements of (a) Group IIIA; (b) Group IVA; (c) Group VA; (d) Group VIA.

3.38 Give the general electronic configuration for the noble gases (except He).

3.39 What is meant by periodicity?

3.40 Of the following pairs of elements, which should have the most similar chemical properties? (a) Na and Al; (b) K and Rb; (c) B and C?

3.41 How does the glow from a mercury lamp or a neon lamp differ from that of sunlight or an ordinary light bulb?

3.42 What is meant by the statement that atomic spectra behave like "fingerprints" for elements?

3.43 Strontium-90 (Sr-90), a product of nuclear fission reactions, is especially dangerous to humans because its chemical behavior is similar to that of another important element in humans. Which one is it?

3.44 Is it true that the most abundant elements in the human body are the same as those in the crust of the earth?

3.45 What measurement was used to obtain the blood levels of lead shown in Figure 3.15?

4 . . . . CHEMICAL BONDING

4.1 INTRODUCTION

In Chapter 2 you saw that chemical reactions involve the breaking of old bonds and the making of new bonds to form new chemical species. In Chapter 3 you found that chemical behavior, or the way in which an atom will enter into a reaction, depends upon its electronic configuration. Here in Chapter 4 we will see how electrons form chemical bonds. Understanding the nature of the chemical bond helps chemists make predictions about the kinds of reactions likely to take place.

Chemical bonds are the attractive forces which join atoms. Bonded atoms are close together. By close we mean that the distance between the centers of two atoms joined by a chemical bond is between 70 pm and 300 pm. Remember that one picometer (1 pm) is 10^{-12} m.

In all molecules of the same compound, the atoms are arranged in the same way, with the same bond distances between two given atoms and the same angles between any two particular bonds. For instance, in H_2O, O is always the central atom. The distance between the center of either H atom and that of the central O atom is 96 pm, as shown in Figure 4.1. You can see in this diagram of a water

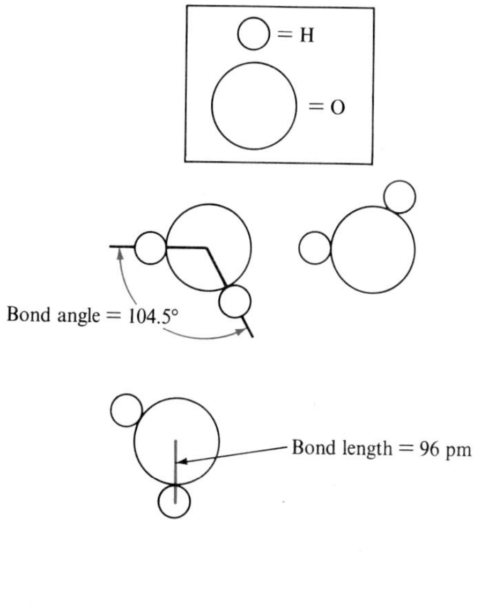

FIGURE 4.1
Water molecule. Every H_2O molecule has a bond angle of 104.5° and an O-H bond length of 96 pm.

molecule that the angle between the two H—O bonds is 104.5°, an angle that is the same for every water molecule.

The energy needed to break a chemical bond between two atoms is called the **bond energy.** For most chemical bonds, bond energies range from about 3×10^{-23} kcal per bond (weak bonds) to 30×10^{-23} kcal per bond (strong bonds). For example, the energy needed to break an H—O bond in the water molecule is 18×10^{-23} kcal.

The way in which many atoms combine to form chemical bonds is intimately related to their electronic structures. In fact, the discovery of electronic configurations of atoms led the way for the breakthrough in theories of chemical bonding. A good bonding theory should be able to predict the formulas of compounds that are known to exist. Any theory which could not predict that H atoms and O atoms can combine to form H_2O molecules would be worthless. Bonding theories should also provide details about the arrangements of atoms within molecules. That O is the central atom in the water molecule and that the molecule is bent must also be suggested by the theory.

Chemical compounds are conveniently divided into two broad classes, called **ionic compounds** and **covalent compounds,** based upon the type of bonds they contain. We will begin our study of bonding theory by examining the physical differences between these two types of compounds.

4.2 TYPES OF COMPOUNDS

Compounds can be classified as ionic or covalent by examining two physical properties, melting point and the ability to conduct electricity. The *ionic compounds* have very high melting points and are good conductors of electricity when they are either melted or dissolved in water. Included in this class are compounds such as ordinary table salt, which is sodium chloride, NaCl. The melting point of NaCl is so high (801°C) that tossing some salt on a skillet and then heating it as much as possible on a kitchen stove will not melt the salt. The melting points of some typical ionic compounds are listed in Figure 4.2*a*. Figure 4.2 also shows an apparatus that could be used to test for electrical conductivity. Any ionic compound, if melted or dissolved in water and placed in the beaker, will complete the circuit and cause the bulb to light. Ionic compounds have high melting points and can conduct electricity because they contain ionic bonds.

Members of the other class of compounds, the *covalent compounds,* have much lower melting points and are poor conductors of electricity. Some covalent compounds are liquids or gases while others are low-melting solids. Some typical covalent compounds and their melting points are listed in Figure 4.2*b*, where we also see that they do not conduct electricity very well. Putting carbon tetrachloride into the beaker shown would not light the bulb in the circuit. Covalent compounds contain covalent bonds.

Few compounds are 100 percent ionic or 100 percent covalent. Indeed, there are some compounds which do not fit comfortably into either class. We will discuss ionic bonding separately from covalent bonding.

Ionic compound	Melting point, °C
Sodium chloride (salt)	801
Calcium fluoride	1360
Potassium sulfate	1069
Magnesium oxide	2800
Radium bromide	728
Barium nitrate	592

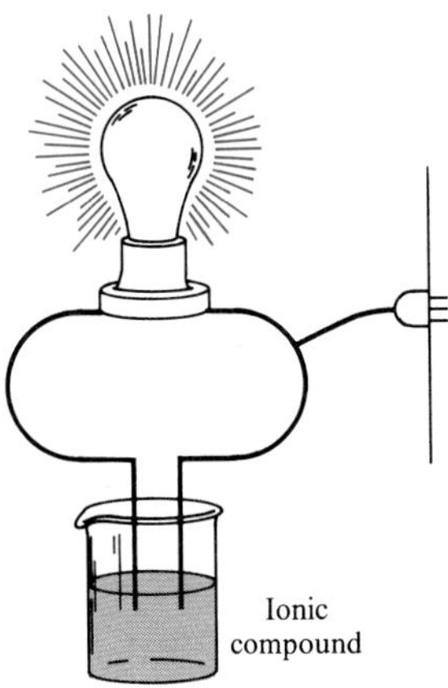

Molten or dissolved ionic compounds complete the circuit because they conduct electricity. The bulb lights.

(*a*)

Covalent compound	Melting point, °C
Sulfur dichloride	−78
Ammonia	−77
Water	0
Carbon tetrachloride	−23
Phosphorus triiodide	61
Arsenic tribromide	33

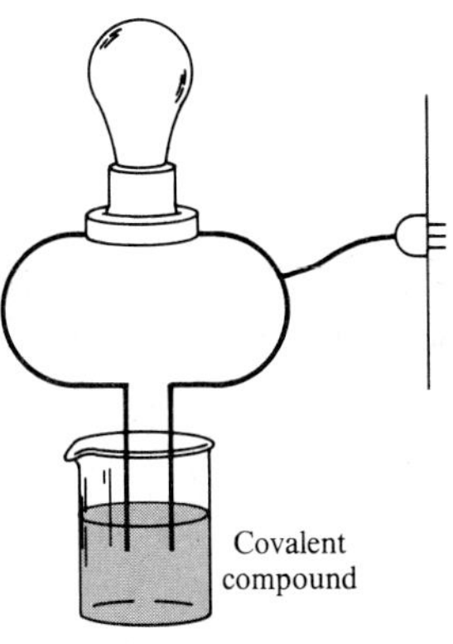

Molten or dissolved covalent compounds do not conduct electricity. The bulb does not light.

(*b*)

FIGURE 4.2
Properties of ionic and covalent compounds. (*a*) Ionic compounds have relatively high melting points. (*b*) Covalent compounds have relatively low melting points.

4.3 FORMATION OF IONS FROM ATOMS

Ionic compounds contain **ions.** Ions are electrically charged species formed when a neutral atom either gains or loses one or more electrons. Positive ions, or **cations,** form when atoms lose one or more electrons. Negative ions, or **anions,** form when atoms gain one or more electrons. An ionic compound is an electrically neutral compound which consists of cations and anions held together by forces of electrical attraction. These attractive forces are called **ionic bonds.** In general, cations form from metallic elements and anions from certain nonmetallic elements. The periodic table in the inside of the front cover shows metallic elements in black symbols; nonmetallic elements in colored symbols; and the remaining elements, the metalloids, which have properties somewhere in between metals and nonmetals, in gray symbols.

We have already mentioned that the highest-energy electrons in atoms are the ones involved in the formation of chemical bonds. Cations form when atoms of metallic elements lose one or more of their highest-energy electrons. Anions form when atoms of nonmetallic elements gain one or more electrons, which enter their highest-energy orbitals. We can make very good predictions about the charges and electronic configurations of the ions that form from the representative elements.

Representative elements are found in the A groups of the periodic table.

The atoms of representative elements tend to lose or gain electrons so that their electronic configurations become identical to those of the noble gas nearest to them in the periodic table.

Like the noble gases, such ion configurations are unusually stable. Only under extreme conditions do the noble gases, helium (He), neon (Ne), argon (Ar), krypton (Kr), xenon (Xe), and radon (Rn), participate in chemical combinations. The electronic configurations of the first four noble gases are

$$
\begin{array}{rl}
{}_{2}\mathrm{He}) & 1s^2 \\
{}_{10}\mathrm{Ne}) & 1s^2\ 2s^2\ 2p^6 \\
{}_{18}\mathrm{Ar}) & 1s^2\ 2s^2\ 2p^6\ 3s^2\ 3p^6 \\
{}_{36}\mathrm{Kr}) & 1s^2\ 2s^2\ 2p^6\ 3s^2\ 3p^6\ 4s^2\ 3d^{10}\ 4p^6
\end{array}
$$

Note that in all the noble gas electronic structures, the outermost orbitals are completely filled. In He the $1s$ orbital contains two electrons, and in Ne, Ar, and Kr the $2p$, $3p$, and $4p$ sets of orbitals all contain six electrons, the maximum possible. Thus the atoms that form ionic compounds will tend to gain or lose electrons to achieve *stable noble gas configurations*.

Cation Formation

Although Li^+ cations and He atoms have the same electronic structures, they are chemically different, since Li^+ ions have three protons and He atoms just two.

The metallic elements of group IA have the general electronic configuration ns^1. To attain a stable noble gas configuration they lose this highest-energy electron. For instance, a lithium atom, Li, loses its $2s$ electron to become Li^+:

$$
\underset{\text{Li atom}}{{}_{3}\mathrm{Li})\ \ 1s^2\ \mathbf{2s^1}} \xrightarrow{-1e^-} \underset{\text{Li}^+\text{ ion}}{{}_{3}\mathrm{Li}^+)\ \ 1s^2}
$$

The electronic configuration of the Li^+ ion is identical to that of helium:

$$
\underset{\text{Helium atom}}{{}_{2}\mathrm{He})\ \ 1s^2}
$$

A sodium atom, Na, loses its $3s$ electron to become Na^+:

$$
\underset{\text{Na atom}}{{}_{11}\mathrm{Na})\ \ 1s^2\ 2s^2\ 2p^6\ \mathbf{3s^1}} \xrightarrow{-1e^-} \underset{\text{Na}^+\text{ ion}}{{}_{11}\mathrm{Na}^+)\ \ 1s^2\ 2s^2\ 2p^6}
$$

The electronic structure of the Na^+ ion is the same as that of the noble gas neon:

$$_{10}\text{Ne})\quad 1s^2\ 2s^2\ 2p^6$$

Ne atom

Since all the elements in group IA have similar electronic structures, one high-energy electron in an *s* orbital, they all lose one electron to form ions with a +1 charge. Note that in this case the charge on the ion is the same as the group number.

The elements of group IIA all have the electronic configuration ns^2 and all form ions with a +2 charge, again the same as the group number. For example, a beryllium atom loses two electrons to become a beryllium ion:

$$_{4}\text{Be})\quad 1s^2\ \mathbf{2s^2} \xrightarrow{-2e^-} {_{4}\text{Be}^{2+}})\quad 1s^2$$

Be atom — Be^{2+} ion

The electronic configuration of the Be^{2+} ion is identical to that of He:

$$_{2}\text{He})\quad 1s^2$$

He atom

Note that the symbol for the charge on an ion includes the number of the charge followed by the sign of the charge. The number 1 is understood and is not written. Magnesium forms the Mg^{2+} ion, which has the same structure as Ne:

$$_{12}\text{Mg})\quad 1s^2\ 2s^2\ 2p^6\ \mathbf{3s^2} \xrightarrow{-2e^-} {_{12}\text{Mg}^{2+}})\quad 1s^2\ 2s^2\ 2p^6$$

Mg atom — Mg^{2+} ion

$$_{10}\text{Ne})\quad 1s^2\ 2s^2\ 2p^6$$

Ne atom

Except for boron, B (a metalloid), the elements of group IIIA, which have the general electronic configuration of ns^2np^1, lose these three highest-energy electrons to form triply charged ions. The electronic structure of the Al^{3+} ion is like that of neon:

$$_{13}\text{Al})\quad 1s^2\ 2s^2\ 2p^6\ \mathbf{3s^2\ 3p^1} \xrightarrow{-3e^-} {_{13}\text{Al}^{3+}})\quad 1s^2\ 2s^2\ 2p^6$$

Al atom — Al^{3+} ion

The general electronic configuration of group IVA elements is ns^2np^2. The metals of this group, Sn and Pb, can lose their highest-energy *p* electrons to form Sn^{2+} and Pb^{2+} ions. These ions do *not* have a noble gas electronic configuration, since they lose only two of their four outermost electrons.

It is much more difficult to predict the cations that are likely to form from the transition metals, those in the group B families. The trends in the stabilities of ions formed from these elements are not very clear at all. Transition metal ions need not have noble gas electronic configurations to be stable. Furthermore, it is not uncommon for transition metal atoms to form more than one cation.

Iron, for instance, forms the double charged Fe^{2+} and the triply charged Fe^{3+} cations.

The name of a cation is simply the name of the element from which it is derived followed by the word "ion." The ions Na^+ and Mg^{2+} are called sodium ion and magnesium ion. When an element forms more than one cation, the names of the cations must include a Roman numeral (in parentheses) to indicate the charge. To name the two iron cations:

Fe^{2+} is the iron(II) ion

and

Fe^{3+} is the iron(III) ion

The names for the Sn^{2+} and Pb^{2+} ions also require Roman numerals because Sn and Pb form other (covalent) compounds in which all four of the highest-energy electrons become involved in the bonding. Thus, Sn^{2+} is called the tin(II) ion and Pb^{2+} is called the lead(II) ion.

Names such as ferrous often appear on product labels.

An old-fashioned naming system for distinguishing between cations formed by the same element is sometimes encountered. The root of the original element name is used with the added suffixes *-ous* or *-ic*. The ending -ous refers to the lower charge number and the ending -ic to the higher one. According to this system the iron cations would be named after the original element name, *ferrum:*

Fe^{2+} is the ferrous ion

and

Fe^{3+} is the ferric ion

The names and symbols for some common cations are listed in Table 4.1.

Anion Formation

Group VIIA elements (F, Cl, Br, I, and At) are called *halogens,* meaning "salt formers" from the Greek roots *hal,* "salt" and *gen,* "produc(er)."

The nonmetallic elements of groups VIA and VIIA gain electrons to form negative ions with stable, noble gas electronic configurations. Atoms from group VIIA elements known as the *halogens* form singly charged anions by gaining one electron to complete their highest occupied *p* orbital. For instance, fluorine, F, gains one electron to become F^-:

$$\underset{\text{F atom}}{{}_9\text{F})\ \ 1s^2\ 2s^2\ 2p^5} \xrightarrow{+e^-} \underset{\text{F}^-\text{ ion}}{{}_9\text{F}^-)\ \ 1s^2\ 2s^2\ 2p^6}$$

The electronic structure of the F^- ion is identical to that of Ne:

$$\underset{\text{Ne atom}}{{}_{10}\text{Ne})\ \ 1s^2\ 2s^2\ 2p^6}$$

Atoms from group VIA elements gain two electrons to form anions. An oxygen atom can gain two electrons to form the anion O^{2-}, which has an electronic structure like that of neon:

TABLE 4.1 **COMMON CATIONS AND THEIR NAMES**

Formula	Name	Formula	Name
From group IA (alkali metals)		**From the B groups**	
Li^+	Lithium	Ag^+	Silver
Na^+	Sodium	Cu^+	Copper(I) or cuprous
K^+	Potassium	Hg^+	Mercury(I) or mercurous
Cs^+	Cesium	Zn^{2+}	Zinc
From group IIA (alkaline earth metals)		Ni^{2+}	Nickel
Mg^{2+}	Magnesium	Fe^{2+}	Iron(II) or ferrous
Ca^{2+}	Calcium	Hg^{2+}	Mercury(II) or mercuric
Sr^{2+}	Strontium	Cu^{2+}	Copper(II) or cupric
Ba^{2+}	Barium	Cr^{2+}	Chromium(II) or chromous
Ra^{2+}	Radium	Cr^{3+}	Chromium(III) or chromic
From group IIIA		Fe^{3+}	Iron(III) or ferric
Al^{3+}	Aluminum	**Others**	
From group IVA		H^+	Hydrogen
Sn^{2+}	Tin(II) or stannous	NH_4^+	Ammonium
Sn^{4+}	Tin(IV) or stannic		
Pb^{2+}	Lead(II) or plumbous		
Pb^{4+}	Lead(IV) or plumbic		

$$\underset{\text{O atom}}{{}_{8}O)\ 1s^2\ 2s^2\ 2p^4} \xrightarrow{+2e^-} \underset{O^{2-}\text{ ion}}{{}_{8}O^{2-})\ 1s^2\ 2s^2\ 2p^6}$$

Anion names are derived from the root of the element name plus the ending *-ide*. For example, to name the anions F^- and O^{2-}:

F is fluorine and F^- is named *fluoride*
O is oxygen and O^{2-} is named *oxide*

Table 4.1 lists some common anions formed from atoms.

SAMPLE EXERCISE 4.1

For the ions which form from the elements K and Cl, give the charge, electronic configuration, name, and noble gas having the same electronic configuration.

Solution:

The electronic structure of $_{19}K$ is $1s^2\ 2s^2\ 2p^6\ 3s^2\ 3p^6\ 4s^1$.
K (group IA) loses one electron to form a cation with a charge of +1.
The electronic structure of $_{19}K^+$ is $1s^2\ 2s^2\ 2p^6\ 3s^2\ 3p^6$.
K^+ has an electronic structure identical to that of Ar.
K^+ is called potassium ion.

The electronic structure of $_{17}Cl$ is $1s^2\ 2s^2\ 2p^6\ 3s^2\ 3p^5$.
Cl (group VIIA) gains one electron to form an anion with a charge of −1.
The electronic structure of $_{17}Cl^-$ is $1s^2\ 2s^2\ 2p^6\ 3s^2\ 3p^6$.
Cl^- has an electronic structure identical to that of Ar.
Cl^- is called chloride.

EXERCISE 4.1

Give the charge, electronic configuration, name, and noble gas having the same electronic configuration for the ions that form from the elements Ca and S.

4.4 POLYATOMIC IONS

It is possible for ions to include two or more atoms. Such polyatomic ions behave as though they were monatomic ions and in fact are often components of ionic compounds.

Polyatomic ions consist of two or more atoms held together by chemical bonds. The group of atoms has a net electrical charge that may be positive or negative. The most frequently encountered polyatomic cation is the ammonium ion, NH_4^+. A multitude of polyatomic anions exist, most of which contain the element oxygen. We will use the common names for these ions even though many of them do not belong to any well-defined system.

Several anions have names that end in *-ide,* including these three:

OH^- hydrox**ide**
CN^- cyan**ide**
O_2^{2-} perox**ide**

Most anions containing oxygen and some other element (except for OH^-) have names taken from the element name or its root modified by the ending *-ate.* For instance, to name the anion that forms from one C atom and three O atoms:

CO_3^{2-} carbon**ate**

Many elements form two anions with oxygen. In this case the anion with fewer O atoms takes the ending *-ite.* Two examples include the anions which contain S and N:

Anions containing O and a nonmetal have names ending in *-ite* (except OH^-).

SO_4^{2-} **sulfate** and SO_3^{2-} **sulfite**

NO_3^- **nitrate** and NO_2^- **nitrite**

Some elements form more than two anions with oxygen. Three elements in group VIIA of the periodic table, namely, Cl, Br, and I, each form four different anions with oxygen. Both prefixes and suffixes are used to distinguish these from each other. For instance, to name the ones derived from Cl and O:

ClO^- **hypochlorite**

ClO_2^- **chlorite**

ClO_3^- **chlorate**

ClO_4^- **perchlorate**

One way to remember that *hypo* refers to the ion with just one O atom and *per-* (derived from *hyper-*) to the one with four O atoms is to recall the meaning of the prefixes hypo- and hyper-. Hypo- means under, as in hypodermic (under the skin) and hyper- means "over-," as in hyperactive (overactive).

The common anions with their formulas and names are given in Table 4.2.

TABLE 4.2 COMMON ANIONS AND THEIR NAMES

Formula	Name	Formula	Name
With a −1 charge		**With a −2 charge**	
F^-	Fluoride	O^{2-}	Oxide
Cl^-	Chloride	S^{2-}	Sulfide
Br^-	Bromide	CO_3^{2-}	Carbonate
I^-	Iodide	SO_3^{2-}	Sulfite
NO_2^-	Nitrite	SO_4^{2-}	Sulfate
NO_3^-	Nitrate	CrO_4^{2-}	Chromate
HCO_3^-	Bicarbonate	$Cr_2O_7^{2-}$	Dichromate
ClO^-	Hypochlorite	SiO_3^{2-}	Silicate
ClO_2^-	Chlorite	O_2^{2-}	Peroxide
ClO_3^-	Chlorate	**With a −3 charge**	
ClO_4^-	Perchlorate		
MnO_4^-	Permanganate	PO_4^{3-}	Phosphate
OH^-	Hydroxide		
CN^-	Cyanide		

4.5 IONIC COMPOUNDS

If an atom which tends to lose electrons approaches an atom which tends to gain electrons, an ionic compound forms. In general, the combination of a metal with a nonmetal produces an ionic compound. For example, if a sodium atom approaches a chlorine atom, the sodium atom will transfer its electron to the chlorine atom to form the ions Na^+ and Cl^-. We can show how this happens by writing the electronic configurations of the Na and Cl atoms in which the highest-energy electrons are represented by dots. The sodium atom with one high-energy electron is written as $\mathrm{Na}\cdot$ and the chlorine atom with 7 is written as $\cdot\underset{\cdot\cdot}{\ddot{\mathrm{Cl}}}:$. The reaction between them is

$$\mathrm{Na}\cdot + \cdot\underset{\cdot\cdot}{\ddot{\mathrm{Cl}}}: \longrightarrow \mathrm{Na}^+ + :\underset{\cdot\cdot}{\ddot{\mathrm{Cl}}}:^-$$

The oppositely charged ions are attracted to each other by electrostatic forces (positive charges attract negative charges) to form the ionic compound sodium chloride, NaCl. The electrostatic force of attraction between Na^+ and Cl^- is called the ionic bond. In general, ionic compounds may contain monatomic ions and/or polyatomic ions.

The total electrical charge in an ionic compound must be zero. That is, the number of positive charges on cations must be equal to the number of negative charges on anions:

$$\text{Sum of charges on cations} = \text{sum of charges on anions}$$

In the formula NaCl there is one positive charge from Na^+ and one negative charge from Cl^-. To form $MgCl_2$, two Cl atoms combine with one Mg atom. Thus in $MgCl_2$ there are two positive charges from Mg^{2+} and two negative charges from the two chloride ions:

$$\mathrm{Mg}: + \begin{matrix}\cdot\underset{\cdot\cdot}{\ddot{\mathrm{Cl}}}: \\ \\ \cdot\underset{\cdot\cdot}{\ddot{\mathrm{Cl}}}:\end{matrix} \longrightarrow \mathrm{Mg}^{2+} + 2\,:\underset{\cdot\cdot}{\ddot{\mathrm{Cl}}}:^-$$

To write formulas for ionic compounds and to name them we must first find the symbols and charges of the ions involved. For the representative elements we can usually make use of the group number and the corresponding electronic configuration to recall ion charges.

The name of an ionic compound is the name of the cation followed by the name of the anion.

For instance, suppose we wish to write the formula and name for the compound containing sodium ions and fluoride ions. Sodium (group IA) loses one electron and fluorine (group VIIA) gains one to form

Na^+ sodium ion

F^- fluoride ion

In formulas for ionic compounds the cation is written on the left.

One Na^+ ion combines with one F^- ion to give the formula

NaF sodium fluoride

NaF is used in water fluoridation and in toothpastes to reduce dental caries.

To write the formula for the ionic compound which contains calcium and chloride ions, we first find the charges on the two ions. Calcium (group IIA) loses two electrons and chlorine (group VIIA) gains one to form

Ca^{2+} calcium ion

Cl^- chloride ion

$CaCl_2$ is used as a drying agent.

Two Cl^- ions (total charge of -2) are needed to balance the charge on one Ca^{2+} ion (total charge of $+2$). The formula is

$CaCl_2$ calcium chloride

If given the name for an ionic compound, we can write its formula by balancing charges, as done in the examples above. For instance, to write the formula for the compound barium phosphate, we begin by finding the charges on the barium and phosphate ions. Barium (group IIA) loses its two highest-energy electrons to form Ba^{2+} ions. The phosphate ion, PO_4^{3-}, is listed in Table 4.2.

Ba^{2+} barium ion

PO_4^{3-} phosphate ion

Three Ba^{2+} ions with a total charge of $+6$ $[3 \times (+2) = +6]$ are needed to balance the charges on two PO_4^{3-} ions $[2 \times (-3) = -6]$. The formula must be

$Ba_3(PO_4)_2$ barium phosphate

Note that the formula for phosphate is enclosed in parentheses to indicate that the subscript 2 refers to the entire phosphate ion (see Section 3.4).

Ionic compounds (except for those in which the cation is H^+) are called **salts.** For instance, the compounds for which we have written formulas in this section, including sodium chloride, $NaCl$, magnesium chloride, $MgCl_2$, sodium fluoride (NaF), calcium chloride ($CaCl_2$), and barium phosphate, $Ba_3(PO_4)_2$, all are salts.

SAMPLE EXERCISE 4.2

Give the formula and name for the salt which forms between the elements radium and bromine, a compound which is used as a radiation source in the treatment of malignant tumors.

Solution:

Radium (group IIA) loses two highest-energy electrons to form Ra^{2+} ions. Bromine (group VIIA) forms Br^- ions since one electron is needed to complete its highest-energy *p* orbital. We need two Br^- ions $[2 \times (-1) = -2]$ to balance the charge on one Ra^{2+} ion $[1 \times (+2) = +2]$. The formula is $RaBr_2$; the name is radium bromide.

EXERCISE 4.2

The elements calcium and sulfur are combined in a compound used as a hair removal agent. Give its formula and name.

SAMPLE EXERCISE 4.3

Write the formula for ferrous carbonate, a compound used in the treatment of anemia. What other name can be used for this compound?

Solution:

Table 4.1 shows that the name ferrous corresponds to Fe^{2+} (recall that ferr*ic* is Fe^{3+}). Table 4.2 shows that carbonate is CO_3^{2-}. We need only one Fe^{2+} ion (total charge of +2) to balance one CO_3^{2-} ion (total charge of −2).
Answer: $FeCO_3$
Ferrous carbonate can also be named iron(II) carbonate

EXERCISE 4.3

The compound magnesium hydroxide is used as an antacid. Give its formula.

TABLE 4.3 **IONIC COMPOUNDS WITH TRIVIAL NAMES**

Formula	Proper name	Trivial name	Medical use
NaCl	Sodium chloride	Salt	Electrolyte replenishment
NaOH	Sodium hydroxide	Caustic soda	
$NaHCO_3$	Sodium bicarbonate	Baking soda	Antacid
Na_2O_2	Sodium peroxide	Sodium superoxide	Acne treatment
CaO	Calcium oxide	Lime	
CaS	Calcium sulfide	Sulfurated lime	Depilatory
KNO_3	Potassium nitrate	Saltpeter	Diuretic*
Li_2CO_3	Lithium carbonate	Lithium	Psychiatric

*A diuretic increases the flow of urine.

Ferrous carbonate is an example of a common, or trivial, name which does not follow any systematic approach but appears in popular literature and in common usage. Some trivial names are considerably less systematic than names such as ferrous carbonate. For example, salt is a trivial name for sodium chloride. A salt-free diet means a diet low in sodium chloride. For other compounds with this sort of trivial name, see the list given in Table 4.3.

4.6 IONIC CRYSTALS AND FORMULA UNITS

The formula for sodium chloride, NaCl, suggests that the ionic bond between sodium and chlorine is an attraction between a particular sodium ion and a particular chloride ion. This is not correct. In reality each sodium ion is attracted to many chloride ions and each chloride ion is attracted to many sodium ions; no one sodium ion can be said to belong to any one chloride ion. The formula NaCl really means that the simplest ratio of sodium atoms to chlorine atoms in the compound sodium chloride is 1 to 1. The arrangement of sodium ions and chloride ions in solid NaCl is pictured in Figure 4.3. In this crystalline structure each sodium ion is surrounded by six chloride ions, and vice versa.

The formula NaCl means that there is one Na^+ for every Cl^-.

For this reason it is not strictly correct to speak of a "molecule" of an ionic compound. The term molecule implies a discrete particular collection of atoms. When we say molecule of NaCl, what we actually mean is that according to the formula NaCl, there is one sodium for every chlorine. The term *formula unit* of NaCl is sometimes used instead of molecule of NaCl.

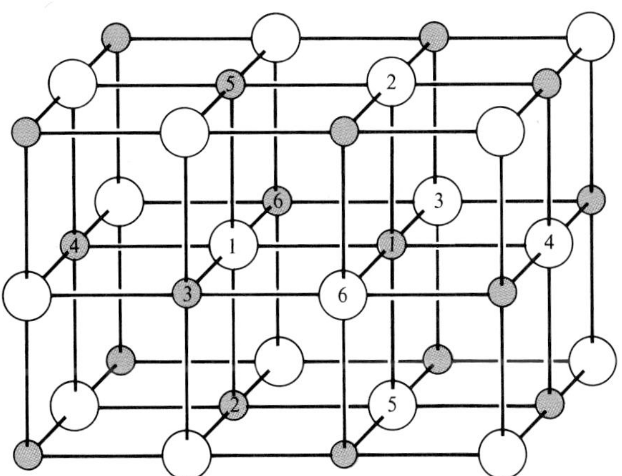

FIGURE 4.3
NaCl crystal. Each Na^+ ion (small circles) is surrounded by six Cl^- ions (large circles) and each Cl^- ion is surrounded by six Na^+ ions. (The ions on the edges are surrounded by ions that are not shown in the diagram.) The ions labeled 1 have six nearest neighbors, labeled 1 through 6.

4.7 IONS AND ELEMENTS

The physical and chemical properties of elements are very different from those of the ions which they produce. The element sodium, Na, is nothing like the sodium cation, Na^+. Sodium is a silvery metal soft enough to be cut with a penknife and is so chemically reactive that it combines readily with air (see color plate 5) and reacts violently with water. Sodium ions are present in compounds such as NaCl, which are nothing like the element sodium.

Often the name of the element is used when we actually mean to refer to its ion. For instance, when you hear that the normal blood level of sodium is about 330 mg per 100 cm^3, it means that the normal blood level of sodium *ions* is about 330 mg per 100 cm^3. Sodium metal in the blood would produce devastating effects! A potassium blood level of 17 mg per 100 cm^3, a calcium blood level of 10 mg per 100 cm^3, and a chloride blood level of 365 mg per 100 cm^3 refer to normal blood levels of potassium ion, K^+, calcium ion, Ca^{2+}, and chloride ion Cl^-.

The "blood level of potassium" refers to K^+, not to K.

4.8 COVALENT BONDING THEORIES

Molten ionic compounds conduct electricity because they are composed of ions which are free to move. Covalent compounds do not conduct electricity (see Figure 4.2). Unlike ionic compounds, covalent compounds do not consist of ions; their atoms do not undergo electron transfer and do not behave like ions. Each covalent molecule is a distinct collection of atoms joined to each other by covalent bonds. Thus covalent compounds, unlike ionic compounds, *do* contain discrete molecules. In water the atoms within each water molecule are attracted more to each other than to the atoms in another neighboring molecule. In Figure 4.4 the

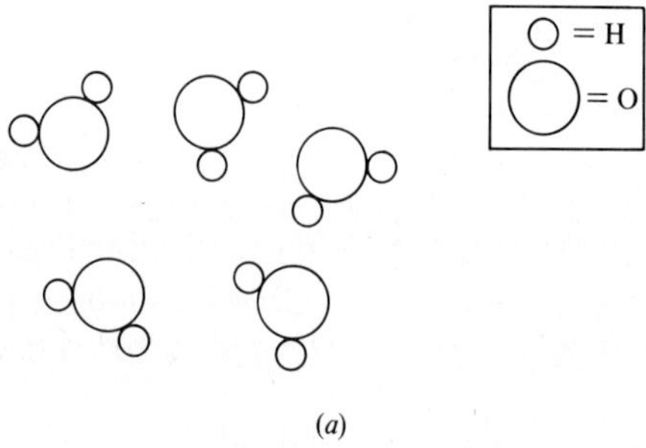

(*a*)

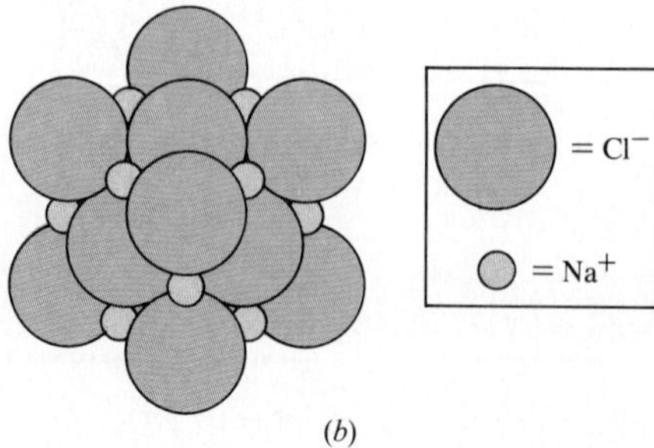

(*b*)

FIGURE 4.4
H_2O compared with NaCl. (*a*) The covalent compound H_2O is composed of distinct molecules. Each O atom belongs with two particular H atoms. (*b*) The ionic compound NaCl is composed of "formula units" of NaCl. No one Na^+ belongs to any one Cl^-.

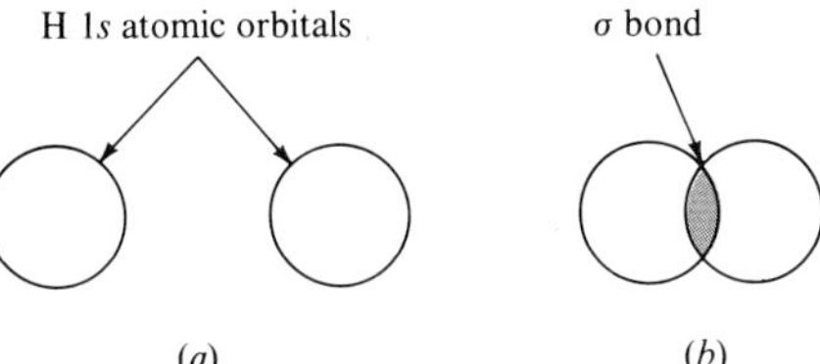

FIGURE 4.5
H atoms form H_2. (*a*) Isolated H atoms. (*b*) H_2 molecule formation. The H_2 molecule forms as the 1*s* orbitals of the isolated H atoms overlap to form a σ bond.

covalent compound water is compared with the ionic compound sodium chloride. The H atoms in each water molecule belong to one particular O atom. For this reason covalent compounds are sometimes called *molecular compounds.*

In general, covalent bonds form between atoms of nonmetallic elements. The forces which operate between these covalently bonded atoms are more complex than the "positive attracts negative" electrostatic forces present in ionic bonding. A covalent bond between two atoms is formed by the *sharing* of one or more pairs of electrons. This is unlike an ionic bond, formation of which involves a *transfer* of electrons.

Using the modern orbital picture of the atom, we can explain how a covalent bond forms. To do this we consider the simplest atom, H, and the simple molecule H_2, which forms when two H atoms bond together. Let us look at two isolated H atoms, each with one electron in a 1*s* orbital, and see what happens as they approach each other (see Figure 4.5). As the two H atoms get closer and closer, their 1*s* orbitals begin to *overlap*. The mutual attraction between the nucleus of one H atom and the electron of the other is responsible for the overlap. The two 1*s* atomic orbitals merge to form a **molecular orbital** of increased electron density. The electrons in the molecular orbital are strongly attracted to both nuclei, and we say that the two electrons in the molecular orbital are *shared* by two H atoms. These shared electrons form a covalent bond. At a distance of about 74 pm between the two nuclei, the H_2 molecule is born as the system of two electrons and two nuclei attains a maximum stability. The stability of the two bonded H atoms is much greater than that of the isolated atoms.

We can now extend the molecular orbital treatment to other covalent molecules. The atomic orbitals that can overlap must be half-filled, that is, they must contain just one electron. The two H 1*s* orbitals that overlap to form the H_2 molecular orbital each contain just one electron. Molecular orbitals contain two electrons and can form from various combinations of half-filled *s* and *p* orbitals, including the ones pictured in Figure 4.6. There are two different kinds of molecular orbitals, MOs, as shown in Figure 4.6. **Sigma** (σ) MOs form from the overlap of *s* with *s* and *p* with *s* and from the head-to-head overlap of two *p* orbitals. The **pi** (π) MOs form from the side-to-side overlap of two *p* orbitals.

Let us look at one more example of the formation of a molecular orbital, this time between two fluorine atoms, which bond together to form the covalently bonded F_2 molecule. To see which atomic orbitals of the F atom can participate in the formation of a molecular orbital, we first look at the electronic configuration of the F atom:

$$\text{F)}\quad 1s^2\ 2s^2\ 2p_x^2\ 2p_y^2\ \mathbf{2p_z^1}$$

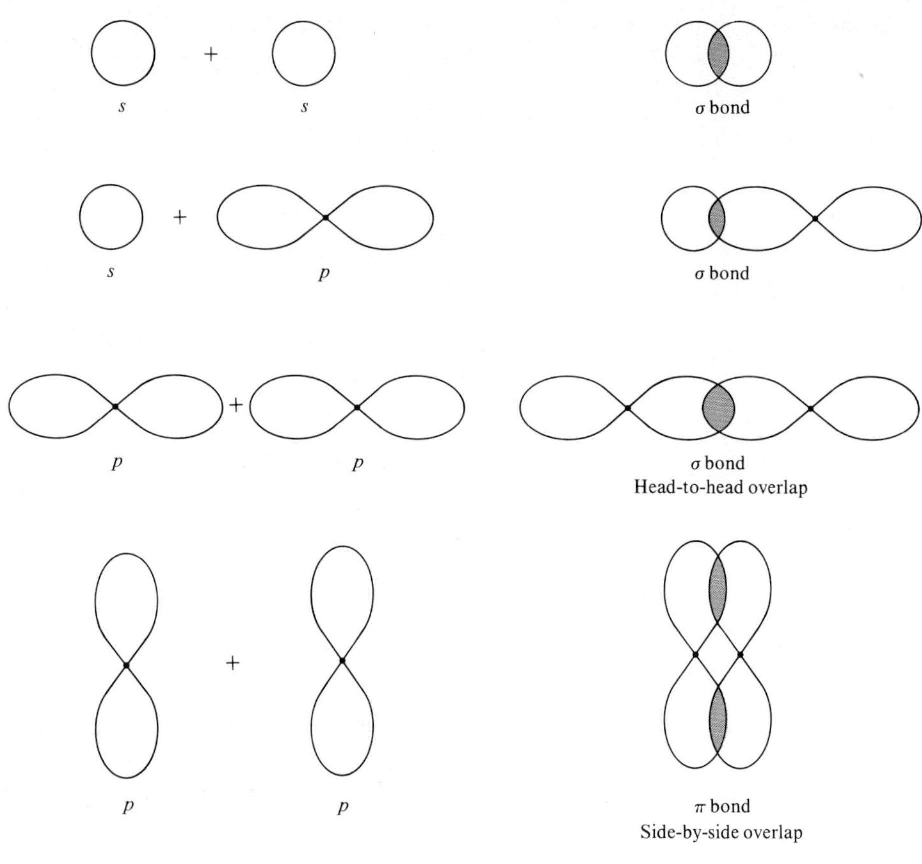

FIGURE 4.6
Sigma and pi molecular orbitals.

We see that each F atom contains one half-filled $2p_z$ orbital. The two $2p_z$ orbitals, one from each F atom, overlap head to head to form a sigma molecular orbital, as shown in Figure 4.7. In this way a covalent bond forms between the F atoms to produce the F_2 molecule. When just two *p* orbitals are available for overlap, it is always the head-to-head overlap that occurs, since the side-to-side overlap requires more energy.

For more complicated covalent molecules than the simple ones we have used so far, the molecular orbital pictures are more difficult to draw. A more convenient way to describe covalent bonds is by using **Lewis structures,** in which the electrons in a molecular orbital are pictured as a pair of dots.

FIGURE 4.7
F atoms form F_2. (*a*) Isolated F atoms. (*b*) F_2 molecule formation. The F_2 molecule forms as the $2p_z$ orbitals of the isolated F atoms overlap.

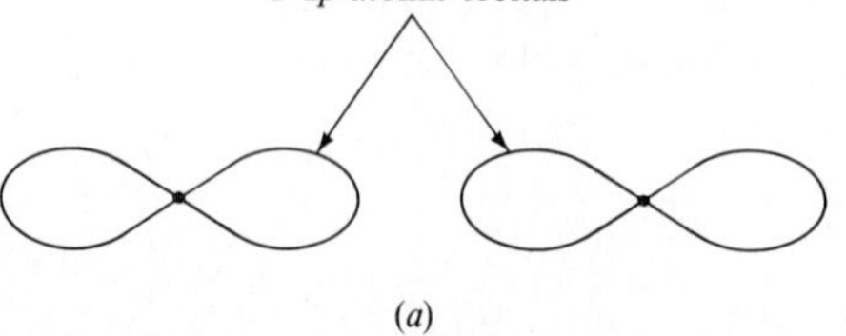

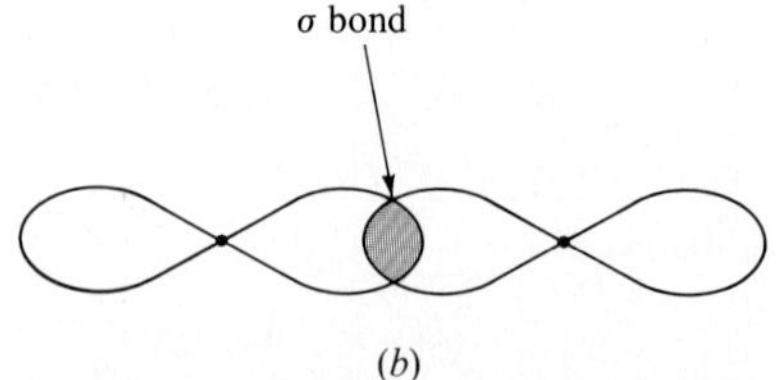

4.9 LEWIS ELECTRON DOT STRUCTURES

Each atom in a covalent bond is surrounded by two or eight electrons

Like molecular orbital theory, the electron dot theory, proposed by the American chemist G. N. Lewis, describes a *covalent bond as a shared pair of electrons.* The Lewis theory predicts the likelihood of formation of covalent molecules by establishing a criterion for their stability. The criterion is that an electronic configuration of each atom be the same as that of one of the noble gases. That is, each atom in the bond must be surrounded by eight electrons or, if the atom is H, by two electrons. This so-called octet rule is followed by most covalently bonded compounds. To see how the rule is applied we can write electron dot structure for some typical covalent molecules. The electrons included in these structures are those which are in the highest-energy level of each atom; these are the electrons available for bonding and are called **valence electrons.** For the representative elements this is the same as the number of the group to which the element belongs.

Valence is derived from the Latin word *valentia,* meaning "capacity" (to form bonds).

We begin by drawing the electron dot structure for the simple molecule H_2. Each H atom has just one electron in a 1*s* orbital and thus has an electron dot structure H·. The two H atoms share their two electrons, so that a pair of electrons forms around each atom:

Isolated H atoms: H· ·H
H_2 molecule: H:H

A dash in a formula refers to an electron pair.

The electron pair which joins the two atoms is a **single covalent bond** and is often indicated by a dash.

H:H can be written H—H

The pair of dots or the dash is analogous to the molecular orbital of our previous discussion.

That a pair of electrons surrounds each H atom can be seen by drawing circles (by pencil or by eye) around each H atom and the electrons around it.

Within each circle there are two electrons.

To write the electron dot structure for the diatomic molecule F_2, we first look at the electronic structure of the F atom. Each F atom (group VIIA) contains seven highest-energy electrons and thus needs one electron to complete its octet. To accomplish this the two F atoms share an electron pair to form a single covalent bond.

Isolated F atoms: $:\ddot{\underset{..}{F}}\cdot \qquad \cdot\ddot{\underset{..}{F}}:$

F_2 molecule: $:\ddot{\underset{..}{F}}:\ddot{\underset{..}{F}}:$

Note that there are six electron pairs that are not bonding the atoms together.

These are called **nonbonding** electron pairs and must be included in the electronic structure to check about whether the octet rule holds. We see that it does for F_2.

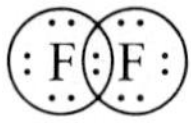

There are eight electrons within each circle.

In writing the structure of the F_2 molecule, the nonbonding pairs may be indicated by dots and are often omitted altogether. The various ways in which we can draw F_2 are

$$:\ddot{\underset{\cdot\cdot}{F}}:\ddot{\underset{\cdot\cdot}{F}}: \quad \text{or} \quad :\ddot{\underset{\cdot\cdot}{F}}—\ddot{\underset{\cdot\cdot}{F}}: \quad \text{or simply F—F}$$

In each case it is the electron pair which joins the F atoms that represents the molecular orbital formed by the overlap of the two $2p_z$ orbitals of the isolated F atoms.

To write the electron dot structure for the water molecule, H_2O, we first examine the electronic configurations of the atoms involved:

$$\text{H)}\ \ 1s^1 \qquad \text{H)}\ \ 1s^1 \qquad \text{O)}\ \ 1s^2 2s^2 2p^4$$

There are six electrons in the second principal energy level of the O atom (group VIA). Thus the O atom has six valence electrons. For H there is one electron available for bonding. The O atom needs two electrons to complete its octet and commonly forms two bonds in its compounds. We say that O has a **covalency** of 2. Hydrogen needs one electron to complete its duet, forms one bond, and has a covalency of 1. The only way to arrange the three atoms so that O can form two bonds and each H atom can form one bond is to put the O atom between the two H atoms:

H O H

We are now ready to distribute the 8 (6 + 1 + 1) electrons according to the octet rule. Each H atom forms a single bond with the central O atom. The remaining four electrons are placed around the O atom as two nonbonding pairs:

Isolated H and O atoms:

$$\text{H}\cdot \qquad \cdot\ddot{\underset{\cdot\cdot}{O}}\cdot \qquad \cdot\text{H}$$

H_2O molecule:

$$\text{H}:\ddot{\underset{\cdot\cdot}{O}}:\text{H} \quad \text{or} \quad \text{H—}\ddot{\underset{\cdot\cdot}{O}}\text{—H} \quad \text{or} \quad \text{H—O—H}$$

We see that this electron dot structure for the water molecule does follow the octet rule.

$$\text{H}(:)\ddot{\underset{\cdot\cdot}{O}}(:)\text{H}$$

	Electronic structures	Valence electrons	Covalency
P	$1s^2 2s^2 2p^6 3s^2 3p^3$	5	3
Cl	$1s^2 2s^2 2p^6 3s^2 3p^5$	$7 \times 3 = 21$	1

Isolated P and Cl atoms

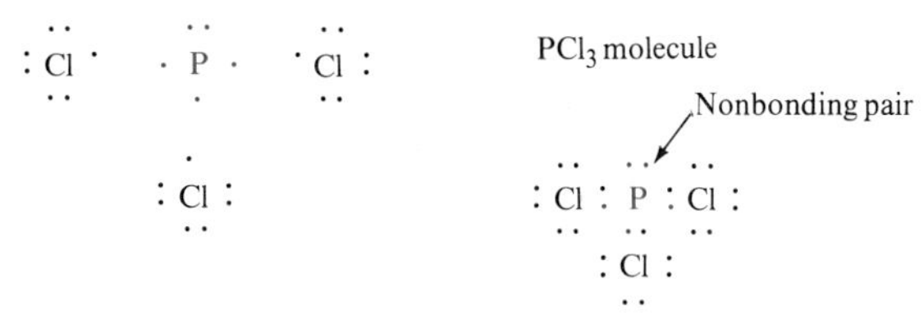

PCl_3 molecule

Nonbonding pair

	Electronic structures	Valence electrons	Covalency
H	$1s^1$	$1 \times 4 = 4$	1
C	$1s^2 2s^2 2p^2$	4	4

Isolated C and H atoms

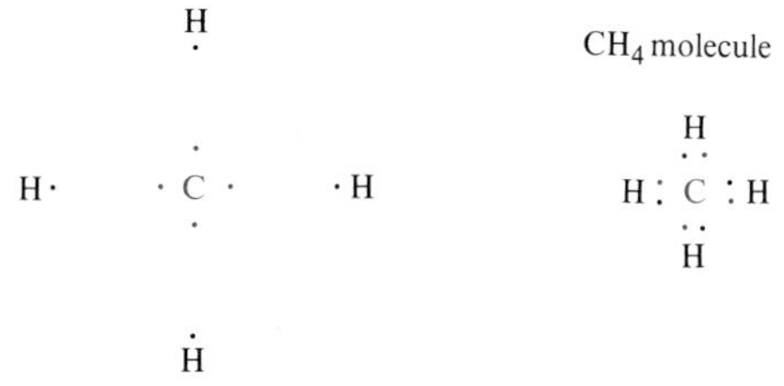

CH_4 molecule

FIGURE 4.8
Lewis structures of PCl_3 and H_2S.

Figure 4.8 guides you through the formation of electron dot structures for two other covalent compounds, PCl_3 and CH_4.

SAMPLE EXERCISE 4.4

Write the Lewis electron dot structure for the ammonia molecule, NH_3.

Solution:

N) $1s^2 2s^2 2p^3$ H) $1s^1$

N, with five valence electrons, needs three electrons to complete an octet. Thus N has a covalency of 3 and forms three bonds. H needs one electron to complete a duet, has a covalency of 1, and forms one bond. N must be the central atom and must be bonded to the three H atoms by three single bonds. The remaining two electrons are placed around N as a nonbonding pair. To distribute the 8 (5 + 1 + 1 + 1) electrons according to the octet rule we must have

```
  H                H               H
  ..               |               |
H:N:H     or    H—N—H     or    H—N—H
  ..               ..
```

EXERCISE 4.4

Give the electron dot structure for hydrogen chloride.

SAMPLE EXERCISE 4.5

The compound chloroform, $CHCl_3$, was at one time used as a general anesthetic. Produce the Lewis electron dot structure for chloroform.

Solution:

C) $1s^22s^22p^2$ H) $1s^1$ Cl) $1s^22s^22p^63s^23p^5$

C, with four valence electrons, needs four electrons to complete an octet and forms four bonds. H needs one electron to complete a pair, and forms one bond. Cl has seven valence electrons, needs one electron, and usually forms one bond. C must be the central atom and must be bonded to one H atom and three Cl atoms by four single bonds. To distribute the 26 (4 + 1 + 7 + 7 + 7) electrons according to the octet rule we must have

```
    H                  H
    ..                 |
Cl:C:Cl     or    Cl—C—Cl
    ..                 |
    Cl                 Cl
```

EXERCISE 4.5

Give the electron dot structure for $SiBr_4$, silicon tetrabromide.

4.10 MULTIPLE COVALENT BONDS

Sometimes more than one electron pair must be placed between two atoms to satisfy the octet rule. Bonds that include more than one electron pair are called **multiple covalent bonds.** In **double bonds** there are two electron pairs and in **triple bonds** there are three.

For instance, consider the Lewis electron dot structure of C_2H_4, a compound called ethene (but more commonly known as ethylene).

$$\begin{array}{c}\text{H}\ \ \text{H}\\ \ddot{}\ \ \ddot{}\\ \text{H:C::C:H}\end{array} \qquad \begin{array}{c}\text{H}\ \ \text{H}\\ |\ \ \ |\\ \text{H—C=C—H}\end{array}$$

The ethene structure includes a total of 12 valence electrons (8 from two C atoms and 4 from four H atoms). The only arrangement of electrons that satisfies the octet rule for the two C atoms is one in which they share four electrons. The four electrons represent two electron pairs, or a double bond, which may be indicated by using a double dash. To see that the octet rule is obeyed, we draw circles around each C atom, making sure to enclose all the surrounding electrons. (Around each H atom there are two electrons.)

$$\begin{array}{c}\text{H}\quad\text{H}\\ \text{H(: C(::)C :)H}\end{array}$$

Without including the double bond between the two C atoms, the octet rule could not be followed.

To write acceptable Lewis dot structures for some compounds, triple bonds must be incorporated. For example, in the compound C_2H_2, called acetylene, the electron dot structure includes a triple bond between the two carbon atoms.

$$\text{H:C:::C:H} \qquad \text{H—C}\equiv\text{C—H}$$

There are 10 valence electrons in this structure (8 from the two C atoms and 2 from the H atoms). By allowing the two C atoms to share six electrons to form the triple bond, the octet rule is satisfied, as we can see in the following:

$$\text{H(:C(:::)C:)H}$$

Multiple bonds have properties that are different from those of single bonds. Multiple bonds are *stronger* and *shorter* than single bonds, and triple bonds are stronger and shorter than double bonds. The lengths and strengths of the single,

TABLE 4.4 COMPARING SINGLE, DOUBLE, AND TRIPLE BONDS BETWEEN C ATOMS

Bond	Type of bond	Length, pm	Strength, kcal/bond	Relative strength compared with C—C
C=C	Double	134	24×10^{-23}	1.8
C≡C	Triple	120	33×10^{-23}	2.5

double, and triple bonds between the two C atoms in the compounds C_2H_6 (ethane), C_2H_4 (ethene), and C_2H_2 (acetylene), respectively, are compared in Table 4.4. One of the great strengths of Lewis electron dot theory is that it correctly predicts the existence of multiple bonds.

SAMPLE EXERCISE 4.6

Write the Lewis electron dot structure for carbon dioxide, CO_2.

Solution:

$$\text{C)}\quad 1s^2 2s^2 2p^2 \qquad \text{O)}\quad 1s^2 2s^2 2p^4$$

Total valence electrons = 4 (from C) + 12 (6 from each O) = 16. To satisfy the octet rule the C atom must be bonded to each O atom by double bonds. The structure includes two nonbonding pairs around each O atom.

:Ö::C::Ö: or :Ö=C=Ö: or O=C=O

• •

EXERCISE 4.6

Give the Lewis electron dot structure for nitrogen, the major component of air. Nitrogen exists in the form of diatomic molecules, N_2.

4.11 EXCEPTIONS TO LEWIS THEORY

So far we have been able to write Lewis electron dot structures which follow the octet rule for all the formulas given. The fact that the compounds represented by these formulas actually exist gives strong support to the Lewis theory. However, we will now look at some exceptions to the rule, that is, some compounds that *do* exist even though Lewis structures which follow the octet rule cannot be drawn for them. Rather than throwing out the theory, we can modify it to include these compounds.

The only way to draw Lewis structures for some molecules is to violate the rule of eight around their central atoms, which may be surrounded by more or less than eight electrons. Two examples of this are the Lewis structures for the compounds PCl_5 and BF_3, in which the octet rule is violated around the central atoms P and B.

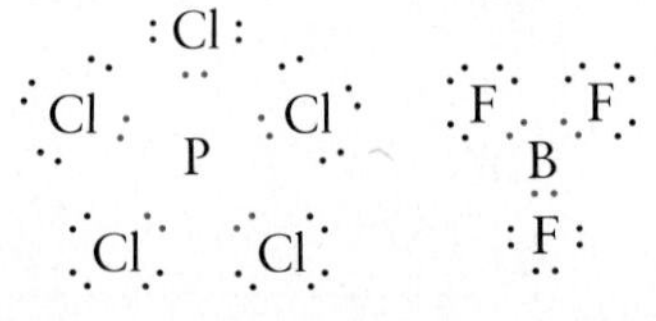

:C̈l:
:C̈l: P :C̈l: :F̈: :F̈:
:C̈l: :C̈l: B
:F̈:

Some compounds do exist even though they do not obey the octet rule.

Around the P atom in PCl_5 there are 10 electrons and around the B of BF_3, only 6. In general, Lewis structures in which the central atom in a structure can be joined to the surrounding atoms by electron pair bonds are acceptable, even though the octet rule may not be satisfied around the central atom.

For some molecules the total number of valence electrons is an odd number, meaning that the octet rule cannot possibly be followed. For instance, to draw the Lewis electron dot structure for NO, which has a total of 11 valence electrons (5 from N and 6 from O), there must be one unpaired electron in the structure. A Lewis structure that we can draw for NO is

$$\cdot\ddot{N}::\ddot{O}:$$

We see that there are only seven electrons around the N atom. However, even though the rule of eight is not obeyed here, this structure does predict an interesting property of NO and other molecules with unpaired electrons. When placed in a magnetic field, compounds such as NO are drawn into the magnetic field. This phenomenon, called *paramagnetism*, can be observed in the laboratory and supports structures such as the one above for NO, even though these structures violate the octet rule.

4.12 MOLECULAR GEOMETRIES

Another great strength of the Lewis electron dot theory is its ability to predict bond angles in molecules and thus to predict the geometry of the entire molecule. The **bond angle** is the angle between two bonds that join two atoms to a third atom. The bond angle between the two H—O bonds of the water molecule is shown below.

O
H H

Bond angle

Once we know all the bond angles in a given molecule, we can predict the three-dimensional spatial orientations of all its constituent atoms. This is the **molecular geometry** of the molecule.

One method used to predict molecular geometries can be applied to molecules with the general formula AX_n, where A is a central atom surrounded by n atoms of X. First, we count the number of electron pairs around A, including both bonding *and* nonbonding pairs. Because these electron pairs are all negatively charged, they move as far apart as possible. The orientation of the electron pairs around the central atom will determine the geometry of the molecule. Let's try to use this method, called the valence-shell electron pair repulsion (VSEPR) theory, to predict the geometries of some molecules.

First we consider the molecules in which the central atom is surrounded by *four* electron pairs.

$$\begin{array}{c} X \\ X : \overset{\cdot\cdot}{\underset{\cdot\cdot}{A}} : X \\ X \end{array}$$

Number of electron pairs around A = 4

Tetrahedron is derived from *tetra*, "four" and *hedra* "faces."

This means that we must allow four charges to repel each other. One way to think about this is to place the four charges in a transparent sphere where they will repel each other so that they land at four different points on the surface of the sphere. To see what figure they make, we connect these four points by lines. In this case, as shown in Figure 4.9, the resulting figure is a regular **tetrahedron.** This geometry provides maximum separation of the four electron pairs. To help you picture a tetrahedron, we have included a model for one in Figure 4.10. By cutting on the solid line and folding on the dotted lines, a tetrahedron is formed as the three corners are brought together to form a solid figure.

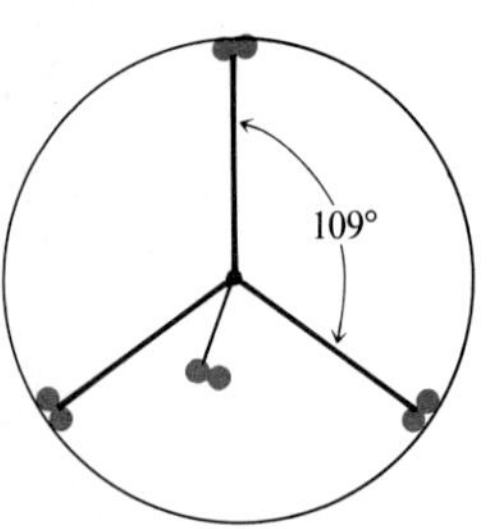

FIGURE 4.9
Tetrahedral arrangement of four charges in a sphere. The black dot is at the center of the sphere. Each pair of colored circles is a "charge" that represents an electron pair. The four charges land at the four corners of a regular tetrahedron.

Thus molecules such as AX_4 will have a *tetrahedral* geometry. In many compounds which form from group IVA elements (C, Si, etc.), such as CH_4, there are four bonding electron pairs around the central atom. The C atom of CH_4 is at the center of the tetrahedron and the four H atoms are at its four corners. That is, the C—H bonds all point toward the four corners of a regular tetrahedron (see Figure 4.11). The H to C to H bond angles are predicted to be 109° (actually 109°29′), an angle known as the *tetrahedral angle.* This is in excellent agreement with experiment. The geometry of CH_4, SiH_4, CCl_4, and other similar compounds *is* tetrahedral, as the theory predicts.

Next we consider compounds such as NH_3, in which the central atom is again surrounded by four electron pairs, one of which is a nonbonding pair. The electronic structure for NH_3 is

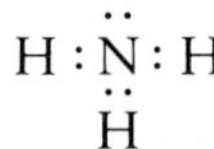

Number of bonding electron pairs: 3
Number of nonbonding electron pairs: 1
Total electron pairs around N: 4

Again the four electron pairs minimize their mutual repulsion by pointing toward the corners of a tetrahedron, and the geometry of the ammonia molecule is predicted to be tetrahedral (see Figure 4.12). We say that the *shape* of the ammonia molecule is *pyramidal* instead of tetrahedral because there are only three bonds around the central atom. Again this is in good agreement with the experimental values for H to N to H bond angles. The measured bond angle is 107° rather than 109°. The reason that the angle is a little less than 109° is that the nonbonding electron pair, called the *lone pair,* repels the other pairs more strongly than would a fourth bonding pair.

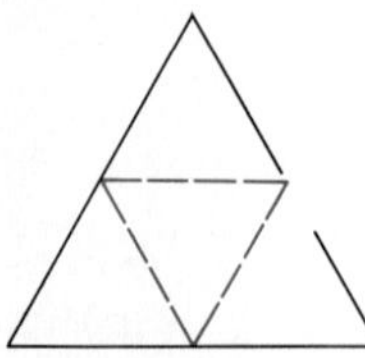

FIGURE 4.10
To make a tetrahedron, trace the figure of an equilateral triangle, as shown above. Cut on the solid lines. Fold on dotted lines so that all three points meet.

We can also use the Lewis theory to predict the geometry of the water molecule.

$$H : \overset{\cdot\cdot}{\underset{\cdot\cdot}{O}} : H$$

Number of bonding pairs: 2
Number of nonbonding pairs: 2
Total number of electron pairs around O: 4

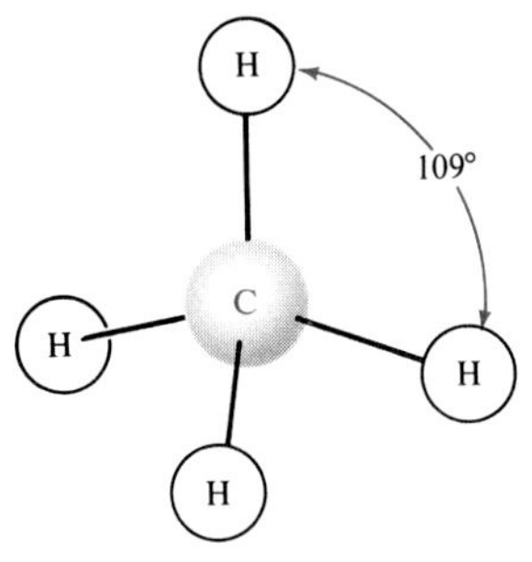

FIGURE 4.11
Geometry of methane. The CH_4 molecule has tetrahedral geometry with 109° bond angles.

Because there is a total of four electron pairs around the central atom, we once again predict a tetrahedral geometry for the water molecule. However, because there are only two, not four, atoms bonded to oxygen, we say that the *shape* of the molecule is *bent* (see Figure 4.13). The observed H to O to H bond angle in water is 104.5°, somewhat less than 109°, because there are two lone pairs to exert extra repulsion and thus to decrease the bond angle below the tetrahedral angle.

In some molecules with the general formula AX_3 there are *three* electron pairs surrounding the central atom:

Number of electron pairs around A: 3

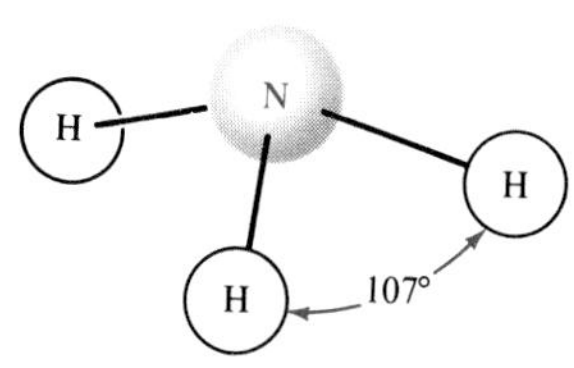

FIGURE 4.12
Geometry of NH_3. The NH_3 molecule is pyramidal in shape. The H-N-H bond angles are a little less than 109°.

Now we must put three like charges into a sphere and imagine the figure they produce. Connecting the points where they land produces a regular triangle, as shown in Figure 4.14.

Thus to determine the geometry of a molecule such as BF_3, we put a B atom at the center of a triangle and the three F atoms at its corners. The B to F bonds point to the corners of a regular triangle, the F to B to F bond angles are 120°, and the molecule is *planar* (see Figure 4.15). We say that the geometry of molecules such as BF_3, in which three electron pairs surround a central atom, is triangular planar. Again, this is in excellent agreement with experimental results, which show that the bond angles in BF_3 are 120°.

When a central atom A is surrounded by only *two* electron pairs, the resulting molecule AX_2 must be *linear*. The maximum repulsion between two electron pairs produces a straight line (see Figure 4.16). One example of this is the covalent compound $BeCl_2$, in which the central Be atom has two bonding electron pairs around it (see Figure 4.17).

$$:\ddot{\underset{\cdot\cdot}{Cl}}:Be:\ddot{\underset{\cdot\cdot}{Cl}}:$$

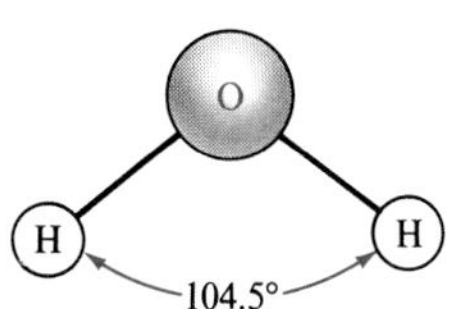

FIGURE 4.13
Geometry of H_2O. The H_2O molecule is bent with a 104.5° bond angle.

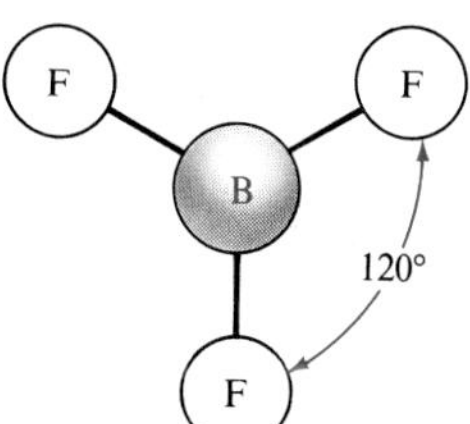

FIGURE 4.15
Geometry of BF_3. The BF_3 molecule is planar with 120° bond angles.

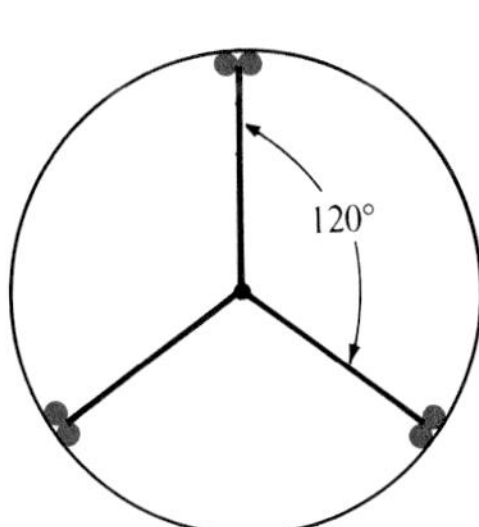

FIGURE 4.14
Three charges in a sphere. The charges point toward the corners of a triangle.

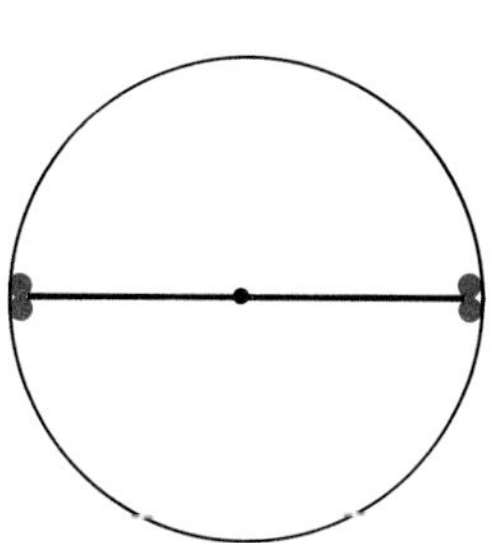

FIGURE 4.16
Two charges in a sphere. Connecting the two charges produces a straight line.

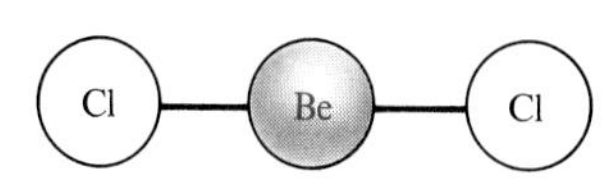

FIGURE 4.17
Geometry of $BeCl_2$. The $BeCl_2$ molecule is linear.

SAMPLE EXERCISE 4.7

What is the shape of the molecule H_2S? (The compound H_2S is called hydrogen sulfide and is responsible for the odor of rotten egg.)

Solution:

To determine the shape we draw the Lewis electron dot structure:

$$H:\overset{..}{\underset{..}{S}}:H$$

Total electron pairs around S: 4

Since there are four electron pairs, the geometry must be tetrahedral. However, since S is bonded to only two atoms, the shape of H_2S is bent.

EXERCISE 4.7

What is the shape of the carbon tetrachloride, CCl_4, molecule?

4.13 ELECTRONEGATIVITY AND POLAR BONDS

When an electron pair (or pairs) involved in a covalent bond is shared by two identical atoms, the sharing is equal. The electron pair cannot be said to be more closely associated with one atom than the other atom. This type of covalent bond is present in diatomic molecules such as H_2, F_2, and N_2:

$$H\text{—}H \qquad F\text{—}F \qquad N\equiv N$$

The electron pair bond in each of the molecules is equally shared by both atoms.

When an electron pair is shared by two different atoms, one atom may have a greater attraction for the electron pair than the other atom. The atom with the greater attraction for the electron pair will assume a partial negative charge relative to the other atom. For example, in the molecule HCl, hydrogen chloride, the Cl atom has a greater attraction for the electron pair than does the H atom. Therefore, the Cl atom becomes partially negative with respect to the H atom. Likewise, the H atom is partially positive relative to the Cl atom. The symbol which indicates a partial charge is the Greek lowercase delta, δ, followed by a + or − sign.

$$\overset{\delta+}{H}:\overset{\delta-}{Cl}$$

The electron pair bond is closer to the Cl atom.

Bonds such as the one in HCl in which the sharing between atoms is not equal are **polar covalent bonds.** An extreme case of the polar covalent bond is

H 2.1																	He —
Li 1.0	Be 1.5											B 2.0	C 2.5	N 3.0	O 3.5	F 4.0	Ne —
Na 0.9	Mg 1.2											Al 1.5	Si 1.8	P 2.1	S 2.5	Cl 3.0	Ar —
K 0.8	Ca 1.0	Sc 1.3	Ti 1.5	V 1.2	Cr 1.6	Mn 1.5	Fe 1.8	Co 1.8	Ni 1.8	Cu 1.9	Zn 1.6	Ga 1.6	Ge 1.8	As 2.0	Se 2.4	Br 2.8	Kr —
Rb 0.8	Sr 1.0	Y 1.2	Zr 1.4	Nb 1.6	Mo 1.8	Tc 1.9	Ru 2.2	Rh 2.2	Pd 2.2	Ag 1.9	Cd 1.7	In 1.7	Sn 1.8	Sb 1.9	Te 2.1	I 2.5	Xe —
Cs 0.7	Ba 0.9	La 1.1	Hf 1.3	Ta 1.5	W 1.7	Re 1.9	Os 2.2	Ir 2.2	Pt 2.2	Au 2.4	Hg 1.9	Tl 1.8	Pb 1.9	Bi 1.9	Po 2.0	At 2.2	Rn —

FIGURE 4.18
Electronegativities.

the ionic bond, in which electron transfer has occurred, producing ions with full charges. The other extreme case is the **nonpolar covalent bond** (as in H_2, F_2, and N_2), in which the bonding electrons are equally shared by both atoms.

The degree of attraction an atom has for a bonding electron pair is the **electronegativity** of the atom. Linus Pauling, whose contributions to chemical bonding theory earned him a Nobel prize in 1954, assigned numbers to represent the electronegativities of atoms; the higher the number, the greater the electronegativity. Figure 4.18 displays the electronegativities of certain elements and their positions in the periodic table of elements.

Note that the most electronegative elements are in the upper right of the periodic table and the least electronegative elements are in the lower left.

The atom with the highest electronegativity, 4.0, is fluorine, which means that F bonded to any other kind of atom will have a greater attraction for the electron pair bond and will always assume a negative charge. The greater the electronegativity difference between two atoms, the more polar the bond that forms between them. According to an arbitrary rule of thumb, when the electronegativity difference is greater than 1.7, the bond between the atoms is considered to be ionic.

To decide whether a bond is ionic, polar covalent, or nonpolar covalent, find the electronegativity difference of the two atoms involved. For instance, we see that the bonds between Na and Cl (in NaCl) and between Ca and O (in CaO) are both ionic.

	Na—Cl	**Ca—O**
Electronegativities	Na (0.9) Cl (3.0)	Ca (1.0) O (3.5)
Difference	2.1	2.5

If the electronegativity difference is zero, it means that the bond between the two atoms is nonpolar covalent, at least to the extent that the electronegativity values assigned are accurate. As stated previously, the only pure nonpolar covalent bond exists between two identical atoms. We see that the C to S bond is nonpolar covalent, and that the H to H bond is pure nonpolar covalent.

	H—H	**C—S**
Electronegativities:	H (2.1) H (2.1)	C (2.5) S (2.5)
Difference:	0	0

Most bonds fall somewhere between the extremes of nonpolar and ionic.

SAMPLE EXERCISE 4.8

Label each of the following bonds nonpolar covalent, polar covalent, or ionic. Are any of the bonds pure nonpolar covalent bonds?
(a) Br—Br (b) Ca—Cl (c) H—O (d) P—H

Solution:

Look up electronegativities for each atom using Figure 4.18. Calculate the electronegativity difference between the two atoms.

(a) Br(2.8) – Br(2.8)
Electronegativity difference = 2.8 – 2.8 = 0. Br—Br is pure nonpolar covalent.
(b) Ca(1.0) – Cl(3.0)
Electronegativity difference = 3.0 – 1.0 = 2.0. Ca—Cl is ionic.
(c) H(2.1) – O(3.5)
Electronegativity difference = 3.5 – 2.1 = 1.4. H—O is polar covalent.
(d) P(2.1) – H(2.1)
Electronegativity difference = 2.1 – 2.1 = 0. P—H is nonpolar covalent.

EXERCISE 4.8

Match each bond below with the correct label.

(a) S—O (1) Ionic
(b) I—I (2) Polar covalent
(c) K—F (3) Pure nonpolar covalent

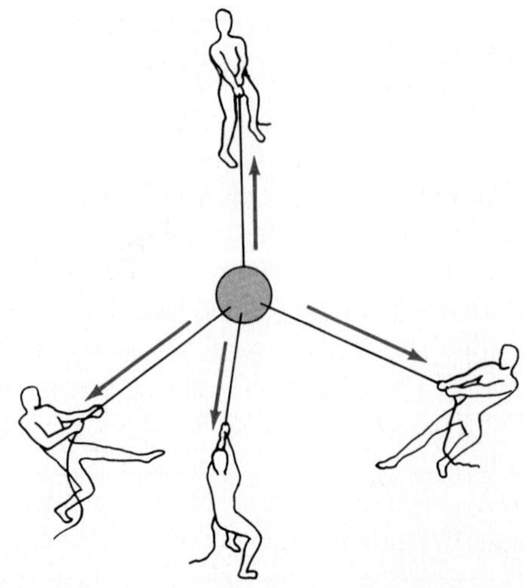

FIGURE 4.19
Tetrahedral arrangement of polar bonds cancelling. The four people are pulling equally on the object. Because they are pulling toward the corners of a regular tetrahedron, their pulling forces cancel and the object does not move.

4.14 POLARITY OF MOLECULES

Some important properties of compounds depend upon whether or not their molecules are polar. To find out if a molecule is polar we check to see if it contains any polar bonds and then find out how the polar bonds are arranged in the molecule. In very symmetrical molecules polar bonds may cancel one another so that the molecule as a whole is nonpolar.

Nonpolar Molecules

Molecules which contain only nonpolar bonds must be nonpolar. This is the case for molecules in which all bonds are between atoms with the same (or very nearly the same) electronegativity values. Molecules such as H_2, O_2, N_2, and P_4, which contain purely covalent bonds, are all nonpolar. Molecules containing only C to S bonds (electronegativity difference of zero) are also nonpolar.

Some nonpolar molecules *do* contain polar bonds, but they are so symmetrical that the polarities cancel. For instance, the compound CF_4, carbon tetrafluoride, is nonpolar even though it contains four C to CF bonds (electronegativity difference = 4.0 − 2.5 = 1.5). (Bond polarity can be indicated by using an arrow that points toward the more electronegative atom in the bond.) For the C to F bond the arrow points toward the F atom. The plus at the tail end of the arrow indicates the least electronegative atom (C, in this case).

$$\overset{+\!\!\longrightarrow}{\text{C—F}}$$

To see why the C to F bond polarities cancel in CF_4 we look at the geometry of the CF_4 molecule, which is tetrahedral:

F
C
F F F

The polarities of the four C to F bonds cancel out because the bonds are arranged so that they point toward the corners of the symmetrical regular tetrahedron. One way to help convince yourself of this is to imagine four people pulling with the same force toward the corners of a regular tetrahedron, as shown in Figure 4.19. Nothing happens! The forces cancel.

Another example of this is the nonpolar molecule CO_2, which is linear. Even though the C to O bonds are polar (electronegativity difference = 3.5 − 2.5 = 1.0), their polarities cancel because of the linear arrangement.

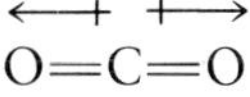

Polar Molecules

Covalent compounds in which bond polarities do not cancel are also polar. For instance, the water molecule is polar because it contains polar O to H bonds and because it is bent so that the polarities do not cancel. Thus, the water molecule has positive and negative ends, as we have shown by using partial charge signs $\delta-$ and $\delta+$.

δ^- O, H δ^+, H δ^+

TABLE 4.5 **POLARITY OF POLYATOMIC MOLECULES**

Name	Formula	Geometry	3D structure
	Polar molecules*		
Ammonia	NH_3	Pyramidal	N; H H H
Water	H_2O	Bent	O; H H
Hydrogen sulfide	H_2S	Bent	S; H H
	Nonpolar molecules†		
Carbon dioxide	CO_2	Linear	O=C=O
Carbon tetrachloride	CCl_4	Tetrahedral	Cl; C; Cl Cl Cl
Methane	CH_4	Tetrahedral	H; C; H H H
Boron trifluoride	BF_3	Planar	F F; B; F

*Bond polarities *do not* cancel for the polar molecules listed.
†The bond polarities *do* cancel for the nonpolar molecules.

The fact that experimental measurements have shown water molecules to be polar proves that the water molecule must be bent. (If water molecules were linear, the bond polarities of the two H to O bonds would cancel, making the molecule nonpolar.)

Table 4.5 lists some other examples of polar and nonpolar molecules.

4.15 NAMING BINARY COVALENT COMPOUNDS

Covalent compounds which contain two nonmetals are called *binary covalent compounds*. Their names conform to a special system similar to that for naming ionic compounds (Section 4.5). The name of the element that is written on the left of the formula (usually the least electronegative element) is simply the name of the element itself. The name of the other element written on the right (usually the more electronegative one) is modified with the suffix *-ide*. Thus HCl is named hydrogen chloride. When more than one atom of an element is present in a formula, the name of the element is preceded by a prefix to indicate the number of atoms. Some of the prefixes are

mono = 1	penta = 5
di = 2	hexa = 6
tri = 3	hepta = 7
tetra = 4	octa = 8

The compound SO_3 is different from the ion SO_3^{2-}, called sulfite.

In most cases the prefix mono- is omitted. For example, SO_3, the compound that forms from one atom of S and three atoms of O, is named sulfur trioxide. A list of names and formulas for binary covalent compounds is presented in Table 4.6.

TABLE 4.6 **NAMES OF COVALENT BINARY COMPOUNDS OF TWO NONMETALS**

Formula	Proper name	Trivial name
CO	Carbon monoxide	
CO_2	Carbon dioxide	
NO	Nitrogen oxide	Nitric oxide
N_2O	Dinitrogen oxide	Nitrous oxide (laughing gas)
NO_2	Nitrogen dioxide	
N_2O_4	Dinitrogen tetroxide	
SO_2	Sulfur dioxide	
SO_3	Sulfur trioxide	
CH_4	Carbon tetrahydride	Methane*
NH_3	Nitrogen trihydride	Ammonia*
H_2O	Dihydrogen oxide	Water*

*The trivial names for CH_4, NH_3, and H_2O are well established and acceptable.

NH_3 is always called ammonia.

Note that several common compounds have trivial names. The compound which forms between two atoms of H and one of O is always called water, not "dihydrogen oxide." The compound with the formula NH_3 is called ammonia rather than "nitrogen trihydride." "Dinitrogen oxide" should be the name of the compound N_2O; however this compound, used as a general anesthetic, is more often called nitrous oxide, or "laughing gas."

4.16 BONDING BETWEEN MOLECULES

The molecules of compounds are attracted to each other by forces which are always present but are much weaker than those which connect the atoms in covalent bonds. The larger the mass of the molecules, the greater are these *intermolecular forces.* We can test this idea by comparing two compounds that have very similar structures, such as CH_4 and GeH_4, both group IVA hydrides. The formula weight of the GeH_4 molecule is 76.6 and that of the CH_4 molecule is 16. Thus GeH_4 molecules are much more attracted to each other than are CH_4 molecules (see Figure 4.20). One way to determine the extent of the intermolecular attractive forces is to measure the boiling point of a compound. The attractive forces between the molecules in a liquid must be overcome before the molecules can escape to become gaseous. From looking at Table 4.7 we see that the boiling point of CH_4 is $-164°C$ compared with the higher boiling point of GeH_4 at $-88°C$, just as would be expected.

Compounds that contain bonds between H and one of the three highly electronegative small atoms F, N, and O have boiling points that are much higher than would be expected from their formula weights. For example, suppose we were asked to guess the boiling point of H_2O (formula weight 18) knowing that H_2Te (formula weight 129.6) boils at $-2°C$, H_2Se (formula weight 81.0) boils at $-41°C$, and H_2S (formula weight 34) boils at $-61°C$. We would be tempted to say that water must boil at a temperature of about $-80°C$ (lower than that for H_2S) and that water must be a gas at room temperature! But, of course, this

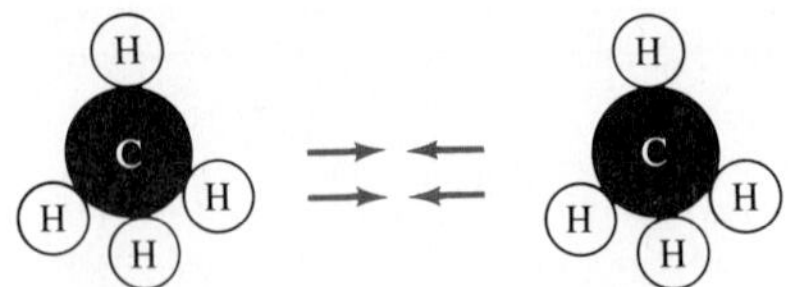

H Ge H H H H Ge H H H

Formula weight GeH_4 = 76.6

FIGURE 4.20
Attraction between GeH_4 molecules compared with CH_4 molecules. At a given separation distance, the attractive forces between GeH_4 molecules are greater than are those operating between the molecules of the less massive CH_4 molecules.

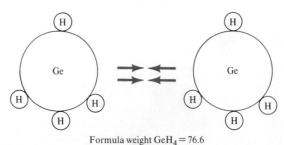

TABLE 4.7 BOILING POINTS OF GROUP IVA THROUGH VIIA

Formula	Name	Formula weight	Boiling point, °C	Physical state, 25°C
	Group IVA hydrides			
CH_4	Methane	16.0	−164	Gas
SiH_4	Silicon tetrahydride (silane)	32.1	−112	Gas
GeH_4	Germanium tetrahydride (germane)	76.6	−88	Gas
SnH_4	Tin tetrahydride (stannane)	122.7	−52	Gas
	Group VA hydrides			
NH_3	Ammonia	17.0	−33	Gas
PH_3	Phosphorus trihydride (phospine)	34.0	−88	Gas
AsH_3	Arsenic trihydride (arsine)	77.9	−55	Gas
SbH_3	Antimony trihydride (stibine)	124.8	−17	Gas
	Group VIA hydrides			
H_2O	Water	18.0	100	Liquid
H_2S	Hydrogen sulfide	34.1	−61	Gas
H_2Se	Hydrogen selenide	81.0	−41	Gas
H_2Te	Hydrogen telluride	129.6	−2	Gas
	Group VIIA hydrides			
HF	Hydrogen fluoride	20.0	20	Gas
HCl	Hydrogen chloride	36.5	−85	Gas
HBr	Hydrogen bromide	80.9	−67	Gas
HI	Hydrogen iodide	127.9	−35	Gas

*Note that the boiling points for ammonia, water, and hydrogen fluoride (in color) are all abnormally high. This is due to hydrogen bonding.

is not so. We know that water is a liquid boiling at 100°C. The compounds HF and NH_3 also have unusually high boiling points compared with those of the other hydrides of their families (see Table 4.7). The presence of an extra attractive force between the molecules of HF, of H_2O, and of NH_3 is responsible for this.

The compounds HF, H_2O, and NH_3 all contain molecules with very polar H—F, H—O, and H—N bonds. Furthermore, the F, O, and N atoms in these bonds all have one or more nonbonding electron pairs:

H—F: O (H, H)   N (H, H, H)

The positive H end of a bond in one of these molecules can form a bridge to the F, O, or N atom of a neighboring molecule (see Figure 4.21, where this is shown for H_2O, NH_3, and HF molecules. This bridge is called a **hydrogen bond.** Hy-

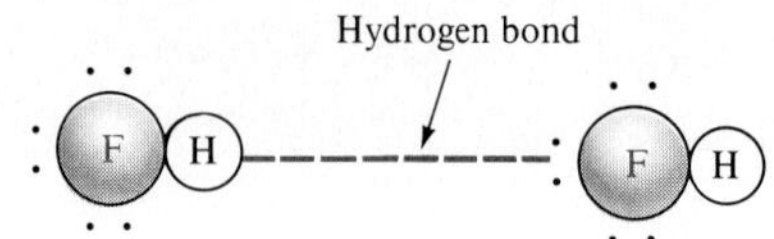

FIGURE 4.21
Hydrogen bonding among H_2O, NH_3, and HF molecules. The hydrogen bonds (in color) form bridges between the H atoms of one molecule and a nonbonding pair on an F, O, and N atom of a neighboring molecule.

drogen bonds are only about one-tenth as strong as ordinary covalent bonds. The approximate energies required to break hydrogen bonds, covalent bonds, and ionic bonds are compared in Table 4.8. Because of hydrogen bonding, the compounds HF, H_2O, and NH_3 all have unusually high boiling points. Any molecule which contains a bond between H and F, O, or N will exhibit hydrogen bonding.

The O—H bonds within one water molecule, H—O—H, are covalent bonds. The bonds between two different water molecules are hydrogen bonds.

The consequences of hydrogen bonding in the world of living matter are far-reaching. Without hydrogen bonding, water would be a gas at ordinary temperatures like its related group VIA hydrides H_2S, H_2Se, and H_2Te. Without liquid water, life as we know it could not exist. Hydrogen bonds cause the protein molecules which make up a large proportion of living tissue to assume their characteristic shapes. It is hydrogen bonding that links two strands of DNA (deoxyribonucleic acid) to form a double helix, which acts as the blueprint for human reproduction.

TABLE 4.8 **STRENGTH OF H BONDS COMPARED WITH TYPICAL IONIC AND COVALENT BONDS**

Bond	Bond strength, kcal/bond
Ionic	30×10^{-23}
Covalent	13×10^{-23}
Hydrogen	1×10^{-23}

SUMMARY

There are two broad classes of chemical bonds, ionic and covalent. Ionic compounds contain ionic bonds and have high melting points and high electrical conductance. Atoms of metallic elements become positive ions, called cations, by losing electrons, and atoms of nonmetals become negative ions, called anions, by gaining electrons. Groups of atoms, called polyatomic ions, may also carry an electrical charge and behave as anions or cations. Ionic compounds are composed of anions and cations held together by the electrostatic attraction between positive and negative charges. To write the name of an ionic compound, first give the cation name and then the anion name. To write formulas of ionic compounds the total charge must be zero. Only the ratio of cations to anions is indicated by the formulas because no one cation belongs to any one anion. In fact, the ions are arranged to form a regular crystalline structure. Hence the word molecule is sometimes replaced by the term formula unit to describe the basic unit of an ionic compound.

Covalent compounds usually form between nonmetallic elements. Covalent bonds are produced by the overlap of atomic orbitals to form molecular orbitals. In Lewis electron dot structures the molecular orbitals are indicated by a shared electron pair. Each atom in a Lewis structure attains a stable noble gas configuration according to the octet rule. All the highest-energy electrons of each atom, called valence electrons, are included to produce electron dot structures for molecules. To follow the octet rule, multiple bonds which include two or three electron pairs may have to be introduced. Multiple bonds are shorter and stronger than single bonds. Although not all compounds can be represented by Lewis structures that obey the octet rule, the ease of application of the Lewis theory and the scope of its success make it enormously useful.

All ionic bonds must be polar, but covalent bonds may be polar or nonpolar. In polar bonds the electrons are shared unequally. Electronegativity is a convenient measure of the degree of attraction which an atom has for a bonding electron pair or pairs. Certain compounds which contain polar bonds may be nonpolar because of their regular geometric shapes, which cause the bond polarities to cancel.

Intermolecular bonds which form between molecules are much weaker than covalent or ionic bonds. All molecules are attracted to each other by forces which increase as the size of the molecule increases. Some molecules, those which contain bonds in which an H atom is joined to one of the very electronegative atoms F, O, or N, also exhibit an extra intermolecular force called hydrogen bonding. Hydrogen bonds are the bridges which form between the H atom of one molecule and the F, O, or N atom of a neighboring molecule.

KEY WORDS

chemical bond
bond energy
ionic compound
covalent compound
ionic bond
covalent bond
cation
anion
polyatomic ion
molecular orbital
pi bond
sigma bond
electron dot structure
valence electrons
octet rule
single bond
multiple bond
double bond
triple bond
electronegativity
polar covalent bond
nonpolar covalent bond
polar molecule
nonpolar molecule
molecular geometry
tetrahedron
hydrogen bonding

EXERCISES

4.9 Compare the electrical conductivity and melting points of ionic compounds and covalent compounds.

4.10 Which of the following elements would be expected to form cations? Why? (**a**) Na; (**b**) Sr; (**c**) S; (**d**) I.

4.11 For the ions which form from K, Ca, and S give the
(**a**) Electronic configuration
(**b**) Symbol
(**c**) Name
(**d**) Noble gas with the same electronic configuration

4.12 Give the symbols and names for the ions which form from (**a**) strontium; (**b**) radium; (**c**) bromine; (**d**) rubidium; (e) indium.

4.13 The element copper forms cuprous and cupric ions. Which one is cuprous, Cu^+ or Cu^{2+}?

4.14 Give the formulas and names for the ionic compounds which form between the following pairs of elements:
(a) Lithium and flourine (b) Cesium and bromine
(c) Potassium and oxygen (d) Barium and sulfur

4.15 Write formulas for the following ionic compounds:
(a) Barium chloride (b) Sodium oxide
(c) Potassium iodide (d) Aluminum fluoride
(e) Radium chloride (f) Sodium sulfide

4.16 Give formulas for the ionic compounds below:
(a) Tin(II) fluoride (b) Mercury(I) oxide
(c) Mercury(II) oxide (d) Cuprous chloride
(e) Stannous chloride

4.17 Write formulas for the following ionic compounds:
(a) Calcium carbonate (b) Sodium phosphate
(c) Calcium sulfate (d) Calcium sulfite
(e) Sodium sulfite (f) Silver nitrate

4.18 Give formulas for the compounds below:
(a) Potassium hydroxide
(b) Sodium cyanide
(c) Sodium peroxide

4.19 There are four possible Cl and O ions. Name the compounds below, using analogous names for those containing I and O.
(a) $NaClO$ (b) $NaClO_2$
(c) $NaClO_3$ (d) $NaClO_4$
(e) $NaIO$ (f) $NaIO_2$
(g) $NaIO_3$ (h) $NaIO_4$

4.20 The compound sodium pertechnetate is used in nuclear medicine to perform brain scans. If technetium (element 43) forms compounds similar to those formed by manganese (Mn), find the formula for sodium pertechnetate using Table 4.2.

4.21 Name the following ionic compounds:
(a) KI (b) Li_2O
(c) SrI_2 (d) $FeBr_2$
(e) $FeBr_3$ (f) $CsCl$
(g) Na_2S (h) Cu_2O

4.22 Name the ionic compounds below:
(a) $Ca(OH)_2$ (b) NH_4I
(c) $NaCN$ (d) $BaCO_3$
(e) $AlPO_4$ (f) $Pb(NO_3)_2$
(g) $K_2Cr_2O_7$ (h) $RaSO_4$
(i) Cr_2O_3 (j) KNO_2
(k) $KClO_4$

4.23 $AuCl_3$ is a compound used in chrysotherapy, that is, treatment of disease by means of gold compounds. Name the compound (containing Au^{3+}) using the Roman numeral system. If gold formed two cations, Au^+ and Au^{3+}, what common name would this compound have?

4.24 The following compounds have medical uses. Complete the table by filling in the missing names or formulas.

Formula	Name	Medical use
?	Sodium nitrite	Vasodilator (dilates blood vessels)
NaF	?	Reduces dental cavities (by water fluoridation)
?	Potassium permanganate	Disinfectant
SrS	?	Depilatory
$Fe(OH)_3$	?	Antidote for arsenic poisoning
?	Sodium bicarbonate	Antacid

4.25 According to Lewis electron dot theory, how many valence electrons are there for the following elements: (a) Phosphorus; (b) iodine; (c) oxygen; (d) sulfur.

4.26 Write Lewis electron dot structures for the following molecules: (a) HI; (b) Cl_2; (c) H_2Se; (d) CBr_4; (e) PI_3.

4.27 Name the compounds from Problem 4.26.

4.28 Write Lewis electron dot structures for the following compounds, which contain multiple bonds. (a) CO_2; (b) HCN.

4.29 Write the Lewis electron dot structure for formaldehyde, CH_2O. (The two H atoms are bonded to the C atom.)

4.30 Name these compounds: (a) P_2O_5; (b) CS_2; (c) NI_3; (d) $GeCl_4$; (e) N_2O_4.

4.31 Write formulas for all the compounds listed in Figure 4.2.

4.32 The name "lithium" is often given to a drug used to treat manic depressives. Is the drug formula most likely to be Li or Li_2CO_3?

4.33 Why is it awkward to talk about "molecules" of NaCl?

4.34 Referring to Figure 4.18, decide whether the following bonds are ionic, polar covalent, nonpolar covalent, or pure nonpolar covalent: (a) C—C; (b) C—Cl; (c) Na—O; (d) S—O; (e) Cl—O; (f) K—F; (g) N—Cl.

4.35 Write the Lewis electron dot structure for SF_4, in which S is the central atom. Is it possible to follow the octet rule?

4.36 In the formation of the Cl_2 molecule, which atomic orbitals of the Cl atoms overlap to form a molecular orbital? Make a sketch showing the two isolated Cl atoms and the Cl_2 molecule.

4.37 In which of the following compounds is the bond between C and N stronger?

```
       H
       |
(a) H—C—N—H      (b) H—C—C≡N
       |  |             |
       H  H             H
```

4.38 Describe the molecular geometry of the following molecules as tetrahedral, pyramidal, bent, linear, or planar. (a) $SiCl_4$; (b) H_2Se; (c) $AsCl_3$.

4.39 For which of the following compounds is the octet rule violated around the central atom? (a) CI_4; (b) SF_6; (c) BCl_3; (d) SbF_3?

4.40 Tell if the following statement is true or false: All molecules with the general formula AX_n, where A is the central atom, must have the same shape. Explain your answer.

4.41 To prevent goiter, ordinary table salt is sometimes "iodized." In what form do you think the element iodine is present?

4.42 For the molecule SiF_4:
(a) Draw the Lewis electron dot structure.
(b) Decide whether or not the molecule is polar.

4.43 Of the following nitrogen oxides, which one must have an unpaired electron in its Lewis dot structure? (a) N_2O; (b) NO_2; (c) N_2O_4?

4.44 Which of the following carbon compounds should exhibit hydrogen bonding?
(a) CH_4
(b) CO_2

```
       H                  H
       |                  |
(c) H—C—O—H      (d) H—C—S—H
       |                  |
       H                  H
```

```
       H
       |
(e) H—C—N—H
       |  |
       H  H
```

4.45 Which of these two compounds should have the higher boiling point? Why? (a) C_2H_6; (b) C_3H_8.

4.46 A representative element E forms compounds such as EF_3 and EF_5. To which group do you think E belongs? Why?

4.47 What are some strengths of the Lewis bonding theory?

4.48 Make a sketch of the hydrogen bonding between two water molecules. How does hydrogen bonding explain the unusually high boiling point of water? What would be the approximate boiling point of water if there were no hydrogen bonding among its molecules?

4.49 Using the old-fashioned naming system for cations, what does the following diagram represent? (Don't take this one too seriously.)

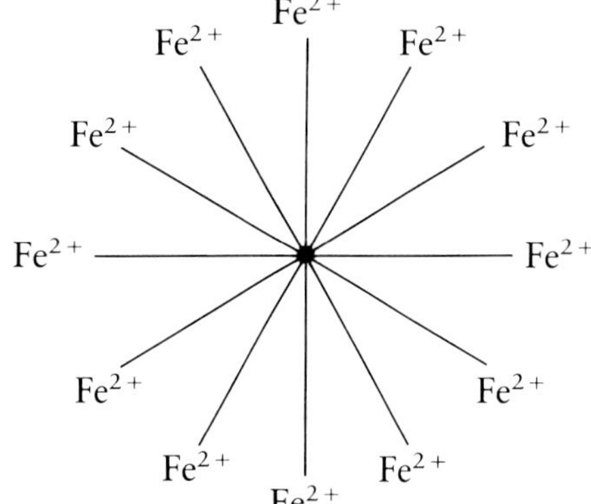

5 ..... THE MOLE AND CHEMICAL CALCULATIONS

5.1 INTRODUCTION

The masses of atoms and molecules are too small to use conveniently. Weighing out single atoms and molecules is impossible.

Chemists *think* in terms of individual atoms and molecules, but they *work* with samples which contain an enormous number of them. For convenience one particular number has been chosen to serve as the "counting unit of chemistry." This number, one of the seven SI base units, is called the *mole.*

5.2 DEFINITION OF THE MOLE

The abbreviation for mole is mol.

One **mole** of a substance is defined as the amount of substance which contains as many particles as there are atoms in 12 g of C-12, a quantity that can be determined by a number of experimental methods. The result of these experiments is a number, called **Avogadro's number**, equal to 602,000,000,000,000,000,000,000, or 6.02×10^{23}.

Thus, one *mole* may also be defined as 6.02×10^{23} particles of substance. By *particles* we mean some well-defined elementary units of which a substance is made. In chemical discussions these particles are usually atoms or molecules. For instance, 1 mol of C-12 contains 6.02×10^{23} C-12 atoms and 1 mol of water contains 6.02×10^{23} molecules of water. In fact, the mole is a number which can be used to refer to any kind of matter. One mole of electrons is 6.02×10^{23} electrons and one mole of apples is 6.02×10^{23} apples.

Distributing Avogadro's number of pennies among the world's population would give each person on earth more than a trillion dollars.

Avogadro's number is so incredibly huge that its size is difficult to comprehend. To give you an idea of just how enormous this is, think of a rope measuring 6.02×10^{23} m in length that would stretch from the earth the whole way to distant galaxies beyond the Milky Way. One mole of apples is 6.02×10^{23} apples, enough apples to provide every human being on the earth with an apple a day for more than 3 billion centuries.

Counting and weighing out 6.02×10^{23} particles of a substance is no more practical than weighing out a single particle. To become a useful working unit, the mole must be able to be converted into a mass than can be measured in the laboratory. The definition of the mole can be expanded to make it more convenient to use. Looking at the definitions for the mole, we see that the mass of 1 mol of C-12 atoms (6.02×10^{23} C-12 atoms) is 12 g, which is numerically identical to the atomic weight of C-12, exactly 12. If we express the atomic weight of C-12 in terms of the unit amu (Section 3.9), we can show that this is true by finding the mass of 6.02×10^{23} atoms of C-12.

$$1 \text{ amu} = 1.66 \times 10^{-24} \text{ g}$$

$$\frac{12 \cancel{\text{amu}}}{1 \cancel{\text{atom C-12}}} \times \frac{1.66 \times 10^{-24} \text{ g}}{1 \cancel{\text{amu}}} \times \frac{6.02 \times 10^{23} \cancel{\text{atoms C-12}}}{1 \text{ mol C-12}} = \frac{12 \text{ g}}{\text{mol C-12}}$$

In general:

One mole of any element or compound has a mass in grams which is numerically equal to its formula weight.

FIGURE 5.1
One mole of salt, soda, and sucrose.

By expressing the formula weight of H_2O as 18.0 amu, we can illustrate this once more.

$$\frac{18.0\ \cancel{\text{amu}}}{1\ \cancel{\text{molecule}\ H_2O}} \times \frac{1.66 \times 10^{-24}\ \text{g}}{\cancel{\text{amu}}} \times \frac{6.02 \times 10^{23}\ \cancel{\text{molecules}\ H_2O}}{1\ \text{mol}\ H_2O} = \frac{18.0\ \text{g}}{\text{mol}\ H_2O}$$

One mole of Cu has a mass of 63.5 g and contains 6.02×10^{23} Cu atoms.

One mole of copper, Cu, has a mass of 63.5 g, since the formula weight of Cu is the same as its atomic weight, 63.5. One mole of glucose ($C_6H_{12}O_6$), which has a formula weight of 180, has a mass of 180 g. Figure 5.1 illustrates one mole of each of several common substances, including table salt (NaCl), sodium bicarbonate ($NaHCO_3$), and sucrose ($C_{12}H_{22}O_{11}$).

SAMPLE EXERCISE 5.1

For 1 mol of oxygen gas, O_2, find

(**a**) The number of molecules (**b**) The mass in grams

Solution:

(**a**) One mole is defined to be 6.02×10^{23} particles. One mole contains 6.02×10^{23} O_2 molecules.

(**b**) The formula weight of O_2 is $2 \times 16.0 = 32.0$. One mole is defined to be the formula weight expressed in grams. One mole contains 32.0 g O_2.

EXERCISE 5.1

What is the mass of 6.02×10^{23} sodium atoms?

5.3 CHEMICAL CONVERSION FACTORS

In the study of chemical calculations it is frequently necessary to convert grams to moles or moles to grams. To do this, the definition of the mole as the formula weight expressed in grams is used directly to generate **chemical conversion factors** that are similar to the conversion factors we have used to perform unit conversions. For instance, we can use the fact that the mass of 1 mol of water is 18.0 g to write the chemical conversion factor

$$1\ \text{mol}\ H_2O = 18.0\ \text{g}\ H_2O$$

We use chemical conversion factors in the same way that we use unit conversion factors such as 1 ft = 12 in.

Chemical conversion factors such as these are applied in the same way as those used to perform unit conversions. As long as the formula for a substance is known, the definition of the mole can be used to make conversions from moles to grams or from grams to moles. Suppose we want to calculate the mass of 2.00 mol H_2O. We can take the same approach as we did in Chapter 1 when we converted from one system of units to another.

1. Decide what units are given and what units are desired.

$$2.00 \text{ mol } H_2O = ? \text{ g } H_2O$$

2. Choose the necessary conversion factor.

$$1 \text{ mol } H_2O = 18.0 \text{ g } H_2O$$

3. Rewrite the conversion factor to make it equal to unity.

$$\frac{1 \text{ mol } H_2O}{18.0 \text{ g } H_2O} = 1 \qquad \frac{18.0 \text{ g } H_2O}{1 \text{ mol } H_2O} = 1$$

4. Multiply by the appropriate conversion factor so that all but the desired units cancel.

$$2.00 \cancel{\text{mol } H_2O} \times \frac{18.0 \text{ g } H_2O}{1 \cancel{\text{mol } H_2O}} = 36.0 \text{ g } H_2O$$

The mass of 2 mol of H_2O is 36.0 g.

Often it is necessary to find the number of moles in a given mass of some substance. For instance, to calculate the number of moles in a 1-lb (454-g) bar of pure gold, Au,

1. 454 g Au = ? mol Au
2. Atomic weight Au = 197; 1 mol Au = 197 g Au
3. $\frac{1 \text{ mol Au}}{197 \text{ g Au}} = 1 \qquad \frac{197 \text{ g Au}}{1 \text{ mol Au}} = 1$
4. $454 \cancel{\text{g Au}} \times \frac{1 \text{ mol Au}}{197 \cancel{\text{g Au}}} = 2.30 \text{ mol Au}$

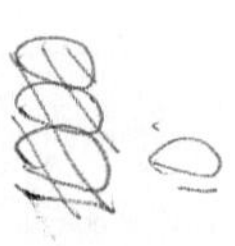

There are 2.30 mol Au in a 1-lb bar of gold.

SAMPLE EXERCISE 5.2

Potassium chloride, KCl, is a compound used to treat potassium deficiency. If a single-dose packet is supposed to contain 0.0200 mol KCl, how many grams of KCl must be placed in the packet?

Solution:

1. 0.0200 mol KCl = ? g KCl
2. Formula weight KCl = 39.1 + 35.5 = 74.6; 1 mol KCl = 74.6 g
3. $\frac{1 \text{ mol KCl}}{74.6 \text{ g KCl}} = 1 \qquad \frac{74.6 \text{ g KCl}}{1 \text{ mol KCl}} = 1$
4. $0.0200 \cancel{\text{mol KCl}} \times \frac{74.6 \text{ g KCl}}{1 \cancel{\text{mol KCl}}} = 1.49 \text{ g KCl}$

1.49 g KCl must be placed in each packet.

EXERCISE 5.2

One antacid tablet is able to neutralize 0.0106 mol HCl (stomach acid). How many grams is this?

SAMPLE EXERCISE 5.3

Solutions containing sodium fluoride, NaF, are used to protect against dental cavities. If 1 L of such a solution contains 2.00 g of sodium fluoride, how many moles of sodium fluoride were used to make up the solution?

Solution:

1. 2.00 g NaF = ? mol NaF
2. Formula weight NaF = 23.0 + 19.0 = 42.0; 1 mol NaF = 42.0 g NaF
3. $\frac{1 \text{ mol NaF}}{42.0 \text{ g NaF}} = 1 \qquad \frac{42.0 \text{ g NaF}}{1 \text{ mol NaF}} = 1$
4. $2.00 \cancel{\text{g NaF}} \times \frac{1 \text{ mol NaF}}{42.0 \cancel{\text{g NaF}}} = 0.0476 \text{ mol NaF}$

There is 0.0476 mol NaF in 1 L of dental rinse solution

EXERCISE 5.3

How many moles of calcium carbonate are in a tablet that contains 240 mg $CaCO_3$?

Calculations such as these are necessary to prepare laboratory solutions and to calculate the quantities of compounds or elements consumed and produced in chemical reactions.

5.4 MORE CHEMICAL CONVERSION FACTORS

From the definition of the mole, the number of atoms or molecules in a given sample of element or compound can easily be calculated. The definition of the mole as 6.02×10^{23} particles provides useful chemical conversion factors, which take this general form

$$1 \text{ mol} = 6.02 \times 10^{23} \text{ particles}$$

For instance, suppose we need to know how many water molecules are in 2 mol H_2O.

1. $2 \text{ mol } H_2O = ? \text{ molecules } H_2O$
2. $1 \text{ mol } H_2O = 6.02 \times 10^{23} \text{ molecules } H_2O$
3. $\dfrac{1 \text{ mol } H_2O}{6.02 \times 10^{23} \text{ molecules}} = 1 \qquad \dfrac{6.02 \times 10^{23} \text{ molecules}}{1 \text{ mol } H_2O} = 1$
4. $2 \cancel{\text{mol } H_2O} \times \dfrac{6.02 \times 10^{23} \text{ molecules}}{1 \cancel{\text{mol } H_2O}} = 12.0 \times 10^{23} \text{ molecules}$

There are 12.0×10^{23} (or twice Avogadro's number) H_2O molecules in 2 mol H_2O.

We can also determine the number of atoms or molecules in a given mass of sample by using the definition of the mole. First the mass in grams must be converted to a number of moles, which in turn is used to find the number of atoms or molecules. To calculate the number of water molecules in 216 g H_2O, enough water to fill an 8-oz glass, we must apply two conversion factors.

1. $216 \text{ g } H_2O = ? \text{ molecules } H_2O.$

   Strategy: $216 \text{ g } H_2O \rightarrow ? \text{ mol } H_2O \rightarrow ? \text{ molecules } H_2O$
2. $1 \text{ mol } H_2O = 18.0 \text{ g } H_2O \qquad 1 \text{ mol } H_2O = 6.02 \times 10^{23} \text{ molecules}$
3. $\dfrac{1 \text{ mol } H_2O}{18 \text{ g } H_2O} = 1 \qquad \dfrac{18 \text{ g } H_2O}{1 \text{ mol } H_2O} = 1$

   and $\dfrac{1 \text{ mol } H_2O}{6.02 \times 10^{23} \text{ molecules}} = 1 \qquad \dfrac{6.02 \times 10^{23} \text{ molecules}}{1 \text{ mol } H_2O} = 1$
4. $216 \cancel{\text{g } H_2O} \times \dfrac{1 \cancel{\text{mol } H_2O}}{18 \cancel{\text{g } H_2O}} \times \dfrac{6.02 \times 10^{23} \text{ molecules}}{1 \cancel{\text{mol } H_2O}} = 72.2 \times 10^{23} \text{ molecules}$

The number of water molecules in an 8-oz glass of water should be an enormous number, and we see that it is.

SAMPLE EXERCISE 5.4

A 1-L balloon contains 0.160 g of helium gas, He. How many He atoms are in the balloon?

Solution:

1. 0.160 g He = ? atoms He
   Again, the strategy is to convert grams to moles and then moles to atoms: 0.160 g He → ? mol He → ? atoms He
2. Atomic weight He = 4.00
   1 mol He = 4.00 g He 1 mol He = 6.02×10^{23} atoms
3. $\frac{1 \text{ mol He}}{4.00 \text{ g He}} = 1 \qquad \frac{4.00 \text{ g He}}{1 \text{ mol He}} = 1$

   and $\frac{1 \text{ mol He}}{6.02 \times 10^{23} \text{ atoms}} = 1 \qquad \frac{6.02 \times 10^{23} \text{ atoms}}{1 \text{ mol He}} = 1$
4. $0.160 \cancel{\text{g He}} \times \frac{1 \cancel{\text{mol He}}}{4.00 \cancel{\text{g He}}} \times \frac{6.02 \times 10^{23} \text{ atoms}}{1 \cancel{\text{mol He}}}$

   $= 0.241 \times 10^{23}$ atoms

   The balloon contains 0.241×10^{23} atoms of He (2.41×10^{22} atoms).

EXERCISE 5.4

Calculate the number of "molecules" (or formula units) of NaCl present in 1 teaspoon (about 11 g) of pure salt.

We can also use the definition of the mole to calculate the masses of atoms and molecules. Since the mass of 6.02×10^{23} particles must be equal to the formula weight in grams, we can calculate the mass of one particle by dividing its formula weight by 6.02×10^{23}. For instance, suppose we want to calculate the mass of a single copper atom, Cu.

$$1 \text{ mol Cu} = 63.5 \text{ g Cu} = 6.02 \times 10^{23} \text{ atoms Cu}$$

The mass of 1 Cu atom is 63.5 g (the mass of 6.02×10^{23} atoms of Cu) divided by 6.02×10^{23}.

$$\frac{63.5 \text{ g}}{6.02 \times 10^{23}} = 1.05 \times 10^{-22} \text{ g}$$

A single atom of copper weighs 1.05×10^{-22} g.

SAMPLE EXERCISE 5.5

Using the definition of the mole, calculate the mass of one molecule of water, H_2O.

Solution:

1 mol H_2O = 18.0 g H_2O = 6.02×10^{23} molecules H_2O

$$\frac{18.0 \text{ g}}{6.02 \times 10^{23}} = 2.99 \times 10^{-23} \text{ g}$$

A single molecule of H_2O weighs 2.99×10^{-23} g.

EXERCISE 5.5

Using the definition of the mole, calculate the mass of one C atom.

One mole is a macroscopic, visible amount. One atom or molecule is microscopic and invisible.

It is important to remember that one atom or one molecule is incredibly small compared with one mole. One mole represents a **macroscopic** amount of substance, that is, an amount which is visible to the naked eye. Atoms and molecules are **microscopic** amounts, which are far too small to be visible. See Figure 5.2, where one mole of water is compared with one molecule of water and one mole of copper is compared with one atom of copper.

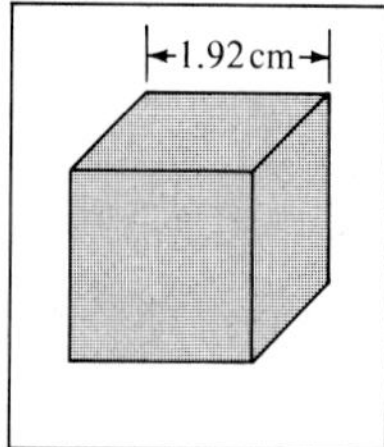

1 mole Cu
6.02×10^{23} Cu atoms
Mass = 63.5 g

1 Cu atom
Mass = 10.5×10^{-23} g

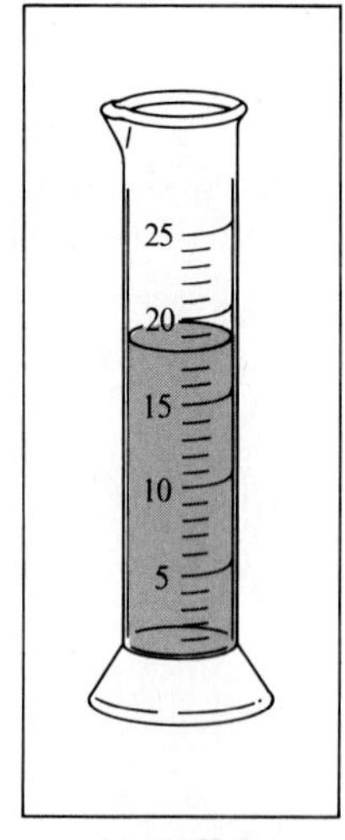

1 mole H_2O
6.02×10^{23} H_2O molecules
Mass = 18.0 g
Volume = 18.0 ml

1 H_2O molecule
Mass = 2.99×10^{-23} g

(*a*) (*b*)

FIGURE 5.2
Comparison of moles to atoms and molecules. (*a*) One mole of Cu and one mole of H_2O. They represent macroscopic quantities that are easily seen. (*b*) One atom of Cu and one molecule of H_2O are drawn to scale. You can see nothing in these boxes because atoms and molecules are invisible microscopic quantities that cannot be seen by the naked eye.

5.5 FORMULAS AND THE MOLE

Formulas give the number of each kind of atom in one molecule. Instead of atoms it is often more useful to think in terms of moles of atoms. Formulas can also be interpreted to give the number of moles of atoms in one mole of that substance. For instance, the formula for water, H_2O, can mean that every molecule of water contains two H atoms and one O atom, but it can also be taken to mean that every mole of water contains 2 mol of H and 1 mol of O.

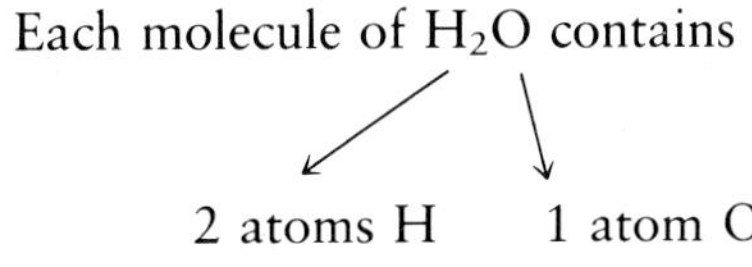

Each molecule of H_2O contains

2 atoms H   1 atom O

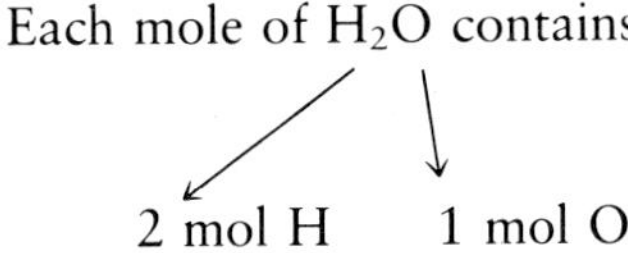

Each mole of H_2O contains

2 mol H   1 mol O

The formula for ethanol is C_2H_6O, which means that

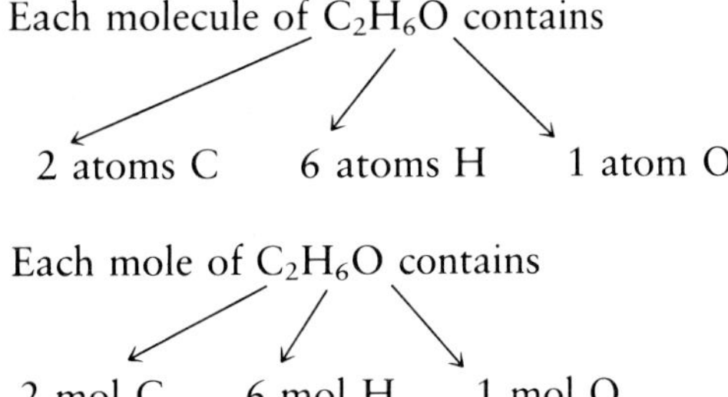

Each molecule of C_2H_6O contains

2 atoms C   6 atoms H   1 atom O

Each mole of C_2H_6O contains

2 mol C   6 mol H   1 mol O

SAMPLE EXERCISE 5.6

How many moles of iron(II) sulfate and of elemental iron are provided by a 167-mg sample of $FeSO_4$?

Solution:

First calculate the number of moles of $FeSO_4$; then use the formula to find the moles of Fe.

1. 167 mg $FeSO_4$ = ? mol $FeSO_4$

$$\text{Formula weight} = \underset{\text{From Fe}}{(1 \times 55.8)} + \underset{\text{From S}}{(1 \times 32)} + \underset{\text{From O}}{(4 \times 16.0)} = 152 \text{ g}$$

2. 1 mol $FeSO_4$ = 152 g $FeSO_4$ and 1000 mg = 1 g

3. $167\ \cancel{mg\ FeSO_4} \times \frac{1\ \cancel{g\ FeSO_4}}{1000\ \cancel{mg\ FeSO_4}} \times \frac{1\ mol\ FeSO_4}{152\ \cancel{g\ FeSO_4}} = 0.00110\ mol\ FeSO_4$

One mole of $FeSO_4$ contains one mole Fe. Thus the sample contains 0.00110 mol Fe.

EXERCISE 5.6

How many moles of lithium are present in a tablet that contains 300 mg of lithium carbonate, Li_2CO_3?

Mass Percent Composition

The formula for a compound may be used to calculate the **mass percent** of each element present in that compound. The mass of one mole of the compound and the mass of each element present in one mole of the compound are calculated by using the formula. The required percentages may then be determined. For instance, to calculate the mass percentages of H and O present in water, we first calculate the mass of one mole of water and then note how much of that mass is contributed by each element.

$$\text{Formula weight } H_2O = (2 \times 1.0) + (1 \times 16.0) = 18.0$$

Thus, 1 mol of water must contain 2 mol H (2×1.0 g $= 2.0$ g) and 1 mol 0 (1×16.0 g $= 16.0$ g) for a total mass of 18.0 g (2.0 g + 16.0 g).

$$1\ mol\ H_2O = \underset{\text{From H}}{(2 \times 1.0\ g)} + \underset{\text{From O}}{(1 \times 16.0\ g)} = 18.0\ g$$

$$\begin{aligned} \%\ H &= \frac{\text{mass of H in 1 mol } H_2O}{\text{mass of 1 mol } H_2O} \times 100\% \\ &= \frac{2.0\ \cancel{g}}{18.0\ \cancel{g}} \times 100\% \\ &= 0.111 \times 100\% \\ &= 11.1\% \end{aligned}$$

$$\begin{aligned} \%\ O &= \frac{\text{mass of O in 1 mol } H_2O}{\text{mass of 1 mol } H_2O} \times 100\% \\ &= \frac{16.0\ \cancel{g}}{18.0\ \cancel{g}} \times 100\% \\ &= 0.889 \times 100\% \\ &= 88.9\% \end{aligned}$$

If the calculations are made carefully, the total of the mass percentages of elements in a compound must be very close to 100 percent, that is, it should range between 99.9 and 100.1 percent. For the examples above we see that the sum of the mass percentages of H and O in H_2O is 100.0% (11.1% + 88.9% = 100.0%).

SAMPLE EXERCISE 5.7

Calculate the mass percentages of the elements present in calcium carbonate, $CaCO_3$.

Solution:

Formula weight $CaCO_3 = (1 \times 40.1) + (1 \times 12.0) + (3 \times 16.0) = 100.1$

$$1 \text{ mol } CaCO_3 = \underset{\text{From Ca}}{(1 \times 40.1 \text{ g})} + \underset{\text{From C}}{(1 \times 12.0 \text{ g})} + \underset{\text{From O}}{(3 \times 16.0 \text{ g})} = 100.1 \text{ g}$$

$$\% \text{ Ca} = \frac{40.1 \text{ g}}{100.1 \text{ g}} \times 100\% \qquad \% \text{ C} = \frac{12.0 \text{ g}}{100.1 \text{ g}} \times 100\% \qquad \% \text{ O} = \frac{48.0 \text{ g}}{100.1 \text{ g}} \times 100\%$$

$$= 0.400 \times 100\% \qquad = 0.120 \times 100\% \qquad = 48.0\%$$

$$= 40.0\% \qquad = 12.0\% \qquad = 48.0\%$$

Check Total: 40.0% + 12.0% + 48.0% = 100.0%

EXERCISE 5.7

Find the mass percentage composition of glucose, $C_6H_{12}O_6$.

Finding mass percentages of elements in a compound can help to identify the compound. Mass percentages calculated according to the method we have just used are compared with the actual mass percentages of elements in compounds as determined by experiment. This can be done in analytical laboratories, where submitted compounds are broken down into their constituent elements and the mass of each element is compared with that of the original sample of compound. This type of procedure is called an *elemental analysis*. A chemist who is trying to prepare a brand new compound may use elemental analysis to prove that the compound has the desired formula.

SAMPLE EXERCISE 5.8

According to a laboratory determination, the mass percentage of N in a compound is found to be 30.4 percent. Which of the following compounds could it be?

(a) NH_3 (formula weight = 17.0)
(b) NO_2 (formula weight = 46.0)
(c) N_2O (formula weight = 44.0)

Solution:

Calculate the mass percentage of N in each of the compounds.

(a) 1 mol NH_3 = 17.0 g contains 14.0 g N

$$\% N = \frac{14.0 \not{g}}{17.0 \not{g}} \times 100\% = 82.4\%$$

(b) 1 mol NO_2 = 46.0 g contains 14.0 g N

$$\% N = \frac{14.0 \not{g}}{46.0 \not{g}} \times 100\% = 30.4\%$$

(c) 1 mol N_2O = 44.0 g contains 28.0 g N

$$\% N = \frac{28.0 \not{g}}{44.0 \not{g}} \times 100\% = 63.6\%$$

The compound is NO_2 (mass percentage N = 30.4%).

EXERCISE 5.8

Match each of the carbon compounds with the correct mass percentage of C.

(a) CH_4 (1) 81.8%
(b) C_2H_6 (2) 80.0%
(c) C_3H_8 (3) 75.0%

In the next sections we will be using mass percentages of elements in compounds to determine formulas, the reverse of what we have just done.

5.6 EMPIRICAL FORMULAS AND MOLECULAR FORMULAS

The **molecular formula** of a compound gives the actual number of each kind of atom in one molecule of the compound. The **empirical formula** of a compound gives the simplest possible whole number ratio of each kind of atom in one molecule. For instance, the molecular formula of hydrogen peroxide is H_2O_2, which means that every molecule of H_2O_2 contains two atoms of H and two atoms of O. The empirical formula of H_2O_2 is simply HO, meaning that each molecule of H_2O_2 contains 1 H atom for every O atom. The molecular formula of dinitrogen tetroxide is N_2O_4, which tells us that the ratio of N atoms to O atoms is 1 to 2. Thus its empirical formula is NO_2.

The empirical formula for some compounds is the same as the molecular formula.

Sometimes the molecular formula of a compound is identical to the empirical formula. The molecular formula for water is H_2O, which is also the empirical formula, the simplest possible formula we can write without using fractional subscripts.

TABLE 5.1 **MOLECULAR AND EMPIRICAL FORMULAS**

Structure and name	Molecular formula	Empirical formula
H—O—O—H Hydrogen peroxide	H_2O_2	HO
H_3C-CH_3 Ethane	C_2H_6	CH_3
H—C≡C—H Acetylene	C_2H_2	CH
C_6H_6 ring (each C bonded to H) Benzene	C_6H_6	CH
$Br_3Si-SiBr_3$ Disilicon hexabromide	Si_2Br_6	$SiBr_3$
$H_3C-CH_2-C(=O)-O-H$ Propanoic acid	$C_3H_6O_2$	$C_3H_6O_2$

In Table 5.1 the structures for several compounds are given, along with their molecular and empirical formulas.

SAMPLE EXERCISE 5.9

Find the empirical formulas for

(a) Glucose, $C_6H_{12}O_6$ (b) Diphosphorus pentoxide, P_2O_5

Solution:

The ratio of C:H:O is 1:2:1. The simplest formula is CH_2O.

The ratio of P to O is 2:5, which cannot be simplified further to give whole numbers. The simplest formula is P_2O_5.

EXERCISE 5.9

What is the empirical formula for stearic acid, $C_{18}H_{36}O_2$, a component of soap?

C_6H_6, C_2H_2, and all other compounds with the empirical formula of CH contain 92.3% C and 7.7% H.

Two compounds whose formulas are multiples of each other must have the same empirical formula. For instance, the formula for benzene, C_6H_6, is three times that of acetylene, C_2H_2. The empirical formula for both these compounds is simply CH. (See Table 5.1.) The weight percentage composition for two compounds which have the same empirical formula must be identical.

5.7 EMPIRICAL FORMULA FROM MASS PERCENTAGES

Phenelzine and several other compounds derived from hydrazine are used as antidepressants.

As mentioned in Section 5.5, experimentally determined mass percentages of the elements in a compound can be used to find the empirical formulas for the compound. For example, suppose we want to find the empirical formula for the compound hydrazine, which contains 87.5 percent by weight nitrogen and 12.5 percent by weight hydrogen. We begin by assuming that we have a 100-g sample of hydrazine. This will simplify our arithmetic in that the masses of the constituent atoms will have the same numerical value as their respective percentages. We can now calculate the masses of N and H in 100-g hydrazine.

$$\text{Mass of N:} \quad 0.875 \times 100 \text{ g} = 87.5 \text{ N}$$

$$\text{Mass of H:} \quad 0.125 \times 100 \text{ g} = 12.5 \text{ g H}$$

The second step is to convert the masses (in grams) of each element to moles.

$$87.5 \cancel{\text{g N}} \times \frac{1 \text{ mol N}}{12.0 \cancel{\text{g N}}} = 6.25 \text{ mol N}$$

$$12.5 \cancel{\text{g H}} \times \frac{1 \text{ mol H}}{1.00 \cancel{\text{g H}}} = 12.5 \text{ mol H}$$

Finally, find the simplest whole number ratio of the moles of each element. The simplest ratio can sometimes be found by simply looking at the numbers. In this case, that would mean noticing that 12.5 is 2 times 6.25. Thus, we have twice as many moles of H as we do of N and the ratio of N atoms to H atoms is also 2 to 1. This gives us an empirical formula of NH_2. Another way to find the ratio is to choose the smallest number of moles calculated in the second step and then divide the number of moles of all other elements by that number. In the example above, the smallest number of moles is 6.25, the number of moles of N. Dividing each number of moles by 6.25 helps to reveal the ratio:

$$\text{N}\ \frac{6.25}{6.25} = 1$$

$$\text{H}\ \frac{12.5}{6.25} = 2$$

Again we see that hydrazine contains 2 mol of mol H for every mole of N, which means that there must be two atoms of H for every atom of N. The empirical formula for hydrazine is thus found to be NH_2.

To find the *molecular formula* for hydrazine, we must also know its formula weight. There are experimental methods by which formula weights for compounds may be obtained in the laboratory *without* knowing the formula. The experimental formula weight is then compared with the empirical formula weight, that is, the formula weight which corresponds to the empirical formula. For instance, suppose that the measured formula weight for hydrazine is 32. To find the molecular formula for hydrazine we first calculate the empirical formula weight:

$$\text{Empirical formula} = NH_2$$

$$\text{Empirical formula weight} = (1 \times 14.0) + (2 \times 1.0) = 16.0$$

Now compare the experimental formula weight and the empirical formula weight by dividing the experimental formula weight by the empirical formula weight. The ratio between the two *must* be very close to a whole number, since the molecular formula is always a whole number multiple of the empirical formula. In this case,

$$\frac{\text{Experimental formula weight}}{\text{Empirical formula weight}} = \frac{32}{16.0} = 2$$

Molecular formulas had to be known before bonding theories could be developed.

Thus, the molecular formula for hydrazine must include twice as many atoms as the empirical formula. Consequently, each subscript in the empirical formula NH_2 must be multiplied by 2.

$$\text{Molecular formula} = N_2H_4$$

SAMPLE EXERCISE 5.10

Find the empirical formula for a compound that contains 50.0 percent S and 50.0 percent O. If the formula weight for this compound is 64, what is the molecular formula?

Solution:

In a 100-g sample we have 50.0 g S and 50.0 g O.
Convert grams to moles:

$$50.0\,\text{g S} \times \frac{1\ \text{mol S}}{32.0\,\text{g S}} = 1.56\ \text{mol S}$$

$$50.0\,\text{g O} \times \frac{1\ \text{mol O}}{16.0\,\text{g O}} = 3.12\ \text{mol O}$$

Find the simplest whole-number ratio of moles of each element:

3.12 is twice 1.56, or $\frac{3.12}{1.56} = 2$

1 mol S for every 2 mol O

Empirical formula = SO_2

Empirical formula weight = $(1 \times 32.0) + (2 \times 16.0) = 64.0$

To find the molecular formula,

$$\frac{\text{Experimental formula weight}}{\text{Empirical formula weight}} = \frac{64}{64.0} = 1$$

Molecular formula = SO_2

EXERCISE 5.10

The formula weight for a compound containing C, H, and O is found to be about 31. If the empirical formula is CH_3O, what is the molecular formula?

5.8 WRITING AND BALANCING CHEMICAL EQUATIONS

In Chapter 2 we gave a very general description of a chemical equation, in which an arrow pointed from the reactants to the products. Now we can improve upon this picture by adding formulas for the compounds or elements that are involved as well as other special symbols. Suppose we want to write the equation which describes the decomposition of solid calcium carbonate to produce solid calcium oxide and carbon dioxide gas. First we need the formulas

Calcium carbonate is $CaCO_3$
Calcium oxide is CaO
Carbon dioxide is CO_2

The reactant is $CaCO_3$ and the products are CaO and CO_2, so the equation is written as

$$CaCO_3 \longrightarrow CaO + CO_2$$

Sometimes the physical state of each reactant and product under the reaction conditions is indicated. Solids are followed by (*s*), liquids by (*l*), and gases by (*g*). With these additions the equation above becomes

$$CaCO_3(s) \longrightarrow CaO(s) + CO_2(g)$$

Special reaction conditions are sometimes indicated with words or symbols written above the equation arrow. For instance, a symbol used for heat supplied to a reaction is Δ. Since the decomposition of $CaCO_3$ requires heat, the equation may be written as

$$CaCO_3(s) \xrightarrow{\Delta} CaO\ (s) + CO_2(g)$$

Figure 5.3 shows the decomposition of mercury(II) oxide to produce mercury

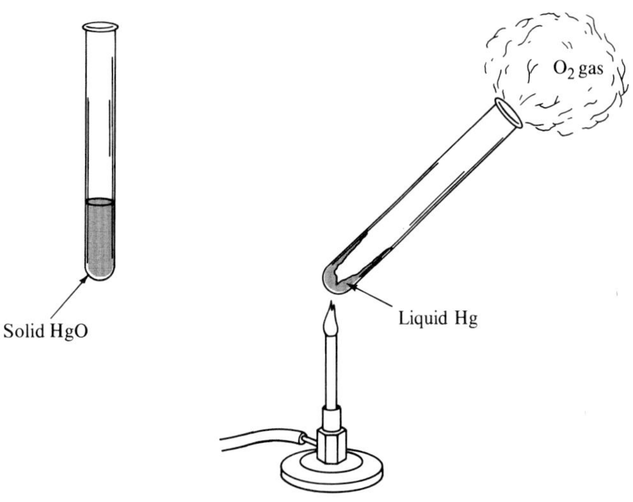

Heat supplied　　One O_2　　Hg + Hg

HgO + HgO

$$2HgO(s) \xrightarrow{\Delta} O_2(g) + 2Hg(l)$$

Solid HgO　　Yields or produces　　Gaseous O_2　　Liquid Hg

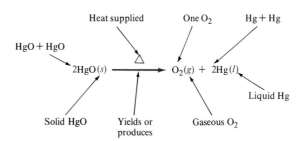

FIGURE 5.3
Symbols used in writing chemical equations. This equation describes the decomposition of mercury(II) oxide by heat to produce gaseous oxygen and liquid mercury.

and oxygen along with its representative chemical equation. A list of some special symbols used in writing chemical equations is given in Table 5.2.

All chemical equations must obey the law of conservation of matter. The mass of the reactants must be exactly equal to the mass of the products. For this to be true the number of each kind of atom in the reactants must be the same as it is in the products. Coefficients placed in front of the formulas in chemical equations are used to equate, or **balance**, the numbers of each kind of atom on both sides of the equation. When the coefficient 1 is used in balancing an equation, it is understood and not written.

Trial and error may be used to find the right set of coefficients. With practice this can be done quickly. We can see that the equation describing the decomposition of $CaCO_3$ is balanced as written; that is, all the coefficients are 1.

The special symbols are sometimes left out of chemical equations.

$$CaCO_3 \longrightarrow CaO + CO_2$$

To check the balancing of an equation, count the atoms on the left side of the arrow and those on the right:

On the left	On the right
1 Ca atom	1 Ca atom
1 C atom	1 C atom
3 O atoms	3 O atoms

In many equations, coefficients other than 1 are needed for balancing. For instance, the chemical equation for the reaction of sodium metal with oxygen to produce sodium oxide is written

$$Na + O_2 \longrightarrow Na_2O$$

That is, one Na atom on the left and two Na atoms on the right and two O

TABLE 5.2 **SYMBOLS USED IN CHEMICAL EQUATIONS**

Symbol	Meaning
$\longrightarrow$	Yields
Δ	Heat
Formula followed by (*g*) or $\uparrow$	Gas
Formula followed by (*s*) or $\downarrow$ or underlined	Solid
Formula followed by (*l*)	Liquid
formula followed by (*aq*)	Dissolved in water
$\leftrightarrows$	Reversible reaction*

*Reversible reactions proceed in either direction, they are discussed in Chapter 10.

atoms on the left but one O atom on the right. We can balance the O atoms by placing a 2 in front of Na_2O. This makes four Na atoms on the right but only one on the left. Placing a 4 in front of Na will balance the Na atoms.

$$4Na + O_2 \longrightarrow 2Na_2O$$

To check, count atoms on both sides of the arrow:

On the left	On the right
4 Na atoms	4 Na atoms
2 O atoms	2 O atoms

It is important to understand that the coefficients in front of the formulas do not modify the formulas. In other words, the symbol $2Na_2O$ means that there are two formula units of sodium oxide, $Na_2O + Na_2O$. It does *not* mean that we have Na_4O_2, which would be a substance chemically different from Na_2O. Thus changing the subscripts in a formula can never be used as a way to balance a chemical equation.

When polyatomic ions appear in an equation, they may be counted as complete units provided that they do not break down in the reaction. To balance the equation which describes the reaction of silver nitrate with lead(II) chloride to produce silver chloride and lead(II) nitrate, the nitrate ion, NO_3^-, can be treated as a unit:

Instead of balancing N and O atoms separately, balance NO_3^- units.

$$AgNO_3 + PbCl_2 \longrightarrow AgCl + Pb(NO_3)_2$$

Placing 2s in front of the AgCl and $AgNO_3$ balances the equation:

$$2AgNO_3 + PbCl_2 \longrightarrow 2AgCl + Pb(NO_3)_2$$

To check this:

On the left	On the right
2 Ag	2 Ag
2 NO_3	2 NO_3
1 Pb	1 Pb
2 Cl	2 Cl

SAMPLE EXERCISE 5.11

The overall reaction for the breakdown of glucose in the body is given below. Balance the equation.

$$C_6H_{12}O_6 + O_2 \longrightarrow CO_2 + H_2O$$

Solution:

In the unbalanced equation there are

6 C atoms on the left, 1 on the right
12 H atoms on the left, 2 on the right
8 O atoms on the left, 3 on the right

Choosing coefficients to balance the C and H atoms is a good way to begin. Place a 6 in front of CO_2 and a 6 in front of H_2O.

$$C_6H_{12}O_6 + O_2 \longrightarrow 6CO_2 + 6H_2O$$

The C and H atoms are now balanced, but the O atoms are not. Note now that there are a total of 18 O atoms on the right. To produce 18 O atoms on the left, the coefficient 6 in front of the O_2 is needed.

$$C_6H_{12}O_6 + 6O_2 \longrightarrow 6CO_2 + 6H_2O$$

Check:

On the left	On the right
6 C	6 C
12 H	12 H
18 O	18 O

EXERCISE 5.11

Balance the equation below, which describes the overall breakdown in the body of palmitic acid, a component of many fats.

$$C_{16}H_{32}O_2 + O_2 \longrightarrow CO_2 + H_2O$$

5.9 CHEMICAL EQUATIONS AND THE MOLE

Chemical equations may be interpreted directly in terms of atoms and molecules. For example, the equation below for the reaction of iron with sulfur to form iron(II) sulfide can be described in this way.

$$Fe + S \longrightarrow FeS$$

In words this equation says that one iron atom plus one sulfur atom gives one iron(II) sulfide molecule. Although perfectly correct, this interpretation of the equation is not very convenient. If we wanted to find out what mass of sulfur would be needed to react with a given amount of iron, we could not do it by measuring out Fe atoms and S atoms.

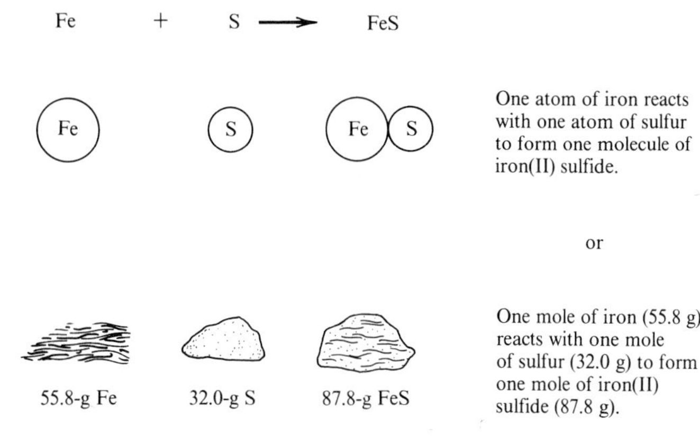
Fe + S → FeS
Fe
S
Fe S
One atom of iron reacts with one atom of sulfur to form one molecule of iron(II) sulfide.
or
55.8-g Fe
32.0-g S
87.8-g FeS
One mole of iron (55.8 g) reacts with one mole of sulfur (32.0 g) to form one mole of iron(II) sulfide (87.8 g).

FIGURE 5.4
The meaning of a chemical equation.

Another much more useful way to interpret an equation is in terms of moles of reactants and products. The equation above also says that one mole of iron plus one mole of sulfur produces one mole of iron(II) sulfide. Moles of substances can be converted to masses which are readily measured in the laboratory. If we do this, the equation says that 55.8 g of iron (1 mol Fe) plus 32.0 g of sulfur (1 mol S) produces 87.8 g of iron(II) sulfide (1 mol FeS). Figure 5.4 summarizes the different ways in which this equation may be interpreted.

5.10 CALCULATIONS FROM CHEMICAL EQUATIONS

Stoichiometry is derived from the Greek words *stoicheion*, meaning "element" and *metron*, meaning "measure."

Balanced chemical equations are used to calculate the quantities of reactants consumed or products formed in a chemical reaction. The use of chemical equations to measure quantities involved in chemical reactions is called **stoichiometry**. In general, stoichiometric calculations are done in the same way as unit conversion calculations. First, we must define some more chemical conversion factors that are derived from given equations.

Balanced chemical equations provide conversion factors which equate any two participants in the reaction that they describe. For instance, from the equation for the combination of hydrogen and oxygen to yield water, three chemical conversion factors are generated. The balanced equation is

$$2H_2 + O_2 \longrightarrow 2H_2O$$

This equation may be read as 2 mol H_2 plus 1 mol O_2 produces 2 mol H_2O. We can use the balanced equation to relate any two quantities in the equation. For instance, 2 mol H_2 is *stoichiometrically equivalent* to 1 mol O_2 because 2 mol H_2 is the exact amount of H_2 which reacts with 1 mol O_2. From this we write a chemical conversion factor as 2 mol H_2 = 1 mol O_2. From the equation above for the formation of water we can write three conversion factors:

2 mol H_2 = 1 mol O_2, meaning that 2 mol H_2 reacts with 1 mol O_2

$2 \text{ mol } H_2 = 2 \text{ mol } H_2O$, meaning that 2 mol H_2 produces 2 mol H_2O

$1 \text{ mol } O_2 = 2 \text{ mol } H_2O$, meaning that 1 mol O_2 produces 2 mol H_2O

Conversion factors that relate two different substances must be linked to a specific chemical equation.

This does not mean that the quantities related to each other in these conversion factors are really the same. Hydrogen, oxygen, and water all have very different physical and chemical properties.

Now we are ready to calculate the amounts of reactants or products involved in chemical reactions. Suppose we wish to find out how many moles of H_2O could be produced by starting with 4.0 mol O_2. To solve any stoichiometry problem, a balanced chemical equation is necessary.

$$2H_2 + O_2 \longrightarrow 2H_2O$$

Now we proceed as though the problem were just like a unit conversion.

1. Decide what is given and what is desired:

$$4.0 \text{ mol } O_2 = ? \text{ mol } H_2O$$

2. Choose the necessary conversion factor. Thus

$$1 \text{ mol } O_2 = 2 \text{ mol } H_2O$$

3. Rewrite the conversion factor to make it equal to unity:

$$\frac{1 \text{ mol } O_2}{2 \text{ mol } H_2O} = 1 \qquad \frac{2 \text{ mol } H_2O}{1 \text{ mol } O_2} = 1$$

Like unit conversions, stoichiometric conversions are done by applying appropriate conversion factors.

4. Multiply by the appropriate conversion factor.

$$4.0 \cancel{\text{mol } O_2} \times \frac{2 \text{ mol } H_2O}{1 \cancel{\text{mol } O_2}} = 8.0 \text{ mol } H_2O$$

Often more than one conversion factor will be needed to solve stoichiometry problems. Suppose this time the reaction is aluminum plus oxygen to produce aluminum oxide and we are trying to find out how many grams of Al are needed to produce 3 mol Al_2O_3. The balanced chemical equation is

$$4Al + 3O_2 \longrightarrow 2\,Al_2O_3$$

1. Decide what is given and what is desired:

$$3 \text{ mol } Al_2O_3 = ? \text{ g Al}$$

We must convert moles of Al_2O_3 to moles of Al before converting to grams of Al. Strategy:

$$3 \text{ mol } Al_2O_3 \longrightarrow ? \text{ mol Al} \longrightarrow ? \text{ g Al}$$

2. Choose the necessary conversion factors:
   4 mol Al = 2 mol Al_2O_3 (from the equation)
   1 mol Al = 27.0 g Al (from the mole definition)
3. Rewrite the conversion factors to make them equal to 1.

$$\frac{4 \text{ mol Al}}{2 \text{ mol Al}_2\text{O}_3} = 1 \qquad \frac{2 \text{ mol Al}_2\text{O}_3}{4 \text{ mol Al}} = 1$$

and

$$\frac{1 \text{ mol Al}}{27.0 \text{ g Al}} = 1 \qquad \frac{27.0 \text{ g Al}}{1 \text{ mol Al}} = 1$$

4. Multiply by the appropriate conversion factors.

$$3 \cancel{\text{mol Al}_2\text{O}_3} \times \frac{4 \cancel{\text{mol Al}}}{2 \cancel{\text{mol Al}_2\text{O}_3}} \times \frac{27.0 \text{ g Al}}{1 \cancel{\text{mol Al}}} = 162 \text{ g Al}$$

SAMPLE EXERCISE 5.12

The balanced chemical equation for the reaction of nitrogen with hydrogen to form ammonia is

$$N_2 + 3H_2 \longrightarrow 2NH_3$$

Starting with 80.0 g H_2, determine how many moles of ammonia can be produced.

Solution:

1. 80.0 g H_2 = ? mol NH_3
   Strategy: 80.0 g H_2 $\longrightarrow$? mol H_2 $\longrightarrow$? mol NH_3
2. 3 mol H_2 = 2 mol NH_3 (from the equation)
   1 mol H_2 = 2.00 g H_2 (from the mole definition)
3. $$\frac{3 \text{ mol H}_2}{2 \text{ mol NH}_3} = 1 \qquad \frac{2 \text{ mol NH}_3}{3 \text{ mol H}_2} = 1$$

   and

   $$\frac{1 \text{ mol H}_2}{2.00 \text{ g H}_2} = 1 \qquad \frac{2.00 \text{ g H}_2}{1 \text{ mol H}_2} = 1$$

4. $$80.0 \cancel{\text{g H}_2} \times \frac{1 \cancel{\text{mol H}_2}}{2.00 \cancel{\text{g H}_2}} \times \frac{2 \text{ mol NH}_3}{3 \cancel{\text{mol H}_2}} = 26.7 \text{ mol NH}_3$$

EXERCISE 5.12

What weight of N_2 is needed to react with 100 g H_2 to form ammonia according to the reaction in the sample exercise above?

In many stoichiometry problems the mass of a reactant or product must be converted to the mass of some other reactant or product. Several conversion factors will be needed. For instance, suppose we want to find out how many grams of calcium metal are needed to react with 100 g of water according to the equation

$$Ca + 2H_2O \longrightarrow Ca(OH)_2 + H_2$$

1. Decide what is given and what is desired.

$$100 \text{ g } H_2O = ? \text{ g Ca}$$

Strategy: $100 \text{ g } H_2O \longrightarrow ? \text{ mol } H_2O \longrightarrow ? \text{ mol Ca} \longrightarrow ? \text{ g Ca}$

2. Choose the necessary conversion factors.
   1 mol Ca = 2 mol H_2O (from the equation)
   1 mol H_2O = 18.0 g H_2O (from the mole definition)
   1 mol Ca = 40.1 g Ca (from the mole definition)
   Rewrite the conversion factors to make them equal to unity.

$$\frac{1 \text{ mol Ca}}{2 \text{ mol } H_2O} = 1 \qquad \frac{2 \text{ mol } H_2O}{1 \text{ mol Ca}} = 1$$

and

$$\frac{1 \text{ mol } H_2O}{18.0 \text{ g } H_2O} = 1 \qquad \frac{18.0 \text{ g } H_2O}{1 \text{ mol } H_2O} = 1$$

and

$$\frac{1 \text{ mol Ca}}{40.1 \text{ g Ca}} = 1 \qquad \frac{40.1 \text{ g Ca}}{1 \text{ mol Ca}} = 1$$

4. Multiply by the appropriate conversion factors.

$$100 \cancel{\text{g } H_2O} \times \frac{1 \cancel{\text{mol } H_2O}}{18.0 \cancel{\text{g } H_2O}} \times \frac{1 \cancel{\text{mol Ca}}}{2 \cancel{\text{mol } H_2O}} \times \frac{40.1 \text{ g Ca}}{1 \cancel{\text{mol Ca}}} = 111 \text{ g Ca}$$

SAMPLE EXERCISE 5.13

The decomposition of ammonium dichromate resembles a volcano spewing out green Cr_2O_3 ash.

Ammonium dichromate decomposes upon heating according to the equation below. How many grams of water are produced from 126 g $(NH_4)_2Cr_2O_7$?

$$(NH_4)_2Cr_2O_7 \longrightarrow Cr_2O_3 + 4H_2O + N_2$$

Solution:

1. 126 g $(NH_4)_2Cr_2O_7$ = ? g H_2O

Strategy: 126 g $(NH_4)_2Cr_2O_7 \longrightarrow$? mol $(NH_4)_2Cr_2O_7 \longrightarrow$? mol $H_2O \longrightarrow$? g H_2O

2. 1 mol $(NH_4)_2Cr_2O_7$ = 252 g $(NH_4)_2Cr_2O_7$ (from the mole definition)
   1 mol H_2O = 18.0 g H_2O (from the mole definition)
   4 mol H_2O = 1 mol $(NH_4)_2Cr_2O_7$ (from the equation)

3.

$$\frac{1 \text{ mol } (NH_4)_2Cr_2O_7}{252 \text{ g } (NH_4)_2Cr_2O_7} = 1 \qquad \frac{252\ (NH_4)_2Cr_2O_7}{1 \text{ mol } (NH_4)_2Cr_2O_7} = 1$$

and

$$\frac{1 \text{ mol } H_2O}{18.0 \text{ g } H_2)} = 1 \qquad \frac{18.0 \text{ g } H_2O}{1 \text{ mol } H_2O} = 1$$

and

$$\frac{4 \text{ mol } H_2O}{1 \text{ mol } (NH_4)_2Cr_2O_7} = 1 \qquad \frac{1 \text{ mol } (NH_4)_2Cr_2O_7}{4 \text{ mol } H_2O} = 1$$

4.

$$126 \cancel{\text{g } (NH_4)_2Cr_2O_7} \times \frac{1 \cancel{\text{mol } (NH_4)_2Cr_2O_7}}{252 \cancel{\text{g } (NH_4)_2Cr_2O_7}} \times \frac{4 \cancel{\text{mol } H_2O}}{1 \cancel{\text{mol } (NH_4)_2Cr_2O_7}}$$

$$\times \frac{18.0 \text{ g } H_2O}{1 \cancel{\text{mol } H_2O}} = 36.0 \text{ g } H_2O$$

• •

EXERCISE 5.13

If 54.0 g H_2O is produced from the decomposition of $(NH_4)_2Cr_2O_7$ (see Sample Exercise 5.13 above), how much N_2 (in grams) is also formed?

SUMMARY

Chemists find the mole to be an especially convenient unit because the number of moles of a substance is directly related to the number of atoms or molecules present in a sample of the substance. One mole of a substance is defined as 6.02×10^{23} particles of a substance; the number 6.02×10^{23} is often called Avogadro's number. One mole of an element or compound contains 6.02×10^{23} atoms or molecules of the element or compound and has a mass in grams equal to the formula weight of the element or compound. It is frequently necessary to convert moles to grams, and vice versa, in order to perform chemical calculations. This is done by direct application of the definition of the mole. By using the definition of the mole it is also possible to calculate the number of atoms or molecules in a given mass of material or to calculate the mass of a single atom or molecule. The mole represents a visible macroscopic amount of substance compared with the invisible, microscopic atoms and molecules.

Chemical formulas may be interpreted in terms of moles of atoms rather than numbers of atoms. Mass percentages of each element in a compound are determined by dividing the masses of each element by the mass of one mole of the compound. Compounds can be broken down into their constituent elements in the laboratory, where experimental determinations of mass percentages can be performed. If the formula of the compound is unknown, the mass percentage data can be used to find the empirical formula, that is, the simplest whole number ratio of atoms. From the empirical formula and an experimental formula weight the actual or molecular formula can be found.

Chemical equations describe chemical reactions with special symbols and chemical formulas. Reactants are the starting substances and products are the newly formed substances. Since the mass of reactants must be exactly equal to the mass of products, all chemical equations must be balanced by equating the numbers of atoms on both sides of the equation. Calculations based on chemical equations are made to determine the quantities of reactants or products involved in chemical reactions. To perform the calculations it is convenient to interpret chemical equations in terms of moles rather than atoms or molecules.

A given quantity may be converted to a desired quantity via a series of conversion factors derived from the definition of the mole and from the balanced chemical equation. A quantity given in grams is first converted to moles so that the chemical equation may be used directly. Chemical conversion factors based upon the balanced chemical equation are used to complete the conversion. Such calculations based upon chemical equations arise often in doing routine experiments in chemical laboratories.

KEY WORDS

mole
Avogadro's number
chemical conversion factor
microscopic
macroscopic
mass percent composition
molecular formula
empirical formula
balancing equation
stoichiometry

EXERCISES

5.14 Convert the following quantities to grams: (a) 1 lb Pb; (b) 1 kg Pb; (c) 1 mol Pb.

5.15 Find the mass in grams of one mole of each of the following substances: (a) C; (b) I_2; (c) O_2; (d) O_3; (e) LiCl; (f) $Ba_3(PO_4)_2$; (g) $K_2Cr_2O_7$; (h) $C_6H_{12}O_6$.

5.16 Calculate the mass in grams of each of the following:
(a) 2.00 mol N_2 (b) 0.500 mol Na
(c) 1.50 mol $AlCl_3$ (d) 0.125 mol CH_3OH
(e) 10.0 mol $(NH_4)_2S$ (f) 1.86 mol Au
(g) 0.0391 mol $AgNO_3$ (h) 15.8 mol SO_2

5.17 What is the mass in grams of 1 mmol H_2O? (Review SI prefixes listed in Chapter 1.)

5.18 Convert the following masses to moles: (a) 360 g H_2O; (b) 360 mg H_2O; (c) 1.00 g H_2; (d) 27.0 g Al; (e) 4.00 lb He; (f) 2.00 kg $BeCl_2$; (g) 150 g C_6H_5N; (h) 1.90 g F_2.

5.19 If a box contains 1-lb pure sodium chloride, how many moles of sodium chloride are in it?

5.20 Why do chemists find the unit *mole* so useful?

5.21 Calculate the number of years that corresponds to one mole of seconds.

5.22 How many molecules are present in the following: (a) 1 mol H_2O; (b) 2.50 mol CS_2; (c) 0.250 mol NH_3; (d) 10^{-4} PCl_3; (e) 10^{-6} mol H_2S; (f) 10.0 mol S_8?

5.23 How many molecules would there be in 100 g of each of the following compounds: (a) CO_2; (b) $SiCl_4$; (c) $C_{12}H_{22}O_{11}$?

5.24 Calculate the number of moles represented by
(a) 6.02×10^{23} Na atoms
(b) 3.01×10^{23} H_2O molecules
(c) 18.06×10^{23} electrons
(d) 12.04×10^{23} Br_2 molecules

5.25 Using the definition of the mole, calculate the mass in grams of the following microscopic units: (a) One NH_3 molecule; (b) one gold atom.

5.26 How many C atoms are there in 2.00 mol of each of the following compounds: (a) CH_4; (b) $NaHCO_3$; (c) C_6H_6; (d)$C_6H_{12}O_6$; (e) $COCl_2$; (f) CH_3CONH_2?

5.27 How many moles of C are present in one mole of each of the compounds listed in Problem 5.26?

5.28 A chemist needs a solution of NaOH that contains 0.500 mol NaOH in enough water to make 1 L of solution. How much NaOH should be weighed out to make exactly 1 L of solution?

5.29 Silver nitrate solutions are used in treating the eyes of newborn babies. If 100 g of this solution contains 1.00 g $AgNO_3$, how many moles of $AgNO_3$ are present? How many moles of water?

5.30 Two different kinds of calcium tablets contain the following amounts of calcium compounds:
(a) 70 mg $CaCO_3$ (calcium carbonate)
(b) 100 mg $Ca(C_3H_5O_3)_2$ (calcium lactate)
Calculate the number of moles of compound in each kind of tablet. Which of the tablets contains more moles of calcium?

5.31 A tablet used to treat potassium deficiency contains the following potassium compounds: (a) 1.12 g KCl; (b) 0.401 g $KHCO_3$; (c) 0.069 g K_2CO_3. Calculate the number of moles of each of the potassium compounds. Calculate the total number of moles of potassium provided by this tablet.

5.32 One lithium carbonate tablet contains 300 mg Li_2CO_3. Blood lithium levels above 0.001 mol/L can cause severe adverse reactions. If one entire tablet were absorbed into the blood stream of an individual at once, would the lithium level be safe? Assume that the volume of blood in this individual is about 5 L.

*5.33 Calculate the number of moles of atoms present in 1 L of iron metal (density 294 lb/ft^3).

5.34 A set of four test tubes each contains 100-g samples of the following elements. If the elements are all monatomic, which test tube contains the largest number of moles: (a) Carbon; (b) potassium; (c) iron; (d) magnesium?

5.35 For the element oxygen (in the form of dioxygen, O_2) find the
(a) Mass of 1 mol of O_2 molecules
(b) Mass of one O_2 molecule
(c) Number of moles in 100 g O_2
(d) Number of O atoms in 1 mol O_2
(e) Number of O_2 molecules in 32 g O_2

5.36 For the compound hydrogen sulfide find the
(a) Mass of 1 mol of H_2S molecules
(b) Mass of one H_2S molecule
(c) Number of moles in 100 g H_2S
(d) Number of S atoms in 1 mol H_2S
(e) Number of H atoms in 1 mol H_2S
(f) Number of H_2S molecules in 34 g H_2S

5.37 Calculate the mass percent of each element in the following compounds: (a) CO_2; (b) NH_4NO_2; (c) $Fe_2(SO_4)_3$; (d) NaOH.

5.38 In which of the following nitrogen compounds is the mass percentage of N the highest: (a) NH_3; (b) NH_4Cl; (c) N_2O; (d) N_2O_5?

5.39 A chemist prepares a new compound, which is to be used as a pain-killer similar to aspirin. The molecular formula is supposed to be $C_{13}H_8O_3F_2$. If the compound is sent out for elemental analysis, what mass percent of C is expected?

5.40 Find the empirical formula which corresponds to each of the following compounds: (a) NH_4NO_2; (b) NH_4NO_3; (c) C_4H_{10}; (d) N_2O_4; (e) $Mg_2P_2O_7$; (f) $C_{14}H_{10}N_2O_2$.

5.41 The formula weight for a compound which has the empirical formula C_3H_2Cl is 147. What is the molecular formula?

5.42 A compound which contains C and H is 92.3 percent C.
(a) What is the empirical formula for the compound?
(b) If the formula weight is about 26, what is the molecular formula?

5.43 A compound which contains C and H is 80.0 percent C.
(a) What is the empirical formula for the compound?
(b) If the formula weight is about 31, what is the molecular formula?

5.44 A compound which contains C and H is 75 percent C.
(a) What is the empirical formula for the compound?
(b) If the formula weight is found to be 16, what is the molecular formula?

5.45 Balance the following equations:
(a) $Na + H_2O \rightarrow NaOH + H_2$
(b) $Al + Br_2 \rightarrow AlBr_3$
(c) $H_2SO_4 + KOH \rightarrow H_2O + K_2SO_4$
(d) $C_4H_{10} + O_2 \rightarrow CO_2 + H_2O$
(e) $C_{12}H_{24}O_2 + O_2 \rightarrow CO_2 + H_2O$

5.46 Write balanced chemical equations to describe the following reactions:
(a) Sulfur dioxide gas reacts with dioxygen gas to produce sulfur trioxide.
(b) Solid mercury(II) sulfide reacts with dioxygen gas to produce liquid mercury and sulfur dioxide gas.
(c) Difluorine plus water yields ozone (trioxygen) and hydrogen fluoride.
(d) Lithium carbonate decomposes upon heating to produce lithium oxide and carbon dioxide.
(e) Magnesium chloride added to silver nitrate produces silver chloride and magnesium nitrate.

5.47 The reaction of some antacids with stomach acid (HCl) may be represented by the following equation:

$$NaHCO_3 + HCl \longrightarrow NaCl + H_2O + CO_2$$

(a) Balance the equation.
(b) How many moles of $NaHCO_3$ are needed to react with 3.00 mol HCl?
(c) How many moles of $NaHCO_3$ produce 0.500 mol CO_2?
(d) How many moles of $NaHCO_3$ are needed to produce 30.0 g H_2O?
(e) What mass in grams of $NaHCO_3$ is needed to react with 2.30 g HCl?

5.48 The reaction of zinc sulfide with oxygen produces zinc oxide and sulfur dioxide according to the following equation:

$$ZnS + O_2 \longrightarrow ZnO + SO_2$$

(a) Balance the equation.
(b) How many moles of O_2 are needed to produce 4.00 mol ZnO?
(c) How many moles of ZnS are needed to produce 4.00 mol ZnO?
(d) If 1.50 mol ZnS reacts with an excess amount of O_2, how many grams of SO_2 will be produced?
(e) What mass in grams of O_2 is needed to react with 100 g ZnS?

5.49 Calcium chloride reacts with sodium carbonate to produce sodium chloride and calcium carbonate.

(a) Write a balanced equation to describe this reaction.

(b) How many grams of sodium carbonate are needed to give 450 g of sodium chloride?

5.50 A laboratory method to produce oxygen gas is based upon the decomposition of potassium chlorate according to the equation below:

$$KClO_3 \longrightarrow O_2 + KCl$$

(a) Balance the equation.

(b) How many grams of $KClO_3$ are needed to provide 1 kg O_2?

5.51 Solutions of hydrogen peroxide, H_2O_2, are sometimes used as antiseptics. Stabilizers must be added to prevent the decomposition reaction below:

$$H_2O_2 \longrightarrow H_2O(l) + O_2(g)$$

(a) Balance the equation.

(b) For every mole of H_2O_2 that decomposes, how many moles oxygen gas are formed?

(c) If a solution containing 3.00 g hydrogen peroxide undergoes complete decomposition, how many grams of oxygen gas will be evolved?

6 . . . . . . NUCLEAR CHEMISTRY

6.1 INTRODUCTION

The nuclei of the atoms of **radioactive isotopes**(**radioisotopes**) are unstable, spontaneously and continuously ejecting particles (see Section 3.5). These particles, moving at high velocity, are capable of much destruction. However, they can also be turned to beneficial purposes, particularly in the field of medicine, where the ejected particles may kill unwanted tissue or may serve as tracers to locate trouble in the body chemistry. Few chapters in the history of chemistry are as exciting as the one in which the discovery of radioactivity took place.

6.2 DISCOVERY OF RADIOACTIVITY

Serendipity, or the finding of something of value while not directly looking for it, has led to many major scientific discoveries. The discoveries of radioactivity and before that of x-radiation were both accidental discoveries made possible by luck and the practiced eyes of experienced scientists. It was Henri Becquerel (1852–1908) who stumbled upon the phenomenon of radioactivity while searching for a source of x-radiation.

The story begins in 1895, when Wilhelm Röntgen (1845–1923) discovered x-radiation and its incredible penetrating power. **X-rays** are massless and chargeless like ordinary visible light radiation but much more energetic. Note in the electromagnetic radiation spectrum shown in Figure 2.8 that x-rays have much shorter wavelengths than does visible light. Thus, as we discussed in Section 2.11, x-ray photons have more energy than visible light photons. X-rays have the ability to penetrate thick black paper, skin, inch-thick pine boards, and aluminum foil, all barriers which would stop visible radiation. Most objects are transparent to x-radiation to some degree. However, bones and heavy metals such as lead are able to absorb x-radiation (see Figure 6.1). The first x-ray picture was taken when

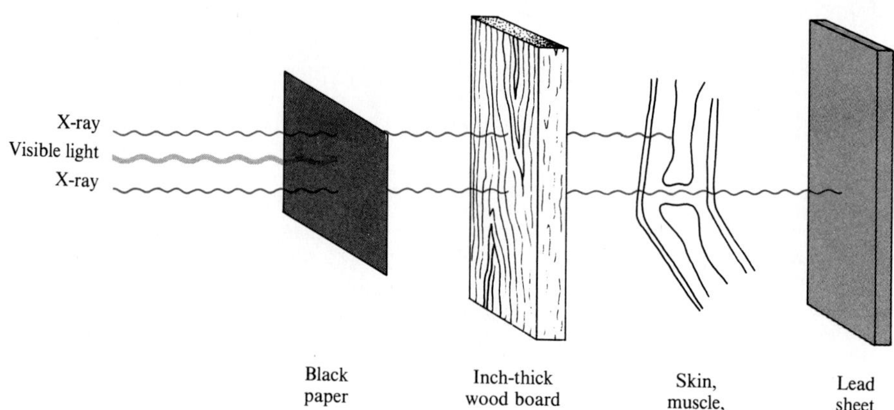

FIGURE 6.1
Penetrative power of x-rays. Visible light is stopped by the black paper. X-rays penetrate black paper, inch-thick board, and skin and muscle but are stopped by the bone and lead sheet.

Initially there was public fear that x-rays could be used to see through clothing.

Röntgen chose the name *x*-rays because he did not know what they were.

Like atoms, molecules have electronic energy levels. Uv from the sun is enough to elevate electrons in some substances. These substances fluoresce as the electrons return to lower levels.

Röntgen allowed x-rays to pass through the bones in his wife's hand. A photographic plate placed behind her hand was blackened everywhere except where the bones were.

The medical profession was quick to pounce upon this new discovery as a diagnostic tool. Physicians could now look through skin into the inside of the body. By passing x-rays through the body, bone fractures could be seen and the presence of tumors could be noted. Members of the scientific commmunity were anxious to find sources for this remarkable radiation. Röntgen had originally discovered x-rays emanating from a fluorescing (glowing) spot on an electric discharge tube, called a cathode-ray tube, a device much like the modern television picture tube. Such a tube is shown in Figure 6.2, where a stream of electrons is aimed at a screen coated with a substance that glows when exposed to an electron beam. It was in the radiation produced by this glow that Röntgen and others found x-rays. The study of this glowing spot led to the theory that *any* substance which fluoresced would produce x-radiation. Figure 6.3 illustrates a Coolidge x-ray tube, which also employs an electron beam to produce x-rays and is used as a source of x-radiation for medical diagnostic procedures.

In Paris Henri Becquerel, professor of physics, was one scientist searching hopefully for the mysterious x-rays among substances which were known to fluoresce upon exposure to sunlight. His technique was to place a substance capable of fluorescing upon a photographic plate covered with thick black cloth. Becquerel then took this apparatus out into the Paris sunshine (see Figure 6.4).

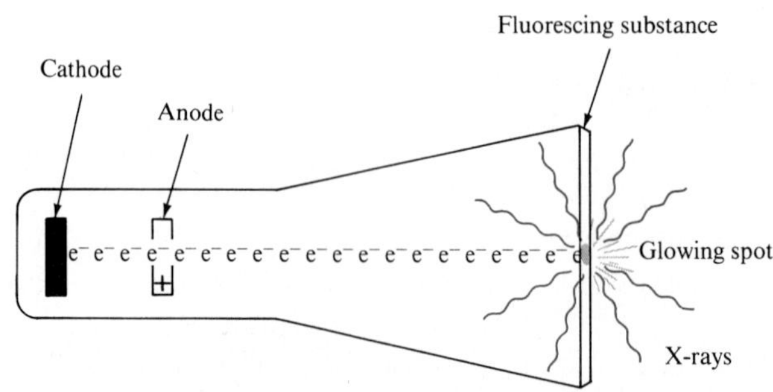

FIGURE 6.2
Cathode ray tube (and x-rays). The cathode emits electrons. The positive anode attracts them and aims them at the screen. Where the electron beam strikes the tub face, a glow appears. The glow is accompanied by x-rays.

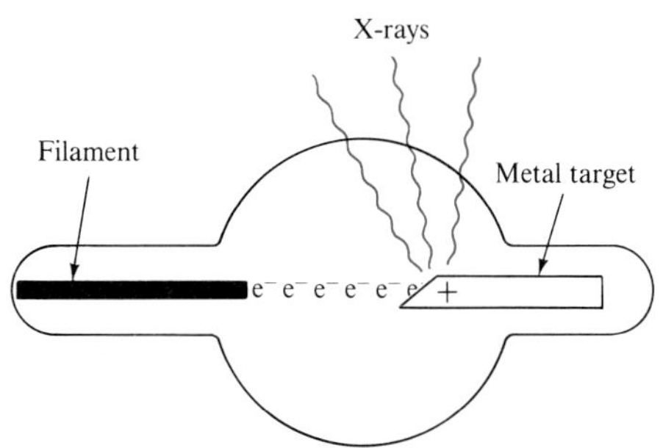

FIGURE 6.3
Coolidge x-ray tube. A tungsten filament emits electrons which are attracted by a positive metal target. The metal target emits the x-rays.

Sun

Fluorescing substance

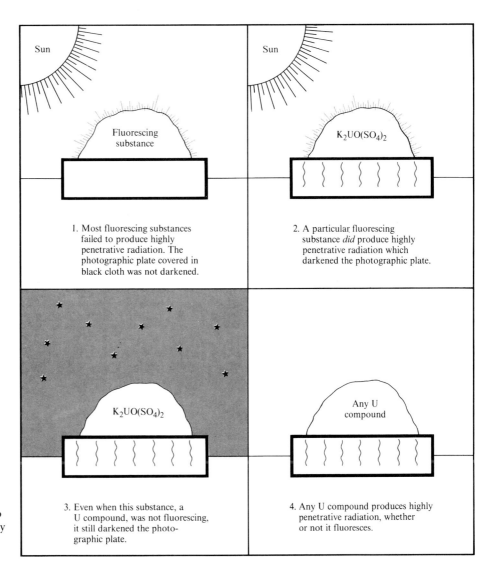

1. Most fluorescing substances failed to produce highly penetrative radiation. The photographic plate covered in black cloth was not darkened.

Sun

$K_2UO(SO_4)_2$

2. A particular fluorescing substance *did* produce highly penetrative radiation which darkened the photographic plate.

$K_2UO(SO_4)_2$

3. Even when this substance, a U compound, was not fluorescing, it still darkened the photographic plate.

Any U compound

4. Any U compound produces highly penetrative radiation, whether or not it fluoresces.

FIGURE 6.4
Discovery of radioactivity. The search for highly penetrative x-rays among fluorescing substances led to the discovery of radioactivity with similar penetrating power.

If x-rays really did come out of fluorescing substances, the plate should have blackened. For a long time Becquerel was unsuccessful. It was on February 24, 1896, that he happened to be testing a particular fluorescing substance with the

U compounds produced energetic radiations without exposure to the sun and thus without fluorescing.

chemical formula $K_2UO(SO_4)_2$. This time the plate blackened! The next day he repeated the experiment in total darkness. Without light there could be no fluorescence and thus no x-radiation. But the plate still blackened (see Figure 6.4). Future experiments showed that *all* uranium compounds produced this penetrating radiation. Furthermore the more uranium present, the greater the radiation produced. Becquerel had uncovered a totally new phenomenon, the *spontaneous* emission of highly penetrating radiation from a substance, that is, emission that occurs with no input of energy. What he had observed was *natural radioactivity.* We will devote the rest of this chapter to the study of the nature of this radioactivity and of the elements that produce it.

Polonium was named after Poland, Marie Sklodowska-Curie's native country.

Other radioactive elements were soon identified. In 1898, with remarkable patience and enthusiam, Marie Curie (1867–1934) and Pierre Curie (1859–1906) isolated tiny quantities of radium (Ra) and polonium (Po) from a huge amount of the uranium ore called pitchblende. Atomic line spectra helped to prove that Ra and Po were brand new elements (see Section 3.15).

6.3 STABILITY OF NUCLEI

Why do some nuclei, such as those of U, Ra, and Po, emit radiation spontaneously while others do not? One fact that can be observed is that the stability of a nucleus depends upon the ratio of neutrons to protons (N/Z) that it contains. Let us see how the N/Z ratio affects the stability of nuclei from three groups of elements, those with atomic numbers $Z < 20$, those with Z from 20 to 83, and those with $Z > 83$.

Elements with $Z < 20$

Nuclei of most stable isotopes with atomic number less than 20 have N/Z ratios of unity or slightly more than unity. In Figure 6.5 the number of neutrons (N) is plotted against the number of protons (Z) for selected isotopes. The shaded area in this plot is known as the **stability zone**. All stable isotopes (indicated on the figure by black circles) must be within the borders of this band. Note that C-12, O-16, and Ca-40 are among the stable isotopes in the stability zone. Some unstable isotopes (shown as colored circles on the plot of N versus Z) may also be located within the band of stability. For instance, C-14 is a radioactive isotope of carbon, but as you can see from looking at Figure 6.5, it is within the stability zone. All isotopes outside the band of stability *must* be radioactive.

Elements with Z 21 to 83

Nuclei of stable isotopes with atomic numbers 21 to 83 have N/Z ratios which increase steadily from 1 to 1.55 (see Figure 6.5). Once again some unstable nuclei do have N/Z ratios between 1 and 1.55, but outside these limits *all* nuclei are unstable.

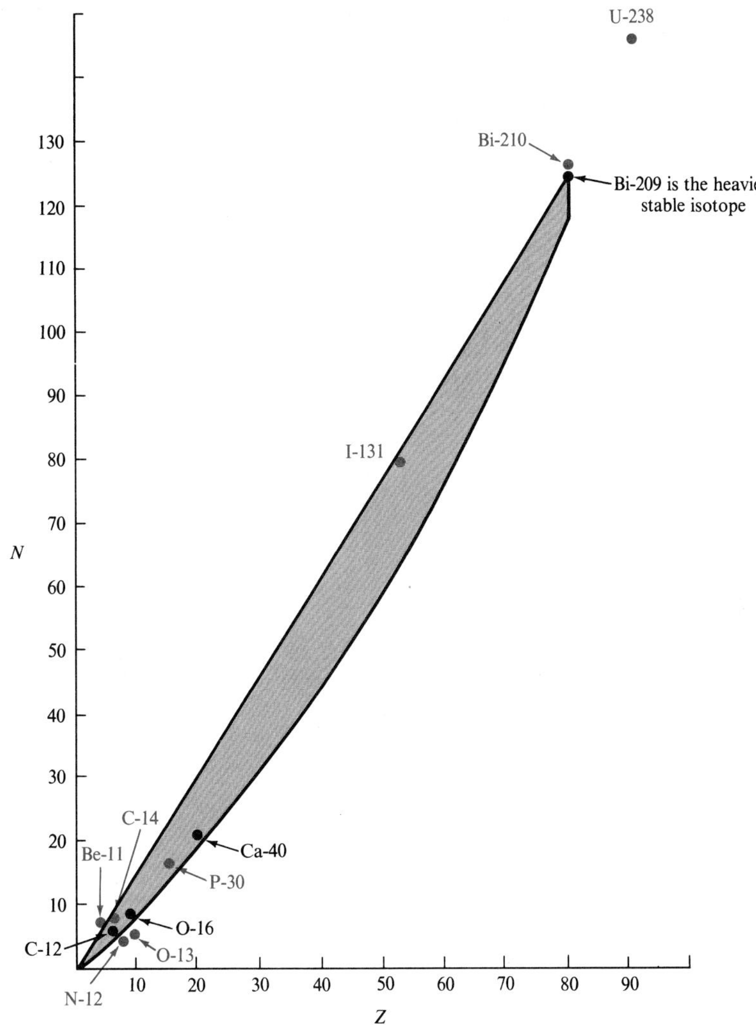

FIGURE 6.5
N/*Z* and stability. The shaded area is the stability zone. Stable isotopes (black circles) must lie within the zone. Unstable isotopes (colored circles) can also be within the zone. All isotopes outside the zone are unstable.

Elements with $Z > 83$

The name technetium comes from the Greek word *technitos*, meaning "artificial."

All elements with *Z* greater than 83 are radioactive. For these elements there is *no* stability zone. (See Figure 6.6, where all the elements that have no stable isotopes are shown in color.) Note from the figure that technetium ($Z=43$) is the one lighter element which has no naturally occurring stable isotopes.

We can make sense of these observations about nuclear stability by examining the interactions of protons and neutrons in the nucleus. As the size of the nucleus increases, so does the number of protons and the repulsive interactions among the protons. If the repulsive forces become too large, the nucleus becomes unstable. A greater ratio of neutrons to protons in such a nucleus helps to reduce the interactions and stabilize the nucleus. The elements with atomic number less than 83 are most stable when *N*/*Z* is between 1:1 and 1.5:1. However, there is a limit to the number of neutrons which a nucleus can accommodate to reduce proton repulsions. This limit is exceeded in all elements with *Z* greater than 83. The

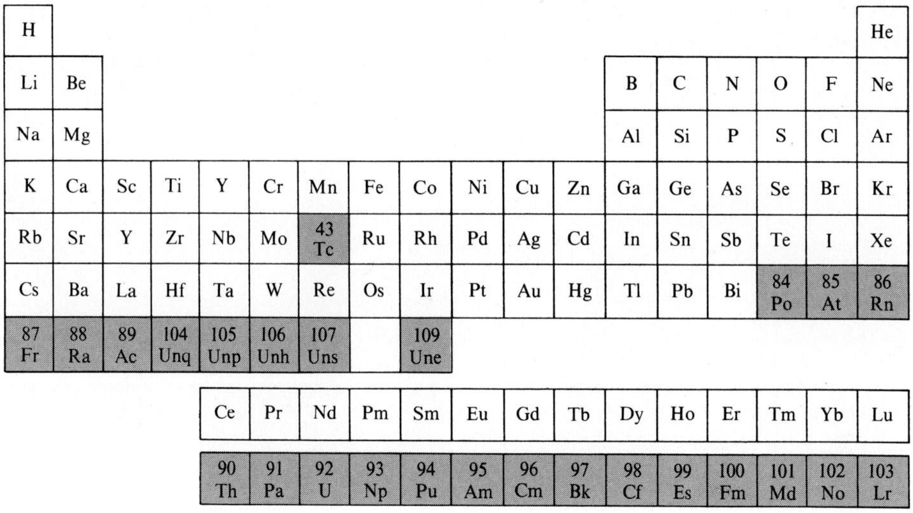

H																	He
Li	Be											B	C	N	O	F	Ne
Na	Mg											Al	Si	P	S	Cl	Ar
K	Ca	Sc	Ti	Y	Cr	Mn	Fe	Co	Ni	Cu	Zn	Ga	Ge	As	Se	Br	Kr
Rb	Sr	Y	Zr	Nb	Mo	43 Tc	Ru	Rh	Pd	Ag	Cd	In	Sn	Sb	Te	I	Xe
Cs	Ba	La	Hf	Ta	W	Re	Os	Ir	Pt	Au	Hg	Tl	Pb	Bi	84 Po	85 At	86 Rn
87 Fr	88 Ra	89 Ac	104 Unq	105 Unp	106 Unh	107 Uns		109 Une									

Ce	Pr	Nd	Pm	Sm	Eu	Gd	Tb	Dy	Ho	Er	Tm	Yb	Lu
90 Th	91 Pa	92 U	93 Np	94 Pu	95 Am	96 Cm	97 Bk	98 Cf	99 Es	100 Fm	101 Md	102 No	103 Lr

FIGURE 6.6
Periodic table showing radioactive elements. The elements for which there are no stable isotopes are shown in color.

heaviest stable nucleus is Bi-209 ($Z=83$), as shown in Figure 6.5, where it fits into the uppermost corner of the stability band.

Radioactive nuclei emit radiation to become more stable by improving their N/Z ratio.

The ways in which they do this is discussed in Section 6.4, with specific illustrations given in Section 6.5.

SAMPLE EXERCISE 6.1

Try to predict from the general guidelines given about nuclear stability whether or not the following isotopes could be stable (nonradioactive).

(a) O-16 (b) Al-27 (c) O-13
(d) Be-11 (e) Ra-228 (f) P-30

Solution:

(a) O-16 ^{16}O $Z = 8$ $N = 8$ $N/Z = 1$

Prediction: Stable isotopes with atomic number less than 20 tend to have N/Z ratios of close to unity. O-16 can be stable.

Fact: The nuclei of O-16 atoms are stable. O-16 is, of course, nonradioactive. It is the most abundant O isotope in nature.

(b) Al-27 ^{27}Al $Z = 13$ $N = 14$ $N/Z = 1.08$

Prediction: Al-27 is nonradioactive because the N/Z ratio is very close to unity.

Fact: Al-27 is not radioactive and accounts for 100 percent of natural Al.

(c) O-13 ^{13}O $Z = 8$ $N = 5$ $N/Z = 0.63$

Prediction: O-13 is radioactive because $N/Z < 1$.

Fact: O-13 is radioactive.

(d) B-11 ^{11}Be $Z = 4$ $N = 7$ $N/Z = 1.75$

Prediction: Be-11 is radioactive because $N/Z > 1.5$.

Fact: Be-11 is radioactive.

(e) P-30 ^{30}P $Z = 15$ $N = 15$ $N/Z = 1$

Prediction: P-30 *could* be stable

Fact: However, P-30 *is* radioactive. Remember that even though stable isotopes with atomic numbers less than 20 tend to have N/Z ratios of about unity, the converse is not true. Some unstable isotopes also have N/Z ratios close to unity. P-30 is one such example.

(f) Ra-228 ^{228}Ra $Z = 88$

Prediction: In this case N/Z need not be calculated. All elements with $Z > 83$ are radioactive.

Fact: Ra-228 and all other Ra isotopes are radioactive.

Exercise 6.1

Which of the following isotopes could be stable?

(a) Si-28 (b) Pu-234 (c) Na-20

6.4 TYPES OF EMITTED RADIATION

Radioactive elements emit three different types of high-velocity penetrating rays called **alpha** (α), **beta** (β), and **gamma** (γ) rays.

Alpha Rays

Of the three the alpha rays are the least penetrative, being unable to go through unbroken skin or clothing or more than a few inches of air. The alpha radiation actually consists of particles identical to the nuclei of helium atoms. In fact, removing the two electrons from a helium atom produces an alpha particle. These alpha particles, like the helium nuclei, possess a nuclear charge of +2 and a mass of 4 amu.

$$\alpha = {}^{4}He \text{ or } {}^{4}_{2}\alpha$$

The line spectrum of He in Color Plate 3*b* was used to identify α particles as He nuclei.

The discovery that alpha particles were so massive made it clear how drastic a process radioactive decay is. An element that emitted something as large as a helium nucleus was undergoing a change which must alter its very identity.

Beta Rays

Beta rays are more penetrating than alpha rays. Ernest Rutherford noticed that beta rays were able to penetrate 12 thin aluminum foils, while alpha rays were stopped by 4 foils. (This is the same type of experiment as the one in which Rutherford discovered the emptiness of the atom—see Section 3.6.) Beta rays consist of particles identical to electrons. Like electrons, beta particles have a charge of −1 and a mass of almost 0:

The mass number of a particle is the integer closest to its mass in atomic mass units.

$$\beta = {}^{0}_{-1}\beta$$

It is also possible for nuclei to emit another kind of beta radiation, in which the particles emitted are identical in mass to electrons but possess a +1 charge. These particles are called **positrons**, and are indicated by the symbol β^+.

$$\beta^+ = {}^{0}_{1}\beta$$

A better symbol for negative beta radiation is β^-. However, when the term beta radiation is used and the sign of the charge is not indicated, it usually refers to the beta particles which are electrons.

Gamma Rays

Gamma radiation is the most penetrating of the three types of radiation. Only $1\frac{1}{2}$ mi of air or a 1-ft-thick lead wall will stop gamma radiation. Gamma rays are very much like x-rays, but the term *gamma ray* is restricted to radiation coming from the nucleus of a radioactive atom. Like x-rays and visible light and any other kind of electromagnetic radiation, gamma rays are chargeless and massless:

Gamma-radiation is part of the electromagnetic radiation spectrum (Figure 2.8).

$$\gamma = {}^{0}_{0}\gamma$$

The properties of alpha, beta, and gamma rays are summarized in Table 6.1, and their penetrative powers are compared in Figure 6.7.

TABLE 6.1 **PROPERTIES OF α-, β-, and γ-RADIATION**

Name	Symbol	Nature of radiation	Mass, amu	Charge
Alpha	α or ${}^{4}_{2}\alpha$	Helium nucleus	4	+2
Beta	β or β^- or ${}^{0}_{-1}\beta$	Electron	0	−1
Beta	β^+ or ${}^{0}_{1}\beta$	Positron	0	+1
Gamma	γ or ${}^{0}_{0}\gamma$	Electromagnetic radiation	0	0

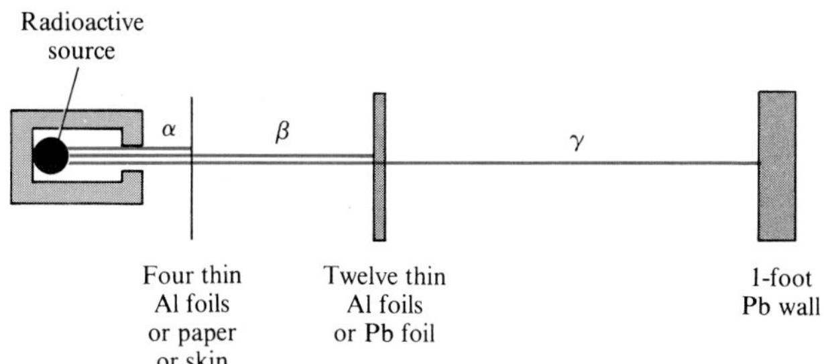

FIGURE 6.7
Penetrative powers of α, β, and γ radiation.

6.5 NUCLEAR DECAY; SPONTANEOUS TRANSMUTATION

During nuclear decay, a radioactive isotope emits alpha, beta, or gamma radiation to become a new element or a new isotope of the same element. The original isotope is sometimes called the **parent** isotope, which gives birth to the decay product called the **daughter** isotope. The nature of the daughter isotope depends upon the type of radiation emitted. The nuclear decay process by which the parent isotope is transformed is often called **spontaneous transmutation.** In all equations that represent transmutations, the total of the charges and of the masses must be the same on both sides of the equation. By balancing the charges and the masses, the new isotope which forms may be identified.

Alpha Emission

When a parent isotope loses an alpha particle, it must lose two protons and two neutrons. The atomic number of the daughter isotope is decreased by two units and the mass number is reduced by four units:

$$^{A}_{Z}[\text{Parent}] \longrightarrow {}^{A-4}_{Z-2}[\text{Daughter}] + {}^{4}_{2}\alpha$$

Note that the sum of the charges and the sum of the masses are equal on both sides of the equation:

Recall that the atomic number Z is equal to the positive charge on the nucleus.

On the left	On the right
Charge $= Z$	Charge $= Z - 2 + 2 = Z$
Mass $= A$	Mass $= A - 4 + 4 = A$

We can describe nuclear decay reactions by following these steps:

1. Write symbols for each known isotope or particle.
2. Write the equation.
3. Balance the charge and the mass.
4. Identify the daughter isotope.

For instance, we can write the equation for the emission of alpha particles from U-238:

1. List the symbols.

$$\text{Alpha} = {}^{4}_{2}\alpha \quad \text{and} \quad \text{U-238} = {}^{238}_{92}\text{U}$$

2. Write the equation.

$${}^{238}_{92}\text{U} \longrightarrow [\text{daughter}] + {}^{4}_{2}\alpha$$

3. Balance the charge and mass.

On the left	On the right
Charge = 92	Charge = ? + 2 = 92
Mass = 238	Mass = ? + 4 = 238

In order for the charge and mass on the right to balance those on the left, the daughter isotope must have an atomic number of 90 and a mass number of 234.

$${}^{238}_{92}\text{U} \longrightarrow {}^{234}_{90}? + {}^{4}_{2}\alpha$$

4. Now identify the daughter isotope.

The ninetieth element in the periodic table is thorium (Th). The completed nuclear equation is

$${}^{238}_{92}\text{U} \longrightarrow {}^{234}_{90}\text{Th} + {}^{4}_{2}\alpha$$

In general, heavy isotopes ($Z > 83$) are unstable because the N/Z ratio is too low. Alpha emission increases the N/Z ratio and thus is one mode of decay for heavy isotopes. The higher N/Z ratio of the daughter isotopes means there is a greater neutron concentration, lower replusive forces among protons, and hence greater stability. For example, in the nuclear decay of U-238 by alpha emission, the N/Z ratio increases as follows:

$${}^{238}_{92}\text{U} \longrightarrow {}^{234}_{90}\text{Th} + {}^{4}_{2}\alpha$$

${}^{238}_{92}\text{U}$	${}^{234}_{90}\text{Th}$
$N = 238 - 92 = 146$	$N = 234 - 90 = 144$
$Z = 92$	$Z = 90$
$N/Z = 146/92 = 1.59$	$N/Z = 144/90 = 1.60$

Beta Emission

When a β^- particle is emitted, the parent isotope loses an electron from its nucleus. At first thought this seems like a very strange idea. How can electrons come shooting out of a nucleus when they are supposed to be circulating around the nucleus? It is not the extranuclear electrons, or circulating electrons, which are ejected. The electrons produced during beta decay actually do come from the nucleus. The process of β^- decay may be visualized by thinking of a neutron as a proton plus an electron:

$$^1_0n = {}^1_1p + {}^{\ 0}_{-1}e$$

Note that the masses and charges are equal on both sides of this equation. Since a β^- particle is identical to an electron, we can also write

$$^1_0n = {}^1_1p + {}^{\ 0}_{-1}\beta$$

Thus electrons, or β^- particles, are ejected from the nucleus when a neutron is transformed into a proton, which appears in its place within the nucleus.

The daughter isotope which forms upon β^- decay must have one more proton than the parent isotope and hence an atomic number one unit higher. The daughter isotope has the same mass number as the parent isotope, since electrons have a mass number of zero.

$$^A_Z[\text{Parent}] \longrightarrow {}_{Z+1}^{\ \ A}[\text{daughter}] + {}^{\ 0}_{-1}\beta$$

On the left	On the right
Charge = Z	Charge = $Z + 1 - 1 = Z$
Mass = A	Mass = $A + 0 = A$

For instance, I-131 emits β^- radiation. To describe this process we begin by listing the symbols needed and then writing the equation and balancing the charge and the mass to identify the daughter isotope.

1. Symbols: I-131 = $^{131}_{53}\text{I}$ and $\beta^- = {}^{\ 0}_{-1}\beta$
2. Equation: $^{131}_{53}\text{I} \longrightarrow [\text{daughter}] + {}^{\ 0}_{-1}\beta$
3. On the left / On the right

On the left	On the right
Charge = 53	Charge = ? − 1 = 53
Mass = 131	Mass = ? + 0 = 131

   The daughter isotope has an atomic number of 54 and a mass number of 131.

   $$^{131}_{53}\text{I} \longrightarrow {}^{131}_{54}[?] + {}^{\ 0}_{-1}\beta$$

4. The fifty-fourth element in the periodic table is xenon (Xe). The completed nuclear equation can now be written.

   $$^{131}_{53}\text{I} \longrightarrow {}^{131}_{54}\text{Xe} + {}^{\ 0}_{-1}\beta$$

The isotope I-131 is unstable because it has an *N*/*Z* ratio which is too high to allow it to fall within the stability zone shown in Figure 6.5. In the decay of I-131 by beta emission, the *N*/*Z* ratio decreases.

$$^{131}_{53}\text{I} \longrightarrow {}^{131}_{54}\text{Xe} + {}^{\ 0}_{-1}\beta$$

$^{131}_{53}\text{I}$	$^{131}_{54}\text{Xe}$
$N = 131 - 53 = 78$	$N = 131 - 54 = 77$
$Z = 53$	$Z = 54$
$N/Z = 1.47$	$N/Z = 1.43$

As mentioned previously, it is possible for radioactive isotopes to emit positive beta particles, β^+, or positrons. This process can be imagined by thinking of a proton as a neutron plus a positron:

$$^{1}_{1}p = ^{1}_{0}n + ^{0}_{1}\beta$$

Note that the charges and masses balance. When a nucleus ejects a positron, a proton is transformed into a neutron.

The new isotope which forms upon β^+ decay must have one more neutron than the parent isotope and one less proton, or an atomic number of one unit less. Since, like electrons, positrons have a mass number of zero, the daughter isotope has the same mass as the parent isotope.

$$^{A}_{Z}[\text{Parent}] \longrightarrow {}_{Z-1}^{A}[\text{daughter}] + ^{0}_{1}\beta$$

On the left	On the right
Charge = Z	Charge = $Z - 1 + 1 = Z$
Mass = A	Mass = $A + 0 = A$

For example, N-12 emits positrons. To write the equation for this decay process:

1. Symbols: Positron = $^{0}_{1}\beta$ and N-12 = $^{12}_{7}N$
2. Equation: $^{12}_{7}N \longrightarrow [\text{daughter}] + ^{0}_{1}\beta$
3. On the left / On the right

On the left	On the right
Charge = 7	Charge = ? + 1 = 7
Mass = 12	Mass = ? + 0 = 12

The daughter isotope has an atomic number of 6 and a mass number of 12.

$$^{12}_{7}N \longrightarrow ^{12}_{6}[?] + ^{0}_{1}\beta$$

4. The new isotope with atomic number 6 must be carbon, C, the sixth element in the periodic table. The completed equation is

$$^{12}_{7}N \longrightarrow ^{12}_{6}C + ^{0}_{1}\beta$$

In general, elements which decay by β^+ emission have *N/Z* ratios which are far too low for stability. Since positron emission adds a neutron to and removes a proton from the new nucleus, the *N/Z* ratio increases to improve stability. As you can see in Figure 6.5, the *N/Z* ratio for N-12 is too low. A favorable *N/Z* value is achieved in the daughter isotope, C-12.

$$^{12}_{7}N \longrightarrow ^{12}_{6}C + ^{0}_{1}\beta$$

$N/Z = 5/7 = 0.71$ (for $^{12}_{7}N$) $N/Z = 6/6 = 1$ (for $^{12}_{6}C$)

In this case positron emission by N-12 produces a particularly stable isotope, C-12, the most abundant isotope of carbon in nature.

Electron Capture

Another method by which a nucleus can increase its *N/Z* ratio is to capture an available orbiting electron. Upon *electron capture*, abbreviated EC, the atomic number is decreased by one unit as a proton combines with the captured electron to create a neutron.

$$^{A}_{Z}[\text{Parent}] + {}^{0}_{-1}e \longrightarrow {}_{Z-1}^{A}[\text{daughter}]$$

For instance, Be-7 undergoes electron capture. To describe this process,

1. Symbols: Be-7 = $^{7}_{4}$Be and electron = $^{0}_{-1}e$
2. Equation: $^{7}_{4}\text{Be} + {}^{0}_{-1}e \longrightarrow$ [daughter]
3. On the left / On the right
   Charge = 4 − 1 = 3 / Charge = ?
   Mass = 7 + 0 = 7 / Mass = ?

   The daughter isotope must have an atomic number of 3 and a mass number of 7.

$$^{7}_{4}\text{Be} + {}^{0}_{-1}e \longrightarrow {}^{7}_{3}[\text{daughter}]$$

4. The daughter isotope is Li-7, a stable isotope of lithium.

$$^{7}_{4}\text{Be} + {}^{0}_{-1}e \longrightarrow {}^{7}_{3}\text{Li}$$

Gamma Emission

When a parent isotope emits gamma radiation, there is no change in mass and no change in atomic number because gamma rays are both massless and chargeless. Why then is the daughter isotope more stable than the parent gamma-emitting isotope? Nuclei which emit gamma radiation have excess energy which they release by this process. This type of energy release is similar to that in which atoms which have excited electrons in high-energy levels release radiation as the electrons return to their lower-energy levels (see Section 3.15 on atomic emission spectroscopy). In fact, many alpha and beta decay processes are accompanied by gamma emission.

An isotope which forms as the result of gamma emission alone has the same atomic number and mass number as the original isotope. To denote the parent isotope we place a lowercase "m" at the upper-right-hand corner of the element symbol E. The m refers to the *metastable* state of the nucleus.

$$\text{E}^{\text{m}} \qquad \text{metastable nucleus}$$

One example of such a gamma emitter is Tc-99m. Since there is no change in *Z* or *A*, we can simply write out the equation.

$$^{99}_{43}\text{Tc}^{\text{m}} \longrightarrow {}^{99}_{43}\text{Tc} + {}^{0}_{0}\gamma$$

The daughter isotope is still Tc-99, but it has a more stable nucleus than the parent isotope, Tc-99m.

Gamma decays involving transitions between isomeric pairs are known as *isomeric transitions*, abbreviated IT.

A metastable nucleus E-m and the corresponding stable nucleus E are called nuclear *isomers*. For instance, Tc-99 and Tc-99m represent a pair of nuclear isomers.

SAMPLE EXERCISE 6.2

Identify the isotope which forms when Bi-210 decays by alpha emission and write an equation for the decay process.

Solution:

1. Symbols: alpha $= {}^{4}_{2}\alpha$ and Bi-210 $= {}^{210}_{83}\text{Bi}$
2. Equation: ${}^{210}_{83}\text{Bi} \longrightarrow\ ? + {}^{4}_{2}\alpha$
3. Balance the charge and mass.

On the left	On the right
Charge = 83	Charge = ? + 2 = 83
Mass = 210	Mass = ? + 4 = 210

The daughter isotope must have an atomic number of 81 (81 + 2 = 83) and a mass number of 206 (206 + 4 = 210).

4. Identify the daughter isotope.

The daughter isotope is thallium ($Z = 81$) and the completed equation is

$${}^{210}_{83}\text{Bi} \longrightarrow {}^{206}_{81}\text{Tl} + {}^{4}_{2}\alpha$$

EXERCISE 6.2

Write an equation to represent the spontaneous transmutation of Ni-63 by β^- emission.

SAMPLE EXERCISE 6.3

Identify the radiation emitted when K-40 decays to become Ca-40.

Solution:

1. Symbols: K-40 $= {}^{40}_{19}\text{K}$ and Ca-40 $= {}^{40}_{20}\text{Ca}$
2. Equation: ${}^{40}_{19}\text{K} \longrightarrow {}^{40}_{20}\text{Ca} +\ ?$
3. Balance the charge and mass.

On the left	On the right
Charge = 19	Charge = 20 + ? = 19
Mass = 40	Mass = 40 + ? = 40

4. Identify the emitted radiation.
   The particle emitted must have a charge of -1 and a mass of 0 and must be β^-.

EXERCISE 6.3

What kind of radiation is emitted when Co-58 becomes Fe-58?

Radioactive elements continue to undergo decay processes until a stable nonradioactive isotope forms. A sequence of decay processes is called a **radioactive series.** Uranium-238 and thorium-232 are two radioactive isotopes which exist in nature. These isotopes decay by a series of steps, which ends with the formation of a stable lead isotope; therefore, the amount of lead on earth is constantly increasing. The uranium series is outlined in Table 6.2.

TABLE 6.2 U-238 DECAY SERIES

U-238 → α + Th-234
Th-234 → β + Pa-234
Pa-234 → β + U-234
U-234 → α + Th-230
Th-230 → α + Ra-226
Ra-226 → α + Rn-222
Rn-222 → α + Po-218
Po-218 → α + Pb-214
Pb-214 → β + Bi-214
Bi-214 → β + Po-214
Po-214 → α + Pb-210
Pb-210 → β + Bi-210
Bi-210 → β + Po-210
Po-210 → α + **Pb-206**

Naturally occurring U-238 decays until the stable isotope Pb-206 is produced according to the reactions above. (Other pathways similar to this one are also possible.)

6.6 MEASURING RADIOACTIVITY

There are several different techniques used to measure the radiation that comes from radioactive elements.

Ionization Detectors

Many devices that are used to detect radioactivity depend upon the ability of alpha, beta, and gamma radiations to convert neutral atoms to charged ions. For instance, argon gas (Ar) is used in some detectors. Ionizing radiation from a disintegrating radioactive substance can displace an electron from an argon atom to create a positive argon ion, Ar^+.

$$\underset{\text{Argon atom}}{Ar} + \underset{\text{Ionizing radiation}}{\alpha, \beta, \text{or } \gamma} \longrightarrow \underset{\text{Argon cation}}{Ar^+} + \underset{\text{Electron}}{e^-}$$

The Ar^+ ion and the electron form what is called an **ion pair**. The presence of ion pairs allows the argon gas to conduct electricity. The popular *Geiger-Müller counter* contains a tube filled with argon gas with a thin entrance window for the radiation. When incoming radiation ionizes the argon, an electric circuit is completed, and clicks or *counts* are detected audibly. The number of counts per minute, abbreviated cpm, measures the quantity of radioactivity. A schematic diagram of a Geiger counter is shown in Figure 6.8.

The pen-type pocket *dosimeter*, worn by persons who work with radioactive substances, operates on the same principle as the Geiger tube but without the sound effect.

Scintillation Detectors

When radiation strikes certain substances, electrons in atoms or molecules of the substance are promoted to higher-energy levels. When the electron subsequently returns to lower-energy levels, energy is released in the form of light flashes called *scintillations*. Different scintillating substances are used to detect different types of radiation. For example, sodium iodide (NaI) crystals mixed with 1 percent thallium(I) iodide (TlI) are widely used to detect gamma radiation.

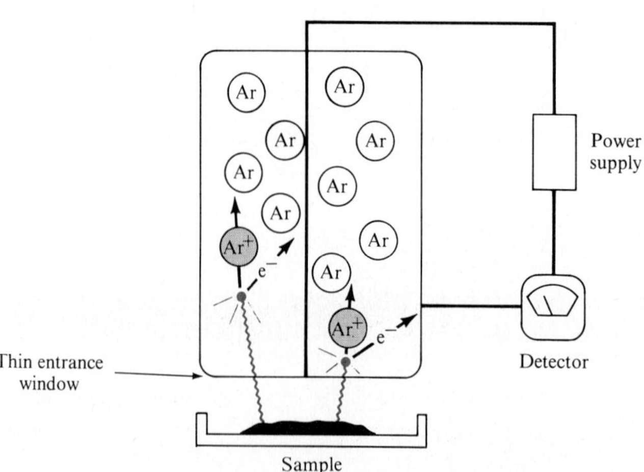

FIGURE 6.8
Geiger counter. Ionizing radiations produce ion pairs (Ar^+ + e) to complete the electric circuit.

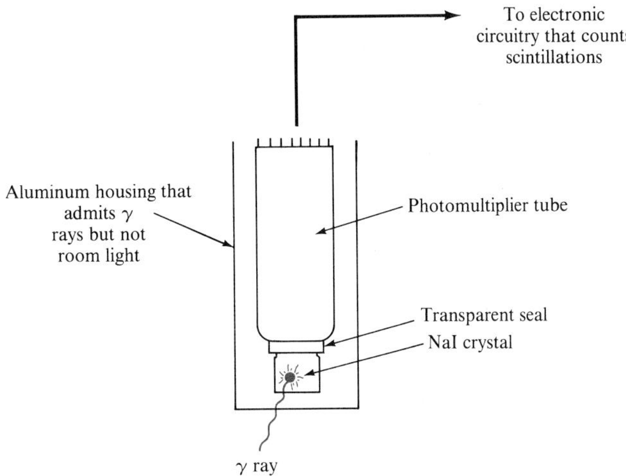

FIGURE 6.9
Gamma-ray energies can be measured by using a scintillation detector in which light flashes fall on a photomultiplier tube.

The original method used to count the light flashes was visual observation, a crude method which gave rise to considerable eye strain. Today special light-sensitive tubes, called *photomultplier tubes*, are used. A typical scintillation counter is pictured in Figure 6.9.

Photographic Detectors

Film "rings" are worn to monitor hand and middle-body exposure.

Radiation is able to darken or fog a photographic plate. Recall that this was the method by which Henri Becquerel first discovered radioactivity. The degree of darkening of the photographic film is a measure of the quantity of radiation to which it is exposed. The *film badge* worn by personnel who are exposed to radiation in their work operates upon this principle. The film in the badges is wrapped in thin paper, which is opaque to ordinary light but is transparent to energetic radiations. For workers who may be exposed to large doses of radiation, such as technicians who give injections of radioisotopes, the badges must be developed as frequently as every day. Other employees, who are simply occupying the area in which such work is done, may have their badges developed as infrequently as once a month.

6.7 RADIOACTIVE LIFETIME

Some radioactive nuclei decay much faster than others. The rate of nuclear decay is measured in terms of the **half-life** ($t_{\frac{1}{2}}$) of the radioisotope. The definition of half-life is

Half-life; ($t_{\frac{1}{2}}$) *is the length of time necessary for one-half of a given mass of radioactive isotope to decay to its distintegration product.*

Half-lives of radioactive isotopes, also called *lifetimes*, range from fractions of picoseconds to longer than 10^{16} years (see Table 6.3). A 1-g sample of the naturally occurring radioisotope C-14 requires 5700 years to decay to 0.5 g of C-14. The half-life of I-131, an isotope used in medical diagnosis, is only 8.0 days. In general, the lifetimes of isotopes used in diagnosis are very short so that the patient will be free of radioactivity in a relatively short time. The specific therapeutic or diagnostic uses are given for many of the radioisotopes listed in Table 6.3.

TABLE 6.3 HALF-LIVES OF RADIOISOTOPES

Isotope	Emission	$T_{1/2}$	Diagnostic or therapeutic use (chemical form)
I-137	β	22s	
In-113m	γ	1.7h	Liver function (In colloid)
Tc-99m	γ	6.0 h	Brain function ($NaTcO_4$)
			Liver function (Tc-S colloid)
I-123	EC	13.3h	Thyroid function (NaI)
Mg-28	β,γ	21.2 h	Magnesium absorption ($MgCl_2$)
Au-198	β,γ	2.7 d	Treatment of prostate and cervical cancers (Au colloid)
Mo-99	β,γ	2.8 d	
Rn-222	α,γ	3.8 d	Treatment of tumors (Rn gas)
Ca-47	β,γ	4.5 d	Bone function ($CaCl_2$)
			Calcium absorption ($CaCl_2$)
Xe-133	β,γ	5.3 d	Lung function (Xe gas)
I-131	β,γ	8.0 d	Thyroid function (NaI)
			Blood volume (I-tagged albumin)
P-32	β	14.2 d	Tumor location* (Na_3PO_4)
Fe-59	β,γ	45 d	Anemia detection ($FeSO_4$)
Sn-113	EC,γ	118 d	
Co-57	EC,γ	270 d	Vitamin B_{12} absorption (vitamin B_{12})
Co-60	β,γ	5.3 years	External therapy
H-3	β	12.3 years	Total body H_2O
Sr-90	β	28 years	Bone tumor diagnosis ($SrCl_2$)
Ra-226	α,γ	1600 years	Treatment of tumors ($RaBr_2$)
C-14	β	5700 years	
U-238	α	4.9×10^9 years	

*Phosphorus accumulates in tumor tissues.

Given the half-life of a radioactive isotope, it is possible to calculate the amount of original isotope which will remain after a given length of time. When the time period is some whole-number multiple of the half-life, the calculation is quite straightforward. For example, to calculate the amount of Sr-90 which will remain if an original mass of 1 g decays for 84 years, we can compute the amount which remains after each half-life. From Table 6.3 we find that the half-life of Sr-90 is 28 years.

The number of half-lives in 84 years is

$$84\cancel{y} \times \frac{1 \text{ half-life}}{28\cancel{y}} = 3 \text{ half-lives}$$

$$\text{After 1 half-life (28 y): Mass Sr-90 remaining} = \frac{1.00 \text{ g}}{2} = 0.500 \text{ g}$$

$$\text{After 2 half-lives (56 y): Mass Sr-90 remaining} = \frac{0.500 \text{ g}}{2} = 0.250 \text{ g}$$

$$\text{After 3 half-lives (84 y): Mass Sr-90 remaining} = \frac{0.250 \text{ g}}{2} = 0.125 \text{ g}$$

The calculation may also be done by using an equation which relates the original mass, m_0, to the mass remaining after n half-lives, m_n:

$$m_n = m_0 \left(\frac{1}{2}\right)^n$$

Now calculating the amount of Sr-90 remaining after three half-lives may be done in a single step:

$$n = 3$$

$$m_0 = 1.00 \text{ g}$$

$$m_3 = \text{mass remaining after 3 half-lives}$$

$$m_3 = 1.00 \text{ g} \times \left(\frac{1}{2}\right)^3$$

$$= 1.00 \text{ g} \times \frac{1}{2} \times \frac{1}{2} \times \frac{1}{2}$$

$$= 1.00 \text{ g} \times \frac{1}{8} = 0.125 \text{ g}$$

Figure 6.10 illustrates the decay of Sr-90 through 10 half-lives.

Calculations involving half-lives are essential for timing the ordering of radioisotopes from suppliers and for determining the amount of activity in patients who have taken therapeutic dosages.

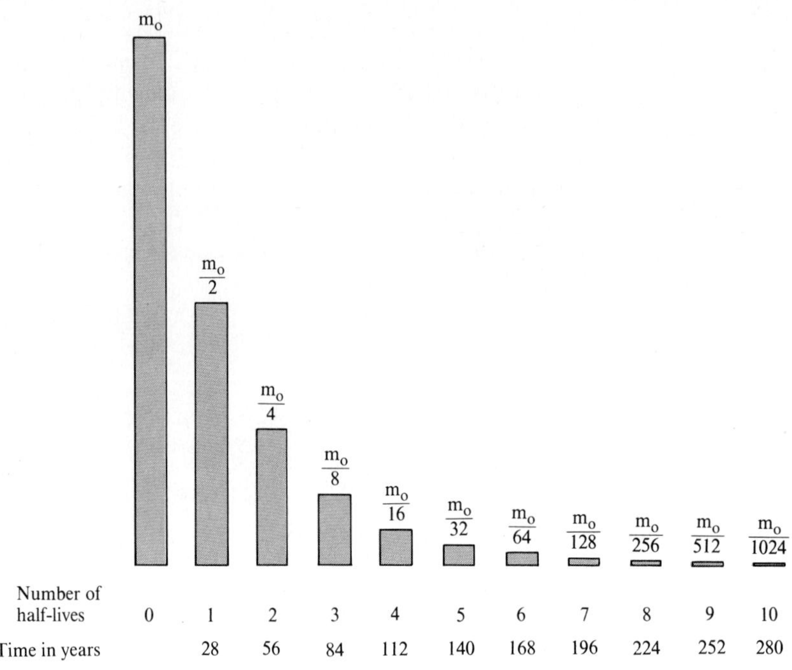

FIGURE 6.10
Decay of Sr-90.

SAMPLE EXERCISE 6.4

A patient receives a 3.0-ng dose of Tc-99m. Calculate the amount of Tc-99m which would remain in the patient after 1 day.

Solution:

From Table 6.3, we find that $t_{\frac{1}{2}}$ for Tc-99m = 6 h
The number of half-lives in 1 day, or 24 h, is

$$24\ \cancel{h} \times \frac{1\ \text{half-life}}{6\ \cancel{h}} = 4\ \text{half-lives}$$

After 1 half-life (6 h): Mass Tc-99m remaining $= \frac{3.0}{2}$ ng $=$ 1.5 ng

After 2 half-lives (12 h): Mass Tc-99m remaining $= \frac{1.5}{2}$ ng $=$ 0.75 ng

After 3 half-lives (18 h): Mass Tc-99m remaining $= \frac{0.75}{2}$ ng $=$ 0.375 ng

After 4 half-lives (24 h): Mass Tc-99m remaining $= \frac{0.375}{2}$ ng $=$ 0.19 ng

Or, using the equation which relates m_n to m_0,

$$m_n = m_0 \left(\frac{1}{2}\right)^n$$

where

$$n = 4$$
$$m_0 = 3.0 \text{ ng}$$
$$m_n = m_4$$

$$m_4 = 3.0 \text{ ng} \times \left(\frac{1}{2}\right)^4$$
$$= 3.0 \text{ ng} \times \frac{1}{16}$$
$$= 0.19 \text{ ng}$$

EXERCISE 6.4

What fraction of I-131 remains in a patient 24 days after the dose is administered?

6.8 RADIOCARBON DATING

From the known rate of decay of the naturally occurring radioactive isotope C-14, it is possible to estimate the age of very old carbon-containing objects, an important technique in the field of archeology. When C-14 decays, it emits beta particles and N-14:

$$^{14}_{6}C \longrightarrow {}^{0}_{-1}\beta + {}^{14}_{7}N$$

The time required for a given mass of C-14 to decay by one-half is 5700 years.

Fortunately the concentration of C-14 in air and food is very small.

All living things contain C-14, which they derive directly or indirectly from the CO_2 of the atmosphere. Plants utilize CO_2 in the photosynthetic process, which converts CO_2 and H_2O to carbohydrate molecules. When animals eat plant foods, they absorb C-14 (see Figure 6.11). As a result of this all living matter

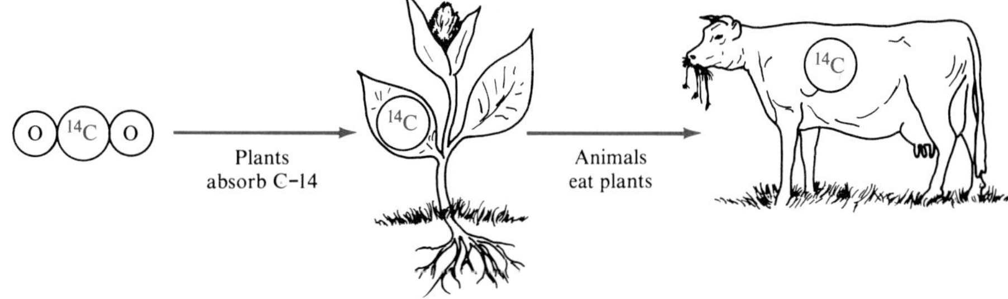

FIGURE 6.11
Radiocarbon dating. One out of every 10^8 CO_2 molecules in the atmosphere contains a C-14 atom. This concentration of C-14 remains constant in living plants and animals.

contains one C-14 atom for every 100 million C-12 atoms. This ratio of C-14 atoms to C-12 atoms remains unchanged as long as the matter is still alive. When death comes, living things no longer breathe or eat and the intake of C-14 ceases. The C-14 in nonliving things decays and is not replenished. Thus, the longer something has been dead, the less C-14 it will contain. By knowing the rate of decay and the amount of C-14 present in a nonliving object compared with that in a living object, it is possible to estimate how much time has passed since the object died and thus to estimate the age of the object.

The activity of the C-14 in the nonliving object is measured with a Geiger counter and is compared to the activity in a living object, which is about 15 disintegrations per minute per gram of carbon. For example, if the activity of C-14 in a sample prepared from an ancient paper scroll is about 7.5 disintegrations per minute per gram of carbon, then one-half of the C-14 in the object has decayed. The time needed for a given mass of C-14 to decay by half is the lifetime of C-14, or 5700 years. The ancient scroll must be about 5700 years old. In very old objects the amount of C-14 remaining may be too small to detect with any degree of accuracy. Only objects less than 57,000 years of age, 10 lifetimes of C-14, may be dated by using the radiocarbon method.

6.9 ARTIFICIAL ISOTOPES

Since radioactivity is easy to detect, small amounts of radioactive substances can be traced as they undergo nuclear decay. One field in which this is done is that of **nuclear medicine**, in which radioactive substances are used to diagnose and treat patients and to study human disease. Many of the important radioisotopes used in nuclear medicine do not occur in nature. In this section we will find out how these artificial radioisotopes are produced, and in Section 6.13 we will return to the subject of nuclear medicine.

Artificial transmutations, unlike spontaneous transmutations, do not occur without the input of energy.

Early alchemists were laughed at as they searched in vain for a method by which they could turn lead into precious gold. Today modern scientists are able to transform many elements into other elements. It is even possible to change lead into gold; however, the cost far exceeds the value of gold. Such induced transformations, or **artificial transformations**, are accomplished by the bombarding of isotopes, called *targets*, with natural forms of radiation, called *bullets*. The target isotope absorbs the bombarding bullet particle to produce a new isotope, along with one or more new energetic particles.

In 1919 Ernest Rutherford succeeded in converting nitrogen into oxygen. The target isotope was naturally occurring N-14 and the bombarding bullet particles were alpha particles emitted from the naturally radioactive element radium. When an N-14 nucleus absorbed an alpha particle, O-17 and another particle were produced.

$$\underset{\text{Target}}{{}^{14}_{7}\text{N}} + \underset{\text{Bullet}}{{}^{4}_{2}\alpha} \longrightarrow {}^{17}_{8}\text{O} + {}^{1}_{1}p$$

Note that the charges and masses on the left balance those on the right.

Another artificial transmutation, in which Be-9 nuclei were bombarded with alpha particles, led to the discovery of the neutron in 1932.

$$^{9}_{4}\text{Be} + ^{4}_{2}\alpha \longrightarrow ^{12}_{6}\text{C} + ^{1}_{0}n$$

For identifying the neutron James Chadwick (1891–1974) received a Nobel prize in physics in 1935.

Radioactive isotopes of all elements may also be produced artificially by bombarding other elements. Many of these are "new" isotopes since they are present in nature in undetectable amounts. For example, when Al-27 is bombarded with alpha particles, radioactive P-30 and neutrons are the products:

$$^{27}_{13}\text{Al} + ^{4}_{2}\alpha \longrightarrow ^{30}_{15}P + ^{1}_{0}n$$

The radioactive P-30 decays spontaneously by positron (β^+) emission:

$$^{30}_{15}\text{P} \longrightarrow ^{0}_{1}\beta + ^{30}_{14}\text{Si}$$

Alpha particles are only able to penetrate lighter nuclei, which have small nuclear charges. Heavier nuclei repel alpha particles because of the large electrostatic repulsions resulting from the approach of the doubly charged α particles. To penetrate nuclei of heavier elements, particles with less charge and/or more energy are necessary. Protons, $^{1}_{1}p$ or $^{1}_{1}\text{H}$, and deuterons, $^{2}_{1}\text{d}$ or $^{2}_{1}\text{H}$, have half the charge of alpha particles and can be produced from ordinary H_2 gas. To give them enough energy to penetrate heavier nuclei, the protons and deuterons are given very high velocities by use of devices called *accelerators*. A typical particle accelerator is diagrammed in Figure 6.12.

The H-2 isotope has a special name, deuterium (D), and H-2 nuclei are called deuterons (d).

Because neutrons have no charge at all, they are able to penetrate target nuclei easily. The number of nuclear transformations produced by use of neutron bullets is greater than the number accomplished by all other particles combined.

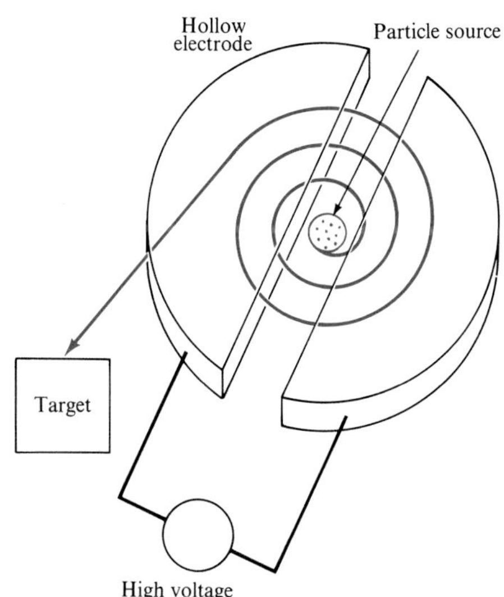

FIGURE 6.12
Particle accelerator. Particles (such as protons or deuterons) are accelerated through the hollow D-shaped electrodes in this particle accelerator called a cyclotron. The accelerated particles then bombard the target element to produce the desired isotope. I-123 is one example of a radioisotope that is prepared in this way.

For example, P-32, commonly used in nuclear medicine, is prepared by bombarding S-32 with high-energy neutrons, which are products of some other artificial transmutation:

$$^{32}_{16}S + ^{1}_{0}n \longrightarrow ^{32}_{15}P + ^{1}_{1}p$$

Transuranium Elements

Before 1940 there were no **transuranium elements**, that is, elements with an atomic number of greater than 92, the atomic number of uranium. By bombarding target isotopes with particles it is possible to create new isotopes with higher mass numbers and higher atomic numbers than uranium. For instance, among the examples above, we showed transmutations in which $^{14}_{7}N$ was converted into $^{18}_{8}O$, $^{9}_{4}Be$ to $^{12}_{6}C$, and $^{27}_{13}Al$ into $^{30}_{15}P$. From this sprang the exciting prospect of bombarding uranium nuclei with particles in the hopes of making the first transuranium element.

Element number 93, neptunium (Np), the first transuranium element, was produced in 1940 by bombarding U-238 with neutrons:

$$^{238}_{92}U + ^{1}_{0}n \longrightarrow ^{239}_{92}U$$

The U-239 decayed by beta emission to produce an isotope of neptunium:

$$^{239}_{92}U \longrightarrow ^{0}_{-1}\beta + ^{239}_{93}Np$$

By emitting β radiation Np-239 yields yet another transuranium element, Pu-239, an isotope of plutonium, element number 94:

$$^{239}_{93}Np \longrightarrow ^{0}_{-1}\beta + ^{239}_{94}Pu$$

The elements uranium, neptunium, and plutonium are named after Uranus, Neptune, and Pluto, the outermost planets in our solar system.

SAMPLE EXERCISE 6.5

What nuclei must be bombarded with neutrons to produce a proton and Co-58, one radioisotope that has been incorporated into the cobalt-containing compound vitamin B-12?

Solution:

$$? + ^{1}_{0}n \longrightarrow ^{58}_{27}Co + ^{1}_{1}p$$

To find the starting isotope balance the mass and charge.

The test for vitamin B-12 absorption by using an oral dose tagged with radioactive cobalt is known as the Schilling test.

On the left	On the right
Charge = ? + 0 = 28	Charge = 27 + 1 = 28
Mass = ? + 1 = 59	Mass = 58 + 1 = 59

For the equation above to balance, the missing isotope must have a nucleus with a charge of 28 (Ni) and a mass of 58. The isotope is thus $^{58}_{28}Ni$ (Ni-58), which accounts for 67.9 percent of naturally occurring nickel.

EXERCISE 6.5

Au-198, one of the medical radioisotopes listed in Table 6.3, is produced by bombarding Au-197 with neutrons. What radiation accompanies this artificial transmutation?

6.10 NUCLEAR FISSION AND FUSION

It was first thought that the Ba was another group IIA element, Ra. But for U (Z = 92) to decay to Ra (Z = 88) it would have to emit 2αs. No αs were found!

The search for transuranium elements, which began in the 1930s, brought about the unexpected discovery of a remarkable phenomenon. While European scientists were trying to produce transuranium elements by bombarding U-238 with neutrons, they were amazed to find lighter elements, such as $_{57}La$ and $_{56}Ba$, among the bombardment products. For these elements to come from $_{92}U$ the uranium nucleus must have split practically in half. This was considered too fantastic to be true. But careful analysis of the bombardment products proved the presence of elements much lighter than U. The name **nuclear fission** was applied to this incredible process, which was not unlike the biological fission of one cell into two cells.

Along with the lighter elements, or fragments, fission reactions produce a great deal of energy and more neutrons than are consumed. Two isotopes which undergo fission readily are U-235, which accounts for only 1 out of every 140 U atoms, and plutonium-239, the artificial transuranium isotope. Figure 6.13 shows a U-235 nucleus splitting into Xe-140 and Sr-94 upon neutron bombardment. Note in the equation below that describes this process that two neutrons are among the products and that the charges and masses balance just as they do for the other nuclear equations we have written.

$$^{1}_{0}n + ^{235}_{92}U \longrightarrow ^{140}_{54}Xe + ^{94}_{38}Sr + 2^{1}_{0}n$$

On the left	On the right
Mass = 1 + 235 = 236	Mass = 140 + 94 + 2 = 236
Charge = 0 + 92 = 92	Charge = 54 + 38 + 0 = 92

The neutrons produced in the original fission are free to bombard additional U-235 nuclei leading to a *branched* reaction, such as the one shown in Figure 6.14. This type of reaction is known as a **chain reaction**. Such chain reactions produce energy, which may be used for weaponry or for peaceful purposes.

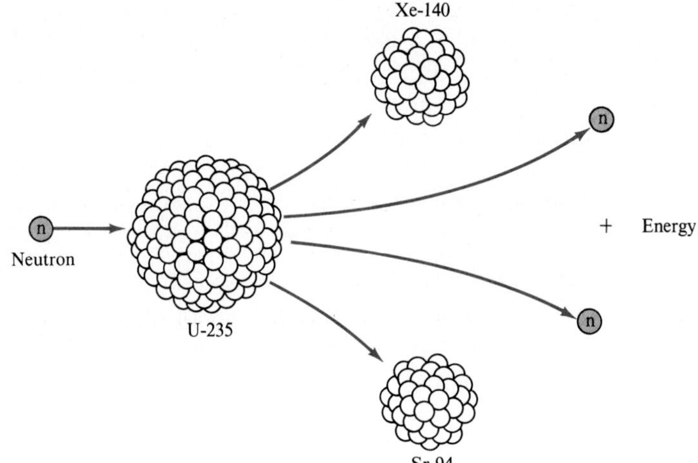

FIGURE 6.13
U-235 fission. Upon bombardment with a neutron, the U-235 nucleus splits into two fragments, Sr-94 and Xe-140, along with two additional neutrons and energy.

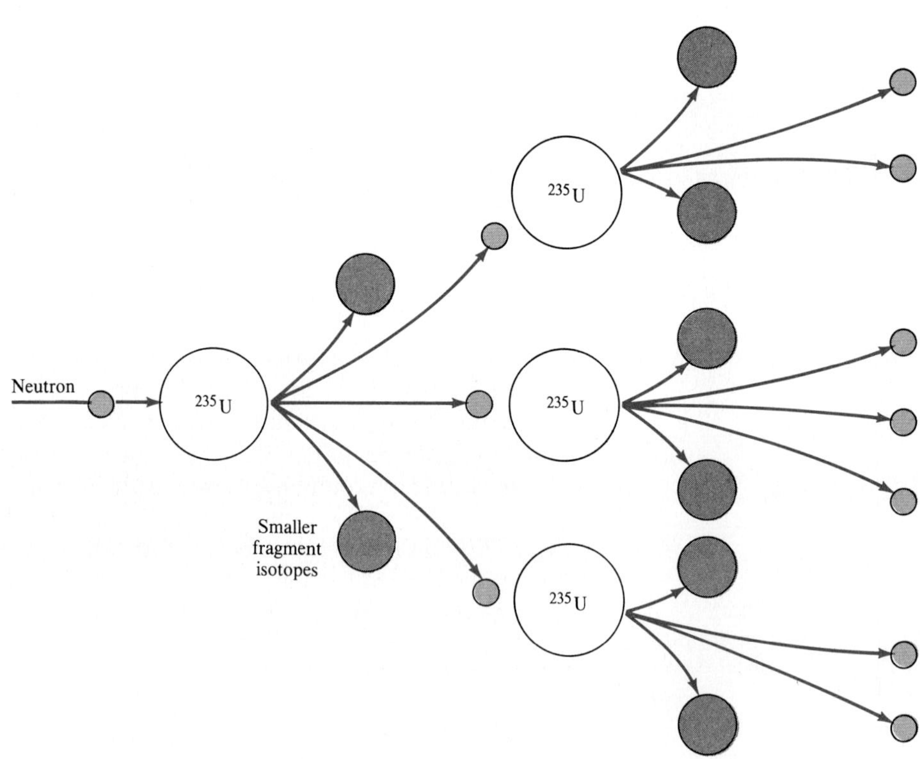

FIGURE 6.14
Chain reaction. Neutrons produced from the fission of U-235 cause additional fissions that lead to a chain reaction.

Atomic Bomb

Because of the tremendous thermal energy produced from fission, the potential for a powerful weapon was obvious. The so-called atomic bomb consists of a *core* of pure fissionable isotope. The harmful effects of the bomb arise from several sources. Thermal energy from the blast causes enormous heat and fire, which is likely to cause complete destruction in an area within a radius of about one-half mile of the blast. Thermal radiation, which is the visible, ultraviolet, and infrared radiation produced from the blast, can cause severe burns, but fortunately has little penetrative power. The eyes are especially sensitive to these flash burns. High-energy neutrons and gamma radiation, products of the nuclear processes, have great penetrative power and cause severe biological damage within one-half mile of the blast. There is much less immediate damage from the radioactive lighter fragments, called *fallout*. However, the fallout presents a long-term hazard, because many of the fragments have long lifetimes. For instance, you saw that Sr-90, a common fission product, has a half-life of 28 years.The special danger of the delayed fallout is that it can be carried away by wind currents to parts of the globe remote from the point of the original blast.

Nuclear Power

In the atomic bomb the branching chain reaction is not controlled, so that the energy derived from the fuel in the bomb is released all at once. However, it *is* possible to control chain reactions. This is done in nuclear reactors, where the energy yielded by fission reactions can be harnessed.

Nuclear reactors work in essentially the same way that atomic bombs do. The crucial difference is that nuclear reactors must be cooled so that the energy they produce does not destroy them. To do this the fuel core is surrounded by heavy concrete walls with passages for *coolants*. Figure 6.15 shows a typical nuclear reactor. Water is well suited as a coolant because it has an unusually high specific heat, meaning that it is an efficient retainer of heat (see Section 2.9).

Water plays a double role in nuclear reactors, as a coolant and moderator.

In addition to the cooling mechanisms, it must also be possible to slow down or stop the fission reaction. To do this certain materials that are particularly good absorbers of neutrons are included as *control rods*. Control rods are made out of the elements boron (B) and cadmium (Cd), which are both excellent neutron absorbers.

The neutrons emitted from a splitting U atom travel much too fast to produce fissions. Thus one other component needed in a nuclear reactor is a *moderator*, a substance used to slow the speed of neutrons. Most modern nuclear reactors use water as a moderator. Other moderating substances include graphite, a form of carbon, and deuterium oxide (D_2O), called "heavy" water.

It is important to realize that even though nuclear reactors may contain enough fissionable material for an explosive chain reaction, there is very little possibility that one of them would explode as does an atomic bomb. Accidental achievement of the very special conditions needed for an atomic blast are highly unlikely. The more realistic safety hazards are malfunctions which would allow the temperature in the core to rise high enough to melt the fuel. The resulting meltdown would cause radiation leakage which would provide a severe hazard for a distance of several miles.

One serious problem associated with the use of nuclear reactors is the question of what to do with the waste radioactive fragments. Some of the fragments can be isolated for use as radioisotopes for medical purposes, including I-131, Cs-137, Ce-144, Sr-90, Tc-99m, and Xe-133. This accounts for only a small proportion of the fragments produced. Most of the waste must be buried somewhere in clay or cement containers.

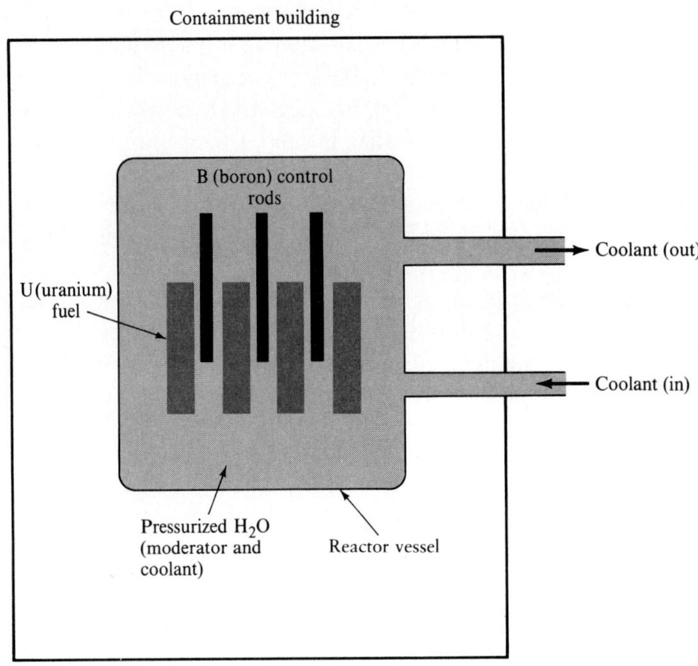

FIGURE 6.15
Nuclear reactor diagram.

Nuclear Fusion

Nuclear *fusion* is an entirely different process from nuclear *fission*. Fusion means joining. During **nuclear fusion** smaller nuclei fuse to form larger nuclei, with the emission of enormous energies. The energy of the sun is due to fusion reaction. However, in order for fusion to occur in the laboratory, incredibly high temperatures, exceeding 100,000,000°C, must be achieved. In fact, the fission bomb, which provides temperatures in this range, is used to activate the fusion process. One fusion reaction involves the joining of two hydrogen isotopes, deuterium and tritium:

$$^{2}_{1}\text{H} + {}^{3}_{1}\text{H} \longrightarrow {}^{3}_{2}\text{He} + 2{}^{1}_{0}n + \text{energy}$$

Note that fusion reactions such as this one do not produce any radioactive fragments. He-3 is stable.

The *hydrogen bomb* got its name from the fact that it utilizes fusion reactions such as the one shown above. But fusion is not the only process involved in the energy released by hydrogen bombs. You can see that neutrons are one product of the fusion reaction. In the hydrogen bomb these neutrons are allowed to bombard uranium that is used as a lining for the bomb, thus causing fission reactions to occur. Thus the energy released from the hydrogen bomb comes from fusion *and* fission reactions, and like the atomic bomb, the hydrogen bomb also produces fallout.

Lasers are being used to obtain the high temperatures.

Efforts to use a fusion process to provide energy for peaceful purposes have been hampered by the difficulty of attaining the necessary high temperatures and of containing gases that are heated to such high temperatures. Since *pure* fusion produces no radioactive fallout and can be fueled with hydrogen obtained from water, it represents a very hopeful energy source for the future.

6.11 UNITS OF RADIOACTIVITY

The **curie** is a unit of radioactive activity. The activity of a radioactive substance is related to the number of decay processes it undergoes in a given amount of time. The definition of one curie (1 Ci) is

One curie equals 3.7×10^{10} nuclear disintegrations per second.

For example, the amount of radium which undergoes 3.7×10^{10} disintegrations in 1 s is exactly 1 g, or 1 Ci Ra = 1.00 g. Other useful prefixed curie units are used when amounts of activity which are much smaller than or much larger than the curie are involved.

One microcurie = 1 μCi = 10^{-6} Ci = 3.7×10^{4} disintegrations per second.

One millicurie = 1 mCi = 10^{-3} Ci = 3.7×10^{7} disintegrations per second.

One megacurie = 1 MCi = 10^{6} Ci = 3.7×10^{16} disintegrations per second.

Dosages of radioisotopes used for medical procedures are given in terms of microcuries or millicuries.

The mass of one curie of any isotope depends upon its rate of nuclear decay and its atomic weight. The mass of one curie of a long-lived isotope of a particular element is greater than that of a short-lived isotope of the same element. For example, the half-life of C-14 is 5700 years and that of C-15 is only 2.4 s. Therefore, more C-14 than C-15 is needed to produce 3.7×10^{10} disintegrations per second.

$$1 \text{ Ci of C-14} = 0.224 \text{ g} \qquad \text{and} \qquad 1 \text{ Ci of C-15} = 3.2 \times 10^{-15} \text{ g}$$

The curie is only a unit of activity and does not indicate the energy of the radiation produced. Therefore, the curie is not a good yardstick to use for the estimation of biological damage.

Roentgen

The **roentgen** is a unit of exposure to x-radiation or to gamma radiation. The various types of nuclear radiation produce ions when they interact with matter, a process that was mentioned in Section 6.6. Each ionization produces a cation and an anion, known as an *ion pair*. The definition of one roentgen (1 R) is based upon the number of ion pairs produced by a quantity of radiation:

One roentgen is the quantity of γ- or x-radiation which will produce 2.08×10^9 ion pairs in one cubic centimeter of dry air at 0°C and 1 atmosphere pressure (ordinary sea level pressure).

It is possible to estimate the effect of exposure to single doses of x- or γ-radiation. For example, a single dose of less than 25 R should not cause clinical effects. On the other hand, exposure of the whole body to a dose of 1000 R would probably be fatal within a few days. The roentgen has limited use in measuring biological damage from radiation because it applies only to x- and γ-radiation. Furthermore, to evaluate the potential toxic effects of a medically useful radioisotope, the radiation actually absorbed by the patient must be estimated.

Rad

Rad is an abbreviation for *r*adiation *a*bsorbed *d*ose.

The quantity of energy deposited in tissue is referred to as the *absorbed dose.* The **rad** is a unit which measures the absorbed dose of ionizing radiation. The definition of one rad (1 rad) is

One rad is the absorbed dose of any kind of ionizing radiation which is accompanied by the liberation of 100 ergs (10^{-5} J) of energy per gram of absorbing material.

Although the rad is a unit of absorbed radiation, it is not quite suitable for determining biological effect. One rad of two different kinds of radiation, alpha and beta, for example, will cause the liberation of 100 ergs of energy per gram of absorbing tissue in both cases but will not produce the same biological effects.

Rem

The **rem**, an abbreviation of "roentgen equivalent man," takes into account the varying abilities of different radiations to produce biological effects. The definition of one rem (1 rem) is given in terms of the relative biological effect of the type of radiation absorbed (RBE):

One rem equals the dose in rads multiplied by the relative biological effect.

The RBE of any given type of radiation is compared with that of gamma radiation, which is assigned a value of 1. The RBE for beta radiation is close to 1, but that for alpha radiation is about 10.

$$\text{RBE } \gamma = 1$$
$$\text{RBE } \beta \approx 1$$
$$\text{RBE } \alpha \approx 10$$

That is, the absorption of 1 rad of alpha radiation produces 10 times the biological

TABLE 6.4 RADIOACTIVITY UNITS

Unit	Abbreviation	General meaning	Specific meaning (1 unit)
Curie	Ci	Decay rate or activity	An amount of radioactive substance that undergoes 3.7×10^{10} disintegrations/s
Roentgen	R	Exposure to γ- or x-radiation	The quantity of γ- or x-radiation that produces 2.08×10^9 ion pairs in 1 cm^3 air
Radiation absorbed dose	rad	Dose of radiation absorbed by material	The absorbed dose which is accompanied by the liberation of 10^{-5} J per gram of absorbing material
Roentgen equivalent man	rem	Dose in rads multiplied by a tissue sensitivity factor	rem = rad $\times$ RBE RBE $\gamma = 1$ RBE $\beta \approx 1$ RBE $\alpha \approx 10$

effect that would be produced by the absorption of 1 rad of either gamma or beta radiation. The meaning of the various radiation units is summarized in Table 6.4.

6.12 BIOLOGICAL EFFECTS OF RADIATION

When high-energy radiation interacts with matter, a number of things may happen. Chemical bonds may be broken, or atoms of one element may be converted into other elements; but in living cells, the ability of nuclear radiations to produce ions is especially important. When high-energy radiation interacts with the atoms or molecules present in a living cell, it may eject electrons from them to produce ion pairs. For example, if the radiation interacts with an oxygen atom, ejects an electron from the atom, and produces an O^+ cation, the ejected electron may be taken up by a C atom to produce a C^- anion. An ion pair, O^+ and C^-, forms:

$$\text{Radiation} + O \longrightarrow \begin{cases} O^+ \\ e^- + C \longrightarrow C^- \end{cases}$$

These highly unstable and energetic ions can react with neighboring atoms and molecules to produce harmful changes in the cell chemistry. It is also possible for the high-energy radiation to produce ion pairs from molecules. The water ions, H_2O^+ and H_2O^-, are extremely unstable and can react with other molecules in the cell. The ionizing radiation may also interact directly with other critical molecules present in the cell. For example, damage to DNA molecules, which direct reproduction, is particularly devastating and may produce mutations.

The effects of radiation sickness can range from mild white blood cell depression to rapid death with convulsions.

Not all tissues are equally susceptible to the effects of radiation. Dense tissue absorbs more radiation than does other tissue. Thus the dense bones of the body are especially vulnerable compared with the less dense organs and muscles. In particular, the white blood cells produced in the bone marrow may be damaged so that they no longer provide resistance to bacterial invasion of the body. Possible effects on cells of any kind include altered chemistry, broken chromosomes, swollen nuclei, cell membrane destruction, and the inability to divide to accomplish normal cell replacement.

The LD_{50} (median lethal dose) for ionizing radiation is 450 rems, the dose that would cause the death of 50 out of every 100 individuals exposed.

The immediate clinical effects of exposure to ionizing radiation depends upon the dose received. Less than 100 rems produces little or no illness, while 1000 rems makes survival unlikely. Long-term effects of exposure to radiation are also possible. These chronic effects include development of cataracts and of cancers and a variety of other life-shortening diseases.

It is impossible to avoid all radiation. The natural radiation always present is called **background radiation**. About 30 percent of this comes from the highly energetic cosmic rays (wavelength $\approx 10^{-5}$nm), which are emitted by the stars and the sun. The rest comes from naturally occurring radioactive isotopes. For instance, 1 out of every 8500 K atoms is radioactive K-40. Heavy radioactive elements such as radium (Ra), uranium (U), polonium (Po), and thorium (Th), are always present in the soil, from which they may enter building materials, drinking water, or body surfaces. The average background radiation in the United States is estimated to be about 0.1 rem, or 100 mrem, per year. Additional radiation over and above background comes from artificial sources, including industry, weapons testing, medical practices. In the United States the average value for this is estimated to be close to that which occurs naturally, or about 100 mrem per year.

Some of the radioactive isotopes that are released during nuclear reactions are especially dangerous because they may concentrate in the milk supply. Two such isotopes are Sr-90 and I-131. Sr-90 behaves chemically like Ca (group IIA) and eventually may concentrate in the bones, where it decays very slowly ($t_{\frac{1}{2}}$ = 28 years) and I-131 ($t_{\frac{1}{2}}$ = 8.0 days) accumulates in the thyroid, where it may cause tumors. These isotopes are particularly dangerous to young children, who are the greatest milk consumers. Some radiation is also absorbed through medical practices, where benefit versus risk must be weighed carefully. During a typical chest x-ray examination the radiation dosage is between 0.1 and 6 mrem for a male and between 0.1 and 15 mrem for a female.

As the absorbed radiation dose increases, the biological response also increases in a predictable, linear fashion. That means that doubling the dose doubles the effect, tripling the dose triples the effect, and so on. The interesting question is whether or not a threshold dose exists below which there is no biological effect. So far, the answer appears to be that there is not.

6.13 NUCLEAR MEDICINE

Radioactive isotopes can be incorporated into chemical compounds in order to diagnose or to treat human disease. Because of the toxic effects of radioisotopes, care must be taken to make certain that the information gained or the effect produced as a result of their use outweighs the risks involved.

Diagnosis

Radioactive isotopes are enormously useful in evaluating the structure or the function of a biological unit of the body. For instance, they can be used to detect the presence of a tumor or to measure differences in blood flow from one part of the body to another. From the outside of the body, radiation detectors can follow the course of injected radiations inside the body. The recorded observation is called a **scan.**

The dose of radioisotope used in diagnosis is too low to cause radiation sickness and should have little effect on patients' visitors, other patients, or medical personnel.

Isotopes used for this purpose must be very carefully chosen. First and foremost, their properties must minimize radiation exposure. Gamma emitters are most useful because they are able to penetrate tissue. The less-penetrating alpha and beta radiations are useless in diagnosis and simply add to the risk of the testing procedure. The half-life of the isotope should be as short as possible, that is, just long enough to permit the physiological event being studied to take place. The isotope must also be able to be incorporated into a compound with the biological behavior needed to allow it to concentrate in the organ or area to be studied. We shall see how these properties are utilized in several important radioisotopes used in diagnostic procedures.

Iodine Isotopes

Of the elements that compose the human body, iodine is unique in that it has two dozen radioactive isotopes. Of these many are useful in nuclear medicine. For instance, iodine radioisotopes in the form of iodide salts (NaI) are given to patients to test for normal thyroid function, that is, normal uptake of iodide by the thyroid. Ingested iodide is so rapidly absorbed from the gastrointestinal tract that it can be detected in the thyroid gland within minutes. In the thyroid the iodide is converted via biochemical reactions to iodine-containing hormones. (Hormones regulate certain metabolic processes.) One of the first isotopes used for thyroid uptake studies was I-131. Since the rate at which the iodine-containing hormones are released by the thyroid happens to be slow compared with the decay of I-131 ($t_{\frac{1}{2}}$ = 8 days), this isotope is practical for studies of thyroid function. However, I-131 is far from an ideal radioactive tracer. Its half-life is longer than necessary for most studies, and furthermore, it emits high-energy beta radiation (see example in Section 6.5). Another isotope of iodine, I-123, has better properties. Its half-life is 13.3 h, long enough for most determinations, and it decays by electron capture, thus emitting no undesirable beta particles.

Another important use of iodine isotopes is in *labeling* compounds of biomedical interest. Iodine atoms replace atoms such as H atoms in some of the molecules of such compounds. The method used is called *iodination* and is illustrated in the reaction below, where R refers to the rest of the compound.

$$\text{R-H} + \text{I}_2 \longrightarrow \text{R-I} + \text{HI}$$

Compounds labeled with a radioisotope are said to be *tagged* with that isotope.

Blood volume determinations are useful for monitoring blood loss during surgery.

Human serum albumin tagged with I-131 is used to determine total circulating blood volume. The tagged albumin is injected. After enough time has passed for complete mixing to occur, a blood sample is withdrawn and its radioactivity is measured. Knowing how much I-131 was originally injected and how much is present in the sample removed leads to a value for the entire volume of circulating blood in the patient.

Technetium-99m

Tc-99m, used in nuclear medicine laboratories, is prepared from the decay of Mo-99: Mo-99 $\longrightarrow$ Tc-99m + β

Because Tc-99m is a gamma emitter with a half-life of 6 h it has excellent characteristics for use in diagnosis. Its short half-life and the absence of beta radiation also allow higher doses of Tc-99m to be administered, which makes Tc-99m easier to detect and reduces the amount of time needed to perform scans. The Tc-99m is incorporated into suitable compounds for studying problems in particular organs.

For many purposes technetium is used as the pertechnetate ion, TcO_4^-. In this form it resembles the iodide ion, I^-, and like the iodide ion, it is taken up by the thyroid gland. One advantage that Tc-99m has in thyroid studies is that it can be taken up by the thyroids of patients whose thyroids do not accumulate iodide. Sodium pertechnetate, $NaTcO_4$, in solution is used in brain scanning. It is effective for this purpose because it is taken up only by unhealthy tumor tissue and is excluded from normal tissue. The presence of radioactivity, or a "hot spot," thus signals a malfunctioning area of the brain. See Figure 6.16, which shows a brain scan that includes a hot spot.

For liver studies, Tc-99m is combined with sulfur to make a ^{99m}Tc-S colloid. (A colloid is a mixture which contains particles with dimensions on the order of 10 to 100 nm.) The colloid-containing Tc-99m is consumed only by healthy liver cells. In this instance, it is the absence of radioactivity, or a "cold spot," which indicates that the liver is not functioning. In Figure 6.17 you can see a cold spot in the scan of a liver which has a large defect.

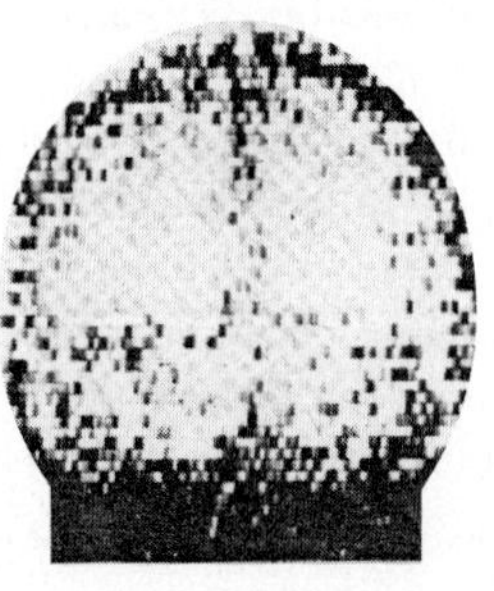

(*a*)

Normal brain scan posterior view

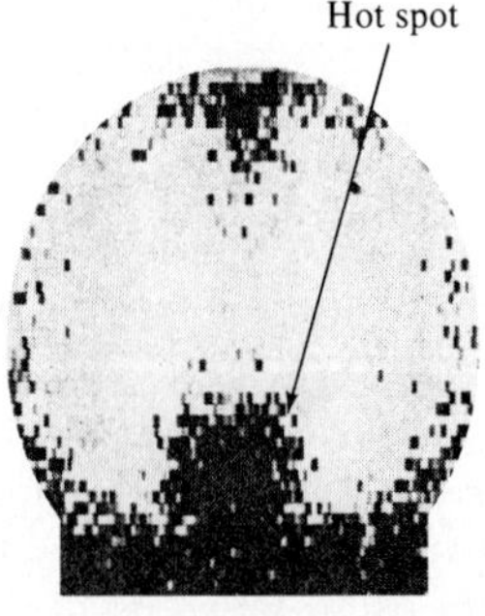

(*b*)

Abnormal brain scan arrow indicates a "hot spot" due to the presence of a tumor.

FIGURE 6.16
Brain scan (hot spot). Arrow indicates the hot spot owing to the presence of a tumor.

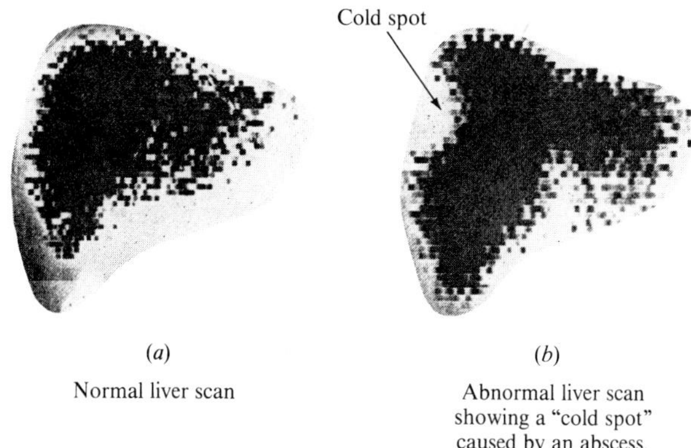
Cold spot
(a)
Normal liver scan
(b)
Abnormal liver scan showing a "cold spot" caused by an abscess.

FIGURE 6.17
Liver scan (cold spot).

Treatment

Mild radiation sickness may appear as a side effect of *treatment* with radioisotopes.

Radioactive isotopes are also used in treating disease. The isotopes are administered in the form of compounds that accumulate in the area to be treated, where emitted radiation kills unwanted tissue. In this case radioisotopes that emit the more destructive beta radiations are desirable. For instance, we have already learned that the thyroid gland has the ability to accumulate iodide. By using much larger doses of sodium iodide which contains I-131 than would be used for diagnosis, we can produce beta radiation that may kill or inhibit the growth of a thyroid tumor.

One of the first uses of radioisotope therapy was in the field of dermatology. The radioisotope P-32 (a beta emitter) in the form of sodium phosphate, Na_3PO_4, was allowed to soak into a small piece of blotter paper, which was then applied to the area requiring treatment. The emitted beta radiation penetrated just far enough to destroy malignant tumors (cancers) and other unwanted growths.

An interesting method used to treat internal cancers involves the production of radioisotopes inside the body. To do this the patient is given nonradioactive boron-10 in the form of $Na_2B_4O_7 \cdot 10H_2O$ (borax). A stream of neutrons is generated in the laboratory, where it may be aimed at the exact spot where the tumor or unwanted growth is located. The neutrons pierce the skin easily and interact with the B-10 to form Li-7 and alpha particles:

$$^{10}_{5}\text{B} + {}^{1}_{0}n \longrightarrow {}^{4}_{2}\alpha + {}^{7}_{3}\text{Li}$$

The biologically destructive alpha particles are concentrated where they are needed to kill unwanted growths.

SUMMARY

Atoms of radioactive elements contain unstable nuclei. The stability of particular isotopes may be estimated by inspection of their N/Z ratios, where N is the number of neutrons and Z is the atomic number of the isotope in question. All stable nuclei have N/Z ratios between 1 and 1.55, the stability zone. All nuclei with Z greater than 83 are unstable.

Radioactive elements emit three types of radiation, alpha (α), beta (β), and gamma (γ). The positively charged

α particles are identical to helium nuclei, $_2He$, with a charge of +2 and a mass number of 4, $^4_2\alpha$. Although they are the least penetrating of the three radiations, massive α particles are capable of producing considerable biological destruction. Beta particles (β^-) are nuclear electrons and thus, like electrons, are almost massless and have a charge of −1. Positrons (β^+) are positive beta particles with a charge of +1. Gamma radiation (γ) is electromagnetic radiation and hence is both massless and chargeless. Gamma rays are more penetrative than α or β rays and have energies similar to those of x-rays.

Spontaneous transmutation occurs when radioactive nuclei of parent isotopes decay to become daughter isotopes. Such nuclear decay can result in the emission of α-, β^--, β^+-, or γ-radiations or can proceed through electron capture (EC). The atomic numbers (or charges) and mass numbers on both sides of the nuclear equation must be balanced. In this way the atomic number and mass number of the daughter isotope, and thus its identity, may be determined.

A number of devices are used to detect radioactive emissions. The Geiger counter produces a signal when radiation ionizes argon gas. Scintillation detectors produce light flashes when substances energized by radiation return to lower-energy levels. Photographic film detectors darken upon exposure to energetic radiation.

Radioactive nuclei decay at different rates. The half-life $t_{\frac{1}{2}}$ of an isotope represents the time required for one-half of a given mass of radioactive isotope to decay. Half-lives range from fractions of seconds to millions of years. The relatively long-lived isotope C-14 ($t_{\frac{1}{2}} = 5700$ years), present in all living matter, may be used to estimate the ages of carbon-containing objects.

It is also possible to accomplish controlled transmutations in which target elements are bombarded with particles such as alpha particles, deuterons, protons, or neutrons. Many isotopes which are not present in nature may be prepared in this way, including many radioisotopes used for medical purposes. Heavy nuclei such as those of uranium ($Z = 92$) may also be bombarded under special conditions to produce transuranium elements ($Z > 92$).

Under some circumstances uranium nuclei can be split into two roughly equal nuclei by bombardment with neutrons. Nuclei which split upon such interaction with neutrons are said to undergo fission. The products of such nuclear fission reactions include the lighter nuclei (fallout), more neutrons, and considerable energy. The energy has been utilized in the development of weaponry and in the production of energy for peaceful purposes in nuclear power plants. Disposal of the waste fragments, or fallout, is an ever-present problem. The fallout problem is not present in nuclear fusion processes, in which two or more nuclei are joined to produce larger nuclei and enormous energy. However, no practical method has yet been devised to harness fusion energy.

Various units are used to measure quantities of radiation. The curie (Ci) measures the number of decays per second, or the activity of the radiation. The roentgen (R) measures exposure to x- or γ-radiation; the rad indicates an absorbed dose of ionizing radiation; and the rem also refers to an absorbed dose of ionizing radiation but includes a weighting factor (RBE), which increases the rem value for more-destructive radiations. Doses necessary to produce biological damage are best expressed in rems.

Biological damage, largely due to the creation of ions from atoms and molecules in living matter, may be caused by the types of radiation present in nature (background) and those created by human activities. One artificial source of radiation exposure comes from the field of nuclear medicine, in which radioisotopes are used to diagnose and treat disease. Here benefit versus risk must be considered before studies or treatments are initiated.

KEY WORDS

x-rays
radioisotopes
stability zone
alpha rays
beta rays
gamma rays
parent isotope
daughter isotope
spontaneous transmutation
positron
electron capture
radioactive series
half-life
nuclear medicine
artificial transmutation
transuranium element
nuclear fission
chain reaction
nuclear fusion
curie
roentgen
rad
rem
background radiation
scan

EXERCISES

6.6 Calculate N/Z for each of the following isotopes. Which of these *must* be unstable? (See Figure 6.5.)
(a) Li-8 (b) B-13 (c) B-10
(d) N-12 (e) O-20 (f) Fe-61
(g) Fe-56 (h) Rn-220 (i) U-235

6.7 Identify the daughter isotopes which form as products of the following processes.
(a) Co-62 $\longrightarrow \beta^- + ?$
(b) PO-120 $\longrightarrow \alpha + ?$
(c) P-28 $\longrightarrow \beta^+ + ?$
(d) Al-26 + $e^- \longrightarrow ?$
(e) Ne-18 $\longrightarrow \beta^+ + ?$
(f) Mo-93m $\longrightarrow \gamma + ?$

6.8 What kind of radiation accompanies the formation of daughter isotopes in each of the reactions shown below?
(a) Mg-27 $\longrightarrow$? + Al-27
(b) F-17 $\longrightarrow$? + O-17
(c) Ba-133m $\longrightarrow$? + Ba-133
(d) I-132 $\longrightarrow$? + Xe-132
(e) Am-243 $\longrightarrow$? + Np-239
(f) Cs-137 $\longrightarrow$? + Ba-137

6.9 Compare the penetrative power of α-, β-, and γ-radiation.

6.10 Why is helium gas found in uranium and thorium ores?

6.11 Identify the parent isotopes in the following decay reactions:
(a) ? $\longrightarrow \alpha$ + Rn-222
(b) ? $\longrightarrow \beta^-$ + Sn-121
(c) ? $\longrightarrow \beta^+$ + Rb-83
(d) ? $\longrightarrow \gamma$ + In-117
(e) ? + $e^- \longrightarrow$ Ar-38
(f) ? $\longrightarrow \beta^+$ + F-19

6.12 Write equations for the following nuclear decay reactions:
(a) Alpha decay of Th-227
(b) Beta decay of Cl-36
(c) Gamma decay of Ba-137m
(d) Electron capture by Pb-202
(e) Positron decay of Mn-50

6.13 Write nuclear decay reactions for the following isotopes used in nuclear medicine (see Table 6.3):
(a) I-123; (b) In-113m; (c) P-32.

6.14 Write the nuclear reaction for the spontaneous decay of Si-26. (*Hint:* Calculate N/Z for Si-26 first.)

6.15 Samples of each of the following isotopes decay for the time periods indicated. In each case calculate the number of half-lives included (see Table 6.3). **(a)** Tc-99m, 1 week; **(b)** C-14, 14,400 years; **(c)** I-137, 1 min 50s.

6.16 A 1-g sample of radium-226 decays by alpha emission. How much radium remains (see Table 6.3) after: **(a)** 1600 years; **(b)** 3200 years; **(c)** 16,000 years.

6.17 What fraction of In-113m should remain in a patient $8\frac{1}{2}$ h after it is given?

6.18 Why must hospitals generate their own supplies of Tc-99m and In-113m?

6.19 How long should it take for 1.00 g of C-14 to decay to 0.250 g? (See Table 6.3.)

6.20 A piece of fabric supposedly used around the year 100 A.D. is discovered. Its C-14 content is measured to be about 15 disintegrations per minute per gram of carbon. Is the fabric authentic?

6.21 Hospitals are able to store short-lived isotopes used in diagnosis in the form of their longer-lived parent isotopes. The short-lived isotopes are removed when needed in a process called "milking." What useful radioisotopes are produced by so-called cow systems that contain the isotopes below? (Refer to Table 6.3.)
(a) Sn-113
(b) Mo-99

6.22 Convert each of the following to curies (Ci):
(a) 1.5 mCi
(b) 0.35 MCi
(c) 25 μCi
(d) 2 g Ra
(e) 2 mg Ra
(f) 7.4×10^4 disintegrations per second

6.23 Two radioisotopes, Fe-59 and Fe-60, have lifetimes of 45 days and 3×10^5 years, respectively. One Ci of which isotope would have the greater mass? Why?

6.24 Why is the rem a better unit for estimating biological damage than the roentgen?

6.25 How is the rad related to the rem?

6.26 Is there anywhere on earth where exposure to radiation produced from decaying nuclei is zero? Why?

6.27 What is the difference between spontaneous and artificial transmutations?

6.28 What radioisotopes, important in nuclear medicine, are products of the following transmutations?
(a) P-31 + H-2 $\longrightarrow$? + ${}^1_1p$
(b) S-34 + ${}^1_0n \longrightarrow$? + ${}^1_1p$
(c) Co-59 + ${}^1_0n \longrightarrow$? + ${}^1_1p$

6.29 Do you think P-31, S-34, and Co-59 (from Exercise 6.28) are naturally occurring or artificial?

6.30 What particles are produced as a result of the following artificial transmutations?
(a) Li-6 + $n \longrightarrow$ H-3 + ?
(b) Mg-26 + H-3 $\longrightarrow$ Mg-28 + ?
(c) N-14 + $\alpha \longrightarrow$ O-17 + ?

6.31 Identify the bombarding particles in the transmutation reactions shown below:
(a) Be-9 + ? $\longrightarrow$ C-12 + n
(b) C-12 + ? $\longrightarrow$ N-13 + γ
(c) N-14 + ? $\longrightarrow$ C-14 + p^+

6.32 A radioactive gas is produced as one decay product of the natural radioactive decay of uranium.
(a) What element is this? (See Table 6.2.)
(b) To what group of the periodic table does it belong?
(c) Do you think a gas mask (which depends on chemical methods of separation) could be used to separate isotopes of this element from air?

6.33 What important characteristics are needed for a radioisotope used in diagnosis?

6.34 Would an α-emitting radioisotope be useful in a diagnostic procedure? Why or why not?

6.35 One of the three iodine isotopes shown in Table 6.3 is not medically useful. Why not?

6.36 Radioactive I-131 can be used in either diagnosis or treatment of disease. What is the major difference in the two procedures?

6.37 The radioisotope I-128 can be used in thyroid studies. Write the equation for its decay by electron capture.

6.38 Explain how the interaction of ionizing radiations with living matter can cause cell damage.

6.39 If a female patient received six chest x-rays in a particular year, how much radiation would she absorb? How does this amount (in mrem) compare with that produced from natural background radiation?

6.40 What is meant by tagging a compound with iodine?

6.41 The equation below represents an organic reaction in which an alcohol (CH_3OH) reacts with an acid (CH_3COOH) to produce an ester (CH_3COOCH_3) and water.

$$CH_3OH + CH_3COOH \searrow CH_3COOCH_3 + H_2O$$

Suppose we suspect that *all* the O atoms in the water product come from the acid reactant (CH_3COOH). How can we prove this?

6.42 What is the difference between nuclear fission and nuclear fusion?

6.43 What is the major difficulty encountered in using nuclear fusion to provide a controlled source of energy?

6.44 How many neutrons are produced as a result of the fission reaction below?

$$n + \text{U-235} \longrightarrow \text{Sr-90} + \text{Xe-143} + ?n$$

6.45 Suppose a neutron causes an atom of U-235 to undergo fission according to the reaction below. One isotope formed is Ba-143. What is the other one?

$$n + \text{U-235} \longrightarrow {}_{56}\text{Ba} + ? + 3n$$

6.46 It is possible for mercury-197 to turn into gold-197 (the most common isotope of gold) via spontaneous transmutation. Write the nuclear equation for this process.

6.47 The body handles Sr-90 in the same way that it handles calcium. In what kind of tissue would you expect Sr-90 to deposit?

6.48 In organ scans used to detect diagnostic radioisotopes, what is meant by the terms hot spot and cold spot?

6.49 Suppose a liver scan is performed by using Tc-S colloid. Would abnormalities appear as hot spots or as cold spots?

6.50 Match each nuclear equation in the table at the bottom of the page with the correct description of its type.

6.51 Why are Sr-90 and I-131 particularly harmful to children?

6.52 What property of alpha particles, protons, and deuterons makes it difficult for them to penetrate nuclei of heavier elements? How can such penetration be accomplished?

6.53 Why are most artificial transmutations done by neutron bombardment?

6.54 Element number 96, called curium after the Curies, is made by bombarding plutonium-239 with α particles. If the isotope of curium formed has a mass number of 240, how many neutrons must accompany this artificial transmutation?

6.55 In Chapter 6 we discussed two cases in which serendipity led to major discoveries. What were they?

6.56 Would C-14 dating be of any use in measuring the age of the earth? Why?

(a) U-235 + n $\longrightarrow$ Sr-90 + Xe-144 + 2n	(1) spontaneous transmutation
(b) U-238 + n $\longrightarrow$ Pu-239 + β	(2) nuclear fission
(c) U-238 $\longrightarrow$ α + Th-234	(3) nuclear fusion
(d) 4 H-1 $\longrightarrow$ He-4 + $2\beta^+$	(4) artificial transmutation

7 . . . . GASES AND THE ATMOSPHERE

7.1 INTRODUCTION

Many important substances exist naturally as gases at room temperature and sea-level pressure. The 11 elements displayed in color on the periodic table on the inside front cover, including life-sustaining O_2, as well as N_2, F_2, Cl_2, H_2 and the noble gases He, Ne, Ar, Kr, Xe, and Rn, are all gases. A large number of low-molecular-weight covalently bonded compounds are gases, including carbon dioxide (CO_2), a waste product of animal metabolism, nitrous oxide (N_2O), used as a general anesthetic, methane (CH_4), a major component of natural gas, and a variety of others, some of which are listed in Table 7.1.

Gases can also be produced when liquids evaporate to become gases. Such gaseous substances, which are liquids under normal conditions, are called **vapors**. Thus we refer to the gaseous water present in air as water *vapor* (not water gas).

In Chapter 2 we gave a brief description of a gas as a substance with no definite volume or shape. Here in Chapter 7 we will look more deeply into the nature of gases and the laws that govern their behavior. In general, the equations that describe gases are relatively simple ones compared with those that are used to treat solids and liquids. The reason for this is that the distances between the molecules in a sample of gas are very large compared with the size of the molecules. (Here we broaden the term "molecule" to include the atoms of He, Ne, Ar, Kr, Xe, and Rn that make up the noble gases.) For instance, the approximate diameter of a nitrogen molecule (N_2) is 0.3 nm and the average distance between two N_2 molecules (at 25°C and sea level) is about 3.5 nm. Thus the distance between the two molecules is roughly 12 (3.5/0.3) times greater than the diameter of a single molecule, as shown in Figure 7.1. In contrast, the distances between molecules of liquids or solids are much smaller (see Figure 7.2). Because gas molecules are so widely separated, the interactions among them are small enough to be ignored, greatly simplifying the laws used to study them. The fact that gas molecules are so far apart is a fundamental assumption of the **kinetic-molecular theory** of gases, from which all the gas laws are derived.

FIGURE 7.1
Distance between N_2 molecules. The distance between two nitrogen gas molecules at 25°C and 1-atm pressure is about 12 times the diameter of each nitrogen molecule.

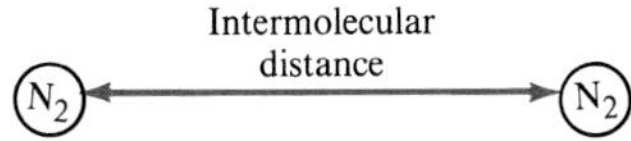

TABLE 7.1 **FORMULAS AND NAMES OF COMMON GASEOUS COMPOUNDS**

Formula	System name	Brief description
CO_2	Carbon dioxide	Metabolic waste product
CO	Carbon monoxide	Toxic product from burning carbon fuels
N_2O	Dinitrogen oxide	General anesthetic (laughing gas)
NO_2	Nitrogen dioxide	Reddish brown smog component
NO	Nitrogen oxide	Readily converted to NO_2 in air
NH_3	Ammonia	Waste product from protein metabolism
SO_2	Sulfur dioxide	Choking odor; respiratory irritant
H_2S	Hydrogen sulfide	Odor of rotten eggs
CH_4	Methane	Natural gas component
HCl	Hydrogen chloride	Hydrochloric acid is aqueous HCl
HCN	Hydrogen cyanide	Highly toxic with odor of almonds
$CClF_3$	A Freon	Refrigerant or propellant
$COCl_2$	Phosgene	War gas
C_3H_6	Cyclopropane	General anesthetic

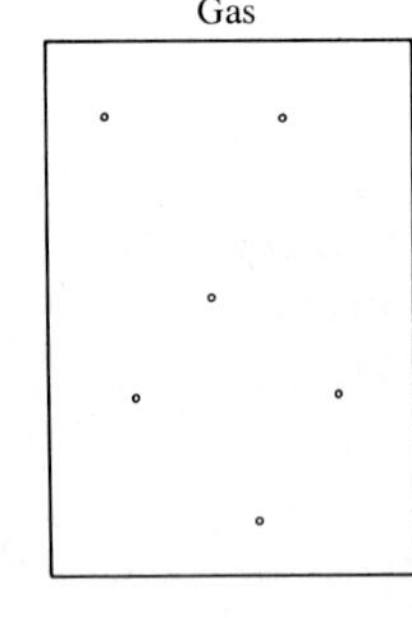

FIGURE 7.2
Intermolecular distances in liquids and solids. Molecules of gases are much farther apart than are those of liquids or solids.

7.2 KINETIC-MOLECULAR THEORY OF GASES

We began this text with a discussion of how chemists try to explain observable properties of matter by building models based upon the invisible miscroscopic particles of which matter is composed. The development of the kinetic-molecular theory is an excellent example of this kind of thinking.

First we present some of the important assumptions of the theory, showing how they fit with the known behavior of gases.

1. *Gas molecules are far apart and so the forces of attraction and repulsion are negligible.* Thus gases can be easily compressed, since there is enough distance between their molecules to move them closer together.
2. *Gas molecules are in constant, rapid motion.* The movement of gas molecules causes collisions with the walls of their containers, giving rise to gas *pressure*. The pressure exerted by air molecules in the lungs keeps the lungs from collapsing. The constant motion of gas molecules causes gases to expand to fill any container. Thus the gases responsible for the odor of cooking foods fill up a room by a process known as *diffusion*.
3. *The speed with which gas molecules move depends upon their temperature.* A gas confined in a rigid container exerts more pressure as the temperature goes up because its molecules move faster and thus collide more frequently with each other and the container walls. Hence, heating an aerosol can may cause it to explode. A gas confined in a flexible container (such as a balloon) will increase in volume if the temperature increases because its molecules move faster and hit the walls with greater force, causing them to expand (see Figure 7.3).

Thus we see that the kinetic-molecular theory of gases explains many familiar properties of gases. So far our discussion about how gases respond to changes in temperature, volume, and pressure has been purely qualitative. In order to make

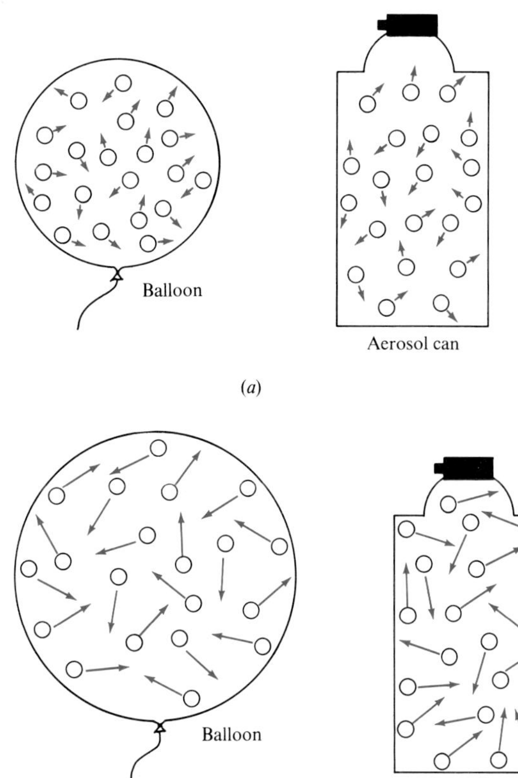

FIGURE 7.3
Gas in flexible and rigid containers. (*a*) At the lower temperature, gas molecules move more slowly. (*b*) When the temperature is increased, the gas molecules move faster. The balloon must expand. Pressure builds up in the aerosol can.

quantitative predictions about gas behavior we must present equations that relate the important variables needed to describe a sample of gas—the temperature, the volume, and the pressure. First let us see how the quantity *gas pressure* is defined and measured.

7.3 GAS PRESSURE

The air which surrounds us exerts a force equivalent to that which would be produced if a mass of 1 kg were pushing in on a surface of about 1 cm^2. We do not notice this because the air inside our bodies is also pushing out with an equal force. The **pressure** exerted by a gas such as air is defined as the amount of force per unit area. Gas pressures are often measured in terms of the height of a column of liquid which the gas will support. The device used to measure the pressure of a gas in this way is called a *barometer.*

Looking at Figure 7.4, you can see how a barometer is constructed. A long glass tube, open on both ends, is placed in a dish of liquid mercury, as in Figure 7.4*a*. The air surrounding the apparatus is pushing down equally on the mercury

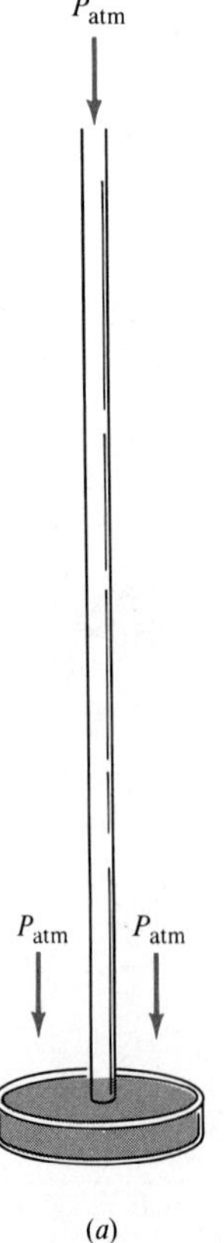

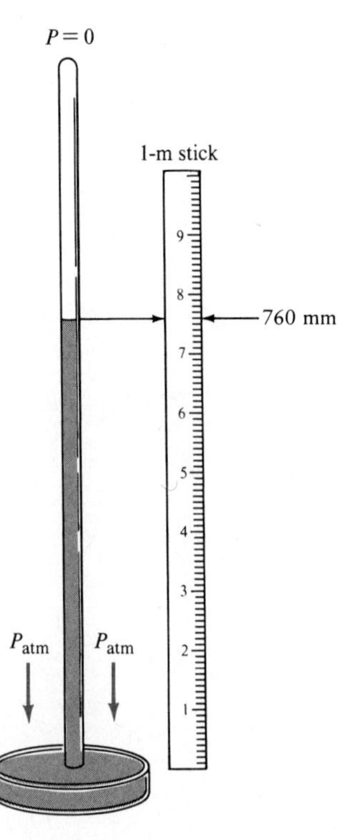

FIGURE 7.4
Barometer. (*a*) The pressure of the atmosphere P_{atm} is exerted on the mercury in the dish and on the mercury in the tube. Thus, the mercury does not rise. (*b*) The pressure of the atmosphere is exerted on the mercury in the dish, but no pressure is exerted on the mercury in the evacuated tube. Thus, the mercury rises in the tube. The height of the mercury is a measure of the atmospheric pressure, which is 760 mmHg in this diagram.

in the dish and the mercury inside the tube. Thus the mercury level stays the same inside and outside the tube. In the apparatus pictured in Figure 7.4*b* all the air is removed from the glass tube, which is then sealed off at the top. There is no air pressure working on the mercury in the tube, but there is pressure exerted on the mercury in the dish thereby causing the mercury to rise in the tube. The greater the pressure, the higher the mercury rises. We can quote the air pressure in terms of the height to which the mercury rises above the level in the dish. In Figure 7.4*b* the measured pressure is said to be 760 mmHg, since the column of mercury supported by the surrounding air is 760 mm in height.

Many different units are used to express gas pressures. One of these is the **atmosphere** (atm), which is approximately equal to the pressure exerted by air in areas around sea level and is exactly equal to 760 mmHg. The unit millimeter of mercury (mmHg) is also referred to as the **torr**, after the Italian physicist Evangelista Torricelli (1608–1647), who first proposed the idea of atmospheric pressure and who invented the barometer to test his ideas. Weather reports in the United States give the barometric pressure in inches of mercury. One atmosphere is the same as 29.9 inHg. In the SI system the unit of pressure is called the **pascal** (Pa), which corresponds to the combination of units below:

The newton (N) is an SI force unit and is equal to 1 (kg)(m)/s^2.

$$1\,\text{Pa} = \frac{\text{kg}}{\text{s}^2 \times \text{m}} = \frac{\text{N}}{\text{m}^2}$$

There are about 101,325 Pa in 1 atm, or about 101 kilopascals (kPa). The pascal is very useful for doing calculations in which other mass and length units already appear but is rarely used for practical work in industry or medicine.

$$1 \text{ atm} = 760 \text{ mmHg} = 760 \text{ torr} = 29.9 \text{ inHg} = 101 \text{ kPa}$$

Table 7.2 lists these and other pressure units and gives their relationship to 1 atm. In much of the work done in medical, industrial, and university laboratories, pressures are expressed in units of millimeters of Hg.

TABLE 7.2 **COMMON PRESSURE UNITS**

Pressure unit	Number in 1 atmosphere
Atmosphere	1
inHg	29.9
cmHg	76.0
mmHg = torr	760
ftH_2O	33.9
lb/in^2	14.7
N/m^2 = pascal (Pa)	1.01×10^5
kilopascal (kPa)	101

At higher altitudes the pressure exerted by gases in the atmosphere is considerably reduced. This happens because near the surface of the earth there is *more* air pushing down from above, thus causing *more* air pressure. As the elevation increases, there is less air to push down and hence a lower pressure. For instance, the atmospheric pressure in Denver, Colorado, the Mile High City, is only 0.83 atm. As the atmospheric pressure decreases, so does the quantity of air per unit area, as well as the quantity of oxygen available for breathing. Human beings are quite sensitive to low oxygen pressure, as we shall discuss further in Section 7.12, but are able to compensate by increasing ventilation, the rate at which fresh air is taken in. The body knows when to do this because chemoreceptors respond to low levels of oxygen in arterial blood by stimulating the nerves which cause ventilation.

Abrupt decreases in barometric pressure may be uncomfortable. In a fast-rising elevator or in an ascending airplane the air pressure outside the body is being reduced more rapidly than that inside the body. As a result eardrums may bulge outward, producing a popping sensation, until the internal body pressure is equally lowered. A very abrupt reduction in atmospheric pressure causes a much more serious condition called ***decompression sickness.*** This happens because nitrogen gas dissolved in body fluids begins to escape in the same way that carbon dioxide gas escapes when a bottle of carbonated beverage is opened. Gas bubbles form in the blood and body tissues, producing a variety of unpleasant symptoms, including severe pain in the joints and chest. The "bends" suffered by deep sea divers coming to the ocean surface too quickly is a type of decompression sickness.

The name "bends" comes from the arching of the back in pain.

SAMPLE EXERCISE 7.1

Calculate the barometric pressure in the city of Denver in millimeters of Hg and torr.

Solution:

$$1 \text{ atm} = 760 \text{ mm Hg} = 1 \text{ torr}$$

$$0.83 \cancel{\text{atm}} \times \frac{760 \text{ mm Hg}}{1 \cancel{\text{atm}}} = 630 \text{ mm Hg} = 630 \text{ torr}$$

EXERCISE 7.1

A weather broadcast gives a barometric reading of 30.0 in of mercury. What is the pressure in atmospheres and in torr?

7.4 BOYLE'S LAW

As a fixed sample of gas is compressed to a smaller volume at constant temperature, its pressure increases. This happens because forcing the same number of molecules into a smaller volume makes for more collisions with their container, thus exerting more pressure (see Figure 7.5). Robert Boyle (1627–1691) turned this qualitative observation into a gas law by compressing and expanding a gas and recording the pressure that corresponded to each volume. A schematic drawing of Boyle's experiment is given in Figure 7.6, where you can see that the product of the pressure P and the volume V always remains the same:

$$P_1V_1 = P_2V_2 = P_3V_3 = P_4V_4$$

or, in general,

$$PV = \text{constant}$$

No such simple relationship between P and V exists for liquids or solids.

As the pressure is increased the volume must decrease, and vice versa. Thus, Boyle's law says that

At constant temperature, the volume of a gas is inversely proportional to pressure.

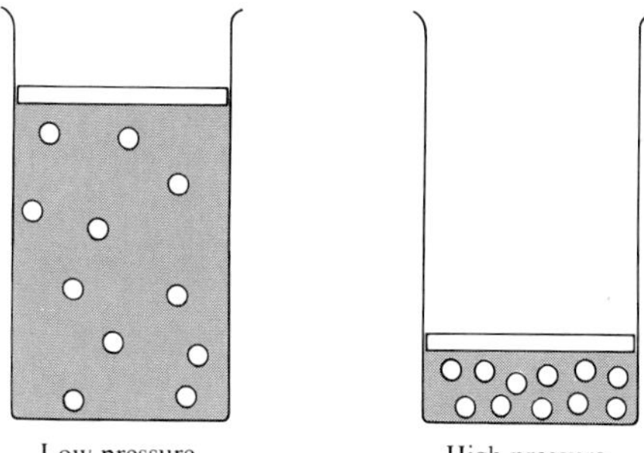

FIGURE 7.5
Molecules forced into smaller volume exert more pressure.

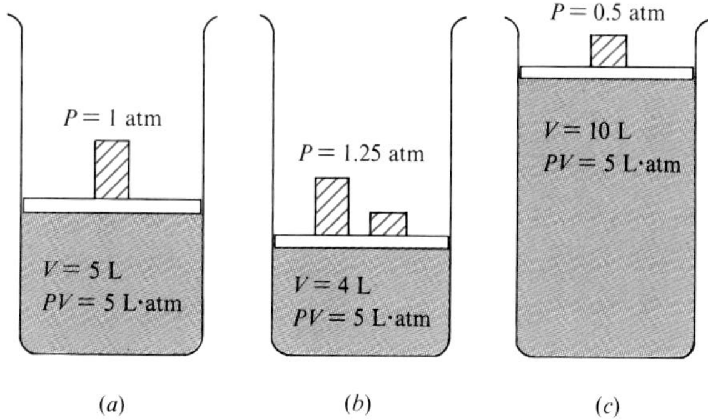

FIGURE 7.6
Boyle's law showing that PV is a constant.

Using Boyle's law, we can calculate the new pressure or volume of a gas of which the original pressure or volume has been changed. For instance, suppose you wish to find the pressure of a gas which originally occupied a 1.00-L container at 1.00 atm pressure and was allowed to expand to fill a 2.00-L container. Use Boyle's law:

$$P_1V_1 = P_2V_2$$

$$P_1 = 1.00 \text{ atm} \qquad V_1 = 1.00 \text{ L}$$

$$P_2 = ? \qquad V_2 = 2.00 \text{ L}$$

$$1.00 \text{ atm} \times 1.00 \text{ L} = P_2 \times 2.00 \text{ L}$$

$$P_2 = \frac{1.00 \text{ atm} \times 1.00 \cancel{\text{L}}}{2.00 \cancel{\text{L}}} = 0.500 \text{ atm}$$

Any pressure or volume units may be used provided they are consistent. In this case both volumes must be expressed in liters (L) so that the units cancel.

Note that the answer, 0.500 atm, makes physical sense; if the volume is doubled, the pressure will be halved, as predicted by Boyle's law.

SAMPLE EXERCISE 7.2

A 2.00-L vessel contains N_2O at a pressure of 1.50 atm. What volume will the gas occupy at a pressure of 1500 torr if the temperature is held constant?

Solution:

Use Boyle's law.

$$P_1V_1 = P_2V_2$$

$$P_1 = 1.50 \text{ atm} \qquad V_1 = 2.00 \text{ L}$$

$$P_2 = 1500 \text{ torr} \qquad V_2 = ?$$

First we must convert P_1 to torr (or P_2 to atm):

$$P_1 = 1.50 \cancel{\text{atm}} \times \frac{760 \text{ torr}}{1 \cancel{\text{atm}}} = 1140 \text{ torr}$$

$$1140 \text{ torr} \times 2.00 \text{ L} = 1500 \text{ torr} \times V_2$$

$$V_2 = \frac{1140 \cancel{\text{torr}} \times 2.00 \text{ L}}{1500 \cancel{\text{torr}}} = 1.52 \text{ L}$$

EXERCISE 7.2

Suppose the pressure of a sample of gas is doubled, keeping the temperature constant. What will happen to the volume?

7.5 CHARLES' LAW

More than 100 years after Boyle's discovery, Jacques Charles (1746–1823) found that the volume of a gas divided by its absolute (Kelvin) temperature remained constant:

$$\frac{V_1}{T_1} = \frac{V_2}{T_2} = \frac{V_3}{T_3} = \frac{V_4}{T_4} \quad \text{and so on}$$

or, in general,

$$\frac{V}{T} = \text{constant}$$

Charles' law is also called the law of Charles and Gay-Lussac (another French scientist who did similar experiments).

For V/T to stay constant, the volume must change in the same direction that the temperature does. Heating a gas increases its volume, as you can see in Figure 7.3, which shows a balloon expanding upon being heated. Cooling a gas decreases its volume. Charles' law says that

At constant pressure, the volume of a gas is directly proportional to its temperature.

In these experiments, the capital T always refers to the absolute temperature, which, as you may recall from Chapter 1, is found by adding 273 to the Celsius temperature t.

Using Charles' law we can calculate the new volume of gas if its temperature is changed. For example, suppose we wish to find the final volume of a 2.00-L gas sample which is cooled from 200 to 100°C.

$$\frac{V_1}{T_1} = \frac{V_2}{T_2}$$

$$V_1 = 2.00 \text{ L} \qquad T_1 = 200°\text{C} + 273 = 473 \text{ K}$$

$$V_2 = ? \qquad T_2 = 100°\text{C} + 273 = 373 \text{ K}$$

Substituting these values into the Charles' law equation, we get

$$\frac{2.00 \text{ L}}{473 \text{ K}} = \frac{V_2}{373 \text{ K}}$$

$$V_2 = \frac{2.00 \text{ L} \times 373 \cancel{\text{K}}}{473 \cancel{\text{K}}} = 1.58 \text{ L}$$

We see that the final volume (1.58 L) is less than the original volume (2.00 L), as it should be when the temperature is lowered.

SAMPLE EXERCISE 7.3

The average size of a single breath of air, called *tidal volume,* is 500 ml. If this amount of air is inhaled at 25°C, calculate the volume it will occupy at body temperature (37°C). Assume the pressure remains at 1 atm.

Solution:

Use Charles' law:

$$\frac{V_1}{T_1} = \frac{V_2}{T_2}$$

$$V_1 = 500 \text{ mL} \qquad T_1 = 25°\text{C} + 273 = 298 \text{ K}$$

$$V_2 = ? \qquad T_2 = 37°\text{C} + 273 = 310 \text{ K}$$

$$\frac{500 \text{ ml}}{298 \text{ K}} = \frac{V_2}{310 \text{ K}}$$

$$V_2 = \frac{500 \text{ ml} \times 310 \cancel{\text{K}}}{298 \cancel{\text{K}}} = 520 \text{ ml}$$

The final volume (520 ml) is greater because our body temperature is higher than the outside temperature.

EXERCISE 7.3

Suppose the Celsius temperature of a sample of gas is doubled from 25 to 50°C at constant pressure. What will happen to the volume?

7.6 COMBINED GAS LAW

Another very useful relationship comes from the combination of Boyle's and Charles' laws. According to the **combined gas law,** the pressure times the volume of a fixed sample of gas divided by its absolute temperature is constant:

$$\frac{P_1V_1}{T_1} = \frac{P_2V_2}{T_2} = \frac{P_3V_3}{T_3} = \frac{P_4V_4}{T_4} \quad \text{and so on}$$

or, in general,

$$\frac{PV}{T} = \text{constant}$$

From the combined gas law equation we can easily generate either Boyle's law or Charles' law. For instance, if the temperature is held constant by setting $T_1 = T_2$, the temperatures cancel:

$$\frac{P_1V_1}{\cancel{T_1}} = \frac{P_2V_2}{\cancel{T_2}}$$

The result is Boyle's law, $P_1V_1 = P_2V_2$. Charles' law is produced in a similar fashion by putting $P_1 = P_2$ in the combined gas law equation to keep the pressure constant:

$$\frac{\cancel{P_1}V_1}{T_1} = \frac{\cancel{P_2}V_2}{T_2}$$

Boyle's and Charles' laws are special cases of the combined gas law.

This time the pressures cancel, leaving Charles' law, $V_1/T_1 = V_2/T_2$.

We can use the combined gas law equation to make calculations about gas samples in which the pressure, temperature, and volume are undergoing change.

SAMPLE EXERCISE 7.4

A 10.0-L gas sample at 1.00 atm pressure and 0°C is heated until its final volume reaches 11.5 L. If the final pressure is 900 mmHg, what must the final temperature be in degrees Celsius?

Solution:

Use the combined gas law:

$$\frac{P_1V_1}{T_1} = \frac{P_2V_2}{T_2}$$

Remember that the units for P_1 and P_2 must be the same.

$$P_1 = 1.00 \text{ atm} = 760 \text{ mmHg} \qquad P_2 = 900 \text{ mmHg}$$

$$V_1 = 10.0 \text{ L} \qquad V_2 = 11.5 \text{ L}$$

$$T_1 = 0°\text{C} + 273 = 273 \text{ K} \qquad T_2 = ?$$

$$\frac{760 \text{ mmHg} \times 10.0 \text{ L}}{273 \text{ K}} = \frac{900 \text{ mmHg} \times 11.5 \text{ L}}{T_2}$$

$$T_2 = \frac{900 \cancel{\text{mmHg}} \times 11.5 \cancel{\text{L}} \times 273 \text{ K}}{760 \cancel{\text{mmHg}} \times 10.0 \cancel{\text{L}}} = 372 \text{ K}$$

$$372 \text{ K} - 273 = 99°\text{C}$$

EXERCISE 7.4

Suppose the volume of a gas is 1.00 L at 37°C and 650 torr. What volume (in cubic centimeters) would this gas occupy at a temperature of 0°C and a pressure of 1.25 atm?

7.7 IDEAL GAS LAW

By measuring the pressure, volume, and temperature of a given amount of gas in the laboratory, we can determine a value for the constant in the combined gas law equation. When the quantity of gas used is exactly 1 mol, the constant is called the **ideal gas constant** R:

$$\frac{PV}{T} = R \text{ (for 1 mol)}$$

For 2 mol of gas R is doubled, for 3 mol it is tripled, and so on.

$$\frac{PV}{T} = 2R \text{ (for 2 mol)}$$

$$\frac{PV}{T} = 3R \text{ (for 3 mol)}$$

If n is used to represent the number of moles of gas, the combined gas law equation can be written

$$\frac{PV}{T} = nR \text{ (for } n \text{ mol)}$$

This equation is called the **ideal gas law** and is usually rearranged to take the form below:

$$PV = nRT$$

By solving this equation for R, we see that $R = PV/nT$. Thus, R must be in units of pressure times volume divided by the product of number of moles and absolute temperature.

$$R \text{ unit} = \frac{\text{pressure unit} \times \text{volume unit}}{\text{mol} \times \text{K}}$$

To find the numerical value for the ideal gas constant R, we can measure the volume of 1 mol of a gas at a given temperature and pressure. We choose a temperature of 0°C and a pressure of 1 atm, a set of conditions known as *standard conditions,* abbreviated STP. At STP 1 mol of a gas occupies 22.4 L. Now we can evaluate R:

STP means 0°C and 1 atm.

$$R = \frac{PV}{nT}$$

and

$$R = \frac{1 \text{ atm} \times 22.4 \text{ L}}{1 \text{ mol} \times 273 \text{ K}} = 0.0821 \frac{(\text{L})(\text{atm})}{(\text{mol})(\text{K})}$$

If instead the pressure is measured in millimeters of Hg, the ideal gas constant becomes

$$R = 62.4 \frac{(\text{L})(\text{mmHg})}{(\text{mol})(\text{K})}$$

The ideal gas law can be used to calculate either the pressure, volume, temperature, or number of moles of a gas provided three of these four quantities are known. For instance, suppose we want to find the volume of 1 mol of a gas at 25°C and 1.50 atm pressure. Since P, T, and n are given, the ideal gas law can be used to find V.

$$PV = nRT$$
$$P = 1.50 \text{ atm}$$
$$T = 0°\text{C} + 273 = 273 \text{ K}$$
$$n = 1 \text{ mol}$$
$$V = ?$$

We choose R in terms of [(L)(atm)]/[(mol)(K)] because the pressure is given in atmospheres.

$$R = 0.0821 \frac{(\text{L})(\text{atm})}{(\text{mol})(\text{K})}$$

$$V = \frac{nRT}{P}$$

$$V = \frac{1 \cancel{\text{mol}} \times 0.0821 (\text{L})(\cancel{\text{atm}}) \times 298 \cancel{\text{K}}}{1.50 (\cancel{\text{atm}}) (\cancel{\text{mol}})(\cancel{\text{K}})} = 16.3 \text{ L}$$

At room temperature and sea-level pressure air behaves like an ideal gas.

Note that the units atm, K, and mol all cancel, leaving the volume unit, L.

Gases that behave as predicted by the kinetic-molecular theory are called **ideal gases.** The behavior of an ideal gas can be predicted by using the ideal gas law (or any of the laws which combine to produce it). This means that values for P, V, T, or n that are calculated using these laws agree with those measured in the laboratory. **Real gases** are gases that deviate from ideal behavior. Equations more complex than the ideal gas law must be used to describe the behavior of real gases. Fortunately, the ideal gas law equation works reasonably well for most gases, including air at room temperature. When pressures get too high and temperatures too low, gas molecules move closer together, and no longer fit the kinetic-molecular model. In fact, at sufficiently high pressures and low temperatures, gases turn into liquids.

SAMPLE EXERCISE 7.5

A sample of the general anesthetic, cyclopropane gas, at 38°C contains 4.00×10^{-3} mol in 1.00 L. What is the gas pressure in millimeters of Hg?

Solution:

We use the ideal gas law.

$$PV = nRT$$

$$T = 38°\text{C} + 273 = 311\text{ K}$$

$$n = 4.00 \times 10^{-3}\text{ mol}$$

$$V = 1.00\text{ L}$$

$$P = ?$$

$$R = 62.4\,\frac{(\text{L})(\text{mmHg})}{(\text{mol})(\text{K})}$$

This value of R is chosen because the pressure is to be found in millimeters of Hg.

Substituting these values onto the ideal gas law

$$P = \frac{nRT}{V}$$

$$P = \frac{4.00 \times 10^{-3}\,\cancel{\text{mol}} \times 62.4\,\frac{(\cancel{\text{L}})(\text{mmHg})}{(\cancel{\text{mol}})(\cancel{\text{K}})} \times 311\,\cancel{\text{K}}}{1.00\,\cancel{\text{L}}} = 77.6\text{ mmHg}$$

EXERCISE 7.5

What is the pressure (in millimeters of Hg) exerted by 29.0 mmol of nitrous oxide at a temperature of 38°C if it is contained in a volume of 1.00 L?

SAMPLE EXERCISE 7.6

A sample of oxygen gas (O_2) at STP has a mass of 16.0 g. What volume does it occupy?

Solution 1:

Use $PV = nRT$. First calculate n from the mass given and the formula weight of O_2, which is 32.0.

$$n = 16.0\ \cancel{g\ O_2} \times \frac{1\ \text{mol}\ O_2}{32.0\ \cancel{g\ O_2}} = 0.500\ \text{mol}\ O_2$$

$$P = 1\ \text{atm}$$

$$T = 0°\text{C} + 273 = 273\ \text{K}$$

$$R = 0.0821\ \frac{(\text{L})(\text{atm})}{(\text{mol})(\text{K})}$$

$$V = ?$$

$$V = \frac{nRT}{P}$$

$$V = \frac{0.500\ \cancel{\text{mol}} \times 0.0821\ \text{L}\ \cancel{\text{atm}} \times 273\ \cancel{\text{K}}}{1\ \cancel{\text{atm}} \qquad (\cancel{\text{mol}})(\cancel{\text{K}})} = 11.2\ \text{L}$$

Solution 2:

The fact that 1 mol of any gas occupies 22.4 L at STP may be used as a conversion factor:

$$1\ \text{mol} = 22.4\ \text{L} \qquad \text{for a gas at STP}$$

We now use this factor to convert 0.500 mol to liters.

$$0.500\ \cancel{\text{mol}} \times \frac{22.4\ \text{L}}{1\ \cancel{\text{mol}}} = 11.2\ \text{L}$$

EXERCISE 7.6

What is the volume at STP of a sample of carbon dioxide gas that weighs 150 g?

7.8 DALTON'S LAW OF PARTIAL PRESSURES

This is the same Dalton who developed the atomic theory (Section 3.2).

Many experiments done on gases involve mixtures of gases rather than pure gaseous substances. Therefore, we need some way to relate the pressure exerted by the components of a mixture to the pressure exerted by the mixture as a whole.

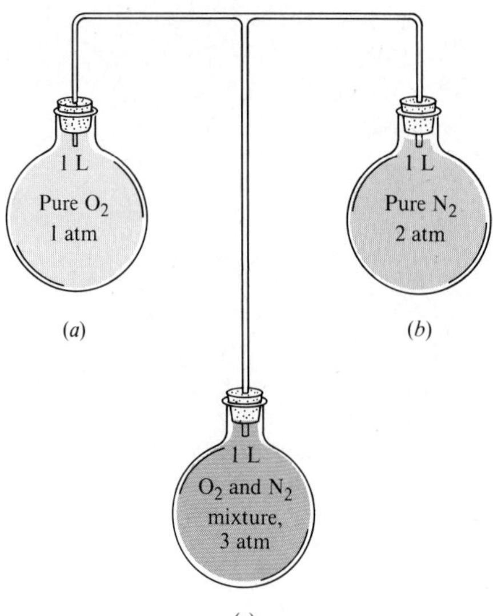

FIGURE 7.7
Mixing gases to illustrate Dalton's law.

To find the pressure exerted by a gaseous mixture **Dalton's law of partial pressures** is applied. The **partial pressure** of a gas is the pressure which that gas would exert if it occupied a container by itself. According to Dalton's law the total pressure P of a mixture of gases is the sum of the partial pressures p of each component gas.

$$P_{\text{total}} = p_1 + p_2 + p_3 \qquad \text{and so on}$$

For example, Figure 7.7 shows what happens to the pressure when a sample of oxygen gas is mixed with nitrogen gas. The 1-L vessel in Figure 7.7*a* contains a sample of pure oxygen gas that exerts a pressure of 1 atm. Figure 7.7*b* is a sample of pure nitrogen gas in another 1-L vessel at a pressure of 2 atm. If the O_2 and N_2 gases are mixed by forcing the O_2 gas into the vessel already containing the N_2 gas, as in Figure 7.7*c*, the total pressure is the sum of the partial pressure of O_2 (1 atm) and the partial pressure of N_2 (2 atm).

$$P_T = p_{O_2} + p_{N_2}$$

$$P_T = 1 \text{ atm} + 2 \text{ atm} = 3 \text{ atm}$$

SAMPLE EXERCISE 7.7

The normal human lung contains about 400 million alveoli.

Alveolar air, a gas mixture contained by an air cell of the lung, called an *alveolus* (see Figure 7.8), exerts a pressure of 1 atm. Using Table 7.3 find the partial pressure of air in such a mixture if the other component is the minimum amount of ether vapor needed to produce general anesthesia.

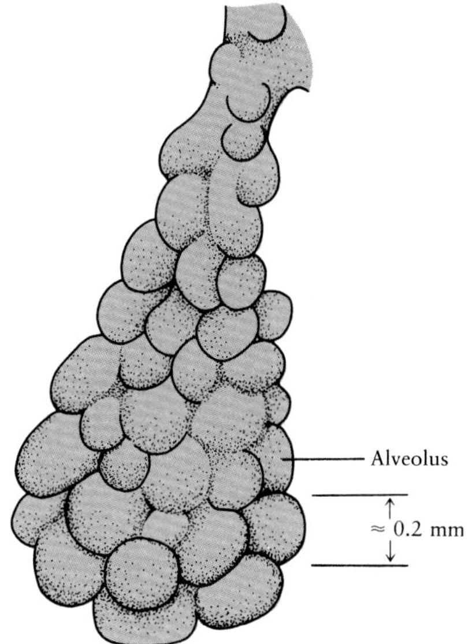

FIGURE 7.8
Clusters of alveoli are connected to air passageways of the lung. The alveoli are in contact with a network of capillaries, where the exchange of gases between the blood and the air takes place.

TABLE 7.3 **MINIMUM PARTIAL PRESSURES OF GENERAL ANESTHETICS IN ALVEOLAR AIR (TOTAL PRESSURE = 760 mmHg)**

Name	Formula	Minimum partial pressure, mmHg
Halothane	$C_2HBrClF_3$	5.8
Ether	$C_4H_{10}O$	14.4
Cyclopropane	C_3H_6	69.9
Nitrous oxide	N_2O	768

Solution:

Table 7.3 shows that the minimum amount of ether needed exerts a partial pressure of 14.4 mmHg. We use Dalton's law.

$$P\ (\text{alveolar air}) = p\ (\text{air}) + p\ (\text{ether})$$

$$p\ (\text{air}) = P\ (\text{alveolar air}) - p\ (\text{ether})$$

$$P\ (\text{alveolar air}) = 1\ \text{atm} = 760\ \text{mmHg} \qquad p\ (\text{ether}) = 14.4\ \text{mmHg}$$

$$p\ (\text{air}) = 760\ \text{mmHg} - 14.4\ \text{mmHg} = 746\ \text{mmHg}$$

EXERCISE 7.7

The partial pressure of air in alveolar air containing air and cyclopropane is 0.950 atm. If the total pressure is 1 atm, will general anesthesia be achieved?

We can show that the partial pressure of a gas is directly related to the number of moles of that gas present in a gaseous mixture. According to the ideal gas law, the pressure of a gas can be expressed in terms of *n*, *R*, *T*, and *V*:

$$PV = nRT \qquad \text{and} \qquad P = \frac{nRT}{V}$$

For a given sample of gas, *R*, *T*, and *V* are constant; only *n* changes.

$$P = n \times \text{constant}$$

Thus, the composition of a gaseous mixture can be expressed in terms of partial pressures. For instance, suppose we have a mixture of two gases. The partial pressure of gas 1 divided by the partial pressure of gas 2 will be the same as the number of moles of gas 1 divided by the number of moles of gas 2:

$$\frac{p\ (\text{gas 1})}{p\ (\text{gas 2})} = \frac{n\ (\text{gas 1})}{n\ (\text{gas 2})}$$

In Table 7.3 the minimum amount of general anesthetic gas (in a mixture with air) that must be administered to a patient is expressed in terms of partial pressures instead of moles.

SAMPLE EXERCISE 7.8

At a temperature of 25°C (298 K), a 10-L flask contains a mixture of 4 mol N_2 gas and 1 mol O_2 gas. Calculate: **(a)** pN_2; **(b)** pO_2; **(c)** pN_2/pO_2.

Solution:

To calculate the pN_2 and pO_2 we use the ideal gas law:

$$P = \frac{nRT}{V}$$

$$pN_2 = \frac{4\ \cancel{\text{mol}} \times 0.0821\ (\cancel{\text{L}})(\text{atm}) \times 298\ \cancel{\text{K}}}{10\ (\cancel{\text{L}})(\cancel{\text{mol}})(\cancel{\text{K}})}$$

$$= 9.79\ \text{atm}$$

$$pO_2 = \frac{1\ \cancel{\text{mol}} \times 0.0821\ (\cancel{\text{L}})(\text{atm}) \times 298\ \cancel{\text{K}}}{10\ (\cancel{\text{L}})(\cancel{\text{mol}})(\cancel{\text{K}})}$$

$$= 2.45\ \text{atm}$$

Thus $pN_2/pO_2 = 9.79/2.45 = 4.00$, or $nN_2/nO_2 = 4$.

EXERCISE 7.8

Suppose a gaseous mixture contains oxygen gas at 1.0 atm pressure and nitrous oxide at 1.0 atm pressure. If 10 mol of O_2 is present, how many moles of nitrous oxide are also there? Do you need to know the temperature and the volume of the gaseous mixture to find the answer?

7.9 DIFFUSION

Gases in a mixture have a tendency to distribute themselves randomly. The process by which gases mix as a result of such random motion is called **diffusion.** You detect the odors of cooking foods or of perfumes because the gases responsible for these scents move through the air by diffusion.

Some gases diffuse more rapidly than others. The heavier the molecules of a gas are, the more slowly their molecules move and the more slowly the gas diffuses. For instance, SO_2 gas (formula weight 64) has a slower rate of diffusion than CH_4 gas (formula weight 16). According to Thomas Graham (1805–1869), the *relative diffusion* rates of two gases (D_1 and D_2) can be expressed in terms of their formula weights (M_1 and M_2) according to the relationship below, called **Graham's law.**

$$\frac{D_2}{D_1} = \sqrt{\frac{M_1}{M_2}}$$

Using Graham's law we find that CH_4 diffuses twice as rapidly as SO_2:

$$\frac{D(CH_4)}{D(SO_2)} = \sqrt{\frac{64}{16}} = \sqrt{4} = 2$$

An easily performed experiment can be done to compare the relative diffusion rates of ammonia, NH_3, and hydrogen chloride, HCl. If NH_3 is allowed to enter one end of a glass tube and HCl the other, a white ring of NH_4Cl forms where the two gases meet, as shown in Figure 7.9. The chemical reaction that takes place is

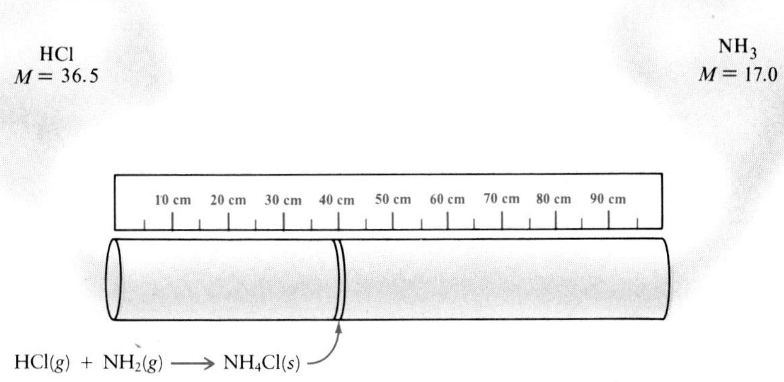

FIGURE 7.9
Diffusion (HCl and NH_3) Where the NH_4Cl forms, NH_3 meets HCl. The NH_3 travels 60 cm, whereas the HCl travels only 40 cm. Since the NH_3 travels 1.5 times farther than HCl, the rate of diffusion of NH_3 must be 1.5 times that of HCl.

$$NH_3(g) + HCl(g) \longrightarrow NH_4Cl(s)$$

The distance traveled by the NH_3 gas divided by the distance traveled by the HCl gas gives an experimental value of 1.5 for their relative rates of diffusion. Now we can apply Graham's law to see how this agrees with the predicted value.

$$\frac{D(NH_3)}{D(HCl)} = \sqrt{\frac{M(HCl)}{M(NH_3)}}$$

$$= \sqrt{\frac{36.5}{17.0}} = 1.47$$

According to Graham's law, NH_3 should diffuse 1.47 times as fast as HCl, in good agreement with the experimental value of 1.5.

Molecular motion resulting in diffusion is not limited to the gaseous state. You can observe the diffusion of a drop of food coloring placed in a glass of water. Eventually the color will be uniformly distributed throughout the water. In living systems, diffusion of molecules plays an important role in moving them from one area of the body to another. Because of the slowness of diffusion this method of transport is only possible over short distances. For instance, it takes only a few seconds for glucose molecules to diffuse from a blood vessel to a point 1 μm away (about one cell diameter), but it would take 11 years for them to diffuse to a point 10 cm away. Fortunately, body cells are close enough to blood vessels so that nutrients and waste products can diffuse rapidly between the cells and the blood.

7.10 GASES IN THE ATMOSPHERE

The *atmosphere* of the earth is the layer of gases which blankets the earth. In this section we will examine the composition of the atmosphere in terms of various units. In the next several sections we go on to consider some of the gases present in the atmosphere in more detail.

There are various unit systems in which the amount of each gas present in the atmosphere can be given. The one used for the major constituents of the atmosphere is volume percent or volume fraction. *Volume fraction* refers to the ratio of the volume of one component gas to the total volume of all component gases. For instance, suppose 100 L of gas mixture is prepared from 78.1 L N_2, 20.9 L of oxygen, and 1.0 L of a mixture of several other gases. Of that volume the N_2 represents a volume fraction of 78.1/100, or 0.781, the O_2 20.9/100, or 0.209, and the remaining gases 1/100, or 0.01. To convert volume fraction to volume percent (vol %) we multiply by 100%, that is, $0.781 \times 100\% = 78.1\%$. Thus 78.1 vol % of this mixture (which is the same as air) is N_2, 20.9 vol % is O_2, and the rest of the gases account for 1.0 vol %.

Because air obeys the ideal gas law, the volume percentages of its components will be the same as the mole percentages, because the volume of an ideal gas at a constant temperature and pressure depends only on the number of moles of that gas.

$$PV = nRT \qquad \text{and} \qquad V = \frac{nRT}{P}$$

It was Avogadro who first noted that equal volumes of gases contain equal numbers of molecules.

Since RT/P is constant provided the temperature and pressure remain constant, V is equal to a constant times n.

$$V = n \times \text{constant}$$

Thus the volume percent and the mole percent will be the same for a particular gas.

Some components of the atmosphere are present in such small amounts that volume percentages or volume fractions are awkward to state. For instance, the volume fraction of helium gas in the atmosphere is only 0.000005 (5×10^{-6}). In cases like this the unit *parts per million,* or ppm, is much more convenient to use. Parts per million refers to the number of molecules of a gas present in a mixture containing one million gas molecules. Volume fraction is converted to ppm by multiplying by 1 million, 10^6.

$$\text{Volume fraction} \times 10^6 = \text{ppm}$$

Thus the amount of helium gas in the atmosphere is $10^6 \times 5 \times 10^{-6}$, or 5 ppm. Two other units used for trace amounts of substance are parts per billion (ppb) and parts per trillion (ppt).

$$\text{Volume fraction} \times 10^9 = \text{ppb}$$

$$\text{Volume fraction} \times 10^{12} = \text{ppt}$$

Table 7.4 lists the constituents of air that do not vary in their concentrations, sometimes called the *permanent gases*. Nitrogen is always present as 78.1 percent of the atmosphere and oxygen as 20.9 percent. Most of the remaining 1 percent is the noble gas argon, which accounts for 0.9 percent. The other permanent components include traces of the other noble gases, neon being the most plentiful after argon, followed by helium, krypton, and xenon, the least plentiful. In addition, traces of hydrogen (H_2) and nitrous oxide, or dinitrogen oxide (N_2O) are present.

Many other gases in the air may show marked changes in their concentrations. These are known as the *variable gases*, the best known of which are carbon dioxide (CO_2) and water vapor, which vary in concentration depending upon the season of the year and the location on earth. Other variable gases include trace amounts of methane (CH_4), carbon monoxide (CO), ozone (O_3), ammonia (NH_3), nitrogen dioxide (NO_2), sulfur dioxide (SO_2), and hydrogen sulfide (H_2S). Many of these variable gases are pollutants, which have elevated concentrations in urban areas, but gases such as ammonia, ozone, hydrogen sulfide, and nitrogen dioxide also have natural origins and can be found anywhere. The amounts of the *variable gases* listed in Table 7.4 are for clean air. Figure 7.10 gives an overall view of the composition of clean, dry air which contains no pollutants and no water vapor.

We will now consider the important gases of the atmosphere individually as we study their sources and their effects on living things.

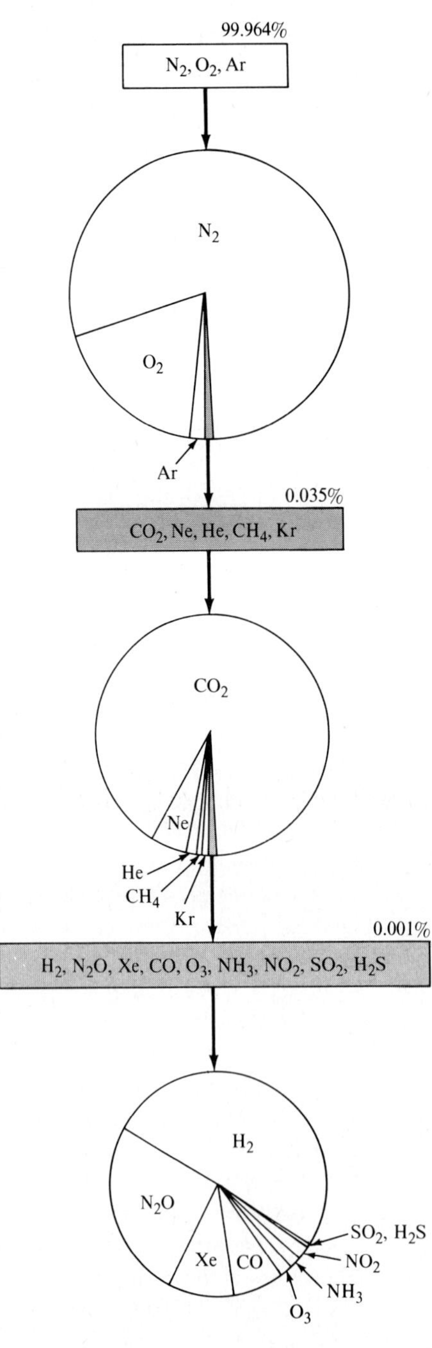

FIGURE 7.10
Pie chart showing composition of clean dry air.

TABLE 7.4 PERMANENT AND VARIABLE GASES IN THE ATMOSPHERE

Gas	Formula	Volume % (volume fraction)	ppm
		Permanent	
Nitrogen	N_2	78.084 (0.78084)	780,840
Oxygen	O_2	20.946 (0.20946)	209,450
Argon	Ar	0.934 (0.00934)	9340
Neon	Ne	0.00182 (0.0000182)	18.2
Helium	He	0.00052 (0.0000052)	5.2
Krypton	Kr	0.00011 (0.0000011)	1.1
Hydrogen	H_2	0.00005 (0.0000005)	0.5
Nitrous oxide	N_2O	0.00003 (0.0000003)	0.3
Xenon	Xe	0.000009 (0.00000009)	0.09
		Variable	
Water vapor	H_2O	0–7 (0–0.07)	0–70,000
Carbon dioxide	CO_2	0.034 (0.00034)	340
Methane	CH_4	0.00015 (0.0000015)	1.5
Carbon monoxide	CO	0.00001 (0.0000001)	0.1
Ozone	O_3	0.000002 (0.00000002)	0.02
Ammonia	NH_3	0.000001 (0.00000001)	0.01
Nitrogen oxide	NO	0.0000002 (0.000000002)	0.0002
Nitrogen dioxide	NO_2	0.0000004 (0.000000004)	0.004
Sulfur dioxide	SO_2	0.00000002 (0.0000000002)	0.0002
Hydrogen sulfide	H_2S	0.00000002 (0.0000000002)	0.0002

7.11 NITROGEN, N_2

Nitrogen molecules, which include nearly 80 percent of all the molecules in air, are very unreactive. You have seen (Section 4.10) that the N atoms in N_2 molecules are joined by a strong triple bond that is difficult to break. Thus N_2 cannot easily react by first dissociating into N atoms. There is also little tendency for the occurrence of other types of reactions in which atoms or groups add onto N_2 molecules. Nitrogen compounds are needed for use in the manufacture of fertilizers. In fact, of the 15 to 20 million tons of ammonia (NH_3) produced every year in the United States, 80 percent is used to make fertilizer. Chemists have developed ways to convert atmospheric nitrogen into useful nitrogen compounds such as ammonia. The process by which atmospheric nitrogen is converted to nitrogen compounds that can be used by plants is called **nitrogen fixation.** One industrial method used for fixing nitrogen is the Haber process, in which the nitrogen gas reacts with hydrogen gas. The reaction is

$$N_2 + 3H_2 \longrightarrow 2NH_3$$

The ammonia can then be converted into other N compounds that eventually are used to nourish the plant life, which in turn nourishes us. Plants utilize N atoms to construct protein molecules, essential for the growth and maintenance of human beings.

Some plants are able to make direct use of the nitrogen in air because they contain special nitrogen-fixing organisms. These are the leguminous plants (peas, beans, alfalfa, clover), which are very useful in returning nitrogen to the soil. Also the seeds of legumes, that is, peas and beans, are good sources of protein, which can be utilized instead of the more expensive animal proteins. For instance, a 100-g portion of beef contains 25 g of protein, the same amount of protein present in a 100-g portion of peanut butter. We will elaborate much more on the structure of proteins and the quality of proteins in foods in Chapter 23.

7.12 OXYGEN, O_2

In contrast with the nonreactive gas nitrogen, oxygen is very reactive and combines with most elements to form oxides. Oxygen participates in *combustion* reactions such as those in which carbon-containing fuel compounds are burned in oxygen to provide energy for heating houses or running automobiles. Methane (CH_4), the chief component of natural gas, reacts with O_2 to provide carbon dioxide and water.

$$CH_4 + 2O_2 \longrightarrow CO_2 + 2H_2O$$

Octane, which has the molecular formula C_8H_{18}, is a typical component of gasoline. With excess supplies of O_2 gas, octane also produces CO_2 and H_2O.

$$C_8H_{18} + \tfrac{25}{2}O_2 \longrightarrow 8CO_2 + 9H_2O$$

However, in automobile engines, where the supply of air and hence O_2 gas is restricted, the combustion products will also include carbon monoxide (CO).

$$C_8H_{18} + \tfrac{17}{2}O_2 \longrightarrow 8CO + 9H_2O$$

In Section 7.16 we will discuss the effect of CO on living things.

Animals inhale air to supply themselves with the oxygen necessary for their survival. To see how much oxygen is actually utilized by humans, we can compare the amount of oxygen in inspired air, the air that enters the lungs, to that in expired air, the air that leaves the lungs. The composition of inspired air is the same as that of the atmosphere, which includes 20.9 percent oxygen and 0.034 percent carbon dioxide. Because some of the oxygen is utilized by the body, producing carbon dioxide as a waste product, expired air contains less oxygen and more carbon dioxide, as we see from looking at Table 7.5. The average composition of expired air includes 16.3 percent oxygen and 4.5 percent carbon dioxide.

Oxygen is carried from the lung alveoli (see Figure 7.8) to the blood vessels by diffusion. More than 98 percent of the oxygen in blood is bound to a giant protein molecule called *hemoglobin*, Hb, which binds with oxygen to form oxyhemoglobin, HbO_2.

TABLE 7.5 **COMPOSITION OF EXPIRED AND INSPIRED AIR**

	Inspired air, vol %	Expired air vol %
N_2	78.9	78.9
O_2	20.9	16.3
CO_2	0.034	4.5

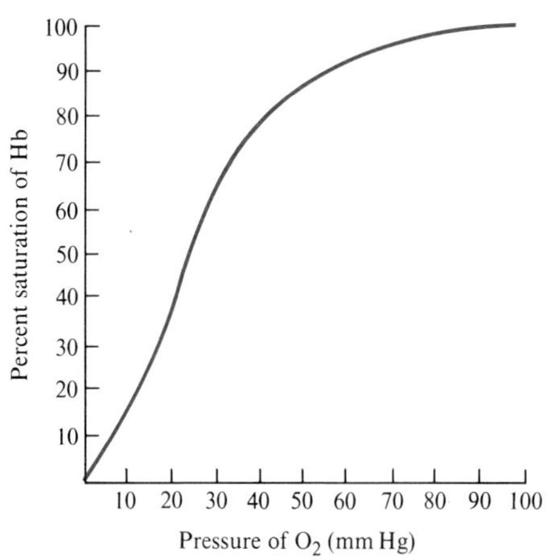

FIGURE 7.11
pO_2 vs. percent saturation of hemoglobin.

$$\underset{\text{(Blue)}}{\text{Hb}} + O_2 \longrightarrow \underset{\text{(Red)}}{\text{HbO}_2}$$

Blood in the veins (which carry blood away from tissues) is bluish because it contains uncombined hemoglobin (Hb), also called deoxyhemoglobin, while arterial blood is red owing to the presence of HbO_2.

For the body to function properly, hemoglobin must be highly saturated with oxygen gas. Figure 7.11 shows how the partial pressure of oxygen available in inspired air affects the percentage saturation of hemoglobin, that is, the percentage of the total hemoglobin that is combined with O_2. You can see that the hemoglobin is 90 percent saturated at a relatively low partial pressure of oxygen, 60 mmHg. (This is low compared with the partial pressure of O_2 in air, which is 159 mmHg, and that in alveolar air, which is only about 105 mmHg.) Thus the body can still function at such low levels of O_2 pressure, levels which could be attained during severe exercise, at high altitudes, or as a result of heart or lung disease.

The alveolar partial pressure of O_2 is only 105 mmHg because 150 ml of each 500-ml breath of air is trapped in lung airways (called dead space) and is unavailable for exchange with blood.

SAMPLE EXERCISE 7.9

Calculate the volume percent of oxygen gas in air at 760 mmHg, if the partial pressure exerted by the O_2 is 60 mmHg.

Solution:

To do this recall from Section 7.8 that partial pressures can be used to give composition by moles and thus volume.

$$\frac{p\ (O_2)}{P\ (\text{total})} = \frac{\text{mol } O_2}{\text{mol (total)}} = \frac{V\ (O_2)}{V\ (\text{total})}$$

Recall that the volume % of O_2 in air is normally 20.9 percent.

$$\frac{60\ \cancel{\text{mmHg}}}{760\ \cancel{\text{mmHg}}} = 0.079\ \text{(volume fraction)} = 7.9\ \text{vol}\ \%$$

EXERCISE 7.9

Suppose a gaseous mixture (air and cyclopropane) to be used as a general anesthetic contains cyclopropane at a partial pressure of 167 mmHg. What is the volume percent of cyclopropane present if the total pressure is 760 mmHg?

7.13 OXIDES OF NITROGEN, NO AND NO_2 (NO_x)

Of the nitrogen oxides the two important pollutants resulting from human activities are NO, properly named *nitrogen oxide* but commonly known as *nitric oxide,* and NO_2, nitrogen dioxide. Together these two oxides are often referred to as NO_x.

NO_x emission occurs as a side reaction of combustion. The air used for combustions includes N_2 as well as O_2. At high temperatures it is possible for the N_2 to react with O_2 to produce NO:

$$N_2 + O_2 \xrightarrow{\Delta} 2NO$$

The necessary high temperatures are present in automobile engines. Most of the NO_x which comes directly from combustion is NO, but the NO in turn produces NO_2. The series of reactions involved may be represented by a simplified version in which NO reacts with O_2 of the air:

$$2NO + O_2 \longrightarrow 2NO_2$$

The concentration of NO in the atmosphere is about 2×10^{-3} ppm and that of NO_2 is about 4×10^{-3} ppm.

Because of their chemical reactivity, the NO_x gases can have harmful effects upon living and nonliving matter. It is possible for NO_2 to lead to the production of the corrosive acidic substance nitric acid, HNO_3, by several different pathways. The one shown in Figure 7.12 involves ozone (O_3), NO_2, and two other oxides of nitrogen, nitrogen trioxide (NO_3) and dinitrogen pentoxide (N_2O_5). Both the nitric acid and the nitrates it produces may have a corrosive effect upon plants and materials.

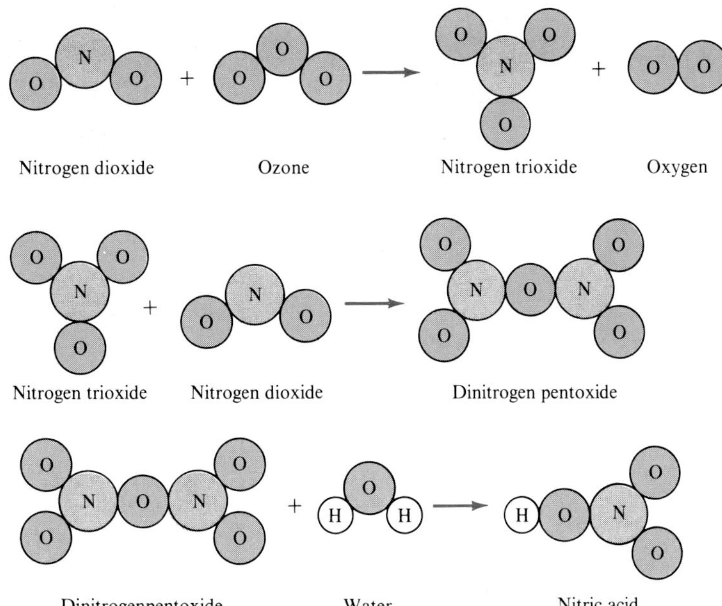

FIGURE 7.12
NO_2 to HNO_3 reaction path.

The gas NO is not poisonous to humans. NO_2, however, is irritating to the lungs, and in very high concentrations of more than 10 ppm it can reduce resistance to respiratory infections. For the relatively low levels present even in urban areas, there is no evidence that exposure to NO_2 produces any chronic effects. Nitrogen dioxide is a brownish-colored gas (see Color Plate 7*a*) and on smoggy days is responsible for brown haze.

7.14 OZONE, O_3

Ozone, O_3, which contains three O atoms per molecule, is another gaseous form of the element oxygen.

Ozone forms naturally in the upper atmosphere when diatomic oxygen interacts with high-energy, short-wavelength radiation. When this happens, the oxygen molecule dissociates into oxygen atoms.

$$O_2 + \text{energetic radiation} \longrightarrow O + O$$

Each O atom then recombines rapidly with an O_2 molecule to form an ozone molecule.

$$(M) + O_2 + O \longrightarrow (M) + O_3$$

(The molecule represented by the letter M is needed for the reaction to take place although M itself is not altered in the reaction.)

An artificial source of ozone is the reaction of the pollutant NO_2 with solar radiation.

$$NO_2 + \text{radiation} \longrightarrow NO + O \qquad \text{and} \qquad O + O_2 \longrightarrow O_3$$

Increased solar radiation in the summer months produces higher levels of ozone. Air pollution in which such photochemical reactions participate is called *photochemical smog,* typified by the brownish Los Angeles type of smog. The average concentration of ozone in the atmosphere is about 0.025 ppm. Urban concentrations may reach levels as high as 1 ppm.

The highly reactive ozone gas which imparts a "fresh" odor to the air in which it is present may have a variety of effects. On the positive side ozone is capable of killing bacteria, and during the 1940s and 1950s lamps which produced ozone were used for this purpose. However, the harmful effects of ozone made the process dangerous and caused it to be discontinued. Ozone causes severe damage to plants and materials. In humans, O_3 attacks the lungs and respiratory system and may cause fatigue and shortness of breath. The performance of an athlete may be affected when ozone levels reach as high as 0.1 ppm and serious irritation sets in at about 0.3 ppm. The typical fresh air odor of ozone can be detected at just 0.015 ppm.

O_3 absorbs uv radiation with wavelength < 300 nm.

The chlorofluorohydrocarbons are known collectively as Freons.

The ozone which is considered a pollutant in the lower atmosphere is an essential component of an upper portion of the atmosphere called the stratosphere (about 50 km altitude). Ozone absorbs ultraviolet radiation from the sun, which would be very harmful to life on earth. In fact, increased ultraviolet radiation has been correlated with increased incidence of skin cancers. One way in which humans have threatened the ozone layer is by introducing compounds known as *chlorofluoromethanes* into the atmosphere. The formula for methane is CH_4. In chlorofluoromethanes the H atoms of methane are replaced by F and Cl atoms. Typical chlorofluoromethanes include compounds such as the ones below.

```
      F                  F                  F
      |                  |                  |
  Cl—C—F            Cl—C—Cl            Cl—C—Cl
      |                  |                  |
      F                  Cl                 F
```

Chlorotrifluoromethane   Trichlorofluoromethane   Dichlorodifluoromethane

This type of compound has found use in aerosol propellants and refrigerants. Eventually the gaseous chlorofluoromethanes diffuse into the stratosphere, where they can destroy ozone molecules by a sequence of reactions. First the halocarbon molecules break down, forming highly reactive Cl atoms, which can decompose O_3 molecules (see Figure 7.13).

$$\text{Chlorofluoromethanes} \longrightarrow Cl$$

$$Cl + O_3 \longrightarrow ClO + O_2$$

To make matters even worse, the ClO molecules may react with O atoms to

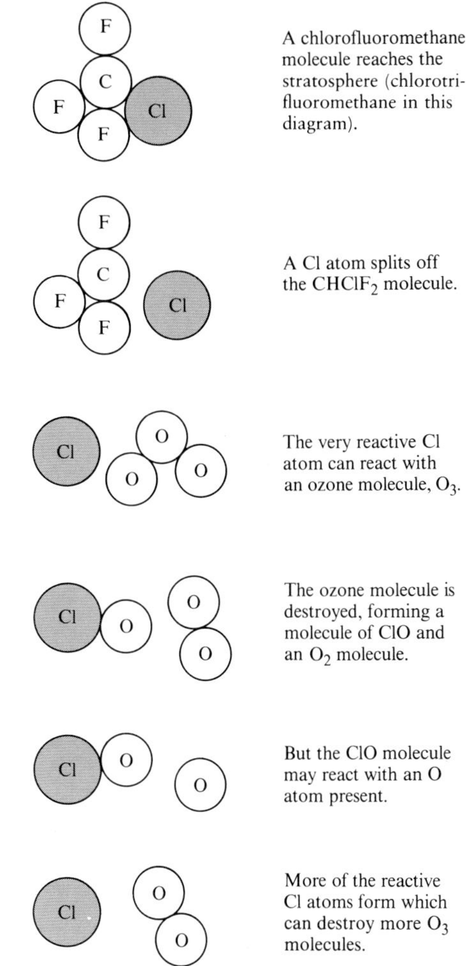

F
C
F
Cl
F
A chlorofluoromethane molecule reaches the stratosphere (chlorotrifluoromethane in this diagram).
F
C
F
Cl
F
A Cl atom splits off the $CHClF_2$ molecule.
Cl
O
O
O
The very reactive Cl atom can react with an ozone molecule, O_3.
Cl
O
O
O
The ozone molecule is destroyed, forming a molecule of ClO and an O_2 molecule.
Cl
O
O
But the ClO molecule may react with an O atom present.
Cl
O
O
More of the reactive Cl atoms form which can destroy more O_3 molecules.

FIGURE 7.13
Decomposition of stratospheric ozone.

regenerate more Cl atoms, which decompose more O_3 molecules, starting a long chain process.

$$ClO + O \longrightarrow Cl + O_2$$

The use of chlorofluoromethanes has been discontinued in many aerosol products to help prevent the harmful accumulation of these compounds.

7.15 WATER VAPOR

The amount of water vapor present in air can vary from as little as zero to as much as 7 percent. Water concentration in air is usually expressed in terms of the *relative humidity*, which is the actual amount of water in the air divided by the maximum possible amount, known as the *saturation amount*.

$$\text{Relative humidity} = \frac{\text{actual amount of } H_2O(g) \times 100\%}{\text{saturation amount of } H_2O(g)}$$

The saturation amount of water vapor in air increases as the temperature increases. At 0°C it is only 0.7 percent, at 20°C it is about 2.5 percent, at 30°C about 4 percent, and at 40°C about 7 percent. Suppose the concentration of water in a sample of air is 2 percent. At 20°C the relative humidity would be higher than at 30°C.

At 20°C:

$$\text{Relative humidity} = \frac{2\% \times 100\%}{2.5\%} = 80\%$$

At 30°C:

$$\text{Relative humidity} = \frac{2\% \times 100\%}{4\%} = 50\%$$

Extreme values of relative humidity can be very uncomfortable. In the winter heated air tends to become very dry. To see why, suppose the relative humidity of the cold air out of doors is 50 percent at 0°C. Then the actual amount of water vapor in the air must be half the saturation value, 0.7%/2, or 0.35%. Now suppose we heat that same cold air to 20°C, a temperature at which the air can hold as much as 2.5 percent water vapor. To calculate the relative humidity of this heated air,

$$\text{Relative humidity (heated air)} = \frac{0.35\% \times 100\%}{2.5\%} = 14\%$$

Thus the relative humidity of the winter air plunged from 50 percent to just 14 percent upon being heated. Relative humidity of less than 15 percent tends to cause respiratory irritations. Since air is constantly coming in from outside, placing pots of water about to counteract the uncomfortable dryness is not particularly effective.

Very high humidity coupled with high temperatures causes discomfort because perspiration from the skin is unable to evaporate into the already nearly saturated air. This evaporation would absorb heat from the body, thus cooling it.

7.16 OXIDES OF CARBON, CO AND CO_2

Of the two common oxides of carbon, one, CO, is highly toxic and the other, CO_2, is harmless.

Carbon Monoxide

Nature produces *carbon monoxide* (CO) from certain types of marine and plant life and from the burning of forests. However, more than 75 percent of the worldwide annual production of CO comes from combustion. Whenever carbon-containing compounds are burned without an adequate supply of air, carbon monoxide forms. As we mentioned in Section 7.12, such a condition is present in the internal combustion engine, where gasoline is burned. In fact, the combustion of gasoline represents the largest artificial source of CO.

The worldwide concentration of CO in the atmosphere averages about 0.1 parts per million (0.1 ppm). However, in some urban areas, where traffic density is high, concentrations can soar as high as hundreds of parts per million.

How dangerous is CO to humans? CO is a colorless, odorless gas, which is relatively unreactive chemically. However, CO is able to combine with the hemoglobin in the blood about 200 times more readily than does oxygen.

$$\text{Hb} + \text{CO} \longrightarrow \text{HbCO}$$

This prevents the hemoglobin from binding oxygen (see Section 7.12). At long exposures (several minutes) to levels of 1000 ppm, death due to suffocation occurs. This is what happens to a person exposed to the exhaust from a car engine allowed to run for a long time in a closed garage. At prolonged exposure to smaller concentrations, inhalation of CO can cause poor judgment (10 ppm), cardiovascular changes (40 ppm), headaches (200 ppm), and loss of consciousness (600 ppm). Fortunately CO does not accumulate in the body because the inhalation of CO-free air for an hour or two removes most of it.

The antidote for carbon monoxide poisoning is oxygen.

Carbon Dioxide

Carbon dioxide is constantly being produced and consumed in nature. The human contribution to the total CO_2 emission comes from combustion of carbon-containing fuels, called *fossil fuels*. Fossil fuels include coal (primarily carbon) and hydrocarbon compounds (compounds containing carbon and hydrogen), such as those occurring in petroleum and natural gas. Carbon dioxide is produced when any of these is burned (recall from Section 7.12 the combustion reactions for the hydrocarbons CH_4 and C_8H_{18}). For coal the reaction is simply $C + O_2 \longrightarrow CO_2$. As a result of these reactions and others like them, the concentration of carbon dioxide in the atmosphere has increased gradually from about 300 ppm in 1896 to about 340 ppm in 1980. What effect has this increased amount of CO_2 had on the earth and its inhabitants? One prediction, known as the "greenhouse effect," was that the higher CO_2 levels would lead to an increase in the temperature of our planet. The reasoning behind this has to do with the ability of CO_2 to absorb infrared (ir) radiation, which is emitted from the surface of the earth. The heat produced by this ir radiation keeps our planet at a temperature at which life thrives. The theory is that increased levels of atmospheric CO_2 will lead to increased ir absorption and thus an increase in the temperature of the earth. So far no such increase has been observed. Although the ecology of the earth must be in some way affected by such a drastic change in the atmosphere, none has yet been clearly detected. Carbon dioxide, a colorless and odorless gas, is not toxic or harmful.

7.17 SULFUR DIOXIDE, SO_2

Sulfur dioxide gas is emitted as a result of various industrial activities. Sulfur in compound form is a common impurity in carbon-containing fuels. When these sulfur-containing fuels are subjected to combustion, the S present reacts with O_2 to produce SO_2:

$$\text{S (in impurities)} + O_2 \longrightarrow SO_2$$

Sulfur dioxide is also a by-product of a metallurgical process in which sulfide ores react with O_2 to produce the free metals. For example, copper is present in nature as copper(II) sulfide. To remove the Cu metal from the sulfide compound,

$$CuS + O_2 \longrightarrow Cu + SO_2$$

Although the average worldwide concentration of SO_2 in the atmosphere is only 0.2 ppb (parts per billion), concentrations in the industrial urban areas are thousands of times greater and average about 0.1 ppm.

The chemically reactive SO_2 can react with air and water to produce highly corrosive sulfuric acid, H_2SO_4. A somewhat simplified version of the reactions involved is portrayed in this sequence:

$$2SO_2 + O_2 \longrightarrow 2SO_3$$

$$SO_3 + H_2O \longrightarrow H_2SO_4$$

The sulfuric acid can corrode metals such as iron.

$$Fe + H_2SO_4 \longrightarrow FeSO_4 + H_2$$

Building materials made of carbonate stones are gradually decomposed by the action of sulfuric acid.

$$CaCO_3 + H_2SO_4 \longrightarrow CaSO_4 + CO_2 + H_2O$$

Increased levels of SO_2 in the atmosphere have led to the production of *acid rain,* containing H_2SO_4. As shown above, acid rain can corrode nonliving things. Many priceless statues are in danger of being ruined by acidic fumes, which are the products of modern industrialization. Acid rain is also dangerous to living things. Acid rainfall can increase the acidity of natural waters, harming or even killing fish. Trees and other plant life are also in danger of being destroyed when subjected to acid rain.

Exposure to 1.5 ppm SO_2 for only a few minutes can cause respiratory problems in healthy individuals.

The effect of SO_2 on humans may also be serious. Sulfur dioxide is a colorless gas with an unpleasant odor and a tendency to produce a choking sensation. The odor of SO_2 can be detected at a concentration of about 0.5 ppm. SO_2 affects the respiratory system and can cause chronic bronchitis. When air levels rise to more than 0.25 ppm, excess deaths may occur in the aged and in those afflicted with respiratory and cardiac disease. During the disastrous London fog of 1952,

SO_2 in combination with soot caused the death rate in London to double. During this time SO_2 concentrations reached levels higher than 1 ppm, about 10 times the normal level. The simple solution of banning the burning of coal with high S content has helped to prevent such awesome fogs.

SUMMARY

The properties of gases are explained by the kinetic-molecular theory, which states that gases are composed of rapidly moving molecules spaced so far apart that the attractive forces between them are negligible.

The amount of force per unit area exerted by a gas is the gas pressure. Sea-level pressure is approximately one atmosphere (1 atm), which is equivalent to 760 mmHg (760 torr). The gas laws relate the pressure P, volume V, and temperature T of a gas sample. According to the combined gas law, PV/T is constant. When T is constant, Boyle's law (PV is constant) is produced, and when P is held constant, the result is Charles' law (V/T is constant).

For n moles of gas PV/T is equal to the quantity $n \times R$, where R is the ideal gas constant; this constitutes the ideal gas law ($PV = nRT$). Gases that obey the ideal gas law (such as air at room temperature and pressure) are called ideal gases.

Gases in mixtures behave independently from each other. Dalton's law of partial pressures says that the total pressure of a gas mixture is the sum of the partial pressures of each component gas. The composition of gaseous mixtures is often given in terms of partial pressures. Gases mix as a result of random motion called diffusion. The greater the formula weight of a gas, the more slowly it diffuses.

The atmosphere is the layer of gases which surrounds the earth. The major constituents of air are N_2 gas, O_2, and Ar (78.1, 20.9, and 0.9 percent, respectively). Other gases present in much lesser amounts include the permanent constituents Ne, He, Kr, Xe, H_2, and N_2O, always present in the same amounts. The variable gases include H_2O vapor, CO_2, CH_4, CO, O_3, NH_3, NO, NO_2, SO_2, and H_2S.

N_2 is unreactive. When it does react to form nitrogen compounds, the process is known as nitrogen fixation. In contrast, O_2 is very reactive. The O_2 in blood needed for respiration is bound to the protein molecule hemoglobin. The oxides of nitrogen, NO and NO_2, called NO_x, are produced as a side product of combustion. They are both highly reactive. NO is not toxic, but the brownish-colored NO_2 irritates the lungs.

Ozone, O_3, is a form of the element oxygen that forms in the upper atmosphere or when NO_2 is irradiated by the sun. The high reactivity of ozone makes it very corrosive. Although a pollutant in the lower atmosphere, O_3 is needed in the stratosphere to absorb uv radiation from the sun which would be destructive to living things on earth. Fluorochloromethanes are dangerous because they eventually diffuse into the stratosphere, where they can decompose O_3 molecules.

The amount of water vapor in air varies from 0 to 7 vol % but is usually expressed in terms of relative humidity, that is, the actual amount of water in the air compared with the amount the air could hold.

Carbon monoxide is a colorless, odorless, toxic gas produced largely from incomplete combustion of carbon-containing fuels. CO_2, also produced from combustion, is not toxic.

The oxides of sulfur, mostly generated from combustion of fuels with S impurities, are toxic and very reactive. Upon reaction with water they form sulfuric acid (H_2SO_4), which is corrosive and is responsible for acid rain.

KEY WORDS

vapor
kinetic-molecular theory
gas pressure
atmosphere (unit)
torr
Boyle's law
Charles' law
combined gas law
ideal gas constant
ideal gas law
ideal gas
real gas
partial pressure
Dalton's law of partial pressures
diffusion
Graham's law
nitrogen fixation
relative humidity

EXERCISES

7.10 How many times greater are the densities of liquids and solids than those of gases? (Use 1 g/ml for solid and liquid densities and g/L for gas density.) How can this calculated value be explained?

7.11 Use the density of air (1.21 g/L) to calculate the mass of air which is contained by a room which measures 3 m × 4 m × 5 m. Remember that 1 L = 1 dm^3 = $10^{-3}m^3$.

7.12 If an average adult takes 15 breaths per minute, inhaling 500 cm^3 of air each time, what mass of air does the person breath in 1 min? (Density of air = 1.21 g/L.)

7.13 Convert the following to pressures in units of millimeters of Hg: (a) 2 atm; (b) 30 inHg; (c) 100 lb/ft^2; (d) 30 cmHg; (e) 0.001 atm; (f) 1 Pa; (g) 100 kPa; (h) 750 torr.

7.14 Calculate the pressure in millimeters of Hg and in atmospheres in an oxygen gas cylinder which contains oxygen at 2200 lb/ft^2.

7.15 Given the ideal gas constant R as 0.0821 (L)(atm)/(mol)(K), find R in terms of: (a) (L)(torr)/(mol)(K); (b) (L)(mmHg)/(mol)(K).

7.16 A sample of gas originally in a 2-L vessel at 1 atm is compressed until the final volume is only 0.5 L. If this is done at constant temperature, what is the final pressure?

7.17 The pressure of a 50-cm^3 sample of air at STP is doubled. If the temperature remains constant, what is the final volume of the air?

7.18 At a constant pressure of 1 atm, 300 ml of nitrogen gas is allowed to expand until the final volume is 450 ml. If the initial temperature is 30°C, what is the final temperature?

7.19 A 20.0-L sample of air exerts a pressure of 750 mmHg at a temperature of 25°C. Calculate the new volume when the pressure is increased to 1250 mmHg and the temperature is increased to 50°C.

7.20 Using the combined gas law equation, derive an expression for the relationship between P and T at constant volume.

7.21 Calculate the volume occupied by 2 mol of an ideal gas at STP.

7.22 Using the ideal gas law, calculate the volume occupied by 150 g of N_2O gas at 20°C and 650 torr.

7.23 What pressure in millimeters of Hg is exerted by 0.25 mol of an ideal gas contained in a 500-ml vessel at 37°C?

7.24 Calculate the number of moles and molecules of O_2 present in one breath (500 ml) if the temperature is 37°C and the partial pressure of O_2 is 159 mmHg.

7.25 A gas mixture used as a general anesthetic must contain oxygen at a partial pressure of at least 114 mmHg. If the total pressure of the mixture is 1 atm, what is the maximum possible partial pressure of the anesthetic gas? Of the gases listed in Table 7.3, which ones would be effective in such a mixture?

7.26 If the partial pressure of water vapor in a sample of wet air is 25 mmHg and the total pressure is 1.2 atm, what is the partial pressure of the air in the mixture?

7.27 Under which of the following sets of conditions would you expect a gas to deviate most from ideal behavior: (a) 1 atm, 37°C; (b) STP; (c) 5 atm, −50°C; (d) 5 atm, 50°C? Explain.

7.28 Carbon monoxide, sulfur dioxide, nitric oxide, nitrogen dioxide, and ozone all behave as air pollutants. Of these gases which has the
(a) Slowest rate of diffusion
(b) Fastest rate of diffusion

7.29 Write balanced chemical equations for the combustion of 1 mol of butane, C_4H_{10}, in which the products are (a) CO_2 and H_2O; (b) CO and H_2O.

7.30 Why might the pollution problem on a sunny Los Angeles day be worse than on a cloudy day?

7.31 The concentration of CO_2 in the atmosphere exhibits seasonal variations. Would you expect the concentration to be higher in summer or in winter? Why?

7.32 Of the 500 ml of air moved in and out of the lungs with each breath (tidal volume), 150 ml is trapped in airways called *dead space* and is unavailable for exchange with blood. In each breath what volume % of oxygen is available for exchange with the blood?

7.33 Write an equation for the formation of sulfur dioxide from the reaction of zinc sulfide (ZnS) with oxygen gas. If 10 mol of ZnS reacts with excess oxygen, how many liters of SO_2 measured at STP will be produced?

7.34 A carbonate stone pillar called Cleopatra's Needle was moved from Alexandria, Egypt, to London, England, where it suffered more deterioration in 70 years than it had in its 3000-year existence. Explain this, using chemical equations.

8 . . . . LIQUIDS AND SOLIDS

8.1 INTRODUCTION

Except for air, most of the substances that you encounter are in a liquid or solid state. In Chapter 7 we were able to develop a detailed theory of gases based upon the kinetic-molecular theory, which depends upon the concept of random motion of independent molecules. We also mentioned that the mathematical treatment of solids and liquids, unlike that of gases, is complicated by the fact that their molecules (or ions or atoms) are close together and thus the forces of attraction or repulsion among them cannot be ignored. Because of the order in solids, it is possible to evaluate the forces operating among their constituent particles. The ions, atoms, or molecules of solids are present in a regular, unchanging arrangement. For instance, Figure 4.3 shows an NaCl crystal, in which the Na^+ and Cl^- ions occupy fixed positions with respect to each other. The study of liquids is complicated by the fact that they do not have the order present in solids, and although their molecules are in constant motion, the motion is not random as it is in gases. Thus theories to describe the behavior of liquids are particularly difficult to develop. Here is this chapter we will present a largely qualitative description of the properties of liquids and solids. We will also take a detailed look at some important liquids and solids, paying special attention to their roles in living systems.

8.2 VAPOR PRESSURE

The term *vapor* is used instead of gas to refer to the gaseous state of substances which are not gases under ordinary conditions (see Section 7.1). Liquids produce vapor when energetic molecules at the liquid surface escape into the gas phase, as shown in Figure 8.1. This is **evaporation** (or vaporization). The equation below describes the evaporation of water.

$$H_2O(l) \longrightarrow H_2O(g)$$

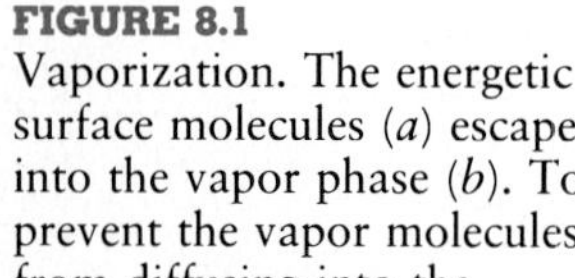

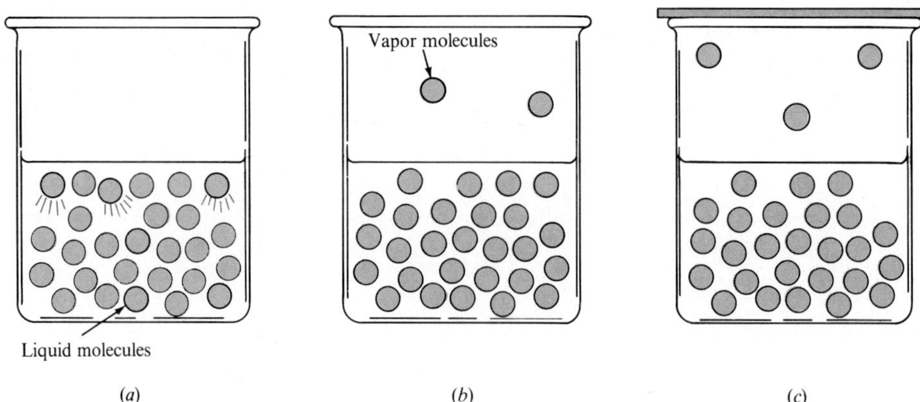

FIGURE 8.1
Vaporization. The energetic surface molecules (*a*) escape into the vapor phase (*b*). To prevent the vapor molecules from diffusing into the atmosphere, the container must be covered (*c*).

The **vapor pressure** of a liquid is the pressure exerted by the gas molecules above a liquid, molecules that are produced from evaporation of the liquid. Vapor pressures of liquids are measured in closed containers so that the vapor produced will not diffuse into the atmosphere (see Figure 8.1*c*).

The device used to measure vapor pressures of liquids consists of a container attached to a U-shaped tube, which is filled with mercury, evacuated, and sealed off at the end. This tube, called a *manometer*, works very much like the barometer used to measure atmospheric pressures. When there is no liquid (or gas) in the container, as shown in Figure 8.2*a*, the mercury levels in the manometer tube are equal, since there is no pressure exerted on the mercury. Then a liquid is placed

FIGURE 8.2
Vapor-pressure measurement. (*a*) The container is empty and there is no difference in the mercury level in the manometer tube. (*b*) The water in the container exerts a vapor pressure of 24 mmHg, the difference in the height of the mercury levels. (*c*) The ethanol, which is more volatile than water, exerts a vapor pressure of 56 mmHg.

in the container. The gaseous molecules produced by the liquid exert pressure (the vapor pressure) on the mercury in the manometer tube. The mercury level in contact with the vapor drops and the level in the other arm rises. The difference in heights of the mercury levels is the vapor pressure of the liquid. The greater the vapor pressure of the liquid, the more pressure is exerted upon the mercury in the U tube and the greater will be the difference in heights. You can see from looking at Figure 8.2*b* and *c* that the vapor pressure of water is 24 mmHg and that of ethanol is 56 mmHg. Liquids that evaporate easily have relatively high vapor pressures and are said to be *volatile*. Thus we can say that ethanol is more volatile than water.

Note in Figure 8.2 that the temperature at which the vapor pressures of water and ethanol are measured is quoted (25°C in this case). Vapor pressures are very sensitive to temperature changes. As the temperature of a liquid increases, so does its vapor pressure. Table 8.1 lists the vapor pressures of some liquids at different temperatures. At 25°C (as shown in Figure 8.2) the vapor pressure of water is 24 mmHg, at 50°C it is 92 mmHg, and at 100°C it is 760 mmHg.

TABLE 8.1 **VAPOR PRESSURES OF COMMON LIQUIDS AT VARIOUS TEMPERATURES**

	Vapor pressure mmHg of				
Temperature, °C	**Water**	**Ethanol**	**Carbon tetrachloride**	**Ether**	**Mercury**
0	5	12	30	185	0.0002
10	9	24	50	292	0.0005
20	17	41	80	378	0.001
25	24	56	98	460	0.002
30	32	79	143	647	0.003
34.5	—	—	—	760	—
40	55	135	216	921	0.006
50	92	222	317	1277	0.013
60	149	353	451	—	0.025
70	234	543	622	—	0.048
76.5	—	—	760	—	—
78.5	—	760	—	—	—
80	355	813	843	—	0.089
90	526	1187	1122	—	0.16
100	760	—	1463	—	0.27
200	11700	—	—	—	17
250		—	—	—	74
300		—	—	—	247
350		—	—	—	673
357		—	—	—	760
400		—	—	—	1574

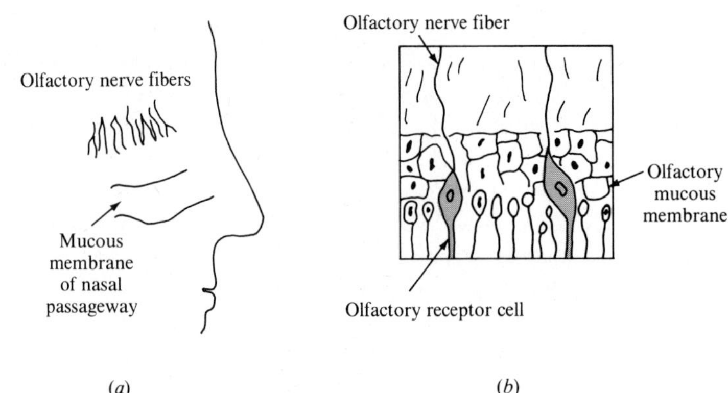

FIGURE 8.3
Olfactory area. (*a*) The nasal area. (*b*) The mucous membrane is magnified to show the olfactory receptor cells. Only volatile substances are able to reach this area.

It is also possible for solids to exert vapor pressures when solid molecules become energetic enough to escape from the solid phase to the gas phase. This process is called **sublimation**. For instance, iodine (I_2), the violet substance used to prepare the anti-infective tincture of iodine, sublimes readily.

$$I_2(s) \longrightarrow I_2(g)$$

The vapor pressures of solids are generally much lower than the vapor pressures of most liquids and are also rather difficult to measure. At 25°C the vapor pressures of the majority of solids lie in a range from close to 0 to about 1 mmHg. Solids that have the highest vapor pressures sublime easily. I_2, for example, has a vapor pressure of about 1 mmHg.

Solids with high vapor pressures may have odors.

The vapor pressure of a solid can be used to predict whether or not it *could* have a detectable odor. A theory advanced to explain the phenomenon of smell is that the olfactory membrane located at the upper part of the nasal cavity contains olfactory receptor sites, which can accommodate molecules of shapes approximately the same as those of the sites. Figure 8.3 illustrates the olfactory area. Whatever the exact physical or chemical principles involved in the mechanism of smell, one essential requirement for odors to be detectable is that the substance to be smelled must produce vapor molecules that come into contact with the olfactory membrane. Thus for solids to have odors they must be volatile. For example, dichlorobenzene (mothballs) and camphor both have strong odors along with relatively high vapor pressures (for solids) of about 1 and 0.3 mmHg, respectively. On the other hand, solids such as metals and sodium chloride, which are odorless, have vapor pressures which are close to zero at room temperature.

8.3 BOILING POINT

As we mentioned in Section 4.16, the attractive forces between the molecules in a liquid must be overcome before the molecules can escape to become gaseous. Adding heat to a liquid increases molecular motion and hence the kinetic energy of its molecules. As the molecules become more energetic, they are able to overcome the attractive forces of neighboring molecules. Some molecules do escape in this way by evaporation, but their escape is hindered by the external atmospheric pressure pushing down on them. As the temperature of a liquid is raised, its vapor pressure increases. Eventually the vapor pressure of the liquid becomes equal to the atmospheric pressure, allowing a great number of molecules to escape. This is the **boiling point**, which is defined as the temperature at which the vapor pressure of the liquid is identical to the external atmospheric pressure above the liquid. The reason that you can see bubbles of vapor in boiling liquids is that the vapor pressure they exert is equal to that applied by the external atmosphere. Before the boiling point is reached, when the vapor pressure in the bubbles is less than that of the atmosphere, the bubbles collapse and are unable to escape from the liquid.

At the boiling point the vapor pressure of a liquid equals the external pressure.

As indicated in color in Table 8.1, the temperature at which the vapor pressure of water reaches a sea-level pressure of 760 mmHg is 100°C. At 100°C the vapor pressure of water becomes equal to the atmospheric pressure, and thus the boiling point of water at 760 mmHg is 100°C. To boil water, heat must be applied until the temperature reaches 100°C. The temperature of the water then remains constant until the liquid has boiled away.

At the normal boiling point the vapor pressure of a liquid equals 760 mmHg.

Because so many boiling points are measured at sea-level pressure, a special term, **normal boiling point**, is used to mean the boiling point measured when the atmospheric pressure is 760 mmHg. Thus we should really say that the *normal* boiling point of water is 100°C. Whenever boiling points are given without an indicated pressure, we must assume that they are normal boiling points. We can use values in Table 8.1 to find normal boiling points. For instance, the temperature at which the vapor pressure of ethanol is 760 mmHg is 78.5°C, and thus the normal boiling point of ethanol is 78.5°C.

In Denver a 3-min egg has the consistency of a $2\frac{1}{2}$-min egg at sea level.

When external atmospheric pressures are different from 760 mmHg, the boiling points are no longer normal boiling points. When the atmospheric pressure is less than 760 mmHg, the boiling temperature decreases. For instance, the atmospheric pressure in Denver, Colorado, is about 630 mmHg. The temperature at which the vapor pressure of water is 630 mmHg is about 94°C. Therefore, it takes longer to cook foods in boiling water at high altitudes, where atmospheric pressure and hence boiling temperatures are reduced, than at sea level. When the atmospheric pressure is greater than 760 mmHg, the boiling temperature is higher than the normal boiling point. For example, at an atmospheric pressure of about 2 atm or 1520 mmHg, water boils at 121°C. This is the principle upon which the pressure cooker operates. Inside the pot, pressures are higher than that of the atmosphere, which increases the boiling temperature of water and decreases the time needed to cook foods in boiling water.

SAMPLE EXERCISE 8.1

At what temperature will water boil when the external pressure is 526 mmHg?

Solution:

Use Table 8.1 to look up the temperature at which the vapor pressure of water is 526 mmHg. At 90°C the vapor pressure of water will equal an external pressure of 526 mmHg. Thus, at this pressure the boiling point of water is 90°C.

EXERCISE 8.1

The weather broadcast on a summer day in the mountains gives a temperature of 90°F and a barometer reading of 25.5 inHg. Will ether boil under these conditions?

8.4 DISTILLATION

Distillation is the process of first vaporizing and then condensing (liquefying) the liquid components of a mixture to separate them from each other or from the solid components which may be present. It is possible to separate or to partially separate two or more liquid components from each other provided that the boiling points of the two substances are sufficiently far apart. For example, suppose a mixture contains two liquids, compound A boiling at 50°C and compound B boiling at 120°C. First the mixture is brought to a boil in a distillation flask or "pot." The first boiling point reached will be close to 50°C, the boiling point of A, and the vapor produced will be very rich in compound A. When most of compound A has boiled away, the boiling temperature will rise to that of com-

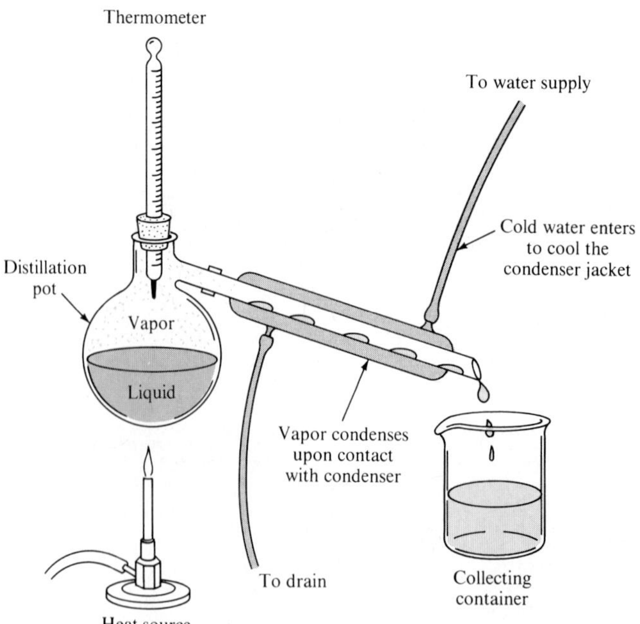

FIGURE 8.4

pound B, 120°C. The liquid produced at each boiling temperature is called a *fraction*. To collect each fraction a cooled condenser tube is attached to the boiling pot. When the vapor reaches the condenser, it returns to the liquid state, where it can be directed into a container. A different container is used to collect each component. Figure 8.4 illustrates a typical distillation apparatus. The fractions obtained by a single distillation process will not be pure A and pure B. Some B vapor will be carried over into the A fraction and some A will remain behind in the B fraction. To achieve even better separation, repeated distillations must be done.

8.5 MELTING POINT

For solids to melt, the constituent particles, atoms, ions, or molecules must increase their energies so that they can overcome their attractive forces and escape from their fixed positions. This happens when heat is applied. The particles of solids vibrate faster and faster until they are free to move. When heated sufficiently, the solid *melts* and changes to a liquid. When liquids are cooled to become

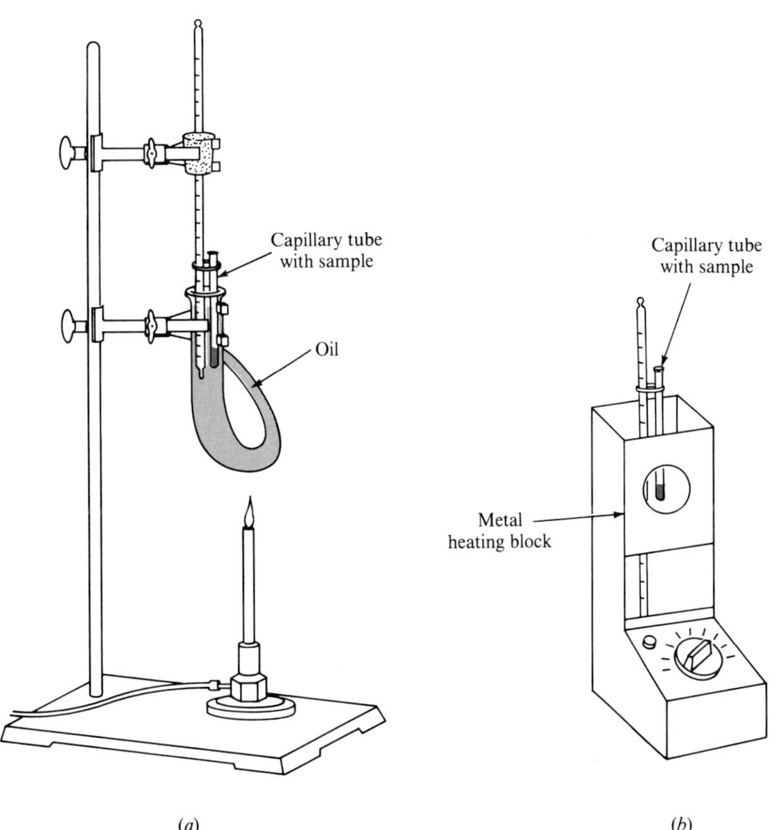

FIGURE 8.5
Melting-point apparatus. (*a*) Thiele tube. (*b*) Electrothermal. Metal heating block makes this apparatus safer than one with an open flame.

solids, the process is called *freezing*. The equations which represent the melting and freezing of water are

$$H_2O(s) \longrightarrow H_2O(l) \qquad \text{melting}$$

$$H_2O(l) \longrightarrow H_2O(s) \qquad \text{freezing}$$

At a pressure of 10 atm ice melts at $-0.075°C$.

The **melting point** is the temperature at which a solid becomes a liquid and is identical to the freezing temperature at which the liquid solidifies. Unlike boiling points, melting points depend very little on atmospheric pressure. The melting point is a valuable identifying property. In particular, the melting points of covalently bonded solids, which are relatively low compared with those of ionic compounds (see Figure 4.2), are conveniently measured in the laboratory. The melting points of covalent compounds are lower than those of ionic compounds because the intermolecular attractive forces in a covalent molecule are less than those between the ions of ionic compounds. Melting points can also be used to indicate the purity of a substance. Pure compounds have sharp melting points and impure compounds melt over a wider temperature range. Two typical melting point devices are given in Figure 8.5.

8.6 PROPERTIES OF LIQUIDS

The ability of liquids to exert pressure and to diffuse are two properties that we have already encountered in our study of the gaseous state.

Liquid Pressure

Liquids exert *pressure* equally in all directions in the same way that gases do. The pressure exerted at any particular point in a container of liquid depends upon the height of the liquid above that point: the greater the height of the liquid, the greater the pressure. For example, the pressure due to water at the bottom of the ocean is much greater than it would be at the surface. This is exactly analogous to the atmospheric pressure exerted by the ocean of air which surrounds the earth. At the bottom of this ocean of air at the surface of the earth, the atmospheric pressure is much higher than it is at higher altitudes.

Viscosity

Viscosity is the resistance of liquids to flow. In general, viscosity depends upon the density of the liquid and the strength of its intermolecular attractions: the higher these are, the more difficult it is for molecules to move over one another, thereby increasing the resistance to flow and hence the viscosity. To measure liquid viscosity, the time required for a liquid to flow from one point to another in a narrow tube is measured with a stopwatch; the more viscous the liquid, the longer it takes. A device used to measure liquid viscosities is the Ostwald vis-

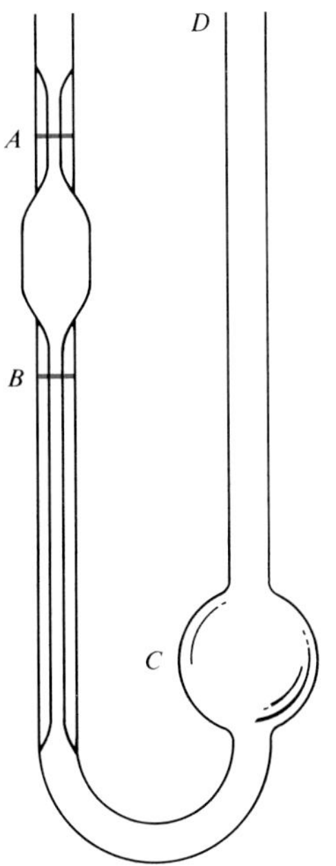

FIGURE 8.6
Viscometer. Point *D* is where the pressure is applied to move the liquid in the reservoir C up the other arm of the tube to point *A*. The time required for the liquid to fall from point *A* to point *B* is a measure of the liquid viscosity.

cometer shown in Figure 8.6. Viscosities of some common liquids relative to that of water are listed in Table 8.2. Note that the viscosities of very "thick" liquids such as glycerol and castor oil are high compared with that of water.

Changes in blood viscosity can influence the pressure exerted by circulating blood upon the walls of blood vessels, that is, the blood pressure. The greater the viscosity, the greater the resistance to flow and the higher the blood pressure. Blood viscosity is normally constant at about 1.025 times the viscosity of water; however, there are circumstances under which this value can increase. For example, an increase in the number of red blood cells, which may occur during muscular exercise or during hot weather, can cause blood viscosity to increase, thus contributing to a rise in blood pressure.

Surface Tension

Surface tension is a characteristic property of liquids which can be observed whenever liquids are in contact with a gas. The molecules at the very surface of the liquid are attracted to the other interior liquid molecules more than they are attracted to the gas molecules with which they are in contact. As a result of these unbalanced forces, the molecules at the surface of a liquid tend to be drawn inward toward the main body of liquid (see Figure 8.7). Therefore the surface of the liquid possesses a certain "toughness" and behaves something like a thick skin, which resists being broken. Many common, everyday observations are the result of surface tension. Objects with a large surface area may float on water, even though their densities are greater than that of water (1 g/cm^3), because of surface tension. For example, a long, thin needle made of stainless steel, which has a density of about 7 g/cm^3, floats on water because of the extra energy needed for the needle to break through the water surface. As a result of surface tension, falling drops of liquid tend to form into spheres because the molecules at the

TABLE 8.2 VISCOSITIES OF COMMON LIQUIDS AS COMPARED WITH WATER

Liquid	Viscosity at 20° C (relative to water)
Ether	0.23
Chloroform	0.58
Methyl alcohol	0.60
Carbon tetrachloride	0.97
Water	1
Blood	1.025
Mercury	1.56
Olive oil	84
Castor oil	986
Glycerol	1490

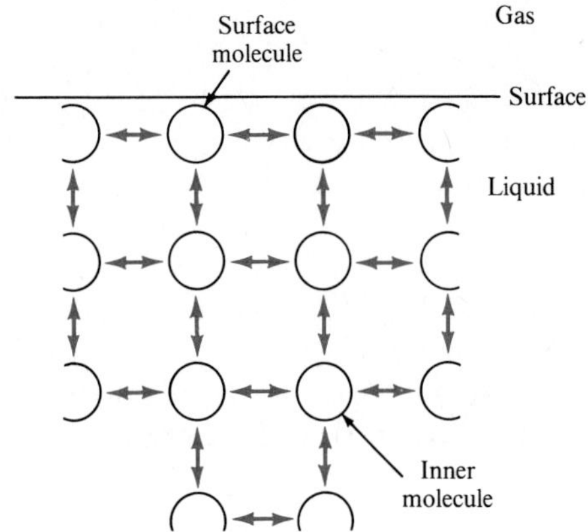

FIGURE 8.7
Surface tension. Attractive forces among inner molecules are exerted equally in all directions. Surface molecules are only attracted to the molecules beneath them and to other surface molecules, creating an imbalance in attractive forces. The result is an attraction of surface molecules down into the inner molecules, causing the phenomenon of surface tension.

surface of the drop are attracted to each other more than to their gaseous surroundings.

Pulmonary surfactants are needed for normal breathing.

The force of surface tension operating in alveolar lung cells can make breathing very difficult. The alveolus is surrounded by a wall through which respiratory gases of alveolar air and blood must be exchanged. An alveolus can be viewed as a bubble filled with air and lined with water (see Figure 8.8). The water lining tends to resist stretching because the surface water molecules are much more attracted to each other than to the molecules of air inside the bubble. Unless this surface tension is somehow counteracted, the alveolus cannot distend itself and the lungs are thus unable to expand to permit normal breathing. Fortunately, the alveolar cells produce compounds called *pulmonary surfactants*. In general *surfactants* reduce surface tension by coming between liquid molecules to reduce the

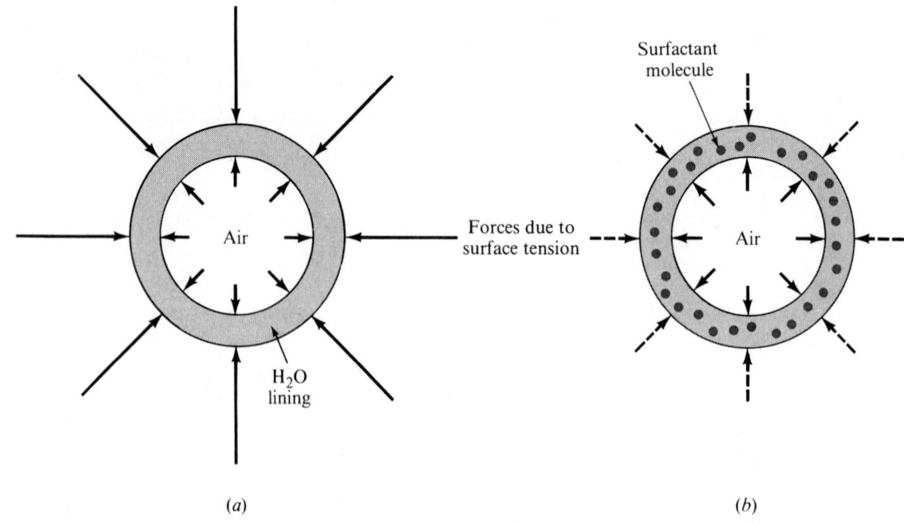

FIGURE 8.8
Expansion of alveolus.
(*a*) The air pressure cannot counteract the force of surface tension, making expansion of the alveolus difficult.
(*b*) Surfactant molecules (in color) reduce the force of surface tension, allowing the air pressure to expand the alveolus to permit normal breathing.

attractive forces between them, as shown in Figure 8.8. Without pulmonary surfactants, only exhausting effort would permit expansion of the alveolus. In premature infants a disease called ***respiratory distress syndrome*** (RDS) is caused by insufficient pulmonary surfactant. The infant afflicted with RDS may have such difficulty breathing that lung collapse and death can result.

8.7 WATER

Out of every 100 molecules in the human body, 99 are water molecules. About 60 percent of the body weight is water. Water owes this unique position as the liquid of living systems to a set of rather peculiar properties. The anomalous properties of water can all be related in some way to the effect of hydrogen bonding, the intermolecular attractive force which is especially important in water. As we discussed in Section 4.16, the force of hydrogen bonding is present because the positive hydrogen atom of one H_2O molecule is attracted to the highly electronegative oxygen atom of a neighboring H_2O molecule (see Figure 4.21*a*). Because of this extra attraction between water molecules, vaporization becomes more difficult, giving water a much higher boiling point than would be expected for a compound with such a low molecular weight. All the group VI hydrides except for water are gases at room temperature and pressure, even though they all have higher molecular weights than water (see Section 4.16).

When most liquids freeze to become solids, they contract. Molten metals contract when they solidify. Solidified wax shrinks so that it can be removed from molds which surround it. But water is different. When water freezes to become ice, it expands. This is a phenomenon familiar to anyone who has inadvertently allowed a container of watery liquid to chill too long in the freezer. If the water happens to freeze, the container is likely to crack. In the winter pipes may burst if the water in them is allowed to freeze. As a result of the fact that water expands when it becomes ice, the density of ice is only about 0.92 g/cm^3, compared with 1 g/cm^3 for liquid water. This explains why ice cubes float in water and icebergs float in the ocean.

This unusual behavior that water exhibits upon freezing can be explained by looking at its crystal structure. The crystal structure of ice shown in Figure 8.9 includes large open channels between groups of water molecules. It is these empty spaces that contribute to the low density of ice compared with that of liquid water. In liquid water the average separation between H_2O molecules is about 0.31 nm, whereas in ice the separation is 0.32 nm. Crystals of most solid substances do not include so much empty space. The open arrangment of water molecules in ice is stabilized by hydrogen bonding between each water molecule and its four nearest neighbors. (See Figure 8.9.)

These unusual properties of water are essential to support life on earth. Without hydrogen bonding, water would not even be a liquid. If water did not expand as it freezes, icebergs would sink, lakes would freeze from the bottom up, and aquatic life would be impossible.

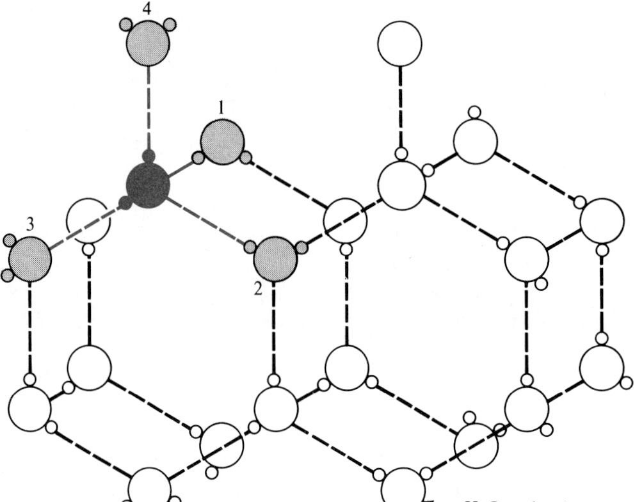

FIGURE 8.9
Solid water and H bonding. The water molecule (indicated in color) is hydrogen-bonded to the four neighboring molecules. The open channels in the crystal structure lower the density of ice compared with that of water.

8.8 CRYSTALLINE SOLIDS

In general solids fall into one of two major classifications; they are either *amorphous* or *crystalline* solids. Amorphous solids do not possess internal order and in some ways resemble liquids, in which the molecules are randomly oriented. Crystalline solids, sometimes called true solids, are highly ordered. Because of their high degree of symmetry crystals are often beautiful to look at. Two particularly striking examples are the copper sulfate crystal shown in Color Plate 8 and the gemstones shown in Color Plate 9.

The characteristic external shape of a crystal is called the *crystal habit*. The physical shape of a macroscopic visible crystal does not necessarily reflect the internal arrangement of atoms, molecules, or ions within the crystal. For example, in Figure 8.10 two different crystal habits of sodium chloride, a cube and an octahedron, are pictured. Although these crystals may look different, their internal structures are identical. The internal arrangement of microscopic units within a crystal is the *crystal structure or crystal lattice structure* (see Figure 4.3 for the crystal structure of NaCl). The term *lattice* refers to a regular arrangement of points in space. In crystals these points are replaced by atoms, ions, or molecules.

It is possible to find the relative positions of the atoms, ions, or molecules which make up a crystal by using a procedure called *x-ray diffraction*. When a beam of x-rays is passed through a crystal, the x-rays are "scattered" in various directions depending upon the three-dimensional arrangement of the particles present in the crystal. From looking at photographs of the x-ray beams after they have passed through the crystal, trained crystallographers are able to deduce the internal arrangement within the crystal. We will find that the crystal structure of the compound DNA gave the clues necessary to find the shape of its molecules and eventually led to the modern theory of heredity (see Chapter 24).

In the next sections we will describe four types of crystalline solids, including ionic crystals, molecular crystals, metallic crystals, and covalent crystals.

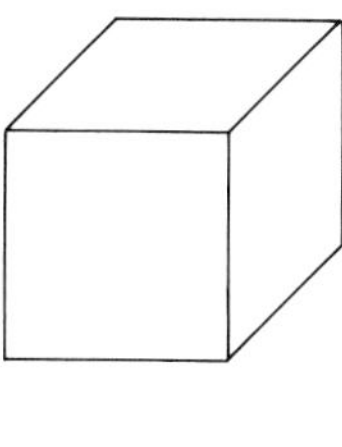

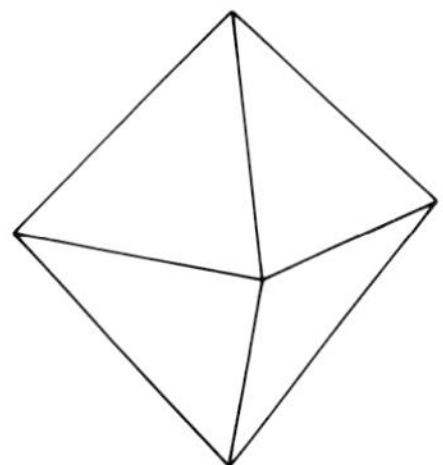

(*a*) (*b*)

FIGURE 8.10
Crystal structure of NaCl and habits. (*a*) A crystal of NaCl shaped like a cube. (*b*) A crystal shaped like an octahedron. Both possess the same internal arrangement of ions, that is, the same crystal structure as shown in Figure 4.3.

8.9 IONIC CRYSTALS AND MOLECULAR CRYSTALS

In *ionic crystals* the positions in the crystal lattice are occupied by cations and anions (see Figure 4.3). Ionic compounds such as NaCl form ionic crystals. In the solid state ionic crystals are unable to conduct electricity because the ions are fixed in their positions and unable to move. Movement of ions or of electrons is necessary for conduction of electricity. Substances which are not good electrical conductors are called insulators; in the solid state ionic crystals are insulators. If ionic solids are melted or dissolved in water, the ions will then be free to move (see Section 4.2). Therefore, molten or dissolved ionic compounds do behave as electrical conductors (see Figure 4.2*a*).

In molecular substances molecules occupy the fixed positions in the crystals. In general, covalent compounds such as H_2O, which contain discrete molecules, form *molecular crystals*. For example, solid H_2O is crystalline ice. In the crystal structure of ice, pictured in Figure 8.9, discrete H_2O molecules occupy the lattice positions. In molecular crystals there are no free electrons available for conduction of electricity because the electrons are all intimately involved in the formation of covalent bonds within the molecules. Therefore, molecular crystals are particularly poor electrical conductors and behave as excellent insulators even when molten or dissolved in water.

8.10 METALLIC CRYSTALS

It may seem odd to think of metals as crystals, but in fact they are. In metallic crystals it is atoms which occupy fixed positions in the crystal lattice. Metals are known to be excellent conductors of electricity, which is explained by the accepted model for the metallic crystal. Typical metal atoms have only one or two valence electrons. As you saw in Section 4.3, the metals lose these valence electrons to form cations. For instance, the metals sodium, magnesium, and silver form the cations Na^+, Mg^{2+}, and Ag^+:

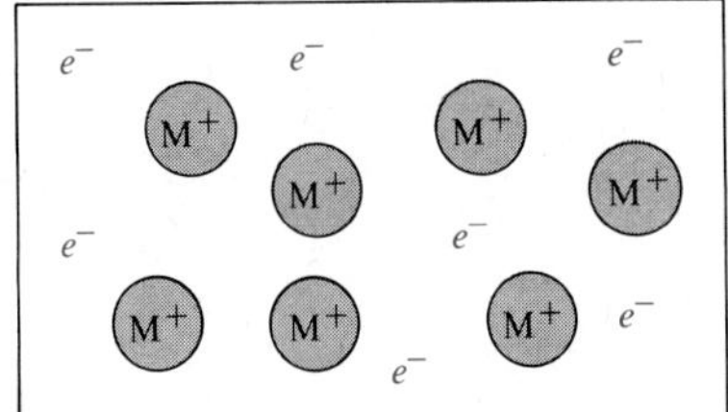

FIGURE 8.11
Metal crystal The valence electrons are free to move among the array of positive M^+ ions.

$$Na \longrightarrow e^- + Na^+$$
$$Mg \longrightarrow 2e^- + Mg^{2+}$$
$$Ag \longrightarrow e^- + Ag^+$$

In the model of a metallic crystal the high-energy valence electrons create a "sea" of electrons in which the positive ions "float." No electron belongs to any one particular metal cation. The model for a crystal of a metal M which forms M^+ cations is shown in Figure 8.11. The valence electrons in metals are not tightly bound to the atoms from which they come and thus are free to move. Electricity is simply a flow of electrons and for this reason all metals are able to conduct electricity.

All metals conduct electricity.

About 75 percent of the elements in the periodic table are metals. (See the periodic table on the front inside cover in which the metallic elements are all indicated by the solid black symbols.) Metals have other characteristic physical properties besides that of high electrical conductivity. They are excellent conductors of heat. Holding a metal spoon which is immersed in a pot of boiling water produces a painful burn because the metal is such a good thermal conductor. Bulk samples of all metals have a shiny surface called a metallic luster. All the metallic elements are solids under ordinary conditions of temperature and pressure except for mercury, which is a liquid. The melting points of the solid metals vary widely from as low as 28°C for cesium ($_{55}Cs$) to as high as 3380°C for tungsten ($_{74}W$). Metals have the ability to combine with each other to form thousands of possible metallic mixtures called *alloys*, which often have more useful properties than any pure metal. For instance, 24-carat gold (100 percent Au) is much too soft to be formed into a piece of jewelry. To give it strength it is mixed with copper and silver in 18-carat gold (75 percent Au) and 14-carat gold (58 percent Au).

Sterling silver is an alloy containing 92.5% Ag and the remainder Cu or some other metal.

The chemical properties of metallic elements are most conveniently discussed according to their positions in the periodic table.

8.11 REPRESENTATIVE METALLIC ELEMENTS

Recall that the elements belonging to the A families, the representative elements, display more regular trends in their properties than do those of the B groups, which contain the transition elements (see Section 3.14).

Group IA, Alkali Metals

Physically the elements of group IA, called the *alkali metals*, do not appear to fit the conventional picture of what metals are supposed to be. The alkali metals are so soft that they can easily be cut with a penknife. They are chemically so highly reactive that they are never to be found uncombined in nature and must be stored covered with an inert substance such as mineral oil to protect them from the atmosphere. Group IA metals react readily with the common substances water and oxygen.

The reactions of Na with O_2 and K with H_2O are shown in Color Plate 5.

$$2K + 2H_2O \longrightarrow 2KOH + H_2$$

$$4Na + O_2 \longrightarrow 2Na_2O$$

Of the alkali metals, sodium and potassium are the most common in the earth's crust as well as the ones required by living organisms, where they are present as Na^+ and K^+. Sodium is the major cation in fluid outside the cell (extracellular fluid), and potassium is the major cation within cells (intracellular fluid) (see Figure 8.12). Both ions play an important role in the mechanism of nerve conduction. Sodium and potassium, along with any other element needed by humans (except for C, H, O, and N), are called **minerals**. Normal diets include adequate amounts of these two group IA minerals. Potassium deficiency, or ***hypokalemia***, caused by gastrointestinal losses, produces neuromuscular disturbances and cardiac abnormalities. Dietary sources of potassium and other minerals needed by humans and the daily requirements for them are given in a table on the back inside cover along with other nutritional data.

Minerals include nonmetals such as I, Cl, S, F, P, and Se, as well as the metals Ca, Mg, Na, K, Cr, Cu, Fe, Mn, Mo, and Zn.

Group IIA, Alkaline Earth Metals

The *alkaline earth metals* of group IIA are somewhat harder and less reactive chemically than their group IA neighbors. The reactions of Ca with water and oxygen are typical of group IIA.

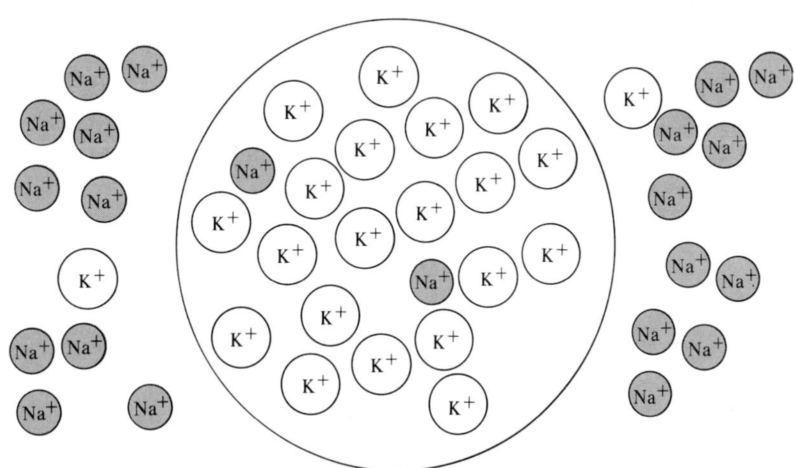

FIGURE 8.12
Na^+ and K^+ concentrations inside and outside the cell. Inside the cell there are about 10 times as many K^+ ions as there are Na^+ ions. Outside the cell, the reverse is true.

$$Ca + 2H_2O \longrightarrow Ca(OH)_2 + H_2$$

$$2Ca + O_2 \longrightarrow 2CaO$$

Calcium and magnesium are the most abundant of the group IIA elements in the earth's crust and occur as the ions Ca^{2+} and Mg^{2+} in living systems. In the body calcium occurs in the form of calcium carbonate, $CaCO_3$, and calcium phosphate, $Ca_3(PO_4)_2$. Calcium is essential for proper development of bones and teeth and for blood clotting, muscle contraction, and nerve conduction. Although calcium is widely present in foods, it is not readily absorbed from some foods. Milk and milk products are excellent sources. Of all the elements, diets are most likely to be deficient in calcium.

Group IIIA, Aluminum

Al is the most abundant metal in the earth's crust (Table 3.2).

Aluminum is the most important group IIIA metal. Pure aluminum metal is both soft and chemically reactive. How then can aluminum metal be used to build airplanes and to make cooking pots? The reactivity of aluminum is greatly reduced by the formation of a thin coating of aluminum oxide, Al_2O_3, on its surface.

$$4Al + 3O_2 \longrightarrow 2Al_2O_3$$

Al_2O_3 is often used as the absorbing solid in chromatography (Color Plate 2).

A fresh scratch mark made on an aluminum pot will at first show the shiny luster of pure aluminum metal, but upon standing it will become coated with a dull layer of protective Al_2O_3. To increase its strength, aluminum metal is mixed with small amounts of other elements such as copper, magnesium, silicon, and manganese, which produces alloys strong enough to be used in construction.

Group IVA, Tin and Lead

The group IVA metallic elements, tin and lead, can form compounds in which either two or four valence electrons are involved. From looking at the electronic structure of Sn it is possible to see why this happens:

$$_{50}Sn)\quad 1s^2 2s^2 2p^6 3s^2 3p^6 4s^2 3d^{10} 5s^2 4d^{10} 5p^2$$

The four electrons in the fifth energy level (in color) are the valence electrons, two of which are *s* electrons and two of which are *p* electrons. Sometimes all four electrons participate directly in the bonding and are shared with some electronegative element. For example, Sn forms covalent tin(IV) oxide, SnO_2. Sometimes the two *s* electrons do not get involved in the bonding. When this happens, Sn forms ions with a +2 charge. Thus Sn can form compounds which are more ionic in nature, such as tin(II) oxide, SnO. Lead can also form both types of compounds, although for lead the tetravalent compounds such as $PbCl_4$ and PbO_2 are less stable than the divalent compounds $PbCl_2$ and PbO.

8.12 LEAD POISONING

In living systems lead compounds can be very harmful. The initial symptoms of ***lead poisoning*** are rather vague, starting with mood changes and irritability. Psychosis and mental retardation appear later. It is sometimes difficult to make the connection between symptoms and disease because the accumulation of lead in the body is slow. Lead may enter the body through compounds of lead which are present in the environment. Lead oxides, which used to be ingredients in outdoor paints, can find their way into the bodies of children who have chewed on windowsills once painted with lead-containing paints. Inside the body, lead compounds are deposited in bone tissue, from which elimination is also very slow. When blood levels of lead exceed 50 μg/dl, toxicity may be observed. Measurements of lead blood levels are made by atomic spectroscopy (see Section 3.15). The devastating effect of lead is due to the fact that lead is able to bind to compounds called *enzymes,* which are necessary for biochemical reactions within the body to proceed at the proper speed. One of these enzymes, called ALA dehydrase, is involved in the synthesis of hemoglobin by red blood cells. Lead interferes with the activity of ALA dehydrase and thus causes a deficiency in hemoglobin formation.

Note that several of the test samples in Figure 3.17 show blood lead levels >50 μ g/dl.

Antidotes for lead poisoning remove Pb^{2+} ions from the blood and tissues by forming a very stable lead compound, which can easily be excreted from the body. Substances used for this purpose are *chelating agents,* which are compounds that enclose metal ions in a pincerlike grasp. One of the most important chelating agents is called ethylenediaminetetraacetic acid, abbreviated EDTA, a compound used widely in the field of analytical chemistry to test for quantities of metal ions present.

The word chelate is derived from *chele,* the Greek word for "claw".

```
       O  H                        H  O
       ‖  |                        |  ‖
H—O—C—C                            C—C—O—H
          |  \      H   H      /   |
          H   \     |   |     /    H
               N—C—C—N
       O  H   /     |   |     \    H  O
       ‖  |  /      H   H      \   |  ‖
H—O—C—C                            C—C—O—H
          |                        |
          H                        H
```

EDTA

EDTA is also used as an antidote for lead poisoning in the form of its ionic calcium disodium salt, abbreviated $CaNa_2EDTA$. The Pb^{2+} ions are able to displace the Ca^{2+} ions from the $CaNa_2EDTA$ salt:

$$CaNa_2EDTA + Pb^{2+} \longrightarrow PbNa_2EDTA + Ca^{2+}$$

The complex $PbNa_2EDTA$, shown in Figure 8.13, dissolves in water, so that it can be eliminated from the body through the urine.

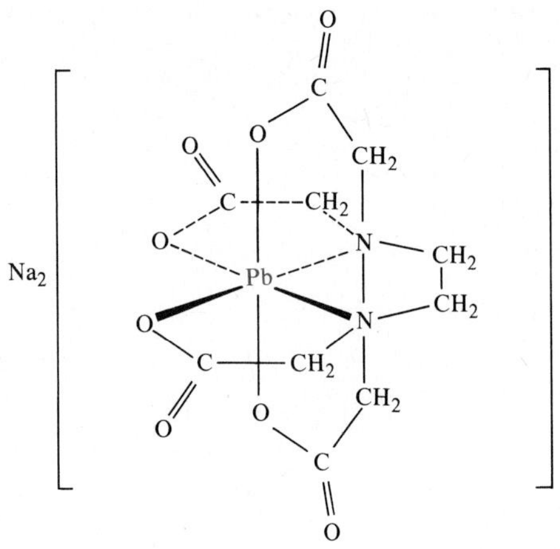

FIGURE 8.13
$PbNa_2$ EDTA complex. EDTA salt "encloses" Pb^{2+} to form a water-soluble complex eliminated in urine.

8.13 TRANSITION METALS

Transition elements have their highest-energy electrons in *d* orbitals.

The transition elements belong to the B groups, which are placed in the middle section of the periodic table of the elements. As we mentioned in Chapter 3, it is much more difficult to predict what ions they are likely to form than it is for the representative elements. In this section we will discuss the properties of some of the more important transition elements.

Copper, Silver, and Gold

Gold forms compounds such as $AuBr_3$, in which the oxidation number of Au is +3.

The coinage metals copper ($_{29}Cu$), silver ($_{47}Ag$), and gold ($_{79}Au$) are found in group IB of the periodic table. These elements are all characterized by their chemical inertness; all can be found uncombined in nature. Silver and gold are used to make decorative pieces and jewelry since their brilliant metallic luster is not easily marred by the atmosphere. As free elements, compounds, or alloys, the coinage metals have a variety of uses including some in the field of medicine. The use of gold compounds in treatment of disease (most often as anti-inflammatory agents) is known as *chrysotherapy*.

K_2S can be administered to prevent the absorption of dietary Cu by converting it to insoluble CuS.

In a rare genetic disease called ***Wilson's disease***, copper is deposited in body tissues. The average daily amount of copper absorbed by the body from dietary sources (see the table on the inside back cover) is about 1 mg. Normally the copper is metabolized and removed from the body, but in individuals with Wilson's disease the copper accumulates in the tissues, particularly in the brain and liver, where the high levels can lead to cirrhosis and neurologic disorders. This happens because of the absence of necessary protein substances, which in normal persons remove the excess copper. To treat Wilson's disease, compounds (EDTA for one) which bind and remove copper as a copper complex must be administered lifelong.

Zinc, Cadmium, and Mercury

The elements zinc ($_{30}Zn$), cadmium ($_{48}Cd$), and mercury ($_{80}Hg$) belong to group IIB of the transition elements. Of these zinc and cadmium are more reactive than mercury. Mercury is the only liquid metal at ordinary temperatures.

The Zn in Zn supplements is often present as $ZnSO_4$.

Zinc is a component of enzymes that catalyze vital metabolic reactions and is thus a required nutrient. However, ingestion of excess zinc from galvanized iron cans causes gastrointestinal distress.

Like lead, mercury forms compounds which are extremely toxic. Symptoms of mercury poisoning begin with memory loss and narrowing of visual field and then accelerate to loss of muscle coordination and severe emotional instability. Mercury used to stiffen felt in the hat industry produced symptoms like these among workers, leading to the expression "mad as a hatter."

Mercury, unlike lead, is concentrated in foods, especially in seafoods, in which form it is ingested by people and animals. Mercury is stored in many tissues, particularly in the liver and the brain, and may have severe toxic effects on the nervous system. The most serious threat to living systems is posed by mercury compounds which are bonded to carbon-containing groups. These so-called organomercury compounds are typified by dimethyl mercury (also called methyl mercury).

```
     H        H
     |        |
 H—C—Hg—C—H
     |        |
     H        H
```

Dimethyl mercury

Bacteria can convert inorganic Hg salts to methyl mercury.

Such mercury compounds are especially dangerous because they are more readily able to pass through the blood-brain barrier than mercury ions from inorganic mercury compounds, that is, those which do not contain hydrocarbon groups.

The antidote for mercury poisoning works in the same way as the antidotes for lead and copper poisoning. A chelating agent called dimercaprol is able to bind mercury and remove it from the body.

```
    H                          H
    |                          |
H—C—S—H                    H—C—S\
    |                          |    Hg
H—C—S—H  + Hg²⁺  ⟶        H—C—S/       + 2 H⁺
    |                          |
H—C—O—H                    H—C—O—H
    |                          |
    H                          H
 Dimercaprol            Mercury dimercaprol
```

Even though the vapor pressure of Hg is small, spilling 1 ml of the liquid element in an average-sized room causes a hazardous concentration in the air.

Alloys of mercury called amalgams are used in dentistry to fill teeth.

Iron

The most abundant source of iron in nature is iron(III) oxide, Fe_2O_3, a compound occurring in the ore hematite. To remove the iron, the ore must be treated with coke (C) in a heated tower called a blast furnace. The two reactions below summarize what happens in the blast furnace.

$$2C + O_2 \xrightarrow{\Delta} 2CO$$

$$3CO + Fe_2O_3 \xrightarrow{\Delta} 2Fe + 3CO_2$$

The iron that is a product of this process contains about 3 percent carbon and is known as pig iron, a very brittle form of iron (like the kind used in cast iron skillets). The much more useful form of iron called *steel* contains only about 1.5 percent C and is often alloyed with other metals as well. Iron is readily converted to its oxide to form the product we know as "rust," according to the equation below.

$$3\ Fe + 2O_2 \longrightarrow Fe_2O_3 \cdot FeO\ (Fe_3O_4)$$

Stainless steel, which is especially resistant to this corrosion, is an iron alloy containing about 10 percent chromium.

Increased need for iron in pregnancy is due to increased blood volume.

Iron is a valuable constituent of plant and animal life. In human organisms iron is part of the oxygen-carrying molecule called hemoglobin (Section 7.12). About 70 percent of the total body iron is present in the form of this essential molecule. Iron is not stored in the body in any great amount and must be present in daily diets so that losses can be replaced. Iron deficiency results in a condition known as ***iron deficiency anemia***, characterized by symptoms of weakness, irritability, and gastrointestinal disturbances. Patients with iron deficiency do not have enough hemoglobin in their red blood cells. The specific treatment for such anemia is the administration of water-soluble iron compounds such as ferrous sulfate [iron(II) sulfate], $FeSO_4$.

8.14 COVALENT CRYSTALS

Covalent crystals form from certain nonmetallic solid elements or from compounds which contain atoms of similar electronegativity. All the atoms present in covalent crystals are bonded together, leaving no discrete molecules. The valence electrons present in such crystals are all involved in the bonding and are confined to regions between the atoms they join. For this reason covalent crystals are often excellent insulators, since there are no freely moving valence electrons. In addition, covalent crystals are unusually brittle and hard, with very high melting points.

The graphite in a pencil is another form of carbon in which the C atoms are arranged in layers.

Many precious gemstones are covalent crystals. Diamond is simply a form of elemental carbon in which all the C atoms are bonded to each other in a tetrahedral arrangement. Rubies and sapphires are both primarily aluminum ox-

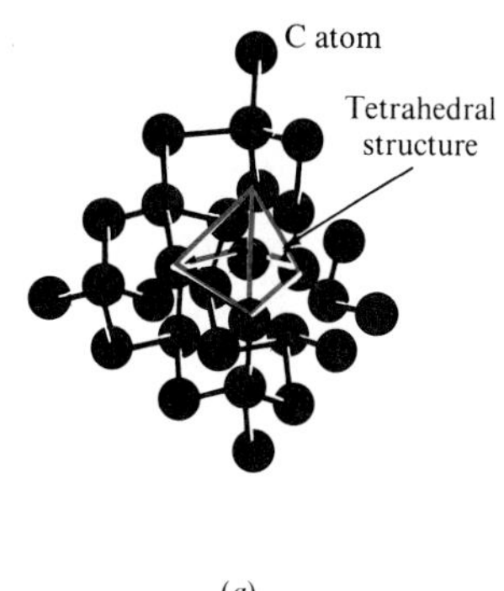

(a)

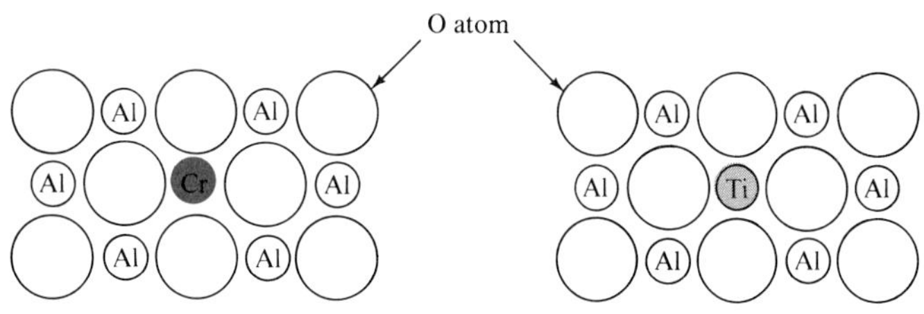

(b) (c)

FIGURE 8.14
Gemstone structures: (*a*) diamond, (*b*) ruby. (*c*) sapphire.

ide, Al_2O_3, in which Al and O atoms are connected by covalent bonds in a crystal lattice. In rubies, the brilliant red comes from chromium impurities. In sapphires, the name applied to all other aluminum oxide gemstones, the impurities may be titanium (Ti) or iron. (In Color Plate 9 you can see that sapphires come in different colors.) Emeralds are a form of the compound beryl, $Be_3Al_2(SiO_3)_6$, which owes its magnificant green to a trace impurity of chromium. Figure 8.14 shows the arrangements of atoms in the covalent crystals of diamond, ruby, and sapphire.

Semiconductors and Transistors

Whereas metallic crystals conduct electricity because they contain valence electrons that are free to move, in most covalent crystals the electrons are not free to move because they are involved in the formation of bonds between atoms within the crystal. However, in some covalent crystals it is possible for the electrons to become energetic enough to be mobile. In germanium (Ge) and in silicon (Si) covalent crystals, light or heat can provide the necessary energy for a measurable conductance to be observed. Silicon and germanium and similar substances are called **semiconductors**. The conductance of semiconductors can be increased by the addition of impurity elements, a process called *doping*. Crystals of Ge and Si which have been doped with impurities are widely used to make **transistors**, which behave as one-way valves for the flow of electrical current. Devices which utilize transistors are called *solid-state devices*. Because of the tremendous convenience associated with the use of transistors, they have virtually revolutionized the modern industrial world.

SUMMARY

Both liquids and solids can exert vapor pressure due to the presence of gas molecules from evaporation or sublimation. Volatile substances have relatively high vapor pressures. In general, liquids are much more volatile than solids.

A liquid boils when its vapor pressure is equal to the pressure of the surrounding atmosphere. The normal boiling point refers to an external pressure of 1 atm. The higher the external pressure, the higher the boiling point. Difference in boiling points are utilized in distillation, a procedure used to separate liquids from each other or from solids.

Like gases, liquids exert pressure. The greater the viscosity of a liquid, the more slowly it flows. Because of surface tension the surfaces of liquids resist being broken.

Water is a unique liquid largely because of the forces of hydrogen bonding that attract its molecules to each other. The boiling point of water is unusually high for its formula weight and water expands when it freezes.

There are many different classes of true solids, that is, the crystalline solids that have order in the arrangement of their microscopic components. Ionic compounds form ionic crystal and covalent compounds form molecular crystals. Metals form metallic crystals, which conduct electricity because they contain electrons that are free to move. Minerals include those metallic elements required in the human diet.

Heavy metal ions are toxic because they bind to enzymes needed to regulate biochemical reactions. Antidotes for lead poisoning and mercury poisoning make use of chelating agents that preferentially bind to the metal ions to form compounds that the body can eliminate.

Covalent crystals are composed of nonmetallic atoms all bonded to one another, which makes them good insulators since they have no free electrons. They are hard, high-melting substances and include gemstones such as diamonds, rubies, sapphires, and emeralds. Some covalent crystals called semiconductors, such as elemental Si and Ge doped with impurities, are able to conduct electricity. Transistors are made out of semiconductors.

KEY WORDS

evaporation
vapor pressure
sublimation
normal boiling point
distillation
melting point
viscosity
surface tension
mineral
ionic crystal
molecular crystal
covalent crystal
semiconductor
transistor

EXERCISES

8.2 Write equations to represent each of the following processes:
(a) Boiling of carbon tetrachloride
(b) Condensation of water
(c) Sublimation of solid carbon dioxide (dry ice)
(d) Melting of ice
(e) Freezing of bromine (Br_2)
(f) Melting of potassium iodide

8.3 According to the definition of vapor we have given in Chapters 7 and 8, which of the following substances would be referred to as vapors and which as gases? (a) $H_2O(g)$; (b) $SO_2(g)$; (c) $Hg(g)$; (d) $Br_2(g)$; (e) $N_2(g)$; (f) $CO(g)$?

8.4 Using Table 8.1, find the boiling point of water at external atmospheric pressures of: (a) 234 mmHg; (b) 1.54 atm; (c) 0.92 cmHg; (d) 29.9 inHg.

8.5 Why must some cooking instructions be modified at high altitudes?

8.6 Using Table 8.1 determine the following:
(a) The boiling point of ethanol when the external atmospheric pressure is reduced to 12 mmHg
(b) The normal boiling point of ether
(c) The external pressure needed for mercury to boil at 100°C
(d) The external pressure needed for carbon tetrachloride to boil at 90°C

8.7 Mercury is odorless. Give one reason why this is true.

8.8 What is meant by the term *normal* boiling point?

8.9 Why is it necessary to specify the external pressure for a boiling point but not for a melting point?

8.10 If a liquid is to be a useful volatile anesthetic, surgical anesthesia must be possible with a partial pressure (in inspired air) which is below its vapor pressure at room temperature. With this in mind evaluate ether and ethanol as *possible* general anesthetics if the partial pressures required are about 15 mmHg for ether and 1.5 mmHg for ethanol.

8.11 Of the following pairs of liquids which do you think could be separated from each other most easily by distillation? Why?
(a) Ethanol and carbon tetrachloride
(b) Ethanol and ether

8.12 To test for lung maturity of the unborn, amniotic fluid is withdrawn from the mother and tested. What general types of compounds are being looked for?

8.13 The fluid portion of the blood called plasma contains high-molecular-weight substances called proteins. If the concentration of these proteins increased, how do you think this would affect blood viscosity and blood pressure?

8.14 Why is possible for a needle to float on water even though it has a density greater than 1 g/ml?

8.15 What unusual properties does water exhibit? How can they be explained?

8.16 "Dry ice" is solid carbon dioxide. What general kind of crystals does it form?

8.17 Which of the following would be good electrical conductors?
(a) Barium
(b) Potassium fluoride (solid)
(c) Potassium fluoride (dissolved in water)
(d) Molten potassium fluoride
(e) Diamond
(f) Lead
(g) Ice

8.18 Sodium metal is an excellent conductor of electricity. Why is it impractical to make sodium wires?

8.19 Draw the formula of the complex which forms from Cu^{2+} and dimercaprol.

8.20 Write chemical equations to describe the following reactions:
(a) Barium with water
(b) Potassium with water
(c) Aluminum with oxygen (O_2)
(d) Strontium (Sr) with oxygen (O_2)

8.21 Can you suggest a general method by which the radioactive metal uranium could be eliminated from the body?

8.22 What is the nutritional meaning of the term *mineral*?

8.23 Rubies and sapphires both contain what common compound? Why do sapphires come in many different colors,while rubies are always red?

8.24 Give the electronic configurations (in terms of *s*, *p*, and *d* orbitals) for the transition elements scandium ($_{21}Sc$) and titanium ($_{22}Ti$). Remember that the 4*s* orbital fills before the 3*d* orbital. How do these configurations differ from that of calcium ($_{20}Ca$)?

8.25 Plastic intrauterine contraceptive devices (IUDs) are wound with copper wire. Why would such a device be dangerous for an individual with Wilson's disease?

8.26 Why can aluminum be used in construction even though it is both soft and chemically very reactive?

8.27 What is a chelating agent?

8.28 A popular new diet book is published which includes as its main source of protein a 4-oz portion of swordfish to be eaten daily. Why might this be dangerous?

8.29 Why is it particularly important that very young children be tested for lead poisoning? How is the test done?

8.30 What function does iron have in humans?

8.31 Why must alkali metals such as Li, Na, and K be stored covered with mineral oil?

8.32 Calcium and sodium are both widely distributed in foods. Why is calcium deficiency sometimes observed anyway?

8.33 What functions does calcium serve in the body?

8.34 For each disorder listed give the mineral involved and specify whether it refers to an abnormally high or abnormally low blood level. (a) Hypocalcemia; (b) hyperkalemia; (c) hypokalemia; (d) hyponatremia.

9 SOLUTIONS

9.1 INTRODUCTION

Air, tap water, foodstuffs, and in fact most of the materials that we come in contact with are present in the form of mixtures rather than pure substances (see Section 2.5). In this chapter we will concentrate our attention upon the *homogeneous mixtures*. Homogeneous mixtures are uniform throughout, meaning that all parts of the mixture have the same composition. There are two general types of homogeneous mixtures, which are distinguished from each other by the size of their component particles. **Solutions** are homogeneous mixtures in which the particle sizes of the components (molecules or ions) range from about 0.1 to 10 nm. **Colloids** contain component particles from 10 to 100 nm in size. It is impossible to see the component particles of solutions or colloids or to separate them by passing the solution or colloid through filter paper. In the sections which follow we will give a brief introduction to the behavior of colloids and a much more detailed discussion of the properties of solutions.

All solutions have certain general properties in common. They all consist of two or more components which remain mixed in solution and have no tendency to separate from the solution. For instance, the salt in a covered saline solution does not suddenly settle out of solution. Although you are most familiar with liquid solutions, solutions can also be gaseous or solid. Air is an example of a gaseous solution and some metal alloys (Section 8.10) are solid solutions. Solutions can form from various combinations of gases, solids, and liquids, as you can see in Table 9.1, which gives the components of some common solutions. Since all solutions are mixtures, all can be separated into their components by some physical means in which no chemical bonds are disturbed. Thus, sodium chloride can be separated from a saline solution by simply evaporating the water or distilling it off to leave pure salt behind. The more sophisticated technique of chromatography (see Section 2.5) must be used to separate the dozens of components of a big-city water supply.

We will devote most of our discussion to solutions that contain only two components, although the ideas and theories presented can be applied to more complex solutions. We will begin by defining the terms used to describe solutions and then establishing some guidelines to predict what components can be mixed together to produce solutions.

TABLE 9.1 **COMMON SOLUTIONS**

Solution	Type	Components	Physical state
Air	Gas in gas	Oxygen, nitrogen, argon, and others (see Table 7.4)	Gas
Natural gas	Gas in gas	Methane, ethane, propane butane, nitrogen	Gas
Carbonated water	Gas in liquid	Water, carbon dioxide	Liquid
Rubbing alcohol	Liquid in liquid	Water, isopropyl alochol	Liquid
Gasoline	Liquid in liquid	Assorted hydrocarbon compounds	Liquid
Saline	Solid in liquid	Water, sodium chloride	Liquid
Corn syrup	Solid in liquid	Glucose, water	Liquid
Novocaine injection mixture	Solid in liquid	Procaine hydrochloride, water, sodium chloride, preservatives	Liquid
Nichrome wire	Solid in solid	Nickel, chromium	Solid

9.2 SOLUTES AND SOLVENTS

In a solution containing two components, one is the **solvent** and the other is the **solute**. For solutions of a solid in a liquid, the *solvent* is taken to be the dispersing medium, that is, the liquid substance that is added to the solid to prepare the solution. The solid is the *solute,* or the dispersed medium. For instance, a saline solution is prepared by adding water to sodium chloride; the water is the solvent and the sodium chloride is the solute. In most cases in which solids are dissolved in liquids, the solvent is also the most abundant component. However, there are exceptions; for instance, it is possible to prepare potassium iodide solutions by adding 100 g H_2O to 200 g KI. Even though KI is the more abundant component in this solution, the solvent is water because water is the dispersing medium. In solutions formed from two liquids it is sometimes convenient to think of the solvent as the more abundant component. For example, in a solution containing 100 ml of alcohol dissolved in 1000 ml of water, the solvent is water and the solute is alcohol. However, in solutions containing water and some other liquid, water is usually considered to be the solvent even if it is not the more-abundant component. For instance, in a rubbing alcohol solution, about 70 percent of the mixture is isopropyl alcohol and the rest is water. But the solvent is still said to be water. As you can see, the terms *solvent* and *solute* are not very precisely defined. Whenever there is any doubt about which is which in any solutions discussed here, we will identify the solvent and the solute.

The process of mixing a solvent and solute (or solutes) to form a solution is called "dissolving," or *dissolution.* It is important to realize that dissolving is not the same thing as melting. Even though the addition of sodium chloride to liquid water produces a liquid solution, the sodium chloride has not "melted"—it has dissolved.

9.3 SOLUBILITY

Note in the data shown in Figure 2.1 that the solubilities are quoted in g/100 cm^3.

The maximum amount of solute which can be dissolved in a particular solvent to make a solution is called the **solubility** of the solute. Solubilities are often expressed in terms of grams of solute per 100 cm^3 of solvent. For example, the solubility of sodium chloride in water is about 36 g per 100 cm^3, which means that it is possible to make a solution by mixing 36 g or less of sodium chloride with 100 cm^3 of water. The solubility of some compounds in water is much less than that of sodium chloride. For example, carbon tetrachloride, CCl_4, is essentially insoluble in water. Other compounds are soluble in water to an infinite extent. Therefore, any amount of the compound may be combined with water to form a solution. Ethanol and water solutions, for instance, may be prepared with any amount of ethanol added to any amount of water. Solubilities in water of some common substance are listed in Table 9.2. Accurate numerical values for solubilities are not always available. Instead we often use a set of general terms to describe solubilities. These usually include "insoluble," "slightly soluble," "soluble," "very soluble," and "infinitely soluble." The term *miscible* is also used to describe two substances (usually liquids) that are infinitely soluble in each other. For instance, we can say that ethanol and water are miscible. Table 9.2 gives the general solubility terms which correspond to the numerical values of the solubilities listed.

TABLE 9.2 SOLUBILITIES OF SELECTED SOLUTES IN WATER AT TEMPERATURES CLOSE TO ROOM TEMPERATURE (20 to 25°C)

Name of compound	Formula	Solubility, g/100 cm^3 H_2O	Solubility general terms*
Ethanol	C_2H_6O	Infinite	∞
Isopropyl alcohol	C_3H_8O	Infinite	∞
Calcium iodide	CaI_2	209	vs
Sucrose	$C_{12}H_{22}O_{11}$	200	vs
Sodium iodide	NaI	184	vs
Sodium nitrate	$NaNO_3$	92	vs s
Sodium chloride	NaCl	36	vs
Ascorbic acid (vitamin C)	$C_6H_8O_6$	30	vs
Ethyl ether	$C_4H_{10}O$	10	s
Lead(II) chloride	$PbCl_2$	1.0	s
Calcium carbonate	$CaCO_3$	0.0015	sl s
Silver chloride	AgCl	0.0002	sl s
Carbon tetrachloride	CCl_4	—†	i
Iron(III) oxide	Fe_2O_3	—	i

*Abbreviations: i = insoluble, sl s = slightly soluble, s = soluble, vs = very soluble, ∞ = infinitely soluble
†The dash (—) in the table means that the numerical value for the solubility is not readily available.

The terms unsaturated, saturated, and supersaturated may be applied to solutions in which the solute has a finite solubility in the solvent. *Unsaturated solutions* contain less solute per 100 cm^3 of solvent than the solubility. *Saturated solutions* contain the amount of solute equal to the solubility, and *supersaturated solutions* actually contain more solute per 100 cm^3 of solvent than the solubility would seem to allow. For example, the solubility of sodium nitrate, $NaNO_3$, in water at 25°C is 92 g per 100 cm^3. An unsaturated aqueous $NaNO_3$ solution contains less than 92 g per 100 cm^3 of water, a saturated solution contains exactly 92 g, and a supersaturated solution contains more than 92 g of $NaNO_3$. Not surprisingly, supersaturated solutions are tricky to prepare. One way to make a supersaturated solution is to evaporate solvent from a solution very slowly. If this is done carefully without agitation or stirring, it is sometimes possible to arrive at a solution which has more solute per 100 cm^3 than the solubility value. Slight agitation, rapid cooling, or the addition of a tiny solute crystal called a *seed* is enough to encourage the appearance of solute crystals from a supersaturated solution. A seed initiates crystal formation because it provides a surface upon which a larger crystal can start to grow. By using this method it is sometimes possible to grow large and beautiful crystals from solutions. In Color Plate 8 the large blue crystal of copper sulfate, $CuSO_4$, was produced by suspending a tiny seed crystal in a supersaturated solution.

SAMPLE EXERCISE 9.1

Using Table 9.2 decide whether the following aqueous solutions are unsaturated, saturated, or supersaturated.

(**a**) 10 g NaCl in 100 cm^3 H_2O (**b**) 18 g ascorbic acid in 50 cm^3 H_2O

Solution:

(**a**) Solubility of NaCl $= \dfrac{36\text{ g NaCl}}{100\text{ cm}^3\text{ H}_2\text{O}}$

$$\underset{\text{Given solution}}{\frac{10\text{ g NaCl}}{100\text{ cm}^3\text{ H}_2\text{O}}} < \underset{\text{Solubility}}{\frac{36\text{ g NaCl}}{100\text{ cm}^3\text{ H}_2\text{O}}}$$

This solution is unsaturated.

(**b**) Solubility of ascorbic acid $= \dfrac{30\text{ g ascorbic acid}}{100\text{ cm}^3\text{ H}_2\text{O}}$

If the given solution contains 18 g ascorbic acid in 50 cm^3 H_2O, then it would contain 36 g ascorbic acid in 100 cm^3 H_2O, or

$$\frac{18 \text{ g ascorbic acid}}{50 \cancel{\text{cm}^3 \text{ H}_2\text{O}}} \times 100 \cancel{\text{cm}^3 \text{ H}_2\text{O}} = 36 \text{ g ascorbic acid}$$

$$\underset{\text{Given solution}}{\frac{36 \text{ g ascorbic acid}}{100 \text{ cm}^3 \text{ H}_2\text{O}}} > \underset{\text{Solubility}}{\frac{30 \text{ g ascorbic acid}}{100 \text{ cm}^3 \text{ H}_2\text{O}}}$$

This solution is supersaturated.

EXERCISE 9.1

Calcium iodide is an expectorant, that is, it helps to dislodge mucus from the respiratory tract. A cough syrup contains 152 mg CaI_2 in 4.5 cm^3 of water. Is the solution saturated, unsaturated, or supersaturated?

9.4 FACTORS INFLUENCING SOLUBILITY

The factors that influence the solubility of one compound in another are complex. However, certain criteria can be established to give at least a qualitative answer to the question of whether or not a solute is likely to be soluble in a particular solvent.

Polarity

For a solute to dissolve in a solvent it must reduce the attractive forces among the solvent molecules so that the solute molecules can "squeeze in" among them. To do this the solute molecules must be attracted to those of the solvent. In this way solute-to-solvent attractive forces will be able to compete with solvent-to-solvent forces. Now we must examine the possible attractive forces that are present among polar molecules and nonpolar molecules.

Polar dissolves polar and nonpolar dissolves nonpolar.

All polar molecules are attracted to each other by forces called *dipole-dipole* forces. In some molecules, such as water, there are additional intermolecular forces due to hydrogen bonding (see Section 4.16). In a polar solvent such as water, only polar solute molecules can compete with the forces operating among the water molecules. For this reason *polar solutes are more soluble in polar solvents.* Likewise, *nonpolar solutes dissolve in nonpolar solvents.* This idea is summarized in the simple rule: Like dissolves like. Let us apply this rule to solutions in which the solvent is water. First suppose the solute is carbon tetrachloride, CCl_4, a nonpolar molecule (see Table 4.5). The polar water molecules are much more attracted to each other than to the nonpolar CCl_4 molecules. It is, therefore, very difficult for a CCl_4 molecule to fit in between two water molecules (see Figure 9.1); no homogeneous mixture is achieved and no solution

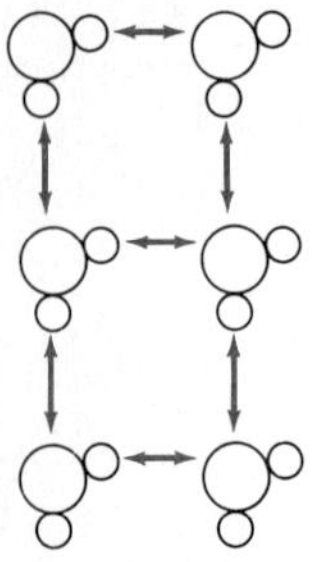

H_2O molecules are attracted to each other by H bonding.

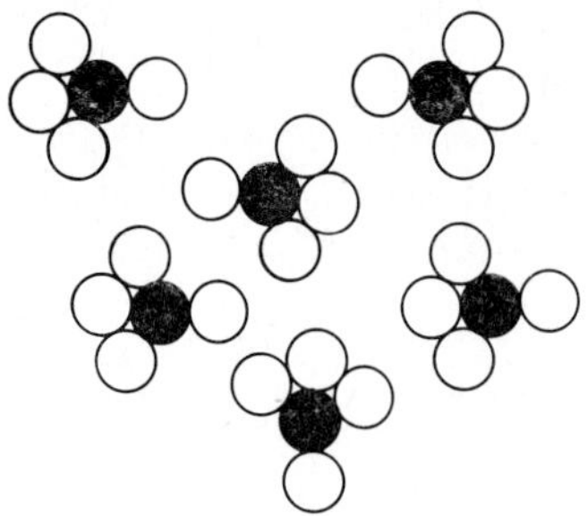

The CCl_4 molecules are not attracted to the H_2O molecules and cannot compete with the forces among the H_2O molecules.

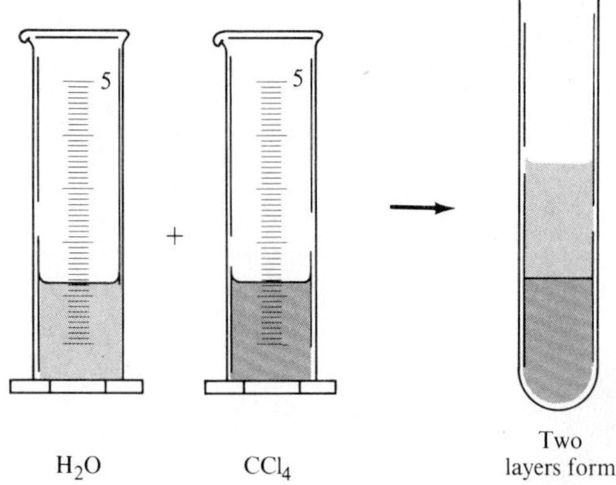

FIGURE 9.1
Mixing CCl_4 and H_2O.

forms. Water and carbon tetrachloride are insoluble in each other. In fact, if H_2O and CCl_4 are shaken vigorously in a test tube, they will separate into two layers. Now suppose we mix ethanol with water. Ethanol is a polar molecule and because it contains an O atom bonded to an H atom, it can participate in hydrogen bonding. The ethanol molecules are attracted to solvent water molecules and are even able to form hydrogen bonds with them. (See Figure 9.2.) Thus ethanol and water molecules can form a uniform, homogeneous mixture, that is, a solution forms. Ethanol is soluble in water. When ethanol is shaken with water in a test tube, no interface forms.

We can apply a similar argument to the dissolution of solid solutes in liquid solvents. For the solute to dissolve, the forces between the molecules or ions in the solid crystal must be reduced by competition with surrounding solvent molecules. Ionic solids are polar and so should be water-soluble. For example, in sodium chloride crystals the sodium ions, Na^+, are attracted to chloride ions, Cl^-. By proper orientation the positive hydrogen end of a water molecule can be attracted to a Cl^- ion and the negative end of a water molecule to an Na^+

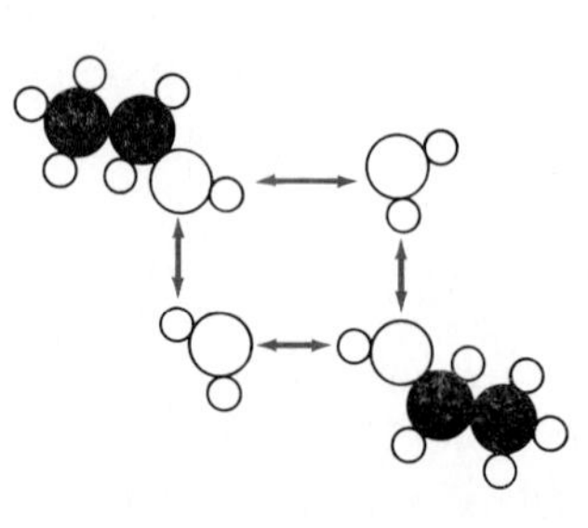

The H_2O and CH_3CH_2OH molecules are attracted to each other by hydrogen bonding.

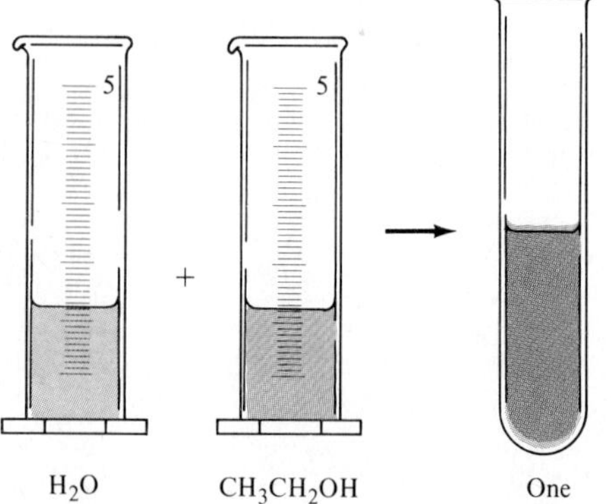

FIGURE 9.2
Mixing ethanol and H_2O.

ion. In this way polar water molecules are able to pull Na^+ and Cl^- ions away from each other and so squeeze in between them. Figure 9.3 illustrates the dissolution of NaCl in water. Note that the ions shown in Figure 9.3*b* are surrounded by water molecules. These ions are said to be *hydrated*. Trying to dissolve NaCl in nonpolar CCl_4 would not be successful because the carbon tetrachloride molecules cannot compete successfully with the strong attractive forces between Na^+ and Cl^- ions.

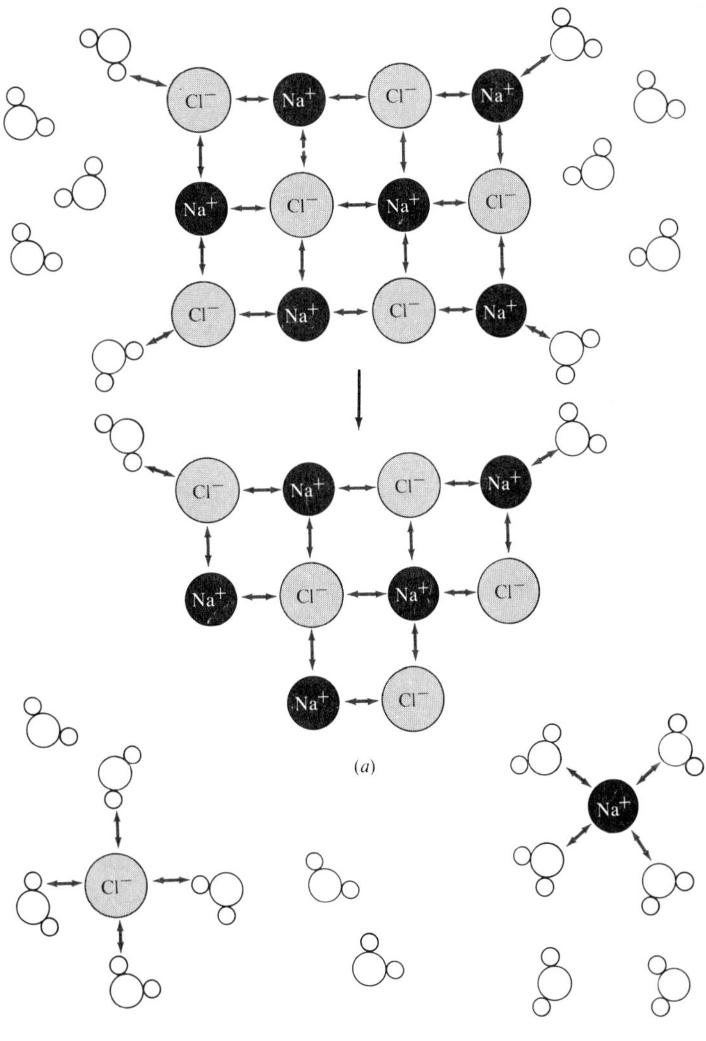

FIGURE 9.3
Mixing NaCl and H_2O.
(*a*) The water molecules are attracted to the Na^+ and Cl^- ions and are thus able to compete with the attractive forces between them. (*b*) A solution forms.

Crystal Lattice Forces

The like-dissolves-like rule serves only as a general guide to what is likely to happen when two compounds are mixed. It simply suggests that polar solvents tend to dissolve polar compounds more readily than nonpolar ones. Other factors are also important; for instance, some ionic compounds are only slightly soluble or practically insoluble in water despite their polarity, because the forces within the crystal lattice which hold the ions in their places are unusually strong. Silver chloride, AgCl, is one example of such an ionic compound. In the AgCl lattice the forces between the Ag^+ ions and Cl^- ions are too great for the polar molecules of water to significantly disrupt the lattice structure. Since the water molecules are unable to squeeze in among the Ag^+ and Cl^- ions, very little AgCl dissolves. As you can see in Table 9.2 the solubility of AgCl in water at room temperature is only about 2×10^{-4} g per 100 cm^3.

Temperature

Most solids are more soluble in hot water than in cold water.

Temperature changes affect solubility. The solubilities of most solid substances increase as the temperature rises because the temperature increase causes greater

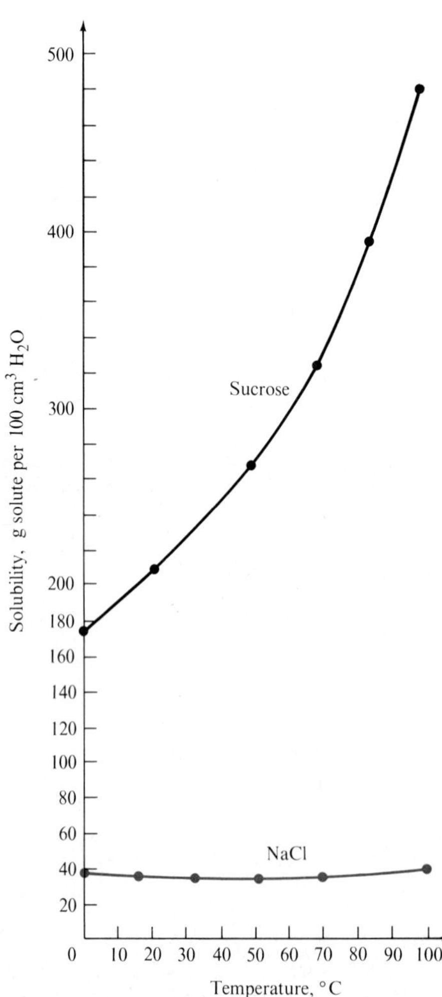

FIGURE 9.4
Solubility of NaCl and sucrose vs. temperature.

movement among solute molecules. This in turn allows the solvent molecules more room to squeeze in. Sucrose, or ordinary table sugar, is much more soluble in boiling water (487 g per 100 cm^3) than it is in ice cold water (179 g per 100 cm^3). Sweetening hot tea is thus much easier than sweetening cold tea. However there are exceptions. The solubility of sodium chloride in water hardly varies, changing from about 35.7 g per 100 cm^3 at 0°C to 39.1 g per 100 cm^3 at 100°C. There are even a few cases in which the solubility of a solute decreases when the temperature increases. Solutions of calcium sulfate, $CaSO_4$, behave this way. In Figure 9.4 the solubilities of sucrose and NaCl are plotted against temperature.

9.5 SOLUBILITY OF GASES IN LIQUIDS

In general the solubility of gases in liquids depends upon the polarity of the solute and solvent, upon temperature, and upon pressure.

Polarity

The like-dissolves-like rule also applies to solutions of gases in liquids. For example, the common gases present in the atmosphere, N_2, O_2, and CO_2, are all nonpolar. (Refer to Section 4.14 for the explanation of why carbon dioxide is

TABLE 9.3 **SOLUBILITY OF GASES IN WATER: EFFECT OF POLARITY AND TEMPERATURE**

Gas	Formula	Structure	Polarity	Solubility, g/100 cm^3 H_2O	Temperature, °C
Nitrogen	N_2	N≡N	Nonpolar	0.0029	0
				0.0018	40
Oxygen	O_2	O=O	Nonpolar	0.0070	0
				0.0035	50
Carbon dioxide	CO_2	O=C=O	Nonpolar	0.34	0
				0.097	40
Chlorine	Cl_2	Cl—Cl	Nonpolar	1.46	0
				0.57	30
Sulfur dioxide	SO_2	O\S//O	Polar	22.8	0
				0.58	90
Hydrogen chloride	HCl	H—Cl	Polar	82.3	0
				56.1	60
Ammonia	NH_3	H–N(–H)–H	Polar	89.9	Cold
				7.4	100
Hydrogen sulfide	H_2S	H–S–H	Polar	437	0
				186	40

nonpolar.) The solubilities of all these gases in water are relatively low, less than 1 g per 100 cm^3. On the other hand, the solubilities of polar gaseous compounds such as HCl, SO_2, and H_2S, are relatively high, ranging from 22.8 g per 100 cm^3 for SO_2 to as much as 437 g per 100 cm^3 for H_2S. The solubilities of various gases in water are listed in Table 9.3.

Temperature

Solubilities of gases *decrease* when the temperature increases (see Table 9.3), because the elevated temperature causes increased movement among the gas molecules (recall the kinetic-molecular theory) and thus gives them a greater chance to escape from the liquid solvent. For example, the solubility of the gaseous mixture air is greater in cold water than it is in hot water. Thus, air bubbles can be seen coming out of water, originally cold from the tap, as it begins to warm to room temperature.

Pressure

The higher the pressure over a solution of a gas in a liquid solvent, the higher the solubility of the gas in the solvent. Carbon dioxide dissolved in carbonated beverages remains dissolved as long as the bottle is capped and the pressure within is maintained. But once the bottle is opened, the pressure above the solution is reduced and carbon dioxide gas begins to bubble out. Another example of the effect of reduced pressure on gas solubility in liquids explains the severe symptoms resulting from decompression sickness, which was discussed in Section 7.3. Nitrogen gas is soluble in body water to the extent of about 10 ml/L. Decrease in pressure causes the solubility of the nitrogen gas in body water to decrease. When this happens, bubbles of nitrogen gas suddenly coming out of solution can form in the blood and in body tissues and by collecting in lung capillaries can cause severe symptoms.

N_2 escaping from body fluids causes the pain of the "bends."

Henry's Law

The solubility of a gas in a liquid solvent can be related quantitatively to the partial pressure of the gas above the solution. **Henry's law**, after William Henry (1774–1836), states that

The solubility of a gas in a liquid is directly proportional to the partial pressure of the gas above the solution in a closed container.

Mathematically, the law can be written in terms of the gas solubility, the partial pressure of the gas, and a constant called the Henry's law constant k:

$$\text{Solubility} = k \times p(\text{gas})$$

Note that Henry's law is in agreement with the qualitative observation that as pressure increases, gas solubility also increases.

Henry's law can be used to estimate the solubility of a gas in a liquid if the partial pressure of the gas over the solution and the appropriate Henry's law constant are known. For example, it is possible to calculate the volume of nitrogen gas, N_2, from inspired air which dissolves in 1 L of body water. The partial pressure of N_2 gas in air is about 0.8 atm and the value of $k(N_2)$ at 37°C is known:

$$p(N_2) = 0.8 \text{ atm}$$

$$k(N_2) = \frac{14 \text{ ml } N_2}{1 \text{ L water} \times 1 \text{ atm}}$$

$$\text{Solubility } (N_2) = k(N_2) \times p(N_2)$$

$$= \frac{14 \text{ ml } N_2 \times 0.8 \cancel{\text{atm}}}{1 \text{ L water} \times 1 \cancel{\text{atm}}} = 10 \text{ ml } N_2/\text{L water}$$

SAMPLE EXERCISE 9.2

The partial pressure of oxygen gas, O_2, in arterial blood is about 100 mmHg, or 0.13 atm. (Although the partial pressure of oxygen in inspired air is about 0.20 atm, some oxygen is lost in air passageways and never reaches the lung alveoli or arterial blood.) Calculate the volume of oxygen gas dissolved in 1 L of arterial blood.

$$\text{Value of } k(O_2) = \frac{22 \text{ ml } O_2}{1 \text{ L blood} \times \text{atm}}$$

Solution:

$$\text{Solubility } (O_2) = k(O_2) \times p(O_2)$$

$$k(O_2) = \frac{22 \text{ ml } O_2}{1 \text{ L blood} \times 1 \text{ atm}}$$

$$p(O_2) = 0.13 \text{ atm}$$

$$\text{Solubility } (O_2) = \frac{22 \text{ ml } O_2 \times 0.13 \cancel{\text{atm}}}{1 \text{ L blood} \times 1 \cancel{\text{atm}}}$$

$$= 3 \text{ ml } O_2/1 \text{ L blood}$$

Actually the oxygen gas content of arterial blood is much greater than the 3 ml oxygen which is physically dissolved in the blood. Another 197 ml oxygen gas, more than 98 percent of the total oxygen, is carried in the red blood cells, where it is bound chemically to hemoglobin molecules.

EXERCISE 9.2

Calculate the volume of CO_2 that is dissolved in a 1-L bottle of carbonated beverage that has been allowed to stand open to the air. Assume that the pressure of CO_2 in the air is about 25 mmHg.

$$k(CO_2) = \frac{730 \text{ ml } CO_2}{1 \text{ L}(H_2O) \times 1 \text{ atm}}$$

9.6 CONCENTRATIONS OF SOLUTIONS

Concentration units tell us how much solute is present for some given quantity of solution or solvent. Of the variety of concentration units in common use, chemists prefer those which express the amount of solute present in terms of moles rather than in terms of grams or milliliters. This is quite natural since the thinking of the chemist revolves about the concept of molecules and ions, which participate in chemical reactions and which are directly related to the mole quantity.

Molarity

Chemists most often express solution concentrations in molarity.

Most of the solutions found on the shelf of a chemistry laboratory will have a label which gives concentration in molarity. To see why molarity is such a convenient unit to use, we look at its definition. **Molarity** (M) is defined as the number of moles of solute dissolved in exactly one liter of solution.

$$\text{Molarity } (M) = \frac{n(\text{solute})}{\text{L(solution)}}$$

One benefit of the use of molarity is the ease of preparing a solution with a given molar concentration. Figure 9.5 shows how this is done. The special flask used

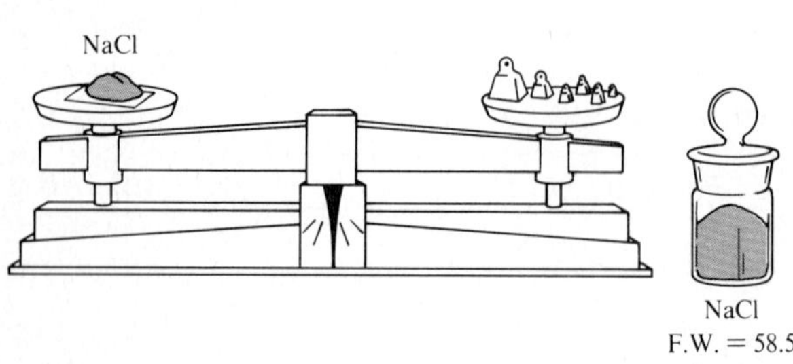

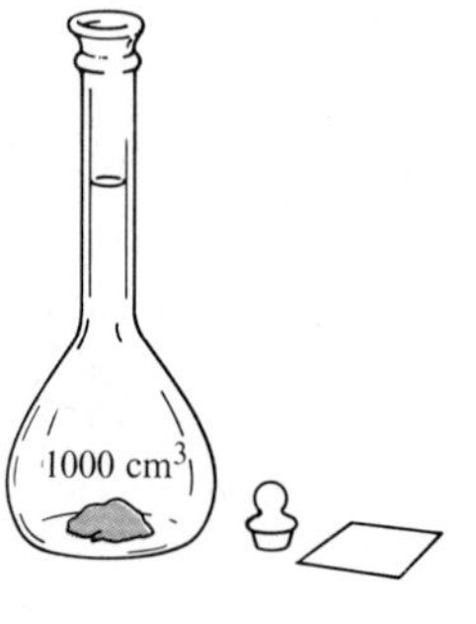

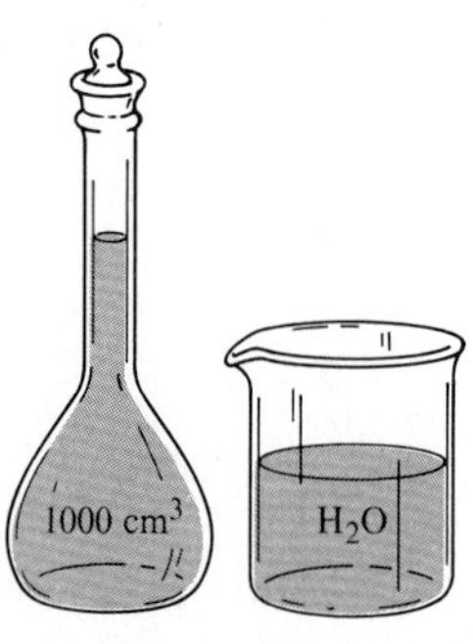

FIGURE 9.5 Making up a 1 M NaCl solution. (1) Weigh out 1 mol (58.5 g) of NaCl. (2) Place the NaCl in a 1-L (1000-cm^3) volumetric flask. (3) Add water up to the 1-L line on the neck of the flask.

is called a *volumetric flask*, that is, a flask which has a circular marking around a narrow neck to indicate a particular volume of solution. The measured amount of solute needed for a particular concentration is placed in the flask and solvent is added up to the mark on the neck of the flask. The 1-L (1000-cm^3) volumetric flask pictured in Figure 9.5 is being used to prepare a solution of NaCl in water which has a molarity of 1.00, that is, which contains 1.00 mol NaCl in 1 L of solution. Since 1 mol of NaCl (formula weight 58.5) has a mass of 58.5 g, a 58.5-g sample of NaCl is weighed out and put into the volumetric flask. Then enough water is added to reach the 1-L mark on the flask neck. The resulting solution has a concentration of 1.00 mol NaCl per liter of solution, which can be written as simply 1.00 *M* and read as "1.00 molar." Square brackets are also used to indicate molar concentrations. The expression [NaCl] means mol NaCl per L solution.

It is not necessary to use 1-L volumetric flasks to make up solutions with a given molarity. Some of the other common sizes available are 5 ml, 10 ml, 25 ml, 50 ml, 100 ml, 250 ml, 500 ml, and 2000 ml. For instance, suppose we want to make up 250 ml of a 1.00 *M* NaOH (formula weight 40.0) solution. The solution contains 1.00 mol NaOH per liter of solution. Paying careful attention to units, we can calculate the mass of NaOH needed. Our strategy is

$$\frac{1.00 \text{ mol NaOH}}{1000 \text{ ml solution}} = \frac{? \text{ g NaOH}}{1000 \text{ ml solution}} = \frac{? \text{ g NaOH}}{250 \text{ ml solution}}$$

Using the information that 1 mol NaOH = 40.0 g NaOH and that the amount of solution we wish to prepare is 250 ml, we get

$$\frac{1.00 \cancel{\text{ mol NaOH}}}{1000 \cancel{\text{ ml solution}}} \times \frac{40 \text{ g NaOH}}{1 \cancel{\text{ mol NaOH}}} \times 250 \cancel{\text{ ml solution}} = 10.0 \text{ g NaOH}$$

Thus, to prepare 250 ml of a 1.0 *M* solution, add 10.0 g NaOH to a 250-ml volumetric flask and dilute with water up to the mark on its neck.

SAMPLE EXERCISE 9.3

Suppose you wish to prepare 500 ml of a 0.200 *M* solution of silver nitrate. How many grams of $AgNO_3$ (formula weight 170) must be weighed out?

Solution:

$$\frac{0.200 \text{ mol AgNO}_3}{1000 \text{ ml solution}} = \frac{? \text{ g AgNO}_3}{1000 \text{ ml solution}} = \frac{? \text{ g AgNO}_3}{500 \text{ ml solution}}$$

$$1 \text{ mol AgNO}_3 = 170 \text{ g AgNO}_3$$

$$\frac{0.200 \cancel{\text{ mol AgNO}_3}}{1000 \cancel{\text{ ml solution}}} \times \frac{170 \text{ g AgNO}_3}{1 \cancel{\text{ mol AgNO}_3}} \times 500 \cancel{\text{ ml solution}} = 17.0 \text{ g AgNO}_3$$

Therefore, 17.0 g $AgNO_3$ must be added to a 500-ml volumetric flask and diluted to the mark to prepare this solution.

EXERCISE 9.3

How many grams of potassium chloride (KCl) are needed to prepare 10 ml of 2.00 *M* solution to be used as a potassium supplement?

Another benefit of the use of molarity is that it is easy to calculate how many moles of a solute there are in a given volume of solution which has a known molar concentration. For instance, suppose we wish to know how many moles of HCl are present in 25.0 ml of a 1.50 *M* HCl solution.

$$\frac{1.50 \text{ mol HCl}}{1000 \text{ ml solution}} = \frac{? \text{ mol HCl}}{25.0 \text{ ml solution}}$$

$$\frac{1.50 \text{ mol HCl}}{1000 \cancel{\text{ ml solution}}} \times 25.0 \cancel{\text{ ml solution}} = 0.0375 \text{ mol HCl}$$

SAMPLE EXERCISE 9.4

A solution of potassium compounds has a concentration which is 3.00 *M* in K^+ ions. Suppose a patient with a potassium deficiency must receive 0.0600 mol K^+ daily. What volume of this solution should be administered?

Solution:

This time it is volume, not moles, we wish to calculate.

$$\frac{1000 \text{ ml solution}}{3.00 \text{ mol } K^+} = \frac{? \text{ ml solution}}{0.0600 \text{ mol } K^+}$$

$$\frac{1000 \text{ ml solution}}{3.00 \cancel{\text{ mol } K^+}} \times 0.0600 \cancel{\text{ mol } K^+} = 20.0 \text{ ml solution}$$

The patient must receive 20.0 ml of 3.00 *M* K^+ solution daily.

EXERCISE 9.4

Calculate the number of moles of ferrous sulfate, or iron(II) sulfate ($FeSO_4$), present in a 5-ml sample of 0.100 *M* solution.

To calculate the molarity of a solution prepared from a given mass of solute and a given mass of solvent, the density of the solution must be known in order to calculate its volume. For instance, suppose a solution is prepared by mixing 117 g NaCl with 360 g H_2O. If the density of the solution is 1.19 g/ml, we can calculate the molarity. We have the mass of the solution:

$$117 \text{ g NaCl} + 360 \text{ g H}_2\text{O} = 477 \text{ g solution}$$

To find the volume of the solution the density is used as a conversion factor.

$$477 \cancel{\text{ g solution}} \times \frac{1 \text{ ml solution}}{1.19 \cancel{\text{ g solution}}} = 400 \text{ ml solution} = 0.400 \text{ L solution}$$

Now we can calculate the molarity (formula weight NaCl = 58.5 g):

$$\frac{117 \cancel{\text{ g NaCl}}}{0.400 \text{ L solution}} \times \frac{1 \text{ mol NaCl}}{58.5 \cancel{\text{ g NaCl}}} = \frac{5.00 \text{ mol NaCl}}{\text{L solution}} = 5.00\ M$$

Molality

A unit that is closely related to the molarity is the molality. Molality units are used in calculations involving the changes in physical properties (such as boiling point and freezing point) that a solvent undergoes when solute is added (see Section 9.7). **Molality** (m) is defined as the number of moles of solute dissolved in exactly one kilogram (1000 g) of solvent.

$$\text{Molality} = \frac{n(\text{solute})}{1 \text{ kg solvent}}$$

For instance, to calculate the molality of a solution prepared by adding 117 g NaCl to 360 g H_2O (0.360 kg H_2O):

$$\frac{117 \text{ g NaCl}}{0.360 \text{ kg H}_2\text{O}} = \frac{? \text{ mol NaCl}}{0.360 \text{ kg H}_2\text{O}}$$

$$1 \text{ mol NaCl} = 58.5 \text{ g NaCl}$$

and

$$\frac{117 \cancel{\text{ g NaCl}}}{0.360 \text{ kg H}_2\text{O}} \times \frac{1 \text{ mol NaCl}}{58.5 \cancel{\text{ g NaCl}}} = \frac{5.56 \text{ mol NaCl}}{\text{kg H}_2\text{O}} = 5.56\ m$$

Note that the molality (5.56 m) that we just calculated for this solution containing 117 g NaCl in 360 g of H_2O is not very different from the molarity (5.00 M) we found for the same solution in the example above. In general, it is not a bad approximation to substitute molarity for molality for most aqueous solutions. Since the density of these solutions is not far from 1 g/ml, the numerical values for molarity and molality will be reasonably close.

SAMPLE EXERCISE 9.5

Compare the molarity and the molality of a 1-L bottle of dextrose solution (used in the preparation of intravenous (I.V.) solutions) in which 0.250 mol of dextrose is dissolved in 970 g water (0.970 kg H_2O).

Solution:

To calculate molarity use the number of moles of dextrose and the volume of solution.

$$\frac{0.250 \text{ mol dextrose}}{1 \text{ L solution}} = 0.250\ M$$

We can calculate molality from the number of moles of dextrose and the mass of solvent.

$$\frac{0.250 \text{ mol dextrose}}{0.970 \text{ kg } H_2O} = 0.258\ m$$

Note that the molarity and the molality of this dextrose solution are not very different.

EXERCISE 9.5

What is the molality of a solution of potassium bromide (KBr) if it is prepared by mixing 119 g KBr with 963 g of water? Compare your answer with the molarity of this solution, which is 1.00 M.

Weight Percent

Although it is based on mass of solute rather than number of moles of solute, the **weight percent** concentration unit is sometimes used in chemistry laboratories and is very frequently used in industrial and medical laboratories. It is nearly always used on labels for household products. The unit of weight percent (sometimes written as % w/w) is defined in terms of a ratio of the weight of the solute divided by the weight of the solution.

$$\text{Percent } w/w = \frac{\text{weight solute}}{\text{weight solution}} \times 100\%$$

For example, suppose an oil solution of dimercaprol, the compound used as an antidote for mercury, gold, or arsenic poisoning (see Section 8.13) is to be prepared by mixing 100 mg of dimercaprol with 700 mg of peanut oil. To calculate the % w/w of dimercaprol in this solution,

$$\text{Weight solute} = 100 \text{ mg}$$

$$\text{Weight solution} = 100 \text{ mg} + 700 \text{ mg} = 800 \text{ mg}$$

$$\text{Weight percent dimercaprol} = \frac{100 \cancel{\text{mg}}}{800 \cancel{\text{mg}}} \times 100\% = 12.5\%$$

Many drug products are described in terms of % w/v, where the units for weight (w) and volume (v) must be specified. For instance, a solution containing 1 g of $MgSO_4$ in a 2-ml ampul may be expressed as 50% w/v.

SAMPLE EXERCISE 9.6

A cough syrup contains 5% w/w alcohol. How many grams of alcohol would there be in a 4-oz bottle of the syrup? (1 oz = 28.3 g)

Solution:

$$\% \text{ w/w} = 5\%$$

$$\text{Weight solution} = 4 \cancel{\text{oz}} \times \frac{28.3 \text{ g}}{1 \cancel{\text{oz}}} = 113 \text{ g}$$

$$5\% = \frac{\text{weight alcohol}}{113 \text{ g}} \times 100\%$$

$$\text{Weight alcohol} = \frac{5\% \times 113 \text{ g}}{100\%} = 5.6 \text{ g}$$

There would be 5.6 g alcohol in the 4-oz bottle of syrup.

EXERCISE 9.6

Calculate the % w/w concentration of a solution made by mixing 10.0 g NaCl with 100 g water.

General Terms: Dilute and Concentrated

The terms *dilute* and *concentrated* are often used to describe solutions. These are purely relative labels which are used to compare actual solution concentrations with the maximum possible concentration. For instance, a solution which contains 30 g NaCl in 100 cm^3 of water is concentrated. This is true because the amount

TABLE 9.4 SUMMARY OF THE MEANING OF VARIOUS CONCENTRATION UNITS

Unit	Meaning	Typical use
Weight percent (% w/w, or wt %)	$\frac{\text{Weight of solute}}{\text{Weight of solution}} \times 100\%$	General purpose
Molality (m)	$\frac{\text{mol solute}}{\text{kg solvent}}$	Calculations, ΔT_f, ΔT_b
Molarity (M)	$\frac{\text{mol solute}}{\text{L solution}}$	Chemistry laboratory
Weight/volume (% w/v)	$\frac{\text{Weight of solute}}{\text{Volume of solution}} \times 100\%$	Diagnostic test results (mg glucose/dl blood); concentrations of drug products
Volume/volume (% v/v)	$\frac{\text{Volume of solute}}{\text{Volume of solvent}} \times 100\%$	Gas concentrations
Proof	200 × v/v	Alcoholic beverage concentrations
Number/volume	$\frac{\text{Count}}{\text{Volume}}$	WBC* or RBC† in blood

*White blood cells
†Red blood cells

of NaCl dissolved is close to the maximum possible amount of 36 g per 100 cm^3 of water, the solubility of NaCl. Using the same reasoning, a solution which contains only 0.30 g NaCl in 100 cm^3 of water is a dilute saline solution. The vague terms dilute and concentrated are used to express only approximate solution concentrations.

A summary of the meaning of the various concentration units we have discussed in this section, as well as some others used to describe drug products and test results, is given in Table 9.4.

9.7 CHANGING SOLUTION CONCENTRATIONS

Solutions used in laboratories are often sold in concentrated form for convenience. Thus it is frequently necessary to dilute such solutions to some desired concentration. Let us see how this is done for solutions with concentrations given in molarity. Suppose we have a 1.00 M solution of HCl in water and we need 250 ml of 0.100 M HCl for an experiment. How much of the original concentrated solution must be placed in a 250-ml volumetric flask to prepare this solution? We first calculate the number of moles required for the more dilute solution and then calculate the volume of the concentrated solution needed to supply that number of moles.

Number of moles needed:

$$\frac{0.100 \text{ mol HCl}}{1000 \cancel{\text{mL solution}}} \times 250 \cancel{\text{mL solution}} = 0.0250 \text{ mol HCl}$$

Volume of 1.00 *M* HCl solution needed:

$$\frac{1000 \text{ ml solution}}{1.00 \cancel{\text{mol HCl}}} \times 0.0250 \cancel{\text{mol HCl}} = 25.0 \text{ ml solution}$$

The new solution is prepared by placing 25.0 ml of the concentrated 1 *M* HCl solution into a 250-ml volumetric flask and then diluting with water.

Essentially what we have done in the example above is make use of a simple equation which relates the original volume and concentration to the final volume and concentration:

$$V(\text{original}) \times C(\text{original}) = V(\text{final}) \times C(\text{final})$$

If the volume is expressed in liters (L) and the concentration in molarity (mol/L), we can show that the equation reduces to mol(original) = mol(final):

$$\text{L}\cancel{(\text{original})} \times \frac{\text{mol(original)}}{\text{L}\cancel{(\text{original})}} = \text{L}\cancel{(\text{final})} \times \frac{\text{mol(final)}}{\text{L}\cancel{(\text{final})}}$$

$$\text{mol(original)} = \text{mol(final)}$$

The quantities *V* and *C* may be expressed in any units provided that they are the same on both sides of the equation.

To repeat the calculation above with the relationship just given

$$V(\text{final}) = 250 \text{ mL}$$

$$V(\text{original}) = ?$$

$$C(\text{final}) = 0.100\ M$$

$$C(\text{original}) = 1.00\ M$$

$$V(\text{original}) \times C(\text{original}) = V(\text{final}) \times C(\text{final})$$

$$V(\text{original}) \times 1.00\ M = 250 \text{ ml} \times 0.100\ M$$

$$V(\text{original}) = \frac{250 \text{ ml} \times 0.100 \cancel{M}}{1.00 \cancel{M}} = 25.0 \text{ ml}$$

SAMPLE EXERCISE 9.7

A 30-ml sample of a stock solution of a drug contains 600 mg of a drug compound mixed with a diluent (5% dextrose solution). For safe administration this drug must be given at a concentration of 50 mg per 500 ml of solution. What volume of the stock solution must be used to prepare 1000 ml of such a solution?

Solution:

$$V(\text{original}) \times C(\text{original}) = V(\text{final}) \times C(\text{final})$$

$$V(\text{original}) = ?$$

$$V(\text{final}) = 1000 \text{ ml}$$

$$C(\text{original}) = 600 \text{ mg}/30 \text{ ml} = 20 \text{ mg/ml}$$

$$C(\text{final}) = 50 \text{ mg}/500 \text{ ml} = 0.10 \text{ mg/ml}$$

Remember that we can use any consistent set of units in the equation above:

$$V(\text{original}) \times 20 \text{ mg/ml} = 1000 \text{ ml} \times 0.10 \text{ mg/ml}$$

$$V(\text{original}) = 1000 \text{ ml} \times \frac{0.10 \cancel{\text{mg/ml}}}{20 \cancel{\text{mg/ml}}} = 5 \text{ ml}$$

Thus we must mix 5 ml of the stock solution with enough dextrose diluent to prepare 1000 ml of the solution to be administered.

EXERCISE 9.7

Suppose you wish to prepare 150 ml of a 1.0% solution of KCl starting with a 10% full-strength solution (too concentrated to be administered directly without producing gastrointestinal disturbances). What volume of the stock solution will be needed?

9.8 COLLIGATIVE PROPERTIES

The properties of solutions are different from those of solvents. For instance, the freezing points of solutions are always lower than those of the pure solvent.

Colligate means to "group together."

Colligative properties such as freezing point depression are properties which depend upon the number of solute particles "collected together" in solution. Colligative properties depend only on the concentration of the dissolved particles, not upon the nature of the dissolved particles. For instance, a 1 *m* (approximately 1*M*) solution of glucose in water and a 1 *m* solution of sucrose in water will both lower the freezing point of water by 1.86°C. This is true even though the formulas and structures of glucose ($C_6H_{12}O_6$) and sucrose ($C_{12}H_{22}O_{11}$) are very different.

There are four colligative properties of solutions that we will discuss:

1. Vapor pressure lowering
2. Boiling point elevation
3. Freezing point depression
4. Osmotic pressure

Since osmotic pressure is particularly important in living systems, we will spend most of our discussion time on this property.

Chemists often use colligative property measurements to determine molecular weights of solutes. Since colligative properties of solutions are directly related to the number of molecules (or ions) of a solute dissolved, we can find out how many moles of solute are in solution by measuring the value of a colligative property. If the weight of the solute used to prepare the solution is also known, the molecular weight can be calculated.

$$\frac{\text{Weight of solute}}{\text{Number of moles of solute}} = \text{molecular weight of solute}$$

Colligative property measurements can thus be used for the determination of molecular weights of *unknown* compounds. In fact, that is how some of the molecular weights used to find molecular formulas from mass composition data were obtained (see Section 5.5).

Vapor Pressure Lowering

The vapor pressure of a solution is always lower than the vapor pressure of the pure solvent at a particular temperature. For example, the vapor pressure of pure water at 100°C is 760 mmHg. The vapor pressure of an aqueous 1 *M* NaCl solution at the same temperature is only 735 mmHg. Thus the vapor pressure is lowered by 25 mmHg as compared with that of pure water.

$$\begin{aligned} p(H_2O) - p(1\ M\ \text{NaCl solution}) &= 760\ \text{mmHg} - 735\ \text{mmHg} \\ &= 25\ \text{mmHg} \end{aligned}$$

The more concentrated the solution, the more the vapor pressure is lowered. The vapor pressure of a 2 *M* NaCl solution at 100°C is 708 mmHg, and the vapor pressure lowering is about twice that of the 1 *M* solution.

$$\begin{aligned} p(H_2O) - p(2\ M\ \text{NaCl solution}) &= 760\ \text{mmHg} - 708\ \text{mmHg} \\ &= 52\ \text{mmHg} \end{aligned}$$

As is typical of all colligative properties, the vapor pressure lowering does not depend upon the nature of the solute but only on the concentration of solute molecules or ions. The vapor pressure lowering for a 1 *M* NaCl solution is the same as that for a 1 *M* KCl solution.

Boiling Point Elevation

Since the vapor pressure of a solution is *lower* than that of the solvent, it follows that the boiling point of the solution must be *higher* than the boiling point of the pure solvent. Extra heat must be supplied to the solution so that the solvent molecules in the solution can attain the vapor pressure of the external atmosphere. For instance, the vapor pressure of pure water at 100°C is 760 mmHg, meaning that the normal boiling point of pure water is 100°C. The vapor pressure of any aqueous solution must be less than 760 mmHg at 100°C. Hence the normal boiling point of any aqueous solution must be greater than 100°C.

The difference between the boiling point T_b of a pure solvent and that of a solution is the **boiling point elevation.** For an aqueous solution boiling at 100.1°C, the boiling point elevation ΔT_b (pronounced delta T_b) is

$$\Delta T_b = T_b(\text{solution}) - T_b(\text{H}_2\text{O})$$

$$T_b(\text{solution}) = 100.1°\text{C}$$

$$T_b(\text{H}_2\text{O}) = 100°\text{C}$$

$$\Delta T_b = 100.1°\text{C} - 100°\text{C} = 0.1°\text{C}$$

The more concentrated the solution, the greater the boiling point elevation. As with all colligative properties, the magnitude of the boiling point elevation depends only upon the concentration of the solution, not on the nature of the solute. The boiling point elevation ΔT_b is directly proportional to the molality of the solution, according to the equation

$$\Delta T_b = k_b \times m$$

The symbol m stands for molality, and k_b is the boiling point elevation constant. Since k_b is expressed in units of degrees Celsius per molal concentration unit, it is known as the *molal boiling point elevation constant.* For water k_b is 0.52°C/m, which means that a 1 m aqueous solution experiences a boiling point elevation of 0.52°C and thus boils at 100.52°C.

Suppose we wish to calculate the boiling point of a solution made by dissolving 0.40 mol of a solute in 1 kg of water. First we find the molality of the solution and then use the equation above to determine ΔT_b.

$$\frac{0.40 \text{ mol solute}}{1 \text{ kg water}} = 0.40\ m$$

$$k_b(\text{H}_2\text{O}) = 0.52°\text{C}/m$$

$$\Delta T_b = k_b \times m$$

$$= \frac{0.52°\text{C}}{\cancel{m}} \times 0.40\ \cancel{m} = 0.21°\text{C}$$

and

$$T_b = 100°\text{C} + 0.21°\text{C} = 100.21°\text{C}$$

Freezing Point Depression

The freezing point of a solution is always lower than the freezing point of the pure solvent. For example, the freezing point of pure water is 0°C while the freezing points of all aqueous solutions are less than 0°C. The difference between the freezing point T_f of a pure solvent and that of a solution is the **freezing point depression.** Freezing point depressions can be calculated from an equation analogous to the one used above to relate boiling point elevations to k_b and m. The freezing point depression ΔT_f depends upon the molal freezing point depression constant k_f and molality m.

$$\Delta T_f = k_f \times m$$

For water the value of k_f is 1.86°C/m. Suppose we wish to calculate the freezing point of the same 0.40 m solution considered in the previous example.

$$\Delta T_f = k_f \times m$$

$$= \frac{1.86°\text{C}}{\cancel{m}} \times 0.40\,\cancel{m} = 0.74°\text{C}$$

and

$$T_f = 0°\text{C} - 0.74°\text{C} = -0.74°\text{C}$$

Antifreeze solutions have freezing points of about −40°C (equals −40°F).

There are many practical applications which take advantage of freezing point depression. Snow is frozen water. To melt snow on winter sidewalks we scatter salt on the snow to lower its freezing point. The freezing point of the snow and salt solution is less than 0°C. Car radiators contain water which might freeze during very cold winter months. The addition of high concentrations of antifreeze compounds prevents the water from freezing by lowering the freezing point below any temperature likely to be encountered even on the coldest of winter days.

SAMPLE EXERCISE 9.8

Calculate the freezing point of a dextrose solution that contains 50 g dextrose (formula weight 180) dissolved in 1.0 kg H_2O. (This concentration is close to that of the diluent we discussed in Sample Exercise 9.7.)

Solution:

To calculate T_f we first find the molality.

$$n(\text{solute}) = 50\ \cancel{\text{g dextrose}} \times \frac{1\text{ mol dextrose}}{180\ \cancel{\text{g dextrose}}}$$

$$= 0.28\text{ mol dextrose}$$

$$\text{Molality} = \frac{0.28 \text{ mol dextrose}}{1.00 \text{ kg } H_2O} = 0.28\ m$$

$$\Delta T_f = k_f \times m$$

$$k_f(H_2O) = 1.86°C/m \qquad \text{and} \qquad m = 0.28$$

$$\Delta T_f = \frac{1.86°C}{\cancel{m}} \times 0.28\ \cancel{m} = 0.52°C$$

$$T_f = 0°C - 0.52°C = -0.52°C$$

The dextrose solution freezes at $-0.52°C$.

EXERCISE 9.8

What is the boiling point of the dextrose solution from Sample Exercise 9.8?

9.9 DISSOCIATION OF IONIC COMPOUNDS IN SOLUTION

When dissolved solutes break down into more than one solute "particle," the colligative properties produced are larger than expected. An example of this phenomenon is the ability of water-soluble ionic compounds to produce ions in aqueous solution. When sodium chloride is dissolved in water, each NaCl produces a sodium ion and a chloride ion.

$$NaCl\ (aq) \longrightarrow Na^+(aq) + Cl^-(aq)$$

Instead of one NaCl particle there are *two* ions which behave like *two* particles. The colligative property effect is thus doubled. The full truth is that the effect is not quite doubled because the ionization is not complete. However, in dilute solutions the assumption of complete ionization will give us good results. Colligative property equations such as $\Delta T_b = k_b \times m$ and $\Delta T_f = k_f \times m$ must be modified to account for the fact that solutes may ionize. In the equations below the i (called the van't Hoff factor) is equal to the number of ions produced by a particular solute.

We will assume that i is always an integer value.

$$\Delta T_b = i \times k_b \times m \qquad \text{and} \qquad \Delta T_f = i \times k_f \times m$$

The value of i for $CaCl_2$, which produces one Ca^+ ion and two Cl^- ions when dissolved in water, is 3. For NaCl, which produces two ions, the value of i is 1.00. Thus, to calculate the freezing point of a 2 m NaCl aqueous solution,

$$\Delta T_f = i \times k_f \times m$$

$$i = 2 \qquad k_f = 1.86°C/m \qquad \text{and} \qquad m = 1.00$$

$$\Delta T_f = 2 \times \frac{1.86°\text{C}}{\cancel{m}} \times 1.00\cancel{m} = 3.72°\text{C}$$

Thus $T_f = 0°\text{C} - 3.72°\text{C} = -3.72°\text{C}$.

9.10 OSMOSIS AND OSMOTIC PRESSURE

Osmosis is the movement of solvent across a special barrier called a **semipermeable membrane**, that is, a membrane that allows certain particles to pass through but not others. Water and other small solvent molecules can pass through a semipermeable membrane while larger solute molecules and ions are held back. When a pure solvent and a solution are separated by such a semipermeable membrane, there is a tendency for solvent to flow through the membrane into the solution. Likewise, when two solutions of different concentrations are separated by a semipermeable membrane

Solvent flows from the less concentrated solution through the membrane into the more concentrated solution.

For example, suppose a semipermeable membrane separates pure water on one side from a sodium chloride solution on the other side. Osmosis occurs. Water flows through the membrane to dilute the sodium chloride solution. The hydrated Na^+ and Cl^- ions are too large to pass through the holes in the membrane, as shown in Figure 9.6. If a semipermeable membrane separates water from a salt solution, water flows through the membrane into the solution (see Figure 9.7*a*). Likewise, water flows from a more dilute solution through a semipermeable membrane to a more concentrated solution (see Figure 9.7*b*). In general, the tendency is for solutions on opposite sides of a semipermeable membrane to become equalized in concentration through osmosis.

As a result of osmosis the pressure on either side of the membranes pictured in Figure 9.7 is different. The liquid level has risen in the right-hand compartment in both cases. **Osmotic pressure** π is the difference between the pressures on both sides of a semipermeable membrane as a result of osmosis. The precise definition of osmotic pressure is the pressure which must be applied to a solution to stop the flow of solvent through a semipermeable membrane. Devices used to measure

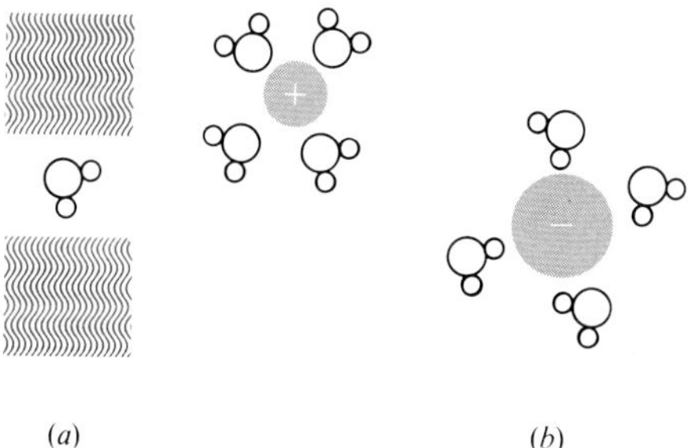

FIGURE 9.6
Holes in semipermeable membrane. (*a*) H_2O molecules can pass through membrane holes. (*b*) Hydrated ions are too large to pass through membrane.

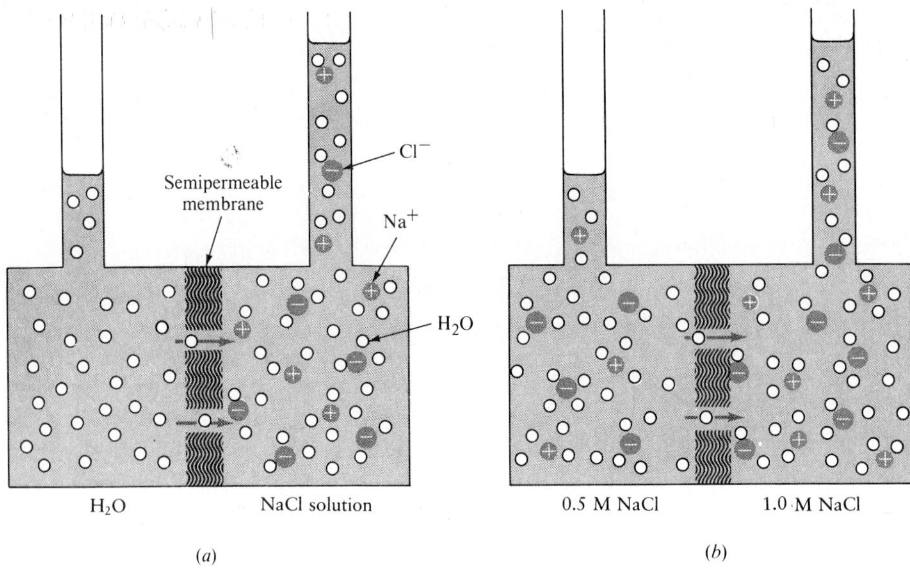

FIGURE 9.7
Process of osmosis. Water flows through the semipermeable membrane to dilute the NaCl solution in the right-hand compartments.

osmotic pressure are called *osmotic pressure cells*. Although they are somewhat more elaborate than the cell diagrammed in Figure 9.8, they operate upon the same principle. In Figure 9.8 pressure is applied to the sodium chloride solution to stop the flow of water into the solution. The measured pressure is the osmotic pressure.

Like all colligative properties, osmotic pressure depends upon the total number of particles present in a solution regardless of whether they are molecules or ions. The higher the concentration of particles in solution, the higher the osmotic pressure. **Osmolarity** is a term used to express concentration in terms of moles of particles in solution per liter of solution and is simply equal to the molarity multiplied by *i*.

$$\text{Osmolarity} = i \times \text{molarity}$$

For example, the osmolarity of a 1 *M* glucose solution is 1 *M* because each glucose molecule represents one solute particle ($i = 1$). That means that 1 mol of glucose molecules produces 1 mol of solute particles. In this case the osmolarity and the molarity are identical. For dissociating ionic solutes, *i* does not equal 1 and osmolarity and molarity are different. For instance, the osmolarity of a 1 *M* NaCl solution is 2 *M* because each sodium chloride unit contributes two solute particles, one Na^+ ion and one Cl^- ion.

The relationship between osmotic pressure and the osmolarity of a solute is expressed by an equation that happens to resemble closely the ideal gas law equation:

$$\pi V = nRT$$

π stands for osmotic pressure.

The symbol π (pi) stands for the osmotic pressure. The other quantities, R, n, T, and V, represent the ideal gas constant, the number of moles of solute particles, the Kelvin temperature, and the volume of solution. Although the osmolarity

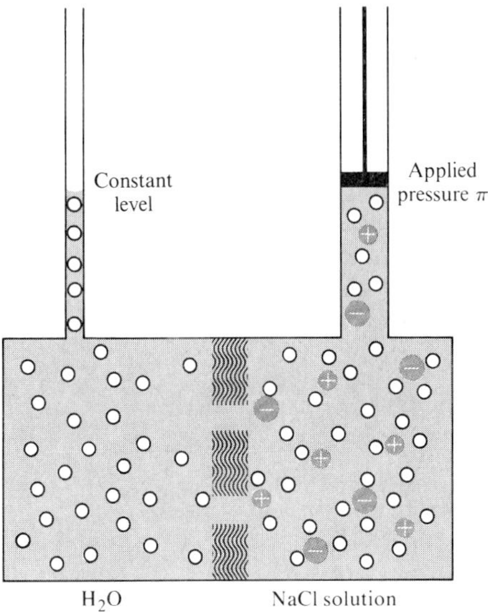

FIGURE 9.8
When the solvent level in the narrow tube (on the left) becomes constant, the flow of solvent has stopped. The applied pressure needed for this to happen is the osmotic pressure (π).

concentration unit does not appear directly in this equation it can be inserted with a simple rearrangement of n and V. The quantity n/V is the number of moles of solute particles divided by the volume (in liters) of the solution and is thus identical to the osmolarity concentration unit, which we will call c.

$$c = \frac{n(\text{solute particles})}{V(\text{volume of solution, L})} = \text{osmolarity}$$

Dividing both sides of the equation above by V puts the concentration (osmolarity) into the equation:

$$\frac{\pi V}{V} = \frac{nRT}{V}$$

$$\pi = \frac{nRT}{V} = \frac{n}{V}RT$$

and thus,

$$\pi = cRT$$

As the concentration increases, so does the osmotic pressure.

Suppose we wish to calculate the osmotic pressure developed in a 0.100 M glucose solution at 25°C. As just noted, glucose molecules do not dissociate and thus the osmolarity c of this solution is 0.100 M.

$$\pi = cRT$$

$$c = 0.100 \text{ mol/L}$$

$$R = 0.0821 \text{ (L)(atm)/(mol)(K)}$$

$$T = 25°\text{C} + 273 = 298 \text{ K}$$

$$\pi = \frac{0.100\ \text{mol}}{\text{L}} \times \frac{0.0821\ (\text{L})(\text{atm})}{(\text{mol})(\text{K})} \times 298\ \text{K} = 2.45\ \text{atm}$$

As you can see from the example above, the osmotic pressure developed by even relatively dilute solutions is a sizable and easily measured quantity. In Section 9.8 we mentioned that colligative properties could be used to find molecular weights. One use for osmotic pressure measurements is in the determination of molecular weights of giant molecules such as proteins (which have molecular weights starting at about 50,000). The molecular weights of such compounds are so large that dissolving a sample of one of them in a solvent produces a solution with a very small number of moles and very low concentration, but the osmotic pressure effect is so great that the measurement can be made anyway. This is not true for other colligative properties such as freezing point depression because the temperature lowering effect would be too small to be observed with any degree of accuracy.

The ΔT_b or ΔT_f of a solution of a very high molecular weight substance is too small to be conveniently measured.

SAMPLE EXERCISE 9.9

Calculate the osmotic pressure which would develop in tissue fluid, which contains 0.150 mol of NaCl per liter. Assume that the temperature is normal body temperature.

Solution:

$$\pi = cRT$$

$$c = 2 \times 0.150\ \text{mol/L} = 0.300\ \text{mol/L}$$

$$R = 0.0821\ (\text{L})(\text{atm})/(\text{mol})(\text{K})$$

$$T = 37°\text{C} + 273 = 310\ \text{K}$$

$$\pi = \frac{0.300\ \text{mol}}{\text{L}} \times \frac{0.0821\ (\text{L})(\text{atm})}{(\text{mol})(\text{K})} \times 310\ \text{K} = 7.64\ \text{atm}$$

An osmotic pressure of 7.64 atm is developed when this tissue fluid is separated from pure water by a membrane permeable to water but not to NaCl.

EXERCISE 9.9

Suppose the osmotic pressure of a potassium chloride (KCl) solution is 7.64 atm when measured at 37°C. How many moles of KCl are present in 1 L of this solution?

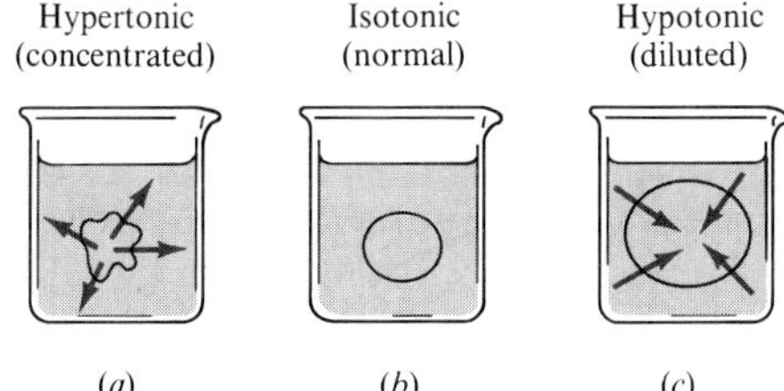

FIGURE 9.9
Red blood cell in isotonic, hypertonic, and hypotonic solutions. (*a*) Water moves out of the cell and it shrinks. (*b*) There is no net movement of water in or out of the cell. (*c*) Water flows into the red blood cell and it swells.

9.11 TONICITY

Water molecules can pass through the holes in cell walls.

Semipermeable membranes are common in the world of living things, where osmosis is an important process. The walls of cells and of the specialized structures within cells, called *organelles*, are semipermeable membranes. Cell membranes can be thought of as membranes containing pores about 0.8 nm in diameter (see Figure 9.6). Water molecules, which measure about 0.3 nm in diameter, pass through freely. Other important species present in body fluids, such as electrolytes cannot. **Electrolytes** are ionic compounds which are soluble in water and form solutions capable of conducting electricity. Ions from electrolytes, such as Na^+, K^+, and Cl^-, present in body fluids are hydrated, which gives them an effective diameter greater than 0.8 nm, as shown in Figure 9.6.

All normal body cells have the same internal osmotic pressure as the tissue fluid which surrounds them. Two solutions which have the same osmolarity are said to be **isotonic**. A cell placed in an isotonic solution neither swells nor shrinks because there is no net movement of water into or out of the cell. For example, the osmolarity of body fluids is about 0.300 *M*. If a cell is placed in a 0.150 *M* sodium chloride solution, which has an osmolarity of 0.300 *M*, the cell neither swells nor shrinks. The 0.150 *M* NaCl solution is said to be isotonic with body fluid. Isotonic saline solutions are used as solvents for drugs to be injected in order to prevent swelling or shrinking of cells at the site of injection.

Fluids used for IV feeding must be isotonic with plasma to prevent pain and tissue trauma, or they must be given through a major vein where high blood flow can dilute the nutrients.

A solution which has a lower osmolarity than is present in normal tissue fluid is said to be **hypotonic**. Cells placed in a hypotonic solution swell because water moves by osmosis from the less concentrated hypotonic solution surrounding the cells across the cell membranes into the cells.

A solution which has a higher osmolarity than that of tissue fluid is **hypertonic**. Cells placed in a hypertonic solution shrink because water from the cell moves across the cell membrane in order to dilute the surrounding hypertonic solution. Figure 9.9 illustrates what happens when a red blood cell is placed in isotonic, hypotonic, and hypertonic saline solutions.

SAMPLE EXERCISE 9.10

A 5% saline solution is prepared when 54.7 g of sodium chloride is added to enough water so that the volume of the solution is 1 L. Is this solution isotonic, hypotonic, or hypertonic with body fluid?

Solution:

Calculate the molarity of this solution to find out.

$$\text{Molarity} = n(\text{solute})/\text{L(solution)}$$

$$1 \text{ mol NaCl} = 58.5 \text{ g NaCl}$$

$$n(\text{solute}) = 54.7 \cancel{\text{g NaCl}} \times \frac{1 \text{ mol NaCl}}{58.5 \cancel{\text{g NaCl}}} = 0.935 \text{ mol}$$

$$\text{Molarity} = 0.935 \text{ mol NaCl/L solution}$$

This solution is hypertonic because the molarity of NaCl is greater than 0.150 *M*.

EXERCISE 9.10

A solution contains 7 mg of NaCl in 1 ml of solution. Is this solution isotonic, hypotonic, or hypertonic with a 0.150 *M* NaCl solution?

To prevent damage to cells it is crucial that fluids within body cells be isotonic with the tissue fluid that surrounds them. When tissue fluid becomes hypertonic, cells shrink as water moves out of the cell from a solution of lower osmolarity to one of higher osmolarity. Two conditions which cause this are body dehydration and excessive intake of salt. Dehydration due to loss of water first affects tissue fluids, which become more concentrated. The body suffers as mucous membranes dry out, abdominal skin becomes inelastic, and urine excretion diminishes. When too much salt is ingested, the fluid surrounding the cells also becomes more concentrated than normal. This time there is no total loss of body water. Again water diffuses out of the cell into the hypertonic solution by osmosis. Extra water collects in body tissues. The resulting condition, characterized by body swelling or puffiness, is called **edema**. When tissue fluids become hypotonic, cells swell as water flows from surrounding tissues across cell walls into the cell. This happens when the body ingests excessive water or when it loses electrolytes. Fortunately the body has mechanisms for maintaining a nearly constant osmolarity of the fluid which surrounds cells by regulating the rate at which the kidneys excrete salt and water into the urine (see Section 9.13).

The word *edema* is derived from the Greek word for swelling, *oidema*

9.12 COLLOIDS

Particle size in colloids is much greater than in solutions.

Solutions, often called the *dissolved state,* contain particles (molecules and ions) ranging in size from 0.1 to 10 nm. Another kind of stable homogeneous mixture can form in which the particle sizes range from about 10 to 100 nm. This particular type of mixture is a **colloid** and belongs to the *colloidal state.* Milk is a colloid which contains particles ranging in size from about 40 to 100 nm. Colloidal particles may consist of single molecules or groups of molecules.

FIGURE 9.10
Tyndall effect. (*a*) Beam is invisible when viewed at 90° (looking down into the beaker) as it passes through a true solution. (*b*) The beam is visible when viewed at 90° as it passes through a colloid, since the beam is scattered in all directions by the colloidal particles.

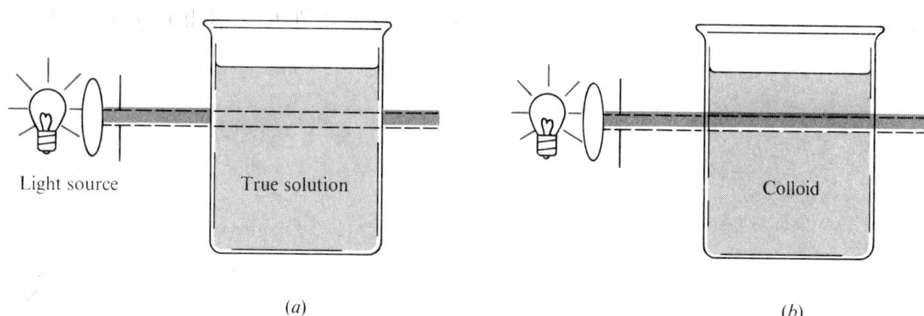

Colloids and solutions share some properties. Both are able to pass through ordinary filter paper. Like solutions, colloids remain uniform and homogeneous. The colloidal particles of homogenized milk do not settle out upon standing.

In other ways the properties of colloids and true solutions are different, largely because of the size of the colloidal particles. For example, liquid solutions are transparent, while liquid colloids may be cloudy. This is because the particles in colloids are large enough to scatter light that is passing through. The scattering, or displacement, of light beams by colloids is called the *Tyndall effect.* Because colloids deflect light, a beam of light passed through a colloid and viewed at an angle is clearly visible. The same beam of light passed through a solution is not deflected, and when viewed at an angle is only weakly visible. The Tyndall effect, illustrated in Figure 9.10, can be used to distinguish colloids from solutions. Because of their size, colloidal particles are unable to pass through certain membranes which are permeable to most solutes. The process of dialysis (Section 9.13) utilizes this property.

Components of colloids are assigned general names which are analogous to the solution terms: solute (the dispersed medium) and solvent (the dispersing medium). The medium in which colloid particles are dispersed is called the *continuous phase* and is roughly comparable with the solvent of a solution. The colloidal particles belong to the *disperse*, or *discontinuous, phase,* which is analogous to the solutes of solutions. Colloids may form from any combination of

TABLE 9.5 COMMON COLLOIDS

Types		
Disperse phase (similar to solute)	**Continuous phase (similar to solvent)**	**General name: examples**
Liquid	Gas	Aerosols: fog, mist
Solid	Gas	Aerosols: smoke
Gas	Liquid	Foams: whipped cream
Liquid	Liquid	Emulsions: mayonnaise, milk
Solid	Liquid	Sol: colloidal gold*
Liquid	Solid	Gels: jellies

*Colloidal gold (Au in H_2O) is used in nuclear medicine (Table 6.3).

liquid, solid, or gas, except for gas and gas. Gases always dissolve in each other to form true solutions. Table 9.5 lists some common colloids.

9.13 DIALYSIS

Capillaries pass water and electrolytes, but not proteins and other large molecules.

The purpose of the kidneys is not only to remove the waste products of metabolism through the formation of urine but also to maintain a constant composition of substances present in the blood. Among the most important of these substances are water and the electrolytes K^+, Na^+, H^+, Ca^{2+}, Mg^{2+}, SO_4^{2-}, and PO_4^{3-}. The amounts of these substances in the blood must be held within very narrow limits for normal biological processes to take place. The first step in urine formation is the filtration of blood through capillary walls. The capillary walls are made of a membrane which allows solution particles (solvents and small solute molecules, including electrolytes) to pass through but not larger, colloidal particles such as protein molecules. Thus the fluid that comes through the capillary walls is protein-free. Most of the substances in this filtered fluid are reabsorbed by the blood. The substances present in excess and the toxic waste materials are secreted and become urine. Damaged kidneys are no longer effective in regulating blood constituents and in excreting wastes. This causes a condition called uremia, or literally, "urine in the blood." Severe kidney malfunction is rapidly fatal.

Uremia may be treated by use of the "artificial kidney," or dialysis machine, an apparatus that eliminates excess ions and wastes that accumulate in the blood when the kidneys fail. **Dialysis** is the process of separating substances from a solution by taking advantage of their differing abilities to pass through porous membranes. In the dialysis machine one kind of porous membrane used is a cellophane tubing, which has characteristics similar to those of capillary walls. The pores of the cellophane are able to pass most solutes but not large colloid particles such as blood protein molecules. The cellophane tubing is allowed to bathe in a salt solution which is similar in ionic concentration to normal body fluid. The bath solution is constantly replaced to maintain normal concentrations.

The removal of waste products through the blood stream is called hemodialysis.

When a patient is put on an artificial kidney machine, blood is pumped from an artery of the arm into the cellophane tubing. The essential blood proteins remain behind in the patient so that respiration is still possible. As the filtered blood flows through the tubing, the solute concentrations within the blood and in the salt bath tend to become equal. For example, suppose the concentration of potassium ions (K^+) is above normal because of malfunctioning kidneys. The potassium ions will diffuse out of the cellophane tubing into the salt bath. Since the salt bath concentration of K^+ ions is held normal by constant replacement of the bath solution, the diffusion occurs until the blood K^+ concentration becomes normal. In the same way waste materials diffuse across the cellophane tubing into the bath until all waste materials are removed from the blood. The constantly replaced bath fluid contains no waste materials at all, so that the diffusion does not stop until the blood is completely cleansed of all toxic wastes. When the filtering procedure is completed, the blood, which now contains normal concentrations of ions and no waste substances, is conducted back into the patient by way of a vein. Because of the existence of artificial kidney machines, patients

The salt bath in an artificial kidney machine is constantly replenished to maintain normal electrolyte concentrations and to remove wastes.

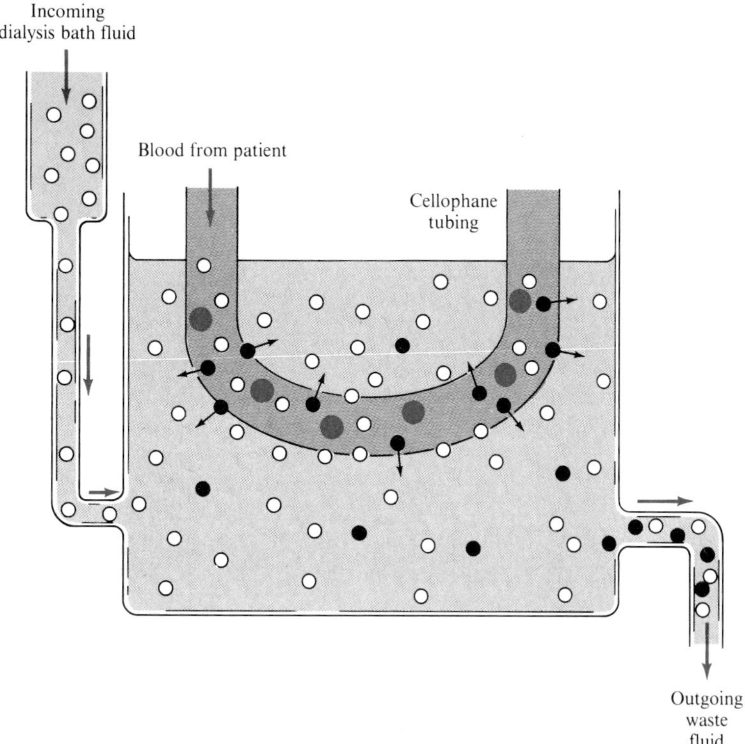

FIGURE 9.11
Dialysis machine. The large red circles represent necessary molecules such as blood proteins that are too large to pass through the walls of the cellophane tubing. Waste molecules, the black circles, can move across the walls and are not replenished, because the incoming bath fluid contains no waste compounds. Glucose and electrolytes, the white circles are also able to pass through the cellophane walls but are replenished by the constantly replaced bath fluid.

with permanent kidney failure can be kept alive and functioning. Figure 9.11 shows a diagram of a typical dialysis machine.

SUMMARY

Solutions are homogeneous mixtures which contain particles (ions and molecules) with dimensions of about 0.1 to 10 nm. The solvent is the solution component which is used to disperse the solute component or components.

The solubility of a solute in a solvent is the maximum amount of solute which can be dissolved in that solvent. Saturated solutions contain a quantity of solute equal to the solubility value. Unsaturated solutions contain less solute than the solubility permits and supersaturated solutions contain more.

Many factors influence the solubility of liquid and solid solutes in liquid solvents. Like dissolves like, meaning that polar dissolves polar and nonpolar dissolves nonpolar. The solubility of most solutes increases with increasing temperature, although there are some exceptions.

The solubility of gases in liquid solvents depends upon polarity, pressure, and temperature. The like-dissolves-like rule is still in effect. According to Henry's law, the solubility of gases in liquid solvents increases as the partial pressure p of the gas above the solution increases. The solubility of gases in liquids decreases as the temperature increases.

The concentrations of solutions can be expressed in various units. The molarity M is the number of moles of solute per liter of solution. The molality m is the number of moles of solute dissolved in 1 kg of solvent. Weight percent of solute, % w/w, is the mass of solute per mass of solution expressed in percent.

Colligative properties of solutions depend upon the number of solute particles dissolved in a solvent but do not depend upon the nature of the particles. The vapor pressure of a solution is lowered as compared with that of the pure solvent. It follows that the boiling points of solutions are always higher than those of pure solvents. The freezing point of a solution is lowered compared with that of the pure solvent. Osmosis occurs when a solution is separated from a less concentrated solution by a semipermeable membrane. Solvent flows from the dilute solution through the membrane into the more concentrated solution, causing osmotic pressure to develop. The magnitude of the vapor pressure lowering, boiling point elevation, freezing point depression, and osmotic pressure developed increases when the concentration of solute particles is increased. The term osmolarity is used for total concentration of solute particles and is found by multiplying molarity by the van't Hoff factor i, which is the number of ions produced by a solute.

The tonicity of body fluids is crucial in maintaining normal cell functions. Hypertonic solutions have osmolarities which are greater than those of normal tissue fluid and hypotonic solutions have osmolarities less than normal. Two solutions which are isotonic have the same osmolarity. If a cell is immersed in an isotonic solution, it remains unchanged, whereas cells placed in hypertonic solutions shrink and those in hypotonic solutions swell.

Colloids are mixtures in which the particle size ranges from about 10 to 100 nm. Because of their larger particles, colloids are sometimes cloudy or opaque. Colloids scatter light beams (the Tyndall effect) while solutions do not. Certain membranes, such as cellophane and capillary walls, are able to pass ordinary solute particles but cannot pass colloidal particles. In kidney machines cellophane tubing can be used to retain protein colloids in the blood by dialysis.

KEY WORDS

solution	molality	semipermeable membrane	hypertonic
solvent	weight percent	osmosis	hypotonic
solute	colligative properties	osmotic pressure	isotonic
solubility	boiling point elevation	osmolarity	colloid
molarity	freezing point depression	electrolyte	dialysis

EXERCISES

9.11 Name the two components of the following solutions. Decide which component is the solvent and which is the solute.
(**a**) A 0.85% saline solution
(**b**) Carbonated water
(**c**) 100 proof vodka (50% by volume ethanol, C_2H_6O)
(**d**) Sterling silver which contains 7.5% copper by weight
(**e**) A helium and oxygen mixture, used as an artificial atmosphere for divers, which contains a percentage of oxygen about the same as that present in air

9.12 Name the solvent in each of the following solutions: (**a**) Blood; (**b**) urine; (**c**) air.

9.13 Decide whether the following aqueous solutions are unsaturated, saturated, or supersaturated (refer to Table 9.2):
(**a**) 300 g sucrose dissolved in 200 ml water
(**b**) 20 g NaCl dissolved in 50 ml water
(**c**) 20 w/w percent saline solution
(**d**) 50 w/w percent NaI solution
(**e**) 0.0010 g calcium carbonate in 100 ml water
(**f**) 0.28 g lead(II) chloride dissolved in 25 ml water

9.14 Decide which of the following compounds should be very water-soluble according to the rule that like dissolves like:
(**a**) $CBr_4(l)$ (**b**) $KF(s)$ (**c**) $CH_4(g)$
(**d**) $HBr(g)$ (**c**) H—C(H)(H)—O—H (**f**) $I_2(s)$

9.15 If 2 ml of CCl_4 is mixed with 2 ml of ethylene glycol, $HOCH_2CH_2OH$, what would you expect to happen? Why?

9.16 Calculate the weight percent of solute, % w/w, for each of the following solutions:
(**a**) 58.5 g NaCl dissolved in 1800 g H_2O
(**b**) 98 g H_2SO_4 dissolved in 1 L H_2O
(**c**) 90.0 g glucose ($C_6H_{12}O_6$) mixed with 900 g H_2O

9.17 Find the molality for each solution in Problem 9.16.

9.18 Is it possible to calculate the molarity of the solutions listed in Problem 9.16. Why?

9.19 Calculate the molarity of each of the following solutions:
(a) 1 mol of solute dissolved in enough solvent to produce 500 ml solution
(b) 20 g NaOH dissolved in enough water to make 500 ml solution
(c) 1 mol of solute dissolved to make up 1000 g of solution with a density of 0.90 g/cm^3

9.20 Describe how you would prepare the following solutions. Be sure to include the amounts of substances and any special equipment that you would need.
(a) 1 L of a 0.10 *M* KCl solution
(b) 50 ml of a 0.10 *M* glucose solution from 500 ml of a 1 *M* glucose solution
(c) 250 ml of a 1 *M* sucrose solution (formula weight 342)
(d) 100 ml of 2 *M* H_2SO_4 solution starting with 1 L of 18 *M* H_2SO_4

9.21 Find the weight percent, % w/w, of solute and solvent in a saturated solution of sodium chloride in water.

***9.22** What is the maximum boiling point of water that could be obtained by the addition of sodium chloride? Assume that the sodium chloride undergoes complete ionization. (*Hint:* Use the solubility of sodium chloride to get started.)

9.23 Calculate the mass in grams of solute needed to prepare the following solutions:
(a) 1 L of 0.500 *M* NaCl
(b) 100 ml of 1 *M* KCl
(c) 1 L of 0.300 *M* NaCl
(d) 2 L of 0.100 *M* glucose ($C_6H_{12}O_6$)

9.24 Determine the freezing point and boiling point of a solution which contains 0.100 mol of (nonionizing) solute dissolved in 1000 g of water. Is it necessary to know the nature of the solute? Why?

9.25 If 100 g of each of the following (nonionizing) solutes is dissolved in 1 kg of water, which one would have the lowest freezing point: (a) Glucose ($C_6H_{12}O_6$); (b) methanol (CH_4O); (c) ethanol (C_2H_6O)?

9.26 What is a semipermeable membrane?

9.27 Make a sketch that illustrates the process of osmosis.

9.28 A lettuce leaf in contact with water remains crisp. When immersed in salty water (or salad dressing), it becomes limp. Why?

9.29 Find the osmotic pressure developed in a 0.0100-*M* solution at 37°C in (a) glucose ($C_6H_{12}O_6$); (b) NaCl.

9.30 Normal blood begins to exhibit hemolysis (destruction of red blood cells) at NaCl concentrations of 0.44% *and less.* How many grams of NaCl would be present in 100 g of a blood sample just beginning to show hemolysis? Is hemolysis bursting or shrinking of blood cells? Explain.

9.31 What is meant by the term osmolarity?

9.32 Barium paper, which is filter paper impregnated with a 10% barium chloride solution, is used in a test for the presence of bile in urine. How many grams of barium chloride are needed to make up 2000 g of solution?

9.33 What do we mean when we say that a solution is isotonic with body fluid?

9.34 One of the two saline solutions below is used as a diluent for an injection solution. Which one do you think it is? Why? (a) 9.0% NaCl (b) 0.9% NaCl

9.35 Calculate the freezing and boiling points of a 0.0200 *m* KCl solution.

9.36 Assuming complete ionization, determine which one of the following solutions should develop the greatest osmotic pressure when separated from pure water by a semipermeable membrane: (a) 0.10 *M* NaCl; (b) 0.10 *M* $CaCl_2$; (c) 0.10 *M* KI.

9.37 Swollen gums may be treated by rinsing the mouth with salt water. What do you think is the principle behind this?

9.38 Of the following particle sizes, which are of solution dimensions and which are of colloidal dimensions? (a) 10 nm; (b) 0.20 nm; (c) 10^{-10} m; (d) 1 Å; (e) 10,000 nm; (f) 10^{-6} m.

9.39 Why is there no such thing as a colloid in which both the continuous and discontinuous phases are gaseous?

9.40 Calculate the volume of N_2 gas in milliliters which will dissolve in 1 L of body water if the partial pressure of the N_2 is 1.50 atm. The Henry's law constant for N_2 is

$$k = \frac{14 \text{ ml } N_2}{1 \text{ L water} \times \text{atm}}$$

How does this compare with the volume of N_2 dissolved when the partial pressure of N_2 is about 0.80 atm, as it is in air at atmospheric pressure? What happens to people who are subjected to sudden reductions in atmospheric pressure?

9.41 How does the semipermeable membrane discussed in Section 9.10 differ from capillary walls and cellophane?

9.42 Explain how an artificial kidney works.

9.43 Why must the bath solution in a dialysis machine be replenished constantly?

***9.44** A 1 % w/w $AgNO_3$ solution is used to treat the eyes of newborn babies. For a density of solution of 1.08 g/ml, calculate the molarity.

10 . . . . CHEMICAL REACTIONS

10.1 INTRODUCTION

At the beginning of this book, we introduced the idea that chemists are interested in the behavior of the atoms and molecules that make up all matter and that their information comes from studying chemical and physical properties of matter. In many of the first nine chapters of this text we have used chemical reactions to describe the chemical properties of various compounds and elements. In this chapter we will take a more detailed look at chemical reactions by dividing them into general classes and by studying the energy changes that accompany them and the rates at which they take place.

10.2 TYPES OF REACTIONS

There are some broad terms used to classify chemical reactions. Most of them indicate by their names the types of reactions that they describe.

Combination

As this name implies, **combination** reactions involve the joining of two substances (elements or compounds) to make a single compound. Using A and B to represent the two species, we can write the combination reaction below:

$$A + B \longrightarrow A\text{-}B$$

There are many examples of combination reactions in which two elements form a compound. One that we have already discussed is the industrial process by which nitrogen gas is combined with hydrogen gas to form ammonia (Section 7.11).

$$N_2 + 3H_2 \longrightarrow 2NH_3$$

A compound and an element can also combine to form a new compound. The organic compound ethene, C_2H_4, contains a double bond between its two C atoms (Section 4.10). When ethene reacts with H_2, a new compound, ethane, forms which has no double bond:

$$\begin{array}{c} \text{H} \quad \text{H} \\ | \quad\; | \\ \text{H—C=C—H} \end{array} + H_2 \longrightarrow \begin{array}{c} \text{H} \quad \text{H} \\ | \quad\; | \\ \text{H—C—C—H} \\ | \quad\; | \\ \text{H} \quad \text{H} \end{array}$$

This particular type of combination reaction is also called an *addition* reaction.

Two compounds can combine to form a single compound, as in the reaction of calcium oxide with carbon dioxide to form calcium carbonate:

$$CaO + CO_2 \longrightarrow CaCO_3$$

Decomposition

In **decomposition** reactions a compound breaks down into two or more elements or new compounds.

$$A\text{-}B \longrightarrow A + B$$

For instance, hydrogen peroxide decomposes to form water and oxygen.

$$2H_2O_2 \longrightarrow 2H_2O + O_2$$

Displacement

In **displacement** reactions a substance A reacts with a compound BC to replace one of the elements in it:

$$A + B\text{-}C \longrightarrow A\text{-}B + C$$

A typical example of this is the reaction of iron metal with aqueous hydrochloric acid, HCl, in which H_2 gas bubbles off.

$$Fe(s) + 2HCl(aq) \longrightarrow FeCl_2(aq) + H_2(g)$$

In this reaction iron displaces hydrogen, in the form of H_2, from HCl.

Double Displacement

In **double displacement** reactions two compounds react with each other. An atom or group of atoms from one of the compounds exchanges with an atom or group of atoms from the other. In the example below the B in AB exchanges with D in CD.

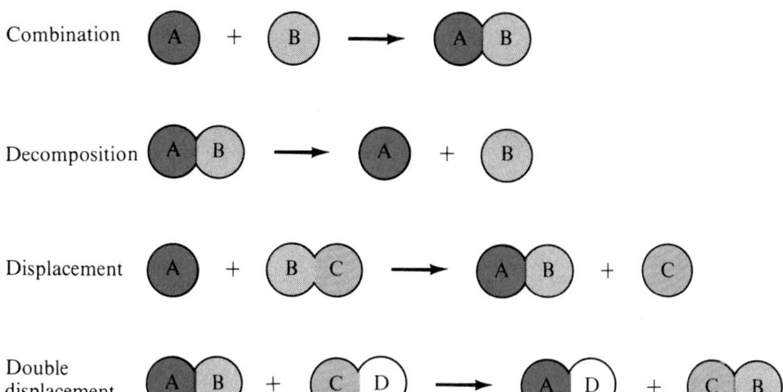

FIGURE 10.1
Types of reactions.

$$A\text{-}B + C\text{-}D \longrightarrow A\text{-}D + C\text{-}B$$

In most cases one of the product compounds is in a different physical state from that of the reactants. For instance, in aqueous solution silver nitrate reacts with sodium chloride to form sodium nitrate and insoluble silver chloride.

$$AgNO_3(aq) + NaCl(aq) \longrightarrow AgCl(s) + NaNO_3(aq)$$

Insoluble compounds which form from solution reactions are called **precipitates.** Sometimes a product which is a precipitate is underlined in a chemical equation or is followed by an arrow (↓). See Table 5.2.

$$AgNO_3(aq) + NaCl(aq) \longrightarrow AgCl\downarrow + NaNO_3(aq)$$

The addition of oxalate to urine to test for calcium by observing precipitation is the Sulkowitch test.

The formation of a precipitate is often used as a test for the presence of some substance. For instance, the test for calcium in urine involves adding the testing reagent ammonium oxalate, $(NH_4)_2C_2O_4$, to a sample of urine. The formation of the insoluble product calcium oxalate, CaC_2O_4, is a positive test for the presence of calcium ions in the urine.

$$CaCl_2 + (NH_4)_2C_2O_4 \longrightarrow CaC_2O_4\downarrow + 2NH_4Cl$$

The precipitate is observed as a turbidity (cloudiness) in the urine. The observed amount of turbidity can be related to the amount of calcium in the urine sample.

Figure 10.1 summarizes all these different types of chemical reactions.

SAMPLE EXERCISE 10.1

Write a balanced chemical equation to describe the reaction below and tell what general class it belongs to. (Refer to Tables 4.1 and 4.2 to help you in writing the formula.)

Heating potassium chlorate produces O_2 and potassium chloride. (This reaction is used in laboratories to prepare small quantities of pure oxygen.)

Solution:

Potassium chlorate is $KClO_3$ and potassium chloride is KCl.

$$2KClO_3 \xrightarrow{\Delta} 2KCl + 3O_2$$

This is a decomposition reaction.

EXERCISE 10.1

Write an equation to describe the reaction that takes place when sodium sulfate is added to lead(II) nitrate in aqueous solution to produce sodium chloride and the insoluble compound lead(II) sulfate.

Although the reaction classes we have just discussed are useful, there are other ways to group chemical reactions. For instance, reactions can be classified according to whether or not electrons are transferred as the reactants are converted to products. In the body, reactions involving electron transfer are required to supply energy for cellular processes and to transform foods into cellular constituents.

10.3 OXIDATION-REDUCTION REACTIONS

We refer to oxidation-reduction reactions as redox reactions.

Reactions in which a net transfer of electrons occurs are **oxidation-reduction** reactions, also known as redox reactions. To decide whether or not a redox reaction is taking place we must see whether or not electrons are transferred by the atoms of any element involved in the reaction. To do this we assign numbers, called **oxidation numbers**, to each element in all the compounds involved in the reaction.

Oxidation Numbers

Oxidation numbers are charges assigned to atoms by assuming that all the bonded electrons are associated with the more electronegative atom. These oxidation numbers serve as a "bookkeeping" device to keep track of electrons that are transferred in a chemical reaction. When electron transfer takes place, the oxidation number of an element in a reactant changes when it becomes part of a product. In most cases two elements from two reactants will be involved. Thus we look for changes in oxidation numbers to identify redox reactions.

Oxidation numbers are assigned by using the following general rules.

1. The oxidation number is *positive* if an element has *lost* electrons or is sharing them with a more electronegative element. The oxidation number is *negative* if the element has *gained* electrons or is sharing them with a less electronegative element.
2. The numerical value of the oxidation number *usually*, but not always, indicates the number of electrons transferred to another element or shared with another element. Thus the oxidation number of an atom of any free element (O_2, Na, S_8, etc.) is zero.

From these rules it follows that the oxidation number of an element that forms an ion is the same as the charge of the ion. For instance, a potassium atom loses one electron to become a K^+ ion and thus has an oxidation number of +1. The oxidation number of oxygen in oxide ions, O^{2-}, is −2 because the O atom gains two electrons to form the ion.

To assign oxidation numbers to elements involved in covalent compounds we can look at their Lewis dot structures. For instance, we can see that the oxidation numbers of H and O are +1 and −2, respectively.

H : O : H   Each O atom shares 2 e^-
             Each H atom shares 1 e^-

The H atoms each share one electron and the central O atom shares two electrons. Since O is more electronegative than H, the oxidation number of O is −2 and that of H is +1. Thus, as mentioned above, the oxidation number of −2 for the O atom in a water molecule is assigned by assuming that the two shared electrons belong to the O atom. The oxidation numbers of −2 for O and +1 for H apply in nearly every compound in which O and H appear.

Table 10.1 lists the common oxidation numbers of some elements and also families of elements. Group IA elements usually have oxidation numbers of +1, group IIA elements of +2, group IIIA elements of +3, group VIIA elements of −1, and group VIA elements of −2. Knowing the common oxidation numbers of combined elements allows us to figure out the oxidation numbers of a large

TABLE 10.1 COMMON OXIDATION NUMBERS OF ELEMENTS AND GROUPS OF ELEMENTS

Element	Common oxidation number	Example compounds
Uncombined	0 (always)	Cu, O_2, H_2, S_8
O	−2	H_2O, NaOH, H_2SO_4, CaO
H	+1	H_2O, NaOH, H_2SO_4, NH_3
Group IA metal	+1	Li_2CO_3, NaCl, KI, etc.
Group IIA metal	+2	$MgSO_4$, $CaCl_2$, Ba_2PO_4
Group VIIA nonmetal	−1	HF, NaCl, CBr_4, KI

number of other elements. This is done by making use of the fact that the sum of all the oxidation numbers in a compound must be zero. For instance, suppose we wish to find the oxidation number of gold in the compound $AuCl_3$. The oxidation number of chlorine is -1 and the compound is neutral.

$$\begin{gathered} AuCl_3 \\ (1 \times ?) + [(-1) \times 3] = 0 \end{gathered}$$

Thus the oxidation number of Au in this compound must be $+3$. To find the oxidation number of S in H_2SO_4 we make use of the fact that the oxidation numbers of O and H are -2 and $+1$, respectively:

$$\begin{gathered} H_2SO_4 \\ [2 \times (1)] + [1 \times (?)] + [4 \times (-2)] = 0 \end{gathered}$$

$$2 + (?) + (-8) = 0$$

The oxidation number of S in H_2SO_4 is $+6$.

SAMPLE EXERCISE 10.2

Find the oxidation numbers of the elements in color in the following:

(a) CH_4 (b) I_2 (c) C_2H_6

Solution:

(a) CH_4

The oxidation number of $+1$ is assigned to H in CH_4:

$$(1 \times [?]) + (4 \times 1) = 0$$

Hence the oxidation number of C in CH_4 is -4.

(b) I_2

The oxidation number of an atom in any element is 0.

(c) C_2H_6

Again the oxidation number for H is $+1$.

$$(2 \times [?]) + (6 \times 1) = 0$$

The oxidation number of C in C_2H_6 is -3.

What are the oxidation numbers of the elements in color in the compounds below?

(a) P_4 (b) $CaCO_3$ (c) $MnCl_2$

Although oxidation numbers of elements involved in covalent compounds are extremely useful in keeping track of the number of electrons transferred in chemical reactions, it is best not to attach too much chemical significance to them. For instance, we just found that the oxidation number of C in CH_4 is -4 and in C_2H_6 it is -3. These numbers give very little insight into the bonding involved in these compounds, as we shall see when we delve further into the bonding in organic compounds, starting in Chapter 12.

Identifying Redox Reactions

As mentioned before, we determine whether or not a reaction is an oxidation reduction reaction by looking for changes in oxidation numbers of elements in the participating compounds. In the reaction below, in which carbon reacts with oxygen to form carbon dioxide, the oxidation numbers of C and O are indicated in the reactants and in the product.

$$\overset{0}{C} + \overset{0}{O_2} \longrightarrow \overset{+4}{C}\overset{-2}{O_2}$$

In all redox reactions changes in oxidation numbers occur and electron transfer takes place.

We see that C loses four electrons when it forms CO_2 and that each O in O_2 gains two electrons to become O^{2-} in CO_2. This reaction involves electron transfer and thus is a redox reaction.

When an O atom in O_2 gains electrons in the reaction above, the oxidation number of O is reduced from 0 to -2. The O_2 is said to be *reduced*. When a compound or element is reduced, its oxidation number becomes more negative. When the C atom loses electrons, it is said to be *oxidized*. When a compound or element is oxidized, its oxidation number becomes more positive.

Oxygen is a common oxidizing agent.

The term **oxidizing agent** is used for the compound (or element) which contains the element that *gains* electrons. Oxidizing agents are thus *reduced*, and their oxidation numbers become more negative. We can think of oxidizing agents as "electron gobblers." In this reaction the oxidizing agent is O_2 because the oxidation number of O in O_2 (0) becomes more negative in CO_2 (-2). In nearly all its reactions O_2 is the oxidizing agent—in fact this is the reason the term was invented. Reducing agents are the compounds (or elements) containing the element that *loses* electrons. **Reducing agents** are *oxidized* and their oxidation numbers become more positive. In the reaction above C is the reducing agent and is itself oxidized; its oxidation number increases from 0 (in C) to $+4$ (in CO_2).

Oxidation cannot take place without reduction, and vice versa.

Since electrons are never "set free," every oxidation reaction must be accompanied by a reduction reaction. In all oxidation-reduction reactions there must be both an oxidizing and a reducing agent. To summarize the terms we have been using:

O_2 *gains* electrons	C *loses* electrons
O_2 is *reduced*	C is *oxidized*
O_2 is the *oxidizing agent*	C is the *reducing agent*

SAMPLE EXERCISE 10.3

In living cells biological oxidations are responsible for producing energy from foodstuffs. The equation below summarizes the reactions which occur when glucose is oxidized in the body to CO_2 and H_2O:

$$C_6H_{12}O_6 + 6O_2 \longrightarrow 6CO_2 + 6H_2O$$

In the reaction above show that glucose loses electrons.

Solution:

We must find the oxidation number of C in glucose and in CO_2. The oxidation numbers of H and O are $+1$ and -2, respectively. In glucose: $C_6H_{12}O_6$

$$(6 \times ?) + (12 \times 1) + (6 \times [-2]) = 0$$
$$(6 \times ?) + 12 - 12 = 0$$
$$6 \times ? = 0$$

In glucose the oxidation number of C is 0. In CO_2 the oxidation number of C is $+4$. The oxidation number of C is more positive in the product CO_2, meaning that glucose has lost electrons.

EXERCISE 10.3

Show that acetylene loses electrons in the combustion reaction below.

$$2C_2H_2 + 5O_2 \longrightarrow 4CO_2 + 2H_2O$$

10.4 REDOX REACTIONS AND BATTERIES

Electricity is produced by the movement of electrons. Since redox reactions involve electron transfer, they are capable of producing electricity. One reaction that can be used for this purpose is the reaction of zinc with copper sulfate, $CuSO_4$, solution

$$\overset{0}{Zn} + \overset{+2}{Cu}SO_4 \longrightarrow \overset{0}{Cu} + \overset{+2}{Zn}SO_4$$

In this reaction Zn loses electrons, or is oxidized:

$$Zn^0 \longrightarrow Zn^{+2}$$

and Cu^{2+} gains electrons, or is reduced:

$$Cu^{2+} \longrightarrow Cu^0$$

Note that none of the atoms of the sulfate group undergo oxidation or reduction. Color Plate 10 shows metallic zinc added to a blue $CuSO_4$ solution, which decolorizes as copper metal and colorless $ZnSO_4$ are formed.

You just saw that placing zinc in a copper sulfate solution produces a chemical reaction. By modifying the conditions under which this reaction occurs, we can use it to generate electricity. Figure 10.2 shows how this can be done. The strips of Cu and Zn metal shown in the diagram are called *electrodes* and the solutions into which they dip are *electrolyte solutions*. (See Section 9.11, where electrolyte solutions were discussed.) The complete apparatus is an electrochemical cell, which is known as a **voltaic cell** and is the same as a **battery**. The cell shown in Figure 10.2 would provide about 1.1 V, compared with the 1.5 V produced by ordinary flashlight batteries.

All batteries include chemicals that participate in a redox reaction.

We assign labels to the electrodes in voltaic cells depending upon the reaction that takes place there. The *cathode* is the electrode at which reduction occurs and the *anode* is the electrode at which oxidation occurs. In this cell the Zn loses electrons ($Zn^0 - 2\,e^- \rightarrow Zn^{+2}$) and is oxidized; thus the Zn electrode is the anode. Ordinary flashlight batteries have Zn anodes, which can be seen as the metal casing (under the paper wrapper). The Cu^{2+} in $CuSO_4$ gains electrons ($Cu^{+2} + 2\,e^- \rightarrow Cu^0$), and the copper electrode is therefore the cathode. (The cathode in a flashlight battery is made of MnO_2.)

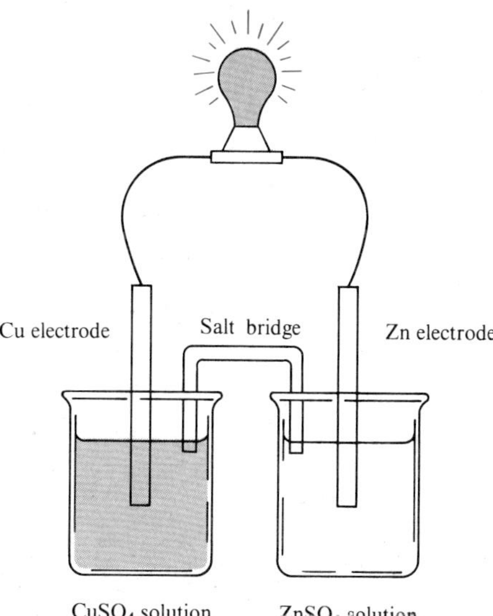

FIGURE 10.2
Voltaic cell. The salt bridge keeps the solutions separate, but still allows the redox reaction to take place.

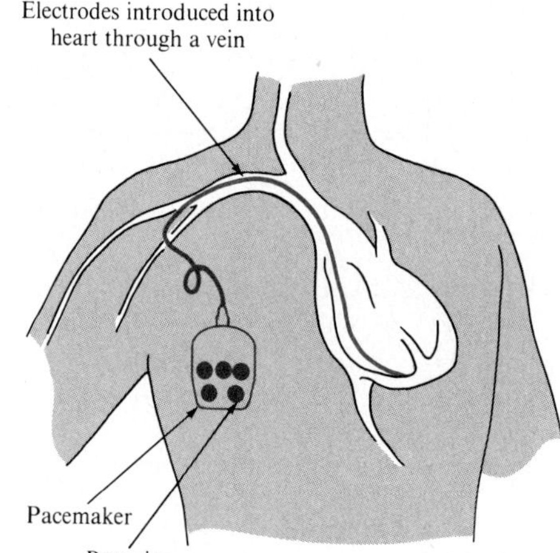

FIGURE 10.3
Pacemaker. The artificial pacemaker is implanted under the skin of a patient in order to deliver an electric pulse to stimulate the heart when the natural-heart pacemaker fails to function.

Tiny long-lived batteries power pacemakers.

A tiny battery powers the electronic device, called a *pacemaker*, that is used to regulate a person's heartbeat by furnishing electrical signals. One battery used for this purpose has a zinc anode and a mercury(II) oxide cathode. The reaction which powers it is

$$HgO + Zn + H_2O \longrightarrow Zn(OH)_2 + Hg$$

One requirement of a pacemaker battery is that it must have a very long lifetime so that the patient need not return to the hospital every year to have it replaced. Figure 10.3 illustrates a pacemaker device.

SAMPLE EXERCISE 10.4

Decide whether a battery could possibly be based upon the reaction below.

$$HCl + NaOH \longrightarrow NaCl + H_2O$$

Solution:

Find the oxidation numbers of Na, H, and O in each reactant and product.

H has an oxidation number of +1 in HCl, NaOH, and H_2O
O has an oxidation number of −2 in NaOH and H_2O
Na has an oxidation number of +1 in NaOH and NaCl

This reaction could not power a battery since it does not involve electron transfer.

EXERCISE 10.4

Show that the reaction of HgO, Zn, and H_2O shown above, which is used to power the pacemaker, is a redox reaction.

10.5 THERMOCHEMISTRY

We have seen that redox reactions can be used to perform electricity, one type of energy. We also saw that some redox reactions, such as the one in which glucose is oxidized, provide energy to power living cells. Some of the energy released by the molecules in food compounds (such as glucose) is released in the form of heat used to maintain body temperature (see Section 2.7). In this section we will take a closer look at the heat changes which take place in all kinds of chemical reactions.

The symbol Δ is used to mean "change in."

Enthalpy is derived from the Greek word *thalpein*, meaning "to heat." *Endo-* means "in" and *exo-* means "out."

The study of the heat changes accompanying chemical reactions is called **thermochemistry**. The term used to describe the heat change which accompanies a chemical reaction (carried out at a constant external pressure) is called the **change in enthalpy** and is written as ΔH (pronounced "delta H"). Reactions that produce or evolve heat are said to be **exothermic**. By convention, the value of ΔH is negative for exothermic reactions. Reactions that absorb heat are **endothermic**, which means that heat must be put in for these reactions to occur. For an endothermic reaction, the change in ΔH is positive.

Combustion reactions provide heat (are exothermic) and so have a negative ΔH value:

$$CH_4 + 2O_2 \longrightarrow CO_2 + 2H_2O + \text{Heat} \qquad \Delta H = -134 \text{ kcal}$$

Exothermic reaction

On the other hand, heat must be supplied to produce the reaction in which nitrogen reacts with oxygen to form nitrogen oxide. The reaction below is endothermic and has a positive ΔH value:

$$\text{Heat} + N_2 + O_2 \longrightarrow 2NO \qquad \Delta H = 43.2 \text{ kcal}$$

Endothermic reaction

The ΔH value for a particular reaction depends upon the number of moles of substances involved. Thus the ΔH value for the formation of 1 mol of nitric oxide according to the reaction above is half of 43.2 kcal, or 21.6 kcal/mol.

The value of ΔH gives chemists an indication of whether or not a particular reaction will proceed spontaneously. To a chemist a **spontaneous reaction** is one that tends to proceed from reactants toward products without any outside influence. For instance, when a piece of sodium metal is mixed with Cl_2 gas, a reaction occurs in which NaCl forms. A mixture of H_2 and O_2 gases can combine to produce water. These are spontaneous reactions. On the other hand, NaCl does not spontaneously decompose into Na metal and Cl_2 gas, nor does H_2O break down into H_2 and O_2 gases unless some outside source of energy is provided. In

Spontaneous chemical reactions are usually exothermic.

nearly all cases, the value of ΔH for a reaction is a good criterion of whether or not a chemical reaction will be spontaneous. Reactions which have a negative value of ΔH are almost always spontaneous, because in reactions which evolve heat, the products tend to be more stable than the mixture of reactants. Reactions which have a positive ΔH value are not usually spontaneous, so that in these reactions the reactants are more stable than the products.

$\Delta H < 0$: Reaction is usually spontaneous

$\Delta H > 0$: Reaction is not usually spontaneous

Spontaneous reactions may be too slow to be observed.

The combustion of methane ($\Delta H = -134$ kcal) is spontaneous. That is why it is possible to use methane as heating fuel. The reaction of nitrogen gas with oxygen gas has a positive value of ΔH (43.2 kcal) and is not spontaneous. This is consistent with our observation that the N_2 and O_2 gases in air do not react with each other. It is important to add one thing to this discussion about spontaneity. Spontaneous chemical reactions are not necessarily fast ones. For instance, the combustion of carbon with O_2 is a spontaneous chemical reaction, meaning that diamond (which is carbon) *can* react with the O_2 in air. However, you can never see this happen because the process is too slow to be observed.

The ΔH quantity is especially useful because the change in enthalpy depends only upon the nature of the reactants and the products, *not* on the path by which the reaction occurs. Furthermore, the ΔH values for each step in a process may be added together to obtain the ΔH for the entire process. For example, suppose the enthalpy change for the combustion of carbon to carbon dioxide is -94.0 kcal:

$$C + O_2 \longrightarrow CO_2 \qquad \Delta H = -94.0 \text{ kcal}$$

This reaction can proceed as a two-step process, with each reaction having a ΔH value:

Step 1:	$C + \frac{1}{2} O_2 \longrightarrow CO$	$\Delta H = -26.4$ kcal
Step 2:	$CO + \frac{1}{2} O_2 \longrightarrow CO_2$	$\Delta H = -67.6$ kcal
Step 1 + step 2:	$C + O_2 \longrightarrow CO_2$	$\Delta H = -94.0$ kcal

We see that the enthalphy change for the overall reaction is the same as the sum of the enthalpy values for the two-step process, which means that we can find ΔH values for complicated multistep processes by using a single reaction which starts with the same reactants and produces the same products.

This is exactly what is done in determining the caloric content of foods. (See the table of nutrition values on the inside cover.) In the human body there are dozens of steps involved in the conversion of carbohydrate molecules such as glucose ($C_6H_{12}O_6$) into the products CO_2 and H_2O, but in the laboratory we can duplicate the reaction in a single step.

In the body: $C_6H_{12}O_6 + 6O_2 \xrightarrow[\text{many steps}]{} 6CO_2 + 6H_2O$

In the lab: $C_6H_{12}O_6 + 6CO_2 \xrightarrow[\text{one step}]{} 6CO_2 + 6H_2O$

The value of ΔH for these two processes will be the same even though one of them requires many more steps than the other. It is relatively easy to measure ΔH for the laboratory version of combustion reactions such as this one by using a device called a *bomb calorimeter*.

10.6 CALORIMETRY

A **bomb calorimeter** is a device that is used to determine the amount of heat produced by oxidizing a substance such as a food sample (see Figure 10.4). The food sample is placed in a holder inside of a well-insulated vessel called a "bomb," which is filled with pure oxygen gas. The sample holder is fitted with ignition wires so that the combustion can be initiated by remote control. The bomb is surrounded by a measured quantity of water. The substance which is to react with O_2 is placed in the bomb and ignited under conditions in which the final products will be CO_2 and H_2O. The heat evolved is measured by noting the change in temperature of the surrounding water and using the specific heat of water to calculate the heat produced (see Section 2.9). By using these data one can determine the value of ΔH for the combustion of the amount of substance placed in the bomb. In fact, this is the way to measure the amount of heat produced from the combustion of glucose. The combustion of 1 mol of glucose has a measured ΔH value of -675 kcal.

$$C_6H_{12}O_6 + 6O_2 \longrightarrow 6CO_2 + 6H_2O \qquad \Delta H = -675 \text{ kcal}$$

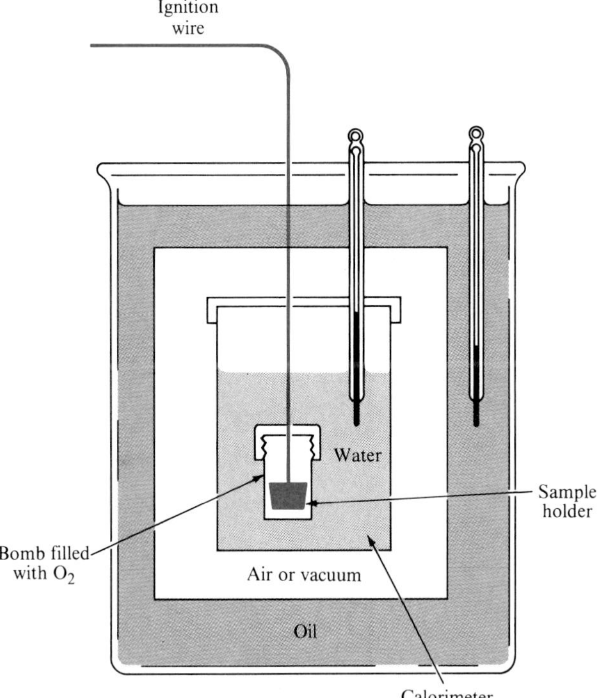

FIGURE 10.4
Bomb calorimeter.

Nutritionists find it much more convenient to quote the heat produced by foodstuffs in terms of kilocalories (kcal, also written Cal with a capital C) per gram, rather than kilocalories per mole. To make this conversion we make use of the fact that the formula weight of $C_6H_{12}O_6$ is 180.

$$1 \text{ mol glucose} = 180 \text{ g glucose}$$

$$\Delta H = \frac{-675 \text{ kcal}}{\cancel{\text{mol glucose}}} \times \frac{1 \cancel{\text{mol glucose}}}{180 \text{ g glucose}} = -3.75 \text{ kcal/g}$$

Other carbohydrates provide slightly different values. For instance, sucrose, which is table sugar, has a ΔH value of -3.95 kcal/g, and for starch ΔH is -4.2 kcal/g. These values must also be modified to account for the fact that the body is not 100 percent efficient, as is a bomb calorimeter. Normal humans digest carbohydrates with 98 to 99 percent efficiency. The approximate value taken for the caloric value of a typical carbohydrate is 4 Cal/g (4 kcal/g or 17 kJ/g). Table 10.2 lists the heats of combustion of carbohydrates, proteins, fats, and alcohol and the approximate fuel value of each of them.

That is how the caloric data in the nutrition value table were obtained.

One way to find the caloric content of various foodstuffs (bread, milk, etc.) is to determine their heats of combustion by placing them in a bomb calorimeter. Another way is to analyze the food for carbohydrates, proteins, and fats and then combine the contributions of these three nutrients present in the food (see table of nutrition values). For instance, suppose the analysis of a sample of 1 cup of whole milk weighing 244 g includes 9 g of protein, 9 g of fat, and 12 g of carbohydrate. To calculate the caloric value of 1 cup of milk,

$$9 \cancel{\text{ g protein}} \times \frac{4 \text{ Cal}}{\cancel{\text{g protein}}} = 36 \text{ Cal}$$

$$9 \cancel{\text{ g fat}} \times \frac{9 \text{ Cal}}{\cancel{\text{g fat}}} = 81 \text{ Cal}$$

$$12 \cancel{\text{ g carbohydrate}} \times \frac{4 \text{ Cal}}{\cancel{\text{g carbohydrate}}} = 48 \text{ Cal}$$

$$\text{Total} = 165 \text{ Cal}$$

TABLE 10.2 CALORIC CONTENT OF AVERAGE NUTRIENTS

Nutrient	ΔH(combustion), Cal	Approximate fuel value	
		in Cal	in kJ
Protein	5.6	4	17
Fat	9.4	9	38
Alcohol	7.1	7	29

Note that this is close to 160 Cal, as listed in the table of nutrition values, a number that was determined by burning the milk in a bomb calorimeter.

SAMPLE EXERCISE 10.5

Using the table of nutrition values find the caloric content of one slice of white enriched bread by using the carbohydrate, protein, and fat composition data and then compare your answer with the measured number of calories given.

Solution:

According to the nutrition value table one slice of bread weighing 23 g contains 2 g protein, 1 g fat, and 12 g carbohydrate.

$$2\ \cancel{\text{g protein}} \times \frac{4\ \text{Cal}}{\cancel{\text{g protein}}} = 8\ \text{Cal}$$

$$1\ \cancel{\text{g fat}} \times \frac{9\ \text{Cal}}{\cancel{\text{g fat}}} = 9\ \text{Cal}$$

$$12\ \cancel{\text{g carbohydrate}} \times \frac{4\ \text{Cal}}{\cancel{\text{g carbohydrate}}} = 48\ \text{Cal}$$

$$\text{Total} = 65\ \text{Cal}$$

The value 65 Cal for one slice of white enriched bread is close to 60 Cal, the caloric value listed in the Table.

EXERCISE 10.5

Using the data in the nutrition value table, estimate the caloric value of an egg from its composition and compare your result with the measured number of calories.

10.7 RATES OF CHEMICAL REACTIONS

As was mentioned in Section 10.6, a ΔH value gives a good indication about the spontaneity of a chemical reaction but nothing about the rate at which a reaction will occur. This belongs to **chemical kinetics**—the rate at which a chemical reaction takes place, which is of great practical significance. In living systems, for instance, biochemical reactions must occur at incredible speeds to support life processes. We shall examine some of the factors that influence reaction rates in this section. In doing so we will make use of the *collision theory* of reaction rates, which says that in order for a reaction to occur between atoms, ions, or molecules, they must first collide. However, some collisions are able to produce a chemical change and others are not. Thus the rate of a reaction depends upon the number of collisions and the fraction of those collisions that are effective.

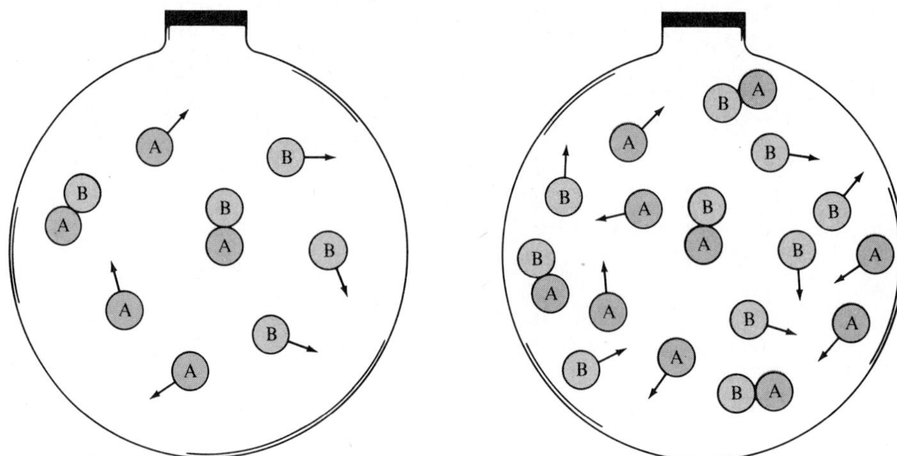

FIGURE 10.5
Increasing the concentration of reactants makes collisions more likely.

Concentration of Reactants

The higher the molar concentration of reactants, the greater the rate of the reaction, because the closer together are the reacting species, the more likely it is that collisions will occur and reactions will take place. Thus the rate of a chemical reaction depends upon the concentration of the reactants (see Figure 10.5).

Activation Energy

Effective collisions must be able to cause the breaking and forming of chemical bonds needed for nearly all chemical reactions to take place. Energy is required for this to happen. The **activation energy** E_a is defined as the minimum amount of energy that the reactants must have so that a reaction can take place. The reactant molecules in all reactions, whether they are endothermic (energy-absorbing) or exothermic (energy-releasing) reactions, must climb an energy barrier before they can react to form product molecules. The activation energy, or energy barrier, can be pictured as a "hill" with a height equal to the activation energy. Figure 10.6 shows that hydrogen and oxygen molecules must be supplied with enough energy to climb this hill before they can form water. The net heat evolved in this reaction, the ΔH for the reaction, is the energy difference between the products and the reactants, as shown in the figure.

The activation energy is much greater for some reactions than for others. The activation energy for endothermic reactions is always greater than the activation energy for exothermic reactions. Figure 10.7 compares the activation energy diagram for an exothermic reaction with that for an endothermic reaction. Note that in the endothermic reaction the energy of the products is higher than that of the reactants, meaning that heat is absorbed. In general, the greater the activation energy, the slower the reaction. The reason that diamond does not react with O_2 at an observable rate is that the activation energy for this particular reaction is very large.

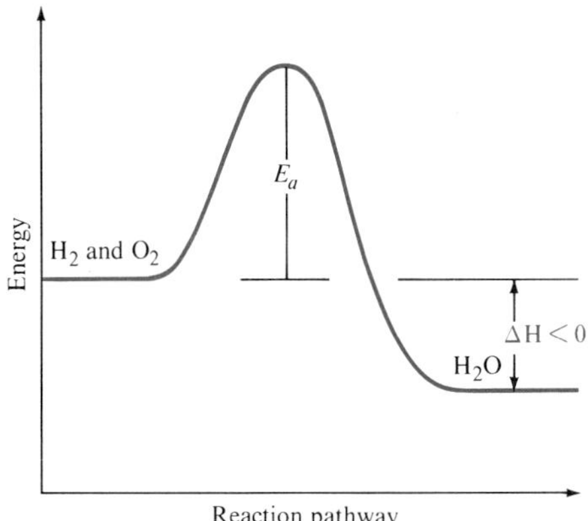

FIGURE 10.6
Activation energy.

One way to provide the needed energy of activation for a reaction is to supply heat by heating or igniting the reactants. Upon ignition hydrogen and oxygen gases react violently to produce water. The hydrogen used to lighten the Hindenburg dirigible coexisted with oxygen gas until a spark precipitated the tragic explosion in 1937.

Another way to overcome energy barriers is to lower the activation energy by the addition of a catalyst. Figure 10.8 illustrates the difference in activation energy for the decomposition of hydrogen peroxide (H_2O_2) with and without a catalyst. The mechanism by which some catalysts work is unknown, whereas other catalysts are known to orient the reactant molecules in such a way that they are more likely to collide with each other. In general, catalysts recovered from reactions are not altered. Furthermore, catalysts affect only the rate of a reaction, not the amount of heat which accompanies it. In biological systems reactions must be catalyzed to lower their energy barriers and permit them to occur at the necessary speeds. Biological catalysts, called **enzymes**, will be discussed in detail in Chapter 25, "Bioenergetics, Enzymes, and Vitamins."

Living organisms could not survive without enzymes.

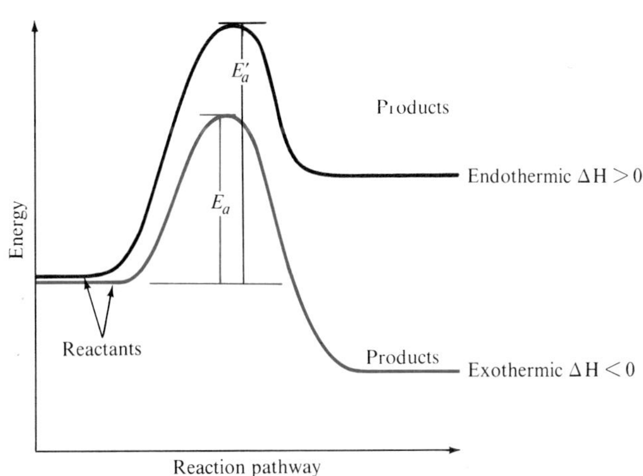

FIGURE 10.7
The endothermic reaction has a higher activation energy (E_a') than does the exothermic reaction.

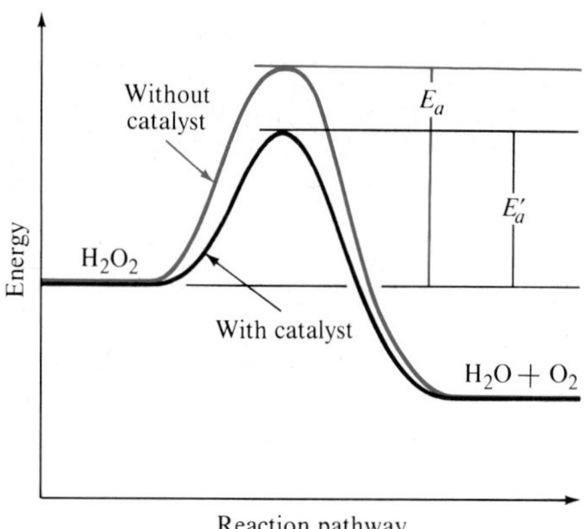

FIGURE 10.8
The catalyzed reaction has a smaller activation energy (E'_a).

Temperature

The more energy the molecules have, the more likely it will be for effective collisions to occur. One way to increase the energy of molecules is to raise their temperature (see Section 7.2). The higher the temperature, the greater will be the fraction of molecules with the necessary activation energies, and the faster the reaction will be. A rule of thumb is that a 10°C rise in temperature causes the reaction rate to double. In the laboratory it is often convenient to speed up reactions by increasing the temperature. The only restrictions are practical ones; for instance, the products must be stable at the reaction temperature chosen. In mammals, whose body temperature is 37°C at all times, temperature does not significantly influence the rate of biochemical reactions.

10.8 CHEMICAL EQUILIBRIUM

In all the reactions we have considered thus far we have assumed that the extent of reaction was 100 percent, that is, that all reactant substances were completely converted into products. In many reactions this is the case. For instance, if we mix 2 mol sodium metal (Na) with 1 mol chlorine gas (Cl_2), 2 mol sodium chloride (NaCl) will be produced and no Na or Cl_2 will remain

	$2Na(s)$	+ $Cl_2(g)$ ⟶	$2NaCl(s)$
Original:	2 mol	1 mol	0 mol
Final:	0 mol	0 mol	2 mol

The extent of reaction in this case is 100 percent because there is no *reverse*, or right-to-left, reaction. The reverse reaction, that is, the decomposition of salt to form sodium and chlorine ($2NaCl \rightarrow 2Na + Cl_2$), does not occur; only the *forward*, or left-to-right, reaction ($2Na + Cl_2 \rightarrow 2NaCl$) takes place. Reactions such as this, which do not proceed in the reverse direction, are **irreversible.**

Irreversible reactions are said to go to completion, with all reactants being consumed. However, not all reactions are like this; one example of a reaction that does not go to completion is that of N_2 gas with H_2 gas to produce gaseous NH_3. If we start with 1 mol N_2 and 3 mol H_2, there will be less than 2 mol NH_3 formed.

	$N_2(g)$	$+\ 3H_2(g)$	$\longrightarrow 2NH_3(g)$
Original:	1 mol	3 mol	0 mol
Final:	0.78 mol	2.34 mol	0.44 mol

The reactants are never completely used up: only 0.22 mol N_2 (1 − 0.78) and 0.66 mol H_2 (3 − 2.34) react and only 0.44 mol NH_3 is produced. The extent of reaction is less than 100 percent (i.e., it does not go to completion) because this reaction is **reversible.** In reversible reactions, two reactions are actually taking place. Reactants are being converted to products as N_2 and H_2 molecules form NH_3 molecules in the forward reaction and at the same time NH_3 molecules are breaking down into N_2 and H_2 molecules in the reverse reaction. To indicate reversible reactions two arrows ($\rightleftharpoons$) are used.

Note that we have previously written the NH_3 synthesis reaction with a single arrow. This is a common practice.

$$N_2 + 3H_2 \rightleftharpoons 2NH_3$$

After some time interval there comes a point at which the rate of formation of NH_3 is the same as the rate of decomposition of NH_3.

Reversible reactions in which the rate of the forward reaction is the same as that of the reverse reaction are said to be in a state of **chemical equilibrium**.

The graph in Figure 10.9 shows that the concentration of products and reactants levels off when equilibrium is reached.

It is important to understand that equilibrium means that the rates of the forward and reverse reactions are equal. It *does not* mean that the amounts of reactants and products are equal. You can see that the equilibrium system described above contains different amounts of the reactants (N_2 and H_2) and of the

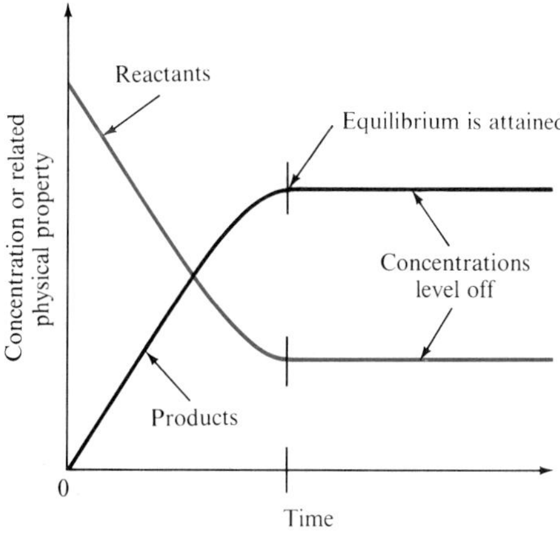

FIGURE 10.9
Equilibrium condition.

product (NH_3). In this particular system the amount of product is less than that of the reactants; the extent of reaction is 22 percent since the number of moles of NH_3 actually formed (0.44 mol) is 22 percent of the number that would form if the reaction went only in the forward direction (2.00 mol). It is also possible for equilibrium systems to contain more product at equilibrium than reactant. That is, the extent of reaction may be closer to 100 percent than to zero.

When a system is at equilibrium, its properties appear to remain constant. For instance, the concentrations of reactants and products at equilibrium stay the same, as shown in Figure 10.9. However, if we could take a microscopic look at the reaction, we would see reactant molecules forming product molecules and product molecules reforming the original reactants at the same rate. Thus equilibrium systems are *static* (unchanging) at the macroscopic level but *dynamic* (changing) at the microscopic level.

To describe the extent of reaction in a given equilibrium system a quantity known as the **equilibrium constant**, abbreviated K_{eq}, is defined. The value of K_{eq} for a given reaction is a constant at a given temperature. The equilibrium constant K_{eq} depends upon the molar concentrations of products compared with those of reactants. We can most easily define K_{eq} by illustrating an equilibrium constant expression for a hypothetical reaction in which a moles of reactant A react with b moles of reactant B to form c moles of product C and d moles of product D.

$$a\mathrm{A} + b\mathrm{B} \rightleftharpoons c\mathrm{C} + d\mathrm{D}$$

For this reaction the equilibrium constant expression is

$$K_{eq} = \frac{[\mathrm{C}]^c[\mathrm{D}]^d}{[\mathrm{A}]^a[\mathrm{B}]^b}$$

The brackets [] refer to molar concentrations (see Section 9.6), and the superscripts a, b, c, and d represent the coefficients in the balanced chemical equation. Note that the concentration of products appears in the numerator of the K expression. Thus the higher the value of K, the greater the extent of reaction and the more nearly the reaction goes to completion or, as is sometimes said, the more it goes to the right. The value of the equilibrium "constant" is constant only at a given temperature; when the temperature changes, the value of K_{eq} also changes.

To write the equilibrium constant expression for the formation of ammonia,

$$\mathrm{N_2}(g) + 3\mathrm{H_2}(g) \rightleftharpoons 2\mathrm{NH_3}(g)$$

$$K_{eq} = \frac{[\mathrm{NH_3}]^2}{[\mathrm{N_2}][\mathrm{H_2}]^3}$$

The value of the equilibrium constant for this reaction at 400°C, the temperature at which the industrial process is carried out, is 1.8×10^{-4}. This value for K_{eq} is much less than unity, which means that the numerator $[NH_3]^2$ is much less than the denominator $[N_2][H_2]^3$. Therefore, this reaction tends to go to the left, favoring the decomposition of NH_3 molecules. At 400°C this reaction is about 20 percent efficient, that is, only about 20 percent of the reactants are actually converted into ammonia gas.

Very large K values indicate high concentrations of products compared with reactants.

As you just saw, the value of K_{eq} can give an indication of the relative amounts of products and reactants. Whenever K_{eq} is greater than unity, it means that at equilibrium the concentration of products is greater than that of the reactants. Conversely, when K_{eq} is less than unity, there must be more reactants than products at equilibrium.

SAMPLE EXERCISE 10.6

Two forms of glucose exist in equilibrium:

$$\alpha\text{-D-glucose} \rightleftharpoons \beta\text{-D-glucose}$$

Write the equilibrium constant expression for this reaction. If K_{eq} is 1.75, which form is more predominant, the α or the β?

Solution:

$$K_{eq} = \frac{[\beta\text{-D-glucose}]}{[\alpha\text{-D-glucose}]}$$

Since $K_{eq} > 1$, the concentration of product, the β form, predominates at equilibrium. Thus this equilibrium favors the formation of product and the reaction goes to the right.

EXERCISE 10.6

The equilibrium constant for the reaction of H_2 and I_2 to produce HI is about 54 at a temperature of 400°C.

$$H_2 + I_2 \rightleftharpoons 2HI$$

Write the equilibrium constant expression for this reaction. In which direction does this reaction tend to go?

10.9 LECHATELIER'S PRINCIPLE

According to **LeChatelier's principle**, whenever a stress is placed on a system in equilibrium, the system will shift in such a direction as to relieve the stress. There are several types of stresses we can use to illustrate how this happens.

Concentration Changes

If the concentration of a reactant or product is increased by adding more of it to the equilibrium reaction, the equilibrium shifts so as to use up the reactant or product. Decreasing the concentration of a reactant or product has exactly the opposite effect. For instance, consider the equilibrium reaction of N_2 and H_2 to make NH_3. Let us see what happens if we add N_2 to this reaction system.

$$N_2 + 3H_2 \rightleftharpoons 2NH_3$$

$$K_{eq} = \frac{[NH_3]^2}{[N_2][H_2]^3}$$

If N_2 is added to this system, the $[N_2]$ term in the denominator of K_{eq} increases. To keep K_{eq} constant the N_2 will react with H_2 to form more NH_3. Thus the reaction must shift to the right, toward product, when N_2 is added.

Suppose we remove NH_3 from the system. What happens then? The $[NH_3]$ decreases, causing N_2 and H_2 molecules to react to form more NH_3. This relieves the stress of removing the NH_3. In this case the reaction also shifts to the right, toward product. Removing a product from an equilibrium reaction as the reaction proceeds is a technique used by chemists to drive the reaction toward completion. For instance, a reaction chemists use to prepare a type of organic compound called an ester is an equilibrium reaction. A typical example of one of these is the reaction below, in which ethanol, CH_3CH_2OH is added to acetic acid, CH_3COOH, to make the ester product, $CH_3COOCH_2CH_3$, and water. The fruity-smelling liquid ester, called ethyl acetate, which is a product of this reaction, is an important industrial solvent used in paint removers and fingernail polish remover.

$$\text{Ethanol} + \text{acetic acid} \rightleftharpoons \text{ester} + \text{water}$$

Removal of a product of an equilibrium reaction drives the reaction to make more product.

To force this reaction to shift toward the ester product, an apparatus has been designed which causes water to be removed from the system. As the water is removed, the reaction shifts toward the right, producing more of the desired ester product.

Temperature

Changing the temperature of the equilibrium system puts a stress on it. How it will respond depends upon whether the equilibrium reaction is exothermic or endothermic. We can think of the heat absorbed or evolved as though it were a reactant or a product. For instance, let us consider ammonia formation, an exothermic reaction, once more:

$$N_2 + 3H_2 \rightleftharpoons 2NH_3 + \text{heat}$$

Suppose we raise the temperature of this reaction, which is equivalent to increasing the amount of heat. To use up the heat added and relieve the resulting stress, this sytem must shift toward the left. Thus, if we wished to force the reaction toward the product NH_3, we would run it at a lower temperature so that the equilibrium will shift toward the right. Unfortunately, industrial processes run at low temperatures are too slow to be practical. A compromise must be made in this case and an intermediate temperature is chosen.

Pressure

Another way to place stress upon an equilibrium system is to increase the total pressure by decreasing the volume or by adding some inert gas such as He or one of the other noble gases. Any system in which the number of *gaseous* moles of reactant and product is different will shift to relieve this stress. To see how, we can look at the NH_3 synthesis again.

$$N_2(g) + 3H_2(g) \rightleftharpoons 2NH_3(g)$$

There is a total of 4 mol of gaseous reactants and only 2 mol of gaseous product. Pressure is caused by collisions of molecules with container walls. The greater the number of moles, the greater the number of molecules and collisions, and hence the greater the pressure. If the pressure of this system is increased, the equilibrium shifts toward the right, that is, toward the product side, on which there is only 2 mol of gaseous substance. Thus the stress of increasing the pressure is relieved as the total number of moles in the system is decreased. In industry the ammonia synthesis is done at pressures of about 250 atm.

Adding a Catalyst

Adding a catalyst to an equilibrium system will *not* shift the equilibrium at all, because the catalyst speeds up *both* the forward and the reverse reactions. The time required to reach equilibrium will decrease, but the equilibrium will not shift.

SAMPLE EXERCISE 10.7

How will the following stresses shift the reaction below, in which NO_2 is in equilibrium with N_2O_4? The reaction is endothermic.

$$N_2O_4(g) \rightleftharpoons 2NO_2(g)$$

(**a**) Temperature is decreased
(**b**) Pressure is increased.
(**c**) $[N_2O_4]$ is increased.

Solution:

(a) Since the reaction is endothermic, heat is absorbed.

$$\text{Heat} + N_2O_4(g) \rightleftharpoons 2NO_2(g)$$

If the temperature is decreased, i.e., if heat is removed, the reaction will shift to the left (to N_2O_4) to produce more heat.

(b) There is 1 mol of reactant and 2 mol of product. Thus the reaction shifts to the reactant (to the left).

(c) The reaction shifts to the right to use up the N_2O_4 added.

EXERCISE 10.7

The gas NO_2 is reddish brown (Section 7.13) and N_2O_4 is colorless. What will happen to the color of the reaction mixture in Sample Exercise 10.7 if it is heated?

Check your answer by referring to Color Plate 7, in which a glass tube containing a mixture of NO_2 and N_2O_4 is photographed at room temperature, at −20°C and at 90°C.

SUMMARY

Reactions can be grouped according to the general way in which the reactants combine or break down. When two substances combine to form a third, the reaction is a combination. In decomposition reactions substances break down into new substances. In displacement reactions an element (or group of elements) is replaced by another element.

In oxidation-reduction (redox) reactions electrons are transferred. To identify a redox reaction the oxidation numbers of each element in each compound can be inspected to see if there is any change from reactants to products. Oxidizing agents gain electrons, their oxidation numbers become more negative, and they are reduced. Reducing agents lose electrons, acquire more positive oxidation numbers, and are oxidized. Redox reactions are used to power batteries in which chemical energy is converted to electrical energy.

Thermochemistry is the study of the heat changes that accompany chemical reactions. The heat changes are changes in enthalpy, or ΔH. Exothermic reactions are heat-evolving reactions and have negative ΔH values, whereas endothermic reactions absorb heat and always have positive ΔH values. It is generally, but not always, true that reactions with negative values of ΔH are spontaneous, that is, they tend to proceed from reactants to products.

The technique of calorimetry is used to determine the caloric value of foodstuffs. The food is subjected to combustion, i.e., reaction with O_2, in a bomb calorimeter, and heat increases in the surrounding water indicate the value of ΔH. Carbohydrates and proteins provide about 4, fats about 9, and alcohol 7 Cal/g.

The study of the rate of a chemical reaction is kinetics. Reaction rates increase with increasing reactant concentrations and temperature. The energy required for reactants to climb an energy barrier so that a reaction can take place is called the activation energy E_a, which can be supplied as heat. For some reactions a catalyst is needed. Biochemical catalysts are called enzymes.

Reactions that do not proceed 100 percent to products are reversible reactions. When the forward and reverse reactions take place at the same rate, a state of equilibrium is achieved. The equilibrium constant K_{eq} is used to estimate whether the reaction tends to go in the forward ($K > 1$) or reverse direction ($K < 1$). According to Le Chatelier's principle, equilibrium reactions shift to relieve stresses placed upon them.

KEY WORDS

combination
decomposition
displacement
double displacement
precipitate
oxidation-reduction
oxidation number
oxidizing agent
reducing agent
battery
thermochemistry
exothermic
endothermic
enthalpy change
spontaneous reaction
bomb calorimeter
kinetics
activation energy
catalyst
reversible reaction
irreversible reaction
chemical equilibrium
equilibrium constant
Le Chatelier's principle

EXERCISES

10.8 Classify the following reactions as combinations, decompositions, displacements, or double displacements.
(a) $2Na(s) + Br_2(l) \longrightarrow 2NaBr(s)$
(b) $2NaBr(s) + Cl_2(g) \longrightarrow 2NaCl(s) + Br_2(l)$
(c) $2HgO(s) \xrightarrow{\Delta} 2Hg(l) + O_2(g)$
(d) $Pb(NO_3)_2(aq) + 2NaI(aq) \longrightarrow PbI_2(s) + 2NaNO_3(aq)$
(e) $Zn(s) + H_2SO_4(aq) \longrightarrow ZnSO_4(aq) + H_2(g)$

10.9 X-rays are used to diagnose stomach ulcers and intestinal disorders. However, x-rays normally pass through these organs. To prevent this the insoluble compound barium sulfate, $BaSO_4$, which is opaque to x-radiation, is given in the form of a syrup. Can you think of a double displacement reaction which would produce $BaSO_4$? (Note: The reactants must be water-soluble. Keep in mind that all nitrates and all sodium salts are water-soluble.)

10.10 Find the oxidation numbers of the underlined elements in the following compounds: (a) $\underline{Pb}Cl_2$; (b) $\underline{Pb}Cl_4$; (c) $H_2\underline{Se}O_4$; (d) $\underline{O}_2$; (e) $\underline{O}_3$; (f) $H\underline{N}O_3$; (g) $K_2\underline{Cr}_2O_7$; (h) $\underline{Cr}_2O_3$; (i) $\underline{Pt}F_4$; (j) $\underline{S}_8$.

10.11 Why are redox reactions applied to the production of batteries?

10.12 Of the following reactions, one is the basis for the operation of a fuel cell (a type of battery) used to supply energy to spacecraft and to provide drinking water as a bonus. Which one must it be? Explain your choice.
(a) $NaOH + HCl \longrightarrow NaCl + H_2O$
(b) $H_2CO_3 \longrightarrow CO_2 + H_2O$
(c) $H_2SO_4 + CaCl_2 \longrightarrow CaSO_4 + H_2O$
(d) $2H_2 + O_2 \longrightarrow 2H_2O$

10.13 In the reactions below, which reactant is the oxidizing agent and which is the reducing agent?
(a) $2Mg + O_2 \longrightarrow 2MgO$
(b) $Mg + Cl_2 \longrightarrow MgCl_2$
(c) $Sn + F_2 \longrightarrow SnF_2$
(d) $ZnO + H_2 \longrightarrow Zn + H_2O$

10.14 The ΔH change for a particular biochemical reaction in which a reactant S (called a substrate) is converted to a product P is -100 kcal/mol.

$$S \longrightarrow P \qquad \Delta H = -100 \text{ kcal}$$

(a) Is the reaction exothermic or endothermic?
(b) What would the value of ΔH be for the reaction

$$2S \longrightarrow 2P$$

(c) If the reaction occurred according to the steps below, where E represents an enzyme catalyst, what would ΔH be for this overall process?

Step 1: $E + S \longrightarrow ES$
Step 2: $ES \longrightarrow P + E$

10.15 Why does the ΔH of combustion per gram of glucose give a good approximate value for its caloric content even though glucose in the body is not metabolized by direct reaction with O_2?

10.16 What are two ways to find the caloric content of a particular food?

10.17 Using the protein, fat, and carbohydrate food composition data in the table of nutrition values, find the caloric content of the following foods and compare your answers with the values measured: (a) One 3-oz hamburger; (b) 1T peanut butter; (c) 1 pat butter; (d) 1 cup yoghurt.

10.18 What is meant by a reversible reaction?

10.19 Comment on the statement: At equilibrium there is no change in the composition of a reaction mixture.

10.20 What happens to reaction rates when the temperature is increased? How important do you think this effect is in mammals?

10.21 What is activation energy? Compare the activation energies of a catalyzed and an uncatalyzed reaction.

10.22 Make a sketch of the activation energy curve for the combustion of methane (CH_4) to yield CO_2 and H_2O. Is this reaction exothermic or endothermic? How do you indicate this on the curve you have drawn?

10.23 What is LeChatelier's principle?

10.24 What happens to the equilibrium system below if the following stresses are applied?

$$2SO_2(g) + O_2(g) \longrightarrow SO_3(g) \qquad \Delta H = -198 \text{ kJ}$$

(**a**) SO_3 is removed from the reaction mixture.
(**b**) O_2 is introduced.
(**c**) The pressure is increased.
(**d**) The temperature is increased.

10.25 The reaction below takes place in automobile engines:

$$\text{Heat} + N_2(g) + O_2(g) \rightleftharpoons 2NO(g)$$

The catalytic converter helps to control the exhaust of NO. Which of the two reasons below could account for this? Explain.
(1) The catalytic converter contains a catalyst.
(2) The catalytic converter is at a lower temperature than the automobile engine.

10.26 How does the numerical value of an equilibrium constant indicate whether a reaction tends to go to the right or to the left?

10.27 How does a catalyst affect a reaction that is at equilibrium?

10.28 Explain how it is possible to produce electrical energy from chemicals. Make a sketch of an apparatus that you could use for this purpose.

10.29 What is meant by a spontaneous reaction?

10.30 Which of the following descriptions apply to exothermic reactions and which to endothermic reactions?
(**a**) Usually spontaneous
(**b**) Evolve heat
(**c**) $\Delta H > 0$
(**d**) Energy of products is less than energy of reactants

10.31 The reaction below is a step in the metabolism of starch.

$$\text{Glucose-1-phosphate} \rightleftharpoons \text{glucose-6-phosphate}$$

In an equilibrium mixture, the concentrations of glucose-1-phosphate and glucose-6-phosphate are 0.0010 *M* and 0.019 *M*, respectively. Calculate the equilibrium constant. In which direction does this reaction tend to go?

11 ACIDS AND BASES

11.1 INTRODUCTION

The Latin word *acidus* means "sour."

Early chemists found that certain compounds fell into one of two categories. One group included sour-tasting substances called *acids*. The tart flavor of lemons and vinegar comes from acids; lemons are rich in citric acid and vinegar is a dilute solution of acetic acid in water. (See Table 11.1 for the formulas of citric and acetic acids.) Acids also produce a burning sensation upon contact with skin, and some of them can "eat" holes through clothing.

In the other group were bitter-tasting compounds originally called *alkali*, after the Arabic words *al kali* for the ashes of the plant which produces one of them (sodium carbonate). We call these substances *bases*. Bases have a "slimy," slippery consistency. One substance that fits this description is soap which is, in fact, a base. (See Table 11.2 for the formula of a typical soap.) Lye contains the base sodium hydroxide (NaOH), and many household cleaning solutions contain the base ammonia (NH_3).

Most metabolic processes are extremely sensitive to the acidity or alkalinity of the fluid in which they occur, which makes this one of the most carefully regulated quantities in all living things. We will begin our study of acids and bases by examining some of their chemical properties. From these we will present a theory that will explain the behavior of acids and bases and allow us to make calculations about the extent of acidity or alkalinity in given solutions.

11.2 PROPERTIES OF ACIDS AND BASES

In this section we will discuss some of the chemical properties that are typical for most acids or bases. We will see that all the characteristic properties of acids and bases are removed when they react with each other.

Acids

One property of acids that we have already mentioned is the sour taste many of them have. Acidic substances such as concentrated sulfuric acid, $H_2SO_4(aq)$, or hydrochloric acid, $HCl(aq)$, do have a sour taste, although they are much too reactive to test in this way. We can more conveniently observe some of their chemical properties. Acids react with certain metals to produce H_2 gas and a salt.

Recall from Section 4.5 that salts are ionic compounds.

$$\text{Acid} + \text{metal} \longrightarrow \text{salt} + H_2$$

For instance, sulfuric acid reacts with magnesium metal to give hydrogen and the salt magnesium sulfate.

$$H_2SO_4(aq) + Mg(s) \longrightarrow MgSO_4(aq) + H_2(g)$$

This reaction belongs to the class of displacement reactions, which we discussed in Section 10.2.

Dilute acids are used to shine metal surfaces by removing dull oxides.

Acids also react with metal oxides to form water and salt as products.

$$\text{Acid} + \text{metal oxide} \longrightarrow \text{salt} + H_2O$$

For example, hydrochloric acid produces copper(II) chloride and water when it reacts with copper(II) oxide:

$$2\ HCl(aq) + CuO(s) \longrightarrow CuCl_2(aq) + H_2O$$

Acids liberate CO_2 from carbonates or from bicarbonates.

$$\text{Acid} + \text{carbonate} \longrightarrow \text{salt} + CO_2(g) + H_2O$$

and

$$\text{Acid} + \text{bicarbonate} \longrightarrow \text{salt} + CO_2(g) + H_2O$$

For instance, antacid tablets containing sodium bicarbonate, $NaHCO_3$, are able to react with stomach acid, HCl, in this way:

$$HCl(aq) + NaHCO_3(aq) \longrightarrow NaCl(aq) + CO_2(g) + H_2O$$

As we mentioned in Section 7.17, the action of acid rain, which contains H_2SO_4, can damage the limestone ($CaCO_3$) of which many statues and buildings are constructed.

$$H_2SO_4(aq) + CaCO_3 \longrightarrow CaSO_4(aq) + CO_2(g) + H_2O$$

Acids undergo a reaction with a dye called litmus to produce a red color. Dyes, such as litmus, that are used to test for acidity are called **indicators**. Paper strips impregnated with litmus dye (litmus papers) turn pinkish red when immersed in lemon juice, vinegar, or any acidic solution, as shown in Color Plate 11.

Bases

Bases react with many salts of heavy metals to produce insoluble hydroxide precipitates in a double displacement reaction (see Section 10.2).

$$\text{Base} + \text{salt} \longrightarrow \text{hydroxide}\downarrow + \text{salt}$$

For example, the base sodium hydroxide reacts with iron(III) nitrate to form the precipitate iron(III) hydroxide:

$$3\ NaOH(aq) + Fe(NO_3)_3(aq) \longrightarrow Fe(OH)_3\downarrow + 3\ NaNO_3(aq)$$

Adding the indicator litmus to a base produces a blue color. Thus, litmus paper dipped into a soapy solution turns blue (see Color Plate 11).

Acid-Base Neutralizations

The properties of both acids and bases are removed when an acid reacts with a base in a reaction called **neutralization**. The products of a neutralization reaction are a salt and water.

$$\text{Base} + \text{acid} \longrightarrow \text{salt} + H_2O$$

TABLE 11.1 SOME COMMON ACIDS

Formula	Name	Use or source
HCl	**Hydrochloric acid** (muriatic acid)	In stomach acid
H_2SO_4	**Sulfuric acid** (oil of vitriol)	In auto battery fluid; dehydrating agent
HNO_3	**Nitric acid**	Starting compound for making fertilizers and explosives
H_3PO_4	**Phosphoric acid**	In some carbonated beverages
$HO{-}\overset{\overset{\large O}{\|}}{C}{-}CH_3$ (HAc)	**Acetic acid**	In vinegar
$HO{-}C(CH_2{-}COOH)_2{-}COOH$ (structure: central C bearing HO, $-\overset{O}{\overset{\|}{C}}-OH$, and two $CH_2-\overset{O}{\overset{\|}{C}}-OH$ groups)	**Citric acid**	In citrus fruits and effervescing antacid tablets
HF	**Hydrofluoric acid**	Used to etch glass; very poisonous
NH_4^+	**Ammonium ion*** ammonium chloride, NH_4Cl	Used to acidify urine

*The ion NH_4^+ is added to solutions as the salt NH_4Cl.

For example, the reaction of NaOH, a base, with HCl, an acid, is a neutralization.

$$NaOH(aq) + HCl(aq) \longrightarrow NaCl(aq) + H_2O$$

If the base is a carbonate or bicarbonate, the products also include CO_2 gas. When $NaHCO_3$ reacts with HCl in the stomach, we say that the $NaHCO_3$ neutralizes stomach acid.

Ingredients in common antacid preparations include $CaCO_3$, $MgCO_3$, $Al(OH)_3$, $Mg(OH)_2$, $NaHCO_3$, and $KHCO_3$.

Tables 11.1 and 11.2 give the formulas and names of a variety of common acids and bases. Now we must find out why it is that some substances behave as acids and others as bases.

TABLE 11.2 **SOME COMMON BASES**

Formula	Name	Use or source
OH^-	**Hydroxide ion*** sodium hydroxide NaOH (lye, caustic soda)	Oven and drain cleaner; "caustic" to remove tissue
	Magnesium hydroxide $Mg(OH)_2$ (milk of magnesia)	Antacid; cathartic
NH_3	**Ammonia**	Household cleaners; product of protein metabolism
HCO_3^-	**Bicarbonate ion*** sodium bicarbonate $NaHCO_3$ (baking soda)	Leavening agent; in fire extinguishers; antacid; used to alkalize urine
CO_3^{2-}	**Carbonate ion*** sodium carbonate Na_2CO_3 (washing soda) calcium carbonate $CaCO_3$	Glass manufacture; antacid, Ca^{2+} supplement; chalk, limestone, pearls
$^-O-C(=O)-CH_3$ or Ac^-	**Acetate ion*** sodium acetate NaAc	Used to alkalize urine
$^-O-C(=O)-(CH_2)_{16}CH_3$	**Stearate ion*** sodium stearate	Hand soap
$CH_2-C(=O)-O^-$ $HO-C-C(=O)-O^-$ $CH_2-C(=O)-O^-$	**Citrate ion*** sodium citrate	Widely found in plant and animal tissue; used to alkalize urine

*The bases OH^-, Ac^-, CO_3^{2-}, HCO_3^-, citrate and stearate are added to solutions in the form of their salts such as the typical ones listed.

11.3 PROTON TRANSFER

Theories that explain the behavior of acids and bases are based upon the differences in the chemical structures of these two types of compounds. An acid-base theory proposed independently by J. N. Brönsted (1879–1947) in Denmark and T. M. Lowry (1874–1936) in England accounts for the acidic or basic properties of most compounds. The **Brönsted-Lowry theory** states that

An acid is a compound that donates a proton and a base is a compound that accepts a proton.

An **acid** is a proton donor.
A **base** is a proton acceptor.

According to the proton transfer theory, all acid-base reactions must involve both an acid (the species that donates the proton) and a base (the species that accepts it). Solvents may behave as acids or bases and *must* be included in acid-base reaction equations.

Let us look at the solutions of HCl and NaOH and see how their components act as proton donors and acceptors. We will write the formula for water as HOH in these reactions to make it easier to follow the transfer of protons to or from the water molecule. When HCl gas dissolves in water, HCl molecules donate protons to water molecules. The H atom indicated below in color is transferred from an HCl molecule to an H_2O molecule (see Figure 11.1, where Lewis electron dot structures of the species involved are included).

$$\underset{\text{Acid}}{HCl} + \underset{\text{Base}}{HOH} \longrightarrow \overset{H^+}{HOH} + Cl^-$$

In this reaction the HCl donates a proton to H_2O and behaves as an acid. The H_2O molecule accepts the proton and hence is a base. The water molecule with the added proton is written as H_3O^+ and is called a *hydronium ion*. Thus the equation can be rewritten as

$$HCl + H_2O \longrightarrow H_3O^+ + Cl^-$$

It is the hydronium ion that gives aqueous acid solutions their acidic properties.

$$\underset{\text{Hydrogen chloride}}{:\ddot{Cl}:H} + \underset{\text{Water}}{:\ddot{\overset{H}{O}}:H} \longrightarrow \underset{\text{Chloride ion}}{\left[:\ddot{Cl}:\right]^-} + \underset{\text{Hydronium ion}}{\left[H:\ddot{\overset{H}{O}}:H\right]^+}$$

FIGURE 11.1
Ionization of HCl. HCl donates a proton to a molecule.

The reaction is sometimes abbreviated in such a way that the water is left out and simply understood ($HCl \rightarrow H^+ + Cl^+$). We will include the water in most of the acid-base reactions that we write. Molecules of HCl do not simply give up protons in water, they *donate* protons to H_2O molecules to form H_3O^+ ions.

In all Brönsted-Lowry acid-base reactions, a new acid called the **conjugate acid** and a new base called the **conjugate base** are formed. The word *conjugate* means joined in pairs. A conjugate pair includes the reacting acid and the new base formed or the reacting base and the new acid formed. For instance, in solutions of HCl in water, the reacting acid is HCl and the reacting base is H_2O.

$$\underset{\text{Reacting acid}}{HCl} + \underset{\text{Reacting base}}{H_2O} \longrightarrow H_3O^+ + Cl^-$$

To find the conjugate acid and base we must look at the products of the reaction. We see that the new acid formed is H_3O^+, which is the conjugate acid, and the new base is Cl^-, the conjugate base. Thus the reacting acid (HCl) forms the conjugate base (Cl^-) while the reacting base (H_2O) forms the conjugate acid (H_3O^+).

Conjugate pair (HCl/Cl^-)

$$HCl + H_2O \longrightarrow Cl^- + H_3O^+$$

Conjugate pair (H_2O/H_3O^+)

Sodium hydroxide (NaOH) is an ionic compound which dissociates into Na^+ and OH^- ions in solution.

This reaction is sometimes abbreviated $NaOH \rightarrow Na^+ + OH^-$.

$$\underset{\text{Acid}}{HOH} + Na^+ + \underset{\text{Base}}{OH^-} \longrightarrow Na^+ + \underset{\text{Conjugate base}}{HO^-} + \underset{\text{Conjugate acid}}{HOH}$$

In this reaction you can see that the OH^- ion accepts a proton from H_2O. Thus, according to the Brönsted-Lowry theory, OH^- must be a base. The water molecule donates a proton to the OH^- ion, and thus in this reaction water behaves like an acid. The new acid formed is also H_2O and the new base is OH^-. In this reaction the conjugate pairs are H_2O (the reacting acid) and OH^- (the conjugate base) and OH^- (the reacting base) and H_2O (the conjugate acid). Note that the Na^+ ions do not participate in the acid-base reaction. Nevertheless (as mentioned in the footnote to Table 11.2), we still say that NaOH is a base because the OH^- is added to a solution in the form of the compound sodium hydroxide.

Ammonia, NH_3, behaves as a base although its formula does not include a hydroxide ion. The ammonia molecule accepts a proton from water to produce hydroxide ions (see Figure 11.2):

$$\underset{\text{H}}{HNH} + HOH \longrightarrow \overset{\text{H}}{\underset{\text{H}}{HNH^+}} + OH^-$$

FIGURE 11.2
Ionization of NH_3. NH_3 accepts a proton from a water molecule.

$$\mathrm{H:\overset{\cdot\cdot}{\underset{\cdot\cdot}{N}}:H + :\overset{\cdot\cdot}{\underset{\cdot\cdot}{O}}: \longrightarrow H:\overset{\cdot\cdot}{\underset{\cdot\cdot}{N}}:H^{+} + :\overset{\cdot\cdot}{\underset{\cdot\cdot}{O}}:^{-}}$$

(Ammonia: N bonded to three H; Water: O bonded to two H; Ammonium ion: N bonded to four H; Hydroxide ion: O bonded to one H)

Ammonia | Water | Ammonium ion | Hydroxide ion

The ammonia is a base and the ammonium ion produced is its conjugate acid.

$$\underset{\text{Base}}{NH_3} + \underset{\text{Acid}}{H_2O} \longrightarrow \underset{\text{Conjugate acid}}{NH_4^+} + \underset{\text{Conjugate base}}{OH^-}$$

We say that NaAc is a base although the base is actually Ac^-.

The compound sodium acetate (NaAc) contains the acetate ion (Ac^-), which is a base (see Table 11.2). Again, the Na^+ ions do not participate in this acid-base reaction. The acetate ion, Ac^-, is the H^+ acceptor.

$$\underset{\text{Base}}{Ac^-} + \underset{\text{Acid}}{HOH} \longrightarrow \underset{\text{Conjugate acid}}{HAc} + \underset{\text{Conjugate base}}{OH^-}$$

Note that OH^- is always produced when a base accepts H^+ from H_2O.

Thus the proton transfer theory explains the basic properties of ions such as Ac^- (in sodium acetate) and HCO_3^- (in sodium bicarbonate).

By noting which reactant is the proton donor and which is the proton acceptor, the Brönsted-Lowry acids and bases can be identified in neutralization reactions. In the neutralization reaction of HCl with NH_3 we see that the acid HCl donates a proton to the base NH_3.

$$NH_3 + HCl \longrightarrow NH_4^+ + Cl^-$$

Often the product of this reaction is written as NH_4Cl.

$$NH_3 + HCl \longrightarrow NH_4Cl$$

The Brönsted-Lowry proton transfer theory can classify many compounds as acids and bases. The proton transfer theory also can be applied in solvents other than water. However, we will limit our discussion to aqueous solutions, since water is the solvent of living systems.

SAMPLE EXERCISE 11.1

Body fluids contain phosphates in several forms, including the monohydrogen phosphate ion, HPO_4^{2-}. This ion behaves like a base. Write the equation for its acid-base reaction with water and label the acid, base, conjugate acid, and conjugate base.

Solution:

Since HPO_4^{2-} is a base, it must accept protons from water. The conjugate acid, $H_2PO_4^-$, will then have a -1 charge.

Note that the total charge is the same on both sides of an ionization equation.

$$\underset{\text{Base}}{HPO_4^{2-}} + \underset{\text{Acid}}{HOH} \longrightarrow \underset{\text{Conjugate acid}}{H_2PO_4^-} + \underset{\text{Conjugate base}}{OH^-}$$

EXERCISE 11.1

Write the reaction in which nitric acid (see Table 11.1) donates a proton to water. Label the acid, base, conjugate acid, and conjugate base.

SAMPLE EXERCISE 11.2

The drug procaine ($C_{13}H_{20}N_2O_2$), or Novocain, is a base which is not very soluble in water. However, it reacts with HCl to form a compound (procaine hydrochloride) that is soluble in water and thus can be used to prepare injections. Write the equation that describes this neutralization reaction.

Solution:

Procaine accepts a proton from HCl.

$$C_{13}H_{20}N_2O_2 + HCl \longrightarrow C_{13}H_{20}N_2O_2H^+ + Cl^- \text{ (or } C_{13}H_{20}N_2O_2HCl)$$

EXERCISE 11.2

Which of the two equations below is a correct description of the neutralization of the base CH_3NH_2 with the acid HAc?

$$CH_3NH_2 + HAc \longrightarrow CH_3NH_3^+ + Ac^- \quad (1)$$

$$CH_3NH_2 + HAc \longrightarrow CH_3NH^- + H_2Ac^+ \quad (2)$$

11.4 STRONG ACIDS AND BASES

In Chapter 10 we said that some reactions are irreversible, that is, the extent of reaction is 100 percent. **Strong acids** and **strong bases** are 100 percent ionized. For instance, HCl is an example of a strong acid. That is, every HCl molecule dissolved in water donates a proton to a water molecule to form a hydronium

TABLE 11.3 STRONG ACIDS

Formula	Name
HCl	Hydrochloric acid
HBr	Hydrobromic acid
HI	Hydroiodic acid
$HClO_4$	Perchloric acid
$HClO_3$	Chloric acid
HNO_3	Nitric acid
H_2SO_4	Sulfuric acid

ion, and no un-ionized or *undissociated* HCl molecules remain. As in all irreversible reactions, we use a single, one-way arrow between the reactants and the products.

$$HCl\ (g) + H_2O \longrightarrow H_3O^+ + Cl^-$$

Table 11.3 lists some other strong acids.

NaOH is one example of a strong base. Every NaOH entity that dissolves in water produces a hydroxide ion and every hydroxide ion accepts a proton.

$$HOH + OH^- + (Na^+) \longrightarrow OH^- + HOH + (Na^+)$$

Group IA elements are the *alkali* metals and group IIA elements are the *alkaline* earth metals.

Table 11.4 lists some strong bases, which include any group IA and group IIA hydroxides that can be dissolved in water.

TABLE 11.4 STRONG BASES

Formula	Name
OH^-	Hydroxide ion
from:	
$LiOH$	Lithium hydroxide
$NaOH$	Sodium hydroxide
KOH	Potassium hydroxide
$RbOH$	Rubidium hydroxide
$CsOH$	Cesium hydroxide
$Mg(OH)_2$	Magnesium hydroxide
$Ca(OH)_2$	Calcium hydroxide
$Sr(OH)_2$	Strontium hydroxide
$Ba(OH)_2$	Barium hydroxide

11.5 WEAK ACIDS AND BASES

Weak acids and **weak bases** do not ionize completely, that is, not every molecule of a weak acid or a weak base dissociates. Equilibrium is established between the molecules of a weak acid or base and the ions that they produce (see Section 10.8). Suppose we use the symbol HA to represent a weak acid and B to represent a weak base. The ionization reactions for HA and B are written as equilibrium reactions, with double arrows separating reactants and products:

HA	$+\ H_2O$	$\rightleftharpoons$	A^-	$+\ H_3O^+$
Acid	Base		Conjugate base	Conjugate acid

B	$+\ H_2O$	$\rightleftharpoons$	BH^+	$+\ OH^-$
Base	Acid		Conjugate acid	Conjugate base

Table 11.5 lists some weak acids and Table 11.6 some weak bases.

TABLE 11.5 WEAK ACIDS

Name	Formula	Ionization	K_a at 25°C	pK_a
Phosphoric acid	H_3PO_4	$H_3PO_4 + H_2O \rightleftharpoons H_2PO_4^{2-} + H_3O^+$	7.5×10^{-3}	2.12
Hydrofluoric acid	HF	$HF + H_2O \rightleftharpoons F^- + H_3O^+$	3.5×10^{-4}	3.46
Acetic acid	HAc	$HAc + H_2O \rightleftharpoons Ac^- + H_3O^+$	1.8×10^{-5}	4.74
Carbonic acid	H_2CO_3	$H_2CO_3 + H_2O \rightleftharpoons HCO_3^- + H_3O^+$	4.3×10^{-7}	6.37
Dihydrogen phosphate ion	$H_2PO_4^{2-}$	$H_2PO_4^{2-} + H_2O \rightleftharpoons HPO_4^- + H_3O^+$	6.2×10^{-8}	7.21
Ammonium ion	NH_4^+	$NH_4^+ + H_2O \rightleftharpoons NH_3 + H_3O^+$	5.7×10^{-10}	9.24
Hydrocyanic acid	HCN	$HCN + H_2O \rightleftharpoons CN^- + H_3O^+$	4.9×10^{-10}	9.31

TABLE 11.6 WEAK BASES

Name	Formula	Ionization	K_b at 25°C	pK_b
Methylamine	CH_3NH_2	$CH_3NH_2 + H_2O \rightleftharpoons CH_3NH_3^+ + OH^-$	3.7×10^{-4}	3.43
Carbonate	CO_3^{2-}	$CO_3^{2-} + H_2O \rightleftharpoons HCO_3^- + OH^-$	1.8×10^{-4}	3.74
Ammonia	NH_3	$NH_3 + H_2O \rightleftharpoons NH_4^+ + OH^-$	1.7×10^{-5}	4.77
Monohydrogen phosphate	HPO_4^{2-}	$HPO_4^{2-} + H_2O \rightleftharpoons H_2PO_4^{2-} + OH^-$	1.6×10^{-7}	6.80
Bicarbonate	HCO_3^-	$HCO_3^- + H_2O \rightleftharpoons H_2CO_3 + OH^-$	2.3×10^{-8}	7.64
Acetate	Ac^-	$Ac^- + H_2O \rightleftharpoons HAc + OH^-$	5.6×10^{-10}	9.25

For instance, acetic acid, which can be abbreviated as HAc, is weakly ionized.

$$HAc + H_2O \rightleftharpoons Ac^- + H_3O^+$$

In 0.1 *M* solutions of acetic acid, only about 1 out of every 100 HAc molecules dissociates into Ac^- and H_3O^+ ions. Thus we can say that this equilibrium reaction favors the reverse reaction, or goes to the left (see Section 10.8).

Ammonia is an example of a weak base, and the ionization equilibrium is written as follows:

$$NH_3 + H_2O \rightleftharpoons NH_4^+ + OH^-$$

To describe the extent of ionization of a weak acid (or base) numbers called acid constants (or base constants) can be defined. We begin by writing the equilibrium constant expression for the ionization of a general weak acid, HA:

$$HA + H_2O \rightleftharpoons H_3O^+ + A^-$$

$$K_{eq} = \frac{[H_3O^+][A^-]}{[HA][H_2O]}$$

We can simplify this expression by making use of the fact that $[H_2O]$ hardly varies in dilute solutions. Thus we can make a very good approximation by combining $[H_2O]$ and K_{eq} to create a new equilibrium constant called the *acid constant* K_a.

$$[H_2O] \times K_{eq} = K_a$$

Now we can rewrite the equilibrium expression without $[H_2O]$:

$$K_a = \frac{[H_3O^+][A^-]}{[HA]}$$

In a similar way we can write an expression for the *base constant* K_b for the ionization of a weak base B:

$$B + H_2O \rightleftharpoons BH^+ + OH^-$$

$$K_b = \frac{[BH^+]\,[OH^-]}{[B]}$$

Tables 11.5 and 11.6 give K_a and K_b values for various weak acids and weak bases.

The ionization constants K_a and K_b give an indication of the relative strengths of acids or bases. The weaker the acid or base, the less it ionizes and the lower will be its K_a or K_b. For instance, from looking at Table 11.5 we see that hydrocyanic acid (K_a, 4.9×10^{-10}) is weaker than acetic acid (K_a, 1.8×10^{-5}).

SAMPLE EXERCISE 11.3

A compound called pyridine (C_5H_5N) undergoes the following ionization reaction. Write the ionization constant expression.

$$C_5H_5N + H_2O \rightleftharpoons C_5H_5NH^+ + OH^-$$

Solution:

Pyridine must be a base since it accepts protons and produces OH^- ions.

$$K_b = \frac{[C_5H_5NH^+][OH^-]}{[C_5H_5N]}$$

EXERCISE 11.3

Write the equation for the ionization in water of the weak acid HClO, hypochlorous acid. Give the expression for the equilibrium constant K_a.

11.6 IONIZATION OF WATER

We have already seen several reactions in which H_2O acts as an acid ($NH_3 + H_2O \rightarrow$) and others where it acts as a base ($HCl + H_2O \rightarrow$). Water by itself ionizes to a very small extent to produce H_3O^+ and OH^- ions. In the reaction below one water molecule (the acid) donates a proton to the other water molecule (the base):

$$\underset{\text{Base}}{HOH} + \underset{\text{Acid}}{HOH} \rightleftharpoons \overset{H}{HOH^+} + OH^-$$

The conjugate acid is the H_3O^+ ion and the conjugate base is the OH^- ion:

$$\underset{\text{Base}}{H_2O} + \underset{\text{Acid}}{H_2O} \rightleftharpoons \underset{\text{Conjugate acid}}{H_3O^+} + \underset{\text{Conjugate base}}{OH^-}$$

The self-ionization of water just described can be represented by an abbreviated equation.

$$H_2O \rightleftharpoons H^+ + OH^-$$

To write the equilibrium constant expression for the ionization of water, $[H_2O]$ is multiplied by K_{eq} to form a new constant K_w, sometimes called the *water constant.*

$$K_{eq} = \frac{[H^+][OH^-]}{[H_2O]} \quad \text{and} \quad K_{eq} \times [H_2O] = K_w$$

$$K_w = [H^+][OH^-]$$

Although they are very small, values for $[H^+]$ and $[OH^-]$ in water can be measured in the laboratory. At 25°C, $[H^+]$ and $[OH^-]$ are each 0.00000010, or 1.0×10^{-7}. From these we can calculate K_w.

$$K_w = [H^+][OH^-]$$

$$[H^+] = [OH^-] = 1.0 \times 10^{-7}$$

and $$K_w = 1.0 \times 10^{-7} \times 1.0 \times 10^{-7} = 1.0 \times 10^{-14}$$

We see that the ionization constant for water is a very small number, which is not surprising since the ionization is slight. Only 2 in every 1 trillion water molecules are ionized at any given time. One liter of water contains only one ten-millionth of a gram of hydrogen ion.

Since water contains an equal concentration of H^+ and OH^- ions, it serves as an excellent standard for acidity measurements.

11.7 MEASURE OF ACIDITY

For convenience we often write H^+, knowing that we really mean H_3O^+.

Acidity is measured in terms of $[H^+]$ present in a solution. The higher the concentration of H^+ ion in the solution, the more acidic it is. Aqueous solutions in which $[OH^-] = [H^+]$ are said to be **neutral**; solutions in which $[H^+]$ is greater than $[OH^-]$ are **acidic**; and conversely, solutions in which $[H^+]$ is less than $[OH^-]$ are **basic** or **alkaline.**

$[H^+] = [OH^-]$ neutral
$[H^+] > [OH^-]$ acidic
$[H^+] < [OH^-]$ basic

Thus water is neutral, since it always produces an equal concentration of OH^- and H^+ ions. At a temperature of 25°C the $[H^+]$ and $[OH^-]$ values are each 1.0×10^{-7}. In acidic solutions $[H^+]$ must be greater than 1.0×10^{-7} and in basic solutions $[H^+]$ must be less than 1.0×10^{-7}.

$[H^+] = 1.0 \times 10^{-7}$ neutral
$[H^+] > 1.0 \times 10^{-7}$ acidic
$[H^+] < 1.0 \times 10^{-7}$ basic

In vinegar, an acidic solution, $[H^+]$ is about 4×10^{-3}, which is greater than 1.0×10^{-7}. In a 1.0 *M* ammonia solution $[H^+]$ is 4×10^{-11}, which is less than 1.0×10^{-7}, as expected for a basic solution.

If we know the hydrogen ion concentration ($[H^+]$) of a given solution, we can use K_w to find $[OH^-]$. For instance, suppose we wish to know $[OH^-]$ in the vinegar solution above.

$$K_w = [H^+][OH^-]$$

$$K_w = 1.0 \times 10^{-14}$$

$$[H^+] = 4 \times 10^{-3}$$

$$[OH^-] = \frac{1.0 \times 10^{-14}}{4 \times 10^{-3}} = 2.5 \times 10^{-12}$$

Neither $[H^+]$ nor $[OH^-]$ is ever zero in an aqueous solution.

No matter how acidic a solution is, there will always be some OH^- ions present, and even very basic solutions always contain some H^+ ions.

SAMPLE EXERCISE 11.4

In a sample of blood the molar concentration of H^+ ions is 6.0×10^{-8} at 25°C. Is the blood acidic or basic? Calculate $[OH^-]$ in the blood sample.

Solution:

$$[H^+] = 6.0 \times 10^{-8} = 0.60 \times 10^{-7}$$

$$0.60 \times 10^{-7} < 1.0 \times 10^{-7}$$

The blood is basic.

$$K_w = [H^+][OH^-] = 1.0 \times 10^{-14}$$

$$[H^+] = 0.60 \times 10^{-7}$$

$$[OH^-] = \frac{1.0 \times 10^{-14}}{0.60 \times 10^{-7}} = 1.7 \times 10^{-7}$$

EXERCISE 11.4

A sample of human saliva has a hydroxide ion concentration of 5.0×10^{-8} *M*. Is the saliva basic or acidic? Calculate the $[H^+]$ present.

11.8 pH AS A MEASURE OF ACIDITY

The numerical values for $[H^+]$ in most of the solutions we will discuss are very small ones, which are usually expressed as exponentials. These numbers are clumsy to use and awkward to speak about. The pH term was invented to provide

In French pH stands for *puissance d'hydrogène*, or "strength of hydrogen."

a more convenient yardstick of acidity in which the numbers quoted are not in exponential form. The pH is directly related to the $[H^+]$ and is defined to be the negative logarithm of $[H^+]$:

$$pH = -\log [H^+]$$

$\log 10^x = x$

The symbol *log* means logarithm to the base 10 and is sometimes written as $\log_{10}$. The **logarithm** of a number is the *exponent* of the number when the number is expressed as a power of 10. Thus the $\log_{10}$ of the number 10^x is x. A list of some numbers and their logarithms is given in Table 11.7. Note that Table 11.7 includes only the whole numbers between 1 and 10. For the intermediate decimal numbers you may estimate or use a more complete table or a calculator.

Let us now illustrate how pH is used to quote the acidity of a given solution. To find the pH of pure water we take the negative log of $[H^+]$.

$$[H^+] = 10^{-7}$$
$$pH = -\log 10^{-7} = -(-7) = 7$$

TABLE 11.7 NUMBERS AND THEIR LOGARITHMS

Number	Expressed as a power of 10	Logarithm of number
0.0000001	10^{-7}	−7
0.000001	10^{-6}	−6
0.00001	10^{-5}	−5
0.0001	10^{-4}	−4
0.001	10^{-3}	−3
0.01	10^{-2}	−2
0.1	10^{-1}	−1
1.0	10^{0}	0
2.0	$10^{0.30}$	0.30
3.0	$10^{0.48}$	0.48
4.0	$10^{0.60}$	0.60
5.0	$10^{0.70}$	0.70
6.0	$10^{0.78}$	0.78
7.0	$10^{0.85}$	0.85
8.0	$10^{0.90}$	0.90
9.0	$10^{0.95}$	0.95
10	10^{1}	1
100	10^{2}	2
1000	10^{3}	3
10000	10^{4}	4
100000	10^{5}	5
1000000	10^{6}	6
10000000	10^{7}	7

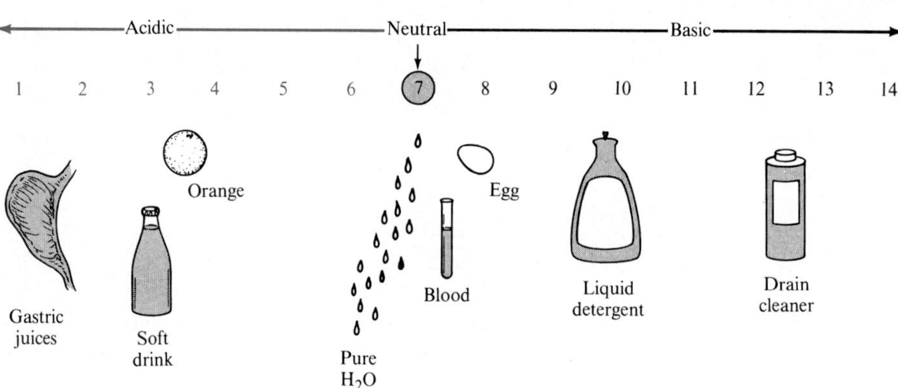

FIGURE 11.3
pH scale and pH values for common substances.

Thus the pH of pure water is 7 and all neutral solutions have a pH of 7. The pH of acidic solutions is always less than 7 and the pH of basic solutions is always greater than 7.

$$\begin{aligned}pH &= 7 \text{ neutral}\\ pH &< 7 \text{ acidic}\\ pH &> 7 \text{ basic}\end{aligned}$$

To find the pH of the vinegar solution with a $[H^+]$ of 4.0×10^{-3}:

$\log(a \times b) = \log a + \log b.$

$$[H^+] = 4.0 \times 10^{-3}$$

$$pH = -\log(4.0 \times 10^{-3})$$

$$= -\log 4.0 - \log 10^{-3}$$

$$\log 4.0 = 0.60 \text{ (from Table 11.7) and } \log 10^{-3} = -3$$

$$pH = -0.60 - (-3) = -0.60 + 3 = 2.4$$

We see that the pH of the acidic vinegar solution is 2.4, which is less than 7. To say that the pH is 2.4 for this vinegar solution is much easier than saying that the hydrogen ion concentration is 4.0×10^{-3}. Figure 11.3 gives pH values for some common substances.

SAMPLE EXERCISE 11.5

Calculate the pH of a blood sample which has $[H^+] = 6.0 \times 10^{-8}$.

Solution:

$$pH = -\log(6.0 \times 10^{-8}) = -\log 6.0 - \log 10^{-8}$$

From Table 11.7 we find that log 6 = 0.78.

$$pH = -0.78 - (-8) = 7.22$$

The pH of this blood > 7, and so this is a slightly basic solution.

EXERCISE 11.5

Find the pH of lemon juice in which the $[H^+]$ is 5.0×10^{-3}.

11.9 CALCULATING pH FROM INITIAL CONCENTRATIONS

If we know the initial concentration of a solution of acid or base, it is possible to calculate the pH. The calculation is easier for a strong acid or base because there is no reverse reaction to consider.

Strong Acids and Bases

Strong acids and bases are 100 percent ionized and thus do not have values of K_a and K_b such as those listed in Tables 11.5 and 11.6. It is possible to calculate the concentrations of ions produced directly from the given concentration of the acid or base. For instance, suppose we wish to calculate the pH of a 0.1 *M* HCl solution. We first write the ionization reaction and then indicate the molar concentrations of HCl and of H_3O^+ and Cl^- present originally and finally. The original concentration of H_3O^+ is considered to be zero because the amount of it produced by the self-ionization of water is negligibly small (0.0000001 *M*) compared with the amount that is produced by the dissolved acid.

	$HCl + H_2O \longrightarrow$	H_3O^+ +	Cl^-
Original:	0.1	0	0
Final:	0	0.1	0.1

Since every HCl molecule ionizes, the final concentration of H_3O^+ is the same as the original concentration of HCl. Now we can calculate the pH of this solution.

$$[H^+] = 0.1 = 10^{-1}$$

$$pH = -\log 10^{-1} = -(-1) = 1$$

To calculate the pH of a 0.1 *M* solution of the strong base KOH we write the acid-base reaction, in which every OH^- present accepts a proton from H_2O:

	$(K^+) + OH^- + H_2O \longrightarrow (K^+) + H_2O +$	OH^-
Original:	0.1	0
Final:	0	0.1

Thus the final concentration of OH^- is 0.1 *M*. Since we know $[OH^-]$ but not $[H^+]$, we cannot calculate pH directly. However, the water constant K_w can be used to calculate $[H^+]$:

$$K_w = 1.0 \times 10^{-14} = [H^+]\,[OH^-]$$

$$[OH^-] = 0.1 = 10^{-1}$$

$$[H^+] = \frac{10^{-14}}{10^{-1}} = 10^{-13}$$

To calculate the pH:

$$pH = -\log 10^{-13} = -(-13) = 13$$

There is another approach we can use to calculate pH given $[OH^-]$. The quantity pOH can be defined in a manner analogous to the definition of pH. That is,

$$pOH = -\log\,[OH^-]$$

The sum of pH and pOH is 14:

$$pH + pOH = 14$$

From $[OH^-]$ we can find pOH and from the equation above, pH. Rewriting the example above this way, we find

$$[OH^-] = 10^{-1}$$

$$pOH = -\log 10^{-1} = -(-1) = 1$$

$$pH = 14 - pOH = 14 - 1 = 13$$

In general, p(quantity) = − log(quantity), a notation commonly used to give values which are expressed as exponentials. For instance, p*K* values are often quoted for K_a and K_b, as you can see in Tables 11.5 and 11.6.

SAMPLE EXERCISE 11.6

Calculate the pH of a 0.2 *M* solution of nitric acid.

Solution:

From looking at Table 11.4 we see that HNO_3 is a strong acid and ionizes completely.

	$HNO_3 + H_2O \longrightarrow$	H_3O^+	$+\ NO_3^-$
Original:	0.2	0	0
Final:	0	0.2	0.2

$$[H^+] = 0.2 = 2 \times 10^{-1}$$

$$pH = -\log (2 \times 10^{-1}) = -\log 2 - \log 10^{-1}$$

$$= -0.3 - (-1) = 0.7$$

EXERCISE 11.6

What is the pH of a cough syrup base that is prepared from a 0.15 *M* solution of hydroiodic acid (an expectorant)?

SAMPLE EXERCISE 11.7

Find the pH of a 0.03 *M* solution of NaOH.

Solution:

NaOH is listed as a strong base in Table 11.4 and is 100 percent ionized.

	$(Na^+) + OH^- + H_2O \longrightarrow$	$(Na^+) + OH^- + H_2O$
Original:	0.08	0
Final:	0	0.08

$$[OH^-] = 0.08 = 8 \times 10^{-2}$$

$$pOH = -\log (8 \times 10^{-2}) = -\log 8 - \log 10^{-2} = -0.9 - (-2) = 1.1$$

$$pH + pOH = 14$$

$$pH = 14 - 1.1 = 12.9$$

EXERCISE 11.7

Find the pH of a solution prepared by adding 0.5 mol KOH to enough water to make 1 L of solution.

Weak Acids and Bases

Weak acids and bases do not ionize 100 percent, and thus the equilibrium constants K_a and K_b must be introduced to find the pH of their solutions. For instance, it is possible to calculate the H^+ concentration of a 0.1 *M* solution of HAc by using its ionization constant, listed in Table 11.5. We will not do the calculation here, but let us compare the calculated $[H^+]$ and pH of a 0.1 *M* HAc solution with those obtained above for the 0.1 *M* solution of the strong acid HCl. The $[H^+]$ of a 0.1 *M* HAc solution is found to be 0.0013 *M*, much less than the 0.1

Other abbreviations for acetic acid (HAc) are HOAc and AcOH.

M we calculated for the HCl solution. The pH of the HAc solution is 2.9. Note that the pH of a 0.1 *M* HCl solution is 1.

The lower the pH, the greater the acidity.

HCl is a strong acid, which ionizes completely as compared with HAc and thus a given HCl solution has a lower pH than an HAc solution of the same concentration.

11.10 MEASURING pH

In the laboratory several different methods are used to determine pH values depending upon the accuracy needed. For very crude measurements pH paper indicators may do, but for more accurate values pH meters and titration techniques are necessary.

pH Paper

In Section 11.2 we mentioned that the indicator litmus turns red in acidic solutions and blue in basic solutions. Nature abounds with many other indicators. The extracts from red cabbage, beets, grapes, colorful autumn leaves, and the petals of a sunflower all change color when their acidity changes. In fact, efforts to use some of these colorings as natural food dyes have been hampered by their sensitivities to the pH of their surroundings. Chemists turn this sensitivity to good use by testing for the pH of solutions with indicators.

A qualitative pH measurement can be made by dipping dye-coated papers into solutions. The dyes are indicators, which are themselves acids or bases. Suppose the indicator is an acid (HInd), which ionizes to form the conjugate base Ind^- and H_3O^+:

$$HInd + H_2O \rightleftharpoons Ind^- + H_3O^+$$

For this indicator to be useful as a visual method for determining pH, the color of HInd must be distinctly different from that of Ind^-. For each indicator equilibrium reaction such as the one above, there will be a pH or a pH range in which the color changes as the equilibrium shifts one way or the other. The $[H^+]$ at which this happens can be determined so that a color change indicates a known pH range. Some pH ranges determined in this way are very broad. For example, litmus-coated papers can do no better than distinguish between acidic and basic solutions by turning red when the pH is less than 7 and blue when the pH is greater than 7. Other, more accurate, papers respond within very narrow pH ranges and can fix the pH to within 1 or even $\frac{1}{2}$ of a pH unit. Papers coated with various dyes each of which change color in given pH ranges are called universal pH papers. Color Plate 12*a* shows a color chart for a universal indicator solution that is able to detect pH values between 4 and 10. In Color Plate 12*b* you can

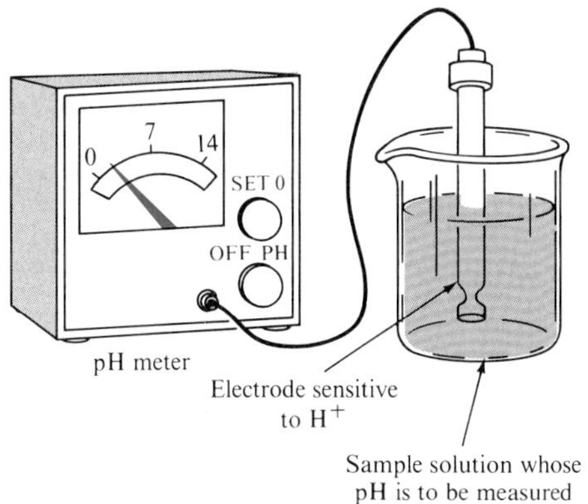

FIGURE 11.4
pH meter. The electrode dipping into the sample is sensitive to pH. The other electrode needed to complete the circuit is inside the pH meter. According to the reading on the dial, the pH of the sample is 2.0.

see the results obtained when a few drops of this indicator are added to several sample solutions. The advantage of testing for pH by using pH papers or indicator solutions is the ease with which such tests can be performed without carrying around any cumbersome equipment. Unfortunately, these tests are not accurate enough for many measurements.

pH Meters

One application in which accurate pH measurements are needed is testing the pH of blood. Normal blood pH lies in a narrow range from 7.36 to 7.44 and thus requires pH measurements which are accurate at least in the first decimal place in order to detect dangerous acid-base imbalance in the blood. An electronic device called a pH meter can be used to obtain a pH reading that is accurate to within 0.01 pH unit in less than 1 min. (See Figure 11.4 for a diagram of a typical pH meter.)

11.11 TITRATION

Titration is a method that is used to determine the concentration of a substance in a given solution sample by allowing the unknown sample to react completely with a solution that has a known concentration. The solution with the known concentration is called a *standard solution*. Titration is a particularly useful method of measuring acidity since acids can be completely neutralized by bases, and vice versa (see Section 11.2). For instance, suppose we want to find the concentration of a sample of HCl solution. A standard solution of NaOH can be added to the HCl solution of unknown concentration until all the HCl has been neutralized. This is called the *equivalence point*. Figure 11.5 shows a titration apparatus in which a standard base solution is added to an acid solution of unknown concentration. A burette designed to deliver accurate volumes is used to hold the standard solution, which is added carefully until neutralization is complete. To-

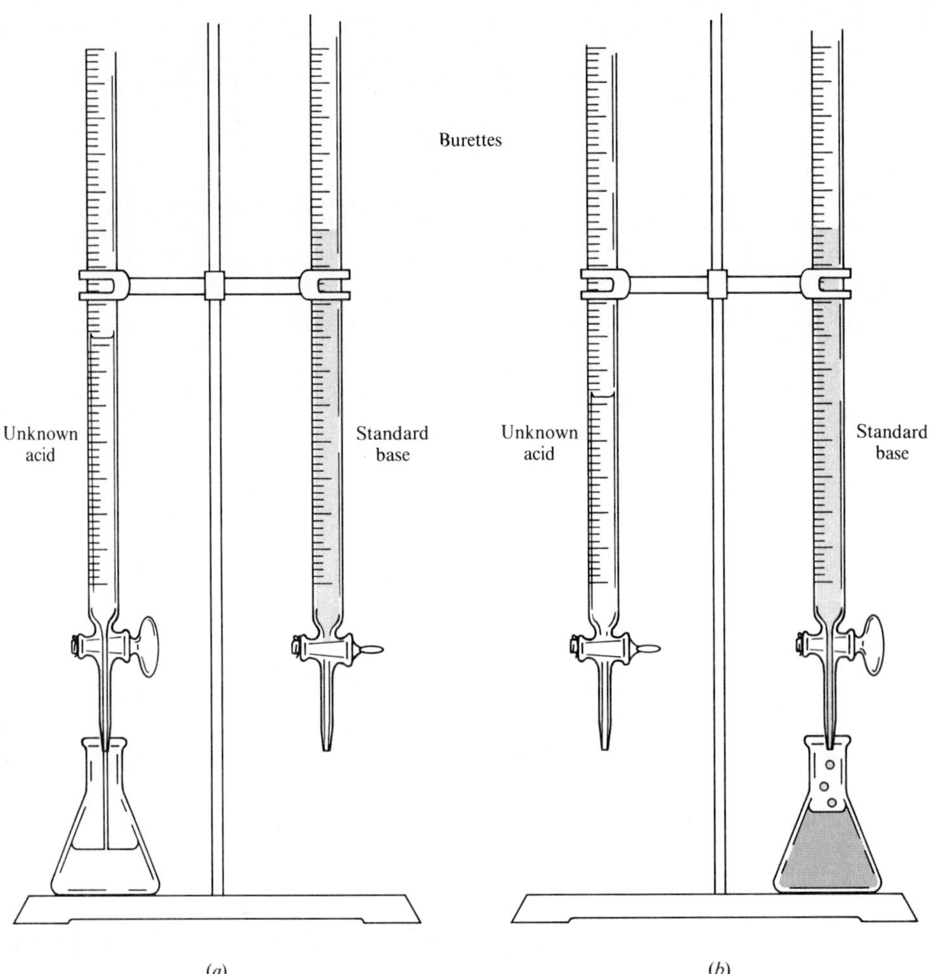

FIGURE 11.5
(*a*) Measure out a volume of acid. (*b*) Titrate with base to the faint pink endpoint color of phenolphthalein. (shown in Color Plate 13)

ward the end of the titration the solution must be added dropwise so that the equivalence point will not be missed.

Indicators

How does the titrator recognize that neutralization is achieved and the equivalence point has been reached? For titrations to be of any practical value there must be some way for the equivalence point to be detected. Indicators are selected that change color near the equivalence point. (It is possible to estimate the equivalence point for most titrations.) In a titration the point at which an indicator changes color is called the *endpoint* of the titration. Ideally, the endpoint and the equivalence point should be the same.

For the titration of HCl with NaOH, the equivalence point will occur at a pH of 7, since the products of the titration, NaCl and H_2O, form a neutral solution. However, as this titration proceeds with the addition of standard base, an abrupt pH change begins at a pH of 4 and increases steeply to a pH of about

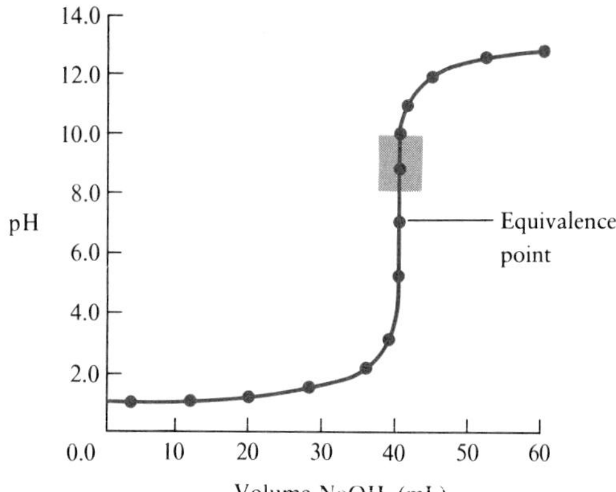

FIGURE 11.6
When about 40-ml of NaOH has been added, pH rises sharply. The colored area marks the sensitivity range of phenolphthalein indicator.

10 with the addition of less than a single drop of standard base, which means that the volume of standard base added is essentially the same anywhere within this 6-unit pH range. Figure 11.6 shows a *titration curve* in which the volume of standard NaOH added is plotted against the pH of the unknown solution. The midpoint of the sharp, vertical rise in pH marks the *equivalence point*, as shown in the figure. However, the indicator chosen for this titration does not have to change color at a pH of exactly 7 or even in a range that includes 7. The *endpoint* of the titration can be anywhere within the range covered by the vertical rise in the titration curve and so an indicator which changes color within this range is a suitable one for this titration. Phenolphthalein is often used for strong acid versus strong base titrations because it changes from colorless in acid solution to a purplish red at pH values of about 8 to 10. This is within the 4 to 10 pH range at which neutralization takes place. The phenolphthalein endpoint is very close to the equivalence point. In titrating HCl with NaOH a few drops of phenolphthalein indicator is added to the acid solution. The endpoint of the titration is revealed when the colorless HCl solution turns a pale purplish red color at the point at which the HCl is completely neutralized, as shown in Color Plate 13. Phenolphthalein is a particularly good indicator to use for this titration because the sudden appearance of color is easy for the eye to detect.

•

Titrations and Calculations

Once the correct volume of a standard base needed to neutralize an unknown acid solution has been experimentally determined, the pH of the unknown acid solution can be found. The number of moles of standard base used can be calculated from the molarity of the standard solution and its volume, as was done in Section 9.6. At the equivalence point the number of moles of HCl and of NaOH must be the same, as we can see by looking at the equation for this reaction.

$$NaOH + HCl \longrightarrow NaCl + H_2O$$

According to the stoichiometry of this equation, 1 mol NaOH reacts exactly with 1 mol HCl. For instance, suppose it takes 25 ml of a 0.4 *M* NaOH solution to reach the equivalence point in a titration of 100 ml of an HCl sample. To find the concentration of the HCl solution, we must first calculate the number of moles of NaOH used up, which will be the same as the number of moles of HCl present in the unknown solution.

$$\frac{0.4 \text{ mol NaOH}}{1000 \cancel{\text{ ml solution}}} \times 25 \cancel{\text{ ml solution}} = 0.01 \text{ mol NaOH}$$

Because NaOH and HCl react in a 1:1 ratio, if 0.01 mol NaOH has been used, then 0.01 mol of HCl has been used as well.

0.01 mol NaOH is equivalent to 0.01 mol HCl

Thus the unknown solution must contain 0.01 mol HCl. The volume of the acid solution is 100 ml, or 0.1 L. To calculate the concentration of the unknown solution,

$$\frac{0.01 \text{ mol HCl}}{0.1 \text{ L}} = 0.1\ M \text{ HCl}$$

From this we can readily calculate the pH since HCl is a strong acid.

$$[H^+] = 0.1 = 10^{-1}$$

$$\text{pH} = -(-1) = 1$$

The pH of the unknown HCl solution is 1.

We can use this same approach even if the neutralization equation does not have 1:1 stoichiometry. For instance, suppose it requires 40 ml of 0.10 M NaOH to neutralize 100 ml of a sample of H_2SO_4. The neutralization reaction is

$$2NaOH + H_2SO_4 \longrightarrow Na_2SO_4 + 2H_2O$$

This time it takes 2 mol NaOH to react completely with 1 mol H_2SO_4. To calculate the concentration of the H_2SO_4 sample, we begin by calculating the number of moles of NaOH used up.

$$\frac{0.1 \text{ mol NaOH}}{1000 \cancel{\text{ ml solution}}} \times 40 \cancel{\text{ ml solution}} = 0.004 \text{ mol NaOH}$$

Since 2 mol NaOH reacts with 1 mol H_2SO_4, we can use the conversion factor

$$2 \text{ mol NaOH} = 1 \text{ mol } H_2SO_4$$

$$0.004 \cancel{\text{ mol NaOH}} \times \frac{1 \text{ mol } H_2SO_4}{2 \cancel{\text{ mol NaOH}}} = 0.002 \text{ mol } H_2SO_4$$

To calculate the concentration of the H_2SO_4 solution,

$$\frac{0.002 \text{ mol } H_2SO_4}{0.1 \text{ L}} = 0.02\ M\ H_2SO_4$$

SAMPLE EXERCISE 11.8

Gastric juices include HCl along with other acids. If 50 ml of 0.10 *M* NaOH solution is needed to neutralize the HCl in 100 ml of gastric juices, what is the concentration of HCl present? If the pH of the gastric juices depended only upon the HCl present, what would it be?

Solution:

First we must calculate the number of moles of NaOH used. This will be equal to the number of moles of HCl present.

$$\text{HCl} + \text{NaOH} \longrightarrow \text{NaCl} + \text{H}_2\text{O}$$

$$\frac{0.10 \text{ mol NaOH}}{1 \text{ L solution}} \times 0.050 \text{ L solution} = 0.0050 \text{ mol NaOH}$$

There must be 0.0050 mol HCl present in the 100 ml (0.10 L). The concentration of the HCl solution is

$$\frac{0.0050 \text{ mol HCl}}{0.10 \text{ L}} = 0.050\ M \text{ HCl}$$

$$\text{pH} = -\log (0.050) = -\log (5.0 \times 10^{-2})$$

$$\text{pH} = -\log 5.0 - \log 10^{-2} = -0.70 + 2 = 1.3$$

The pH of the gastric juices would be 1.3 if HCl were the only source of acidity.

EXERCISE 11.8

Suppose it requires 30 ml of 0.050 *M* NaOH to neutralize the HCl present in a 75-ml sample of gastric juice. What is the pH?

11.12 TITRATIONS AND NORMALITY

Any calculation involving titrations *can* be done with the mole concept and the stoichiometry that we used in the previous section. However, you will probably encounter another method in which different terminology is used. Titration as described in the previous section measures the point at which the substance to be titrated is stoichiometrically equivalent to that in the standard solution. Knowing the stoichiometric equivalency between acid and base, that is, the number of moles of acid needed to react with a given number of moles of base, allows us to define another useful quantity, the **gram equivalent weight** (also called an *equivalent*) of an acid or a base. One gram equivalent weight of an acid is the number of grams of acid that donate one mole of H^+ ions. One gram equivalent weight of a base is the number of grams of the base that accepts one mole of H^+ ions.

To find the gram equivalent weight of an acid or a base we must first know the reaction in which it participates. For instance, suppose we wish to determine the gram equivalent weights of NaOH and HCl in the neutralization reaction

$$NaOH + HCl \longrightarrow NaCl + H_2O$$

In this reaction the NaOH accepts one proton and the HCl donates one proton. That is, one mole of NaOH accepts one mole of protons and one mole of HCl donates one mole of protons. Thus the gram equivalent weights of NaOH and HCl are the same as their molar weights.

$$1 \text{ mol HCl} = 36.5 \text{ g HCl}$$

$$1 \text{ gram equivalent weight HCl} = 36.5 \text{ g HCl}$$

and

$$1 \text{ mol NaOH} = 40 \text{ g NaOH}$$

$$1 \text{ gram-equivalent weight NaOH} = 40 \text{ g NaOH}$$

The unit milliequivalent (meq) is often used: 1 meq = 10^{-3} eq.

One gram equivalent weight of HCl, or one equivalent of HCl, weighs 36.5 g and corresponds to one mole of H^+ ions. One equivalent of NaOH weighs 40 g and corresponds to one mole of H^+ ions.

SAMPLE EXERCISE 11.9

Calculate the gram equivalent weights of H_2SO_4 and NaOH according to the neutralization reaction below:

$$H_2SO_4 + 2NaOH \longrightarrow Na_2SO_4 + 2H_2O$$

Solution:

Each NaOH accepts one proton.

$$\text{Equivalent weight NaOH} = \text{molar weight NaOH} = 40 \text{ g NaOH}$$

Each H_2SO_4 donates two protons.

$$\text{Equivalent weight } H_2SO_4 = \frac{\text{molar weight } H_2SO_4}{2}$$

$$= \frac{98 \text{ g } H_2SO_4}{2} = 49 \text{ g } H_2SO_4$$

In other words, only 0.5 mol H_2SO_4 is needed to donate 1 mol protons. One equivalent of NaOH weighs 40 g and one equivalent of H_2SO_4 weighs 49 g.

• •

EXERCISE 11.9

KOH and H_3PO_4 participate in the neutralization reaction below. Find their equivalent weights.

$$3KOH + H_3PO_4 \longrightarrow K_3PO_4 + 3H_2O$$

The equivalent weight of an acid or base is most commonly expressed by a concentration unit called *normality*. **Normality** (N) is the number of equivalents per liter of solution. Knowing the normality of an unknown solution allows $[H^+]$ and the pH to be calculated directly. For instance, suppose we wish to calculate the pH of 30 ml of an unknown acid solution which requires 30 ml 0.01 N NaOH for neutralization. To begin, calculate the number of equivalents (eq) of NaOH used.

$$\frac{0.01 \text{ eq NaOH}}{1000 \text{ \sout{ml solution}}} \times 30 \text{ \sout{ml solution}} = 0.0003 \text{ eq NaOH}$$

Since one equivalent of base reacts with one equivalent of acid, this gives the number of equivalents of acid present.

0.0003 eq NaOH reacts exactly with 0.0003 eq acid

Now we can calculate the normality of the acid:

$$\frac{0.0003 \text{ eq acid}}{0.03 \text{ L solution}} = 0.01\ N \text{ acid}$$

The normality gives the $[H^+]$ since 0.01 eq of acid per liter corresponds to 0.01 mol of H^+ ions per liter.

$$[H^+] = 0.01 = 10^{-2}$$
$$pH = -\log 10^{-2} = -(-2) = 2$$

The pH of this acid solution is 2. Note that it makes no difference what unknown acid is being titrated as long as we know the equivalent weight of NaOH.

Using concentrations expressed in normality makes acid-base titration calculations very straightforward. The number of equivalents of acid and base that react in a neutralization must be the same:

$$eq_{acid} = eq_{base}$$

We can express eq_{acid} and eq_{base} in terms of normality of solution times volume of solution in liters:

$$eq_{acid} = N_{acid} \times V_{acid}$$

$$eq_{base} = N_{base} \times V_{base}$$

Now the expression $eq_{acid} = eq_{base}$ can be rewritten as

$$N_{acid} \times V_{acid} = N_{base} \times V_{base}$$

Any consistent volume units (for V_{acid} and V_{base}) may be used in applying this equation since they will cancel anyway. Let us rework the example above.

$$N_{NaOH} = 0.01 \qquad V_{NaOH} = 30 \text{ ml}$$

$$N_{acid} = ? \qquad V_{acid} = 30 \text{ ml}$$

$$N_{acid} \times V_{acid} = N_{base} \times V_{base}$$

$$N_{acid} \times 30 = 0.01 \times 30$$

$$N_{acid} = \frac{0.01 \times 30}{30} = 0.01$$

Again we see that there must be 0.01 eq acid per liter of solution, 0.01 mol H^+ per liter, and a pH of 2.

SAMPLE EXERCISE 11.10

Urine, which is normally slightly acid (normal range 6 to 7), contains a variety of acids and bases. It is possible to determine the total acidity (that is, $[H^+]$) produced by the acids present by titrating with 0.1 *N* NaOH solution after first removing the basic compounds present. Suppose a 150-ml sample of urine requires 50 ml of 0.1 *N* NaOH solution for neutralization. What was the $[H^+]$ contributed by the acids in the urine?

Solution:

We can calculate N_{acid} from

$$N_{acid} \times V_{acid} = N_{base} \times V_{base}$$

$$N_{acid} = ? \qquad V_{acid} = 150 \text{ ml}$$

$$N_{base} = 0.1 \qquad V_{base} = 50 \text{ ml}$$

$$N_{acid} \times 150 = 0.1 \times 50$$

$$N_{acid} = \frac{0.1 \times 50}{150} = 0.033$$

Thus there must be 0.033 eq of acid per liter, which corresponds to 0.033 mol of H^+ ions per liter. The $[H^+]$ produced by the acids in the urine is 0.033 *M*.

EXERCISE 11.10

A 100-ml sample of unknown acid solution requires 25 ml of 0.2 *N* NaOH to reach the equivalence point in a titration. What is the $[H^+]$ and the pH of the acid solution?

11.13 BUFFERS

Biological catalysts called *enzymes* regulate body chemistry in a narrow range of acidity. Even slight changes in the pH of blood can upset the body chemistry, causing disease or, in cases in which the pH falls below 6.8 or rises above 7.8, death. Many factors affect the pH of body fluids. Acids and bases are taken in by ingestion of acidic or basic foods and by the formation of acidic or basic products of metabolism in the body. Fortunately the body has a built-in mechanism to prevent pH from varying far from normal: body fluids contain *buffers*. **Buffer** solutions resist changes in pH even when mixed with strong acids or strong bases.

Buffer solutions contain an acidic species to react with invading bases and a basic species to react with invading acids. To make a buffer solution, a weak acid is combined with its conjugate base (in the form of a salt of the weak acid). For instance, a typical buffer solution can be prepared from acetic acid (HAc) and sodium acetate (NaAc). By looking at Tables 11.5 and 11.6 you see that the HAc is a weak acid and that Ac^- (from NaAc) is a weak base. The acetic acid can neutralize bases such as NaOH.

$$\text{HAc} + \text{NaOH} \longrightarrow \text{NaAc} + \text{H}_2\text{O}$$

And the acetate can accept protons and neutralize acids such as HCl.

$$\text{Ac}^- + \text{HCl} \longrightarrow \text{HAc} + \text{Cl}^-$$

Buffer solutions can also be made from weak bases and their conjugate acids.

The ability of buffers to resist pH changes is remarkable. We can see how a buffer works by comparing what happens to the pH of water (which has no buffering action) and the pH of a buffer solution upon the addition of strong acid. Suppose we add 0.01 mol HCl to 1 L of water. The pH will plummet from the neutral value of 7 for water to a value of 2. (In doing this calculation we will assume that the volume remains at 1 L even after the HCl sample has been added.)

Now let us see what happens if the same 0.01 mol of HCl is added to a buffer solution prepared by mixing equal concentrations of acetic acid and its salt sodium acetate. Suppose we add 0.01 mol HCl to 1 L of such a buffer made from 0.1 *M* HAc and 0.1 *M* NaAc. The pH of the buffer itself is 4.74, which is the same as the p*K* value for acetic acid, listed in Table 11.6. In fact, for any buffer containing equal concentrations of a weak acid and its salt, the pH is always equal to the p*K* of the weak acid. (We will not show the detailed calculation here.) Upon addition of the HCl sample, the pH does decrease since an acid is being added, but only to 4.65, less than 0.1 pH unit. The sodium acetate in the buffer was able to react with the acid to prevent a drastic pH change. Thus the same amount of acid which caused water to experience a 5-unit drop in pH hardly changed the pH of an equal volume of buffer solution.

The buffer solution is equally resistant to the addition of a base. Adding 0.01 mol NaOH to 1 L of water causes the pH to rise sharply from 7 to 12, compared with a small increase from 4.74 to 4.83 when the same amount of base is added to the buffer solution. This is illustrated in Color Plate 12*c*, where you can compare the colors produced when universal indicator solution is added to pure water (green), to pure water with added NaOH (turns purple), to the buffer solution (red), and to the buffer with added NaOH (stays reddish).

SAMPLE EXERCISE 11.11

Suppose you wished to make a buffer solution containing NH_3. What other compound (besides water) would you need?

Solution:

The conjugate acid of NH_3 is NH_4^+. You would need to use an ammonium salt such as NH_4Cl.

EXERCISE 11.11

What is the pH of a buffer made from 0.2 *M* HAc and 0.2 *M* NaAc?

Bicarbonate Buffer

There are several buffering systems found in body fluids. One of the most important ones is the *bicarbonate buffering system*. The *bicarbonate buffer* consists of the weak acid carbonic acid, H_2CO_3, and its conjugate base, HCO_3^-, in the form of the salt sodium bicarbonate, $NaHCO_3$.

The carbonic acid neutralizes any base by reacting with OH^- ions and the bicarbonate ion neutralizes any acid by reacting with H^+ ions.

$$H_2CO_3 + OH^- \longrightarrow HCO_3^- + H_2O$$

$$HCO_3^- + H^+ \longrightarrow H_2CO_3$$

Note in Table 11.6 that the pK listed for carbonic acid is 6.37, which is about 1 unit away from 7.4, the normal pH of blood. An *equimolar* buffer solution of H_2CO_3 and HCO_3^- would have a pH of 6.37 and thus would not be an effective buffer for blood. However, the bicarbonate system *is* a remarkably effective buffer because in the body the molar concentration of HCO_3^- (0.025 *M*) is about 10 times that of H_2CO_3 (0.0025 *M*), which produces a buffer solution with a pH close to 7.4. The bicarbonate system in the body works remarkably well. If we add to 1 L of blood plasma at a pH of 7.4 the same 0.01 mol of HCl that we added to 1 L of water and to 1 L of acetate buffer, the pH does drop, but only to 7.2.

Bicarbonate buffer is constantly being replenished in the body. Carbon dioxide, a product of normal metabolism, renews the supply of H_2CO_3:

$$CO_2 + H_2O \rightleftharpoons H_2CO_3$$

The respiratory system increases or decreases the rate at which CO_2 is removed from the blood and thus influences the buffer system and the acid-base balance in the blood. Adding CO_2 to the blood shifts the equilibrium above to the right, thus producing more H_2CO_3 and a greater $[H^+]$ in the body fluids (see Section 10.8). Removing CO_2 has the opposite effect. Conversely, the $[H^+]$ in the blood also influences respiration rate. An increase in $[H^+]$ stimulates the respiration rate so that CO_2 can be eliminated, thus driving the equilibrium above to the left and consuming the acid, H_2CO_3.

The chemical buffering system and the respiratory system react quickly to counteract changes in the pH of body fluids but they do not completely restore the proper acid-base balance. The kidneys are needed to bring about complete acid-base balance, which they accomplish by adjusting the rate at which H^+ ions are secreted into the urine. (See Section 9.13, where the function of the kidneys in maintaining proper concentration of ions such as H^+ in body fluids is discussed.)

11.14 ACIDOSIS AND ALKALOSIS

Blood pH values of >7.55 or <7.25 are called "panic values" because they are life-threatening.

The pH of normal blood is 7.4 ± 0.04 pH units. In ***acidosis*** the pH dips below 7.36; in ***alkalosis*** it rises above 7.44. One way in which these conditions can be achieved is through abnormal breathing.

Respiratory Acidosis and Alkalosis

Respiratory acidosis results from inefficient removal of CO_2 from the lungs. The level of CO_2 builds up in the blood, thus driving the equilibrium $CO_2 + H_2O \rightleftharpoons H_2CO_3$ to the right. This produces more H_2CO_3 and increases the acidity of body fluids (see Table 11.8). Such a condition arises from *hypoventilation*, a

TABLE 11.8 ACID-BASE IMBALANCES: $CO_2 + H_2O \rightleftharpoons H_2CO_3$

Condition	pH urine	pCO_2(or H_2CO_3)*	HCO_3^-*
Respiratory acidosis	↓	↑	↑
Metabolic acidosis	↓	↓	↓
Respiratory alkalosis	↑	↓	↓
Metabolic alkalosis	↑	↑	↑

*The changes which lead to each condition are shown in color.

lowered breathing rate associated with respiratory diseases such as emphysema and asthma. The kidneys can eventually compensate for this by eliminating H^+ ions in the urine but not fast enough to prevent some acidosis from occurring during active periods. Treatment consists of correcting the underlying causes of respiratory difficulty.

Respiratory alkalosis is caused by excessive elimination of CO_2 by the lungs, which consumes H_2CO_3 to replenish the supply of CO_2. Such a condition can occur at high altitudes and during extreme emotional anxiety, situations in which abnormally rapid deep breathing, *hyperventilation*, occurs. The urine of individuals with respiratory alkalosis is alkaline and their CO_2 level and H_2CO_3 concentration are reduced (Table 11.8). Again, treatment is designed to correct the respiratory problem. One way to do this is by use of a rebreathing bag, in which the patient rebreathes air, which becomes richer in CO_2 with each breath.

Metabolic Acidosis and Alkalosis

A more serious form of acid-base imbalance comes from abnormal metabolism or accidental ingestion in which excessive amounts of acids or bases are released into the bloodstream. A common example of metabolic acidosis is that in diabetics, who accumulate acidic substances from the metabolism of fats. Another cause of *metabolic acidosis* is reduced HCO_3^- concentration caused by diarrhea. When HCO_3^- is reduced, H_2CO_3 is also reduced to keep HCO_3^-/H_2CO_3 constant (see Table 11.8). Immediate treatment of acute metabolic acidosis requires administration of $NaHCO_3$, followed by efforts to correct the underlying metabolic problem.

Severe cases of acidosis are treated with injection of $NaHCO_3$ and those of alkalosis with NH_4Cl.

Metabolic alkalosis results from an elevated HCO_3^- level, which can be caused by prolonged vomiting or by ingestion of a base. Patients with metabolic alkalosis have alkaline urine and elevated HCO_3^- and CO_2 levels (Table 11.8).

It is possible to use the data listed in Table 11.8 to distinguish among the four types of acid-base imbalances listed above (assuming that the patient is suffering from no more than one of them) by measuring the pH of the urine and the CO_2 or bicarbonate level in the blood. For instance, acidic urine and elevated HCO_3^- or CO_2 indicate respiratory acidosis, while acidic urine and lowered HCO_3^- or CO_2 point to metabolic acidosis.

SUMMARY

The Brönsted-Lowry proton transfer theory defines acids as proton donors and bases as proton acceptors. An acid, HA, donates protons to water molecules to form a hydronium ion H_3O^+ and an anion A^-. The anion is a new base, called the conjugate base, and the hydronium ion is a new acid, the conjugate acid. A base B accepts a proton from water to form a conjugate acid BH and a conjugate base OH^-.

Strong acids or bases are 100 percent ionized. Weak acids and bases are less than 100 percent ionized and exist in equilibrium with the ions they produce. The larger the ionization constant K_a or K_b, the greater the concentrations of ions formed and the stronger the acid or base.

Water ionizes very slightly to form 10^{-7} *M* H^+ and OH^-. The product of $[H^+]$ and $[OH^-]$ is a constant $K_w = 10^{-14}$. Instead of expressing acidity as $[H^+]$, the pH, which is defined as $-\log [H^+]$, is used. In neutral solutions, such as pure water, $[H^+] = [OH^-] = 10^{-7}$ and pH = 7. In acidic solutions, $[H^+] > [OH^-]$, $[H^+] > 10^{-7}$, and pH < 7. In basic or alkaline solutions, $[H^+] < [OH^-]$, $[H^+] < 10^{-7}$, and pH > 7.

In solutions of strong acids or bases, the given concentration of the acid or base allows the pH to be calculated. In solutions of weak bases, the ionization constant as well as the initial concentration must be known.

Indicators containing dyes that change color at specified pH ranges can be used to make crude pH measurements. More accurate measurements such as those needed to measure blood pH require the use of pH meters.

An acid-base titration is performed to find the concentration of an unknown acid (or base) by using a standard (known concentration) solution of base (or acid). The equivalence point of an acid-base titration occurs when the neutralization reaction is complete. The endpoint of the titration is the point at which the indicator changes color.

Concentrations of solutions used in titrations are sometimes expressed in normality (*N*), gram equivalent weights, or equivalents of acid or base per liter of solution. One equivalent of an acid (or base) is the number of grams of acid (or base) that donates (or accepts) one mole of H^+ ions. Normality units are very useful for making titration calculations, since $N_{acid} \times V_{acid} = N_{base} \times V_{base}$.

Buffer solutions resist pH changes upon addition of acids or bases. Buffers can be prepared from a weak acid and its conjugate base, added as a salt, or from a weak base and its conjugate acid, added as a salt. In the body the bicarbonate buffering system works to maintain the pH of blood near 7.4. The HCO_3^- neutralizes acids and the H_2CO_3 neutralizes bases.

In acidosis the pH drops below 7.36 and in alkalosis it rises above 7.44. Respiratory acidosis is caused by reduced ventilation, which thereby increases CO_2, H_2CO_3, and acidity. Respiratory alkalosis is due to increased ventilation, which lowers CO_2, H_2CO_3, and acidity. Metabolic acidosis (from lowered HCO_3^-) and metabolic alkalosis (from increased HCO_3^-) are more serious conditions, which arise from abnormal metabolism.

KEY WORDS

indicator
neutralization
Brönsted-Lowry theory
acid
base
conjugate acid
conjugate base
strong acid
strong base
weak acid
weak base
neutral
acidic
basic
alkaline
logarithm
pH
titration
gram equivalent weight
normality
buffer
acidosis
alkalosis

EXERCISES

11.12 A magician displays four beakers of colorless liquid, one of which is a strong acid solution. After performing a trick which involves taking a sip from beakers selected by a member of the audience, the magician must prove that the fourth beaker does contain the acid. Suggest a chemical reaction that could be used.

11.13 Complete the following reactions:
(a) $Zn(s) + HCl(aq) \longrightarrow$
(b) $H_2SO_4(aq) + K_2CO_3(aq) \longrightarrow$
(c) $KOH(aq) + FeCl_3(aq) \longrightarrow$

11.14 Write equations for the acid-base reactions in which each of the bases below accept protons from water: (a) LiOH; (b) KCN; (c)$CH_3CH_2NH_2$. (In **a** and **b** the Li^+ and K^+ ions do not participate in acid-base reactions.) In each case identify the conjugate acid and base and the conjugate pairs.

11.15 Write equations for the acid-base reactions with water for each of the following compounds or ions. Identify the conjugate acid, conjugate base, and conjugate pairs in each case. Refer to Tables 11.3 to 11.6 to see which are acids and which are bases. (a) HBr; (b) NH_4^+; (c) CH_3NH_2.

11.16 In each of the following decide whether the underlined species is an acid or a base:
(a) $\underline{HPO_4^{2-}} + H_2O \rightleftharpoons H_2PO_4^- + OH^-$
(b) $\underline{HS^-} + H_2O \rightleftharpoons S^{2-} + H_3O^+$
(c) $\underline{CH_3NH_2} + HCl \rightleftharpoons CH_3NH_3Cl$
(d) $\underline{HSO_4^-} + H_2O \rightleftharpoons H_3O^+ + SO_4^{2-}$
(e) $\underline{CH_3NH_3^+} + H_2O \rightleftharpoons CH_3NH_2 + H_3O^+$

11.17 The weak acid butyric acid ($CH_3CH_2CH_2COOH$) is an obnoxious-smelling liquid, which is a constituent of "fat" compounds present in butter and is responsible for the odor of rancid butter.
(a) Write the acid-base reaction for butyric acid in water. (It is the H atom indicated in color, the "acidic" H, that is donated.)
(b) Write the K_a expression for butyric acid.

11.18 Calcium carbonate is the chief component of many commercial antacid tablets. Write the equation that describes how it neutralizes stomach acid.

11.19 Determine the logarithms of the following numbers using Table 11.7: (a) 10; (b) 10^4; (c) 10,000; (d) $\frac{1}{10}$; (e) 0.01; (f) 200; (g) 3000; (h) 0.07; (i) 0.0000008; (j) $\frac{1}{2}$; (k) $10^{-8.5}$; (l) $10^{0.3}$.

11.20 Calculate the pH of solutions which have the following molar H^+ concentrations, $[H^+]$, and decide whether they are neutral, acidic, or basic: (a) 0.1; (b) 0.0001; (c) 0.003; (d) 10^{-8}; (e) 0.000000003; (f) 0.0000001.

11.21 Approximate pH values are given for the fruits listed below. Arrange the fruits from the least acidic to the most acidic. Apples (pH~3); pears (pH~4); lemons (pH ~2).

11.22 Why do you think the pH scale is a more convenient measure of acidity than $[H^+]$?

★11.23 A plaque pH <5.5 is needed to initiate dental caries. Calculate the approximate $[H^+]$ corresponding to this, using Table 11.7. (Plaque is a viscous bacteria-laden film present on the surface of teeth).

11.24 What is meant by the quantity pOH? How is it related to pH?

11.25 Calculate the $[OH^-]$ present in the following solutions:
(a) A solution in which $[H^+]$ is 10^2
(b) A solution with a pH of 4

11.26 Is it possible for a highly acidic aqueous solution to have $[OH^-] = 0$? Explain.

11.27 Calculate the $[H^+]$ and the pH of a solution in which $[OH^-]$ is 0.01.

11.28 Calculate the pH of solutions of: (a) 0.1 *M* HBr (strong acid); (b) 10^{-3} *M* NaOH (strong base).

11.29 The $[OH^-]$ in a sample of "normal" body fluid is 10^{-12}. Is the fluid likely to be: (a) Blood; (b) urine; (c) gastric juice?

11.30 It takes 1 L of 0.100 *M* NaOH solution to neutralize exactly 1 L of HCl solution. Calculate the $[H^+]$ and the pH of the acid solution.

11.31 What is the difference between the equivalence point of a titration and the endpoint?

11.32 The curve pictured below describes a titration of NH_3 with standard HCl solution. Would phenolphthalein be a suitable indicator for this titration? Why?

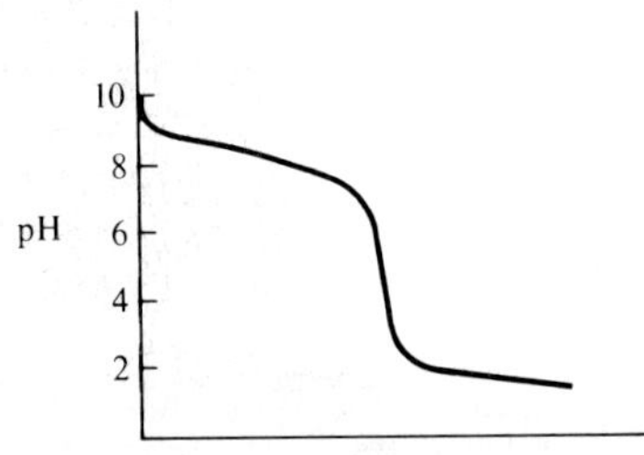

Volume HCl added

11.33 The endpoint of a titration occurs when 40 ml of a 0.01 *M* solution of standard NaOH has been added to 20 ml of an HCl solution of unknown concentration. What is the $[H^+]$ and the pH of the HCl solution?

11.34 It takes 30 ml of 0.10 *N* NaOH to neutralize the acid in a 100-ml acidic solution. Find the $[H^+]$ and pH of this solution.

11.35 What are the gram equivalent weights of the reacting acids and bases in the following neutralization reactions?
(a) $HBr + NaOH \longrightarrow NaBr + H_2O$
(b) $H_2SO_4 + 2KOH \longrightarrow K_2SO_4 + 2H_2O$
(c) $2HCl + Ca(OH)_2 \longrightarrow CaCl_2 + 2H_2O$

11.36 According to their reactions in Exercise 11.35, calculate the number of grams needed to prepare 1 L of 0.1 *N* solutions of the following: (a) HBr; (b) KOH; (c) H_2SO_4.

11.37 If it takes 1 L of 0.1 *M* KOH solution to neutralize 2 L of nitric acid solution, calculate the H^+ and the pH of the nitric acid solution.

11.38 What two general types of components must be present in all buffer solutions?

11.39 What other component would be needed in an aqueous buffer solution containing HCN?

11.40 The pK_a value for hemoglobin (Hb) in venous blood is 7.8. The pK_a value for oxyhemoglobin (HbO_2) in arterial blood is 7.0. Which is the weaker acid?

11.41 A buffer solution contains acetic acid (HAc) and sodium acetate (NaAc). Write equations for the reactions that take place upon adding the following substances to this buffer solution: (a) KOH; (b) HBr.

11.42 When is the pH of an acetic acid–sodium acetate buffer solution identical to the pK value of acetic acid?

11.43 Why are NH_4Cl solutions acidic?

11.44 What are the components of the bicarbonate buffer system?

11.45 Using equations show how the bicarbonate buffer would neutralize added HCl or NaOH.

11.46 How does the body replenish H_2CO_3?

11.47 What is meant by acidosis and alkalosis?

11.48 What is the difference between respiratory acidosis and metabolic acidosis?

11.49 Why does hyperventilation (rapid deep breathing) cause alkalosis?

11.50 Why does hypoventilation (reduced breathing rate) cause acidosis?

11.51 Three blood samples from three different patients have the following concentrations of H^+. Do any of these individuals suffer from acidosis or alkalosis? (a) 3×10^{-7} *M*; (b) 3×10^{-8} *M*; (c) 6×10^{-8} *M*.

11.52 One liter of a KOH solution contains 100 g KOH. What is the normality of the solution?

11.53 A 50-ml ampul contains a solution used in the treatment of acute metabolic acidosis. If the ampul contains 44.6 milliequivalents (meq) of $NaHCO_3$, what is the normality of the solution? How many milligrams of $NaHCO_3$ are present in the ampul?

11.54 Using the universal indicator chart shown in Color Plate 12*a*, give the color of the following solutions, to which a few drops of indicator have been added:
(a) 10^{-5} *M* HCl
(b) 10^{-4} *M* KOH
(c) HAc-NaAc buffer prepared with equal concentrations of HAc and NaAc.

11.55 In cases of severe metabolic alkalosis, chemical neutralization of the excess bicarbonate is possible. Which one of the following salts could be used to do this? (a) NaAc; (b) KCN; (c) NH_4Cl; (d) $CaCO_3$.

12 ALKANES

12.1 INTRODUCTION

In this chapter we begin our study of organic chemistry, a subject which is most often defined as *the chemistry of the compounds of carbon*. Some of the organic carbon compounds that we have discussed are methane (CH_4), ethene (C_2H_4), acetylene (C_2H_2), benzene (C_6H_6), octane (C_8H_{18}), acetic acid (CH_3CO_2H), and ethanol (C_2H_6O); these represent only a few of the 3 million organic compounds known.

The term "organic" was chosen because scientists thought that *organic* compounds could be derived from organic matter (plants and animals) only. *Inorganic*, on the other hand, was used to describe compounds not found in living matter. It was believed that the driving force of life, called the "vital force," was necessary to make organic compounds and that it was therefore impossible to make them in scientific laboratories. In fact, before the year 1828 no scientist had ever been able to synthesize an organic compound starting with one or more inorganic compounds. It was in that year that the vital force theory began to crumble when a German chemist, Friedrich Wöhler (1800–1882), heated an *inorganic* compound, ammonium cyanate, and obtained an *organic* compound, urea.

$$\underset{\text{Ammonium cyanate}}{NH_4NCO} \xrightarrow{\Delta} \underset{\text{Urea}}{H_2N\text{—}\overset{\overset{\displaystyle O}{\|}}{C}\text{—}NH_2}$$

The vital force theory was not completely abandoned until about 1850.

In Wöhler's landmark experiment, urea, a component of urine, was produced in a laboratory vessel instead of the bladder of an animal. This was the first time that an organic compound had been synthesized in the laboratory without the assistance of any vital force.

As more and more organic compounds were made in laboratories, a whole new era of chemistry evolved. The field of modern organic chemistry was born, a field which would provide drugs, building materials, and a host of organic chemicals for use in every area of modern living.

It is important to note that not all carbon-containing compounds are classified as organic compounds. Among the inorganic carbon compounds are several that we have mentioned in the first 11 chapters of this text. The oxides of carbon (CO and CO_2), carbonic acid (H_2CO_3), carbonates ($CaCO_3$ and Na_2CO_3), bicarbonates ($NaHCO_3$), hydrocyanic acid (HCN), and cyanides (NaCN) are considered to be inorganic compounds even though they contain the element carbon.

12.2 UNIQUENESS OF CARBON

The Latin word for "chain" is *catena.*

The reason that there are so many possible organic compounds is that the carbon atom has unique bonding characteristics, being able to form long chains by bonding to other carbon atoms. Formation of chains is called *catenation.* Some other group IVA elements can also form chains, although they are very short and much less stable than carbon chains. Silicon, for instance, can form chains as long as six atoms

Si—Si—Si—Si—Si—Si

but carbon has an unlimited capacity to undergo catenation.

Carbon can form straight chains,

—C—C—C—C—C—C—C—C—C—C—C—C—C—

as well as branched chains,

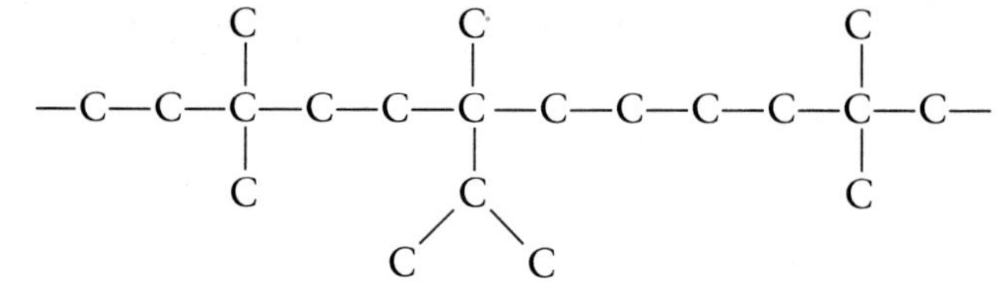

```
          C           C                    C
          |           |                    |
 —C—C—C—C—C—C—C—C—C—C—C—C—
          |           |                    |
          C           C                    C
                     / \
                    C   C
```

and ring structures,

```
     C
    / \
   C   C
   |   |
   C   C
    \ /
     C
```

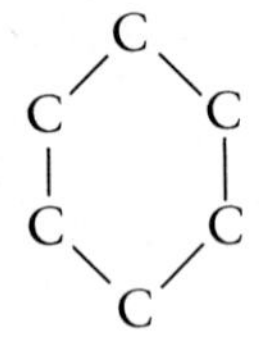

In addition, carbon atoms can form double and triple bonds with other carbon atoms or with nonmetals.

C=C   C≡C   C=O   C≡N

The nonmetallic elements that appear most often in organic compounds are O, N, S, P, the halogens (F, Cl, Br, and I) and H, an element which is present in almost all organic compounds. The **hydrocarbons** are organic compounds consisting of only two elements, C and H. To better study the huge number of possible organic compounds that can form from C and these other elements, organic compounds are organized into classes of compounds which share similar structural features. Even the hydrocarbons are so complex and varied that they must be subdivided into classes. Our study of organic chemistry begins with a class of hydrocarbons called the *alkanes*.

12.3 ALKANES: GENERAL FORMULA

Alkanes are hydrocarbons which contain only single bonds between any two C atoms. All alkanes share the same general formula:

$$C_nH_{2n+2} \qquad \text{General alkane}$$

If we set $n = 1$, the general formula becomes CH_4:

$$C_1H_{(2\times 1)+2} \qquad \text{or} \qquad CH_4$$

TABLE 12.1 FORMULAS AND NAMES OF THE FIRST 20 ALKANES

Molecular formula	Name
CH_4	Methane
C_2H_6	Ethane
C_3H_8	Propane
C_4H_{10}	Butane
C_5H_{12}	Pentane
C_6H_{14}	Hexane
C_7H_{16}	Heptane
C_8H_{18}	Octane
C_9H_{20}	Nonane
$C_{10}H_{22}$	Decane
$C_{11}H_{24}$	Undecane
$C_{12}H_{26}$	Dodecane
$C_{13}H_{28}$	Tridecane
$C_{14}H_{30}$	Tetradecane
$C_{15}H_{32}$	Pentadecane
$C_{16}H_{34}$	Hexadecane
$C_{17}H_{36}$	Heptadecane
$C_{18}H_{38}$	Octadecane
$C_{19}H_{40}$	Nonadecane
$C_{20}H_{42}$	Eicosane

When $n = 2$, the alkane formula generated becomes

$$C_2H_{(2\times 2)+2} \quad \text{or} \quad C_2H_6$$

The molecular formulas of alkanes for which $n = 1$ to $n = 20$ are listed in Table 12.1. Note that each alkane in the table differs from the one nearest to it by one C atom and two H atoms. A series of organic compounds in which adjacent members differ by one repeating unit is called a **homologous series.**

SAMPLE EXERCISE 12.1

Find the molecular formula and the formula weight for the alkane which contains 29 C atoms, a compound found in the leaves of members of the cabbage family.

Solution:

We set $n = 29$ in the general formula for an alkane.

$$C_{29}H_{(2\times 29)+2} \quad \text{or} \quad C_{29}H_{60}$$

To calculate the formula weight,

$$\text{Atomic weight C} = 12.0$$

$$\text{Atomic weight H} = 1.0$$

$$\text{Formula weight} = (29 \times 12.0) + (60 \times 1.0) = 408.0$$

EXERCISE 12.1

The formula for an another alkane present in cabbage leaves includes 64 H atoms. How many C atoms must the formula contain?

The name which corresponds to each alkane formula includes a prefix followed by the ending *-ane*. The prefixes for the first four alkanes are *meth-*, *eth-*, *prop-*, and *but-*:

meth- (1 C)	CH_4	Methane
eth- (2 Cs)	C_2H_6	Ethane
prop- (3 Cs)	C_3H_8	Propane
but- (4 Cs)	C_4H_{10}	Butane

The prefixes for the next six alkanes correspond to the roots of the Greek words for the numbers 5 to 10 and are thus easier to remember:

C_5H_{12}	Pentane
C_6H_{14}	Hexane

C_7H_{16}	Heptane
C_8H_{18}	Octane
C_9H_{20}	Nonane
$C_{10}H_{22}$	Decane

The names for the rest of the first 20 alkanes are listed in Table 12.1.

12.4 THE CARBON ATOM AND BONDING

In Chapter 4 you saw that covalent bonds between nonmetallic atoms result from the overlap of half-filled atomic orbitals (see Section 4.8). To find out how many bonds an atom will form in its compounds we can count the number of electrons in half-filled atomic orbitals. Looking at the electronic configuration for the C atom, we see that there are two orbitals which contain a single electron, that is, there are two half-filled orbitals:

$$1s^2 2s^2 2p_x^{\,1} 2p_y^{\,1}$$

Because each lone (unpaired) electron can pair with a lone electron from another atom, we would expect that C atoms should form two single bonds in their covalent compounds. For instance, C and H would be expected to form a compound CH_2 and C and Cl would be expected to form CCl_2. But this is not what happens. We know that the molecular formula for the singly bonded compound formed between C and H is CH_4 (methane) and that the analogous compound between C and Cl is CCl_4 (carbon tetrachloride). This does not mean that covalent bonding theory has failed in this case; it does mean that the electronic configuration for an isolated, unbonded C atom shown above differs from that for a bonded C atom. The configuration for the bonded C atom actually consists of *four* unpaired electrons, not two. The third and fourth unpaired electrons are produced when one of the paired $2s$ electrons is promoted to a higher energy level.

Promotion

The $2p_z$ orbital in the electronic configuration for an unbonded C atom is empty. It is possible for one of the $2s$ electrons in the C electronic configuration to be raised in energy, that is, **promoted**, so that it occupies a $2p_z$ orbital:

$\uparrow$ $2p_x$ $\uparrow$ $2p_y$ __ $2p_z$		$\uparrow$ $2p_x$ $\uparrow$ $2p_y$ $\uparrow$ $2p_z$
$\uparrow\downarrow$ $2s$	$\xrightarrow{\text{promotion}}$	$\uparrow$ $2s$
$\uparrow\downarrow$ $1s$		$\uparrow\downarrow$ $1s$
$1s^2 2s^2 2p_x^{\,1} 2p_y^{\,1} 2p_z^{\,0}$		$1s^2 2s^1 2p_x^{\,1} 2p_y^{\,1} 2p_z^{\,1}$

Looking at this promoted electronic configuration of carbon, you can see that there are four half-filled orbitals. The four half-filled orbitals can overlap with four other half-filled atomic orbitals to produce four single covalent bonds. This explains why carbon forms compounds such as CH_4 and CCl_4.

However, another discrepancy exists. Experimental data indicate that there is only *one* kind of C—H bond in CH_4, as there is only one kind of C—Cl bond in CCl_4. That is, all C—H bonds in CH_4 are identical and all C—Cl bonds in CCl_4 are identical. But we see that the promoted electronic configuration contains *two* kinds of bonding atomic orbitals. Three of the half-filled orbitals are $2p$ orbitals and the other is a $2s$ orbital. This would suggest that there should be two different kinds of bonds with a C atom, one kind involving overlap with the $2p$ orbitals and the other with the $2s$ orbital. To give an adequate explanation of the bonding in singly bonded C compounds, we must produce an electronic configuration on which all four half-filled atomic orbitals are identical.

Hybridization

Hybridization of atomic orbitals means mixing of atomic orbitals to produce new orbitals called *hybrid orbitals*. In this case we "mix" the $2s$ orbital with the three $2p$ orbitals of C to produce four new *identical* hybrid orbitals:

$$\begin{array}{c} \underline{\uparrow}\ \underline{\uparrow}\ \underline{\uparrow} \\ 2p_x\ 2p_y\ 2p_z \\ \\ \underline{\uparrow} \\ 2s \end{array} \xrightarrow{\text{hybridization}} \begin{array}{cccc} \underline{\uparrow} & \underline{\uparrow} & \underline{\uparrow} & \underline{\uparrow} \\ 2sp^3 & 2sp^3 & 2sp^3 & 2sp^3 \end{array}$$

The newly formed hybrid orbitals are called **sp^3 orbitals** because they are formed from one s orbital and three p orbitals. In this particular case they are called $2sp^3$ orbitals, since they were produced from the mixing of second energy level orbitals.

Now we can rewrite the electronic configuration of the C atom in terms of sp^3 hybrid orbitals:

$$1s^2(2sp^3)^1(2sp^3)^1(2sp^3)^1(2sp^3)^1$$

The C atom is said to be sp^3 hybridized.

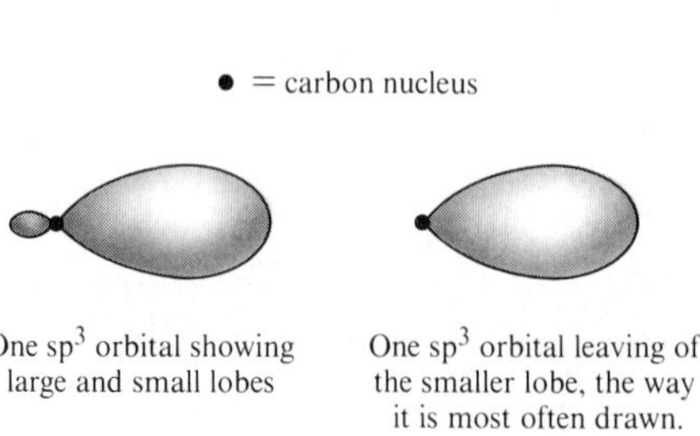

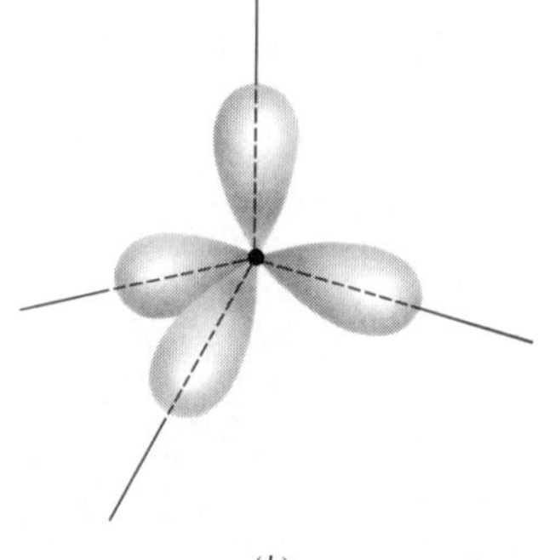

FIGURE 12.1
(*a*) An sp^3 orbital. (*b*) The four sp^3 orbitals of C.

sp^3 hybrid orbitals have both s and p character.

We can describe the hybrid orbitals using pictures to represent the combinations. In Figure 3.8 you saw that *s* orbitals are spherical and *p* orbitals are shaped like dumbbells. The hybrid sp^3 orbitals are shaped like lopsided dumbbells with one lobe of the dumbbell much larger than the other one, although we often omit the smaller lobe when drawing an sp^3 orbital (see Figure 12.1*a*). The four sp^3 orbitals are oriented so that they point toward the corners of a regular tetrahedron, as shown in Figure 12.1*b*.

12.5 BONDING IN ALKANES

Now we can use the sp^3 hybrid orbitals of C to draw the structure of the methane molecule, in which four H atoms are attached to a central C atom. Each H atom has an electron in a spherical 1*s* orbital. The four 1*s* orbitals of the H atoms approach the four sp^3 hybrid orbitals of the central C atom, as shown in Figure 12.2. Each 1*s* orbital of H overlaps with one of the sp^3 hybrid orbitals to form four sigma (σ) bonds (see Section 4.8). In Figure 12.2 the overlap is indicated by the colored regions.

The bonding in all the alkanes is described by use of sp^3 hybridized C atoms. Figure 12.3 illustrates the bonding in ethane, C_2H_6.

Drawing the orbital overlap bonding pictures becomes more and more cumbersome as the molecules get larger and larger. To avoid this we can adopt Lewis electron dot structures (Section 4.9) to describe the bonding in alkanes. In these structures an electron dot pair represents the overlap of two atomic orbitals to form single bonds. The number of valence electrons is the same as the group number of a representative element and so for carbon (group IVA) there are *four* valence electrons.

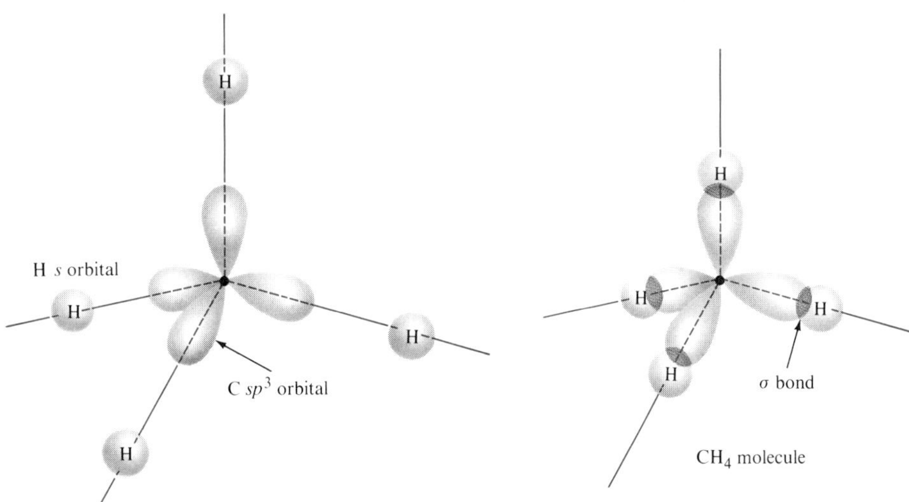

FIGURE 12.2
Bonding in methane.

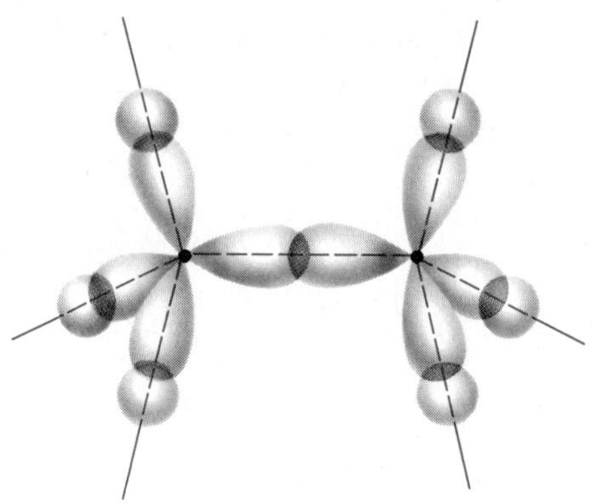

FIGURE 12.3
Bonding in ethane.

C forms four bonds in its compounds.

Thus C needs four electrons to complete its octet and forms four bonds in its compounds.

In the electron dot structure for methane, C must be the central atom and must form four single bonds with the four H atoms. The eight valence electrons (four from the C atom and four from the H atoms) are distributed to satisfy the octet rule.

$$\begin{array}{c} \mathrm{H} \\ \mathrm{H}:\overset{\cdot\cdot}{\underset{\cdot\cdot}{\mathrm{C}}}:\mathrm{H} \\ \mathrm{H} \end{array} \quad \text{or} \quad \begin{array}{c} \mathrm{H} \\ | \\ \mathrm{H{-}C{-}H} \\ | \\ \mathrm{H} \end{array}$$

In most of the organic structures we write, the covalent bonds will be shown as dashes instead of dots.

In ethane (C_2H_6) each of the two C atoms must form four bonds, one with each other and three with H atoms. The 14 valence electrons (8 from the C atoms and 6 from the H atoms) are distributed so that the octet rule is obeyed:

$$\begin{array}{c} \mathrm{H\ H} \\ \mathrm{H}:\overset{\cdot\cdot}{\underset{\cdot\cdot}{\mathrm{C}}}:\overset{\cdot\cdot}{\underset{\cdot\cdot}{\mathrm{C}}}:\mathrm{H} \\ \mathrm{H\ H} \end{array} \quad \text{or} \quad \begin{array}{c} \mathrm{H\quad H} \\ |\quad\ | \\ \mathrm{H{-}C{-}C{-}H} \\ |\quad\ | \\ \mathrm{H\quad H} \end{array}$$

In the previous section we said that the four sp^3 hybrid orbitals of C are arranged so that they each point to the corners of a regular tetrahedron. This agrees exactly with the model derived from the electron dot theory and valence-shell electron pair repulsion (VSEPR) theory. According to the VSEPR theory, compounds in which a central carbon atom is bonded to four other atoms are tetrahedral, which means that the atoms bonded to the C atom point toward the

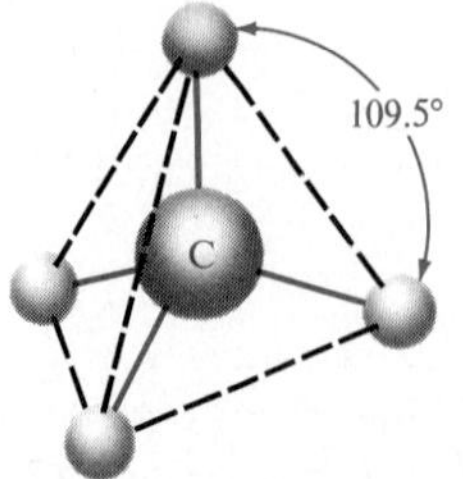

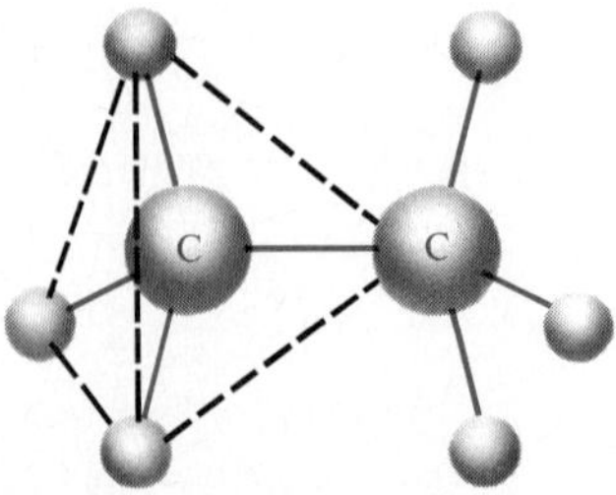

FIGURE 12.4

corners of a regular tetrahedron (see Figure 4.10 to help you in visualizing a tetrahedron). The tetrahedral structures of methane and ethane are shown in Figure 12.4.

SAMPLE EXERCISE 12.2

Draw the electron dot structure for propane.

Solution:

Propane has three C atoms. To find the formula we set $n = 3$ in the general alkane formula:

$$C_3H_{(3\times 2)+2} \quad \text{or} \quad C_3H_8$$

Each of the C atoms forms four bonds with other atoms. The three C atoms are joined to each other. The end C atoms are bonded to three H atoms each and the middle C to only two H atoms. To distribute the 20 valence electrons (12 from the C atoms and 8 from the H atoms),

```
   H H H              H   H   H
   ¨ ¨ ¨              |   |   |
 H:C:C:C:H    or   H—C—C—C—H
   ¨ ¨ ¨              |   |   |
   H H H              H   H   H
```

EXERCISE 12.2

The partial electron dot structure for butane below includes only the four C atoms that are bonded to each other. Complete the structure by adding the H atoms and the remainder of the valence electrons.

C:C:C:C

12.6 STRUCTURAL ISOMERISM

Isomer is derived from *iso-* meaning "equal" and *meros* meaning "part."

Structural isomers are two or more compounds which have the same molecular formula but a different arrangement of atoms. The arrangement of atoms is represented by a formula called the **structural formula.** Thus structural isomers have the same molecular formulas but different structural formulas.

We did not encounter any structural isomerism in inorganic chemistry, where it is not common. The molecular formula for most inorganic compounds represents only one arrangement of atoms. For instance, H and O combine to form water H_2O. In every molecule of water, the O is the central atom, which is connected to two H atoms. The structural formula for water is thus H—O—H. Since the formula H_2O stands for that one arrangement of atoms, we say that it has only one structural isomer. The formula H_2SO_4 corresponds to one structural formula and also corresponds to a single structural isomer.

```
        O
        |
H—O—S—O—H
        |
        O
```

In organic chemistry a molecular formula may correspond to many different arrangements of atoms. For example, the molecular formula C_2H_6O represents two very different compounds, dimethyl ether and ethanol:

```
   H     H                 H  H
   |     |                 |  |
H—C—O—C—H      and     H—C—C—O—H
   |     |                 |  |
   H     H                 H  H
```

Dimethyl ether (C_2H_6O) Ethanol (C_2H_6O)

Structural isomers have different properties.

Ethanol and dimethyl ether are structural isomers because they have the same molecular formulas but different structural formulas. In general, structural isomers have different physical and chemical properties. The boiling point of the dimethyl ether is −23°C, compared with 78.5°C for ethanol. Ethanol is much more reactive chemically than is dimethyl ether. Some properties of ethanol and dimethyl ether are compared in Table 12.2.

Because of structural isomerism the molecular formula is not the best way to represent an organic compound. Structural formulas which indicate how the atoms are connected to each other are necessary.

TABLE 12.2 **COMPARING PROPERTIES OF STRUCTURAL ISOMERS**

	Ethanol	**Dimethyl ether**
Molecular formula	C_2H_6O	C_2H_6O
Structural formula	H—C(H)(H)—C(H)(H)—OH	H—C(H)(H)—O—C(H)(H)—H
Freezing point	−117°C	−138°C
Boiling point	78.5°C	−23°C
Physical state	Liquid	Gas
Reactivity	High	Low

12.7 WRITING STRUCTURAL FORMULAS

As mentioned above, we use dashes to represent covalent bonds in organic structural formulas. But "full" structural formulas, in which all bonds are indicated by dashes, consume a considerable amount of space. To condense the structural formula, the H atoms that are connected to a particular C atom are written to the right of that atom, and a subscript is used to give the number of attached H atoms. The dashes for bonds between C atoms in a chain are often omitted and simply understood. The dashes for bonds between side chains and the main C chain are usually included. For instance, the full organic structural formula shown below can be condensed:

```
    H   H   H   H   H
    |   |   |   |   |
H — C — C — C — C — C — H
    |   |   |   |   |
    H   H   H   |   H
                |
            H — C — H
                |
                H
```

Full structural formula

```
CH3—CH—CH2—CH2—CH3
    |
    CH3

CH3CHCH2CH2CH3
   |
   CH3
```

Condensed structural formulas

The two-dimensional structural formula simply indicates how the atoms are connected to each other to form the molecule. You can see that the structural formulas above do not show that the bond angles in alkanes are tetrahedral. In general, the bond angles in structural formulas need not have any significance. In spite of the fact that they are drawn with different bond angles, the four structural formulas for butane (C_4H_{10}) shown below all represent one compound in which four C atoms are bonded to each other to form a continuous chain. To prove to yourself that the structures really are the same, you can trace a line through the C—C bonds in each one without lifting your pencil off the page.

```
CH3       CH2            CH3—CH2—CH2
   \     /   \                    |
    CH2       CH3                 CH3

CH3—CH2—CH2—CH3          CH2—CH2
                         |    |
                         CH3  CH3
```

For alkanes with very long C—C chains, it is convenient to shorten the structural formulas by enclosing all CH_2 links in parentheses with a subscript to indicate how many CH_2 links are included. For instance, we can write the structural formula for decane ($C_{10}H_{22}$) in two ways:

$$CH_3CH_2CH_2CH_2CH_2CH_2CH_2CH_2CH_2CH_3 \quad \text{or} \quad CH_3(CH_2)_8CH_3$$

Model sets are very useful in helping to visualize the atoms and bonds in organic molecules. Three different models of the ethanol molecule, CH_3CH_2OH, are shown in Figure 12.5.

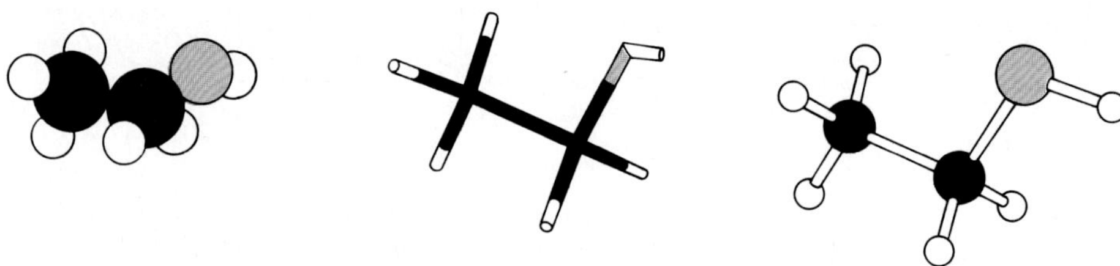

FIGURE 12.5
Model sets. Each model represents CH_3CH_2OH, ethanol. The C's are black, the H's are white and the O's are in color.

SAMPLE EXERCISE 12.3

Write the molecular formula and the condensed formula that correspond to the full alkane formula below.

```
          H                   H
          |                   |
       H—C—H               H—C—H
          |                   |
    H     |   H   H   H   H   |   H   H   H
    |     |   |   |   |   |   |   |   |   |
 H— C  —  C — C — C — C — C — C — C — C — C—H
    |     |   |   |   |   |   |   |   |   |
    H     H   |   H   H   H   |   H   H   H
              |               |
           H—C—H           H—C—H
              |               |
              H               H
```

Solution:

To write the molecular formula count the number of C atoms and use the general alkane formula to find the number of H atoms (or count them). There are 14 C atoms and thus there must be 30 H atoms ($[2 \times 14] + 2$). The molecular formula is $C_{14}H_{30}$.

To write the condensed structural formula we count the H atoms attached to each C atom in the structure and write them next to the atom to which they are attached. The leftmost C above is attached to three H atoms, the next C to the right is attached to one H and to one CH_3 group, and so on.

```
        CH3                                   CH3
        |                                     |
CH3—CH—CH—CH2—CH2—CH2—C—CH2—CH2—CH3
             |                        |
            CH3                      CH3
```

$$
\begin{array}{l}
\quad\;\; CH_3 \qquad\qquad\qquad\qquad\qquad\qquad\quad CH_3 \\
CH_3-CH-CH-CH_2-CH_2-CH_2-C-CH_2-CH_2-CH_3 \\
\qquad\qquad\; CH_3 \qquad\qquad\qquad\qquad\qquad\quad CH_3
\end{array}
$$

We could also have written this formula without using the horizontal dashes. Note how much more information about the structure of this compound there is in any form of the structural formula than in the molecular formula.

EXERCISE 12.3

Give the molecular formula and the full formula that corresponds to the condensed formula for the alkane below, a compound that is used as a standard for gasoline performance.

$$\begin{array}{c} CH_3 \\ | \\ CH_3-C-CH_2CHCH_3 \\ || \\ CH_3CH_3 \end{array}$$

12.8 STRUCTURAL ISOMERS OF ALKANES

All alkanes that have more than three C atoms have at least two structural isomers. To see why this is so we can look carefully at the possible arrangements of the C and H atoms in the first five alkanes.

Methane, CH_4

In CH_4 the central C atom forms four single bonds with four H atoms.

$$CH_4 \qquad \begin{array}{c} H \\ | \\ H-C-H \\ | \\ H \end{array} \qquad CH_4 \qquad (1)$$

Molecular formula — Full structural formula — Condensed structural formula

This is the only way in which these five atoms can be arranged; thus methane has only one possible structural formula. We say that CH_4 has one structural isomer.

Ethane, C_2H_6

Only one arrangement of the eight atoms of ethane (two C atoms and six H atoms) is possible. The C atoms must be joined to each other and each must be attached to three H atoms.

$$C_2H_6 \qquad \begin{array}{c} H\ \ H \\ |\ \ \ | \\ H-C-C-H \\ |\ \ \ | \\ H\ \ H \end{array} \qquad CH_3CH_3 \qquad (1)$$

Molecular formula — Full structural formula — Condensed structural formula

There is only one structural isomer corresponding to C_2H_6, ethane.

Propane, C_3H_8

As we saw in Sample Exercise 12.2, there is only one way to arrange the three C atoms and the eight H atoms of C_3H_8.

$$\underset{\text{Molecular formula}}{C_3H_8} \qquad \underset{\text{Full structural formula}}{\text{H}-\overset{\overset{\text{H}}{|}}{\underset{\underset{\text{H}}{|}}{\text{C}}}-\overset{\overset{\text{H}}{|}}{\underset{\underset{\text{H}}{|}}{\text{C}}}-\overset{\overset{\text{H}}{|}}{\underset{\underset{\text{H}}{|}}{\text{C}}}-\text{H}} \qquad \underset{\text{Condensed structural formula}}{CH_3CH_2CH_3} \qquad (1)$$

Thus there is only a single structural isomer for C_3H_8, propane.

Butane, C_4H_{10}

Butane, C_4H_{10}, is the first member of the alkane series to have more than one structural isomer. There are two different ways to arrange the 4 C atoms and the 10 H atoms in C_4H_{10}. The 4 C atoms can be connected to form a C—C—C—C chain (as in Exercise 12.3):

$$\underset{\text{Molecular formula}}{C_4H_{10}} \qquad \underset{\text{Full structural formula}}{\text{H}-\overset{\overset{\text{H}}{|}}{\underset{\underset{\text{H}}{|}}{\text{C}}}-\overset{\overset{\text{H}}{|}}{\underset{\underset{\text{H}}{|}}{\text{C}}}-\overset{\overset{\text{H}}{|}}{\underset{\underset{\text{H}}{|}}{\text{C}}}-\overset{\overset{\text{H}}{|}}{\underset{\underset{\text{H}}{|}}{\text{C}}}-\text{H}} \qquad \underset{\text{Condensed structural formula}}{CH_3CH_2CH_2CH_3} \qquad (1)$$

This form of any alkane is often called the **straight-chain** form. The term "straight" means that all the C atoms are attached to each other to form a continuous chain with no branches. Because the bond angles are all tetrahedral (109.5°), the chain is actually zigzag, not straight, as you can see from looking at Figure 12.6.

Another way to arrange the 14 atoms in C_4H_{10} is to form a C—C—C chain with three C atoms and then bond the fourth C atom to the middle atom of the chain to form a **branched chain**:

$$\underset{\text{Molecular formula}}{C_4H_{10}} \qquad \underset{\text{Full structural formula}}{\text{H}-\overset{\overset{\text{H}}{|}}{\underset{\underset{\text{H}}{|}}{\text{C}}}-\overset{\overset{\text{H}}{|}}{\underset{\underset{\text{H}-\underset{\underset{\text{H}}{|}}{\text{C}}-\text{H}}{|}}{\text{C}}}-\overset{\overset{\text{H}}{|}}{\underset{\underset{\text{H}}{|}}{\text{C}}}-\text{H}} \qquad \underset{\text{Condensed structural formula}}{CH_3\underset{\underset{CH_3}{|}}{C}HCH_3}$$

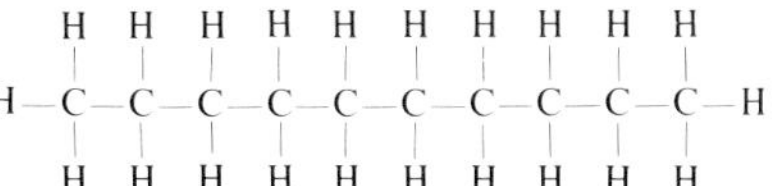

(a)

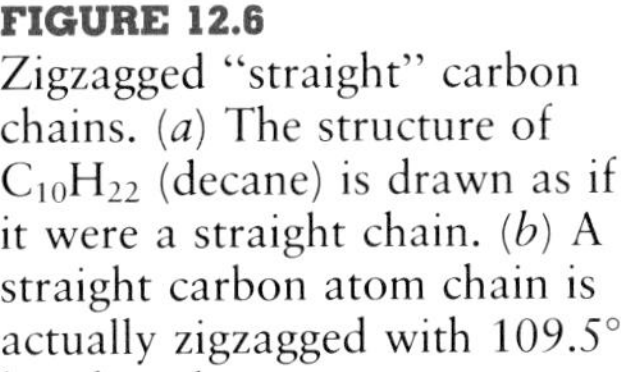

FIGURE 12.6
Zigzagged "straight" carbon chains. (*a*) The structure of $C_{10}H_{22}$ (decane) is drawn as if it were a straight chain. (*b*) A straight carbon atom chain is actually zigzagged with 109.5° bond angles.

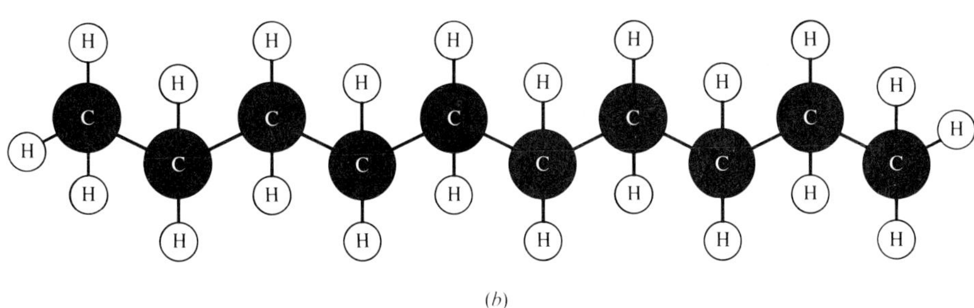

(b)

We see that there are two possible arrangements of the atoms in C_4H_{10}, and thus two structural isomers are possible for butane. Structures of the straight-chain and the branched butane isomers are shown in Figure 12.7.

Pentane, C_5H_{12}

There is a systematic way in which we can list all the different structural isomers of a particular alkane. First start with the straight-chain compound. Next shorten the chain by one C atom and write structural formulas for all the branched isomers with this chain length. Continue making shorter chains until all possible combinations of the available atoms have been exhausted. Let us apply this method to find all the structural isomers of pentane.

C_4H_{10} $\quad CH_3CH_2CH_2CH_3$

C_4H_{10} $\quad CH_3CHCH_3$ (with CH_3 branch on the middle C)

FIGURE 12.7
Structural isomers of butane.

$$
C_5H_{12} \qquad
\begin{array}{ccccccccccc}
 & & H & & H & & H & & H & & H \\
 & & | & & | & & | & & | & & | \\
H & - & C & - & C & - & C & - & C & - & C & - & H \\
 & & | & & | & & | & & | & & | \\
 & & H & & H & & H & & H & & H
\end{array}
\qquad CH_3CH_2CH_2CH_2CH_3 \qquad (1)
$$

Molecular formula — Full structural formula — Condensed structural formula

Next we see how many isomers we can draw with a C—C—C—C chain. There is one isomer with a CH_3 attached to the next to last C atom in this chain.

$$
C_5H_{12} \qquad
\begin{array}{ccccccccccc}
 & & H & & H & & H & & H & & \\
 & & | & & | & & | & & | & & \\
H & - & C & - & C & - & C & - & C & - & H \\
 & & | & & | & & | & & | & & \\
 & & H & & | & & H & & H & & \\
 & & & & | & & & & & & \\
 & & H & - & C & - & H & & & & \\
 & & & & | & & & & & & \\
 & & & & H & & & & & &
\end{array}
\qquad
\begin{array}{l}
CH_3CHCH_2CH_3 \\
\quad\;\; | \\
\quad CH_3
\end{array}
\qquad (2)
$$

Molecular formula — Full structural formula — Condensed structural formula

Finally there is one more structural isomer of pentane in which a C—C—C chain forms the backbone of the molecule. The other two C atoms branch off from the center C atom of the chain:

$$
C_5H_{12} \qquad
\begin{array}{ccccccccc}
 & & & & H & & & & \\
 & & & & | & & & & \\
 & & H & - & C & - & H & & \\
 & & & & | & & & & \\
 & & H & & | & & H & & \\
 & & | & & | & & | & & \\
H & - & C & - & C & - & C & - & H \\
 & & | & & | & & | & & \\
 & & H & & | & & H & & \\
 & & & & | & & & & \\
 & & H & - & C & - & H & & \\
 & & & & | & & & & \\
 & & & & H & & & &
\end{array}
\qquad
\begin{array}{ccccc}
 & & CH_3 & & \\
 & & | & & \\
CH_3 & - & C & - & CH_3 \\
 & & | & & \\
 & & CH_3 & &
\end{array}
\qquad (3)
$$

Molecular formula — Full structural formula — Condensed structural formula

There is no other way to arrange the 17 atoms in pentane to form a structure which is truly different from the three already given. Some which may seem to be different are revealed to be the same if closely examined. For instance, the two structures below are not different from the ones already listed.

$$
\begin{array}{l}
CH_3CH_2CHCH_2 \\
\qquad\quad\;\; | \\
\qquad\quad CH_3
\end{array}
\qquad
\begin{array}{l}
CH_3CH_2CH_2CH_2 \\
\qquad\qquad\quad\; | \\
\qquad\qquad\quad CH_3
\end{array}
$$

The one on the left is identical to isomer 2, the pentane structure with the four-carbon chain; it has simply been "flipped over."

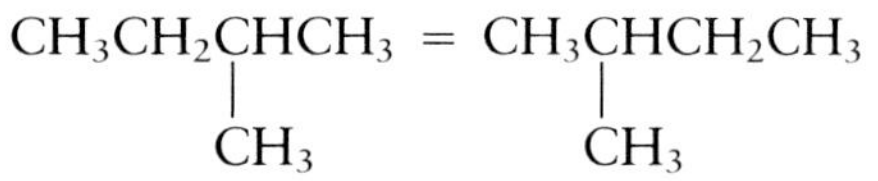

$$CH_3CH_2\underset{\underset{\displaystyle CH_3}{|}}{C}HCH_3 = CH_3\underset{\underset{\displaystyle CH_3}{|}}{C}HCH_2CH_3$$

The other structure is the same as isomer 1, the straight-chain form, because the C atoms are linked one to another to form a continuous five-carbon chain. The fact that one of the C atoms has been drawn as though at an angle to the others is insignificant (see Section 12.7).

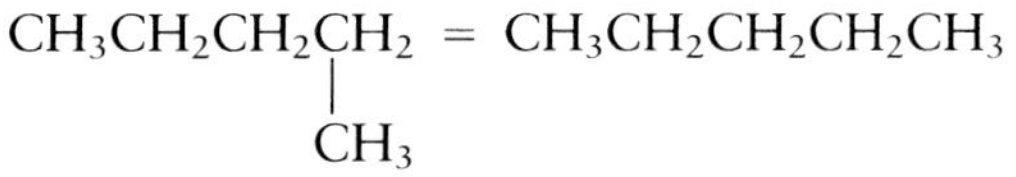

$$CH_3CH_2CH_2\underset{\underset{\displaystyle CH_3}{|}}{C}H_2 = CH_3CH_2CH_2CH_2CH_3$$

Thus we see that C_5H_{12}, pentane, has three structural isomers, pictured in Figure 12.8.

As the number of carbons in an alkane increases, the number of structural isomers possible escalates rapidly. Hexane (C_6H_{14}) has 5 isomers, heptane (C_7H_{16}) has 9, and octane (C_8H_{18}) has 18. The alkane with 20 C atoms ($C_{20}H_{42}$) has 366,319 structural isomers! (Although their structures can be drawn, not all of these isomers have been prepared.) In Table 12.3 the numbers of structural isomers possible for the first 20 alkanes are listed.

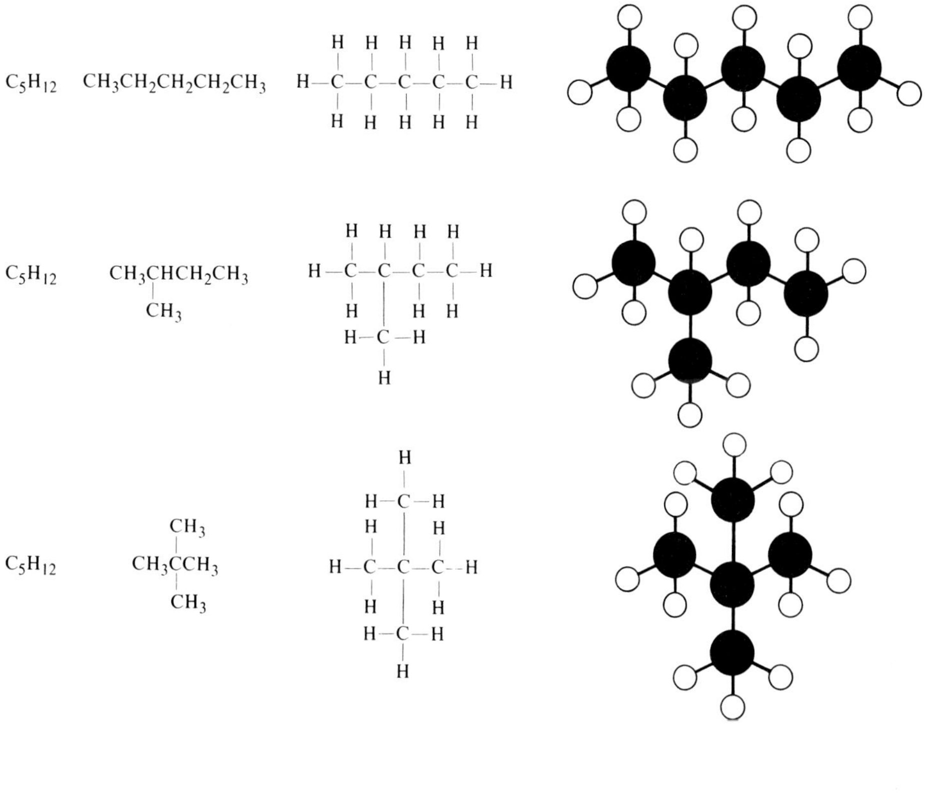

C_5H_{12} $CH_3CH_2CH_2CH_2CH_3$

C_5H_{12} $CH_3\underset{\underset{\displaystyle CH_3}{|}}{C}HCH_2CH_3$

C_5H_{12} $CH_3\overset{\overset{\displaystyle CH_3}{|}}{\underset{\underset{\displaystyle CH_3}{|}}{C}}CH_3$

FIGURE 12.8
Structural isomers of pentane.

TABLE 12.3 NUMBERS OF STRUCTURAL ISOMERS OF ALKANES

Name	Number of C atoms	Molecular formula	Number of structural isomers
Methane	1	CH_4	1
Ethane	2	C_2H_6	1
Propane	3	C_3H_8	1
Butane	4	C_4H_{10}	2
Pentane	5	C_5H_{12}	3
Hexane	6	C_6H_{14}	5
Heptane	7	C_7H_{16}	9
Octane	8	C_8H_{18}	18
Nonane	9	C_9H_{20}	35
Decane	10	$C_{10}H_{22}$	75
Undecane	11	$C_{11}H_{24}$	159
Dodecane	12	$C_{12}H_{26}$	355
Tridecane	13	$C_{13}H_{28}$	802
Tetradecane	14	$C_{14}H_{30}$	1858
Pentadecane	15	$C_{15}H_{32}$	4347
Hexadecane	16	$C_{16}H_{34}$	10,359
Heptadecane	17	$C_{17}H_{36}$	24,895
Octadecane	18	$C_{18}H_{38}$	60,523
Nonadecane	19	$C_{19}H_{40}$	148,284
Eicosane	20	$C_{20}H_{42}$	366,319

SAMPLE EXERCISE 12.4

Draw the structural formulas for the isomers of hexane, C_6H_{14}.

Solution:

We start with the straight-chain form of hexane.

$$CH_3CH_2CH_2CH_2CH_2CH_3 \quad (1)$$

Next we look for isomers with C_5 chains. There are two of these:

$$\underset{\displaystyle CH_3}{CH_3\underset{|}{C}HCH_2CH_2CH_3} \ (2) \quad \text{and} \quad CH_3CH_2\underset{\underset{\displaystyle CH_3}{|}}{C}HCH_2CH_3 \ (3)$$

Now we shorten the longest chain to just four C atoms to produce two more isomers:

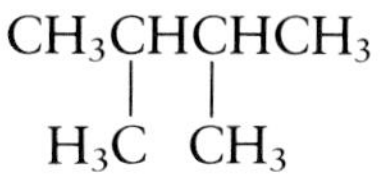

$$\begin{array}{l} CH_3CHCHCH_3 \\ \quad | \quad | \\ H_3C \; CH_3 \end{array} (4) \quad \text{and} \quad CH_3-\overset{\displaystyle CH_3}{\underset{\displaystyle CH_3}{\overset{|}{\underset{|}{C}}}}-CH_2CH_3 \; (5)$$

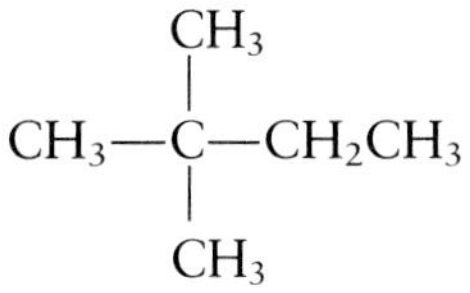

These are the five structural isomers for C_6H_{14}.

EXERCISE 12.4

Of the formulas shown below, which ones represent structural isomers of heptane?

(**a**) $CH_3CH_2CH_2CH_2CH_2CH_3$

(**b**) $CH_3CH_2\underset{\displaystyle CH_3}{\underset{|}{C}}HCH_2CH_2CH_2CH_3$

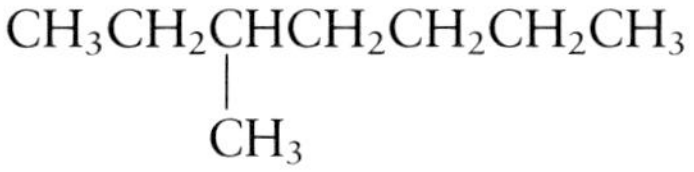

(**c**) $CH_3-\overset{\displaystyle CH_3}{\overset{|}{\underset{\displaystyle H_3C}{\underset{|}{C}}}}-\underset{\displaystyle CH_3}{\underset{|}{C}}HCH_3$

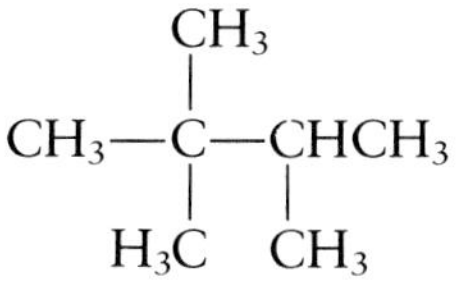

(**d**) $CH_3(CH_2)_5CH_3$

Structural isomers are different compounds and must have different names.

Because of the fact that one molecular formula can represent so many different alkane compounds, the naming system we introduced in Section 12.3 must be refined. Two isomeric compounds with different properties cannot be assigned the same name. Butane, C_4H_{10}, has two different isomers with different properties: the straight-chain form of butane boils at 0.5°C and the branched butane at −12°C; the straight-chain butane has a melting point of −138°C while the branched form melts at −159°C. We cannot call both these compounds "butane."

The IUPAC also recommended the SI unit system.

In 1957 the International Union of Pure and Applied Chemistry (IUPAC, pronounced "eye you pack") adopted the definitive set of rules which apply to the nomenclature of all organic compounds. The IUPAC system for naming alkanes names the branches (side groups) and the longest chain to which they are attached. We have already learned how to name straight-chain alkanes in Section 12.3. Before we can make use of the IUPAC system for naming alkanes, we must also learn how to name attached groups.

12.9 ALKYL GROUPS

The groups of atoms, called **alkyl** groups, which branch off from the main chain of an alkane are derived by removing an H atom from an alkane molecule.

$$\text{Alkane} - \text{H atom} = \text{alkyl group}$$

Alkyl group names are derived from parent alkane names by substituting the suffix *-yl* for *-ane*. The alkyl groups which appear most often as side branches contain either one, two, three, or four carbon atoms. Let us see how they are derived from their parent alkanes.

Methyl

Methyl contains one C atom.

The *methyl* group is derived by removing any H atom from the alkane methane:

$$\begin{array}{c}\text{H}\\ |\\ \text{H—C—H}\\ |\\ \text{H}\\ \text{Methane}\end{array} - \text{H} = \begin{array}{c}\text{H}\\ |\\ \text{H—C—}\\ |\\ \text{H}\\ \text{Methyl}\end{array} \quad \text{or} \quad CH_3\text{—}$$

Ethyl

Ethyl contains two C atoms.

The *ethyl* group is produced by removing any H atom from ethane:

$$\begin{array}{c}\text{H}\ \ \text{H}\\ |\ \ \ |\\ \text{H—C—C—H}\\ |\ \ \ |\\ \text{H}\ \ \text{H}\\ \text{Ethane}\end{array} - \text{H} = \begin{array}{c}\text{H}\ \ \text{H}\\ |\ \ \ |\\ \text{H—C—C—}\\ |\ \ \ |\\ \text{H}\ \ \text{H}\\ \text{Ethyl}\end{array} \quad \text{or} \quad CH_3CH_2\text{—}$$

The formula C_2H_5— is sometimes used instead of CH_3CH_2— to represent the ethyl group.

Propyl

Propyl contains three C atoms.

In methane (and ethane) it did not matter which H atom was removed, since they were all equivalent. However, all the H atoms in propane are *not* the same. The six H atoms attached to the end C atoms are different from the two H atoms (in color below) attached to the middle C atom.

$$\begin{array}{c}\text{H}\ \ \text{H}\ \ \text{H}\\ |\ \ \ |\ \ \ |\\ \text{H—C—C—C—H}\\ |\ \ \ |\ \ \ |\\ \text{H}\ \ \text{H}\ \ \text{H}\end{array}$$

The alkyl group called *propyl* is produced by the removal of any one of the six H atoms attached to an end C atom.

$$\begin{array}{c}\text{H}\ \ \text{H}\ \ \text{H}\\ |\ \ \ |\ \ \ |\\ \text{H—C—C—C—H}\\ |\ \ \ |\ \ \ |\\ \text{H}\ \ \text{H}\ \ \text{H}\\ \text{Propane}\end{array} - \text{an end H} = \begin{array}{c}\text{H}\ \ \text{H}\ \ \text{H}\\ |\ \ \ |\ \ \ |\\ \text{H—C—C—C—}\\ |\ \ \ |\ \ \ |\\ \text{H}\ \ \text{H}\ \ \text{H}\\ \text{Propyl}\end{array} \text{or } CH_3CH_2CH_2\text{—}$$

Isopropyl

The iso*prop*yl group also has three C atoms.

If one of the two H atoms attached to the middle C atom of propane is removed, another three-carbon alkyl group is produced. This one is called *isopropyl.*

Molecular formula	Condensed structural formula	Full structural formula	Three-dimensional structure
CH_3—	CH_3 —	H H—C— H	Methyl
C_2H_5—	CH_3CH_2—	H H H—C—C— H H	Ethyl
C_3H_7—	$CH_3CH_2CH_2$—	H H H H—C—C—C— H H H	*n*-propyl or propyl
C_3H_7—	CH_3CHCH_3 |	H H H H—C—C—C—H H H	isopropyl or 2-propyl
C_4H_9—	$CH_3CH_2CH_2CH_2$—	H H H H H—C—C—C—C— H H H H	*n*-butyl or butyl
C_4H_9—	$CH_3CH_2CHCH_3$ |	H H H H H—C—C—C—C—H H H H	secondary-butyl or *s*-butyl
C_4H_9—	CH_3CHCH_2 CH_3	H H H H—C—C—C— H H H—C—H H	isobutyl
C_4H_9—	CH_3 CH_3C — CH_3	H H—C—H H H—C—C— H H—C—H H	*t*-butyl

FIGURE 12.9
Alkyl groups.

$$\begin{array}{c} \text{H}\ \ \text{H}\ \ \text{H} \\ | \quad | \quad | \\ \text{H—C—C—C—H} \\ | \quad | \quad | \\ \text{H}\ \ \text{H}\ \ \text{H} \end{array} \ - \text{ a middle H} = \begin{array}{c} \text{H}\ \ \text{H}\ \ \text{H} \\ | \quad | \quad | \\ \text{H—C—C—C—H} \\ | \qquad \ \ | \\ \text{H} \qquad \text{H} \end{array} \text{ or } CH_3\underset{|}{C}HCH_3$$

Propane Isopropyl

We can say that the propyl and isopropyl groups are structural isomers since they both have the same formula, C_3H_7—.

Butyl Groups

Butyl groups contain four C atoms.

There are four possible *butyl* groups, C_4H_9—. These are included in Figure 12.9, where all the important alkyl group structures are summarized.

12.10 IUPAC NOMENCLATURE FOR ALKANES

With use of the names methyl, ethyl, propyl, and isopropyl, it is possible to name practically all alkanes by following the IUPAC nomenclature rules. In this system each different alkane has a different name.

Rule I *Choose the longest C to C chain. The name of the alkane with this number of C atoms is the parent alkane name.*

For instance, in the formula below the longest chain has 6 C atoms.

$$CH_3—CH_2—CH_2—\underset{\displaystyle CH_3}{\underset{|}{C}H}—CH_2—CH_3$$

The parent name of this alkane is thus hexane. This is true even though the molecular formula for the compound is C_7H_{16}, a heptane formula.

Rule II *Number the longest C to C chain. Assign the number 1 to the C atom on the end of the chain which is closest to any side branching.*

For example, for the compound shown above, the number 1 is given to the C atom on the right of the longest chain.

$$\overset{6}{C}H_3—\overset{5}{C}H_2—\overset{4}{C}H_2—\underset{\displaystyle CH_3}{\underset{|}{\overset{3}{C}H}}—\overset{2}{C}H_2—\overset{1}{C}H_3$$

The methyl group in color is a branch group because it is attached to the longest chain but is not part of it. The numbering system given in rule II is adopted so that the branch groups are on the C atoms with the lowest possible numbers. With the correct numbering of C atoms, the methyl group is on the carbon in position 3 (C-3). (Incorrect numbering, from left to right, would put the methyl groups on the C-4 atom.)

Rule III *Complete the name by giving the number of the C atom to which a branched group is attached, followed by the name of the group and then by the name of the parent alkane.*

We can now complete the name for the compound in which the branch group methyl is attached to C-3 and the parent name is hexane.

$$\overset{6}{CH_3}-\overset{5}{CH_2}-\overset{4}{CH_2}-\underset{\displaystyle CH_3}{\overset{3}{CH}}-\overset{2}{CH_2}-\overset{1}{CH_3}$$

The full name for this alkane is 3-methylhexane. In IUPAC alkane names, hyphens separate letters from numbers. There is no space between the name of the alkyl group and the parent alkane.

Often more than one alkyl group is attached to the longest chain of an alkane. Rule IIIA applies when the groups are identical.

Rule IIIA *When identical alkyl groups are attached to the longest C chain, use the prefixes* di-, tri-, *and* tetra- *to indicate two, three, and four alkyl groups, respectively.*

For example, to name these two alkanes,

$$\overset{6}{CH_3}-\overset{5}{CH_2}-\overset{4}{CH_2}-\underset{\displaystyle CH_3}{\overset{3}{CH}}-\underset{\displaystyle CH_3}{\overset{2}{CH}}-\overset{1}{CH_3}$$

2,3-*Di*methylhexane

and

$$\overset{6}{CH_3}-\overset{5}{CH_2}-\overset{4}{CH_2}-\overset{3}{CH_2}-\underset{\displaystyle CH_3}{\overset{\displaystyle CH_3}{\overset{2}{C}}}-\overset{1}{CH_3}$$

2,2-*Di*methylhexane

Note that two numbers are separated by commas, and that the number is repeated if both alkyl groups are on the same C atom.

Rule IIIB *When two different alkyl groups are attached, they are listed in either of two ways: (1) alphabetical order; (2) order of "complexity."*

Larger groups are considered to be more complex than smaller ones; thus ethyl is more complex than methyl. Branched groups are taken to be more complex than straight chain groups; thus isopropyl is more complex than propyl.

To name the alkane below we can apply either system:

$$\overset{1}{CH_3}\overset{2}{CH_2}\overset{3}{\underset{\displaystyle CH_3}{\underset{|}{C}}H}\overset{4}{CH_2}\overset{5}{\underset{\displaystyle \underset{\displaystyle CH_3}{\underset{|}{CH_2}}}{\underset{|}{C}}H}\overset{6}{CH_2}\overset{7}{CH_2}\overset{8}{CH_2}\overset{9}{CH_3}$$

More chemists prefer the complexity system.

This alkane can be named either 3-methyl-5-ethylnonane (complexity) or 5-ethyl-3-methylnonane (alphabetical).

SAMPLE EXERCISE 12.5

Name the three isomers of pentane according to the IUPAC rules.

Solution:

$$CH_3CH_2CH_2CH_2CH_3 \quad (1)$$

Pentane

$$CH_3\underset{\displaystyle CH_3}{\underset{|}{C}}HCH_2CH_3 \quad (2)$$

The longest chain is four C atoms long and the numbering starts from the left. The attached group is methyl.

$$\overset{1}{CH_3}\overset{2}{\underset{\displaystyle CH_3}{\underset{|}{C}}H}\overset{3}{CH_2}\overset{4}{CH_3}$$

2-Methylbutane

The longest chain is three C atoms long, the numbering starts from either end, and the attached groups are methyls.

$$CH_3-\underset{\displaystyle CH_3}{\underset{|}{\overset{\displaystyle CH_3}{\overset{|}{C}}}}-CH_3 \quad (3) \qquad \overset{1}{CH_3}-\underset{\displaystyle CH_3}{\underset{|}{\overset{\displaystyle CH_3}{\overset{|}{\overset{2}{C}}}}}-\overset{3}{CH_3}$$

2,2-Dimethylpropane

In the IUPAC system each pentane isomer is assigned a different name.

EXERCISE 12.5

Name the five hexane isomers. (See Sample Exercise 12.4.)

SAMPLE EXERCISE 12.6

Give the IUPAC name for the alkane below. Of what straight-chain alkane is it a structural isomer? (See Table 12.1.)

```
CH3CHCH2CHCH2CH3
   |    |
   CH3  CH2
        |
        CH2
        |
        CH2
        |
        CH3
```

Solution:

The longest C to C chain is eight C atoms long. (Note that the longest chain need not be written horizontally.) The attached groups are methyl and ethyl. Correct numbering puts the methyl on C-2 and the ethyl on C-4.

```
1  2   3  4
CH3CHCH2CHCH2CH3
   |    |
   CH3 5CH2
        |
       6CH2
        |
       7CH2
        |
       8CH3
```

The name is 2-methyl-4-ethyloctane or 4-ethyl-2-methyloctane.

You can count C atoms by inspecting the formula above to find that the molecular formula for this compound is $C_{11}H_{24}$, meaning that it is an isomer of undecane. A quicker way to discover this is to add the number of C atoms in each part of the name:

1 (methyl) + 2 (ethyl) + 8 (octane) = 11 (undecane isomer)

EXERCISE 12.6

Give the IUPAC name for the compound below. This compound (the standard for gasoline performance) is a structural isomer of what straight-chain alkane?

$$\begin{array}{c} CH_3 \\ | \\ CH_3-C-CH_2CHCH_3 \\ |\qquad\quad | \\ CH_3 \quad\; CH_3 \end{array}$$

SAMPLE EXERCISE 12.7

Give the IUPAC name for the following compound:

$$\begin{array}{l} CH_3CH_2CH_2CH_2CHCH_2CH_2CH_3 \\ \qquad\qquad\qquad\quad | \\ \qquad\qquad\qquad\quad CHCH_3 \\ \qquad\qquad\qquad\quad | \\ \qquad\qquad\qquad\quad CH_3 \end{array}$$

Solution:

The longest C chain is eight C atoms in length and the attached group is isopropyl. The numbering should begin on the right, closest to the branched group.

$$\begin{array}{l} \overset{8}{C}H_3\overset{7}{C}H_2\overset{6}{C}H_2\overset{5}{C}H_2\overset{4}{C}H\overset{3}{C}H_2\overset{2}{C}H_2\overset{1}{C}H_3 \\ \qquad\qquad\qquad\quad | \\ \qquad\qquad\qquad\quad CHCH_3 \\ \qquad\qquad\qquad\quad | \\ \qquad\qquad\qquad\quad CH_3 \end{array}$$

The name is 4-isopropyloctane.

EXERCISE 12.7

What is the IUPAC name of this compound?

$$\begin{array}{l} \qquad\quad CH_3 \\ \qquad\quad | \\ CH_3-C-CHCH_2CH_2CH_2CH_3 \\ \qquad\quad |\quad | \\ \qquad CH_3CH_2 \\ \qquad\qquad\;\; | \\ \qquad\qquad\;\; CH_2 \\ \qquad\qquad\;\; | \\ \qquad\qquad\;\; CH_2 \\ \qquad\qquad\;\; | \\ \qquad\qquad\;\; CH_3 \end{array}$$

12.11 WRITING FORMULAS FROM NAMES

Given the IUPAC name for a compound, we can draw its structural formula using the following steps:

1. Draw the C to C chain that corresponds to the parent alkane name and number the C atoms.
2. Attach the branched groups to the appropriate C atoms.
3. Fill in the H atoms needed to give each C atom in the formula a covalency of 4.

For instance, suppose we wish to write the structural formula for 2,4-dimethylhexane.

1. Hexane (C_6H_{14}) is the parent alkane.

```
1   2   3   4   5   6
C—C—C—C—C—C
```

2. Methyl groups are attached to the C-2 and C-4 atoms.

```
1   2   3   4   5   6
C—C—C—C—C—C
    |       |
   CH3     CH3
```

3. The C-1 and C-6 atoms each need three H atoms, C-2 and C-4 each need one H atom, and C-3 and C-5 each need two. The complete formula is

```
CH3CHCH2CHCH2CH3
    |     |
   CH3   CH3
```

SAMPLE EXERCISE 12.8

Write the structural formula for 2,4-dimethyl-4-ethylheptane.

Solution:

1. Draw a seven-carbon chain for heptane.

```
1   2   3   4   5   6   7
C—C—C—C—C—C—C
```

2. Put one methyl on the C-2 atom. Put the ethyl and the other methyl on the C-4 atom.

$$
\begin{array}{ccccccccccccc}
 & & & & & & \mathrm{CH_3} & & & & & & \\
1 & & 2 & & 3 & & 4\,| & & 5 & & 6 & & 7 \\
\mathrm{C} & - & \mathrm{C} & - & \mathrm{C} & - & \mathrm{C} & - & \mathrm{C} & - & \mathrm{C} & - & \mathrm{C} \\
 & & | & & & & | & & & & & & \\
 & & \mathrm{CH_3} & & & & \mathrm{CH_2} & & & & & & \\
 & & & & & & | & & & & & & \\
 & & & & & & \mathrm{CH_3} & & & & & &
\end{array}
$$

3. Fill in H atoms to give each C atom a covalency of 4: three each on C-1 and C-7; two each on C-3, C-5, C-6; one on C-2; and none on C-4.

$$
\begin{array}{l}
\qquad\qquad\quad \mathrm{CH_3} \\
\qquad\qquad\quad | \\
\mathrm{CH_3CHCH_2CCH_2CH_2CH_3} \\
\qquad\;\, | \qquad\;\, | \\
\quad\;\; \mathrm{CH_3} \quad \mathrm{CH_2} \\
\qquad\qquad\quad | \\
\qquad\qquad\quad \mathrm{CH_3}
\end{array}
$$

EXERCISE 12.8

What is the structural formula for 3,3,5-trimethyloctane?

12.12 COMMON NAMES FOR ALKANES

In Chapter 4 we found that inorganic compounds are often called by common or trivial names which are not part of a well-defined naming system. The use of common names is even more prevalent in organic chemistry. One example of this is the use of the prefix **normal** (abbreviated *n*) to refer to straight-chain alkanes. Using this system, we call the seven-carbon alkane below normal heptane, or *n*-heptane, instead of heptane.

$$\mathrm{CH_3CH_2CH_2CH_2CH_2CH_2CH_3}$$

Heptane or *n*-heptane

Alkanes which have a methyl group attached to the next to last C atom are often called **isoalkanes**. For instance, the C_6H_{14} isomer below, named 2-methylpentane in the IUPAC system, is also called isohexane.

$$
\begin{array}{l}
\mathrm{CH_3CH_2CH_2CHCH_3} \\
\qquad\qquad\quad\;\; | \\
\qquad\qquad\quad \mathrm{CH_3}
\end{array}
$$

2-Methylpentane or isohexane

Isoalkane formulas can always fit inside of a fish,

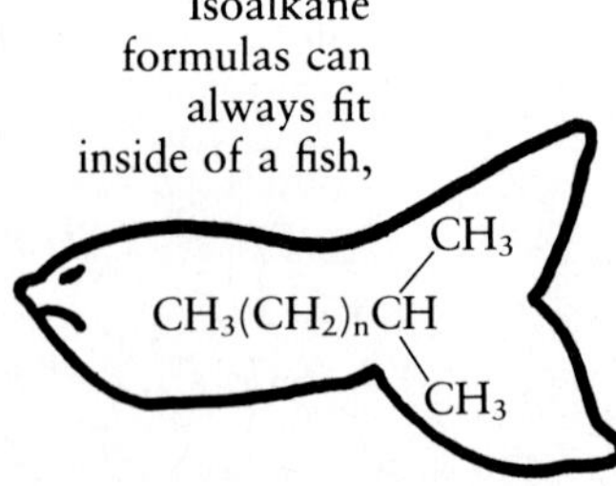

Isoalkanes can be drawn so that the branched end resembles a fishtail.

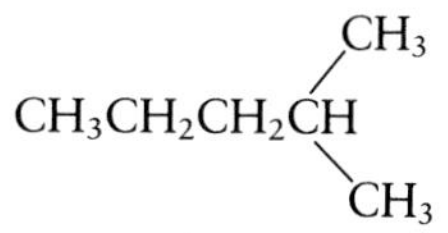

$$\begin{array}{l} \qquad\qquad\qquad\quad CH_3 \\ CH_3CH_2CH_2CH \\ \qquad\qquad\qquad\quad CH_3 \end{array}$$

Isohexane

Common names such as isoalkane do appear on product labels and are routinely used in laboratories.

SAMPLE EXERCISE 12.9

Give the IUPAC and common names for this alkane:

$$\begin{array}{l} CH_3CH_2CHCH_3 \\ \qquad\quad\;\; | \\ \qquad\quad CH_3 \end{array}$$

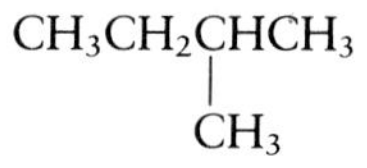

Solution:

In the IUPAC system the longest chain is four C atoms long, the numbering starts from the right in order to give the lowest possible number to the carbon atom that has the branch group. The attached group is a methyl.

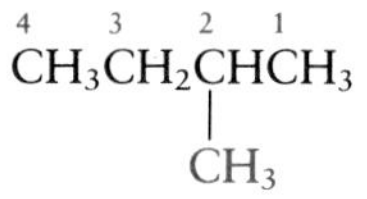

$$\begin{array}{l} \overset{4}{CH_3}\overset{3}{CH_2}\overset{2}{CH}\overset{1}{CH_3} \\ \qquad\quad\;\; | \\ \qquad\quad CH_3 \end{array}$$

The IUPAC name is 2-methylbutane.

This compound can also be named as an isoalkane:

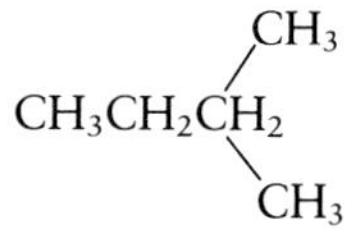

$$\begin{array}{l} \qquad\qquad\quad CH_3 \\ CH_3CH_2CH_2 \\ \qquad\qquad\quad CH_3 \end{array}$$

The common name is isopentane.

EXERCISE 12.9

What are the IUPAC and common names for this alkane?

$$\begin{array}{l} CH_3CHCH_2CH_2CH_2CH_3 \\ \qquad\;\; | \\ \qquad CH_3 \end{array}$$

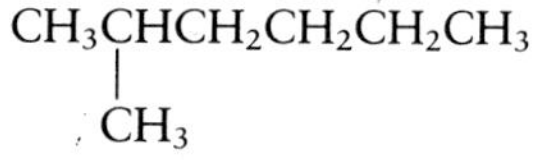

12.13 PHYSICAL PROPERTIES OF ALKANES

Alkanes, like all hydrocarbon molecules, contain covalent bonds between C atoms and between H and C atoms. Thus they all have the general characteristics of covalent compounds that we mentioned in Section 4.2, including low melting points and poor electrical conductivity. In fact, all the general properties of the alkanes apply to hydrocarbons as a group as well. Let us now look at some specific properties.

Solubility

Since the electronegativities of C and H are very close (2.5 and 2.1, respectively), the covalent bonds in alkanes are only slightly polar. Therefore, alkanes are essentially nonpolar. As we discussed in Chapter 9 (Section 9.4), nonpolar solutes tend to dissolve in nonpolar solvents but not in polar solvents. Alkanes all have little or no polarity and so are soluble in each other and in nonpolar solvents such as carbon tetrachloride (CCl_4). Alkanes are not soluble in water. For instance, mixing gasoline (which includes a mixture of alkanes and other hydrocarbons) with water produces two layers (Figure 12.10*a*).

Physical States

The greater the formula weight, the higher the intermolecular forces and the higher the boiling point.

In general, boiling points of compounds depend on the attractive forces operating between their molecules (see Section 4.16). For alkanes, all of which share similar structural features, the boiling points increase as their formula weights increase. Under ordinary conditions of pressure and temperature (1 atm and 25°C), as we can see from looking at Table 12.4, the lower-formula-weight alkanes are gases and the rest are liquids or solids. The first four alkanes, namely, methane, ethane, propane, and butane, are all gases:

$$C_1 \text{ to } C_4 \quad \text{gases}$$

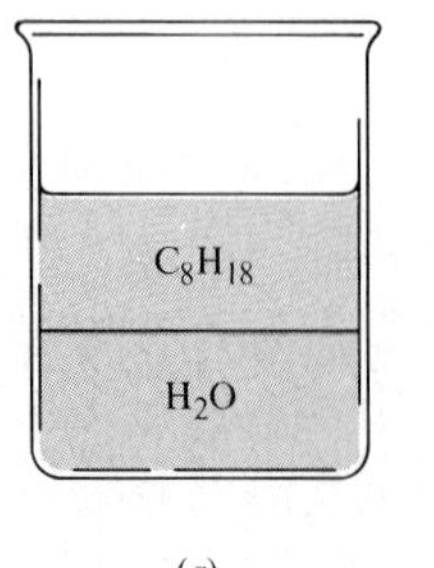

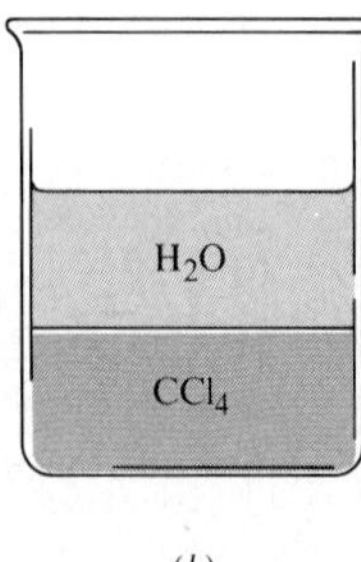

FIGURE 12.10
Densities of hydrocarbons and halohydrocarbons. (*a*) The density of gasoline (octane C_8H_{18} isomers and other liquid hydrocarbons) is less than 1 g/ml. (*b*) The density of CCl_4 (and of most chlorinated, brominated, and iodinated hydrocarbons) is greater than 1 g/ml.

TABLE 12.4 **PHYSICAL PROPERTIES OF STRAIGHT-CHAIN ALKANES**

Name	Formula	Formula weight	Boiling point, °C	Melting point, °C	Physical state at 25°C
Methane	CH_4	16	−164	−182	Gas
Ethane	CH_3CH_3	30	−89	−183	Gas
Propane	$CH_3CH_2CH_3$	44	−42	−188	Gas
Butane	$CH_3CH_2CH_2CH_3$	58	−0.5	−138	Gas
Pentane	$CH_3(CH_2)_3CH_3$	72	36	−130	Liquid
Hexane	$CH_3(CH_2)_4CH_3$	86	69	−95	Liquid
Heptane	$CH_3(CH_2)_5CH_3$	100	98	−91	Liquid
Octane	$CH_3(CH_2)_6CH_3$	114	126	−57	Liquid
Nonane	$CH_3(CH_2)_7CH_3$	128	151	−54	Liquid
Decane	$CH_3(CH_2)_8CH_3$	142	174	−30	Liquid
Pentadecane	$CH_3(CH_2)_{13}CH_3$	212	271	10	Liquid
Heptadecane	$CH_3(CH_2)_{15}CH_3$	240	302	22	Liquid
Octadecane	$CH_3(CH_2)_{16}CH_3$	254	316	28	Solid
Eicosane	$CH_3(CH_2)_{18}CH_3$	282	343	37	Solid

Natural gas is primarily methane but also includes some of the other gaseous alkanes (see Table 9.1). Alkanes which have from 5 to 17 C atoms are liquids:

C_5 to C_{17} liquids

Gasoline includes the alkanes with 5 to 12 C atoms, *kerosene* contains those with 12 to 15 C atoms, and home heating oil fuels contain those with 15 to 18 C atoms in their formulas. Alkanes with 18 or more C atoms in their formulas are solids:

C_{18} and up solids

The paraffin wax from which candles and wax paper are made contains alkanes with more than 25 C atoms. Paraffin waxes are also present in plant leaves and fruit skins.

Density

Densities of substances which contain high-atomic-weight elements tend to be higher than those containing lower-atomic-weight elements. Since hydrocarbons contain the low-atomic-weight elements C and H, they have relatively low densities, less than 1 g/cm^3. The densities of liquid and solid alkanes are between 0.6 g/cm^3 and 0.8 g/cm^3. When gasoline and water are mixed to form two layers, it is the gasoline which floats on top of the water layer (see Figure 12.10*a*).

12.14 CHEMICAL PROPERTIES OF ALKANES

At room temperature the alkanes do not react with acids, bases, oxidizing agents, or most other reagents.

A name sometimes used instead of alkane is *paraffin,* a word derived from Greek meaning "little affinity" (for other compounds). In fact, it is true that alkanes are chemically not very reactive. Violent explosions involving alkane fuels occur only under very special conditions in which their vapors mix with air in the presence of a flame or spark. Alkane fuels for running automobiles and heating homes can be safely stored in gas tanks and pipe lines. Although alkanes are relatively unreactive organic compounds, they do undergo several important reactions. We will discuss two of them, combustion and substitution.

Combustion

In Chapter 7 (Section 7.12) you saw that when alkanes are burned in the presence of oxygen, CO_2 and H_2O are produced; and that if insufficient O_2 is available, CO is also a possible product. The effects of CO poisoning are discussed in Section 7.16. The two reactions below describe the combustion of methane and octane to produce CO_2 and H_2O. A small flame or a spark is needed to supply the necessary activation energy, yet the overall reactions are heat-producing, or exothermic (see Section 10.5).

Assume that one product of the combustion of a hydrocarbon is CO_2 unless otherwise specified.

$$CH_4(g) + 2O_2 \longrightarrow CO_2 + 2H_2O + \text{HEAT}$$

$$2C_8H_{18} + 25O_2 \longrightarrow 16CO_2 + 18H_2O + \text{HEAT}$$

Substitution

In a **substitution reaction** an H atom in an alkane is *substituted* by a chlorine (Cl) or bromine (Br) atom on treating the alkane with Cl_2 or Br_2. Energy must be supplied in the form of heat or ultraviolet radiation for these reactions to take place. For instance, we can write the reaction in which one methane H atom is replaced with a Cl atom:

Recall from Section 2.11 that the energy of a photon is $h \times \nu$.

$$\mathrm{H{-}\overset{\displaystyle H}{\underset{\displaystyle H}{\overset{|}{\underset{|}{C}}}}{-}H} + \mathrm{Cl{-}Cl} \xrightarrow{h\nu \text{ or } \Delta} \mathrm{H{-}Cl} + \mathrm{H{-}\overset{\displaystyle H}{\underset{\displaystyle H}{\overset{|}{\underset{|}{C}}}}{-}Cl}$$

Using condensed formulas, the reaction is

$$CH_4 + Cl_2 \xrightarrow{h\nu \text{ or } \Delta} HCl + CH_3Cl$$

The products of this reaction are hydrogen chloride and chloromethane.

SAMPLE EXERCISE 12.10

Write a balanced chemical equation for the complete combustion of propane.

Solution:

The reactants are propane (C_3H_8) and O_2 and the products are CO_2 and H_2O.

$$C_3H_8 + O_2 \longrightarrow CO_2 + H_2O$$

We need three C atoms and eight H atoms on the right. To accomplish this we use the coefficients 3 for CO_2 and 4 for H_2O.

$$C_3H_8 + O_2 \longrightarrow 3CO_2 + 4H_2O$$

To balance the O atoms the coefficient 5 is placed in front of the O_2.

$$C_3H_8 + 5O_2 \longrightarrow 3CO_2 + 4H_2O$$

EXERCISE 12.10

Write a balanced equation for the combustion of butane.

SAMPLE EXERCISE 12.11

Give the equation for the reaction of ethane with Br_2.

Solution:

Ethane is C_2H_6 and bromine is Br_2. Using full structural formulas makes it easier to see what the products will be.

$$\begin{array}{c} \text{H}\quad\text{H} \\ |\quad\ | \\ \text{H—C—C—H} \\ |\quad\ | \\ \text{H}\quad\text{H} \end{array} + \text{Br—Br} \xrightarrow{h\nu \text{ or } \Delta} \underset{\text{Hydrogen bromide}}{\text{H—Br}} + \underset{\text{Bromoethane}}{\begin{array}{c} \text{H}\quad\text{H} \\ |\quad\ | \\ \text{H—C—C—Br} \\ |\quad\ | \\ \text{H}\quad\text{H} \end{array}}$$

Or, using condensed formulas,

$$CH_3CH_3 + Br_2 \xrightarrow{h\nu \text{ or } \Delta} HBr + CH_3CH_2Br$$

EXERCISE 12.11

Write the reaction for the formation of CH_3CH_2Cl, starting with ethane and Cl_2.

In actual practice, when halogens react with alkanes, more than one haloalkane product is possible. For instance, the chlorination of methane can produce four different products, in which one, two, three, or all four H atoms are replaced with Cl atoms:

$$CH_4 + Cl_2 \longrightarrow HCl + CH_3Cl$$

$$CH_4 + 2Cl_2 \longrightarrow 2HCl + CH_2Cl_2$$

$$CH_4 + 3Cl_2 \longrightarrow 3HCl + CHCl_3$$

$$CH_4 + 4Cl_2 \longrightarrow 4HCl + CCl_4$$

Typically, it is difficult to limit the product of a particular organic reaction to a single desired compound. In most cases mixtures of products are produced which must be separated by use of chromatographic techniques such as the ones we discussed in Chapter 2 (see Section 2.5).

Alkane H atoms cannot be substituted directly by F or I atoms. Fluorine (F_2) is so reactive that when it reacts with alkanes, it causes the rupture of C—C bonds. Iodine (I_2) is so unreactive that it cannot replace alkane H atoms. To prepare fluoro- or iodoalkanes, other types of reactions must be used.

12.15 HALOGENATED ALKANES

Halogenated hydrocarbons have a variety of uses in industry and medicine, and in future chapters we will be introducing many more of these compounds. In this section we will learn how to name haloalkanes and what some of their important properties are.

Nomenclature

The elements F, Cl, Br, and I belong to group VIIA, the halogens.

Halogenated alkanes are named as derivatives of alkanes according to the IUPAC rules. The halogen substituent atom is indicated by a prefix of the form *halo-:*

Cl- chloro-
Br- bromo-

F- fluoro-
I- iodo-

For instance, in the IUPAC system we name the products of the chlorination of methane as methane derivatives. These compounds also have common names, some of which (e.g., chloroform) are used more often than the IUPAC names.

$CHCl_3$ is nearly always called *chloroform.*

CH_3Cl	chloromethane	or	methyl chloride
CH_2Cl_2	dichloromethane	or	methylene chloride
$CHCl_3$	trichloromethane	or	chloroform
CCl_4	tetrachloromethane	or	carbon tetrachloride

We can also name more complicated halogenated alkanes using the IUPAC system rules given in Section 12.10. Suppose we wish to name the halogenated alkane shown below:

$$\begin{array}{l} CH_3\underset{\large Br}{\underset{|}{C}}HCH_2\underset{\large CH_3}{\underset{|}{C}}HCH_2CH_2CH_3 \end{array}$$

First we find the longest chain (seven C atoms) and then number starting from the left. This places the Br on C-2 and the CH_3 on C-4.

$$\overset{1}{C}H_3\underset{\large Br}{\underset{|}{\overset{2}{C}}}H\overset{3}{C}H_2\underset{\large CH_3}{\underset{|}{\overset{4}{C}}}H\overset{5}{C}H_2\overset{6}{C}H_2\overset{7}{C}H_3$$

The name is 2-bromo-4-methylheptane.

SAMPLE EXERCISE 12.12

Name the compound below.

$$Cl\underset{\large Cl}{\underset{|}{C}}HCH_2Cl$$

Solution:

In this case the longest chain has two C atoms. Two of the Cl atoms are attached to the C-1 atom and one to C-2. Assigning the numbers in this way puts the smallest possible numbers in the name.

$$Cl\underset{\large Cl}{\underset{|}{\overset{1}{C}}}H\overset{2}{C}H_2Cl$$

The name of this common industrial solvent is 1,1,2-trichloroethane.

EXERCISE 12.12

Give two names for CH_3CH_2Cl, a compound that acts like a local anesthetic when sprayed on the skin.

Properties

Most of the halogenated alkanes are liquids; the exceptions are those containing F atoms, which are gases. Those with molecules which have more than one Cl atom, or any Br or I atoms are denser than most other organic compounds. In Figure 12.10*b* you can see that water floats on top of a layer of CCl_4.

Chloroform was banned from use in drug and household products in 1976.

Halogenated hydrocarbons resist combustion and are thus *nonflammable.* This serves as a plus for the use of haloalkanes in situations where danger of fire would be a serious drawback. Their toxicity, on the other hand, is a minus. Carbon tetrachloride is toxic to the liver and kidneys and is especially dangerous because it can be absorbed through the skin as well as by inhalation of vapors. Chloroform, $CHCl_3$, and many other haloalkanes are suspected carcinogens.

Uses

Halogenated hydrocarbons are useful in the dry cleaning industry, where their lack of flammability and ability to dissolve dirt and grease make them very effective.

Haloalkanes containing fluorine and chlorine are used as refrigerants and propellants. Collectively they are called Freons, and each has a number to identify it. The first Freon made was the compound below, dichlorodifluoromethane, which is known as Freon 12.

```
      Cl
      |
  Cl—C—F
      |
      F
```

Freon 12

Cl atoms from Freon molecules react with ozone.

Freons have replaced propane as refrigerants because their lack of flammability makes them much safer to use. Freons can escape from refrigerator coils or other containers, reach the stratosphere, and damage the ozone layer (Section 7.14). Freons in aerosol propellants represent the most serious threat to ozone, since they are released into the air, whereas refrigerator coils are sealed.

Phosgene poisoning produces the symptoms of pneumonia.

At one time carbon tetrachloride was used in fire extinguishers because of its resistance to combustion. However, in the presence of O_2, CCl_4 can decompose upon heating to produce a highly toxic compound known as *phosgene:*

```
      O
      ‖
  Cl—C—Cl
```

Phosgene

Halothane induces anesthesia rapidly and causes few side effects.

Haloalkanes have a variety of uses in the field of medicine. Chloroethane, also called ethyl chloride, is used as a topical anesthetic. When sprayed on the skin it vaporizes rapidly, drawing heat from the skin and thus deadening the nerve endings. Halothane and halopropane are used as general anesthetics administered by inhalation.

```
    F  Cl              F   F   H
    |  |               |   |   |
F—C—C—Br        F—C—C—C—Br
    |  |               |   |   |
    F  H               H   F   H
```

Halothane Halopropane

12.16 CYLCO ALKANES

Each intersection of a geometric figure stands for one C and two H atoms.

```
\      \
 >  =   CH2
/      /
```

Hydrocarbons in which a single-bonded C to C *ring* is present are **cycloalkanes.** The general molecular formula for a cycloalkane is C_nH_{2n}, where n is equal to or greater than 3. Cycloalkanes are named by affixing the prefix *cyclo-* to the open-chain alkane that has the same number of C atoms. There are various ways to represent the structures of cycloalkanes. We will look at those in which n is 3, 4, 5, or 6.

The first cycloalkane is *cyclopropane,* C_3H_6, in which two H atoms are attached to each of the three-ring C atoms to give each carbon atom its normal covalency of 4. Ring formulas such as these are most often represented by geometric figures in which each intersection represents a C atom. The H atoms attached to each ring C atom are not included but are assumed to be there.

```
    H   H
     \ /
      C                CH2
     / \              /   \
H—C———C—H        CH2—CH2        △
    |     |
    H     H
```

Cyclopropane structures

In cyclopropane the C—C bond angles are 60°:

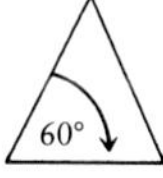

The molecular formula of *cyclobutane* is C_4H_8 and its structural formula is written as a square, with a carbon atom in each of the four corners:

```
    H  H
    |  |
H—C—C—H       H2C—CH2
    |  |           |     |
H—C—C—H       H2C—CH2        □
    |  |
    H  H
```

Cyclobutane structures

The C—C bond angles in cyclobutane are 90°:

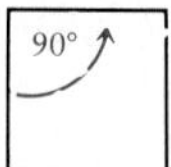

The structural formula for *cyclopentane,* C_5H_{10}, is written as a pentagon:

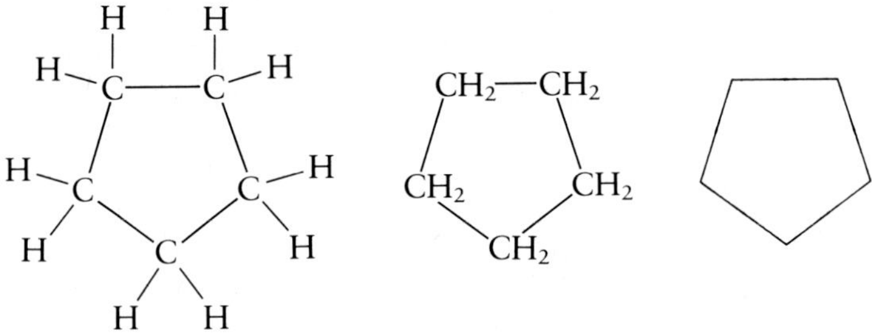

In cyclopentane the C—C bond angles are 108°:

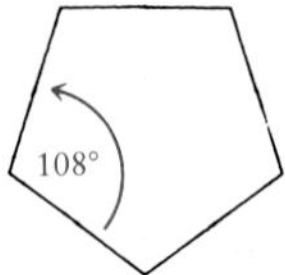

Cyclohexane, C_6H_{12}, is represented by a hexagonal structural formula:

However, cyclohexane is not a planar, or "flat," molecule as the structures above would suggest. In a three-dimensional view the cyclohexane ring is puckered to form one of two structures, one known as the *boat* form and the other as the *chair* form.

109.5° 109.5°

Chair Boat

TABLE 12.5 **ANGLE STRAIN IN CYCLOALKANES**

Cycloalkane	Structure	Bond angles	Angle strain
Cyclopropane		60°	49.5°
Cyclobutane		90°	19.5°
Cyclopentane		108°	1.5°
Cyclohexane		109.5°	0°

Stability of Cycloalkanes

The angle strain for cyclopropane is 109.5° − 60°, or 49.5°.

Cycloalkanes in which the C—C bond angles are closest to the tetrahedral angle of 109.5° are the most stable ones. The difference between the bond angles in a particular cycloalkane and 109.5° is called the **angle strain**. The greater the angle strain, the less stable is the cycloalkane. Looking at Table 12.5 you can see that the angle strain is largest for cyclopropane (49.5) and cyclobutane (19.5°) and smallest for cyclopentane and cyclohexane.

Cyclopropane cannot be used in operations in which electrocautery is needed to coagulate or destroy tissue.

To relieve the angle strain both cyclopropane and cyclobutane undergo reactions in which their rings open up to form open-chain compounds. Cyclopropane has been used as a general inhalation anesthetic. However, it is so highly flammable and can produce such violent explosions that great care must be taken to eliminate sparks or static of any kind from the operating room.

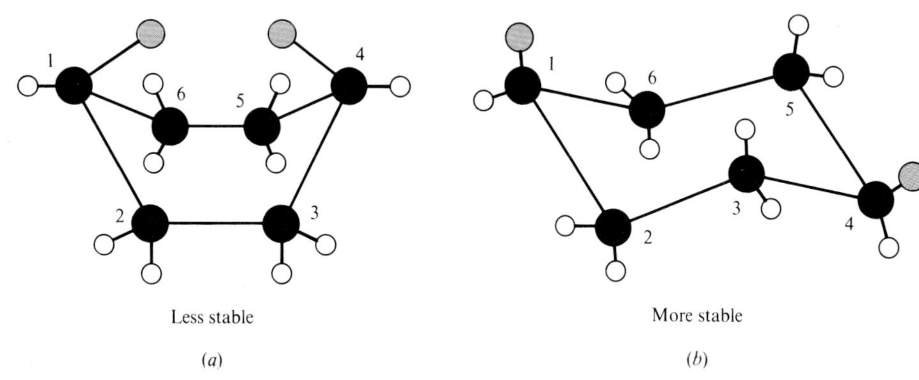

FIGURE 12.11
(*a*) Boat and (*b*) chair forms of cyclohexane. In the boat form, C atoms 1 and 4 are pulled close together, as are the hydrogen atoms attached to them (in color).

You just saw above that there are two forms of cyclohexane, the chair and the boat, both of which have the preferred 109.5° angles and thus no angle strain. Despite this, the chair form is much more stable than is the boat, because cyclic structures in which H atoms stay as far away from each other as possible are more stable than are those in which they are crowded closer together. Note that in the model of the boat form, shown in Figure 12.11, the H atoms on C-1 and C-4 (in color) are much closer together than they are in the chair form. In fact, the chair form of cyclohexane is a particularly stable structure, which is essentially free of any strain at all. Six-membered rings such as cyclohexane are widespread in nature, as we will see when we discuss carbohydrates in Chapter 21.

Substituted Cycloalkanes

One or more H atoms in cycloalkanes may be replaced by other atoms or groups. To name substituted cycloalkanes we give the name of the substituent plus the name of the cycloalkane. For instance, the names of the substituted cyclohexane and cyclopentane shown below are constructed in this way:

$—CH_3$ —Br

Methylcyclohexane   Bromocyclopentane

When more than one substituent is present, the ring C atoms must be numbered. The numbers are assigned so that the resulting cycloalkane name has the *lowest* possible numbers. One substituent must always be at the 1 position and the others are given the next lowest numbers possible. For instance, to name the dimethylcyclohexane shown below, the number 1 is assigned to the position of one methyl group and the other methyl is at the 3 position.

1 $—CH_3$

2

3

CH_3

1,3-Dimethylcyclohexane

SAMPLE EXERCISE 12.13

Give the condensed formula and the name of this substituted cycloalkane:

$—CH_2CH_3$

Solution:

This is a cyclopentane because it contains a five-membered ring. Each ring C atom is bonded to two H atoms, except for the C bonded to the ethyl group, which has only one attached H atom.

$$\begin{array}{ccc} CH_2 & \text{—} & CH\text{—}CH_2CH_3 \\ | & & | \\ CH_2 & & CH_2 \\ & \diagdown\ \diagup & \\ & CH_2 & \end{array}$$

The compound is named ethylcyclopentane.

EXERCISE 12.13

Give the condensed formula and name for the cycloalkane shown below:

CH_3 CH_3

Properties of Cycloalkanes

In general, the physical and chemical properties of cycloalkanes are similar to those of the open-chain alkanes. Cyclopropane and cyclobutane, like propane and butane, are gases, and cyclopentane and cyclohexane, like pentane and hexane, are liquids. Because they are relatively inert, the cycloalkanes, like the alkanes, can be found in nature, where they appear in petroleum deposits.

12.17 FOSSIL FUELS

Most of the world's energy needs are provided by the combustion of the **fossil fuels**, namely, coal, natural gas, and petroleum or oil.

Petrolatum and other petroleum jellies contain high-molecular-weight alkanes.

Coal is more than 90 percent carbon. Natural gas, also known as marsh gas, consists mostly of methane and is often found along with oil deposits. Petroleum contains a complex mixture of hydrocarbons, most of which are alkanes or cycloalkanes. Of the alkanes present, the most abundant are straight-chain alkanes (the least reactive), 2-methylalkanes, and cyclohexanes.

Crude petroleum is refined by distillation (Section 8.4), in which the various hydrocarbons are separated into fractions with similar boiling points and molecular sizes. Figure 12.12 gives a diagram of the apparatus used and the common

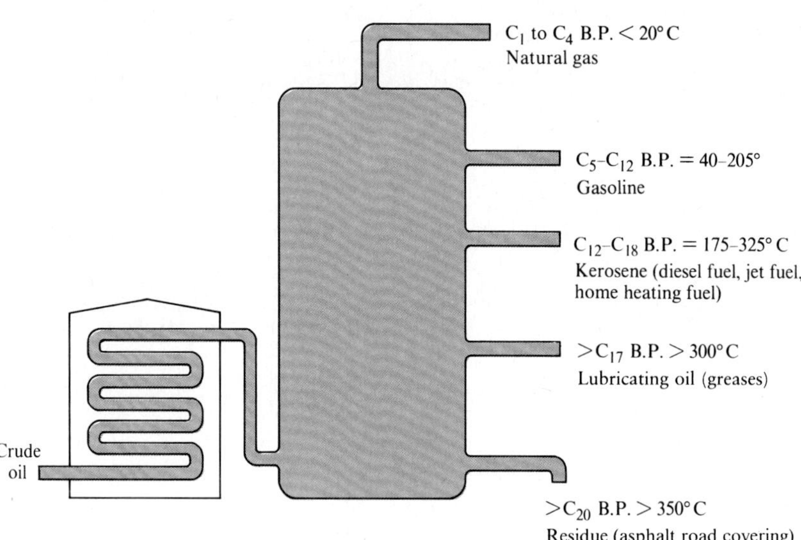

FIGURE 12.12
Petroleum distillation.

names and approximate boiling ranges of the fractions removed.

Before the advent of the automobile there was little use for the gasoline fraction, the fraction which is now of the greatest commercial importance. Unfortunately the best gasoline is composed of highly branched alkanes, which, as mentioned above, are the least abundant in nature. Chemical processes may be used to transform straight-chain alkanes and other hydrocarbons into the highly branched ones. The octane number rating system for gasoline compares the performance of a gasoline with that of a mixture of two standard compounds, heptane (octane number 0) and 2,2,4-trimethylpentane (octane number 100). The percentage of 2,2,4-trimethylpentane in the comparison mixture that exactly matches the performance of a gasoline is the octane number of that gasoline. For instance, a gasoline that performs just like a mixture containing 88 percent 2,2,4-trimethylpentane and 12 percent heptane has an octane number of 88.

Petroleum can also provide small molecules to be used as building blocks for the synthesis of other organic compounds, including many of those to be discussed in Chapters 13 through 19, where we continue our coverage of the different classes of organic compounds.

SUMMARY

Organic chemistry is the chemistry of carbon compounds. Carbon forms millions of compounds because the C atom has an unlimited capacity to form chains and can form multiple bonds with other C atoms or with O or N atoms.

Hydrocarbons contain the elements C and H. Alkanes are hydrocarbons in which all the C—C bonds are single. The fact that C atoms form four bonds in their compounds is explained by promotion of one of the 2*s* electrons of the unbonded C atom to the empty $2p_z$ orbital to give four unpaired electrons. The fact that the four bonds formed in alkanes are all equivalent is explained by mixing the orbitals containing the unpaired electrons (2*s*, $2p_x$, $2p_y$, and $2p_z$) to produce four hybrid sp^3 orbitals. The electronic configuration of the single-bonded C atom is $1s^2(2sp^3)^1\ (2sp^3)^1\ (2sp^3)^1\ (2sp^3)^1$. A sigma ($\sigma$) bond between a C atom and another atom is formed by overlap of the sp^3 hybrid orbital of C with an orbital from the other atom, as indicated by a dash.

Structural isomers are two or more compounds with the same molecular formulas but different structural formulas, that is, formulas that indicate the arrangements of atoms in a compound. Full structural formulas show all the bonds with dashes. In condensed formulas H atoms bonded to C atoms are written next to the C atom without a dash. Straight-chain alkanes have a continuous C to C chain and branched alkanes have one or more C atom branches attached to the longest main chain of a compound.

IUPAC names for alkanes are based upon assigned names ending in the suffix *-ane*, including methane (one C atom), ethane (two C atoms), propane (three C atoms), butane (four C atoms), pentane (five C atoms) and so on, with prefixes used to indicate the numbers 6 through 10. The parent alkane name is derived from the longest continuous C to C chain in a compound. The C atoms in this chain are numbered in such a way that the number 1 is closest to the end with any side branching. The branched groups are named as alkyls by replacing *-ane* in the corresponding alkane name with *-yl* and are located by indicating the number of the C atom to which they are attached. Attached alkyl groups are listed in order of complexity or alphabetically. Common names instead of the systematic names are often used for some alkanes and for many other organic compounds.

Alkanes are nonpolar, insoluble in water, and less dense than water. Gaseous alkanes have 1 to 4 C atoms, liquids 5 to 17 C atoms, and solids more than 18 C atoms.

Chemically the alkanes are relatively inert. They undergo combustion reactions as they burn in air to produce CO_2 (or CO) and H_2O. The typical reactions of alkanes are substitution reactions in which one or more alkane H atoms are replaced by Cl or Br atoms.

Halogenated alkanes are named by using the appropriate halo- prefix (chloro-, bromo-, etc.) with the name of the corresponding alkane. Halogenated hydrocarbons are nonflammable and toxic to varying degress. In medicine many of them, particularly halothane, serve as general inhalation anesthetics.

Cycloalkanes are hydrocarbons containing a single-bonded C to C ring. Their properties are similar to those of the alkanes.

KEY WORDS

organic chemistry
hydrocarbon
alkane
homologous series
promotion
hybridization
sp^3 hybrid orbitals
structural isomers
structural formula
straight chain
branched chain
IUPAC system
alkyl
normal
isoalkane
substitution reaction
halogenated alkane
cycloalkane
angle strain
fossil fuels

EXERCISES

12.14 What special bonding properties of carbon explain the fact that carbon forms so many more compounds than does any other element?

12.15 Write molecular formulas for the following alkanes: (**a**) Ethane; (**b**) butane; (**c**) pentane; (**d**) octane.

12.16 Calculate the formula weight of the alkane which has 12 carbon atoms.

12.17 Spinach leaves contain alkanes with 33, 35, and 37 carbon atoms. Give the molecular formulas for these three alkanes.

12.18 Why does the electronic configuration of carbon have to be modified to explain the formation of compounds such as the alkanes?

12.19 Draw Lewis electron dot structures for the two structural isomers of butane.

12.20 Rewrite the full structural formulas below in condensed form.

```
         H   H   H   H
         |   |   |   |
(a)  H—C—C—C—C—H
         |   |   |   |
         H   |   H   H
             |
          H—C—H
             |
             H
```

(b)
$$\begin{array}{ccccccccccccc}
 & & & & H & & & & & & & & \\
 & & & & | & & & & & & & & \\
 & & & H- & C & -H & & & & & & & \\
 & & H & & | & & H & & H & & H & & \\
 & & | & & | & & | & & | & & | & & \\
H & - & C & - & C & - & C & - & C & - & C & - & H \\
 & & | & & | & & | & & | & & | & & \\
 & & H & & | & & H & & H & & | & & \\
 & & & H- & C & -H & & & & H- & C & -H & \\
 & & & & | & & & & & & | & & \\
 & & & & H & & & & & & H & &
\end{array}$$

12.21 What are the IUPAC names for the compounds in Exercise 12.20?

12.22 Why are molecular formulas not sufficient to describe the structures of most organic compounds?

12.23 For heptane:
(a) List the structural isomers.
(b) Give the IUPAC name for each isomer.
(c) Do any of the isomers have common names?

12.24 Give the IUPAC names for the following alkanes:

(a) $CH_3CH_2\underset{\displaystyle CH_3}{\underset{|}{C}}HCH_3$ (b) $CH_3\underset{\displaystyle CH_3}{\underset{|}{C}}HCH_2CH_3$

(c) $CH_3(CH_2)_7CH_3$

(d) $CH_3\underset{\displaystyle CH_3}{\underset{|}{C}}HCH_2\underset{\displaystyle CH_3}{\underset{|}{C}}HCH_2CH_3$

12.25 Give the IUPAC names for the alkanes below:

(a) $CH_3-\overset{\displaystyle CH_3}{\overset{|}{\underset{\displaystyle CH_3}{\underset{|}{C}}}}-CH_2\underset{\displaystyle CH_3}{\underset{|}{C}}HCH_2CH_3$

(b) $CH_3CH_2CH_2\underset{\displaystyle \underset{\displaystyle CH_3}{\underset{|}{CH_2}}}{\underset{|}{C}}HCH_2\underset{\displaystyle CH_3}{\underset{|}{C}}HCH_2CH_3$

(c) $CH_3CH_2\underset{\displaystyle \underset{\displaystyle CH_3}{\underset{|}{CH_2}}}{\underset{|}{C}}HCH_3$

(d) $CH_3CH_2CH_2\underset{\displaystyle \underset{\displaystyle CH_3}{\underset{|}{CHCH_3}}}{\underset{|}{C}}HCH_2CH_2CH_3$

12.26 Write structural formulas which correspond to the following IUPAC and common names.
(a) 3-Ethylpentane (b) 2-Methylheptane
(c) 2,3-Dimethylhexane (d) Isobutane

12.27 What structural formulas correspond to the following IUPAC and common names?
(a) 2-Methylpropane
(b) *n*-Octane
(c) 2-Methyl-4-ethylnonane
(d) 2,2,5-Trimethylheptane

12.28 A pheromone is a substance secreted by an animal in order to communicate with other animals. Give the formula for 2-methylheptadecane, a pheromone secreted by tiger moths.

12.29 What is the IUPAC name for isopentane?

12.30 Why are these IUPAC names "impossible"? (a) 1-methylpentane; (b) 2-octylbutane; (c) 3-methylbutane?

12.31 The following pairs of liquids form mixtures in which two layers form. For each pair, which liquid is the top layer: (a) Chloroform and water; (b) hexane and water?

12.32 Which of the following alkanes are liquids? Gases? Solids? (The pressure is 1 atm and the temperature is 25°C.)
(a) Heptane
(b) Ethane
(c) 2,2,4-Trimethylpentane
(d) 2-Methyldecane
(e) Eicosane (see Table 12.1)
(f) Propane

12.33 The compound 2,2,4-trimethylpentane, used to measure gasoline performance, is most often called *isooctane* in the petroleum industry. Is 2,2,4-trimethylpentane really isooctane?

12.34 These compounds are structural isomers of what straight-chain alkanes? (a) 2,2-dimethylpentane; (b) 2-methyl-4-ethyloctane; (c) 5-propylnonane?

12.35 Write balanced chemical equations for the combustion of the following compounds, assuming that the products are CO_2 and H_2O:
(a) Ethane; (b) 2-Methylbutane;
(c) Cyclohexane.

12.36 What is meant by a substitution reaction?

12.37 Write the reactions for the bromination of 1 mol methane with: (a) 1 mol Br_2; (b) 2 mol Br_2; (c) 3 mol Br_2; (d) 4 mol Br_2. Name all the products using IUPAC names and common names.

12.38 Give the structural formulas and the names for the two possible products which could form by a substitution reaction in which one H atom of propane is replaced with a Cl atom.

12.39 What advantage do the general anesthetics halothane and halopropane have over cyclopropane?

12.40 Give the IUPAC names for halothane and halopropane from their formulas, given in Section 12.15.

12.41 The iodine compound CHI_3 is a yellowish crystalline powder used locally as an antiseptic and anesthetic. What are the IUPAC and common names for this compound? Can it be produced by the direct reaction of iodine with methane?

12.42 Why are cyclopropane and cyclobutane less stable than cyclopentane and cyclohexane?

12.43 Give the condensed cycloalkane formulas that correspond to the geometric figures below:

12.44 Name the following cycloalkanes:

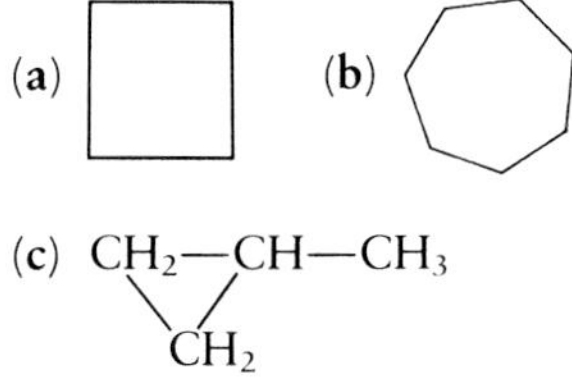

12.45 Name the di- and tri-substituted alkanes below:

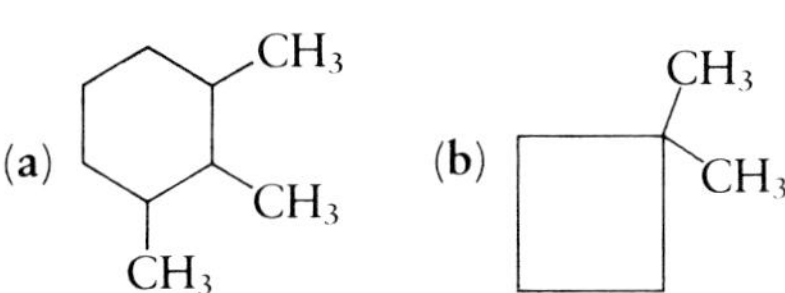

(c) cyclopentane ring bearing CH_2CH_3 and CH_3CH_2 substituents

CH_2CH_3

CH_3CH_2

12.46 Why are Freons safer to use as refrigerants than propane?

12.47 What is the IUPAC name for Freon 12 (see Section 12.15)?

12.48 What are the fossil fuels?

12.49 Which of the undecanes below is most likely to be found in large amounts in an oil deposit?

(a) $CH_3CHCH_2CH_2CHCHCH_2CH_3$ (with CH_3 on the second carbon, and H_3C and CH_3 on the fifth and sixth carbons)

(b) $CH_3(CH_2)_9CH_3$

12.50 Cyclohexane is the most abundant cycloalkane in petroleum, followed by cyclopentane, and very distantly by cyclobutane and cyclopropane. Why do you think this is true?

12.51 We most often draw a regular hexagon to represent cyclohexane. Is this an accurate representation of the actual three-dimensional structure of cyclohexane? Why?

13 ALKENES AND ALKYNES

13.1 INTRODUCTION

FIGURE 13.1
(*a*) Single-bonded C atoms are bonded to *four* other atoms. (*b*) Double-bonded C atoms form bonds with *three* other atoms. (*c*) Triple-bonded C atoms form bonds with only *two* other atoms.

You saw in Chapter 12 that carbon atoms are tetravalent and thus can bond to four other atoms at most. This is what happens in alkanes; in Figure 13.1 you can see that each C atom in the alkane shown is bonded to four other atoms. Alkanes are said to be **saturated** because the C atoms in their formulas are bonded to the maximum possible number of atoms; that is, their capacity to form bonds with other atoms is saturated. The carbon-carbon bonds in saturated compounds are all single bonds. Hydrocarbons in which multiple bonds are present are **unsaturated**, because their molecules include C atoms that are bonded to fewer than four atoms. For instance, the double-bonded C atoms in ethene are each bonded to only three other atoms, one C atom and two H atoms. Hydrocarbons such as ethene, which contain a carbon to carbon double bond, are called **alkenes**. In ethyne (common name, acetylene) each of the triple-bonded C atoms is joined to two other atoms, a C atom and an H atom. Hydrocarbons such as ethyne, which contain a carbon to carbon triple bond, are called **alkynes**.

We will find that the unsaturated hydrocarbons (alkenes and alkynes) are physically similar to the alkanes but chemically very different. The multiple bonds in unsaturated hydrocarbons are much more reactive than the single bonds in alkanes.

13.2 ALKENES: GENERAL FORMULA

The general formula for an alkene hydrocarbon is

$$C_nH_{2n}$$

Note that the number of H atoms in a given alkene is two less than that in the corresponding alkane (general formula C_nH_{2n+2}). Alkanes are saturated with H and alkenes are unsaturated. Because a double bond requires at least two carbon

TABLE 13.1 FORMULAS AND NAMES OF ALKENES (n = 2 TO 20)

Molecular formula	Name
C_2H_4	Ethene (ethylene)
C_3H_6	Propene (propylene)
C_4H_8	Butene
C_5H_{10}	Pentene
C_6H_{12}	Hexene
C_7H_{14}	Heptene
C_8H_{16}	Octene
C_9H_{18}	Nonene
$C_{10}H_{20}$	Decene
$C_{11}H_{22}$	Undecene
$C_{12}H_{24}$	Dodecene
$C_{13}H_{26}$	Tridecene
$C_{14}H_{28}$	Tetradecene
$C_{15}H_{30}$	Pentadecene
$C_{16}H_{32}$	Hexadecene
$C_{17}H_{34}$	Heptadecene
$C_{18}H_{36}$	Octadecene
$C_{19}H_{38}$	Nonadecene
$C_{20}H_{40}$	Eicosene

Alkenes contain one double bond.

atoms, there is no alkene in which $n = 1$. If we set $n = 2$, the alkene formula becomes

$$C_2H_{(2\times 2)} \quad \text{or} \quad C_2H_4$$

which represents ethene (Figure 13.1*b*). When $n = 3$, the formula produced is C_3H_6, the formula of propene.

Alkene names are derived from the name assigned to the alkane with the same number of carbon atoms by replacing the alkane suffix *-ane* with *-ene*. For instance, the name of the four-carbon alkene C_4H_8 is but*ene,* derived from the name of the four-carbon alkane but*ane*. For some of the lower members of the alkene family a name of the type "alkylene" instead of alkene is often used. For example, ethene (C_2H_4) and propene (C_3H_6) are also called ethylene and propylene. The molecular formulas and names for the alkenes in which $n = 2$ to 20 are given in Table 13.1. Each alkene listed differs from an adjacent alkene by one repeating unit (a CH_2 unit) and thus the alkenes represent a homologous series (see Section 12.3).

SAMPLE EXERCISE 13.1

Find the molecular formula and the name for the alkene which contains eight carbon atoms.

Solution:

Formula: $C_8H_{2\times 8} = C_8H_{16}$

The name is *octene*, derived from the name of the eight-carbon alkane octane with the *-ene* suffix replacing *-ane*.

EXERCISE 13.1

What is the name of an alkene whose molecular formula contains 20 hydrogen atoms?

13.3 THE ALKENE DOUBLE BOND

In Chapter 12 (Section 12.4) you saw how a carbon $2s$ electron can be promoted to the $2p_z$ energy level to produce an electronic configuration in which there are four unpaired electrons available for bonding.

$$1s^2 2s^1 2p_x^1 2p_y^1 2p_z^1$$

The hybridization of the $2s$ and $2p$ orbitals to produce four identical sp^3 hybrid orbitals explained the bonding in compounds such as CH_4 and the other alkanes. However, sp^3 hybridization will not explain the bonding in compounds such as ethene. In the ethene structure there are three atoms (two H atoms and a C atom) bonded to each of the double-bonded C atoms, not four as there are in an alkane. Furthermore, in ethene each C atom is involved in two different kinds of bonds, two C—H single bonds and one C=C double bond. A different set of hybrid orbitals is required for a double-bonded C atom surrounded by three other atoms.

Hybridization

The carbon atoms in ethene undergo promotion and hybridization to produce three *hybrid* orbitals and one *unhybridized* $2p_z$ orbital (in color below). This is accomplished by mixing the $2s$ orbital with only two of the $2p$ orbitals:

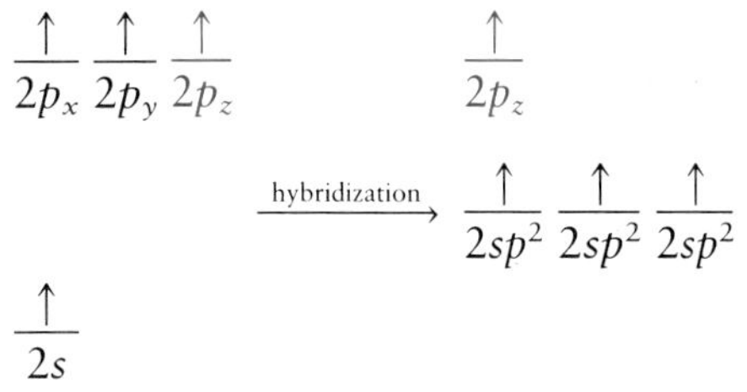

$$\begin{array}{ccc} \underline{\uparrow}\;\underline{\uparrow}\;\underline{\uparrow} & & \underline{\uparrow} \\ 2p_x\;2p_y\;2p_z & & 2p_z \\ & \xrightarrow{\text{hybridization}} & \underline{\uparrow}\;\underline{\uparrow}\;\underline{\uparrow} \\ & & 2sp^2\;2sp^2\;2sp^2 \\ \underline{\uparrow} & & \\ 2s & & \end{array}$$

The newly formed hybrid orbitals are called ***sp*² orbitals** because they are formed from one *s* orbital and two *p* orbitals. We can rewrite the electronic configuration

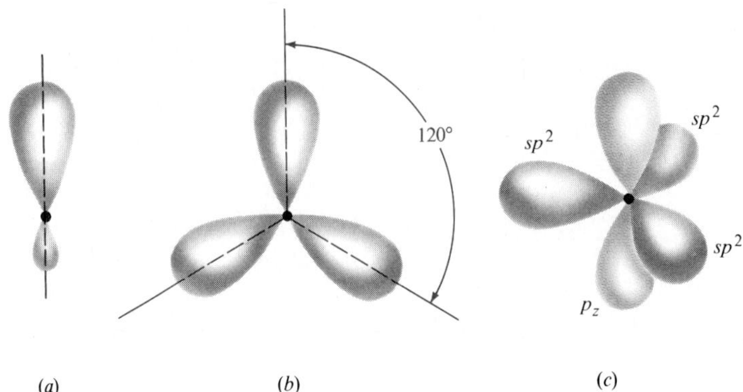

FIGURE 13.2
(*a*) An sp^2-hybrid orbital. (*b*) The three sp^2 hybrids of carbon showing only the larger lobes. (*c*) The axis of the $2p_z$ orbital is perpendicular to the plane of the sp^2 orbitals.

for a doubly bonded carbon atom in terms of sp^2 hybrid orbitals and the unhybridized $2p$ orbital:

$$1s^2(2sp^2)^1(2sp^2)^1(2sp^2)^1 2p_z^{\,1}$$

We say that doubly bonded carbon atoms are sp^2 hybridized. Like the sp^3 hybrid orbitals (Figure 12.1), the sp^2 hybrid orbitals resemble lopsided dumbbells, as shown in Figure 13.2*a*. The three sp^2 hybrid orbitals all lie in the same plane with each orbital pointing toward one corner of an equilateral triangle, which makes the angles between orbitals 120° (see Figure 13.2*b*). The unhybridized p orbital is pictured (in color) in Figure 13.2*c*, where you can see that it lies perpendicular to the three sp^2 orbitals.

To draw the structure of the simplest alkene, ethene, we use the sp^2 hybridized carbon atoms. Figure 13.3 shows a step-by-step construction of the ethene orbital

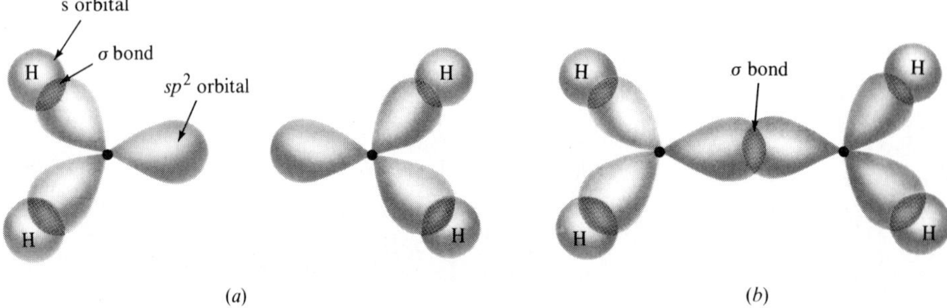

π bond
p orbital
H
H
H
H
Using dashes to represent σ bonds
(c)

H
H
π
C
C
π
H
H
H
H
σ
π
H
H
(d)

FIGURE 13.3
Bonding in ethene. (*a*) Four σ bonds form as four H *s* orbitals overlap with four sp^2 hydrid orbitals. (*b*) A σ bond forms from the remaining sp^2 orbitals. (*c*) A π bond forms as the two unhydridized *p* orbitals overlap. (*d*) The π bond is drawn as a cloud above and below the plane.

structure. First we draw the three sp^2 orbitals around each of the two C atoms in ethene. Two of these sp^2 orbitals from each C atom overlap with H 1*s* orbitals to form the four C—H single bonds. Next one bond of the C═C double bond forms as the remaining two sp^2 orbitals (one from each C atom) overlap to form a sigma (σ) bond (Section 4.8). All the bonds shown in the structure so far are σ bonds, and this part of the structure is sometimes called the sigma framework. To complete the picture the unhybridized $2p_z$ orbitals (one from each C atom) overlap to form a pi (π) bond, thus completing the double bond between the C atoms. Note that *the C to C double bond includes one σ bond and one π bond.* The double-bonded carbon atoms and the H atoms (or C atoms) to which they are bonded all lie in the same plane (see Figure 13.4).

The C to C double bond has both a σ and a π character.

In Chapter 4 we found that C to C double bonds were stronger than C to C single bonds. The bond energy for the C to C double bond is 146 kcal/mol compared with 82 kcal/mol for a C to C σ bond. From these values the energy of the π bond in ethene has been estimated to be (146 − 82) kcal/mol, or 64 kcal/mol. Thus the π bond in ethene (bond energy 64 kcal/mol) is only about two-thirds as strong as the σ bond (bond energy 82 kcal/mol). We will see that this dual nature of the C—C double bond explains some important properties of alkenes.

Since the drawing of orbital pictures for larger alkenes is inconvenient, Lewis electron dot structures are often used instead. In Chapter 4 we used the electron

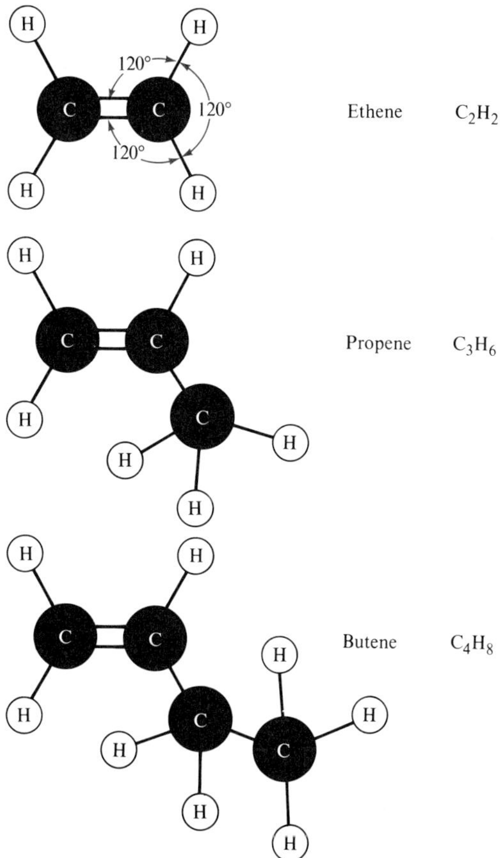

FIGURE 13.4
Alkene structures. Double-bonded C atoms and the atoms to which they are bonded are all in the same plane.

dot structure of ethene as one example of a molecule in which a multiple bond was needed to satisfy the octet rule (see Section 4.10). The Lewis dot structures for ethene and propene are given below:

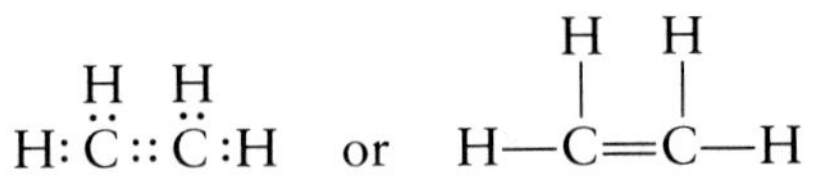

$$\mathrm{H\!:\!\overset{H}{\underset{}{\ddot{C}}}\!::\!\overset{H}{\ddot{C}}\!:\!H} \quad \text{or} \quad \mathrm{H{-}\overset{H}{\overset{|}{C}}{=}\overset{H}{\overset{|}{C}}{-}H}$$

Ethene

$$\mathrm{H\!:\!\overset{H}{\underset{H}{\ddot{\underset{..}{C}}}}\!:\!\overset{H}{\ddot{C}}\!::\!\overset{H}{\ddot{C}}\!:\!H} \quad \text{or} \quad \mathrm{H{-}\overset{H}{\overset{|}{\underset{H}{\underset{|}{C}}}}{-}\overset{H}{\overset{|}{C}}{=}\overset{H}{\overset{|}{C}}{-}H}$$

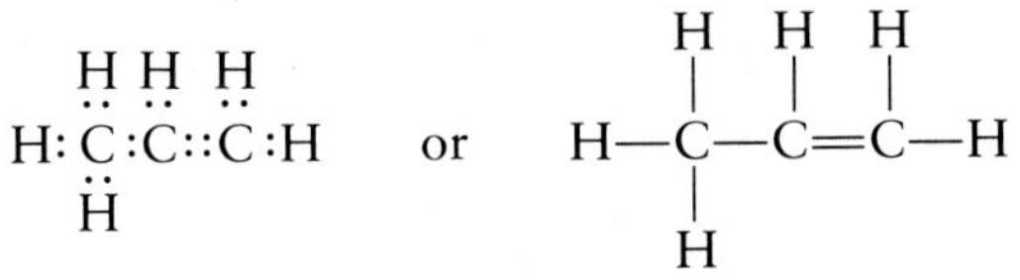

Propene

SAMPLE EXERCISE 13.2

In the structure shown below, give the hybridization of each C atom.

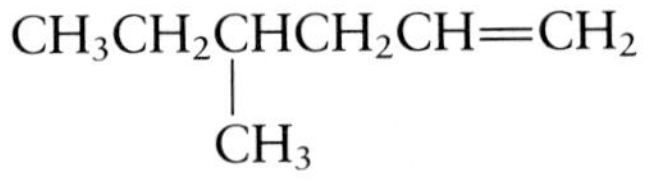

$$\mathrm{CH_3CH_2\underset{\underset{CH_3}{|}}{C}HCH_2CH{=}CH_2}$$

Solution:

The two C atoms in the double bond are sp^2 hybridized. The rest are sp^3 hybridized since they form four single bonds.

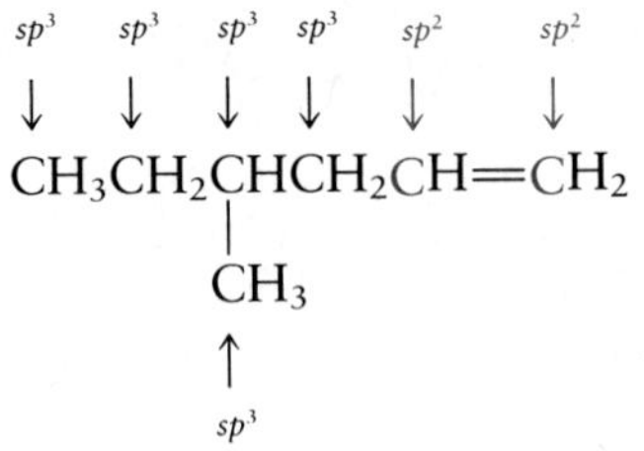

$$\begin{array}{cccccc} sp^3 & sp^3 & sp^3 & sp^3 & sp^2 & sp^2 \\ \downarrow & \downarrow & \downarrow & \downarrow & \downarrow & \downarrow \end{array}$$

$$\mathrm{CH_3CH_2\underset{\underset{\underset{\underset{sp^3}{\uparrow}}{CH_3}}{|}}{C}HCH_2CH{=}CH_2}$$

EXERCISE 13.2

What is wrong with this alkene formula?

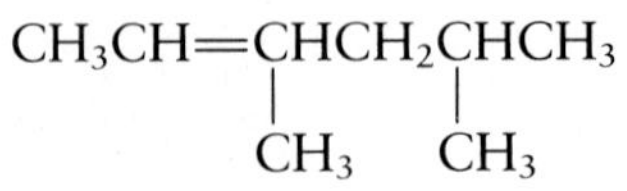

$$\mathrm{CH_3CH{=}\underset{\underset{CH_3}{|}}{C}HCH_2\underset{\underset{CH_3}{|}}{C}HCH_3}$$

13.4 STRUCTURAL ISOMERS OF ALKENES

The double-bonded structural isomers of a particular alkene may have different carbon skeletons, different placement of the double bond, or both. To list the isomers for an alkene, start with the straight-chain isomer and put the double bond in all possible positions. To find more isomers shorten the main chain by one C at a time, as we did when listing alkane isomers (Section 12.8). Then attach the branch group (or groups) and move the double bond around in the new main chain looking for all the possible combinations of branch position and double-bond location.

Ethene

There is only one way to arrange the two C atoms and the four H atoms to form the double-bonded ethene molecule.

C_2H_4	$CH_2{=}CH_2$	(1)
Molecular formula	Condensed structural formula	

Thus ethene has just one structural isomer.

Propene

Cyclopropane, C_3H_6, is a structural isomer of propene but it has no double bond.

For the molecular formula C_3H_6 there is only one propene isomer.

C_3H_6	$CH_3CH{=}CH_2$	(1)
Molecular formula	Condensed structural formula	

Butene

There are two possible butene structures which include a four-carbon chain. In one of them the double bond involves one of the end C atoms.

$$C_4H_8 \qquad CH_2{=}CHCH_2CH_3 \qquad (1)$$

In the other one, the double bond is located between the two middle C atoms of the chain.

$$C_4H_8 \qquad CH_3CH{=}CHCH_3 \qquad (2)$$

There is one more structural isomer of butene in which the double bond is part of a three-carbon chain.

$$C_4H_8 \qquad CH_2{=}\underset{\underset{\displaystyle CH_3}{|}}{C}{-}CH_3 \qquad (3)$$

SAMPLE EXERCISE 13.3

Write condensed formulas for the alkene structural isomers of pentene, C_5H_{12}.

Solution:

There are two pentene isomers which contain a five-carbon chain. In one the double bond is between the end C atoms, whereas in the other it is between two middle C atoms.

Isomer 1: $CH_2{=}CHCH_2CH_2CH_3$ Isomer 2: $CH_3CH_2CH{=}CHCH_3$

There are three pentene isomers with four-carbon chains, in each of which there is an attached methyl group. In two of these the double bond is located between the end C atoms.

Isomer 3: $CH_2{=}CH\underset{|\atop CH_3}{C}HCH_3$ Isomer 4: $CH_2{=}\underset{|\atop CH_3}{C}{-}CH_2CH_3$

The third isomer with a four-carbon chain has the double bond between the middle C atoms:

Isomer 5: $CH_3CH{=}\underset{|\atop CH_3}{C}{-}CH_3$

Pentene has a total of five alkene isomers.

EXAMPLE 13.3

Which of the formulas below represent structural isomers of hexene?

(a) $CH_3CH_2CH_2CH_2CH_2CH_3$ (b) $CH_3\underset{|\atop CH_3}{C}HCH_2CH{=}CH_2$

(c) $CH_3CH{=}\underset{|\atop CH_3}{C}CH_2CH_3$ (d) $CH_2{=}CHCH_2\underset{|\atop CH_3}{C}HCH_2CH_3$

(e) $CH_3\underset{|\atop CH_3}{C}{=}\underset{|\atop CH_3}{C}CH_3$ (f) $CH_3(CH_2)_3CH{=}CH_2$

13.5 ALKENE NOMENCLATURE

The IUPAC rules for naming alkenes are similar to those for naming alkanes. An extra rule is needed to specify the location of the double bond.

Rule I *Choose the longest C to C chain which includes the double bond. The parent name of the alkene is the alkene name corresponding to that number of carbon atoms.*

For instance, the longest chain in the formula below contains six C atoms.

$$CH_2{=}CHCH_2CH_2\underset{\displaystyle CH_3}{\underset{|}{C}}HCH_3$$

Thus the parent name of this alkene must be hexene.

Rule II *Number the C to C chain. Assign the number 1 to the C atom on the end closest to the double bond.*

For example, for the hexene shown, the numbering must start from the end nearest to the double bond, the left end in this case.

$$\overset{1}{C}H_2{=}\overset{2}{C}H\overset{3}{C}H_2\overset{4}{C}H_2\underset{\displaystyle CH_3}{\underset{|}{\overset{5}{C}}}H\overset{6}{C}H_3$$

In numbering alkene C chains the double bond takes precedence over branch groups.

The naming system for alkenes is designed to give the lowest possible numbers to the C atoms bearing the double bond regardless of where the branch groups may be attached.

Rule III *Indicate the position of the double bond using the lowest-numbered double-bonded C atom. Place this number in front of the parent alkene name.*

According to this rule the hexene example is a 1-hexene since its double bond is located between C-1 and C-2.

Rule IV *Complete the name by giving the number of the C atom to which a branched group is attached followed by the name of the branched group, using the same rules applied to the alkanes. These substituent names always come before the parent alkene name.*

According to these rules the name of the hexene example shown is 5-methyl-1-hexene:

$$\overset{1}{C}H_2{=}\overset{2}{C}H\overset{3}{C}H_2\overset{4}{C}H_2\underset{\displaystyle CH_3}{\underset{|}{\overset{5}{C}}}H\overset{6}{C}H_3$$

5-Methyl-1-hexene

SAMPLE EXERCISE 13.4

Name the three isomers of butene according to the IUPAC rules.

Solution:

(1) $CH_2{=}CHCH_2CH_3$
Number from the left. The double bond is between C-1 and C-2.

$$\overset{1}{C}H_2{=}\overset{2}{C}H\overset{3}{C}H_2\overset{4}{C}H_3$$

1-Butene

(2) $CH_3CH{=}CHCH_3$
Number from either end. The double bond is between C-2 and C-3.

$$\overset{1}{C}H_3\overset{2}{C}H{=}\overset{3}{C}H\overset{4}{C}H_4$$

2-Butene

(3) $CH_3{-}\underset{\displaystyle CH_3}{\underset{|}{C}}{=}CH_2$

Number from the right as this formula is written. The methyl is attached to the C-2 atom. The parent compound can be written as propene (instead of 1-propene), since there could not be a 2-propene. (Although it is also true that there could not be a 1-methyl- or 3-methylpropene, the number 2 is usually included in the name.)

$$\overset{3}{C}H_3{-}\underset{\displaystyle CH_3}{\underset{|}{\overset{2}{C}}}{=}\overset{1}{C}H_2$$

2-Methylpropene

EXERCISE 13.4

Name the five pentene isomers listed in Sample Exercise 13.3

SAMPLE EXERCISE 13.5

Name this alkene, a compound that is used as an intermediate in the synthesis of some laundry detergents.

$$CH_3\underset{\displaystyle CH_3}{\underset{|}{C}}HCH_2\underset{\displaystyle CH_3}{\underset{|}{C}}HCH_2\underset{\displaystyle CH_3}{\underset{|}{C}}HCH{=}CHCH_3$$

Solution:

The longest chain is nine C atoms in length. The numbering must start from the right, closest to the double bond.

$$\overset{9}{C}H_3\overset{8}{C}H\overset{7}{C}H_2\overset{6}{C}H\overset{5}{C}H_2\overset{4}{C}H\overset{3}{C}H{=}\overset{2}{C}H\overset{1}{C}H_3$$
(with CH_3 groups on C-8, C-6 and C-4)

The name is 4,6,8-trimethyl-2-nonene

EXERCISE 13.5

What is the name of this alkene?

$$CH_3CH{=}CCH_2CHCH_2CH_3$$
(with CH_3 groups on the third and fifth carbons from the left)

Trivial names are often used for some of the simpler alkenes which include one of the two unsaturated groups below. Because they appear in the structures of so many compounds these groups are given the special names *vinyl* and *allyl.*

$CH_2{=}CH{-}$	$CH_2{=}CHCH_2{-}$
Vinyl	Allyl

Thus the compounds below can be named vinyl chloride and allyl chloride instead of chloroethane and 3-chloropropene.

$CH_2{=}CHCl$	$CH_2{=}CHCH_2Cl$
Vinyl chloride (chloroethene)	Allyl chloride (3-chloropropene)

13.6 WRITING ALKENE FORMULAS FROM NAMES

To draw the structural formula for an alkene from its name, do the following:

1. Draw a C to C chain corresponding to the parent alkene name and number the C atoms.
2. Insert the double bond.
3. Attach branched groups.
4. Fill in the H atoms needed to give each C atom in the formula a covalency of 4.

For example, suppose we want to write the structural formula for the compound named 2,4-dimethyl-2-pentene.

1. Draw a five-carbon chain for pentene and number the C atoms.

$$\overset{1}{C} \quad \overset{2}{C} \quad \overset{3}{C} \quad \overset{4}{C} \quad \overset{5}{C}$$

2. Insert the double bond between C-2 and C-3.

$$\overset{1}{C} \quad \overset{2}{C}{=}\overset{3}{C} \quad \overset{4}{C} \quad \overset{5}{C}$$

3. Attach methyl groups to C-2 and C-4.

$$\overset{1}{C} \quad \underset{CH_3}{\overset{2}{C}}{=}\overset{3}{C} \quad \underset{CH_3}{\overset{4}{C}} \quad C$$

4. Fill in the H atoms needed to give each C atom a covalency of 4: three each on C-1 and C-5, none on C-2, and one each on C-3 and C-4.

$$CH_3\underset{CH_3}{C}{=}CH\underset{CH_3}{C}HCH_3$$

SAMPLE EXERCISE 13.6

Write the formula for 4,5-dimethyl-3-octene.

Solution:

1. Draw an eight-carbon chain.

$$\overset{1}{C} \quad \overset{2}{C} \quad \overset{3}{C} \quad \overset{4}{C} \quad \overset{5}{C} \quad \overset{6}{C} \quad \overset{7}{C} \quad \overset{8}{C}$$

2. Insert the double bond between C-3 and C-4.

$$\overset{1}{C} \quad \overset{2}{C} \quad \overset{3}{C}{=}\overset{4}{C} \quad \overset{5}{C} \quad \overset{6}{C} \quad \overset{7}{C} \quad \overset{8}{C}$$

3. Attach one methyl group to the C-4 and one to the C-5 atom.

$$\overset{1}{C} \quad \overset{2}{C} \quad \overset{3}{C}{=}\underset{CH_3}{\overset{4}{C}} \quad \underset{CH_3}{\overset{5}{C}} \quad \overset{6}{C} \quad \overset{7}{C} \quad \overset{8}{C}$$

4. Fill in the H atoms, three each on C-1 and C-8, two each on C-2, C-6, and C-7, one each on C-3 and C-5, and none on C-4.

$$\begin{array}{l} \overset{1}{CH_3}\overset{2}{CH_2}\overset{3}{CH}=\overset{4}{C}-\overset{5}{CH}\overset{6}{CH_2}\overset{7}{CH_2}\overset{8}{CH_3} \\ \qquad\qquad\quad | \quad\;\; | \\ \qquad\qquad\; CH_3\,CH_3 \end{array}$$

EXERCISE 13.6

Give the formula for 2,4,4-trimethyl-2-pentene.

13.7 CIS-TRANS GEOMETRIC ISOMERISM

So far we have been discussing alkene structural isomers which have the same molecular formula but different structural formulas. Now we introduce another type of isomerism called *geometric isomerism*. **Geometric isomers** are compounds which have the same molecular formula *and* the same structural formula but a different arrangement of their atoms in space. Certain alkenes exhibit this kind of isomerism, namely, those that contain two different atoms (or groups of atoms) on *both* doubly bonded C atoms. For instance, the one alkene formula shown below (in which X and Y are different groups or atoms) represents two different compounds.

$$YXC=CXY$$

To show the two different compounds that correspond to the formula above, we draw more detailed structural formulas, which show the actual geometry of the molecules. The two compounds are

(1) X and X above, C=C, Y and Y below — is different from (2) X above left, Y above right, C=C, Y below left, X below right

In Latin *cis* means "on this side" and *trans* means "across."

In compound (1), called the **cis isomer**, the two X's are on the same side of the double bond, as are the two Y's. In compound 2, the **trans isomer**, the X's are on different sides, as are the two Y's.

(1) X and X above, C=C, Y and Y below

X's on the same side
Y's on the same side
Cis isomer

(2) X above left, Y above right, C=C, Y below left, X below right

X's on opposite sides
Y's on opposite sides
Trans isomer

The reason that formulas 1 and 2 represent different compounds is that there is no rotation about the C to C double bond. The double bond is *rigid* and is said to be *hindered* in its rotation. Because of the hindered rotation molecule 1 cannot be twisted around the double bond to become molecule 2. This is different from the free rotation possible about a single bond (Figure 13.5*a*). The reason for the rigidity of the C to C double bond can be seen by looking at the orbital bonding picture. Rotation about the double bond would destroy the maximum overlap attained when the two p_z atomic orbitals of C are side by side, as shown in Figure 13.5*b*.

One of the three butene isomers, 2-butene, exhibits cis-trans isomerism.

$$CH_3CH{=}CHCH_3$$
2-Butene

Each of the double-bonded C atoms has two different attachments, a methyl group and an H atom. In the cis isomer the H atoms are on the same side of the double bond and in the trans isomer they are on opposite sides. The full names of the compounds must include the prefixes cis- and trans-.

$$\begin{matrix} CH_3 & & CH_3 \\ & C{=}C & \\ H & & H \end{matrix} \qquad \begin{matrix} CH_3 & & H \\ & C{=}C & \\ H & & CH_3 \end{matrix}$$
cis-2-Butene *trans*-2-Butene

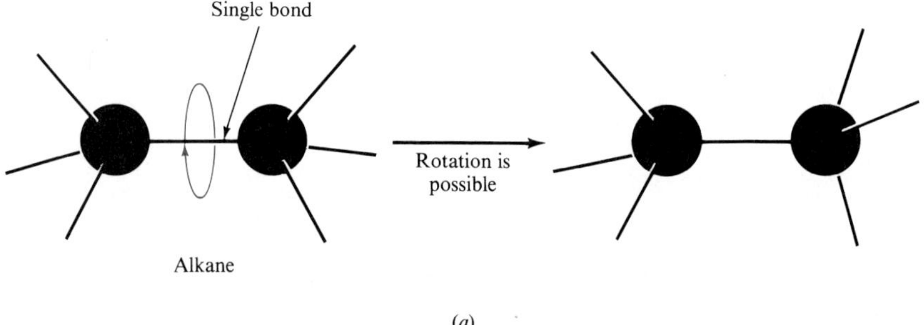

(*a*)

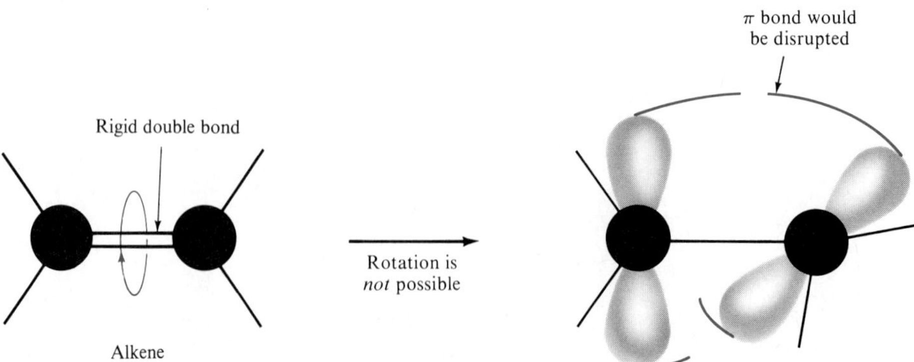

FIGURE 13.5

Cis and trans isomers have different chemical and physical properties; for example, *cis*-2-butene boils at 4°C, compared with *trans*-2-butene, which boils at 1°C (see Table 13.2, where the physical properties of ethene, propene, the butenes, and pentenes are summarized). Also note that the boiling points of *cis*-2-butene and *trans*-2-butene are different from those of the other butene isomers, 1-butene and 2-methylpropene.

The X's and the Y's in the general formula for alkenes that exhibit cis-trans isomerism need not be identical. For instance, the compound 2-pentene has a cis and a trans isomer; on one double-bonded C atom there is a methyl group and an H atom and on the other an ethyl and an H atom.

TABLE 13.2 **PHYSICAL PROPERTIES OF ALKENES**

Name	Formula	Boiling point, °C	Melting point, °C	Density, g/ml (liquids at 20°)
Ethene	$CH_2{=}CH_2$	−102	−169	Gas
Propene	$CH_2{=}CHCH_3$	−48	−185	Gas
1-Butene	$CH_2{=}CHCH_2CH_3$	−7	−185	Gas
cis-2-Butene	$(CH_3)(H)C{=}C(CH_3)(H)$ (CH₃ groups cis)	4	−139	Gas
trans-2-Butene	$(CH_3)(H)C{=}C(H)(CH_3)$ (CH₃ groups trans)	1	−106	Gas
2-Methylpropene	$CH_2{=}C(CH_3)CH_3$	−7	−141	Gas
1-Pentene	$CH_2{=}CHCH_2CH_2CH_3$	30	−138	0.640
cis-2-Pentene	$(CH_3)(H)C{=}C(CH_2CH_3)(H)$ (cis)	37	−151	0.655
trans-2-Pentene	$(CH_3)(H)C{=}C(H)(CH_2CH_3)$ (trans)	36	−136	0.648
3-Methyl-1-butene	$CH_2{=}CHCH(CH_3)CH_3$	20	−169	0.627
2-Methyl-1-butene	$CH_2{=}C(CH_3)CH_2CH_3$	31	−138	0.650
2-Methyl-2-butene	$CH_3C(CH_3){=}CHCH_3$	39	−134	0.662

$$CH_3CH{=}CHCH_2CH_3$$

The isomer in which the methyl and the ethyl are on the same side of the double bond is the cis isomer.

$$\underset{\textit{cis}\text{-2-Pentene}}{\overset{CH_3\qquad CH_2CH_3}{\underset{H\qquad\quad H}{C{=}C}}}\qquad\underset{\textit{trans}\text{-2-Pentene}}{\overset{CH_3\qquad H}{\underset{H\qquad CH_2CH_3}{C{=}C}}}$$

In general, the cis geometric isomer is the one in which the most similar groups are on the same side of the double bond and the trans isomer is the one in which they are on opposite sides.

To see if an alkene has cis and trans isomers examine the groups attached to the double-bonded C atoms.

Cis-trans isomerism in alkenes is possible *only* if both C atoms in the double bond bear two different atoms or groups. If either double-bonded C atom contains two identical atoms or groups, there can be no cis-trans isomerism. For instance, 1-chloro-1-bromoethene does not exhibit cis-trans isomerism; the C-1 atom is bonded to different atoms (a Cl and a Br) but the C-2 atom is bonded to two H atoms. Only one arrangement in space is possible. The formulas drawn below represent the same molecule since one formula can simply be "flipped over" to produce the other.

$$\underset{\text{1-Chloro-1-bromoethene}}{\overset{Cl\qquad H}{\underset{Br\qquad H}{C{=}C}}}\quad\text{is the same as}\quad\underset{\text{1-Chloro-1-bromoethene}}{\overset{Br\qquad H}{\underset{Cl\qquad H}{C{=}C}}}$$

SAMPLE EXERCISE 13.7

Write the formulas for the cis and trans isomers of 1,2-dichloroethene, $C_2H_2Cl_2$.

Solution:

In the formula for 1,2-dichloroethene we see that there are two different atoms, a Cl and an H, on each double-bonded C atom.

$$ClCH{=}CHCl$$

In the cis isomer the Cl atoms are on the same side of the double bond and in the trans isomer they are on opposite sides.

$$\underset{\textit{cis}\text{-1,2-Dichloroethene}}{\overset{Cl\qquad Cl}{\underset{H\qquad H}{C{=}C}}}\qquad\underset{\textit{trans}\text{-1,2-Dichloroethene}}{\overset{Cl\qquad H}{\underset{H\qquad Cl}{C{=}C}}}$$

Cis- and *trans*-1,2-dichloroethene are different compounds with different boiling points (60.3°C for the *cis*-isomer and 47.5°C for the *trans*-isomer).

EXERCISE 13.7

Give the structural formulas for the cis and trans isomers of 2,3-dibromo-2-butene.

SAMPLE EXERCISE 13.8

Decide whether 1-hexene or 2-hexene exhibits cis-trans isomerism. If so, give the names and formulas of the two isomers.

Solution:

We must examine both doubly bonded C atoms of 3-hexene. If either one contains two identical groups, no cis-trans isomerism exists.

$$\overset{1}{C}H_2{=}\overset{2}{C}H\overset{3}{C}H_2\overset{4}{C}H_2\overset{5}{C}H_2\overset{6}{C}H_2$$

3-Hexene

The C-1 atom contains 2 H atoms.

No cis-trans isomerism is possible for 1-hexene.

$$\overset{1}{C}H_3\overset{2}{C}H{=}\overset{3}{C}H\overset{4}{C}H_2\overset{5}{C}H_2\overset{6}{C}H_3$$

2-Hexene

In 2-hexene, the C-2 atom contains an H and a methyl group and C-3 contains an H and a propyl group. Thus there must be both a *cis*-2-hexene and a *trans*-2-hexene.

```
CH3           CH2CH2CH3    CH3            H
   \         /                \          /
    C = C                      C = C
   /         \                /          \
 H             H            H             CH2CH2CH3
```

cis-2-Hexene   *trans*-2-Hexene

EXERCISE 13.8

Decide whether 3-hexene or 2-methyl-2-pentene exhibits cis-trans isomerism. If so, give the names and formulas of the two isomers.

13.8 PROPERTIES OF ALKENES

The physical properties of alkene hydrocarbons are similar to those of the alkanes (see Section 12.13). Alkenes are nonpolar compounds which dissolve readily in nonpolar solvents and are insoluble in water. Table 13.3 compares the boiling points and densities of straight-chain alkenes with those of the alkanes (and alkynes).

The alkenes are physically similar to the alkanes but chemically much more reactive.

Most of the chemical properties of the alkenes are very different from those of the relatively unreactive alkanes. Like alkanes, the alkenes undergo combustion reactions with oxygen of the air.

$$\text{Alkene} + O_2 \longrightarrow CO_2 + H_2O$$

However, it is the reactions involving the double bond which are the characteristic reactions of the alkenes. The more loosely held π electrons (see Section 13.3) are available for the formation of new bonds in chemical reactions with other substances.

An atom or group of atoms which determines the properties of a molecule is said to be a ***functional group.***

The functional group of an alkene is the double bond.

Consider the chemical oxidation of alkenes using cold, dilute aqueous potassium permanganate ($KMnO_4$) solution. This reaction, milder than the combustion reaction above, disrupts only the double bond of the alkene, leaving the rest of the molecule intact. The products include an organic compound known as a diol and manganese(IV) oxide, MnO_2.

$$\underset{\text{Alkene}}{-\overset{|}{C}=\overset{|}{C}-} + \underset{\text{Potassium permanganate}}{KMnO_4} + H_2O \longrightarrow \underset{\text{Organic product (diol)}}{-\underset{OH}{\overset{|}{\underset{|}{C}}}-\underset{OH}{\overset{|}{\underset{|}{C}}}-} + MnO_2 + KOH \quad \text{(unbalanced)}$$

Potassium permanganate forms a bright purple solution, which upon reaction gives a brown precipitate of MnO_2. This reaction is the basis for a useful analytical test known as the Baeyer test, which is used to identify alkenes. If an unknown compound does cause the purple color of potassium permanganate to disappear, it *might* be an alkene. However, since many other types of organic compounds also react with $KMnO_4$ solutions, further tests must be done to make a more definitive identification. The reaction of an alkene with potassium permanganate is shown in Color Plate 14.

The characteristic reactions of alkenes are addition reactions.

The most important class of reactions in which the alkene double bond participates are **addition reactions**, in which two reactant molecules, an alkene A and some other molecule B, add together to form one product molecule AB.

$$A + B \longrightarrow AB$$

To see why addition to double bonds is so favorable, let us consider the reaction

TABLE 13.3 PHYSICAL PROPERTIES OF ALKANES, ALKENES, AND ALKYNES

Alkane	bp, °C	Density, g/ml at 20°C	Alkene	bp, °C	Density, g/ml at 20°C	Alkyne	bp, °C	Density, g/ml at 20°C
Methane	−164	Gas						
Ethane	−89	Gas	Ethene	−102	Gas	Ethyne	−84	Gas
Propane	−42	Gas	Propene	−48	Gas	Propyne	−23	Gas
Butane	−0.5	Gas	1-Butene	−7	Gas	1-Butyne	8	Gas
Pentane	36	0.63	1-Pentene	30	0.64	1-Pentyne	40	0.69
Hexane	69	0.66	1-Hexene	63	0.67	1-Hexyne	71	0.72
Heptane	98	0.68	1-Heptene	94	0.70	1-Heptyne	100	0.73
Octane	126	0.70	1-Octene	121	0.71	1-Octyne	125	0.75

pictured in Figure 13.6 in which the other compound B has the formula XY. Earlier we said that it is the weaker π bond of the alkene double bond which determines an alkane's reactivity. Two new single bonds (C—X and C—Y) form as the X—Y and the alkene π bonds break to form the product molecule as shown in Figure 13.6 where the bonds involved are in color. The product bonds (two σ's) are stronger than the reactant bonds (one π and one σ), which means that the product is more stable than the reactants. Reactions such as this, in which the products are more stable than the reactants, are exothermic. Recall from Chapter 10 that exothermic reactions are almost always spontaneous (Section 10.5) and hence addition reactions are spontaneous.

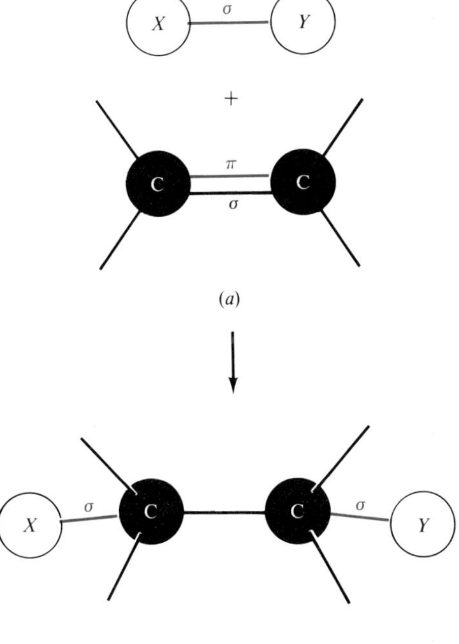

Addition to alkenes. (*a*) The bonds (in color) that will be broken include one σ and one π. (*b*) The newly formed bonds (in color) include two σ bonds X-C and C-Y.

13.9 ADDITION REACTIONS OF ALKENES

We do not burn alkenes for fuel because they are too valuable as synthetic intermediates.

Pyrolysis comes from *pyr* "fire" and *lysis* "loosening."

Alkenes are valuable starting materials in the synthesis of organic compounds. Because they undergo addition readily and thus are so reactive, the amounts of alkene present in nature are very small. However, alkenes can be prepared by heating alkanes, the main components of natural gas and petroleum (Section 12.17). The process, called **pyrolysis,** breaks one large alkane molecule down into a mixture of smaller alkane and alkene molecules. A typical example of one of these reactions, called *cracking* reactions, is shown below. Heating hexane under pressure produces a mixture which includes a large amount of ethene (about 40 percent) along with smaller amounts of propene (about 20 percent), methane, and other compounds.

$$\underset{\text{Hexane}}{CH_3CH_2CH_2CH_2CH_2CH_3} \xrightarrow{\Delta} \underset{\text{Methane}}{CH_4} + \underset{\text{Ethene}}{CH_2{=}CH_2} + \underset{\text{Propene}}{CH_3CH{=}CH_2}$$

Various substances can be added to the double bonds of ethene, propene, and other alkenes to produce useful products. Ethene, for instance, can be converted into polyethylene, ethyl alcohol, and ethyl chloride. In this section we will see how products such as these are formed as we discuss the addition of H_2, Cl_2, Br_2, hydrogen halides, H_2O, and alkenes themselves to alkenes.

Addition of H_2

When H_2 is added to an alkene, the product is an alkane.

$$\text{Alkene} + H_2 \longrightarrow \text{alkane}$$

This general type of reaction, in which a double bond is converted to a single bond by the addition of hydrogen gas, is called **hydrogenation.** We say that hydrogen *adds across* the double bond.

$$\underset{\text{Alkene}}{-\overset{|}{C}{=}\overset{|}{C}-} + \underset{\text{Hydrogen}}{H{-}H} \longrightarrow \underset{\text{Alkane}}{-\overset{|}{\underset{H}{\underset{|}{C}}}-\overset{|}{\underset{H}{\underset{|}{C}}}-}$$

When hydrogen is added to ethene, the product is ethane

$$\underset{\text{Ethene}}{H-\overset{H}{\overset{|}{C}}{=}\overset{H}{\overset{|}{C}}-H} + \underset{\text{Hydrogen}}{H{-}H} \longrightarrow \underset{\text{Ethane}}{H-\overset{H}{\overset{|}{\underset{H}{\underset{|}{C}}}}-\overset{H}{\overset{|}{\underset{H}{\underset{|}{C}}}}-H}$$

or, using condensed formulas,

$$CH_2{=}CH_2 + H_2 \longrightarrow CH_3CH_3$$

Similarly, adding hydrogen to 1-butene or 2-butene produces butane.

$$\underset{\text{1-Butene}}{CH_3CH_2CH{=}CH_2} + H_2 \longrightarrow \underset{\text{Butane}}{CH_3CH_2CH_2CH_2CH_3}$$

$$\underset{\text{2-Butene}}{CH_3CH{=}CHCH_3} + H_2 \longrightarrow \underset{\text{Butane}}{CH_3CH_2CH_2CH_3}$$

All these reactions are exothermic. The hydrogenation of ethene, for instance, evolves about 33 kcal/mol ($\Delta H = -33$ kcal/mol).

$$CH_2{=}CH_2 + H_2 \longrightarrow CH_3CH_3 + 33\ \text{kcal/mol}$$

In fact, the heats of hydrogenation for all alkenes are about 30 kcal/mol.

In Chapter 10 you learned that spontaneous reactions are not necessarily fast ones (Section 10.5). Without a catalyst the hydrogenation of alkenes would proceed at a very slow rate. To make the reaction practical, a finely divided metal catalyst such as platinum, palladium, or nickel must be added to lower the energy barrier between the reactants and products (See Section 10.7 for a discussion of catalysis.)

$$CH_2{=}CH_2 + H_2 \xrightarrow{\text{Pt, Pd, or Ni}} CH_3CH_3$$

Addition of Cl_2 or Br_2

Like H_2, bromine (Br_2) and chlorine (Cl_2) can be added across alkene double bonds. (F_2 is too reactive to use and I_2 is not reactive enough.) Unlike hydrogenation, the halogenation of alkenes is fast and does not require a catalyst. The products of such reactions are 1,2-dihaloalkanes, sometimes called vicinal dihalides, which are used as starting materials to prepare other organic compounds. One halogen bonds to each of the double-bonded C atoms. For instance, when Cl_2 is added to ethene, the product is 1,2-dichloroethane.

In Latin the word *vicinus* means "neighbor."

```
  H  H                         H  H
  |  |                         |  |
H—C=C—H  +  Cl—Cl   ——→    H—C——C—H
                               |  |
                               Cl Cl
 Ethene      Chlorine      1,2-Dichloroethane
```

Using condensed formulas,

$$\underset{\text{Ethene}}{CH_2{=}CH_2} + Cl_2 \longrightarrow \underset{\text{1,2-Dichloroethane}}{ClCH_2CH_2Cl}$$

Ethene is a gas and the product 1,2-dichloroethane is an oily liquid. It is this reaction that gave rise to the name *olefiant gas*, meaning "oil-forming gas," a name once used for ethylene. At one time the alkenes were known as *olefins*.

1,2-Dibromoethane is a dense toxic liquid that smells like chloroform.

The addition of bromine to ethene gives 1,2-dibromoethene.

$$\underset{\text{Ethene}}{CH_2{=}CH_2} + Br_2 \longrightarrow \underset{\text{1,2-Dibromoethane}}{BrCH_2CH_2Br}$$

The fact that compounds with C to C double bonds are able to absorb bromine rapidly can be used as a qualitative test for the presence of alkenes. Bromine is a vibrantly colored, reddish orange liquid. Alkenes and the product haloalkanes are colorless. When the highly colored bromine is added to an unknown sample, two things can happen. If the red color persists, the bromine has not reacted with the sample compound, meaning that no C to C double bonds are present and the compound cannot be an alkene. If the red color does disappear (this happens nearly instantaneously), an addition reaction has occurred and the unknown compound could be an alkene.

Reaction with bromine is one way to distinguish an alkane from an alkene. Without sunlight or heat the substitution reaction of Br_2 with alkanes is so slow that no reaction appears to occur. Suppose a student has two hydrocarbon samples, one of which is known to be pentane and the other pentene. They are both low-boiling colorless liquids with similar densities (see Table 13.3), so they cannot easily be distinguished on the basis of their physical properties. But pentane does not react readily with Br_2, whereas pentene does.

$$\underset{\text{Pentane (colorless)}}{CH_3CH_2CH_2CH_2CH_3} + \underset{\text{Bromine (red)}}{Br_2} \longrightarrow \underset{\text{(remains red)}}{\text{no immediate reaction}}$$

$$\underset{\text{1-Pentene (colorless)}}{CH_2{=}CHCH_2CH_2CH_3} + \underset{\text{Bromine (red)}}{Br_2} \longrightarrow \underset{\text{1,2-Dibromopentane (colorless)}}{BrCH_2\underset{\displaystyle Br}{\underset{|}{C}}HCH_2CH_2CH_3}$$

If the red color disappears, the unknown hydrocarbon must be pentene; if it stays, it must be pentane (see Color Plate 15). The Baeyer test discussed in Section 13.8 can also be used to decide which compound is which. The pentane is not oxidized by $KMnO_4$ and so will not decolorize the purple $KMnO_4$ solution, whereas the pentene will.

SAMPLE EXERCISE 13.9

Write equations to describe the reaction of propene with

(a) O_2 (b) H_2 (c) Cl_2

Solution:

(a) This is a combustion reaction, yielding CO_2 and water.

$$CH_3CH{=}CH_2 + O_2 \longrightarrow CO_2 + H_2O$$

It is easier to see how to balance the equation if the molecular formula for propene (C_3H_6) is used.

$$C_3H_6 + \tfrac{9}{2}O_2 \longrightarrow 3CO_2 + 3H_2O$$

or, using integer coefficients,

$$2C_3H_6 + 9O_2 \longrightarrow 6CO_2 + 6H_2O$$

(**b**) This is an addition reaction (specifically, hydrogenation), which produces an alkane.

$$CH_3CH{=}CH_2 + H_2 \xrightarrow{\text{Pt.Pd, or Ni}} \underset{\text{Propane}}{CH_3CH_2CH_3}$$

(**c**) The product of this addition reaction is a dihaloalkane.

$$CH_3CH{=}CH_2 + Cl_2 \longrightarrow \underset{\text{1,2-Dichloropropane}}{CH_3\underset{\substack{|\\ Cl}}{C}HCH_2Cl}$$

EXERCISE 13.9

The compound 1,2-dibromobutane can be prepared by the bromination of 1-butene. Write an equation to describe this reaction.

Addition of Hydrogen Halides

The hydrogen halides HCl, HBr, and HI can be added to alkenes to produce haloalkanes. The H atom bonds to one of the double-bonded C atoms and the halogen atom to the other. For instance, the addition of HCl to ethene produces the local anesthetic chloroethane (ethyl chloride). The properties and uses of the alkyl halide products were discussed in Section 12.15.

$$\underset{\text{Ethene}}{H{-}\underset{\substack{|\\ H}}{C}{=}\underset{\substack{|\\ H}}{C}{-}H} + H{-}Cl \longrightarrow \underset{\text{Chloroethane}}{H{-}\overset{\substack{H\\ |}}{\underset{\substack{|\\ H}}{C}}{-}\overset{\substack{Cl\\ |}}{\underset{\substack{|\\ H}}{C}}{-}H}$$

$$\underset{\text{Ethene}}{CH_2{=}CH_2} + HCl \longrightarrow \underset{\text{Chloroethane}}{CH_3CH_2Cl}$$

Adding HI to 2-butene produces 2-iodobutane.

$$CH_3CH{=}CHCH_3 + HI \longrightarrow CH_3CH_2\underset{\displaystyle I}{\underset{|}{C}}HCH_3$$

2-Butene 2-Iodobutane

So far the example alkenes we have used in the addition of hydrogen halides have been symmetrical. That is, the two carbon atoms bearing the double bond are each bonded to the same atoms and groups and those are indistinguishable from each other. Suppose we choose an alkene that is not symmetrical—propene, for instance. One of the double-bonded C atoms in propene is attached to two H atoms and the other to a methyl group and an H atom:

$$CH_3{-}\underset{\displaystyle H}{\underset{|}{C}}{=}\underset{\displaystyle H}{\underset{|}{C}}{-}H$$

Now there are two possible products which might be expected to form when a hydrogen halide is added, that is, the H atom could be directed to either C atom. Suppose HCl is added to propene. If the H atom bonds to the C-1 atom, the product will be 2-chloropropane.

$$\overset{3}{C}H_3\overset{2}{C}H{=}\overset{1}{C}H_2 + H{-}Cl \longrightarrow CH_3\underset{\displaystyle Cl}{\underset{|}{C}}H\underset{\displaystyle H}{\underset{|}{C}}H_2 \text{ or } CH_3\underset{\displaystyle Cl}{\underset{|}{C}}HCH_3$$

Propene 2-Chloropropane

If the H atom adds to C-2, a different product, 1-chloropropane, will form:

$$\overset{3}{C}H_3\overset{2}{C}H{=}\overset{1}{C}H_2 + H{-}Cl \longrightarrow CH_3\underset{\displaystyle H}{\underset{|}{C}}H\underset{\displaystyle Cl}{\underset{|}{C}}H_2 \text{ or } CH_3CH_2CH_2Cl$$

Propene 1-Chloropropane

Vladimir Markovnikov (1838–1904), from the University of Moscow, did important work on hydrocarbon chemistry.

In fact, only one of these products, 2-chloropropane, actually does form in any appreciable amount. We can predict the product of reactions such as this one above by adhering to **Markovnikov's rule**, which states that the H atom goes to the double-bonded C atom which already has the most H atoms. An easy way to remember this rule is that "the rich (with H) C atoms get richer (with H)." Now let us look again at the addition of HCl to propene. We see that the C-1 atom has two H atoms and the C-2 atom has only one. Thus, according to Markovnikov's rule the product must be 2-chloropropane, the compound that forms when the H atom of HCl bonds to the C-1 atom of propene.

SAMPLE EXERCISE 13.10

Give the two possible products of the addition of HBr to 1-butene. Which one predominates?

Solution:

The H atom of HBr can add to the C-1 atom of 1-butene:

$$CH_3CH_2CH{=}CH_2 + HBr \longrightarrow \underset{\text{2-Bromobutane}}{CH_3CH_2\underset{\displaystyle Br}{\underset{|}{C}}HCH_3}$$

Or the H atom can add to the C-2 atom:

$$CH_3CH_2CH{=}CH_2 + HBr \longrightarrow \underset{\text{1-Bromobutane}}{CH_3CH_2CH_2CH_2Br}$$

According to Markovnikov's rule 2-bromobutane is the predominant product, since the H atom will add to the doubly bonded carbon (C-1), which already has the most H atoms.

EXERCISE 13.10

Write the reactions for the formation of the two possible products formed when we add HI to 2-pentene. These two products are formed in approximately equal amounts. Why?

Addition of H_2O

Water adds across the alkene double bond in the presence of an acid catalyst to produce oxygen-containing organic compounds called *alcohols*. Alcohols, which contain the functional group —OH, will be discussed in detail in Chapter 15. To write equations for these reactions we write the water formula as H—OH. The H atom is joined to one of the double-bonded C atoms and the OH to the other.

$$\underset{\text{Alkene}}{-\overset{\displaystyle H}{\overset{|}{C}}{=}\overset{\displaystyle H}{\overset{|}{C}}-} + H{-}OH \xrightarrow{H^+} \underset{\text{Alcohol}}{-\underset{\displaystyle OH}{\underset{|}{\overset{\displaystyle H}{\overset{|}{C}}}}-\underset{\displaystyle H}{\underset{|}{\overset{\displaystyle H}{\overset{|}{C}}}}-}$$

For instance, the reaction of ethene with water produces an alcohol called ethyl alcohol (ethanol).

$$\underset{\text{Ethene}}{CH_2{=}CH_2} + H{-}OH \xrightarrow{H^+} \underset{\text{Ethyl alcohol}}{H{-}CH_2CH_2{-}OH \text{ or } CH_3CH_2OH}$$

The addition of water to alkenes also obeys Markovnikov's rule. When water adds across the propene double bond, there are two possible products; isopropyl alcohol is the one that forms as the H atom of water goes to the C-1 atom, the one which already has two H atoms.

$$\overset{3}{C}H_3\overset{2}{C}H{=}\overset{1}{C}H_2 + H{-}OH \xrightarrow{H^+} CH_3\underset{\displaystyle OH}{\underset{|}{C}}HCH_2{-}H \quad \text{or} \quad CH_3\underset{\displaystyle OH}{\underset{|}{C}}HCH_3$$

Propene — Isopropyl alcohol

The addition of water to alkenes, the hydration of alkenes, is an important industrial process for making alcohols. In fact, isopropyl alcohol is the major ingredient in rubbing alcohol (a 70% solution of the alcohol in water).

SAMPLE EXERCISE 13.11

Give the two possible products of the hydration of 1-butene. One of these, used as an organic reagent, industrial cleaner, and solvent, is actually prepared by the hydration of butene. Which of the reactions below is involved?

Solution:

Water could add across the double bond of 1-butene in two possible ways.

$$(1)\ CH_3CH_2CH{=}CH_2 + H{-}OH \longrightarrow CH_3CH_2\underset{\displaystyle OH}{\underset{|}{C}}HCH_2{-}H$$

$$\text{or} \quad CH_3CH_2\underset{\displaystyle OH}{\underset{|}{C}}HCH_3$$

$$(2)\ CH_3CH_2CH{=}CH_2 + H{-}OH \longrightarrow CH_3CH_2CH_2\underset{\displaystyle H}{\underset{|}{C}}H{-}OH$$

$$\text{or} \quad CH_3CH_2CH_2CH_2OH$$

Reaction 1 is useful because it is the one in which the H atom adds to the C that already has two H atoms, thus satisfying the Markovnikov rule.

EXERCISE 13.11

Another way to make one of the products above, $CH_3CH_2\underset{\displaystyle OH}{\underset{|}{C}}HCH_3$, is by the hydration of 2-butene. Give the reaction for this. Can the other product, $CH_3CH_2CH_2CH_2OH$, be made this way?

Addition of Alkenes

It is possible for one alkene molecule to add across the double bond of another alkene molecule. For instance, at high pressure and temperature ethene can be added to itself.

$$\underset{\text{Ethene}}{\mathrm{H{-}\overset{H}{\overset{|}{C}}{=}\overset{H}{\overset{|}{C}}{-}H}} + \underset{\text{Ethene}}{\mathrm{H{-}\overset{H}{\overset{|}{C}}{=}\overset{H}{\overset{|}{C}}{-}H}} \longrightarrow \underset{\text{1-Butene}}{\mathrm{H{-}\overset{H}{\overset{|}{\underset{H}{\underset{|}{C}}}}{-}\overset{H}{\overset{|}{\underset{H}{\underset{|}{C}}}}{-}\overset{H}{\overset{|}{C}}{=}\overset{H}{\overset{|}{C}}{-}H}}$$

We will discuss the polymerization of other alkenes in Chapter 19.

The product, 1-butene, still has a double bond, to which yet another ethene molecule can be added. The butene is a *dimer* (two parts) because it was formed from two single ethene units called *monomers*. Continued additions lead to giant

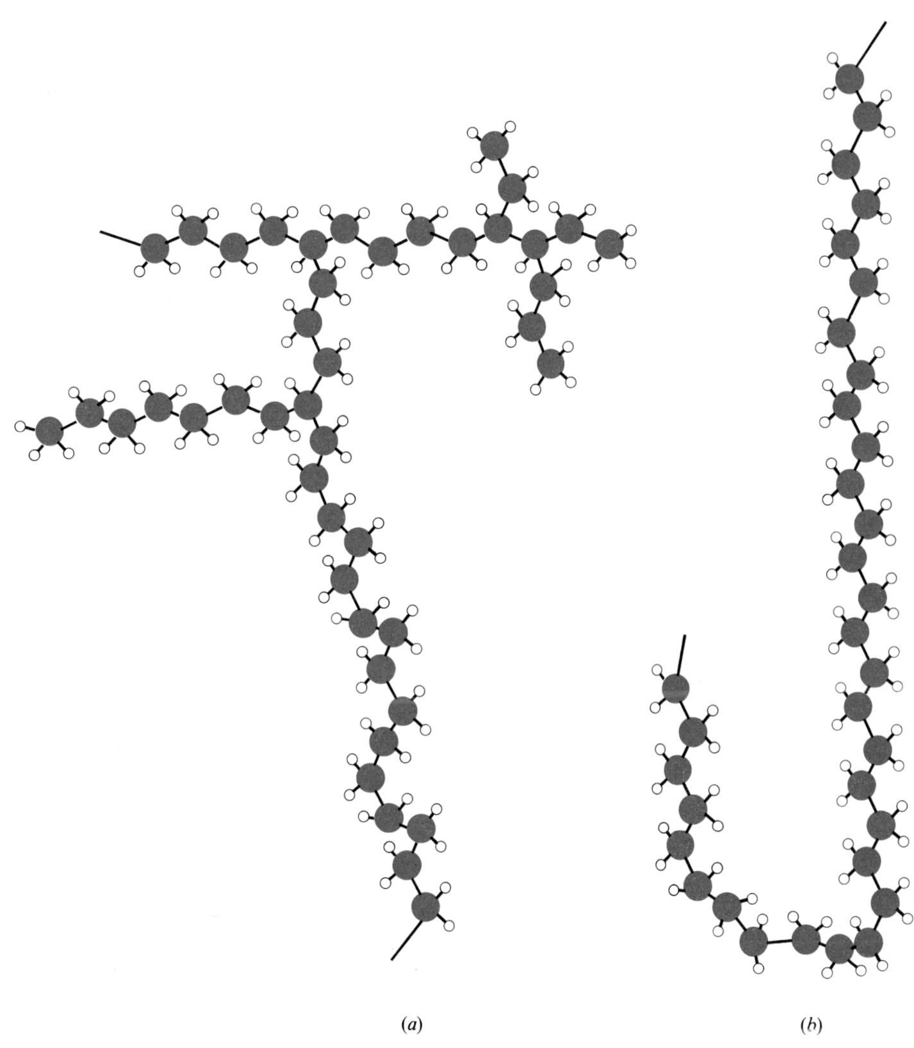

FIGURE 13.7
Polyethylene chains. (*a*) Branched polyethylene segment. (*b*) Linear polyethylene segment.

molecules called *polymers* (many parts), the subject of Chapter 19. The polymer molecule that forms from the polymerization of ethene is called polyethene (commonly known as polyethylene) and consists of a long single-bonded C to C chain, which may be linear or branched depending on the conditions of the reaction (see Figure 13.7). Polyethylene (or polyethene) is composed of carbon-carbon single bonds, just as alkane molecules are. Thus, like an alkane, polyethylene is relatively unreactive and is insoluble in water. Polyethylene is one of the most useful of all polymers, being used in the form of plastic wrap and molded objects such as toys, housewares, and bottles.

In medicine polyethylene is used for drains, catheters, and tubing.

13.10 CYCLIC ALKENES

In Chapter 12 (Section 12.16) you saw that alkanes can exist as ring compounds called cycloalkanes. Alkenes can likewise exist as ring compounds, called in this case **cycloalkenes.** Cycloalkenes have one or more double bonds in their rings. Both formulas below represent the structure of cyclohexene, C_6H_{10}.

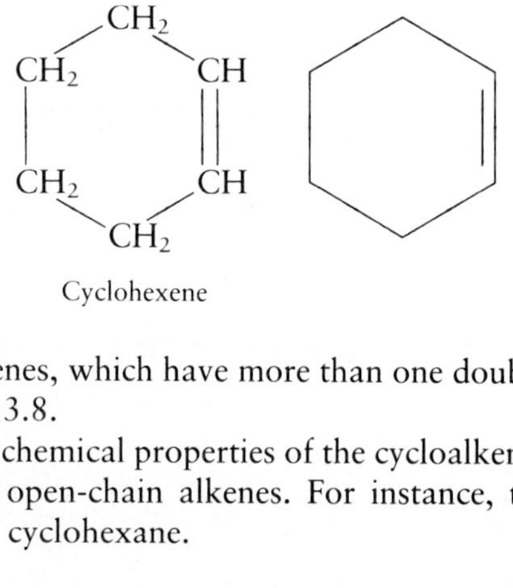

CH_2 CH_2 CH CH_2 CH CH_2

Cyclohexene

Some other cyclic alkenes, which have more than one double bond in their rings, are shown in Figure 13.8.

The physical and chemical properties of the cycloalkenes are similar to those of the corresponding open-chain alkenes. For instance, the addition of H_2 to cyclohexene produces cyclohexane.

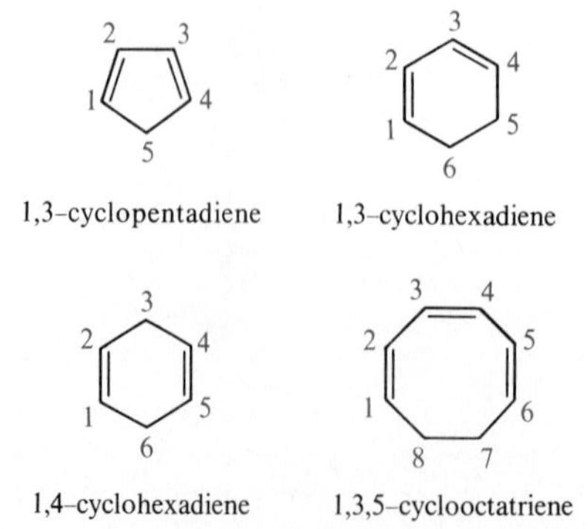

1,3-cyclopentadiene

1,3-cyclohexadiene

1,4-cyclohexadiene

1,3,5-cyclooctatriene

FIGURE 13.8
Cyclic alkenes.

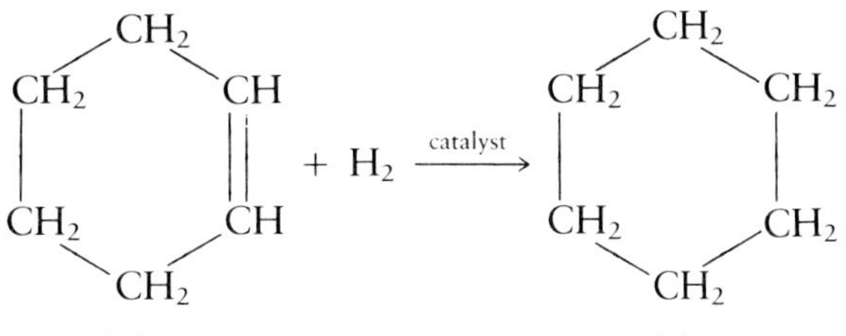

$$\begin{array}{c} CH_2 - CH_2 - CH = CH - CH_2 - CH_2 \text{ (ring)} \end{array} + H_2 \xrightarrow{\text{catalyst}} \text{cyclo-}(CH_2)_6$$

Cyclohexene   Cyclohexane

Also like hexene, cyclohexene decolorizes bromine. Since, in cycloalkanes, ring carbon positions are numbered consecutively to give the substituents the lowest possible numbers (Section 12.16), the product of this reaction is called 1,2-dibromocyclohexane.

$$\text{Cyclohexene} + Br_2 \longrightarrow \text{ring } CH_2-CH_2-CH_2-CH_2-CH(Br)-CH(Br)$$

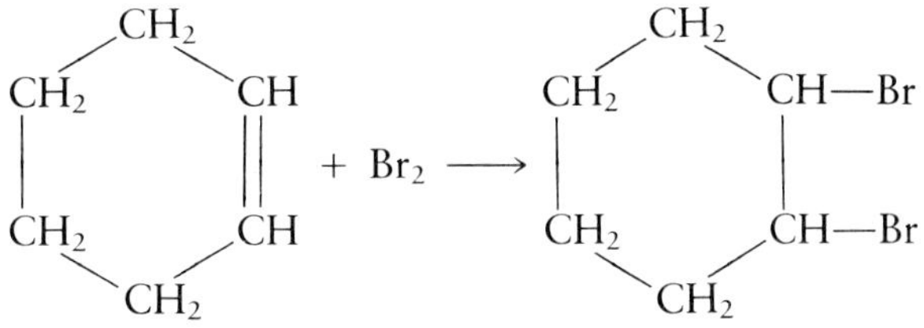

Cyclohexene   1,2-Dibromocyclohexane

13.11 DIENES AND TERPENES

Alkenes that include two C to C double bonds are **dienes**. The most important diene is the four-carbon compound 1,3-butadiene.

$$\overset{1}{C}H_2{=}\overset{2}{C}H{-}\overset{3}{C}H{=}\overset{4}{C}H_2$$

In Section 13.9 we saw that alkenes could be added to alkenes to form polymer molecules. Butadiene can also be added to butadiene, forming polymers which have rubbery, elastic properties. The addition of a methyl derivative of butadiene (called *isoprene*) to itself produces the same structure as that of natural rubber from rubber tree plants.

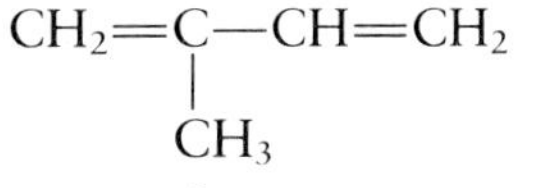

$$CH_2{=}\underset{\displaystyle CH_3}{\underset{|}{C}}{-}CH{=}CH_2$$

Isoprene

A segment of the product of the polymerization, called polyisoprene, is shown in Figure 13.9*a*. Note that polyisoprene still contains one double bond for each repeating unit. Furthermore, the two C atoms involved in the double bond are each bonded to two different "groups," one being attached to an H atom and to the remaining part of the polymer chain, while the other is attached to a methyl

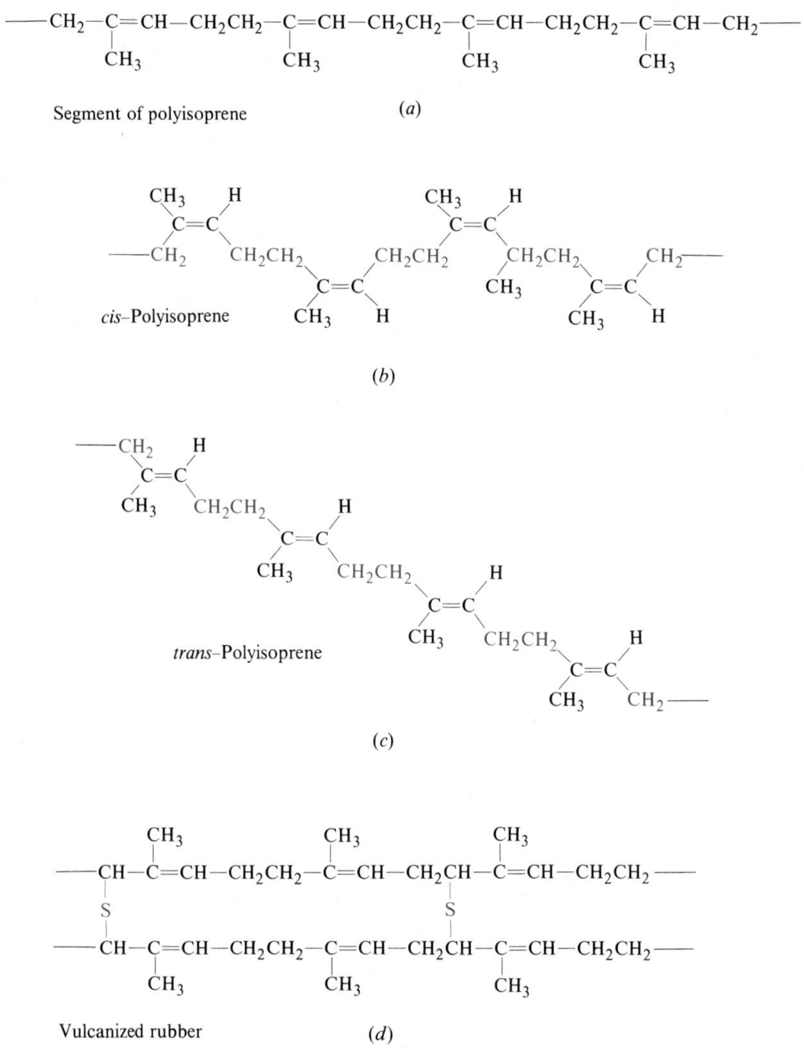

$$—CH_2—\underset{\displaystyle CH_3}{\underset{|}{C}}=CH—CH_2CH_2—\underset{\displaystyle CH_3}{\underset{|}{C}}=CH—CH_2CH_2—\underset{\displaystyle CH_3}{\underset{|}{C}}=CH—CH_2CH_2—\underset{\displaystyle CH_3}{\underset{|}{C}}=CH—CH_2—$$

Segment of polyisoprene (*a*)

cis-Polyisoprene (*b*)

trans-Polyisoprene (*c*)

Vulcanized rubber (*d*)

FIGURE 13.9
Polyisoprene. (*a*) Segment of polyisoprene. (*b*) Natural rubber. The CH_2CH_2 groups are on the same side of the double bond. (*c*) The CH_2CH_2 groups are on opposite sides of the double bond. (*d*) Vulcanized rubber.

group and the rest of the chain. Thus the polyisoprene molecule exhibits cis-trans isomerism and can exist in two forms, *trans*-polyisoprene and *cis*-polyisoprene, as shown in Figure 13.9*b*.

The American Charles Goodyear (1800–1860) discovered vulcanization.

These two compounds have very different properties. Natural rubber is *cis*-polyisoprene. The trans form of polyisoprene is a stiff, brittle substance known as gutta percha, the material used as a covering for golf balls. Because polyisoprene contains double bonds, it is more reactive than polymers such as polyethylene and can be degraded by reaction with oxidizing agents. Its reactivity can also be put to practical use by treating *cis*-polyisoprene with sulfur to link neighboring polymer chains (Figure 13.9*c*). This process, called *vulcanization*, gives the rubber enough strength to allow it to be used in rubber tires.

Natural rubber is an example of a **terpene**, a naturally occurring compound which includes isoprene fragments. Both cyclic and straight-chain terpenes, such as those shown in Figure 13.10, are widespread in nature. Figure 13.11*a* shows the formula of *β-carotene*, a terpene in which there are eight isoprene units. The

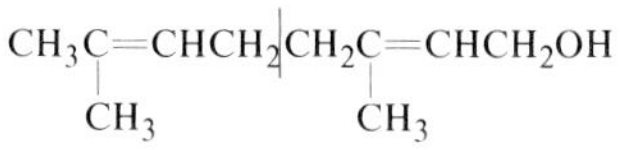

$CH_3C{=}CHCH_2|CH_2C{=}CHCH_2OH$ (with CH_3 on each C=)

Geraniol (in geranium oil)

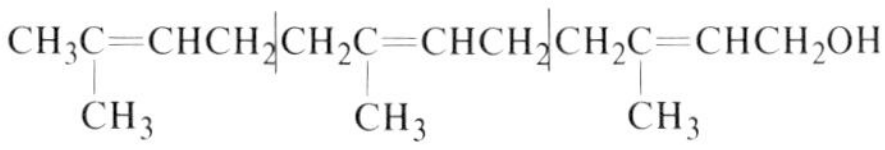

$CH_3C{=}CHCH_2|CH_2C{=}CHCH_2|CH_2C{=}CHCH_2OH$ (with CH_3 on each C=)

Farneseol (in flower oils)

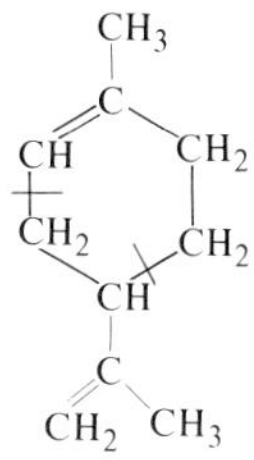

Limonene (in lemon oil)

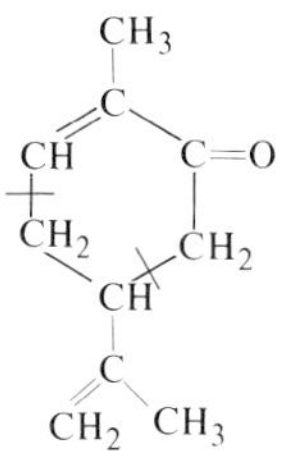

Carvone (in caraway oil and spearmint)

FIGURE 13.10
Terpenes. Colored markers separate the C_5 isoprene units. Geraniol contains two isoprene units and farnesol contains three. The cyclic terpenes, limonene and carvone, each contain two isoprenes.

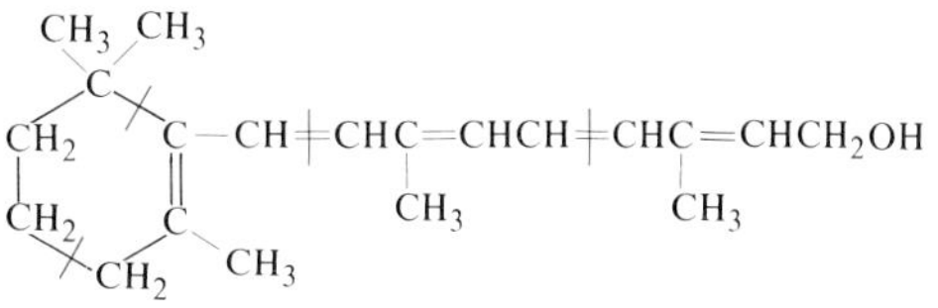

Vitamin A

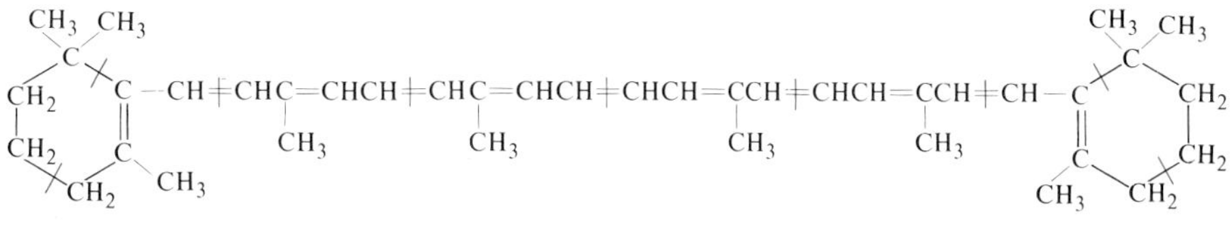

β-Carotene (in carrots)

FIGURE 13.11
β-Carotene and vitamin A are also terpenes. The body can synthesize vitamin A from β-carotene.

The conversion of carotenes to vitamin A takes place in the intestine.

carotenes are precursors in the biological synthesis of another terpene called *retinol,* a form of *vitamin A* (Figure 13.11). Note that vitamin A includes four isoprene units, which means that one molecule of carotene can provide two molecules of vitamin A. The structure and function of vitamin A are discussed further in Chapter 22 on lipids, where we will see how retinol is involved in the visual cycle.

13.12 ALKYNES

Alkynes are unsaturated hydrocarbons containing a C to C triple bond. An alkyne has two less H atoms than a corresponding alkene and four less than an alkane.

Alkane: C_nH_{2n+2}
Alkene: C_nH_{2n}
Alkyne: C_nH_{2n-2}

Alkynes contain one triple bond.

Since the formation of a triple bond requires at least two C atoms, there are no alkynes in which $n = 1$. When n is 2, the alkyne formula is C_2H_2, and when it is 3, the formula becomes C_3H_4.

The names of alkynes are derived by dropping the *-ane* from the name of the alkane with the same number of carbon atoms and adding the suffix *-yne*. For instance, the name of the two-carbon alkyne is ethyne, a name which is almost always replaced by the common name *acetylene*.

We usually write the acetylene formula as HC≡CH rather than CH≡CH.

$$HC\equiv CH$$

Ethyne, or acetylene

The IUPAC rules for naming alkyne compounds are the same as those we used for the alkenes. The two isomers of butyne below are called 1-butyne and 2-butyne.

$$HC\equiv CCH_2CH_3 \qquad CH_3C\equiv CCH_3$$

1-Butyne 2-Butyne

A common system is also used in which alkynes are named as derivatives of acetylene. For instance, propyne is sometimes called methylacetylene.

$$CH_3C\equiv CH$$

Propyne, or methylacetylene

No cis-trans isomerism is possible for alkynes. The triple bond is rigid as is the double bond, but in an alkyne molecule only one atom or group of atoms can be bonded to each triple-bonded C atom. Thus only one arrangement in space is possible.

SAMPLE EXERCISE 13.12

Give the formulas and names for the isomers of pentyne.

Solution:

First list those which contain a five-carbon chain.

$$(1)\ \overset{1}{H}\overset{2}{C}\equiv\overset{3}{C}\overset{4}{C}H_2\overset{5}{C}H_2CH_3 \qquad (2)\ \overset{1}{C}H_3\overset{2}{C}\equiv\overset{3}{C}\overset{4}{C}H_2\overset{5}{C}H_3$$

1-Pentyne 2-Pentyne

There is one more isomer, a butyne derivative.

(3) $\overset{1}{H}\overset{2}{C}{\equiv}\overset{3}{C}\overset{4}{C}HCH_3$ with a CH_3 branch on C-3

3-Methyl-1-butyne

There are three isomers of pentyne.

EXERCISE 13.12

Name this alkyne:

$$CH_3CH_2CH_2\underset{\displaystyle CH_3}{\underset{|}{C}}HC{\equiv}CCH_2CH_3$$

13.13 THE ALKYNE TRIPLE BOND

In alkenes each of the triply bonded C atoms forms bonds with only *two* neighboring atoms. In acetylene, H—C≡C—H, each C atom forms a triple bond with the other C atom and a single bond with H. The triply bonded carbon atoms in alkynes are *sp hybridized.* One 2*s* orbital mixes with only one of the 2*p* orbitals to produce a set of two hybrid orbitals called **sp orbitals** and two unhybridized *p* orbitals, in color below.

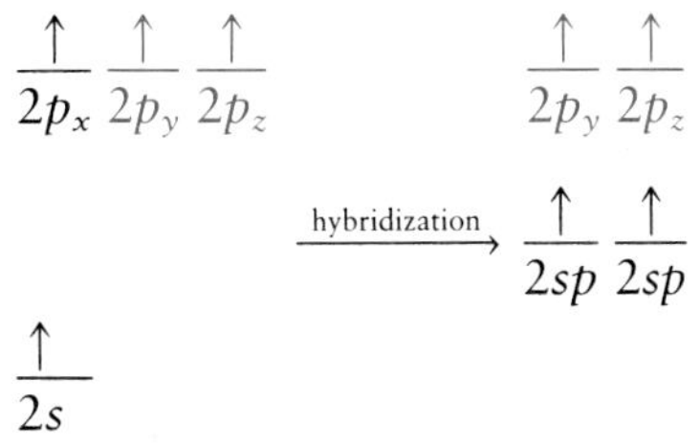

$$\begin{array}{ccc} \underline{\uparrow}\ \underline{\uparrow}\ \underline{\uparrow} & & \underline{\uparrow}\ \underline{\uparrow} \\ 2p_x\ 2p_y\ 2p_z & & 2p_y\ 2p_z \\ & \xrightarrow{\text{hybridization}} & \underline{\uparrow}\ \underline{\uparrow} \\ & & 2sp\ 2sp \\ \underline{\uparrow} & & \\ 2s & & \end{array}$$

We write the electronic configuration for a triply bonded carbon atom as follows:

$$1s^2(2sp)^1(2sp)^1 2p_y{}^1 2p_z{}^1$$

The two *sp* hybrid orbitals are shaped like lopsided dumbbells and are arranged about the C atom nucleus so that they fall in a straight line, as shown in Figure 13.12.

The orbital bonding picture of the simplest alkyne, ethyne or acetylene, is shown in Figure 13.13. The two *sp* hybrid orbitals are drawn around the two triply bonded C atoms. The two H atoms of acetylene are singly bonded to each of the two C atoms by overlap of H 1*s* orbitals with C *sp* hybrid orbitals, as

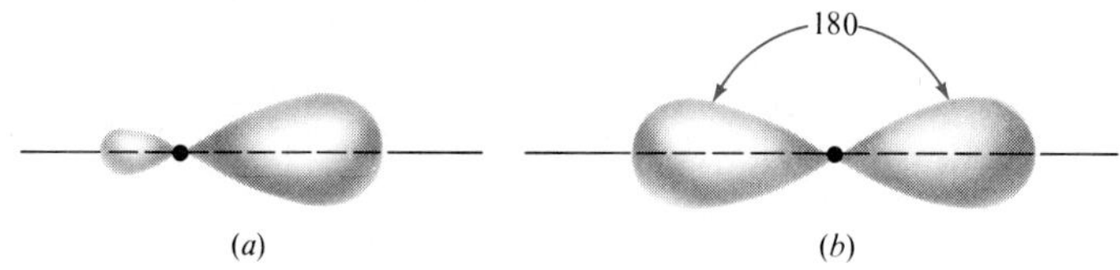

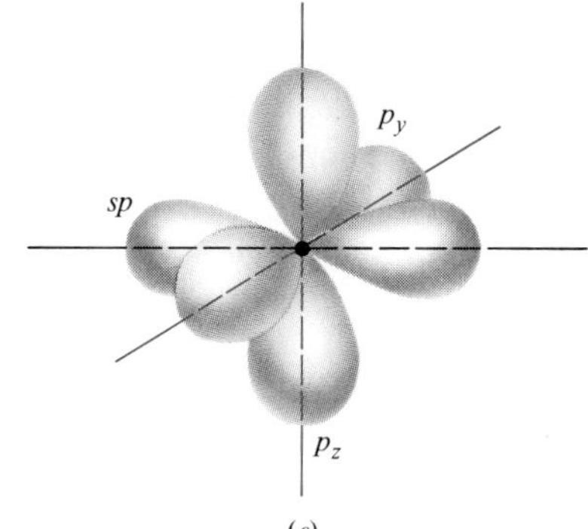

FIGURE 13.12
(*a*) An *sp*-hybrid orbital. (*b*) The *sp*-hybrid orbitals of C. (*c*) *sp*-hybrid orbital and two unhybridized *p* orbitals (in color).

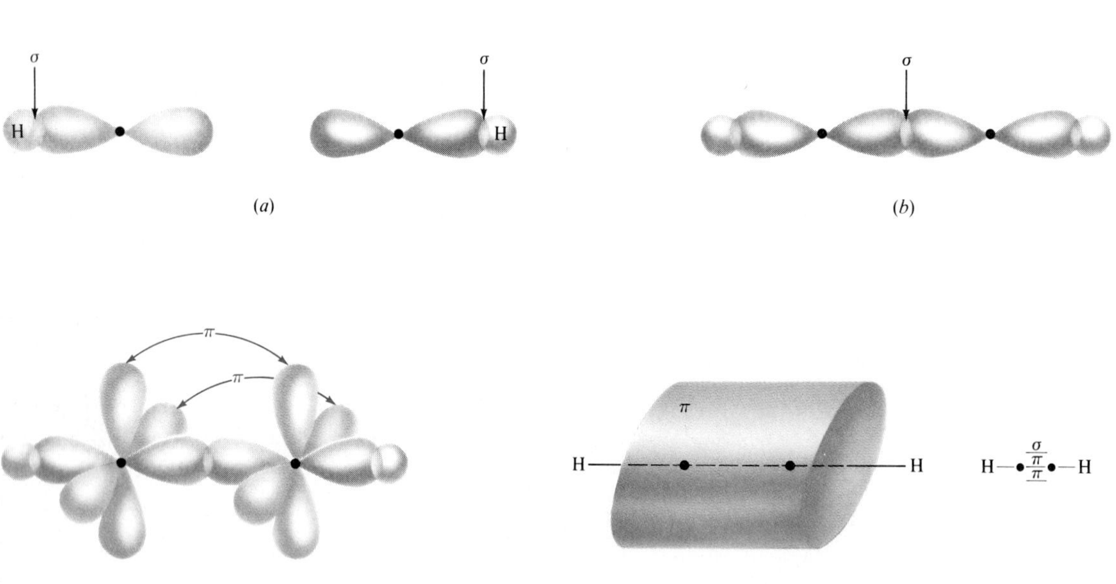

FIGURE 13.13
Bonding in acetylene. (*a*) Two σ bonds from two H 1*s* orbitals overlap with two *sp*-hybrid orbitals. (*b*) A σ bond forms as the remaining sp orbitals overlap. (*c*) Two π bonds form from the overlap of both pairs of unhydridized *p* orbitals. (*d*) The triple bond is two-thirds π and one-third σ.

shown in Figure 13.13*a*. The remaining two *sp* orbitals (one from each C atom) overlap with each other to form the σ bond of the triple bond. This much of the structure of acetylene contains σ bonds only and is the σ framework (see Figure 13.13*b*). To complete the triple bond the unhybridized p_y and p_z orbitals from each C atom overlap to form two π bonds, one from the two unhybridized p_y orbitals and another from the two unhybridized p_z orbitals. The complete picture of the acetylene bonding is given in Figure 13.13*c*. The acetylene triple bond is thus one-third σ and two-thirds π in character. As in alkenes, the loosely held π electrons are available to participate in chemical reactions.

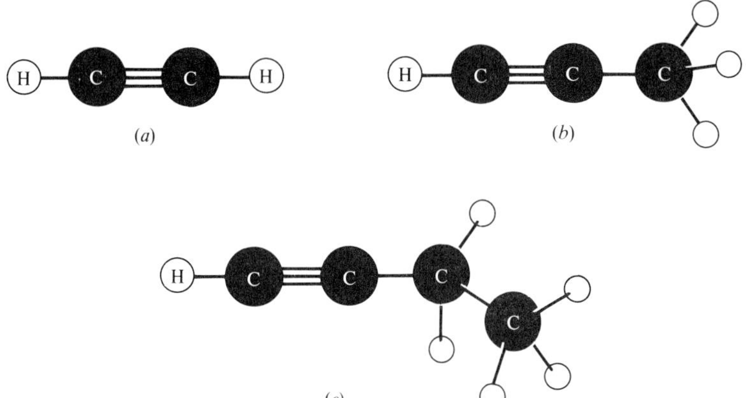

FIGURE 13.14
Alkyne structures. (*a*) Ethyne C_2H_2 (acetylene). (*b*) Propyne C_3H_4. (*c*) Butyne C_4H_6.

The C≡C triple bond has both σ and π character.

The Lewis electron dot structure for C_2H_2 is drawn by including a triple bond between the two C atoms, thus satisfying the octet rule.

$$\mathrm{H{:}C{:}{:}{:}C{:}H} \qquad \text{or} \qquad \mathrm{H{-}C{\equiv}C{-}H}$$

Figure 13.14 shows the structures of ethyne (acetylene), propyne, and butyne.

13.14 PROPERTIES OF ALKYNES

The functional group of an alkyne is the triple bond.

Physically the alkynes are similar to the corresponding alkenes or alkanes (see Table 13.3). Chemically they are very reactive because of the triple bonds they contain.

The reactions of alkynes, like those of alkenes, involve addition across the multiple bond. We can write the addition reactions of alkynes as though they occurred in two steps, the first converting the triple bond to a double bond and the second converting the double bond to a single bond. For instance, we can write the reaction for the hydrogenation of acetylene, forming first ethene and then ethane.

$$\mathrm{H{-}C{\equiv}C{-}H + H{-}H \longrightarrow H{-}\overset{\overset{\displaystyle H}{|}}{C}{=}\overset{\overset{\displaystyle H}{|}}{C}{-}H}$$

$$\mathrm{H{-}\overset{\overset{\displaystyle H}{|}}{C}{=}\overset{\overset{\displaystyle H}{|}}{C}{-}H + H{-}H \longrightarrow H{-}\underset{\underset{\displaystyle H}{|}}{\overset{\overset{\displaystyle H}{|}}{C}}{-}\underset{\underset{\displaystyle H}{|}}{\overset{\overset{\displaystyle H}{|}}{C}}{-}H}$$

However, what we write on paper is not always possible in the laboratory. In practice the addition to alkynes provides a mixture of saturated (alkane) and unsaturated (alkene) products. For some reactions it is possible to choose conditions under which one of the steps is much faster than the other. For instance, the reaction above can produce an excellent yield of alkene when carried out in the presence of a palladium catalyst which has been partially deactivated (*poisoned*). Compared with alkenes, alkynes undergo hydrogenation so fast in the presence of palladium that the poisoned catalyst is active enough to permit hydrogenation of the alkyne but is not a good enough catalyst for addition of hydrogen to alkenes. Thus the majority of product that forms is alkene and not alkane.

Alkynes also undergo addition with hydrogen halides, water, and halogens. In the reactions below propene reacts with Cl_2 to form an alkene and an alkane.

$$\underset{\text{Propyne}}{CH_3C{\equiv}CH} + Cl_2 \longrightarrow \underset{\text{1,2-Dichloropropene}}{CH_3C(Cl){=}CH(Cl)} \xrightarrow{Cl_2} \underset{\text{1,1,2,2-Tetrachloropropane}}{CH_3CCl_2{-}CHCl_2}$$

The mixture that forms in this reaction contains about three times as much alkane as alkene product.

The combustion of alkynes produces CO_2 and H_2O, as in the reaction below for acetylene:

$$2HC{\equiv}CH + 5O_2 \longrightarrow 4CO_2 + 2H_2O$$

The amount of heat evolved in this reaction is greater than that produced by the combustion of other hydrocarbons, which is why the burning of acetylene provides a flame hot enough (about 2800°C) to join metal parts by a process called *welding*.

SAMPLE EXERCISE 13.13

Write a two-step reaction for the the combination of 1-butyne with bromine to form a tetrabromobutane.

Solution:

First we add Br_2 across the butyne triple bond to form a dibromobutene:

$$\underset{\text{1-Butene}}{CH_3CH_2C{\equiv}CH} + Br{-}Br \longrightarrow \underset{\text{1,2-Dibromobutene}}{CH_3CH_2C(Br){=}CH(Br)}$$

Then another Br_2 adds across the double bond:

$$\mathrm{CH_3CH_2C(Br){=}CH(Br) + Br{-}Br \longrightarrow CH_3CH_2C(Br)_2{-}CH(Br)_2}$$

1,2-Dibromobutene → 1,1,2,2-Tetrabromobutane

EXERCISE 13.13

Give the structures and names of the alkene and alkane produced by the hydrogenation of propyne.

Acetylene can be produced in the laboratory from simple inorganic materials. First charcoal (C) reacts with lime (CaO) when heated to form a compound called calcium carbide:

$$3C + CaO \xrightarrow{\Delta} CaC_2 + CO$$

The carbide ion, C_2^{2-}, includes a triple bond and can be written as $C{\equiv}C^{2-}$. Dripping water over calcium carbide converts it into acetylene:

$$2H_2O + Ca^{2+}(C{\equiv}C)^{2-} \longrightarrow HC{\equiv}CH + Ca(OH)_2$$

Thus by starting with charcoal, lime, and water it is possible to make the organic compound acetylene and from acetylene to make other valuable organic compounds.

SUMMARY

Alkenes and alkynes are unsaturated hydrocarbons because they contain multiple bonds. Physically they are very much like the alkanes; chemically they are vastly different because of the extra reactivity of the multiple bonds.

Alkenes (general formula C_nH_{2n}) are hydrocarbons which contain a double bond. The alkene double bond forms from the overlap of two sp^2 hybrid orbitals to produce the σ part of the double bond and from the overlap of two unhybridized p orbitals to form the π part. The π bond is estimated to be only two-thirds as strong as the σ bond. The double bond and its attached atoms all lie in the same plane.

Alkene names are derived from those of the alkane with the same number of carbon atoms by replacing the *-ane* suffix with *-ene*. The IUPAC nomenclature system for alkenes is similar to that for alkanes except that the double bond takes precedence and a number must be included to specify the position of the double bond.

Alkenes exhibit a special type of isomerism called cis-trans isomerism. This is an example of geometric isomerism in which compounds with the same structural formula are different because their atoms are arranged differently in space. In alkenes restricted rotation about the double bond because of the π bonding "traps" similar groups on the same side of the double bond (cis isomer) or on opposite sides (trans isomer). Cis and trans isomers have different physical and chemical properties.

Alkenes are highly reactive as compared with alkanes because of the availability of the π electrons in the double bond. Alkenes can be oxidized by $KMnO_4$ to produce diols. The typical reactions of alkenes are addition reactions in which hydrogen, halogens, hydrogen halides, water, and alkenes themselves add across the double bond. The addition of hydrogen halides and water to unsymmetrical alkenes obeys Markovnikov's rule, which states that the H goes to that doubly bonded C atom which has the most H atoms. The addition of alkenes to each other produces giant molecules called polymers.

Cycloalkenes are ring compounds with one or more double bonds. Dienes are open-chain alkene compounds with two double bonds. Terpenes, such as rubber, carotenes, and vitamin A, are naturally occurring compounds containing isoprene units.

Alkynes (general formula C_nH_{2n-2}) contain a triple bond. The σ part of the triple bond forms from the overlap of two *sp* hybridized orbitals; the remaining two components of the triple bond arise from the overlap of two unhybridized p_y orbitals and two unhybridized p_z orbitals. The triply bonded C atoms and the atoms bonded to them all lie in a straight line. Alkynes are named in the same way as alkenes except that their parent names end in *-yne*. Ethyne is nearly always called acetylene. Like alkenes, alkynes undergo addition reactions. These occur in two steps, with an alkene forming first, then an alkane. Some reactions can be stopped after the first step.

KEY WORDS

saturated
unsaturated
alkene
alkyne
sp^2 orbital
sp orbital
geometric isomerism
cis
trans
functional group
pyrolysis
addition reaction
hydrogenation
hydration
Markovnikov's rule
cycloalkene
diene
terpene

EXERCISES

13.14 Draw electron dot structures for (**a**) propene; (**b**) propyne.

13.15 What is meant by the terms saturated and unsaturated?

13.16 Give the molecular formulas for each of the following hydrocarbons: (**a**) heptane; (**b**) heptene; (**c**) heptyne.

13.17 The formula weight of an open-chain hydrocarbon with 10 carbon atoms is 138. What is its molecular formula? What type of compound is it?

13.18 Why is it impossible to explain the bonding in ethene and ethyne (acetylene) by using sp^3 hybrid orbitals?

13.19 Compare the strengths of the π and σ bonds that contribute to the C to C double bond.

13.20 Give the hybridization for each C atom in the formulas below:

(**a**) $\begin{array}{l} CH_2{=}CHCHCH_3 \\ \qquad\quad\ \ | \\ \qquad\quad CH_3 \end{array}$ (**b**) $CH_3CH_2C{\equiv}CH$

13.21 Rewrite the following formulas in condensed form.

(**a**) $\begin{array}{ccccc} H & & & & H \\ & \diagdown & & \diagup & \\ & & C{=}C & & \\ & \diagup & & \diagdown & \\ H & & & & F \end{array}$

(**b**) $\begin{array}{ccccccccccc} & & H & & H & & H & & H & & H \\ & & | & & | & & | & & | & & | \\ H & - & C & = & C & - & C & - & C & - & C & - & H \\ & & & & & & | & & | & & | \\ & & & & & & H & & H & & H \end{array}$

(**c**) $\begin{array}{ccccccccccc} & & Cl & & & & & & H & & \\ & & | & & & & & & | & & \\ Cl & - & C & - & C & = & C & - & C & - & H \\ & & | & & | & & | & & | & & \\ & & H & & H & & | & & H & & \\ & & & & & H & - & C & - & H & \\ & & & & & & & | & & & \\ & & & & & & & H & & & \end{array}$

(**d**) $\begin{array}{ccccccccccc} & & H & & & & & & H & & H & & \\ & & | & & & & & & | & & | & & \\ H & - & C & - & C & \equiv & C & - & C & - & C & - & H \\ & & | & & & & & & | & & | & & \\ & & H & & & & & & H & & H & & \end{array}$

13.22 Ethylene and one of its derivatives, trichloroethylene, have both been used as general inhalation anesthetics. Give their structural formulas.

13.23 Name the following unsaturated hydrocarbons:

(a) $HC{\equiv}CH$

(b) $\begin{array}{ccccc} CH_2{=}CH & CH & CH_2 & CH & CH_3 \\ & | & & | & \\ & Cl & & CH_3 & \end{array}$

(c) $\begin{array}{ccccc} CH_3 & C & {=}CH & CH & CH_3 \\ & | & & | & \\ & CH_3 & & Br & \end{array}$

(d) $\begin{array}{ccc} CH_3CH{=}CH & CH & CH_3 \\ & | & \\ & CH_2 & \\ & | & \\ & CH_3 & \end{array}$

(e) $CH_3CH_2C{\equiv}CCH_3$

(f) $\begin{array}{ccc} & CH_3 & \\ & | & \\ CH_3 & C & CH_2CH_2CH{=}CHCH_3 \\ & | & \\ & CH_3 & \end{array}$

13.24 What structural feature is needed for an alkene to exhibit cis-trans isomerism?

13.25 Of the compounds in Exercise 13.23, which exhibit cis-trans isomerism? For each one that does, give the full structures and names of both isomers.

13.26 Why don't alkynes or alkanes exhibit cis-trans isomerism?

13.27 Write structural formulas which correspond to the following names:
(a) 2-Hexene
(b) 2-Hexyne
(c) 1,1-Dibromopropene
(d) 1,2-Dibromopropene
(e) 5,5,6-Trimethyl-3-octene
(f) Diiodoacetylene
(g) Propylene
(h) Cyclobutene
(i) 1,3-Pentadiene

13.28 The formulas below correspond to the straight-chain structural isomers of what alkene? Name each one. Do any of them exhibit cis-trans isomerism? For any that do, draw the structures of the cis and trans isomers.
(a) $CH_2{=}CHCH_2CH_2CH_2CH_2CH_2CH_3$
(b) $CH_3CH{=}CHCH_2CH_2CH_2CH_2CH_3$
(c) $CH_3CH_2CH{=}CHCH_2CH_2CH_2CH_3$
(d) $CH_3CH_2CH_2CH{=}CHCH_2CH_2CH_3$

13.29 Identify what is wrong with each of the formulas below:
(a) $CH_2{\equiv}C{-}CH_3$
(b) $\begin{array}{ccc} CH_2{=} & CH & CH_2CH_2CH_3 \\ & | & \\ & CH_3 & \end{array}$
(c) $CH_3C{=}CHCH_2CH_2CH_3$
(d) $\begin{array}{ccc} CH_3CH_2C{\equiv} & C & CH_2CH_2CH_3 \\ & | & \\ & Cl & \end{array}$

13.30 Why are the following IUPAC names "impossible"?
(a) 2-Propene
(b) 3-Butene
(c) 2,2-Dimethyl-2-pentene
(d) 2-Methyl-1-butyne
(e) 2-Methyl-4-pentene
(f) *cis*-1-Butene

13.31 The compound tetrafluoroethene is the starting material for the production of the polymer called Teflon. Give the full structural formula for tetrafluoroethene.

13.32 Write a balanced equation for the combustion of 1-hexene, assuming that the products are carbon dioxide and water.

13.33 Why are there mostly alkanes in petroleum rather than alkenes and alkynes? How do we get alkene compounds from petroleum products?

13.34 What is the difference between a substitution reaction and an addition reaction? Give an example of each one.

13.35 Complete the following reactions and name all organic reactants and products:
(a) $CH_2{=}CH_2 + H_2 \xrightarrow{\text{catalyst}}$
(b) $CH_2{=}CHCH_2CH_3 + Cl_2 \longrightarrow$
(c) $CH_2{=}CH_2 + H_2O \xrightarrow{H^+}$
(d) $CH_3CH{=}CHCH_3 + HI \longrightarrow$
(e)  $+ Br_2 \longrightarrow$

13.36 Is it necessary to balance addition reactions? Why?

13.37 Write the reaction for 1-pentene and potassium permanganate solution. (You need not balance this one.) How will the appearance of this reaction mixture change as the reaction proceeds?

13.38 Using Markovnikov's rule complete the following reactions, giving both possible products. In each case specify which product is the predominant one.
(a) $CH_3CH_2CH{=}CH_2 + HCl \longrightarrow$
(b) $\begin{array}{ccc} CH_3CH{=} & C & CH_2CH_2CH_3 + H_2O \xrightarrow{H^+} \\ & | & \\ & CH_3 & \end{array}$

13.39 Why does rubbing alcohol contain isopropyl alcohol and not propyl alcohol?

13.40 The labels have come off two bottles which contain 1-hexene and hexane. What chemical tests could you perform to replace the correct label on each bottle? Write chemical equations for any reactions involved. Suppose you wished to identify the compounds using a density measurement. How many significant figures would you need to include in your density determinations?

13.41 The compound below is sometimes called by the trivial name propylene dichloride because it is made from propylene.

$$\underset{\displaystyle\quad\;\; Cl}{ClCH_2\overset{|}{C}HCH_3}$$

Write the equation for the reaction of which this compound is a product. What is its IUPAC name?

13.42 Complete the necessary equations for carrying out each of the following alkyne reactions in two steps:

(a) $HC{\equiv}CH + H_2 \longrightarrow$

(b) $HC{\equiv}CCH_3 + Cl_2$

(c) $HC{\equiv}CCH_3 + HCl \longrightarrow$

13.43 Starting with water, charcoal, and calcium oxide, can you think of a way to make ethane?

13.44 What singly bonded hydrocarbon is a structural isomer of propene?

13.45 There are two singly bonded hydrocarbons that have the molecular formula C_4H_8. Of what alkene are they structural isomers? Give their structures.

13.46 The hydrocarbon formula below represents squalene, a precursor in the biological synthesis of cholesterol. In what way does this compound resemble natural rubber? To what general class of compounds does squalene belong? How many isoprene units are present in squalene?

$$CH_3\underset{CH_3}{\underset{|}{C}}{=}CHCH_2CH_2\underset{CH_3}{\underset{|}{C}}{=}CHCH_2CH_2\underset{CH_3}{\underset{|}{C}}{=}CHCH_2CH_2CH{=}\underset{CH_3}{\underset{|}{C}}CH_2CH_2CH{=}\underset{CH_3}{\underset{|}{C}}CH_2CH_2CH{=}\underset{CH_3}{\underset{|}{C}}CH_3$$

13.47 In measuring the vitamin A content of foods, a unit called the retinol equivalent (RE) is sometimes used. The definition of this unit is

$$1 \text{ RE} = 1\ \mu g \text{ vitamin A}$$
$$1 \text{ RE} = 6\ \mu g\ \beta\text{-carotene}$$

If the body were 100 percent efficient in synthesizing vitamin A from β-carotene, what amount of β-carotene in micrograms should corresond to 1 RE?

14 . . . . BENZENE AND THE AROMATIC HYDROCARBONS

14.1 INTRODUCTION

So far most of the compounds we have studied have been open-chain compounds. We also discussed a few ring compounds, the cycloalkanes and cycloalkenes, and found their properties to be very much like their counterparts, the alkanes and alkenes. Open-chain compounds and their corresponding ring compounds are known as **aliphatic compounds.** Thus the pentane and pentene shown below are aliphatic compounds because they have open chains.

$$\underset{\text{Pentane}}{CH_3CH_2CH_2CH_2CH_3} \quad \text{and} \quad \underset{\text{1-Pentene}}{CH_2{=}CHCH_2CH_2CH_3}$$

Moreover the ring compounds, cyclopentane and cyclopentene are also aliphatic because their properties are like those of pentane and 1-pentene.

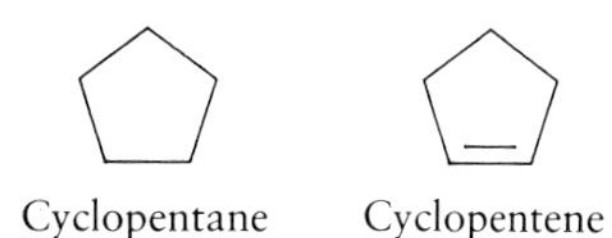

Cyclopentane Cyclopentene

The term aliphatic comes from the Greek word *aleiphar,* which means "oil". When we discuss fat molecules in Chapter 22, we will find that their carbon-containing portions are all aliphatic.

In this chapter we will introduce another class of organic compounds called the *aromatics* (see Figure 14.1). Benzene and its derivatives were originally called aromatic compounds because of their rather pleasant aromas. Some aromatic compounds which are responsible for the odors of flavorings and spices are shown in Figure 14.2, where you can see that they all have a benzene ring in their structures. The term **aromatic** now refers to any compound which has a benzene ring in its structure or has chemical properties similar to those of benzene. In the sections that follow we will describe the structure and the properties of benzene and many of its derivatives.

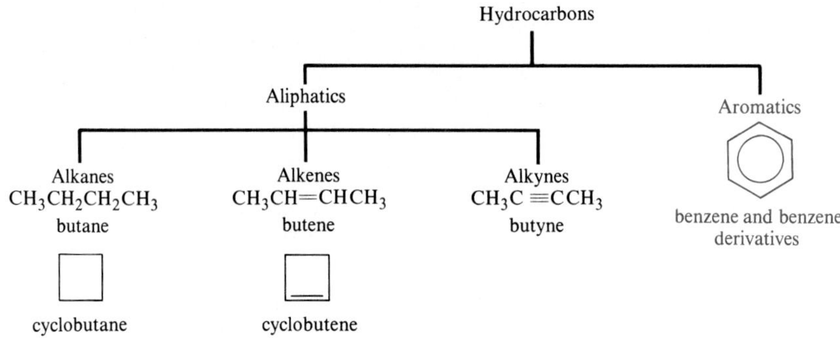

FIGURE 14.1
Types of hydrocarbons.

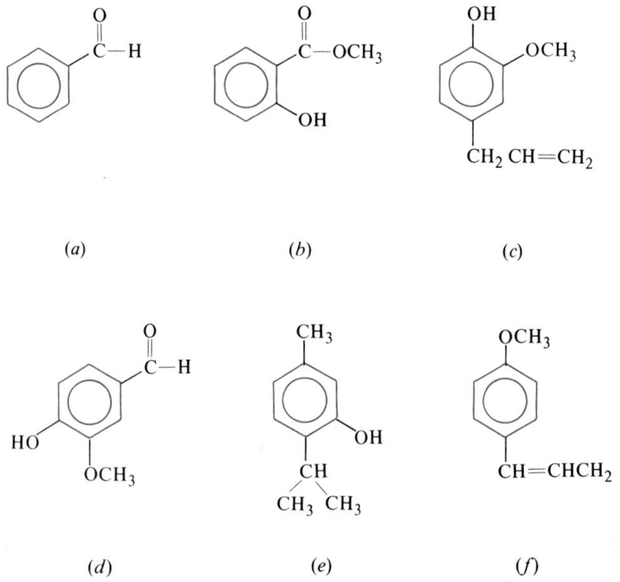

(*a*) (*b*) (*c*)

(*d*) (*e*) (*f*)

FIGURE 14.2
Some aromatic flavorings. (*a*) Almond (benzaldehyde); (*b*) wintergreen (methyl salicylate); (*c*) cloves (eugenol); (*d*) vanilla (vanillin); (*e*) thyme (thymol); (*f*) anise (anethole).

14.2 RING STRUCTURE OF BENZENE

In the 1820s a pure liquid hydrocarbon called benzene was first isolated. Chemists found that the empirical formula of benzene was CH and determined its formula weight to be 78. As you saw in Chapter 5 (Section 5.6), this information can be used to find the molecular formula.

$$\frac{\text{Experimental formula weight}}{\text{Empirical formula weight}} = \frac{78}{13} = 6$$

In this way chemists were readily able to establish the molecular formula of this new substance as C_6H_6, but it would take some time for them to figure out a structure which was consistent with the properties of benzene. Let us see why they were so baffled.

From its molecular formula it would seem that the benzene molecule must be highly unsaturated. Hexyne, the six-carbon alkyne with a molecular formula of C_6H_{10}, has more H atoms per C atom than benzene. Any open-chain structure proposed for benzene would have to include more than one multiple bond. For instance, the open-chain structure with the molecular formula C_6H_6 shown below has one triple bond and two double bonds.

$$CH_2{=}CH{-}C{\equiv}C{-}CH{=}CH_2$$

Molecular formula C_6H_6

In Chapter 13 you saw that compounds containing multiple bonds are particularly reactive and participate readily in addition reactions across the multiple bonds. Bromine added to alkenes and alkynes decolorizes almost at once (see Color Plate 15). Thus if the structure above were correct, we would expect an immediate reaction of benzene with bromine. But that is not what happens, as shown in Color Plate 16. Bromine reacts very slowly with benzene. In fact, bromine reacts with benzene at about the same rate as it reacts with alkanes, and like alkanes, benzene undergoes *substitution* with bromine.

$$\text{Alkene} + Br_2 \longrightarrow \text{very fast}$$

$$\text{Alkyne} + Br_2 \longrightarrow \text{very fast}$$

$$\text{Alkane} + Br_2 \longrightarrow \text{very slow}$$

$$\text{Benzene} + Br_2 \longrightarrow \text{very slow}$$

Kekulé was originally a student of architecture.

Thus, an open-chain structure for benzene could not be correct. The chemist August Kekulé (1829–1896) proposed an alternative structure in which the six carbon atoms of benzene are joined together to form a hexagon with each ring C atom bonded to an H atom. The inspiration for this idea supposedly sprang from a daydream in which Kekulé visualized "long rows (of atoms) . . . , all twining and twisting in snakelike motion," and then saw that "One of the snakes had seized hold of its own tail. . . ." (Historians insist that the account of his daydream, supposedly scribbled immediately upon his awakening, actually underwent considerable rewriting.) In any case, Kekulé's structure turned out to be correct. Benzene *is* a ring compound.

To satisfy the tetravalency of the C atom, three alternating double bonds had to be introduced into the benzene ring.

Kekulé structure for benzene

However, this structure also failed to answer many questions about the properties of benzene. If the structure above were correct, benzene would still be expected to be highly reactive because of the three double bonds it contains. (Cyclohexene, with just one double bond in its ring, undergoes a rapid reaction with bromine.) Furthermore, if the benzene ring really did have alternating single and double bonds, the distance between doubly bonded C atoms would be shorter than that between singly bonded C atoms (see Table 4.4), yet all physical measurements showed that the six C to C bond distances were identical. Furthermore, if there were two different kinds of bonds in the benzene ring, two different disubstituted benzene compounds with substituents on adjacent C atoms should be possible. To show why this is true, suppose we replace two adjacent H atoms in the benzene rings with Cl atoms. We have two choices about where to put them. The Cl atoms could be placed on two double-bonded ring C atoms (as shown in dichlorobenzene structure 1) or on two single-bonded C atoms (structure 2).

Dichlorobenzene 1 Dichlorobenzene 2

These two different compounds have never been isolated. There is only one dichlorobenzene known in which two Cl atoms substitute for two adjacent H atoms.

We will see that all these properties of benzene can be accounted for by an orbital bonding picture of the benzene molecule.

14.3 BONDING IN BENZENE

To draw the orbital bonding diagram for the benzene molecule, we must first decide on what kind of hybrid C orbitals to use. There are *three* atoms attached to each C atom in benzene (two C atoms and one H atom). The bond angles in the benzene molecule are 120° and the molecule is planar (see Figure 14.3). Recall that the three sp^2 orbitals that we used to describe the double-bonded C atoms in the alkenes make 120° bond angles with each other and all lie in the same plane (see Section 13.3). In fact, we use sp^2 hybrid orbitals for the C atoms in benzene as we did for the double-bonded C atoms in alkenes.

Benzene C atoms are sp^2 hybridized.

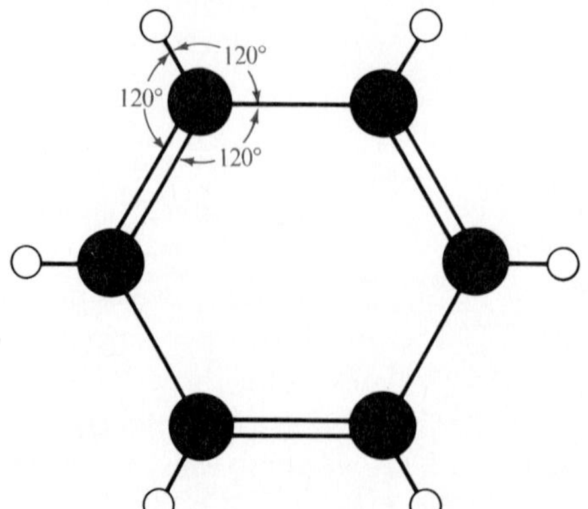

FIGURE 14.3
Geometry of benzene. Bond angles in the benzene molecule are 120°.

$$\frac{\uparrow}{2p_x}\ \frac{\uparrow}{2p_y}\ \frac{\uparrow}{2p_z} \qquad\qquad \frac{\uparrow}{2p_z}$$

$$\xrightarrow{\textit{hybridization}} \frac{\uparrow}{2sp^2}\ \frac{\uparrow}{2sp^2}\ \frac{\uparrow}{2sp^2}$$

$$\frac{\uparrow}{2s}$$

The step-by-step construction of the molecular orbitals for benzene is shown in Figure 14.4. First we draw the sigma framework. Each C to H bond is formed by the overlap of a 1*s* orbital of H with an sp^2 hybrid orbital of C (Figure 14.4*a*).

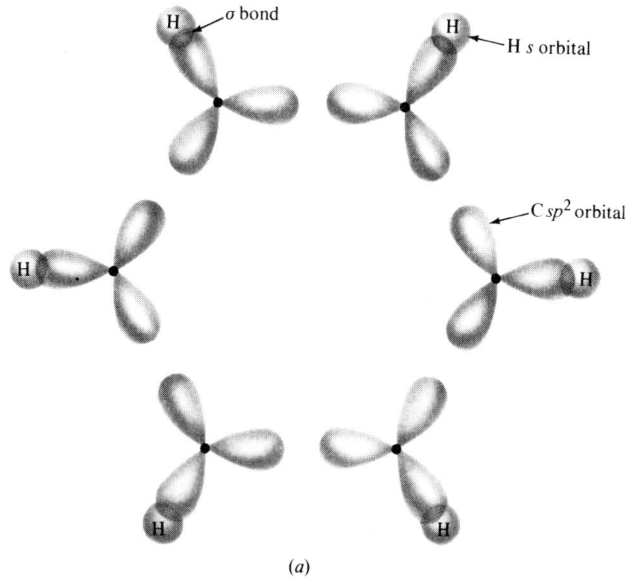

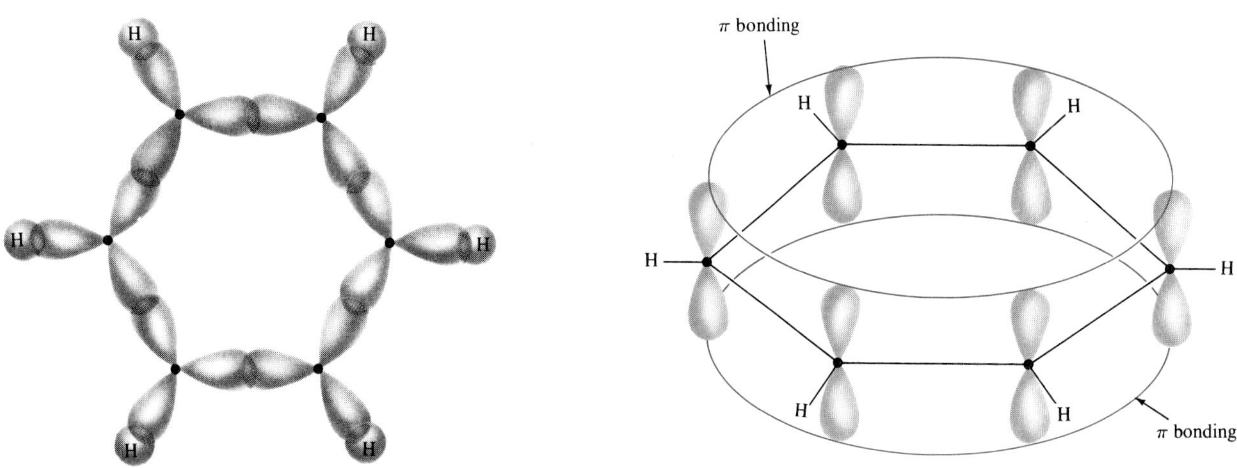

FIGURE 14.4
Benzene bonding. (*a*) C-H σ bonds; (*b*) σ framework; (*c*) continuous π bond.

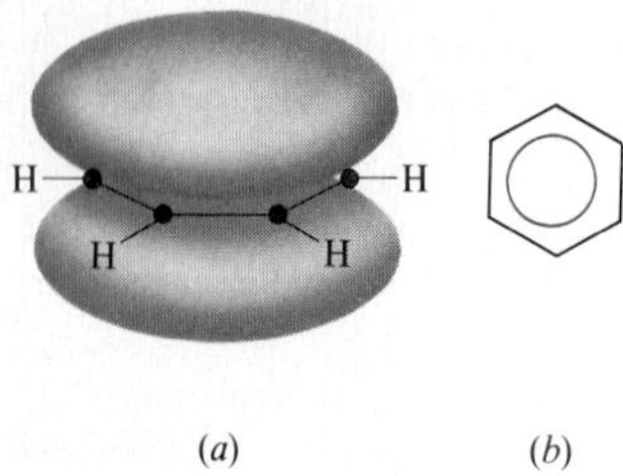

FIGURE 14.5
(*a*) The π bonds are shown as a continuous ring above and below the plane of the benzene ring. (*b*) The symbol for benzene, in which the circle represents the continuous π bond.

To complete the sigma framework the C atoms are all bonded to each other by overlap of their remaining two sp^2 orbitals (Figure 14.4*b*). Each carbon atom also has one unhybridized *p* orbital containing one electron. These are shown (in color) above and below the plane of the sigma framework in Figure 14.4*c*. To finish the bonding picture a *p* orbital from each C atom overlaps with the *p* orbitals of two neighboring C atoms to form the π bonds (Figure 14.4*c*). These overlapping *p* orbitals form a continuous π bond about the benzene ring, as you can see in Figure 14.5, where they are drawn as two "doughnuts" above and below the benzene ring. Because each *p* orbital overlaps with two other *p* orbitals, the π electrons are not localized between any two carbon atoms. Rather, all six π electrons are *delocalized* over the entire ring.

Now let us see how this picture of the bonding in benzene is consistent with its properties. According to the structure shown, all the C to C bonds in benzene should be identical, as in fact they are known to be. Each bond is formed from the overlap of one *p* orbital with two other *p* orbitals and thus should be weaker and longer than the double bond in ethene. From looking at Table 14.1 you can see that the bond length of the C to C bonds in benzene is intermediate between that of the single bond of ethane and the double bond of ethene. Thus benzene does not contain any double bonds and hence does not participate in addition reactions. In fact, the delocalization of the π electrons confers great stability on benzene, and in nearly all chemical reactions in which benzene participates the benzene ring itself survives. Only extreme reaction conditions (such as those favoring combustion) are able to destroy the benzene ring.

The benzene ring remains intact in nearly all its reactions.

TABLE 14.1 **LENGTHS OF C TO C BONDS**

Type of bond	Name of compound	Formula of compound	C to C bond length, pm
Single	Ethane	H H | | H—C—C—H | | H H	154
Double	Ethene	H H | | H—C=C—H	134
"One and one-half"	Benzene	H | H C H C C (ring with circle) C C H C H | H	140

14.4 STRUCTURAL FORMULAS FOR BENZENE

We can draw the benzene hexagon structure as .

The drawing we use to represent the structure of benzene is a hexagon with a circle inside it. At each corner of the hexagon a C atom bonded to an H atom is understood. The circle represents the continuous π bonding about the benzene ring.

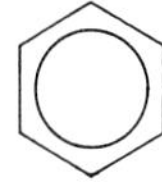

Benzene structure

Another commonly encountered depiction of benzene is the following:

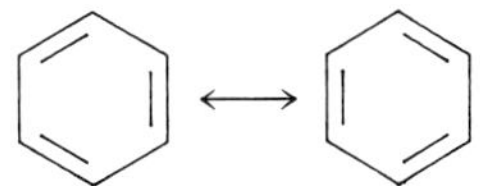

Resonance structures of benzene

There is only *one* benzene structure.

If you look carefully at this second structure, you can see that we have simply exchanged the positions of the single and double bonds. Two structures such as the ones above used to represent a single compound are called **resonance structures.** In writing resonance structures for a compound, a double-headed arrow is placed between them. The meaning of the arrow is that *both* structures contribute to the structure of benzene but neither structure is a complete representation—there is only *one* benzene. The actual structure of benzene is a composite of the resonance structures shown. [The arrow does *not* mean that the two benzene structures are in equilibrium with each other. Remember that we used double arrows ($\rightleftharpoons$) to indicate equilibrium.]

The first structure above, in which the delocalized π electrons are emphasized by putting a circle in the benzene hexagon, is the one that is most consistent with the properties of benzene and the one that we will use in this text.

14.5 NOMENCLATURE OF BENZENE COMPOUNDS

The compounds that form when one or more H atoms of benzene are substituted with other atoms or groups of atoms are named as derivatives of benzene. The rules for doing this are most conveniently presented by sorting benzene compounds into classes according to the number and kind of substituents present.

Monosubstituted Benzenes

In monosubstituted benzenes *one* H atom is replaced by another atom or group X.

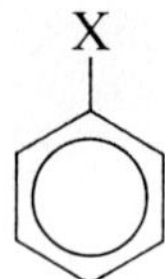

To name the compound above, the name of the substituent X is followed by the word *benzene*. For instance, if a chlorine atom is the substituent, the compound is called *chlorobenzene*

Cl

Chlorobenzene

and if the attached group is nitro ($-NO_2$), the name of the compound is *nitrobenzene*.

NO_2

Nitrobenzene

See Table 14.2 for the names and formulas of some possible substituents of benzene.

Many of the monosubstituted benzenes have common names which are retained in the IUPAC nomenclature system. For instance, when a methyl group is substituted on a benzene ring, the resulting compound is called *toluene* and not methylbenzene.

TABLE 14.2 **FORMULAS AND NAMES OF SUBSTITUENTS**

Formulas	Names
$-OH$	Hydroxy
$-NH_2$	Amino
$-NO_2$	Nitro
$-OCH_3$	Methoxy
$-\overset{O}{\overset{\|}{C}}-H$	Formyl
$-\overset{O}{\overset{\|}{C}}-OH$	Carboxy
$-C\equiv N$	Cyano

Toluene

Table 14.3 gives the names and formulas of some monosubstituted benzenes which have common names. We will return to most of these compounds in future chapters as the functional groups with which they are substituted are introduced.

Disubstituted Benzenes (Same Groups)

There are three different ways to place two substituents on a benzene ring. First let us draw the possible isomers for benzene substituted with two identical groups X. We can place them adjacent to one another

TABLE 14.3 **NAMES AND FORMULAS OF MONOSUBSTITUTED BENZENES**

Formula	Systematic name	Common name
$C_6H_5-CH_3$	Methylbenzene	Toluene
C_6H_5-OH	Hydroxybenzene	Phenol
$C_6H_5-NH_2$	Aminobenzene	Aniline
$C_6H_5-C(=O)-OH$	Carboxybenzene	Benzoic acid
$C_6H_5-OCH_3$	Methoxybenzene	Anisole
$C_6H_5-C(=O)-H$	Formylbenzene	Benzaldehyde

or the groups could be one carbon atom away from each other

or at opposite ends of the ring

Disubstituted benzenes in which the substituents are identical are also named as benzene derivatives, but there are two ways to do this.

Method 1: *Number the positions of the benzene ring so that the substituents are on the positions with the lowest possible numbers. Use the prefix di- to indicate that there are two substituents.*

We can use this method to name the three possible dichlorobenzenes below.

1,2-Dichlorobenzene

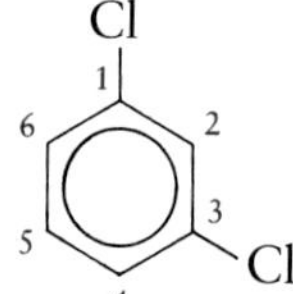

1,3-Dichlorobenzene

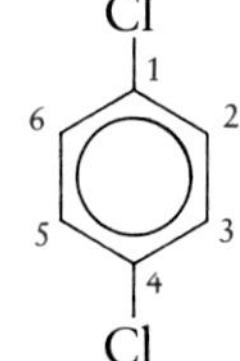

1,4-Dichlorobenzene

Alternatively, we can use a method in which the prefixes ***ortho-, meta-*** and ***para-*** replace the numbers (1,2-, 1,3-, and 1,4-, respectively) used in the example above.

Method 2: *Use the prefix* ortho- *for adjacent substituents,* meta- *for those separated by one C atom, and* para- *for substituents on opposite ring positions.*

Naming the three dichlorobenzene isomers by this method,

p-Dichlorobenzene is used in mothballs.

ortho-Dichlorobenzene (*o*-dichlorobenzene)

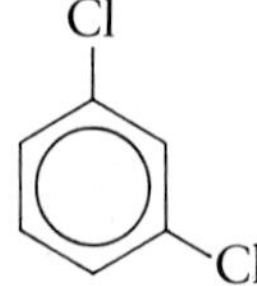

meta-Dichlorobenzene (*m*-dichlorobenzene)

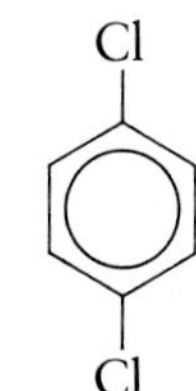

para-Dichlorobenzene (*p*-dichlorobenzene)

Some disubstituted benzene compounds have common names. For instance, the benzene compounds in which there are two methyl groups attached are called *xylenes*. The three isomers are distinguished by using the ortho, meta, para system.

Commercial xylene is a mixture of all three isomers.

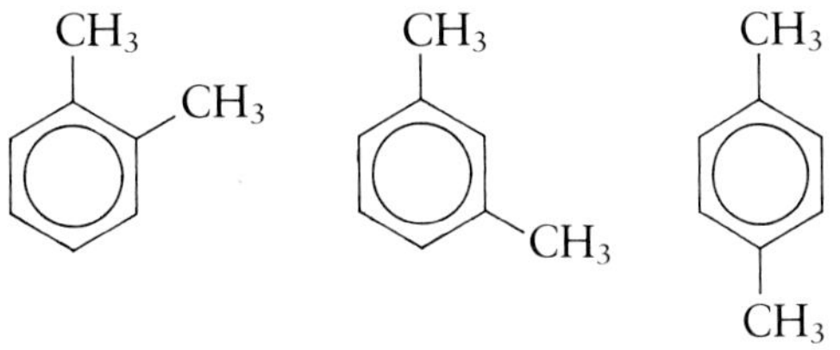

o-Xylene *m*-Xylene *p*-Xylene

Disubstituted Benzenes (Different Groups)

There are various ways to name benzenes substituted with two different groups. They can be named as derivatives of benzene itself. In using this system the ring is numbered to give the lowest numbers to occupied ring positions, with number 1 assigned to the substituent that is lower in alphabetical order. The substituents and their numerical locations are then listed, followed by the parent name benzene. For instance, to name the benzene compounds below using this system,

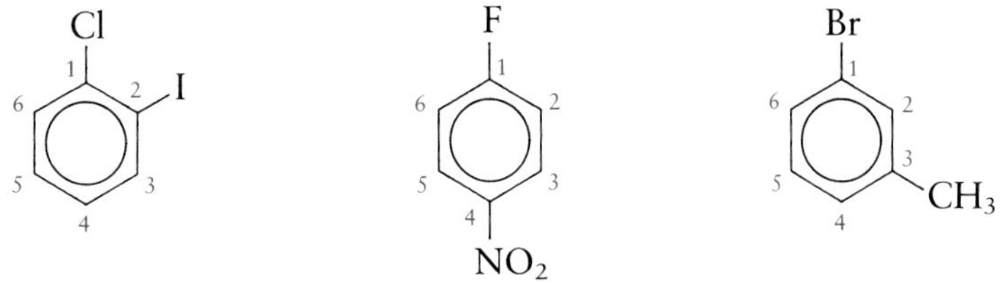

1-Chloro-2-iodo***benzene*** 1-Fluoro-4-nitro***benzene*** 1-Bromo-3-methyl***benzene***

Disubstituted benzene compounds can also be named as derivatives of one of the monosubstituted benzenes with common names (see Table 14.3). For instance, the compound 1-bromo-3-methylbenzene is most often named as a derivative of toluene. In this system the group which is a part of the monosubstituted benzene parent is understood to be on the C-1 atom of the ring. Using the numbering system, we name this compound 3-bromotoluene. (Note that the number 1 does not appear in the name.) The name *m*-bromotoluene is also used.

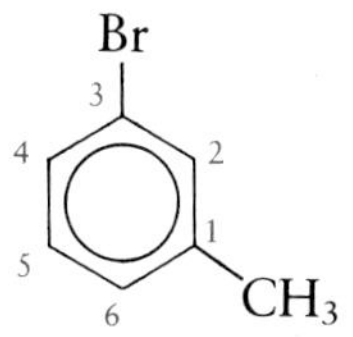

3-Bromo***toluene*** or *m*-bromo***toluene***

In compounds in which both the attached groups impart a common name to benzene, there is an order of priority about which of the substituents forms the parent name. The order of precedence for some functional groups is given in

TABLE 14.4 **ORDER OF PRECEDENCE FOR FUNCTIONAL GROUPS**

Formula of group	Name of group	Priority
		Highest
$-\overset{\overset{\displaystyle O}{\|}}{C}-OH$	Carboxy	
$-\overset{\overset{\displaystyle O}{\|}}{C}-H$	Formyl	
$-OH$	Hydroxy	
$-NH_2$	Amino	
$-OCH_3$	Methoxy	
$-CH_3$	Methyl	
		Lowest

Table 14.4, where the group with the lowest priority is at the bottom of the list. For instance, you can see that the amino group ($-NH_2$) is above the methyl group, which means that a compound containing both a methyl and an amino group should be named as an aniline and not as a toluene.

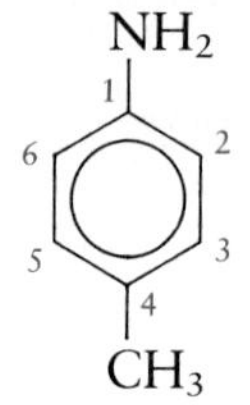

4-Methyl***aniline*** or *p*-methyl***aniline***

Polysubstituted Benzenes

To name benzene compounds in which there are three or more substituents, the numbering system is used in such a way as to give the substituents the lowest possible numbers. For example,

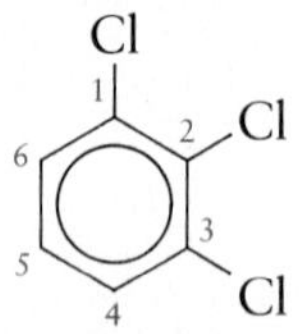

1,2,3-Trichlorobenzene 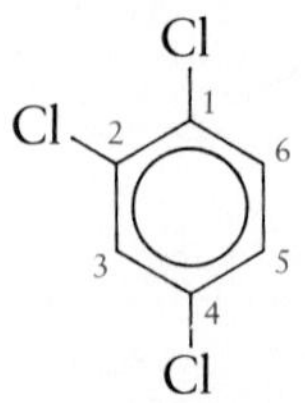 1,2,4-Trichlorobenzene

Polysubstituted benzenes that include one of the substituents listed in Table 14.4 are named as derivatives of monosubstituted benzenes, such as the one below named as a toluene derivative.

Since this is a toluene derivative, the methyl group is on the C-1 atom.

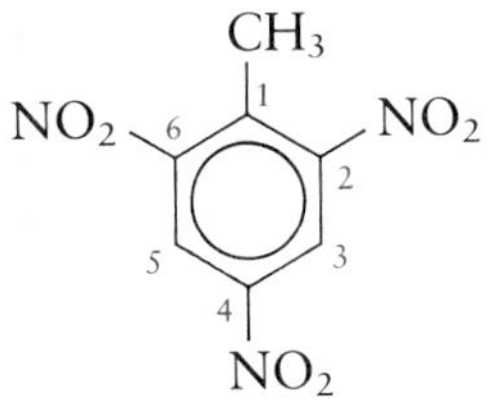

2,4,6-trinitro***toluene***

Nitro compounds which have a high percentage of N in their formulas are explosive. One of these is the compound above called TNT (trinitrotoluene), which explodes upon detonation and is used to fill bombs and hand grenades.

SAMPLE EXERCISE 14.1

Name the following benzene compounds:

(**a**) (**b**)

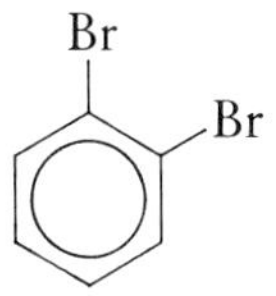

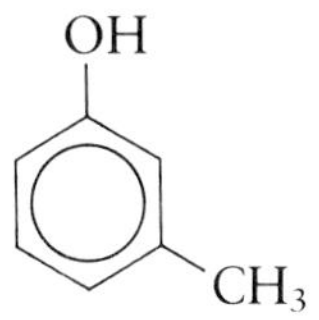

Solution:

(**a**) Since there are two identical atoms on adjacent C atoms, this compound is named as a benzene derivative.

1,2-dibromo***benzene*** or *o*-dibromo***benzene***

(**b**) Looking at Table 14.4 we see that —OH takes precedence over —CH_3. Thus we name the compound as a derivative of phenol:

3-methyl***phenol*** or *m*-methyl***phenol***

This compound, used as a germicide, is also known by the trivial name *meta*-cresol or *m*-cresol.

EXERCISE 14.1

The compound below, abbreviated PABA, prevents sunburn by absorbing ultraviolet radiation. What name is the abbreviation based upon?

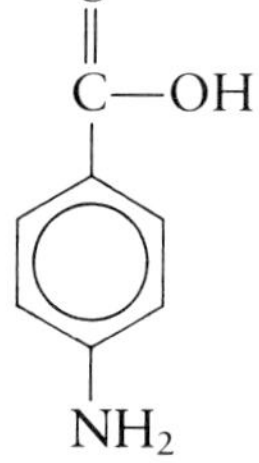

SAMPLE EXERCISE 14.2

Give the formula for 2,3-dichlorotoluene.

Solution:

The parent compound is toluene and so we number the ring C atoms by putting the methyl group on the C-1 atom.

CH_3

Toluene

To complete the formula attach the chlorines at the 2 and 3 positions.

CH_3 Cl Cl

EXERCISE 14.2

Write the formula for 2-amino-4,6-dichlorophenol.

14.6 PHENYL GROUP

Some benzene compounds are more conveniently named by considering the benzene itself to be a substituent. The benzene substituent, which is named **phenyl,** is formed by removing one H atom from the benzene ring. (This, as you will recall from Chapter 12, is how we formed the methyl group from methane, ethyl from ethane, and so on).

The phenyl group is sometimes abbreviated with the Greek letter phi, ϕ or by *Ph*.

– H = or

Phenyl

For instance, the compound below can be named as a derivative of methane by using the phenyl group as a substituent.

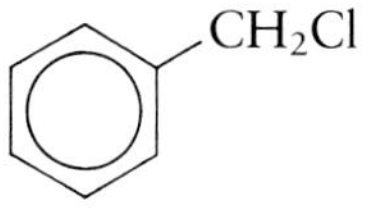

C_6H_5–CH_2Cl

Chlorophenyl*methane*

Compounds in which benzene appears more than once are named by making use of the phenyl name. The compound below, formed when two benzene rings are bonded together through two of their C atoms (with the loss of two H atoms), is called *biphenyl.*

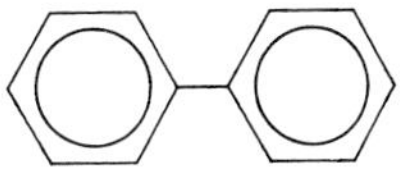

Biphenyl

The compound which results when chlorine atoms are placed on every ring position is known as *polychlorinated biphenyl* (abbreviated PCB), a highly toxic substance with a variety of industrial uses.

Symptoms of PCB poisoning include chloracne, a skin eruption caused by chlorinated hydrocarbons.

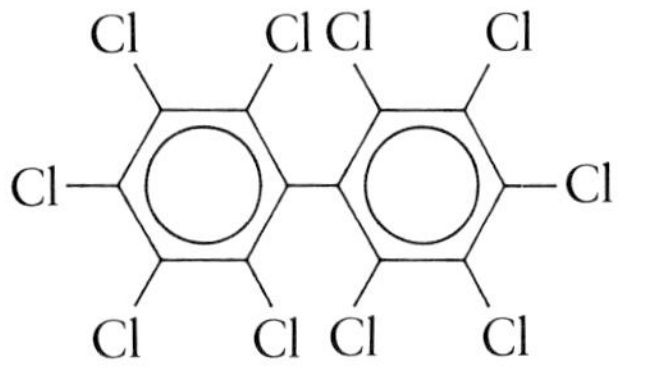

Polychlorinated biphenyl or PCB

The usefulness of PCB in industry is largely due to its flame resistance and to its stability toward acids, bases, and heat. Because it is so stable, PCB is poorly metabolized in the bodies of mammals and tends to accumulate in their fatty tissues because it is also water-insoluble. Thus PCB that escapes into the environment is a particularly hazardous pollutant.

SAMPLE EXERCISE 14.3

Name this aromatic compound:

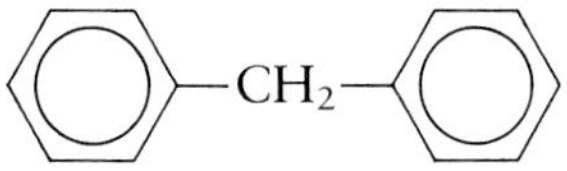

C_6H_5–CH_2–C_6H_5

Solution:

We can name this as a derivative of methane, diphenylmethane.

EXERCISE 14.3

Name the compound below as an alkane derivative.

C_6H_5—$CH_2CH_2CH_3$

14.7 CHEMICAL PROPERTIES OF BENZENE

We have already said in Section 14.3 that the aromatic ring system of benzene remains intact in nearly all its reactions. There is no addition across the carbon–carbon bonds of benzene. The reactions that do take place are **aromatic substitution** reactions, in which one or more ring H atoms are replaced by other atoms or groups of atoms.

Halogenation

Benzene reacts with bromine or chlorine to form bromobenzene or chlorobenzene in the presence of an iron catalyst (Fe, $FeBr_3$ or $FeCl_3$). When Cl_2 reacts with benzene as shown below, the products are chlorobenzene and hydrogen chloride.

$$C_6H_6 + Cl_2 \xrightarrow{\text{Fe or FeCl}_3} C_6H_5Cl + HCl$$

Chlorobenzene Hydrogen chloride

Introducing the second halogen into the benzene ring is much more difficult than introducing the first one. Thus the halogenation of benzene provides primarily a monohalogenated product, unlike the halogenation of alkanes, in which a mixture forms (see Section 12.14).

Nitration

Nitrobenzene can be prepared by reacting benzene with nitric acid (HNO_3) in the presence of sulfuric acid (H_2SO_4).

When we write the reaction of benzene and nitric acid we can easily remember the reaction products by using the formula HO—NO_2 for nitric acid and "lassoing" a water molecule, one H of which comes from the benzene ring.

$$C_6H_5\text{—}\boxed{H + HO}\text{—}NO_2 \xrightarrow{H_2SO_4} C_6H_5\text{—}NO_2 + H_2O$$

Nitrobenzene

Nitrobenzene is a yellowish liquid with an almondy odor. It was once used as a flavoring called "artificial oil of bitter almonds"; this use was discontinued when it was discovered that nitrobenzene is highly toxic. Because it has only one nitro group, it is not explosive like TNT, which has three nitro groups (see Section 14.5).

Nitrobenzene is rapidly absorbed through the skin.

SAMPLE EXERCISE 14.4

Starting with benzene, write a reaction for the formation of bromobenzene.

Solution:

In this halogenation we need Br_2 and Fe or $FeBr_3$ as a catalyst.

$$C_6H_6 + Br_2 \xrightarrow{\text{Fe or FeBr}_3} C_6H_5Br + HBr$$

Bromobenzene

EXERCISE 14.4

Write the reaction in which chlorobenzene reacts with Cl_2 to form *o*-dichlorobenzene.

14.8 ARENES

The arene toluene consists of benzene (aromatic) and a methyl group (aliphatic).

Hydrocarbons such as the alkylbenzenes toluene and ethylbenzene, which have both aliphatic and aromatic components, are called **arenes.** (For the formulas and names of some important arenes, see Table 14.5.) Because arenes have both aromatic and aliphatic character, they also have properties of aliphatic as well as of aromatic compounds.

Physically the arenes—and benzene itself—are like the aliphatic hydrocarbons. They are nonpolar and insoluble in water and have densities lower than that of water (see Table 14.5). The arenes are used as solvents and as starting materials for the synthesis of most other complicated aromatic compounds. They have an aromatic, not unpleasant, aroma. However, arenes can be absorbed through the skin and must be handled with care in well-ventilated areas since many of them are toxic. Benzene itself is more toxic than any of the arenes. The reason for this is related to the inertness of benzene, which makes it difficult for the body to eliminate it. The body rids itself of toxic substances by converting them into compounds that are soluble in body fluids and can be removed as

TABLE 14.5 ARENES

Name	Formula	Bp, °C	Density, g/ml
Benzene	C_6H_6	80	0.879
Toluene	C_6H_5—CH_3	111	0.866
Ethylbenzene	C_6H_5—CH_2CH_3	136	0.867
p-Xylene	CH_3—C_6H_4—CH_3 (para)	138	0.861
m-Xylene	CH_3—C_6H_4—CH_3 (meta)	139	0.864
o-Xylene	CH_3—C_6H_4—CH_3 (ortho)	144	0.880
Cumene	C_6H_5—$CHCH_3$ with CH_3	152	0.862
Mesitylene	$C_6H_3(CH_3)_3$ (1,3,5)	165	0.864
Styrene	C_6H_5—$CH{=}CH_2$	145	0.907

waste. In biological systems the benzene is metabolized by conversion to an oxide, which is eliminated, though very slowly, from the body.

Benzene is toxic when ingested or inhaled.

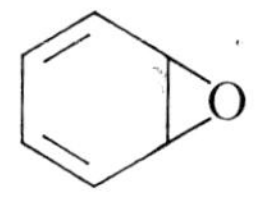

Benzene oxide

Unfortunately, oxides such as the one above are **carcinogenic** (cancer-causing) or can be converted in the body to carcinogens. Thus the formation of benzene oxide provides one explanation for the fact that benzene is known to cause cancer, in particular leukemia.

The alkylbenzenes undergo reactions common to both benzene and the alkanes and are more reactive than either. In Section 13.8 you saw that alkanes unlike alkenes, can not be oxidized by chemical oxidizing agents such as $KMnO_4$; however, the side chains of alkylbenzenes *can* be oxidized by hot $KMnO_4$ solution to produce a compound called *benzoic acid* (see Table 14.3). As in nearly all reactions that involve benzene derivatives, the very stable benzene ring remains intact (Section 14.3). In writing these oxidation reactions we will include only the carbon-containing compounds. (Thus, the O and H atoms will not balance.)

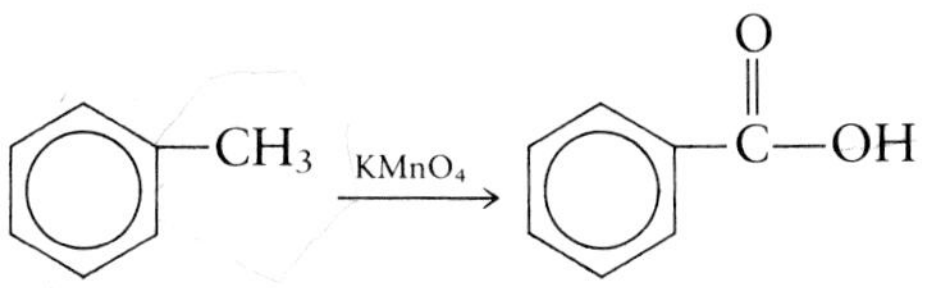

$$C_6H_5\text{—}CH_3 \xrightarrow{KMnO_4} C_6H_5\text{—}\overset{\overset{\displaystyle O}{\|}}{C}\text{—}OH$$

Methylbenzene (toluene) | Benzoic acid

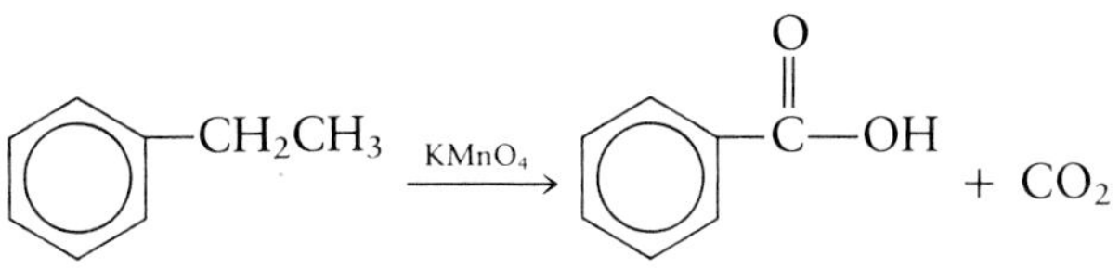

$$C_6H_5\text{—}CH_2CH_3 \xrightarrow{KMnO_4} C_6H_5\text{—}\overset{\overset{\displaystyle O}{\|}}{C}\text{—}OH + CO_2$$

Ethylbenzene | Benzoic acid

Alkylbenzenes are less toxic than benzene since the body can convert them to nontoxic benzoic acid.

Oxidation reactions provide a route by which the body can convert alkylbenzenes to more water-soluble substances, which can be eliminated from the body. Benzoic acid is nontoxic, and in fact derivatives of benzoic acid are used as food preservatives and in suntan lotions. Thus compounds such as toluene and xylene, although still toxic, are not as toxic when ingested as is benzene. When evaluating the toxicity of an ingested substance, it is important to consider not only the compound itself but the toxicity of all possible compounds that the body can make from it. Compounds produced during metabolism are known as *metabolites*.

14.9 FUSED-RING AROMATICS

A **fused-ring aromatic** is a compound that forms when two or more aromatic rings are joined at two or more C atoms. The source of fused-ring aromatics (and of arenes and benzene itself) is a substance called coal tar, the liquid residue produced when coal is heated in the absence of air:

$$\text{Coal (carbon)} \xrightarrow{\Delta} \underset{\text{Impure carbon}}{\text{coke}} + \underset{\text{Gaseous residue}}{\text{coal gas}} + \underset{\text{Liquid residue}}{\text{coal tar}}$$

The simplest fused-ring aromatic is naphthalene, a compound used in some mothballs:

$C_{10}H_8$

Naphthalene

Anthracene is the compound that forms when three benzene rings are joined side by side:

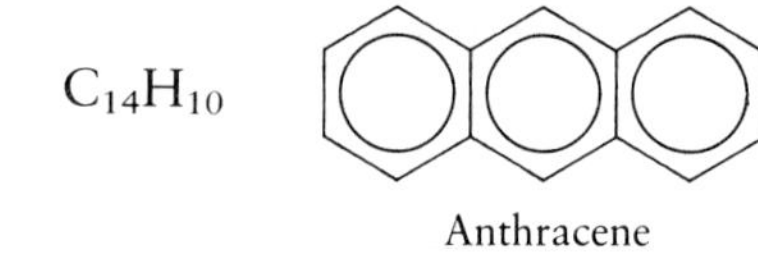

Another compound containing three fused rings is phenanthrene.

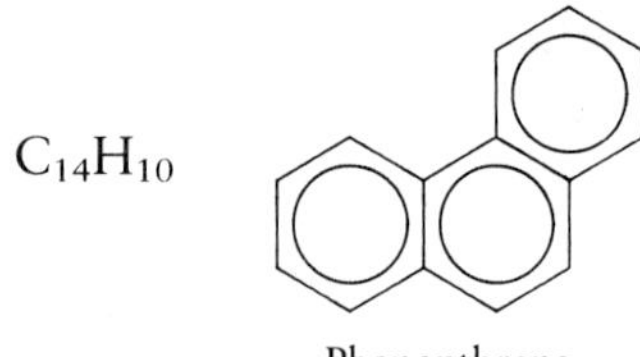

Many of the fused-ring compounds are known to be carcinogenic. The presence of 3,4-benzpyrene in the soot left from incomplete combustion of coal was found to cause the unusually high incidence of cancer in London chimney sweeps.

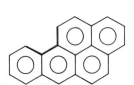

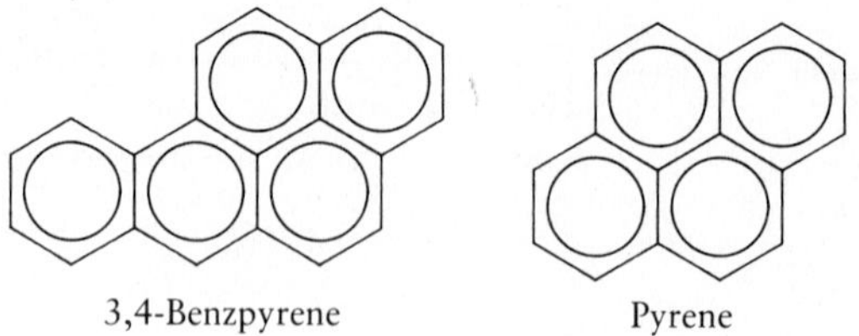

1,2-benzanthracene

3,4-benzphenanthrene

1,2,5,6-dibenzanthracene

3,4-benzpyrene

FIGURE 14.6
Known fused-ring carcinogens. The colored line shows the "bay region."

Figure 14.6 shows the fused ring aromatics which are known carcinogens.

The carcinogenic fused-ring aromatics all have similar structural features.

There are very interesting relationships between the molecular structures of the fused-ring aromatics and carcinogenicity. According to one hypothesis, the carcinogenic ones must contain an enclosed region, shown in color in Figure 14.6, called the "bay region." Metabolites of the carcinogenic fused-ring aromatics are known to cause alterations in the structure of DNA molecules. As we will learn in Chapter 24, such damage can lead to genetic mutations, which increases the likelihood of cancer formation in living things. The reason that the bay regions are thought to be important is that molecules which contain them produce metabolites that are not planar. It has been proposed that flat planar molecules can fit into the DNA structure without disrupting it, but nonplanar ones cannot.

SAMPLE EXERCISE 14.5

The compound shown below is called naphthacene.

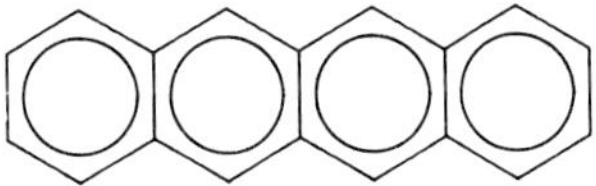

(a) Find the molecular formula for naphthacene.
(b) Is naphthacene likely to be a potent carcinogen?

Solution:

(a) We can rewrite the geometric structure to include all the constituent C and H atoms:

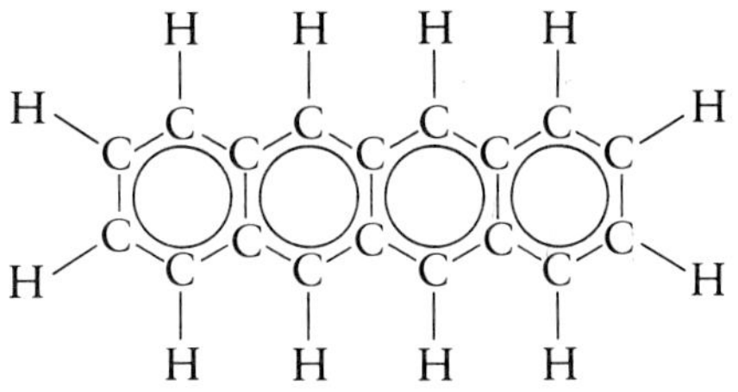

Thus the molecular formula is $C_{18}H_{12}$.

(b) No, because naphthacene does not contain a bay region, it is not likely to be appreciably carcinogenic.

EXERCISE 14.5

Give the molecular formula for the compound below, called methylcholanthrene. Is it likely to be a potent carcinogen?

CH_3

CH_2-CH_2

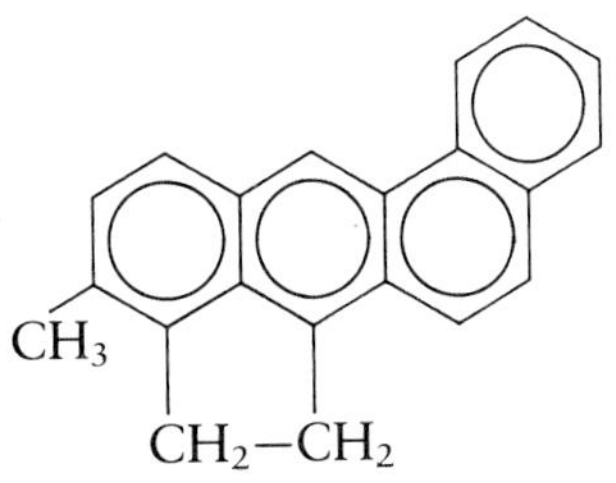

SUMMARY

Benzene and its derivatives belong to the class of organic compounds called the aromatics. The parent compound, benzene itself, has a molecular formula of C_6H_6 and a ring structure in which the six C atoms form a hexagon. The sp^2 hybrid orbitals (three on each C atom) produce the sigma framework of the molecule; each C atom forms three sigma bonds, two with the neighboring C atoms and one with an H atom. The six unhybridized *p* orbitals overlap to form a continuous delocalized π bond around the benzene ring, thus giving the ring extra stability. The C to C bonds are all the same, with a bond length intermediate between that of a single bond and a double bond. This bonding picture is consistent with the measured bond lengths in benzene and with the chemical inertness of the benzene ring structure. The structure we use for benzene shows the π bond as a circle inside a hexagon which represents the sigma framework .

Monosubstituted benzene compounds are named by adding the substituent prefix to the word *benzene*. Positions of substituents in disubstituted benzenes are indicated by using the numbering system or the ortho (1,2), meta (1,3), para (1,4) system. For polysubstituted benzenes the numbering system only is used. Benzene compounds are also named as derivatives of monosubstituted benzenes which have common names. The name phenyl is used for a substituent benzene ring.

Like alkanes, the aromatic compounds typically undergo substitution reactions. Halogenation in the presence of an iron or iron halide catalyst produces halobenzenes. Treating benzene with nitric acid and sulfuric acid forms the product nitrobenzene.

Arenes are alkylbenzene compounds and have properties of both aliphatics and aromatics. The aliphatic side chain can be oxidized to produce the nontoxic compound called benzoic acid. Benzene is more toxic than the other alkylbenzenes because it has no side chain and in the body is converted to a carcinogenic oxide.

Fused-ring aromatic compounds have benzene rings attached to each other through two or more C atoms. Some of these are metabolized in the body to form potent carcinogens. Theories suggest that the carcinogenic ones all have structural features which cause them to disrupt the structure of DNA.

KEY WORDS

aliphatic
aromatic
benzene
resonance structures
ortho
meta
para
phenyl
aromatic substitution
arene
fused-ring aromatic
carcinogen

EXERCISES

14.6 In Section 14.2 a structure for an open-chain compound with the molecular formula C_6H_6 is given. Can you think of any other possible structures? Why did chemists think that structures such as these were unlikely for benzene?

14.7 Give the names and molecular formulas for each of the following compounds.

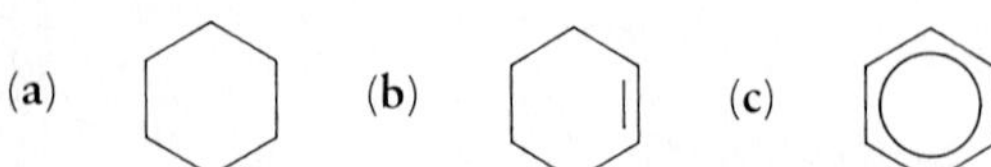

14.8 Give the molecular formulas for each of the six-carbon compounds below. In which of them is the number of H atoms the smallest?
(a) Cyclohexane (b) Hexane (c) Cyclohexene
(d) Hexene (e) Hexyne (f) Benzene

14.9 Name the following benzene compounds using both the numbering and the *o*-, *m*-, and *p* systems for the disubstituted ones:

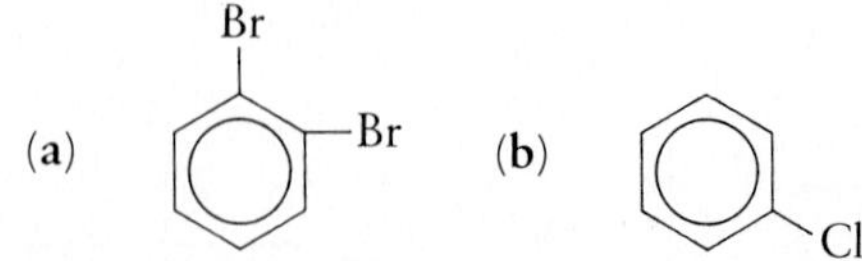

(c) 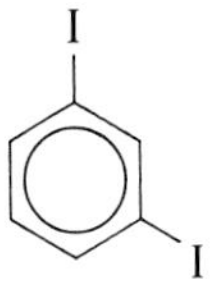 (d)

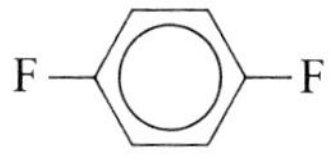

14.10 Give names for the benzene compounds below:

(a) 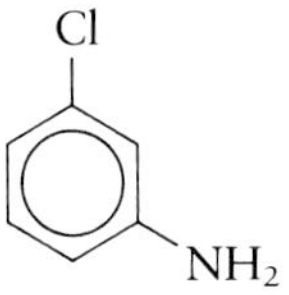 (b)

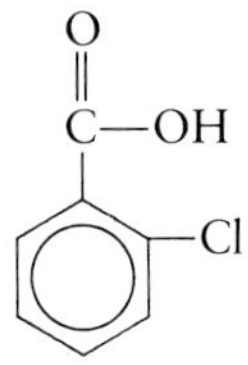

(c) 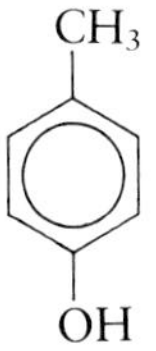 (d)

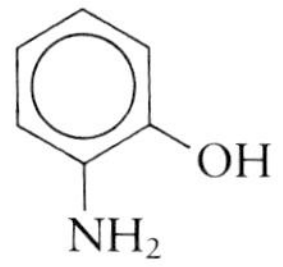

14.11 Name the polysubstituted benzenes below.

(a) 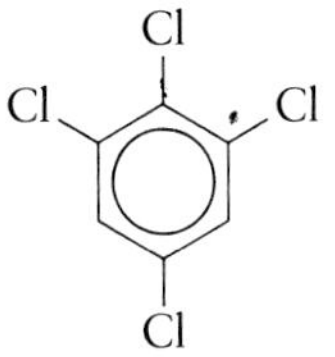 (b)

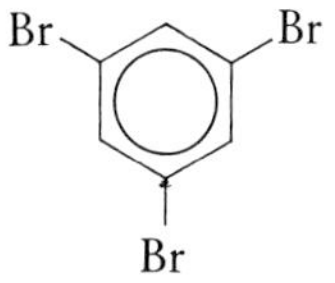

14.12 Can the compounds in Exercise 14.11 be named by using the ortho, meta, para system?

14.13 The formula below is for salicylic acid, used to prepare several important analgesic drugs, including aspirin. Give another name for salicylic acid. (*Hint:* See Table 14.4.)

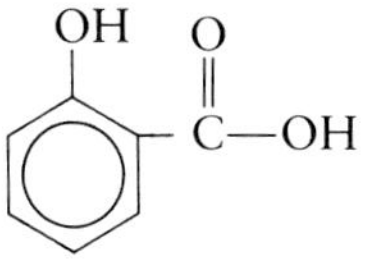

14.14 Give another name for mesitylene. (See Table 14.6 for its formula.)

14.15 Name these two disubstituted benzenes. (*Hint:* MD is not an element or a group of elements!)

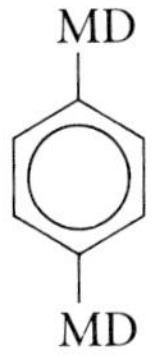

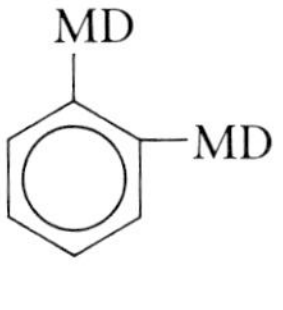

14.16 Picric acid is a compound that has been used topically as an antiseptic and astringent (shrinks tissues). Give another name for picric acid. Picric acid must be stored in a cool place and must be shipped very carefully. Why?

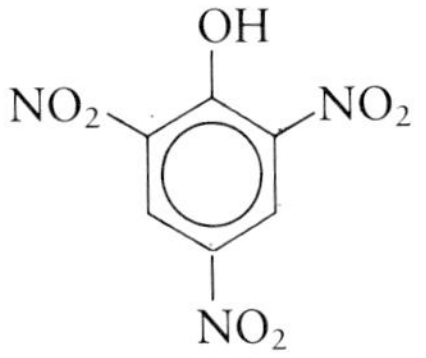

Picric acid

14.17 Name the following aromatic compounds as alkane derivatives.

(a) 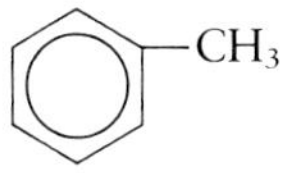 (b)

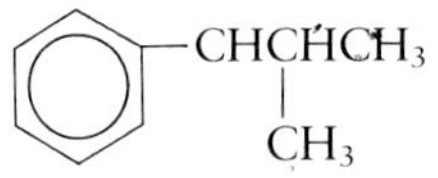

(c)

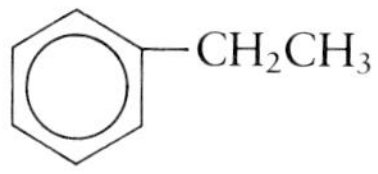

14.18 Why are the C to C bonds in benzene sometimes referred to as "$1\frac{1}{2}$" bonds?

14.19 How does the double-headed arrow (↔) used between the resonance structures for benzene differ from the double arrows (⇌) used for equilibrium reactions?

14.20 Give the formulas which correspond to the following names. Do any two of these names refer to the same compound?

(a) Nitrobenzene
(b) *p*-Dibromobenzene
(c) *m*-Chlorotoluene
(d) 2-Iodoaniline
(e) 1,3,5-Trinitrobenzene
(f) *p*-Xylene
(g) 3-Chlorotoluene
(h) 2,4-Dichlorotoluene

14.21 Why are the following names "impossible"?

(a) *m*-Toluene
(b) 5,6-Dichlorobenzene
(c) 2,4,6-Trichlorobenzene
(d) 1,3,4-Trinitrobenzene

14.22 The formula below represents the insecticide DDT.

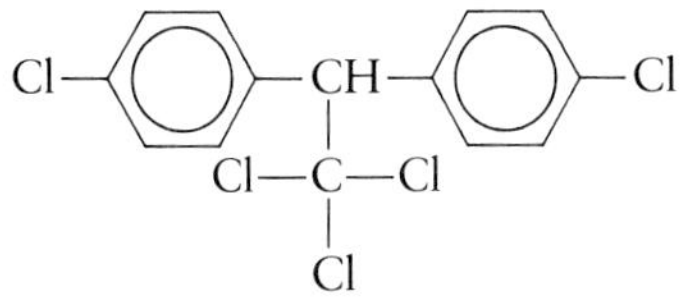

The first D is for dichloro (the Cl atoms on the phenyl rings) and the second D for diphenyl. The T stands for what halogenated hydrocarbon?

14.23 Describe what happens when Br_2 is added to benzene without a catalyst.

14.24 What chemical test could you use to distinguish between the two liquid compounds toluene and heptene?

14.25 Complete the following reactions by supplying the missing reactant, catalyst or product.

(a) 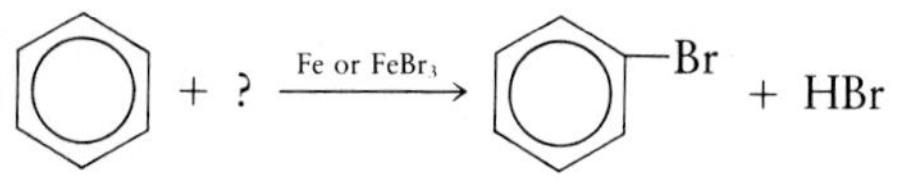 C_6H_6 + ? $\xrightarrow{\text{Fe or FeBr}_3}$ C_6H_5Br + HBr

(b) 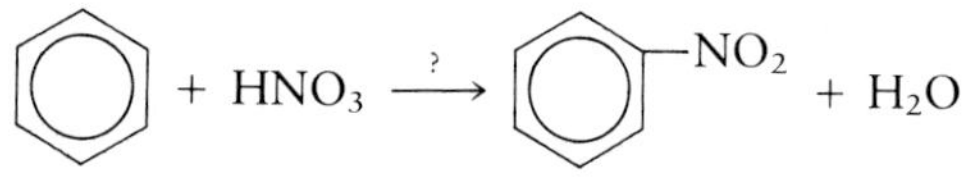 C_6H_6 + HNO_3 $\xrightarrow{?}$ $C_6H_5NO_2$ + H_2O

14.26 The compound hydrazine has the formula below.

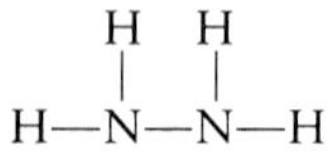

H—N(H)—N(H)—H

Give the formulas for:

(**a**) Phenylhydrazine, a substance which causes hemolysis (destruction of red blood cells)

(**b**) 2,4-Dinitrophenylhydrazine, a compound used to identify aldehydes and ketones (Chapter 16), including sugars.

14.27 The compound called phenylthiourea has a very interesting property which makes it useful in genetic studies. Depending upon the heredity of the taster it is either bitter or tasteless. Thiourea is

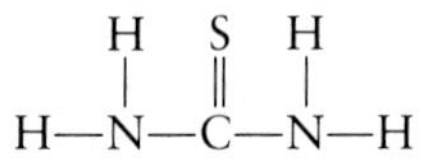

H—N(H)—C(=S)—N(H)—H

To which atom must the phenyl group be bonded? Give the formula for phenylthiourea.

14.28 What is meant by an arene?

14.29 Styrene is an arene that contains an unsaturated aliphatic group. Can you give two other possible names for styrene?

14.30 Why is benzene more toxic than toluene and other alkylbenzenes?

14.31 What is the organic product of the oxidation of the following alkylbenzenes with hot $KMnO_4$ solution: (**a**) Toluene; (**b**) ethylbenzene; (**c**) propylbenzene?

14.32 What is a fused-ring aromatic compound?

14.33 Give the molecular formula for the fused-ring aromatic compound shown below:

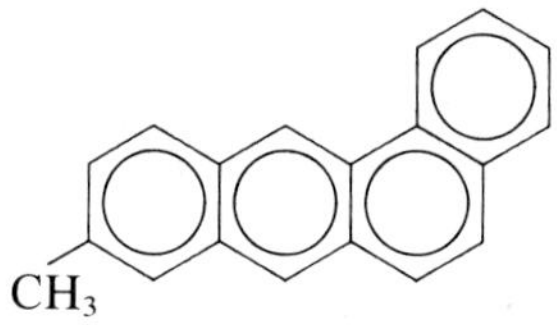

CH_3

According to the criteria given in Section 14.9, would you expect this compound to be a potent carcinogen? Why?

14.34 Why is biphenyl not classified as a fused-ring aromatic?

14.35 What three-letter abbreviation could be applied to the compound below?

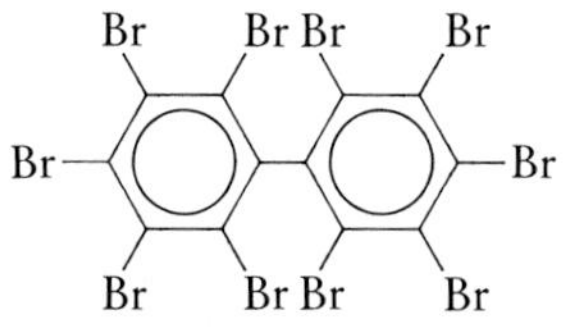

Br Br Br Br
Br Br
Br Br Br Br

15 ALCOHOLS AND ETHERS

15.1 INTRODUCTION

In the next few chapters we will introduce the organic compounds which have oxygen atoms in their functional groups. Two of these are the *alcohols* and the *ethers*. From studying their structures we will be able to understand how ethanol, beverage alcohol, is metabolized in the body, why certain phenols can be used as food preservatives, and how general anesthetics such as ethyl ether are transported to the brain.

We can produce the structures of both classes of compounds starting with a water molecule, HOH. By replacing one of the H atoms in water with a C atom, we have the general formula of an **alcohol**, written ROH, where the R refers to a hydrocarbon group.

R—OH

General alcohol formula

For instance, if the R is a methyl group, the alcohol formula is

$$CH_3OH$$

and when R is a phenyl group, the alcohol is phenol (see Table 14.3).

OH (phenol structure: OH attached to benzene ring)

To produce the **ether** structure both H atoms of water are replaced with hydrocarbon groups. We write the ether general formula with an R and an R′ (R prime), meaning that the attached hydrocarbon groups can be the same or different.

R—O—R′

General ether formula

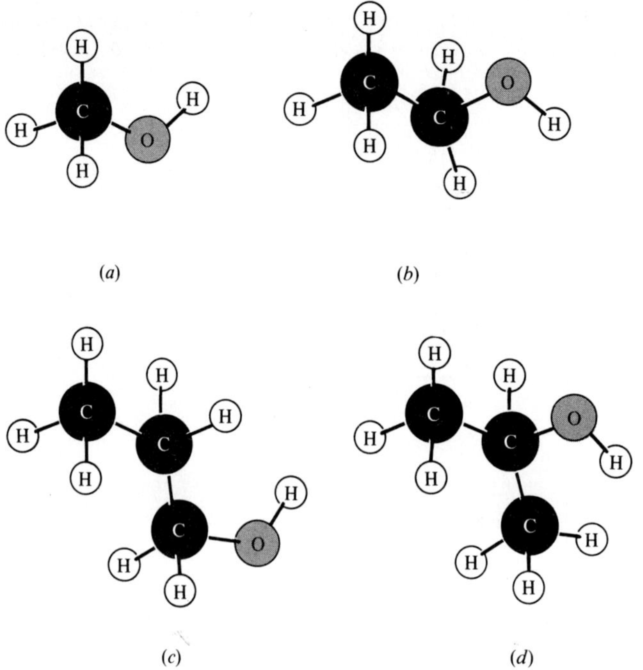

FIGURE 15.1
Structures of some common alcohols. (*a*) Methyl alcohol; (*b*) ethyl alcohol; (*c*) propyl alcohol; (*d*) isopropyl alcohol

One ether used as a general anesthetic is the one in which both R and R′ are ethyl groups (diethyl ether):

$$CH_3CH_2OCH_2CH_3$$

In mixed ethers, the attached hydrocarbon groups are different. In methyl phenyl ether, a phenyl and a methyl group are attached to the O atom.

$$C_6H_5\text{—}OCH_3$$

Some alcohol and ether structures are shown in Figures 15.1 and 15.2.

As you might expect, as compared with ethers the properties of the alcohols are more like those of water, since their formulas still contain one H atom bonded to an O atom. But we will see that the presence of the R group in alcohols does make their chemical behavior very different from that of water.

FIGURE 15.2
Structures of some ethers. (*a*) Dimethyl ether; (*b*) ethyl methyl ether; (*c*) diethyl ether.

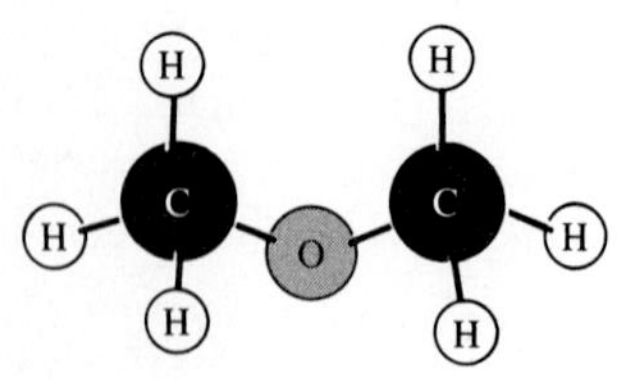

(*a*)

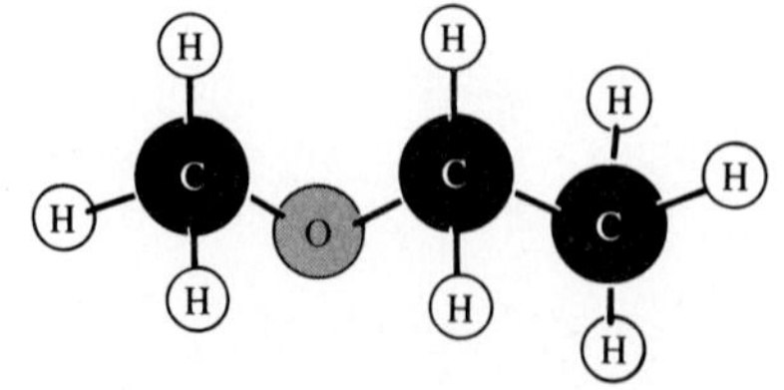

(*b*)

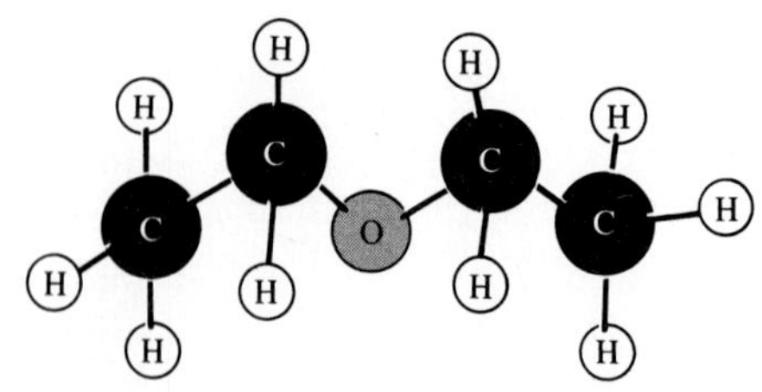

(*c*)

15.2 NAMING ALCOHOLS

Alkyl alcohols can be named as alkanols, a name derived by dropping the *e* from alkane and adding *ol*. For instance, the name of the alcohol derived from the simplest alkane comes from changing methane to methanol:

$$CH_3OH$$

Methanol

Ethanol is a two-carbon alcohol:

$$CH_3CH_2OH$$

Ethanol

At one time alcohols were named as alkyl alcohols (e.g., methyl alcohol and ethyl alcohol), names which are still in use and often appear on bottle labels.

To name any alcohol more complex than these we must indicate the location of the OH group as well as those of any other branch groups. To do this we follow the rules below.

Rule I *Choose the longest C to C chain to which the OH group is attached. This gives the parent alcohol name.*

For instance, in the formulas below the longest chain is four C atoms long, so all three compounds are butanols.

$$CH_3CH_2CH_2CH_2OH \qquad CH_3\underset{\underset{\displaystyle OH}{|}}{C}HCH_2CH_3 \qquad CH_3\underset{\underset{\displaystyle CH_3}{|}}{C}HCH_2CH_2OH$$

Rule II *Number the C atoms so that the C atom bonded to the OH group has the lowest possible number.*

Thus we number the compounds above as shown:

$$\overset{4}{C}H_3\overset{3}{C}H_2\overset{2}{C}H_2\overset{1}{C}H_2OH \qquad \overset{1}{C}H_3\underset{\underset{\displaystyle OH}{|}}{\overset{2}{C}}H\overset{3}{C}H_2\overset{4}{C}H_3 \qquad \overset{4}{C}H_3\underset{\underset{\displaystyle CH_3}{|}}{\overset{3}{C}}H\overset{2}{C}H_2\overset{1}{C}H_2OH$$

Rule III *Form the name by placing the number of the C atom to which the OH is attached in front of the parent alcohol. Indicate any branched groups according to the rules of alkane nomenclature.*

Using these rules, we can name the compounds above:

$$\overset{4}{C}H_3\overset{3}{C}H_2\overset{2}{C}H_2\overset{1}{C}H_2OH \qquad \overset{1}{C}H_3\underset{\underset{\displaystyle OH}{|}}{\overset{2}{C}}H\overset{3}{C}H_2\overset{4}{C}H_3 \qquad \overset{4}{C}H_3\underset{\underset{\displaystyle CH_3}{|}}{\overset{3}{C}}H_2\overset{2}{C}H_2\overset{1}{C}H_2OH$$

1-Butanol 2-Butanol 3-Methyl-1-butanol

The functional group of an alcohol is the hydroxyl group.

The OH group is called the **hydroxyl group** and is named *hydroxy-* when it appears as a substituent. This is done in compounds which contain a hydroxyl group and another functional group of higher priority (see Table 14.4). Thus the compound below is named as a derivative of benzoic acid with a hydroxy substituent rather than as an alcohol

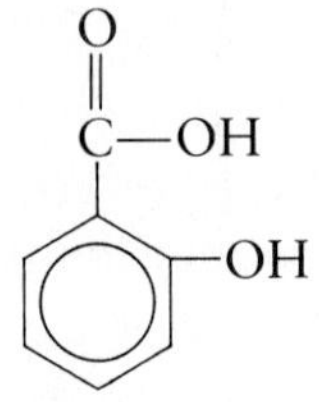

O
||
C—OH
(benzene ring)—OH

o-Hydroxybenzoic acid
salicylic acid

SAMPLE EXERCISE 15.1

Name the two alcohols below.

(**a**) CH_3CHOH with CH_3 on the second C

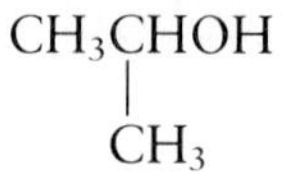

(**b**) $CH_3CH_2CHCHCH_2CH_3$ with H_3C and OH on the third and fourth C atoms

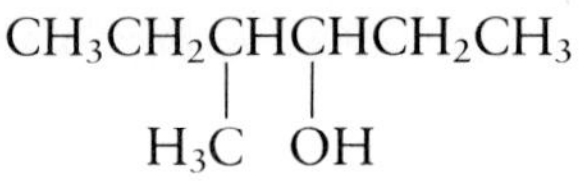

Solution:

(**a**) The longest chain is three C atoms long, so this alcohol is named as a propanol.

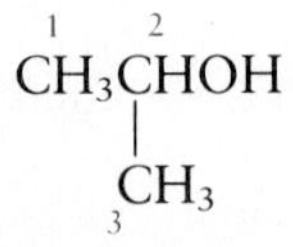

$$\overset{1}{CH_3}\overset{2}{C}HOH\text{ with }\overset{3}{CH_3}\text{ on C-2}$$

2-Propanol

This compound is very frequently called isopropyl alcohol, since it is an isopropyl group that is attached to the OH group. Labels on rubbing alcohol are most likely to read "isopropyl alcohol."

(**b**) This is a hexanol. Correct numbering puts the OH on the C-3 atom and the methyl on C-4.

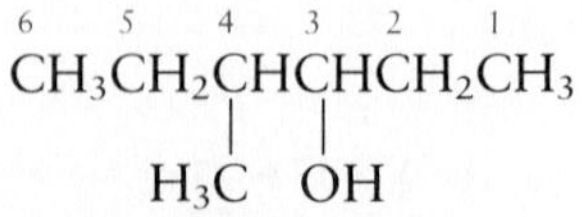

$$\overset{6}{CH_3}\overset{5}{CH_2}\overset{4}{C}H\overset{3}{C}H\overset{2}{CH_2}\overset{1}{CH_3}\text{ with }H_3C\text{ on C-4 and }OH\text{ on C-3}$$

4-Methyl-3-hexanol

EXERCISE 15.1

Name the following alcohols.

(a) $CH_3CH_2\underset{\displaystyle CH_3}{\underset{|}{C}}HCH_2CH_2OH$ (b) $CH_3CH_2\underset{\displaystyle CH_3}{\underset{|}{C}}HCH_2CH_2\underset{\displaystyle OH}{\underset{|}{C}}HCH_2CH_3$

Alcohols with more than one hydroxyl group are **polyhydric alcohols** and are named as alkane derivatives. The ones with two hydroxyl groups are called alkanediols (or dihydroxyalkanes); those with three, triols (or trihydroxyalkanes); and so on. Two important ones are

$HOCH_2CH_2OH$ $HOCH_2\underset{\displaystyle OH}{\underset{|}{C}}HCH_2OH$

1,2-Ethanediol (1,2-dihydroxyethane) 1,2,3-Propanetriol (1,2,3-trihydroxypropane)

Both these compounds are much more often called by their trivial names. Another name for a diol is *glycol.* The compound 1,2-ethanediol, used as antifreeze (see Section 9.8), is usually called *ethylene glycol,* and 1,2,3-propanetriol is almost always called *glycerol* (or sometimes glycerine).

$HOCH_2CH_2OH$ $HOCH_2\underset{\displaystyle OH}{\underset{|}{C}}HCH_2OH$

Ethylene glycol Glycerol (or glycerine)

The prefix *glyc-* used in both trivial names above means "sweet" and was originally used to form the name for glycerol because it is a sweet-tasting liquid. The same prefix was later used to name diols (even though they are not all sweet-tasting). We will encounter the prefix again (*gluc-* instead of *glyc-*) when we talk about the sugar glucose.

Mannitol has a sweet taste and is added to sugarless gum.

Mannitol, a hexahydric alcohol that is widespread in nature, belongs to a class of compounds known as the *sugar alcohols* because their structures are related to those of sugars (sugar structures are discussed in detail in Chapter 21).

$$HOCH_2\underset{\displaystyle OH}{\underset{|}{C}}H\underset{\displaystyle OH}{\underset{|}{C}}H\underset{\displaystyle OH}{\underset{|}{C}}H\underset{\displaystyle OH}{\underset{|}{C}}HCH_2OH$$

If a poison can be excreted in the urine, mannitol given intravenously may help to eliminate it.

Mannitol is used medically to promote diuresis (water loss).

You saw in Chapter 14 that phenol is hydroxybenzene and its monosubstituted derivatives may be named by using the prefixes *ortho-*, *meta-*, and *para-*, or numbers to locate the other group. For instance, to name the phenols below:

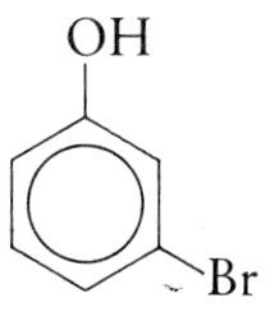

m-Bromophenol (3-bromophenol)

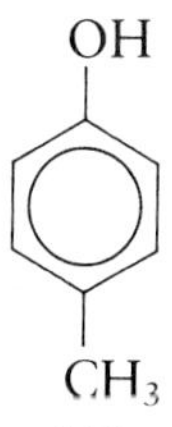

p-Methylphenol (4-methylphenol)

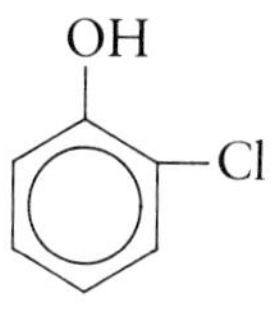

o-Chlorophenol (2-chlorophenol)

Many phenol derivatives may be called by their common names. Those which have a methyl substituent are *cresols*.

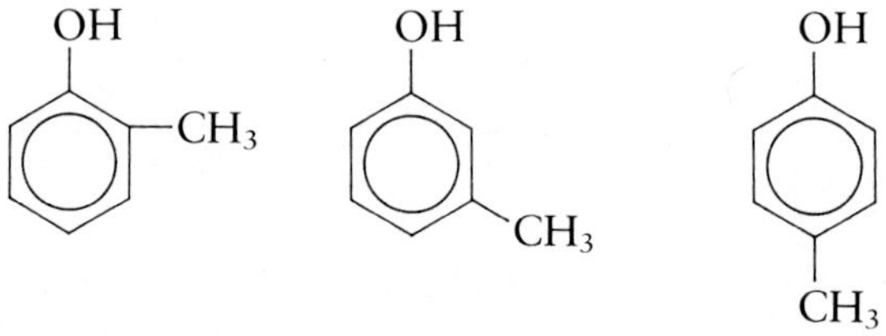

A mixture of the three cresols is called tricresol. The cresols are used as disinfectants.

o-Cresol (2-methylphenol) | *m*-Cresol (3-methylphenol) | *p*-Cresol (4-methylphenol)

Three different common names are used for the three dihydroxybenzenes:

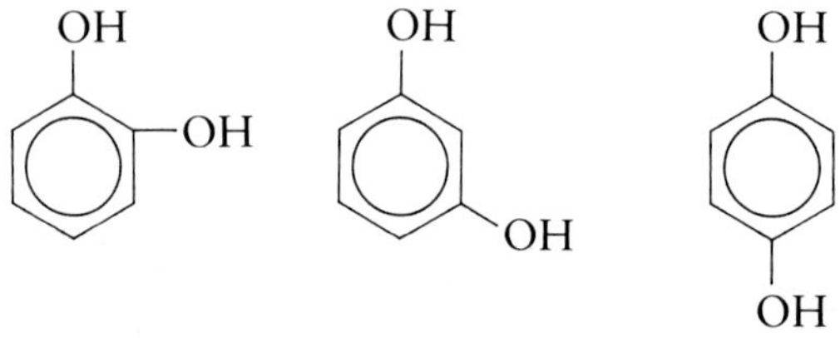

Derivatives of catechol are neurotransmitters such as adrenalin.

Catechol | Resorcinol | Hydroquinone

Aromatic alcohols in which the hydroxyl group is bonded to an alkyl group are named in several ways. For instance, we can give two names to the compound below, a substance used as a bactericide, that is, an agent that kills bacteria.

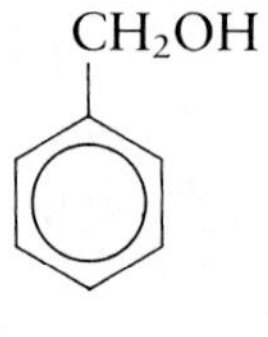

CH_2OH

This compound is most frequently called benzyl alcohol, the prefix *benzyl-* being used for the group formed by the removal of an H atom from toluene.

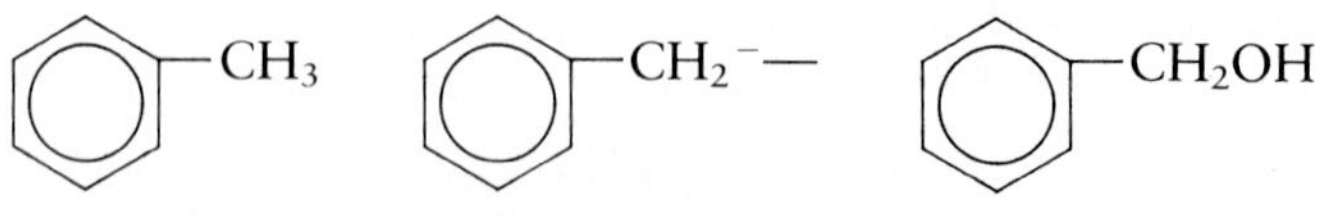

Toluene | Benzyl group | Benzyl alcohol

The phenyl ring can also be considered as a substituent and the alcohol named as a methanol derivative, phenylmethanol.

Table 15.1 lists the formulas, names, uses, and average fatal doses for humans of some common alcohols.

TABLE 15.1 **NAMES, FORMULAS, USES, AND TOXICITY OF IMPORTANT ALCOHOLS**

System name and formula	Other name(s)	Use	Human toxicity: average fatal dose*
Methanol CH_3OH	Methyl alcohol, wood alcohol, carbinol	Solvent, cooking fuel, denaturing agent for ethanol	100–250 ml
Ethanol CH_3CH_2OH	Ethyl alcohol	Industrial solvent, drug solvent and preservative, alcoholic beverages	
2-Propanol CH_3CHOH (with OH on C)	Isopropyl alcohol	Solvent, rubbing alcohol, disinfectant, after-shave lotion, denaturing agent for ethanol	100 ml
1,2-Ethanediol $HOCH_2CH_2OH$	Ethylene glycol	Antifreeze, solvent, polymer synthesis	100 ml
1,2,3-Propanetriol $HOCH_2CHCH_2OH$ (with OH on central C)	Glycerol, glycerine	Solvent, skin lubricant, metabolic intermediate	
Phenol C_6H_5–OH	Carbolic acid	Topical anesthetic; synthesis of polymers, medical compounds, and dyes	15 g

*Fatal doses can be less than this.

SAMPLE EXERCISE 15.2

Name these two aromatic alcohols:

(a) OH on benzene ring with NO_2 on adjacent carbon

(b) CH_2CH_2OH on benzene ring

Solution:

(**a**) This is a phenol derivative. Its name is *o*-nitrophenol or 2-nitrophenol.
(**b**) This alcohol can be named as a derivative of ethanol.

$$\overset{2}{C}H_2\overset{1}{C}H_2OH$$ (attached to benzene ring)

2-Phenylethanol

EXERCISE 15.2

The aromatic alcohol below, called thymol and found in thyme oil, is used topically as a bactericide and fungicide. Name it as a derivative of phenol

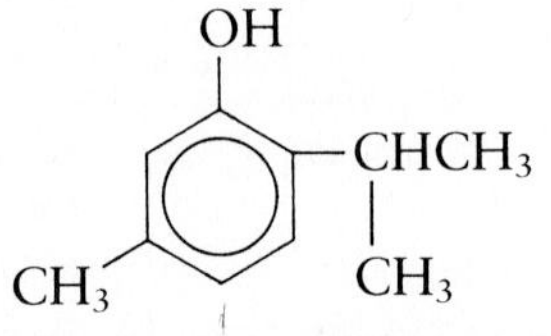

OH

$CHCH_3$

CH_3 CH_3

You can be reasonably sure that compounds which have names ending in *ol* include a hydroxyl group somewhere in their structures. For instance, the compound below, called eugenol and widely used in dentistry, is the main chemical constituent of clove oil and has antibacterial and analgesic properties.

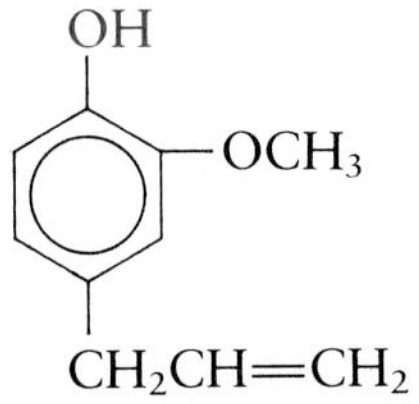

OH

OCH_3

$CH_2CH{=}CH_2$

Eugen***ol***

Cholesterol, a component of most animal tissues, includes a hydroxyl group attached to a complex ring structure.

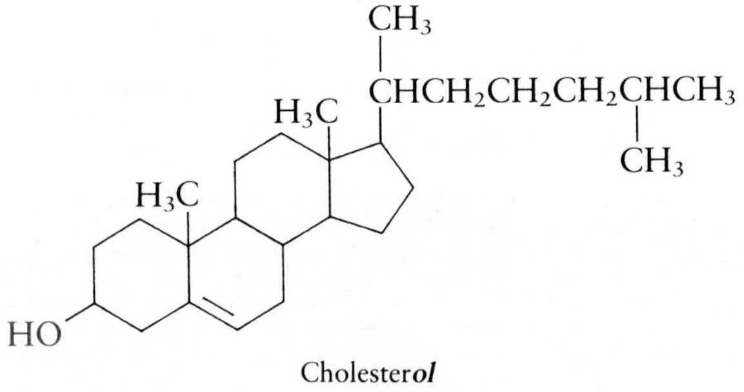

CH_3

$CHCH_2CH_2CH_2CHCH_3$

H_3C CH_3

H_3C

HO

Cholester***ol***

15.3 PHYSICAL PROPERTIES OF ALCOHOLS

We found that many of the physical properties of water depended upon its *inter*molecular hydrogen bonding (see Section 8.7). This is also true of alcohol molecules. The formula for an alcohol includes an O atom bonded to an H atom, and thus alcohols satisfy the criterion for hydrogen bonding. The electropositive H atom of one alcohol molecule is attracted to the electronegative O atom of a neighboring molecule, as shown in Figure 15.3

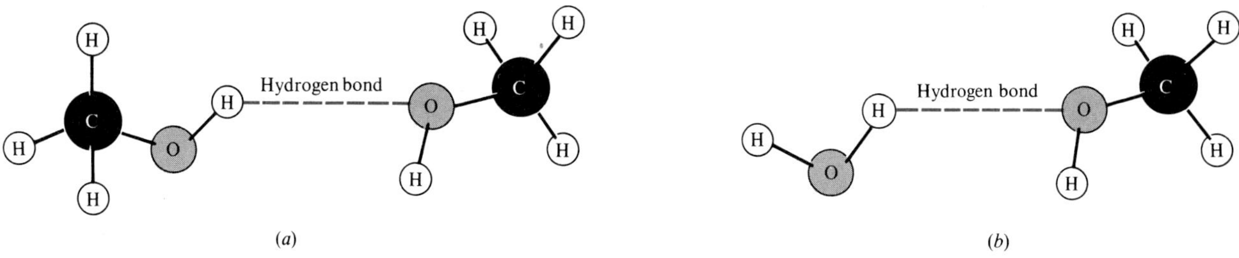

FIGURE 15.3
(*a*) Hydrogen bonding in methanol. The electropositive H atom of one methanol molecule is attracted to the electronegative O atom of another to form a hydrogen bond. (*b*) Hydrogen bonding in methanol and alcohol solutions. The electropositive H atom of a water molecule is attracted to the electronegative O atom of a methanol molecule to form a hydrogen bond.

Boiling Point

Hydrogen-bonded compounds have higher boiling points than expected from estimates based upon their formula weights (see Section 4.16). For instance, the formula weight of methanol is nearly the same as that of ethane.

CH_3OH	CH_3CH_3
Methanol	Ethane
(formula weight 32)	(formula weight 30)

Because molecules of methanol are hydrogen-bonded to each other, extra energy must be supplied to break the hydrogen bonds between them before vaporization can take place. Thus methanol is a liquid (boiling point 65°C), and ethane, which does not exhibit hydrogen bonding, is a gas (boiling point −89°C). Similar comparisons given in Table 15.2 show that the boiling points of all alcohols are unusually high for their formula weights.

Solubility

In Chapter 9 we used the "like dissolves like" rule to predict whether or not compounds would be soluble in each other. Thus we expect alcohols to dissolve

TABLE 15.2 **BOILING POINTS OF ALCOHOLS COMPARED WITH ALKANES OF SIMILAR FORMULA WEIGHT**

Compound	Formula	Formula weight	Boiling point, °C
Ethane	CH_3CH_3	30	−89
Methanol	CH_3OH	32	65
Propane	$CH_3CH_2CH_3$	44	−42
Ethanol	CH_3CH_2OH	46	78.5
Butane	$CH_3CH_2CH_2CH_3$	58	−0.5
1-Propanol	$CH_3CH_2CH_2OH$	60	97
Pentane	$CH_3CH_2CH_2CH_2CH_3$	72	36
1-Butanol	$CH_3CH_2CH_2CH_2OH$	74	118

TABLE 15.3 SOLUBILITIES OF ALCOHOLS

Alcohol Formula	Name	Solubility/100 g H_2O
CH_3OH	Methanol	∞*
CH_3CH_2OH	Ethanol	∞
$CH_3CH_2CH_2OH$	1-Propanol	∞
$CH_3CH(OH)CH_3$	2-Propanol	∞
$CH_3CH_2CH_2CH_2OH$	1-Butanol	8
$CH_3CH_2CH_2CH_2CH_2OH$	1-Pentanol	3
$CH_3CH_2CH_2CH_2CH_2CH_2OH$	1-Hexanol	0.6
$CH_3CH_2CH_2CH_2CH_2CH_2CH_2OH$	1-Heptanol	0.1
$CH_3CH_2CH_2CH_2CH_2CH_2CH_2CH_2OH$	1-Octanol	0.05
$HOCH_2CH_2CH_2CH_2CH_2CH_2OH$	1,6-Hexanediol	∞

*∞ = infinitely soluble.

in water, since they are polar molecules and particularly since alcohol and water molecules can form hydrogen bonds with each other, as shown in Figure 15.3*b*. This reasoning is correct provided that the hydrocarbon chains of the alcohol molecules are not too long. As the hydrocarbon chains get longer and longer, the alcohol molecules become increasingly nonpolar and less able to compete with the attractive forces operating among the very polar water molecules. Thus the longer-chain alcohol molecules are unable to fit in among the water molecules and two layers form (see Section 9.4). A useful rule of thumb is that water solubility begins to decrease markedly when the chain length of an alcohol exceeds four C atoms for each hydroxyl group. You can see this trend in Table 15.3, which gives the solubilities of some alcohols. Note that one of the compounds listed is 1,6-hexanediol, which although it has six C atoms, is still water-soluble, since it has two hydroxyl groups and thus only three C atoms per hydroxyl group.

Alcohols with less than five C atoms are water-soluble.

15.4 PRIMARY, SECONDARY, AND TERTIARY ALCOHOLS

Alkyl alcohols can be divided into one of three classes (primary, secondary, or tertiary), depending upon the type of C atom to which their hydroxyl groups are attached. In **primary alcohols** the hydroxyl group is attached to a *primary C atom*, that is, a carbon atom that is bonded to only *one* other C atom. The alcohols shown below all have a hydroxyl group attached to a primary C atom and so are classified as primary alcohols.

CH_3CH_2OH	$CH_3CH(CH_3)CH_2OH$	C_6H_5–CH_2OH
Ethanol	2-Methyl-1-propanol	Benzyl alcohol

In **secondary alcohols** the hydroxyl group is attached to a *secondary C atom*, that is, a carbon atom that is bonded to *two* other C atoms. The following alcohols are thus secondary alcohols.

$$\begin{array}{c} CH_3CHOH \\ | \\ CH_3 \end{array} \qquad \begin{array}{c} CH_3CH_2CHOH \\ | \\ CH_3 \end{array} \qquad \begin{array}{c} CH_3 \\ | \\ CH_3-C-CH_2CHOH \\ |\qquad | \\ CH_3 \quad CH_3 \end{array}$$

2-Propanol　2-Butanol　4,4-Dimethyl-2-pentanol

In each of the **tertiary alcohols** shown below, the hydroxyl group is attached to a *tertiary C atom*, a C atom which forms bonds with *three* other C atoms.

$$\begin{array}{c} CH_3 \\ | \\ CH_3COH \\ | \\ CH_3 \end{array} \qquad \begin{array}{c} CH_3 \\ | \\ CH_3CH_2COH \\ | \\ CH_3 \end{array}$$

2-Methyl-2-propanol　2-Methyl-2-butanol

The alkyl group in 2-methyl-2-propanol is called tertiary butyl for *tert-butyl.*

$$\begin{array}{c} CH_3 \\ | \\ CH_3C- \\ | \\ CH_3 \end{array}$$

tert-Butyl

The term *tert*-butyl is almost always used to name compounds in which this group appears.

$$\begin{array}{c} CH_3 \\ | \\ CH_3COH \\ | \\ CH_3 \end{array} \qquad \begin{array}{c} CH_3 \\ | \\ CH_3CCl \\ | \\ CH_3 \end{array}$$

tert-Butyl alcohol　*tert*-Butyl chloride

The chemistry of the alcohols is essentially the chemistry of the hydroxyl group. Because the environment of the hydroxyl group is different for primary, secondary, and tertiary alcohols, so too are many of their chemical properties.

SAMPLE EXERCISE 15.3

Label the following alcohols as primary, secondary, or tertiary.

(**a**) 2-Pentanol　(**b**) 4-Methyl-1-hexanol

Solution:

Write the structural formulas for each compound and then examine the C atom attached to the hydroxyl group.

(**a**) This alcohol contains a five-carbon chain and has the hydroxyl group on the C-2 atom.

$$\overset{1}{C}H_3\overset{2}{C}H\overset{3}{C}H_2\overset{4}{C}H_2\overset{5}{C}H_3 \quad (OH \text{ on C-2})$$

$$\begin{array}{l} CH_3\underset{\displaystyle OH}{\underset{|}{C}}HCH_2CH_2CH_3 \end{array}$$

The C-2 atom is bonded to two other C atoms. Thus 2-pentanol is a secondary alcohol.

(**b**) There is a methyl group on C-4 and a hydroxyl group on C-1 in this hexanol.

$$\begin{array}{l} \overset{6}{C}H_3\overset{5}{C}H_2\underset{\displaystyle CH_3}{\underset{|}{\overset{4}{C}}}H\overset{3}{C}H_2\overset{2}{C}H_2\overset{1}{C}H_2OH \end{array}$$

Since C-1 is attached to only one other C atom, it is a primary C atom and this is a primary alcohol.

• •

EXERCISE 15.3

Decide whether 2-methyl-2-pentanol is a primary, secondary, or tertiary alcohol.

15.5 OXIDATION OF ALKYL ALCOHOLS

In general, alcohols are relatively reactive compounds which undergo many different kinds of reactions and can be used as starting materials for the preparation of other compounds. As mentioned before, the chemistry of alcohols is the chemistry of the hydroxyl group. Although phenols also contain hydroxyl groups, we will discuss them separately since the presence of the aromatic ring attached to the hydroxyl has a significant effect on the properties of phenol and its derivatives. In this section we will consider the oxidation reactions of alkyl alcohols, including some which take place in the body.

Alcohols can be burned to produce carbon dioxide and water. The combustion of methanol is sometimes used to provide heat for tabletop cooking or warming.

$$2CH_3OH + 3O_2 \rightarrow 2CO_2 + 4\,H_2O$$

Because of their high oxygen content alcohols burn with a bluish flame, compared with the yellowish flame that you see when hydrocarbons burn.

Alcohols can also undergo milder oxidation reactions. In these reactions the products are organic compounds instead of CO_2, and the oxidizing agent is a compound such as potassium permanganate ($KMnO_4$) or potassium dichromate ($K_2Cr_2O_7$) instead of the O_2 of the air. In Chapter 10 we defined oxidation as a loss of electrons (Section 10.3). The *oxidation* reactions of organic compounds that we discuss here are also accompanied by a *gain in O atoms* or a *loss of H atoms*. In the reactions below we will indicate the oxidizing agent by using the symbol for oxygen in brackets [O]. The products of the oxidation of alcohols depend upon whether the alcohol is primary, secondary, or tertiary.

When primary alcohols are oxidized, two H atoms (in color below) are removed to form the product called an *aldehyde*.

R represents any hydrocarbon group or H.

$$\underset{\text{Primary alcohol}}{R-\overset{\overset{\displaystyle H}{|}}{\underset{\underset{\displaystyle H}{|}}{C}}-OH} + [O] \longrightarrow \underset{\text{Aldehyde}}{R-\overset{\overset{\displaystyle O}{\|}}{C}-H} + H_2O$$

In the aldehyde product a hydrogen atom and an oxygen atom are both bonded to the C atom, as shown in the formula. To satisfy the tetravalency of carbon we must include a double bond between the C and O atoms. Because the aldehyde product contains two less H atoms in its formula than does the reactant alcohol, this type of reaction is also known as a **dehydrogenation.** In fact, the name *aldehyde* was originally derived from the words alcohol dehydrogenation.

The oxidation of a primary alcohol can be stopped at the aldehyde stage or it can be carried further as the aldehyde undergoes oxidation to another organic compound called a *carboxylic acid.*

$$\underset{\text{Aldehyde}}{R-\overset{\overset{\displaystyle O}{\|}}{C}-H} + [O] \longrightarrow \underset{\text{Carboxylic acid}}{R-\overset{\overset{\displaystyle O}{\|}}{C}-OH}$$

Carboxylic acids (covered in Chapter 17) contain the *carboxyl* functional group, which consists of a C atom double-bonded to an O atom and single-bonded to an OH group ($\overset{\overset{\displaystyle O}{\|}}{C}-OH$). Many of the weak acids, such as acetic acid, which we discussed in Chapter 11, are carboxylic acids.

The body metabolizes ethanol by first oxidizing it to an aldehyde called acetaldehyde. An enzyme called alcohol dehydrogenase acts as a catalyst in this reaction.

$$\underset{\text{Ethanol}}{CH_3CH_2OH} + [O] \xrightarrow{\text{alcohol dehydrogenase}} \underset{\text{Acetaldehyde}}{CH_3\overset{\overset{\displaystyle O}{\|}}{C}H} \qquad \text{(unbalanced)}$$

Then the acetaldehyde is further oxidized to acetic acid with the assistance of a different enzyme called aldehyde dehydrogenase.

$$\underset{\text{Acetaldehyde}}{CH_3\overset{\overset{\displaystyle O}{\|}}{C}H} + [O] \xrightarrow{\text{aldehyde dehydrogenase}} \underset{\text{Acetic acid}}{CH_3\overset{\overset{\displaystyle O}{\|}}{C}OH}$$

The acetic acid enters major metabolic pathways in the body and is eventually broken down into the waste products carbon dioxide and water.

$$CH_3\overset{\overset{\displaystyle O}{\|}}{C}OH + [O] \longrightarrow CO_2 + H_2O \qquad \text{(unbalanced)}$$

For 1 mole of ethanol (formula weight 46) the amount of energy produced is 46×7, or 322 kcal.

The overall reaction in which ethanol is converted to carbon dioxide and water takes place with the release of about 7 kcal (7 food calories) per gram of alcohol ingested (see Table 10.2), which corresponds to 322 kcal per mole.

The 7 Cal/g derived from alcohol are often called "empty" calories.

$$CH_3CH_2OH + 3O_2 \longrightarrow 2CO_2 + 3H_2O + 322 \text{ Cal}$$

Thus alcohol can provide energy but it has no nutritive value.

The term 100 proof alcohol means 50% pure alcohol by volume.

In the average person the metabolism of alcohol takes place at an essentially constant rate of about 10 ml of pure alcohol per hour regardless of the alcohol level in the blood. We can use this rate to calculate the time required to metabolize an amount of alcohol that produces a particular effect. From Table 15.4 you can see that it takes about 1 mg of pure alcohol, called *absolute alcohol*, per milliliter of blood to produce mild intoxication. In an average person this level results from the consumption of about 50 ml of pure ethanol. (Since vodka, gin, and whiskey contain only 40 to 50 percent by volume of ethanol, this corresponds to a volume of 100 to 120 ml, or the amount in a 4-oz drink.) To find the time required to metabolize 50 ml of absolute alcohol, use the given rate:

$$50\cancel{\text{ml}} \times \frac{1 \text{ h}}{10\cancel{\text{ml}}} = 5 \text{ h}$$

Thus it takes about 5 h to eliminate the alcohol that produces mild intoxication.

The oxidation of ethanol is the basis of the Breathalyzer test used to estimate blood alcohol levels. The oxidizing agent is a yellowish orange solution of $K_2Cr_2O_7$ mixed with H_2SO_4, which reacts with breath alcohol to form acetic acid and chromium (III) sulfate, as shown in the reaction below:

$$\underset{}{3CH_3CH_2OH} + 8H_2SO_4 + \underset{\text{Yellow-orange}}{2K_2Cr_2O)_7} \longrightarrow 3CH_3\overset{\overset{\displaystyle O}{\|}}{C}OH + 2K_2SO_4 + \underset{\text{Violet}}{2Cr_2(SO_4)_3} + 11H_2O$$

As the reaction proceeds, $K_2Cr_2O_7$ is consumed, changing the color of the original solution. In Color Plate 17 you can thereby see that addition of ethanol to a test dichromate solution changes its color from yellow-orange to violet. The Breathalyzer device used to perform this test (see Figure 15.4) uses photomultiplier tubes instead, devices which are able to detect light intensity. The color of a test solution of $K_2Cr_2O_7$, that is, the one that reacts with the breath alcohol, is compared with that of a standard unreacted solution. The greater the amount of breath alcohol,

The breath alcohol level is related to the percentage of blood alcohol.

TABLE 15.4 **ALCOHOL BLOOD LEVEL VERSUS EFFECTS**

Blood level		
mg alcohol/ml blood	**wt %**	**Effect**
<0.5	<0.05	Small
1	0.1	Mild intoxication*
2	0.2	Intoxication
3	0.3	Stupor
4	0.4	Coma
>6	>0.6	Death

*Intoxication is characterized by euphoria, aggressiveness, lengthened reaction time, and impairment of vision and muscle coordination.

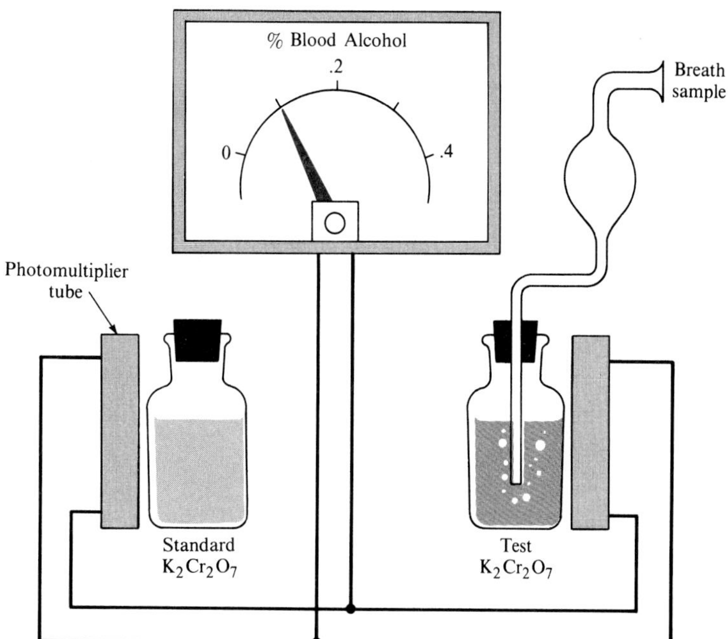

FIGURE 15.4
The breathalyzer machine. Any ethanol present in the breath sample reacts with test $K_2Cr_2O_7$ oxidizing solution, making the test solution less yellow. The photomultiplier tubes detect differences in yellowness in the test and standard $K_2Cr_2O_7$ solutions.

the greater the difference in coloration of the two solutions, and the greater is the deflection of the needle on the instrument.

When secondary alcohols are oxidized, the organic product formed is a *ketone* (see Chapter 16), a compound in which a C atom is double-bonded to an O atom and also to two hydrocarbon groups. Note that the ketone product has two less H atoms than the original alcohol.

$$\underset{\text{Secondary alcohol}}{\text{R—}\overset{\text{OH}}{\overset{|}{\text{C}}}\text{H—R}'} + [\text{O}] \longrightarrow \underset{\text{Ketone}}{\text{R—}\overset{\text{O}}{\overset{\|}{\text{C}}}\text{—R}'} + \text{H}_2\text{O}$$

For instance, isopropyl alcohol (2-propanol) is oxidized to a ketone called acetone.

$$\underset{\text{Isopropyl alcohol}}{\text{CH}_3\overset{\text{OH}}{\overset{|}{\text{C}}}\text{HCH}_3} + [\text{O}] \longrightarrow \underset{\text{Acetone}}{\text{CH}_3\overset{\text{O}}{\overset{\|}{\text{C}}}\text{CH}_3} + \text{H}_2\text{O}$$

Tertiary alcohols do not undergo oxidation under mild conditions.

$$\underset{\text{Tertiary alcohol}}{\text{R}'\text{—}\underset{\underset{\text{R}''}{|}}{\overset{\overset{\text{R}}{|}}{\text{C}}}\text{—OH}} + [\text{O}] \longrightarrow \text{no reaction}$$

SAMPLE EXERCISE 15.4

Give the structure for the aldehyde products of the following reaction:

$$\overset{4}{C}H_3\overset{3}{C}H_2\overset{2}{C}H_2\overset{1}{C}H_2OH + [O] \longrightarrow$$

The reactant, 1-butanol, is a primary alcohol which loses two H atoms to form the corresponding four-carbon aldehyde (called butyraldehyde). In the product formula the C-1 atom forms a double bond with the O atom and a single bond with an H atom.

$$\underset{\text{1-Butanol}}{CH_3CH_2CH_2OH_2OH} + [O] \longrightarrow \underset{\text{Butyraldehyde}}{CH_3CH_2CH_2\overset{\overset{\displaystyle O}{\|}}{C}—H} + H_2O$$

EXERCISE 15.4

What is the structure of the aldehyde product in the reaction below?

$$CH_3\underset{\underset{\displaystyle CH_3}{|}}{C}HCH_2OH + [O] \longrightarrow$$

15.6 DEHYDRATION OF ALCOHOLS

In **dehydration reactions** a reactant is converted to a new organic product with the loss of a molecule of water. Alcohols can be dehydrated when treated with hot sulfuric acid (H_2SO_4); the product that forms depends upon the temperature at which the reaction is run.

Alkene Formation

Alcohols can be dehydrated to form alkenes when heated with sulfuric acid. For instance, ethanol is converted to ethene when treated with H_2SO_4 at a temperature of 170°C. It is easiest to see what happens by using a full formula for the reactant alcohol.

$$\underset{\text{Ethanol}}{H—\underset{\underset{\displaystyle H}{|}}{\overset{\overset{\displaystyle H}{|}}{C}}—\underset{\underset{\displaystyle OH}{|}}{\overset{\overset{\displaystyle H}{|}}{C}}—H} \xrightarrow[170°]{H_2SO_4} \underset{\text{Ethene}}{H—\overset{\overset{\displaystyle H}{|}}{C}=\overset{\overset{\displaystyle H}{|}}{C}—H} + H_2O$$

Tertiary alcohols undergo dehydration most easily, followed by secondary and then by primary alcohols.

Ether Formation

At lower temperatures alcohols treated with sulfuric acid can be dehydrated by the elimination of *one* molecule of water from *two* molecules of alcohol. The product has the general formula of ROR, an ether. We can show how the reaction takes place by writing the alcohol formula twice with the hydroxyl groups facing each other.

$$R—O—H + H—O—R \xrightarrow{H_2SO_4} R—O—R + H_2O$$

For instance, at a temperature of 140°C ethanol is dehydrated to form the general anesthetic diethyl ether.

$$\underset{\text{Ethanol}}{CH_3CH_2OH + HOCH_2CH_3} \xrightarrow[140°C]{H_2SO_4} \underset{\text{Diethyl ether}}{CH_3CH_2OCH_2CH_3} + H_2O$$

The reaction above is actually used as the industrial preparation for diethyl ether. It is also possible to run this type of reaction by using two different alcohols, ROH and R′OH; however, that will result in the formation of a mixture of three ethers with the formulas ROR, R′OR′, and ROR′.

SAMPLE EXERCISE 15.5

Write the products which form when propanol is dehydrated in the presence of H_2SO_4 to form

(a) An alkene (140°C) (b) An ether (100°C)

Solution:

(a) One molecule of water is eliminated from one propanol molecule to form propene.

$$\underset{\text{Propanol}}{H—\overset{H}{\underset{H}{C}}—\overset{H}{\underset{H}{C}}—\overset{H}{\underset{OH}{C}}—H} \xrightarrow[140°C]{H_2SO_4} H_2O + \underset{\text{Propene}}{H—\overset{H}{\underset{H}{C}}—\overset{H}{C}=\overset{H}{C}—H} \quad \text{or} \quad CH_3CH=CH_2$$

(b) One molecule of water is eliminated from two molecules of propanol to form an ether called dipropyl ether.

$$\underset{\text{Propanol}}{CH_3CH_2CH_2OH + HOCH_2CH_2CH_3} \xrightarrow[100°C]{H_2SO_4} \underset{\text{Dipropyl ether}}{CH_3CH_2CH_2OCH_2CH_2CH_3} + H_2O$$

EXERCISE 15.5

Write the products which form when 1-butanol is dehydrated to form

(a) An alkene (b) An ether

15.7 ACIDITY OF ALCOHOLS

Alcohols can donate protons to water molecules to form hydronium ions and **alkoxide ions,** RO^-. However, most alkyl alcohols are even weaker acids than pure water, that is, they have K_a values that are less than 10^{-14} (see Section 11.5):

$$ROH + HOH \rightleftharpoons HOH_2^+ + RO^- \quad K_a \approx 10^{-16} \text{ to } 10^{-18}$$

$$HOH + HOH \rightleftharpoons HOH_2^+ + HO^- \quad K_a = 10^{-14}$$

Another name for phenol is *carbolic acid.*

Phenols, which have K_a values of about 10^{-10}, are considerably more acidic than alkyl alcohols. In the ionization shown below phenol itself donates a proton to water, forming the phenoxide ion.

$$C_6H_5{-}OH + HOH \rightleftharpoons HOH_2^+ + C_6H_5{-}O^- \quad K_a = 1.2 \times 10^{-10}$$

Phenoxide ion

Phenols are much more acidic than alkyl alcohols because the phenoxide ion is more stable than any alkoxide ion. The unshared electron pair from the negatively charged O atom is shared with the benzene ring, which stabilizes the phenoxide ion. Thus, phenol releases an H^+ ion from its hydroxyl group more easily than does an alkyl alcohol.

Phenol undergoes reactions typical of other weak acids, including neutralization. When phenol reacts with sodium hydroxide, the product is the salt sodium phenoxide, also called sodium phenolate.

$$C_6H_5OH + NaOH \longrightarrow C_6H_5ONa + H_2O$$

Phenol — Sodium phenoxide

15.8 OXIDATION OF PHENOLS

Phenols lose electrons readily and are thus very easily oxidized. Phenol itself can react with the oxygen in air to produce a mixture of products, including a compound called quinone, as shown below.

Quinone is only one of many possible oxidation products of phenol.

$$C_6H_5{-}OH + O_2 \longrightarrow O{=}C_6H_4{=}O + H_2O$$

Phenol — Quinone

Quinone, a yellow solid, contributes to the discoloration of phenol, which in pure form is a colorless solid.

Phenols can also undergo oxidation reactions in which they lose one electron and the hydroxyl H atom. The product is an example of a **free radical**, that is, a species which contains one unpaired electron. The phenoxy free radical is produced from phenol.

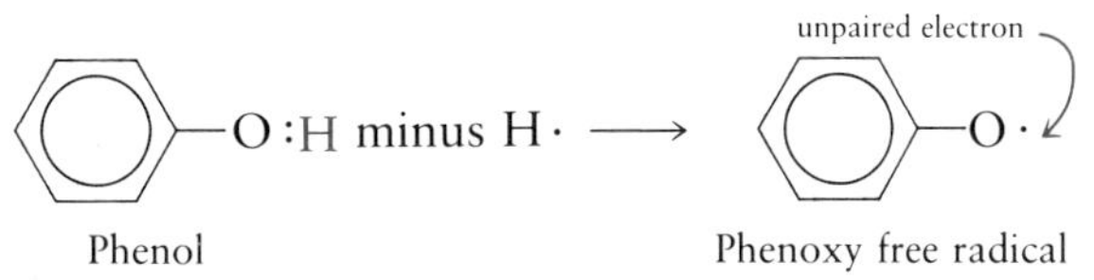

Free radicals are highly reactive species because they seek one electron in order to achieve a stable octet and tend to extract that electron from whatever substance is available, thereby producing more free radicals. Free radicals present in a substance or a mixture can initiate chemical reactions, often undesirable ones. The phenoxy free radical, however is much less chemically reactive than most other free radicals. This makes it is possible to use phenol (and phenol derivatives) as *free radical traps.* The phenol compound readily gives up its H atom and electron to any other free radical present, producing the phenoxy free radical. The product phenoxy free radial is much less reactive, and therefore less harmful, than the original free radical, indicated below by R·.

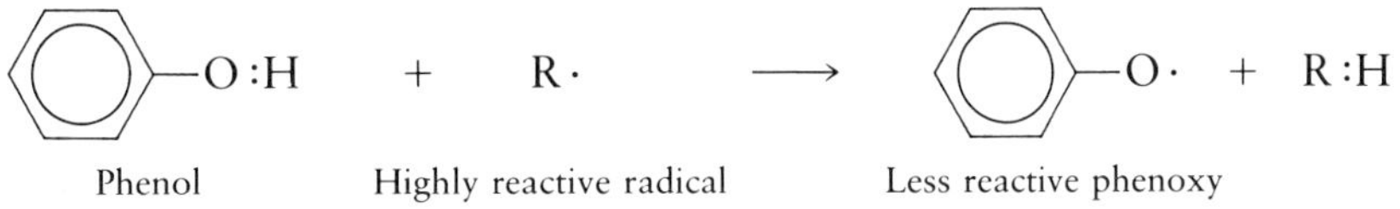

The R radicals are trapped and are said to be *scavenged* by the phenol, thus preventing them from initiating unwanted reactions.

Phenols are so easily oxidized compared with most substances that they are added to certain products as **antioxidants**. For instance, when fats are oxidized, they turn rancid because of the formation of oxidation products with unpleasant odors. To prevent this from happening, the phenol derivatives called butylated hydroxyanisole (BHA) and butylated hydroxytoluene (BHT), shown in Figure 15.5, are added to the fatty foods. The more easily oxidized phenols are preferentially attacked by the oxidizing agents, thereby protecting the fats.

BHA or BHT free radicals are relatively stable.

Vitamin E, a derivative of phenol called *α-tocopherol* (shown in Figure 15.6), is a powerful antioxidant which protects fats present in biological membranes from molecular oxygen and from free radicals. Like other phenol compounds, vitamin E is able to trap free radicals by combining with them to produce the phenoxy free radical.

Vitamin E is a biological antioxidant.

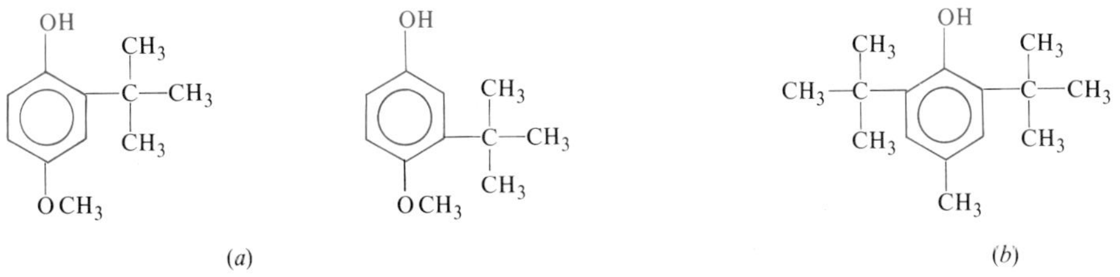

FIGURE 15.5
Phenol derivatives as antioxidants. (*a*) BHAs. (*b*) BHT.

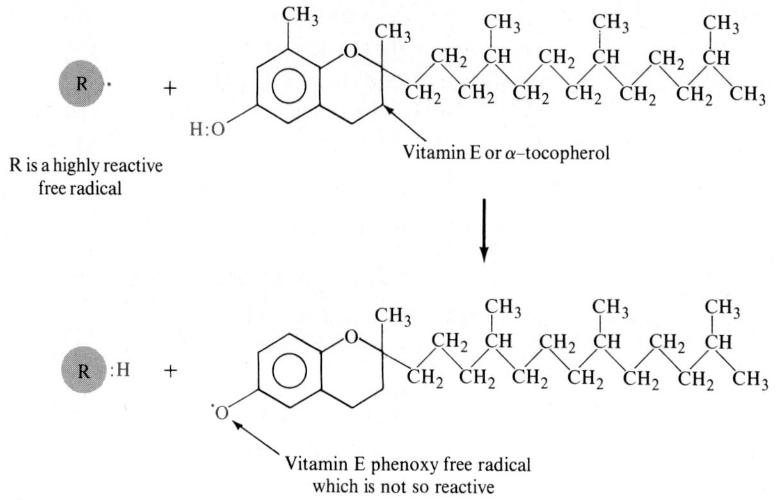

R · + [vitamin E structure, H:O]

R is a highly reactive free radical

Vitamin E or α-tocopherol

R :H + [vitamin E phenoxy radical structure]

Vitamin E phenoxy free radical which is not so reactive

FIGURE 15.6
Reaction of vitamin E with free radicals.

Vitamin E	+	R·	$\longrightarrow$	vitamin E·	+	R:H
A phenol		free radical		A phenoxy radical		

The phenoxy free radical is less reactive and less damaging to body constituents than other types of free radicals.

15.9 IMPORTANT ALCOHOLS

We can now look at the properties of some alcohols encountered in medicine, applying the chemical principles we have just studied.

Ethanol

In industry ethanol is prepard by hydration of ethene (see Section 13.9).

$$CH_2{=}CH_2 + H_2O \xrightarrow{H^+} CH_3CH_2OH$$

Ethanol, like all alkyl alcohols, is a central nervous system (CNS) depressant, producing the effects listed in Table 15.4. In reasonable doses neither ethanol nor its metabolities, acetaldehyde and acetic acid, are toxic. Acetaldehyde and acetic acid do have unpleasant sour odors, which may linger on the breath of an individual who has ingested large quantities of alcohol. A buildup of acetaldehyde in the body can cause a violently unpleasant illness called ***acetaldehydemia.*** This illness is produced when the action of aldehyde dehydrogenase, the one that catalyzes the metabolism of acetaldehyde, is inhibited.

$$\underset{\text{Ethanol}}{CH_3CH_2OH} \xrightarrow{\text{alcohol dehydrogenase}} \underset{\text{Acetaldehyde}}{CH_3\overset{\overset{O}{\|}}{C}H} \xrightarrow{\text{aldehyde dehydrogenase}} \underset{\text{Acetic acid}}{CH_3\overset{\overset{O}{\|}}{C}OH}$$

$$\begin{array}{l} CH_3CH_2 \\ \quad\quad\quad\;\; N-\overset{O}{\overset{\|}{C}}-S-S-\overset{O}{\overset{\|}{C}}-N \\ CH_3CH_2 \end{array} \begin{array}{l} CH_2CH_3 \\ \\ CH_2CH_3 \end{array}$$

FIGURE 15.7
Disulfuram, or Antabuse.

A drug called by the trademark Antabuse, the chemical name of which is disulfuram (see Figure 15.7), is thought to inhibit aldehyde dehydrogenase and thus to cause buildup of acetaldehyde in persons who ingest alcohol. This drug is sometimes used to help in the treatment of ***alcoholism***; a person suffering from alcoholism may elect to take disulfuram, knowing that in combination with alcohol the drug will produce acetaldehydemia. To avoid the unpleasant symptoms of this illness, which include flushing, nausea, vomiting, labored breathing, chest pain, and throbbing headache, the patient has to refrain from drinking alcohol. However, persons treated with disulfuram must remember that the drug will work even if the ethanol ingested comes from vanilla extract or cough medicine instead of liquor. The alcohol content of some common household and drug products is listed in Table 15.5

A teaspoon of alcohol is enough to produce the symptoms of acetaldehydemia in patients treated with disulfuram.

Ethanol is an important industrial solvent, which has germicidal properties and is used as a solvent and preservative for many drugs. Alcoholic solutions of medicinal substances are called *tinctures*. The iodine preparation known as tincture of iodine is less irritating to the skin than "strong" tincture of iodine, which contains much more alcohol (see Table 15.5). Ethanol used for purposes other than drinking is untaxed, which makes it as much as 20 times cheaper than the alcohol used in liquor. However, to prevent it from being used for drinking purposes, unpleasant and difficult to remove substances are added to untaxed alcohol. Ethanol treated in this way is known as *denatured alcohol*.

TABLE 15.5 **ALCOHOL CONTENT OF COMMON PRODUCTS**

Product	% Ethanol	Product	% Ethanol
Flavorings		**Mouthwashes**	
Vanilla extract	35	Listerine	25
Almond extract	50	Scope	18
Cough and cold remedies		Colgate 100	17
		Cepacol	14
Pertussin Plus	25	Lavoris	5
Nyquil	25	**Miscellaneous**	
Dristan	12		
Vicks 44	10	"Strong" iodine tincture	83
Robitussin	3.5	Perfumes	75–90
Robitussin CF, DM, PE	1.4	Iodine tincture	46
		Paregoric tincture	45
		Terpin hydrate	42
		Benadryl elixir	14
		Donnagel suspension	4

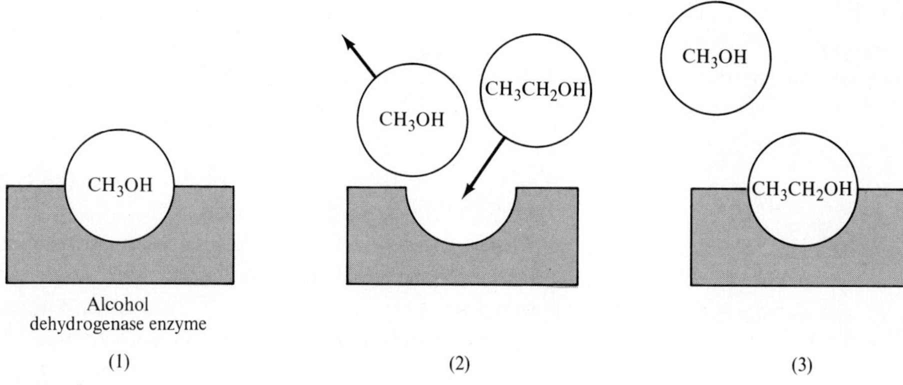

FIGURE 15.8
Ethanol as an antidote for methanol poisoning. (1) When methanol only is present, the enzyme alcohol dehydrogenase oxidizes it to formaldehyde, which is toxic. (2) Ethanol has a greater affinity for alcohol dehydrogenase than does methanol. Ethanol molecules displace methanol molecules (3) The enzyme alcohol dehydrogenase oxidizes ethanol to acetaldehyde, which is much less toxic.

Methanol

Methanol is sometimes called *wood alcohol* because wood can be heated to produce a liquid rich in methanol. Drinking methanol is very dangerous because when it is oxidized during metabolism, two toxic metabolites, formaldehyde and formic acid, are produced.

$$\underset{\text{Methanol}}{CH_3OH} \xrightarrow{\text{alcohol dehydrogenase}} \underset{\text{Formaldehyde}}{H\overset{\overset{\displaystyle O}{\|}}{C}H} \xrightarrow{\text{aldehyde dehydrogenase}} \underset{\text{Formic acid}}{H\overset{\overset{\displaystyle O}{\|}}{C}OH}$$

Formaldehyde is toxic to the retina of the eye and can cause blindness. Formic acid causes acidosis, the condition in which the pH of body fluids dips below normal (see Section 11.14).

Enough ethanol to maintain a blood level of 1 mg/ml is given as an antidote for methanol poisoning.

From looking at the reactions above you can see that the same enzymes which catalyze the metabolism of ethanol also catalyze the metabolism of methanol. However, ethanol has an affinity for alcohol dehydrogenase which is 10 times as great as that of methanol. Thus it is possible to use ethanol as an antidote for methanol poisoning! The ethanol administered occupies alcohol dehydrogenase and thus prevents the formation of the toxic metabolite formaldehyde, as illustrated in Figure 15.8.

Isopropyl Alcohol (2-Propanol)

Spores have been known to survive for years in alcohol.

In the form of a 70 percent aqueous solution, isopropyl alcohol is used both as a rubbing alcohol and as a disinfectant. Ethanol and isopropyl alcohol, the main alcohols used to kill microorganisms, work best in solution because the solution is able to penetrate bacteria cell walls more effectively than pure alcohol. Alcohols do not kill spores or viruses and may simply diminish the growth of bacteria rather than killing them. For this reason alcohols cannot be used alone for sterilization procedures in which complete destruction of microbial forms is required.

Isopropyl alcohol is also unfit for drinking (see Table 15.1 where the lethal doses of all the common alcohols are listed).

Glycerol

The common name glycerine and the systematic name 1,2,3-propane-triol are also used in place of the name glycerol. The clear, syrupy liquid is infinitely

Glycerol and other polyhydric alcohols form H bonds with water, thus preventing loss of water and "drying out."

soluble in water, as expected, because its formula contains one hydroxy group for every C atom. In medicine glycerol is used as a solvent for other medications and as a skin lubricant.

Phenol

Phenol, a colorless solid which melts at 43°C, used to be called "carbolic acid," a name chosen because of its acidity. Phenol is an important compound in industry, where it serves as a starting material for the production of polymers, including Bakelite, a hard, durable substance which is highly resistant to both heat and chemicals. In medicine phenol is used as a topical anesthetic and along with sodium phenoxide (also called sodium phenolate) is used as an ingredient in some lozenges and mouthwashes used to treat throat irritations.

Phenol also acts as a disinfectant. In fact, phenol is used as a standard for germ-killing ability. Other germicidal compounds are compared with a 5% phenol solution by defining a number called the *phenol coefficient*. For instance, a compound which kills *Staphylococcus aureus* bacteria five times more effectively than phenol is said to have a phenol coefficient of 5. Hexachlorophene, the chlorinated phenol compound pictured below, has an unusually high phenol coefficient of 125. Phenol coefficients for alcohol disinfectants are listed in Table 15.6.

The phenol coefficients of ethanol and isopropylalcohol are 0.039 and 0.054, respectively.

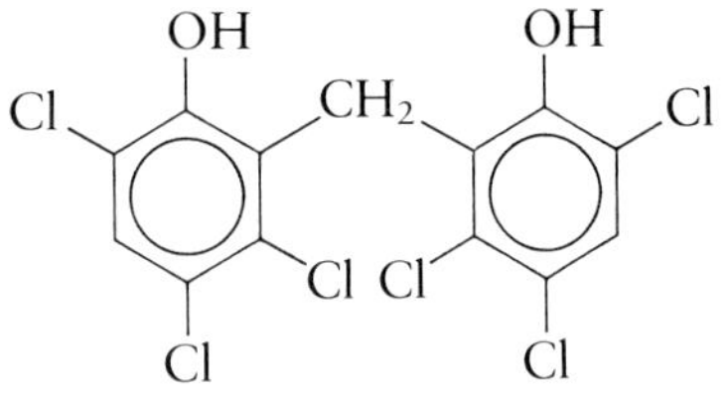

OH OH
Cl CH_2 Cl
Cl Cl
Cl Cl

Hexachlorophene

Because of their germicidal properties phenolic compounds are incorporated into soaps and scrubs. Their use must be somewhat restricted because phenols are skin irritants and are toxic when ingested in high concentrations or absorbed through the skin.

15.10 NAMING ETHERS

Ethers are named by giving the names of the R and R′ hydrocarbon groups in the general formula ROR′, in alphabetical order, followed by the word ether. When the R and R′ groups are the same, the name of the R group is given only once or the prefix *di-* is used in the name. Using this method we can name the ethers below:

$CH_3CH_2OCH_2CH_3$	$CH_3OCH_2CH_3$	C_6H_5—OCH_2CH_3
Diethyl ether (ethyl ether)	Ethyl methyl ether	Ethyl phenyl ether

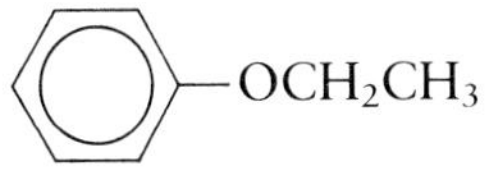

PHENOL COEFFICIENTS FOR ALCOHOL DISINFECTANTS

		Phenol coefficients against	
Alcohol	**Formula**	***Staphylococcus***	***Salmonella***
p-Heptylphenol	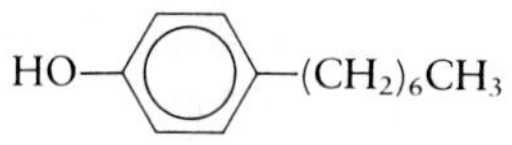 $HO-\bigcirc-(CH_2)_6CH_3$	625	16–17
p-Hexylphenol	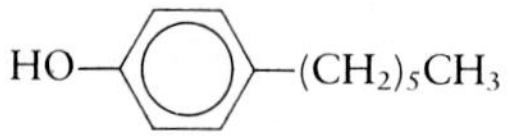 $HO-\bigcirc-(CH_2)_5CH_3$	313	33.3
Hexachlorophene	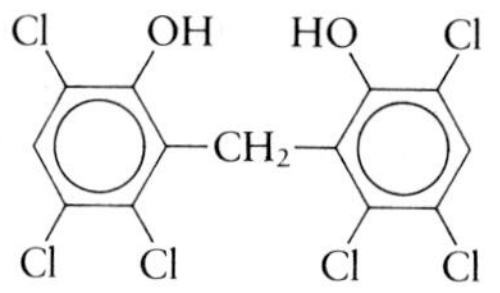 Cl OH HO Cl $\bigcirc-CH_2-\bigcirc$ Cl Cl Cl Cl	125	
p-Propylphenol	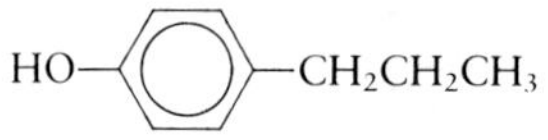 $HO-\bigcirc-CH_2CH_2CH_3$	16.3	18.3
o-Cresol	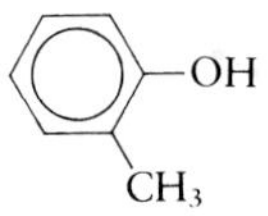 $\bigcirc-OH$ CH_3	2.3	2.3
m-Cresol	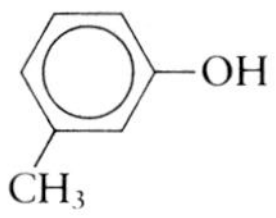 $\bigcirc-OH$ CH_3	2.3	2.3
p-Cresol	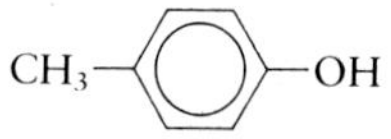 $CH_3-\bigcirc-OH$	2.3	2.3
Phenol	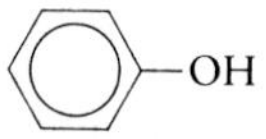 $\bigcirc-OH$	1	1
1-Octanol	$CH_3(CH_2)_7OH$	0.63	21
1-Pentanol	$CH_3(CH_2)_4OH$	0.63	0.78
1-Propanol	$CH_3CH_2CH_2OH$	0.082	0.10
2-Propanol	CH_3CHOH $\vert$ CH_3	0.054	0.064
Ethanol	CH_3CH_2OH	0.039	0.04

The aromatic ether in which R is methyl and R′ is phenyl has the common name anisole.

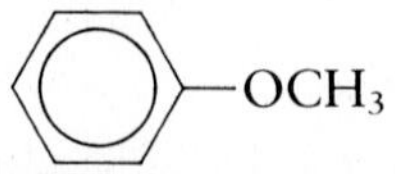

$$\bigcirc-OCH_3$$

Methyl phenyl ether (anisole)

The common names for ethers are used much more often than the IUPAC names.

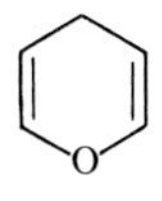

Ethylene oxide   Pyran   Furan

FIGURE 15.9
Cyclic ethers.

Ethers can also be named as hydrocarbon derivatives containing the substituent OR, called **alkoxy** (when R is alkyl). The more complex hydrocarbon group (see Section 12.10) forms the parent hydrocarbon name and the other group the alkoxy prefix. Since the phenyl group is more complex than the methyl group, anisole is named methoxybenzene ($C_6H_5OCH_3$).

Cyclic ethers contain one or more C—O—C bonds, which are part of a ring structure. Some important cyclic ethers, along with their names and uses, are shown in Figure 15.9. We will encounter the pyran and furan ring structures again in the study of carbohydrate chemistry (Chapter 21), where they appear as components of carbohydrate molecules.

SAMPLE EXERCISE 15.6

Name the ethers below.

(a) CH_3OCH_3

(b) 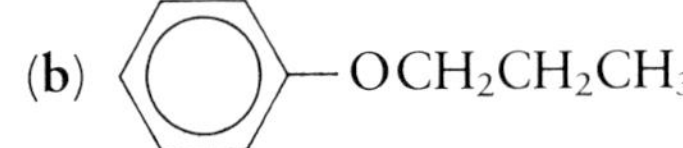

Solution:

(a) Since both hydrocarbon groups are methyl, this compound is named dimethyl ether or methyl ether.
(b) The hydrocarbon groups are phenyl and propyl, so this ether is phenyl propyl ether. As a benzene derivative it is called propoxybenzene.

EXERCISE 15.6

Write the formula for diisopropyl ether.

15.11 PHYSICAL PROPERTIES OF ETHERS

As you can see from looking at the general formula for an ether, ROR′, there is no H atom bonded to the ether O atom. Thus ether molecules do not form hydrogen bonds with each other as alcohol molecules do. Thus, we can expect the boiling points of ethers to be lower than those of alcohols of the same formula weight. For instance, the structural isomers ethanol and dimethyl ether both have the formual C_2H_6O. Ethanol is a liquid and dimethyl ether is a gas.

CH_3CH_2OH	CH_3OCH_3
bp 78.5°C	bp −23°C

Table 15.7 compares the boiling points of ether and alcohol isomers. In each case the boiling point of the ether is considerably lower than that of its isomeric alcohol.

TABLE 15.7 PHYSICAL PROPERTIES OF ETHERS

Name	Formula	Boiling point, °C Ether	Boiling point, °C Isomeric alcohol
Dimethyl ether	CH_3OCH_3	−23	78.5 (ethanol)
Ethyl methyl ether	$CH_3CH_2OCH_3$	11	97 (1-propanol)
Diethyl ether	$CH_3CH_2OCH_2CH_3$	34.5	118 (1-butanol)
Ethyl propyl ether	$CH_3CH_2CH_2OCH_2CH_3$	64	138 (1-pentanol)
Dipropyl ether	$CH_3CH_2CH_2OCH_2CH_2CH_3$	91	157 (1-hexanol)

Ether molecules are polar because they contain polar C—O bonds and because, like water, their molecules are bent so that the bond polarities do not cancel (see Section 4.14). Although ether molecules cannot form hydrogen bonds with each other, they can form hydrogen bonds with water molecules. Thus, like alcohols, ethers which have fewer than five C atoms are somewhat soluble in water. Diethyl ether has a solubility of about 10 g per 100 g water, comparable with that of 1-butanol (8 g per 100 g water).

The fact that ethyl ether is much more soluble in blood than most compounds used as general anesthetics has a great influence on the rate at which anesthesia is achieved with ethyl ether and the rate at which the patient recovers from it. For general anesthesia to be achieved, a minimum alveolar concentration of anesthetic gas is necessary. (See Table 7.3 for the minimum alveolar concentrations of some general anesthetic gases.) Furthermore, the effective inhaled pressure of anesthetic gas must be *maintained* in the alveoli for anesthesia to be induced. When the general anesthetic is administered, there is exchange between the lung alveoli and the blood, as shown in Figure 15.10. Because ethyl ether is so soluble in blood, the partial pressure of ether in the lungs is constantly being reduced as the gaseous ether is transported through the pulmonary membrane to the blood-

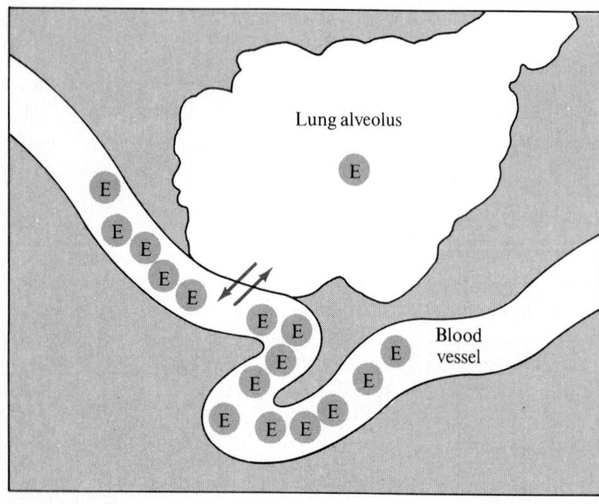

(*a*)

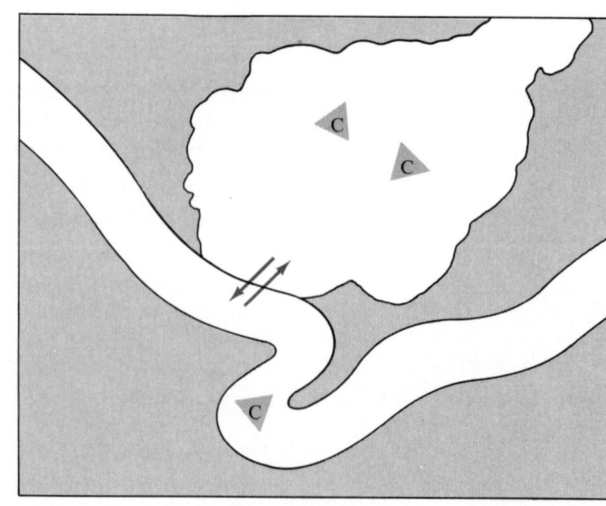

(*b*)

FIGURE 15.10 (*a*) The solubility in blood of diethyl ether is 15, meaning that the concentration of ether in blood is 15 times greater than in the lung at equilibrium. (*b*) The solubility of cyclopropane is 0.5, meaning that the concentration of cyclopropane in the blood is one-half of what it is in the lung at equilibrium.

TABLE 15.8 **SOLUBILITIES OF GENERAL ANESTHETICS AT 37–38°C**

Anesthetic	Concentration in blood/ concentration in alveolar air	Concentration in lipid/ concentration in water
Diethyl ether	15	3.2
Chloroform	7.3	100
Halothane	2.3	220
Cyclopropane	0.5	34
Nitrous oxide	0.5	3.2
Ethylene	0.1	14

It takes only 1 or 2 min to induce anesthesia with cyclopropane.

stream. Thus it takes longer for general anesthesia to be produced with ethyl ether than with cyclopropane, which has a low solubility in blood. The high solubility of ethyl ether in blood also explains the fact that recovery from it is slower. Its concentration in blood and body tissues remains higher longer than that of a less soluble substance such as cyclopropane. Table 15.8 compares the concentrations of various general anesthetic compounds in blood with their concentrations in the gaseous anesthetic mixture at body temperature when equilibrium between the two phases has been achieved. Note that the value for diethyl ether is 15, compared with only 0.5 for cyclopropane.

15.12 CHEMICAL PROPERTIES OF ETHERS

Ethers do not react with many substances, a property which makes them useful as inert solvents in which to carry out reactions. However, ethers can undergo oxidation and must be handled carefully because the oxidation produces **organic peroxides**, which are explosive and dangerous compounds. To form a peroxide, an ether reacts with O_2 from the air in a complex series of steps.

$$\underset{\text{Ether}}{\text{R—O—R}} + O_2 \xrightarrow{\text{many steps}} \underset{\text{Peroxide}}{\text{R—O—O—R}} \qquad \text{(unbalanced)}$$

It can thus be very dangerous to heat an ether since the liquid ether will boil away and leave any higher-boiling peroxides which might be present. Heating the peroxide residue can cause an explosion violent enough to blow the roof off a building. To be safe, ethers should never be evaporated to dryness unless it is certain that there are no peroxides present.

15.13 ETHYL ETHER AND GENERAL ANESTHETICS

Recall that halogenated hydrocarbons are not flammable.

We have mentioned many compounds used as **general anesthetics**, including cyclopropane, halothane, nitrous oxide, chloroform, and diethyl ether, the first one used successfully (in the year 1845, when it was administered for dental surgery).

$CH_3CH_2OCH_2CH_3$ — Diethyl ether

N_2O — Nitrous oxide

$CH_2{=}CH_2$ — Ethylene

$CH_2{=}CHOCH{=}CH_2$ — Divinyl ether

CH_3CH_2Cl — Chloroethane

$CHCl_3$ — Chloroform

Br—CH(Cl)—C(F)(F)—F — Halothane

CH_2—CH_2 (ring with CH_2) — Cyclopropane

Xe — Xenon

FIGURE 15.11
General anesthetic compounds. They all behave as general anesthetics but not all are in use.

Figure 15.11 shows the structures of a variety of compounds which behave as general anesthetics. What is striking about this collection of compounds is that there is no one structural feature that they all have in common. Xenon, for instance, is nothing like any of the others. In fact, why any of them work is not really well understood. There is a theory, however, that explains how they get to the site at which they act, that is, the central nervous system (brain and spinal cord). Once inhaled, the anesthetic is carried to the blood, which then transports it to brain tissue, as shown in Figure 15.12. Brain tissue is very rich in nonpolar substances called *lipids* (Chapter 22). The one thing that the general anesthetic substances have in common is that they are more soluble in nonpolar substances (brain lipids) than in polar ones (such as blood). In Table 15.8, which compares the solubilities of some general anesthetics in lipid with their solubilities in blood, you can see that these ratios are all greater than unity. Thus general anesthetics are able to be transported from the blood to the brain, where they can begin to act. Even ether, one of the most polar of the anesthetics, as we mentioned above, is still more soluble in lipids than it is in water. This theory explains only how the general anesthetics get to the site of action but not how they act. An ideal general anesthetic would be nonflammable, potent, and rapidly induced, cause no postoperative side effects, and be nontoxic after repeated use. No one com-

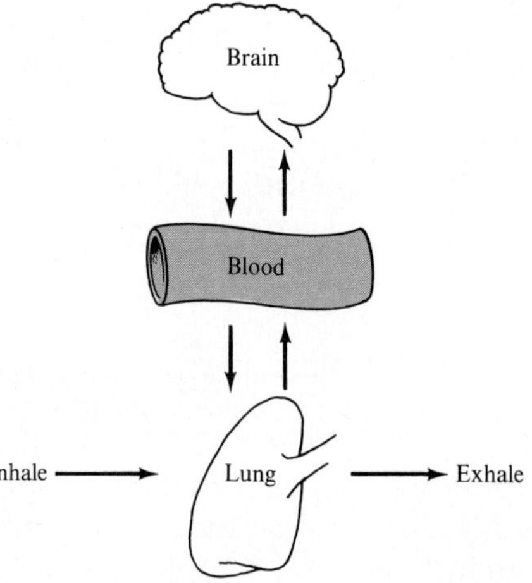

FIGURE 15.12
The brain is rich in lipids. All general anesthetics are more soluble in lipid than in blood, allowing them to reach the brain.

Note that the potency of a general anesthetic is not always directly related to rate of induction.

pound is rated good in all these areas, as you can note from looking at Table 15.9. The lack of understanding of their mechanism of action makes it difficult to design perfect general anesthetic drugs.

TABLE 15.9 **PROPERTIES OF GENERAL ANESTHETICS**

Compound	Potency	Rate of induction	Postoperative side effects	Flammability	Toxicity
$CH_3CH_2OCH_2CH_3$ Diethyl ether	+	−	−	−	+
$CF_3CHClBr$ Halothane	+	±	±	+	±
N_2O Nitrous oxide	−	+	−	+	+
CH_2—CH_2 \ / CH_2 Cyclopropane	+	+	+	−	+

In this table a plus (+) is good, minus (−) is poor, and (±) is intermediate.

SUMMARY

Alcohols are organic compounds which contain a hydroxyl group (OH) attached to a C atom. The general formula for an alcohol is ROH, where R can be an aliphatic or an aromatic hydrocarbon group. Saturated aliphatic alcohols are named either as alkyl alcohols (common) or as alkanols (IUPAC). When they are named as alkanols, numbers are used to specify the location of the hydroxyl group and any other substituents. Aromatic alcohols in which the OH is bonded directly to the benzene ring are named as derivatives of phenol.

Like water, alcohols participate in hydrogen bonding and thus have unusually high boiling points for their formula weights. Alcohols with four or less C atoms are water-soluble.

Alcohols are classified according to the nature of the C atom to which their hydroxyl groups are bonded. In primary alcohols the OH is attached to a primary C atom, that is, a C atom bonded to only one other C atom. Secondary alcohols have OH groups attached to secondary C atoms (bonded to two other C atoms) and tertiary alcohols have the OH group on a tertiary C atom (bonded to three other C atoms).

When treated with chemical oxidizing agents such as potassium dichromate ($K_2Cr_2O_7$), primary alcohols are initially oxidized to form aldehydes ($R{-}\overset{\displaystyle O}{\overset{\|}{C}}{-}H$), which are further oxidized to carboxylic acids ($R{-}\overset{\displaystyle O}{\overset{\|}{C}}{-}OH$). Secondary alcohols undergo oxidation to form ketones ($R{-}\overset{\displaystyle O}{\overset{\|}{C}}{-}R'$), and tertiary alcohols are not easily oxidized. Alcohols can be dehydrated in the presence of sulfuric acid (H_2SO_4) to form alkenes or ethers (ROR). For a given alcohol, say ethanol, the alkenes are formed at a higher temperature (170°C) and ethers at a lower temperature (140°C).

Phenols are more acidic than alkyl alcohols and can form salts called phenoxides when they react with a base such as NaOH. Phenols can be oxidized to form a phenoxide free radical (PhO·), which is much less reactive than other free radicals. Thus phenols are used as free radical traps to replace very reactive free radicals with much less reactive phenoxide free radicals. Since phenols are readily oxidized, they are used as antioxidants to protect other compounds from being attacked by oxidizing agents.

Ethanol is drinking alcohol and is metabolized in the body to produce acetaldehyde, then acetic acid, and eventually CO_2 and water. Methanol, which metabolizes to form formaldehyde and formic acid, is toxic. Alkyl alcohols and phenols have germicidal properties and are used as disinfectants.

The general formula for an ether is ROR′, where the R and R′ stand for aliphatic or aromatic hydrocarbon groups. Ethers are most often named by giving the hydrocarbon names in alphabetical order and adding the word *ether*.

Because ether molecules do not participate in hydrogen bonding with each other, ethers have lower boiling points than corresponding alcohols. Ethers are polar and form hydrogen bonds with water molecules: thus they are soluble in water if their formulas include less than five C atoms. In general, ethers are fairly unreactive, although they can be oxidized to form explosive peroxides. Many ethers, including ethyl ether, are used as general inhalation anesthetics.

KEY WORDS

alcohol	primary alcohol	dehydration reaction	free radical
ether	secondary alcohol	alkoxide ion	alkoxy group
hydroxyl group	tertiary alcohol	phenols	organic peroxide
polyhydric alcohol	dehydrogenation	antioxidant	general anesthetic

EXERCISES

15.7 Can the R in the general formula for an alcohol be an H atom? Why?

15.8 Can the R or R′ in the general formula for an ether be an H atom? Why?

15.9 Name the following alcohols:

(a) $CH_3CH_2CH_2OH$ (b) 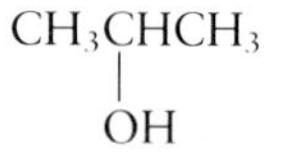 CH_3CHCH_3 with OH on C-2

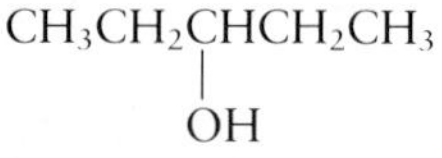

(c) $CH_3CH_2CHCH_2CH_3$ with OH on C-3 (d) 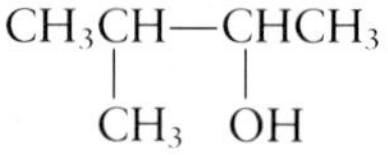 $CH_3CH—CHCH_3$ with CH_3 on C-2 and OH on C-3

15.10 Name the alcohols below:

(a) $HOCH_2CH_2CH_2CH_2CH_2CH_3$

(b) 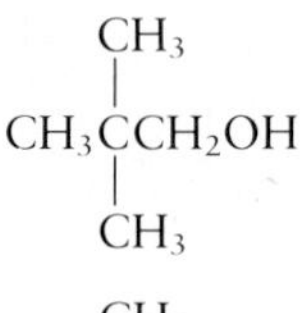 CH_3CCH_2OH with two CH_3 on the central C (c) $HOCH_2CH_2CH_2OH$

(d) 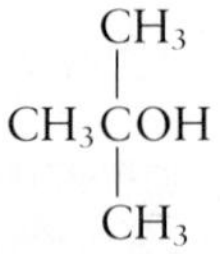 CH_3COH with two CH_3 on the central C

15.11 Classify each alcohol in Exercises 15.9 and 15.10 as primary, secondary, or tertiary.

15.12 Name the following aromatic alcohols. Which can be classified as phenols?

(a) 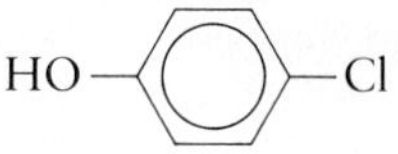 HO—C_6H_4—Cl (para)

(b) C_6H_5—$CH_2CHCH_2CH_3$ with OH on the CH

(c) C_6H_4 with OH and CH_3 (meta) (d) 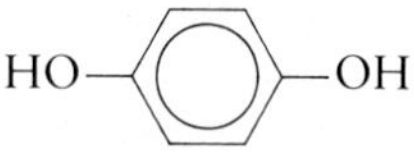 HO—C_6H_4—OH (para)

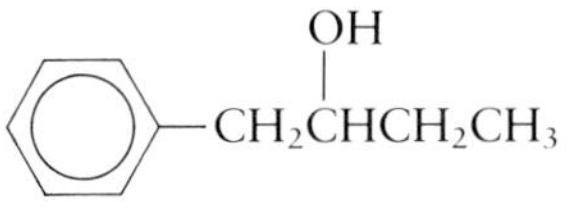

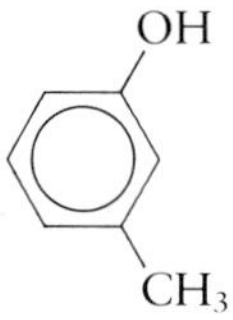

15.13 Write the structure for 4-hexylresorcinol, a compound which is used as an antiseptic, germicide, and remedy for intestinal worms. (See page 456.)

15.14 Name the compound called eugenol as a phenol.

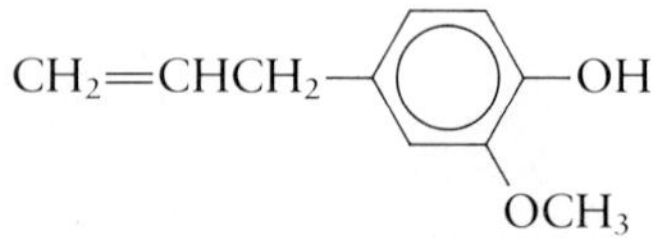

$CH_2{=}CHCH_2$—C_6H_3—OH with OCH_3 ortho to OH

(*Hint*: Recall that $CH_2{=}CHCH_2—$ is called allyl.)

15.15 The compound below, called isoeugenol, occurs in oil of nutmeg. How is its structure different from that of eugenol?

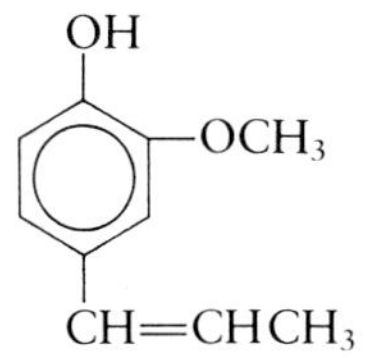

OH
(benzene ring)—OCH_3
CH=CHCH$_3$

15.16 Give the structural formulas for the following alcohols: (**a**) Methanol; (**b**) 2-butanol; (**c**) 3-heptanol; (**d**) 2,4-dimethyl-2-pentanol; (**e**) *p*-bromophenol; (**f**) diphenylhydroxymethane; (**g**) 1,2-propanediol.

15.17 There are four alcohol isomers of butanol. (**a**) Write their structures and name them. (**b**) Label each one as primary, secondary, or tertiary.

15.18 Why do alcohols have unusually high boiling points compared with alkanes with the same formula weight?

15.19 What is the rule of thumb about the water solubility of alcohols?

15.20 The structure of sucrose (table sugar) is pictured below. Why is sucrose soluble in water even though its formula includes 12 C atoms?

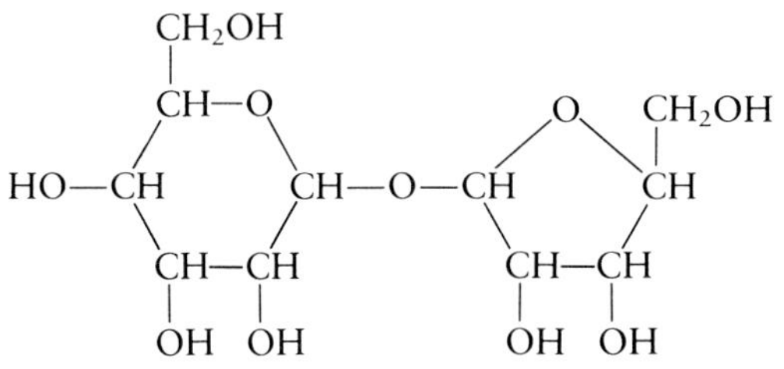

```
        CH2OH
        |
        CH—O                    O     CH2OH
       /     \               /    \   |
HO—CH          CH—O—CH              CH
       \     /          \         /
        CH—CH            CH—CH
        |   |            |   |
        OH  OH           OH  OH
```

15.21 Name the polyhydric alcohol mannitol as an alkane derivative.

15.22 Why was the name carbolic acid originally used for the compound phenol?

15.23 Give the structures for all the ether isomers with the formula $C_5H_{12}O$.

15.24 Arrange the following four compounds according to increasing boiling point: butane, propanol, methyl ethyl ether, pentanol.

15.25 Name the following ethers:

(**a**) $CH_3CH_2CH_2CH_2OCH_2CH_3$

(**b**) $CH_3CHOCH_2CH_3$ (with CH_3 on the CH)

(**c**) CH_3O—(benzene ring)

(**d**) $CH_3CH_2CH_2CH_2O$—(benzene ring)

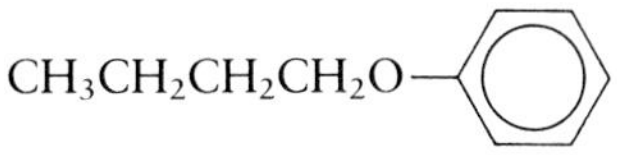

15.26 The liquid compound styrene (phenylethene) forms solid polymers in the presence of free radicals. Why do you think the additive hydroquinone (1,4-dihydroxybenzene) is added to reagent bottles of styrene?

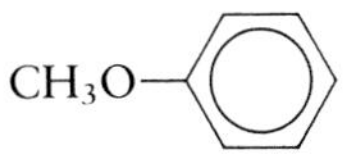

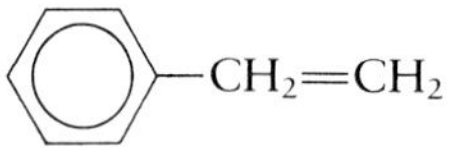

(benzene ring)—CH_2=CH_2 Styrene

15.27 Two phenol compounds used as antioxidants are the butylated derivatives of the phenols shown below.

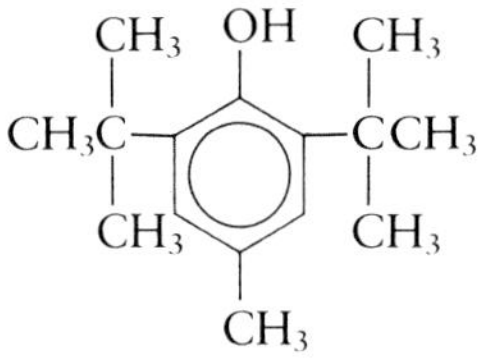

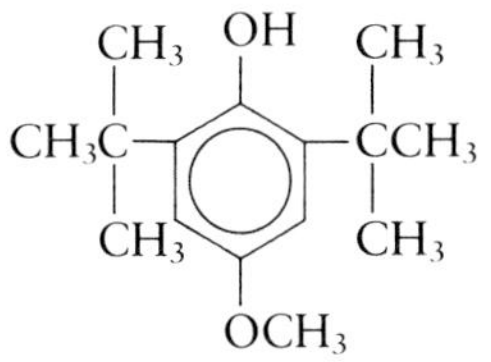

(benzene ring with OH; two $C(CH_3)_3$ groups (CH_3C with CH_3 above and below; CCH_3 with CH_3 above and below) ortho to OH; CH_3 para to OH)

(benzene ring with OH; two $C(CH_3)_3$ groups (CH_3C with CH_3 above and below; CCH_3 with CH_3 above and below) ortho to OH; OCH_3 para to OH)

(**a**) One of these compounds is abbreviated BHT and the other BHA. What do BHT and BHA stand for? (*Hint*: B stands for butylated.)

(**b**) Why are phenols good antioxidants?

15.28 Give formulas for the organic products of the following reactions:

(**a**) $CH_3CH_2OH + [O] \rightarrow$ (an aldehyde)

(**b**) $CH_3CH_2CH_2CH_2CH_2OH + [O] \rightarrow$ (an aldehyde)

(**c**) $CH_3CH_2CHOH + [O] \longrightarrow$ (a ketone) (with CH_3 on the CH)

15.29 Write the reactions for the following conversions:

(**a**) Ethanol to acetaldehyde

(**b**) Acetaldehyde to acetic acid

(**c**) Methanol to formaldehyde

(**d**) Formaldehyde to formic acid

15.30 Suppose a person consumed about 100 ml of absolute ethanol, enough to produce a blood level of 200 mg alcohol per 100 ml blood.

(**a**) About how many milliliters of 50% ethanol would be consumed?

(**b**) What would be the effect on the person?

(**c**) How long would it take the person to metabolize the alcohol?

15.31 Why is it so dangerous to consume methanol? How

can ethanol behave as an antidote for methanol poisoning?

15.32 Suppose a person taking disulfuram used the cough medication described below. What would happen? Ingredients (in each 5 ml): active ingredient 2.5 mg, alcohol 5%, sugar, water, glycerol, ammonium chloride, sodium citrate, raspberry flavoring, caramel.

15.33 The compound below is used in acne preparations. What type of organic compound is this?

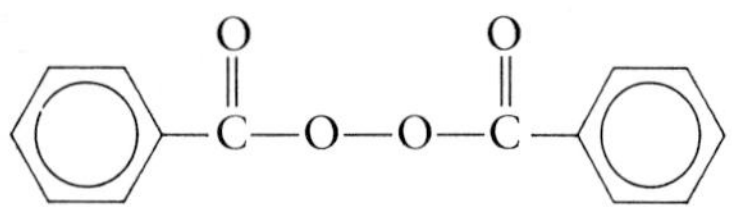

$$\mathrm{C_6H_5{-}\overset{\overset{\displaystyle O}{\|}}{C}{-}O{-}O{-}\overset{\overset{\displaystyle O}{\|}}{C}{-}C_6H_5}$$

15.34 What is meant by the statement that a substance has a phenol coefficient of 2?

15.35 Write the reaction in which
(**a**) Ethanol is dehydrated to form ethene
(**b**) Methanol is dehydrated to form methyl ether

15.36 Are there compounds besides ethanol which could react with the oxidizing agent used in the Breathalyzer machine?

15.37 Why do ethers have lower boiling points than alcohols of the same formula weight?

15.38 What are the important features that should be present in a compound to be used as a general anesthetic? Why is it difficult to design the ideal general anesthetic?

15.39 Give the name for the general anesthetic compound below:

$$\mathrm{CH_2{=}CH{-}O{-}CH{=}CH_2}$$

Do you think it would be safe to use this compound in an operation for which electrocautery is required? Why or why not?

15.40 Why does it take longer for ethyl ether to produce general anesthesia than it does for cyclopropane to do so?

15.41 The compound below, called methoxyflurane (Penthrane), is a potent general anesthetic. To what class of compounds does Penthrane belong? Would you expect this compound to be highly flammable?

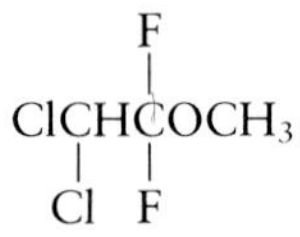

$$\mathrm{Cl\underset{\underset{\displaystyle Cl}{|}}{C}H\overset{\overset{\displaystyle F}{|}}{\underset{\underset{\displaystyle F}{|}}{C}}OCH_3}$$

15.42 Enflurane (Enthrane) is a potent general anesthetic with properties similar to those of halothane. What kind of compound is this? Should it be flammable?

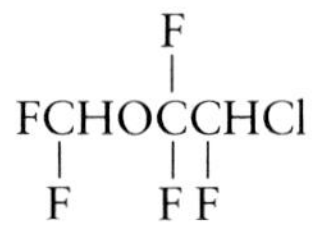

$$\mathrm{F\underset{\underset{\displaystyle F}{|}}{C}HO\overset{\overset{\displaystyle F}{|}}{\underset{\underset{\displaystyle F}{|}}{C}}\underset{\underset{\displaystyle F}{|}}{C}HCl}$$

15.43 Why is nitrous oxide most often used in a mixture of general anesthetic gases rather than by itself?

15.44 What property shared by all the general anesthetics allows them to be transported to the central nervous system?

15.45 Note from Table 15.6 that 1-octanol has a very high set of phenol coefficients compared with 2-propanol or ethanol. Why isn't octanol used to make disinfectant solutions?

16 . . . . ALDEHYDES AND KETONES

16.1 INTRODUCTION

In this chapter we will discuss the structures and properties of two closely related classes of compounds, the *aldehydes* and the *ketones*. In the last chapter we found that aldehydes are produced when primary alcohols are oxidized (see Section 15.5)

$$\underset{\text{Primary alcohol}}{RCH_2OH} + [O] \longrightarrow \underset{\text{Aldehyde}}{R{-}\overset{\overset{\displaystyle O}{\|}}{C}{-}H} + H_2O$$

and that the oxidation of a secondary alcohol gives a ketone

$$\underset{\text{Secondary alcohol}}{R{-}\overset{\overset{\displaystyle OH}{|}}{C}H{-}R} + [O] \longrightarrow \underset{\text{Ketone}}{R{-}\overset{\overset{\displaystyle O}{\|}}{C}{-}R'} + H_2O$$

When writing general formulas for aldehydes and ketones, it is important to specify the nature of any R groups that appear. In the general formula for an **aldehyde** the R can be a hydrogen atom or a hydrocarbon group.

$$\underset{\text{Aldehyde formula}}{R{-}\overset{\overset{\displaystyle O}{\|}}{C}{-}H} \qquad \text{where R is an H atom or a hydrocarbon group}$$

However, in the **ketone** formula both the R and the R′ must be hydrocarbon groups, not hydrogen atoms, since otherwise the formula converts to that of an aldehyde.

$$\underset{\text{Ketone formula}}{R{-}\overset{\overset{\displaystyle O}{\|}}{C}{-}R'} \qquad \text{where R and R' are hydrocarbon groups}$$

Many of the typical reactions of aldehydes and ketones discussed in this chapter will be seen again when we begin out study of the carbohydrates (Chapter

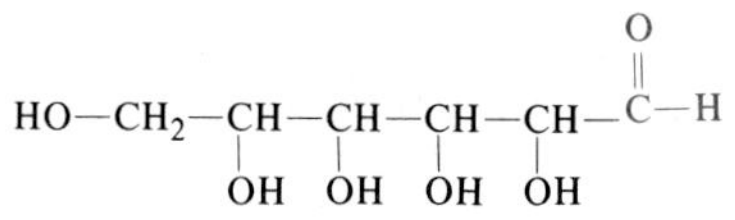

$$HO-CH_2-\underset{OH}{\underset{|}{CH}}-\underset{OH}{\underset{|}{CH}}-\underset{OH}{\underset{|}{CH}}-\underset{OH}{\underset{|}{CH}}-\overset{O}{\overset{\|}{C}}-H$$

Glucose

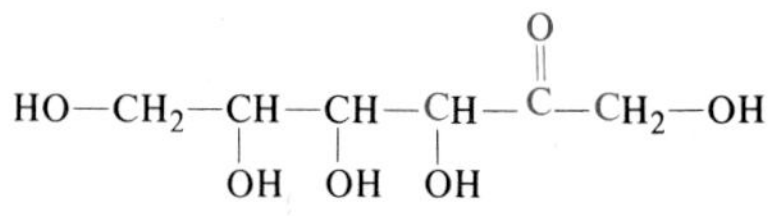

$$HO-CH_2-\underset{OH}{\underset{|}{CH}}-\underset{OH}{\underset{|}{CH}}-\underset{OH}{\underset{|}{CH}}-\overset{O}{\overset{\|}{C}}-CH_2-OH$$

Fructose

FIGURE 16.1
Glucose (an aldehyde) and fructose (a ketone).

21), which are themselves aldehydes or ketones. Figure 16.1 gives the structures of two important carbohydrate molecules, the sugars fructose and glucose. A close look at their structures shows that glucose is an aldehyde and that fructose is a ketone.

16.2 THE CARBONYL GROUP

Figure 16.2*a* shows the structures of some aldehydes and Figure 16.2*b* shows some ketones where you can see that their common structural feature is a carbon atom double-bonded to an oxygen atom, comprising a **carbonyl group.**

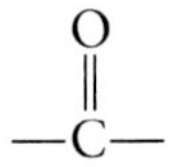

$$-\overset{O}{\overset{\|}{C}}-$$

Carbonyl group

Most of the chemical reactions of the aldehydes and ketones involve the carbonyl group.

The carbonyl double bond undergoes addition reactions like the alkene double bond. But unlike the alkene double bond, the carbonyl double bond is polar because the carbonyl O atom is much more electronegative than the C atom to which it is bonded.

$$\overset{\delta+}{C}=\overset{\delta-}{O} \qquad\qquad C=C$$

Polar carbonyl double bond — Nonpolar alkene double bond

We will find that many more kinds of compounds can be added across the carbonyl double bond because of its polarity.

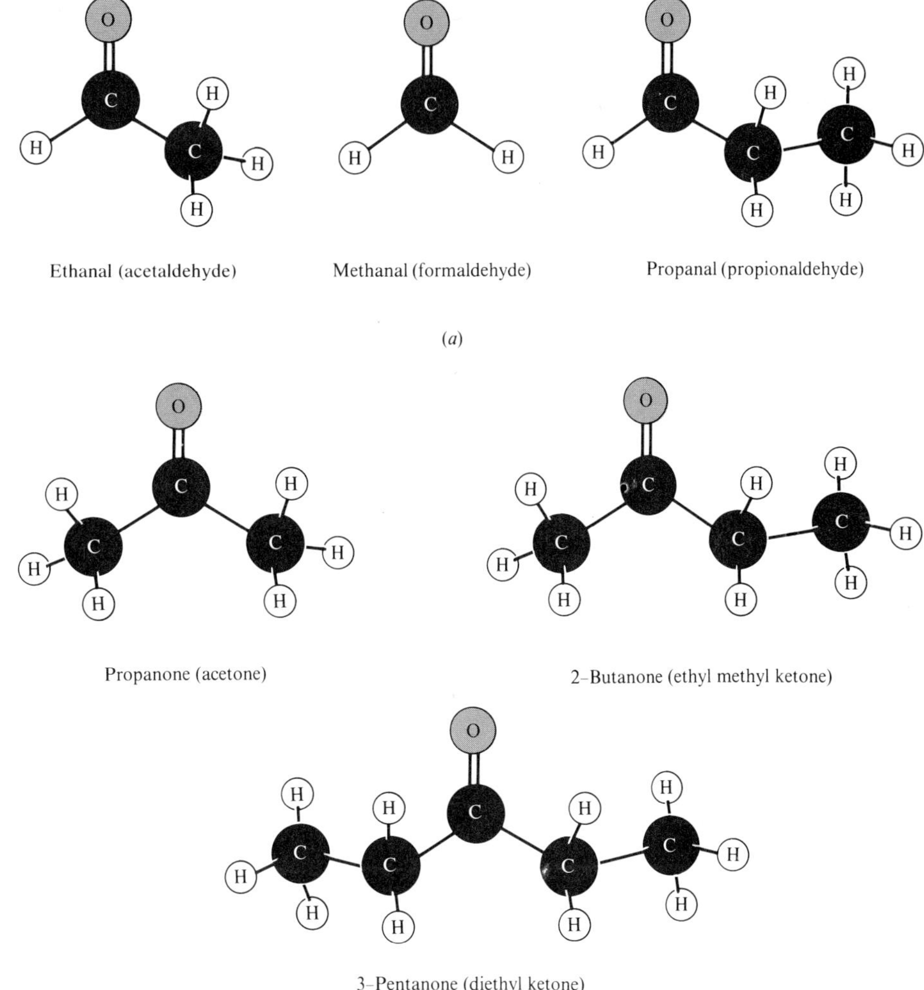

FIGURE 16.2
(*a*) Structures of aldehydes.
(*b*) Structures of ketones.

16.3 NAMING ALDEHYDES

Aliphatic Aldehydes

Unsubstituted aldehydes are named by dropping the *-e* from the alkane name with the same number of C atoms and adding the suffix *-al* (for *al*dehyde). The carbonyl C atom *is* included in the carbon atom total. For instance, to name the aldehyde below, which has five C atoms in its formula, the name pentane is modified by dropping the *-e* and adding *-al* to form pentanal.

Pentan***al***

Many low-molecular-weight aldehydes have common names derived from carboxylic acid names. A carboxylic acid, $R-\overset{\overset{\displaystyle O}{\|}}{C}-OH$, is produced by the oxidation of an aldehyde $R-\overset{\overset{\displaystyle O}{\|}}{C}-H$, as we discussed in Section 15.5. The common aldehyde names are derived by dropping the *-ic acid* from the carboxylic acid name and then adding the suffix *-aldehyde*. For instance, the name of the two-carbon carboxylic acid ($CH_3\overset{\overset{\displaystyle O}{\|}}{C}OH$) is *acet*ic acid and the name for the corresponding aldehyde ($CH_3\overset{\overset{\displaystyle O}{\|}}{C}H$) is *acet*aldehyde. The one-carbon and two-carbon aldehydes are usually referred to as *form*aldehyde (from *form*ic acid) and acetaldehyde rather than methanal and ethanal.

$$H\overset{\overset{\displaystyle O}{\|}}{C}H \qquad\qquad CH_3\overset{\overset{\displaystyle O}{\|}}{C}H$$

Formaldehyde or methanal   Acetaldehyde or ethanal

Table 16.1 lists the IUPAC names and the most used common names for the first 10 members of a homologous series of aldehydes, as well as the names of the carboxylic acids from which the common names are derived.

The IUPAC names of more complex aldehydes, that is, those in which the R group is branched or contains a substituent, are named by using a numbering system. The carbonyl C atom is assigned the number 1 and the other C atoms in the longest chain of the aldehyde R group are numbered consecutively. For example, the three aldehydes below are named as derivatives of butanal.

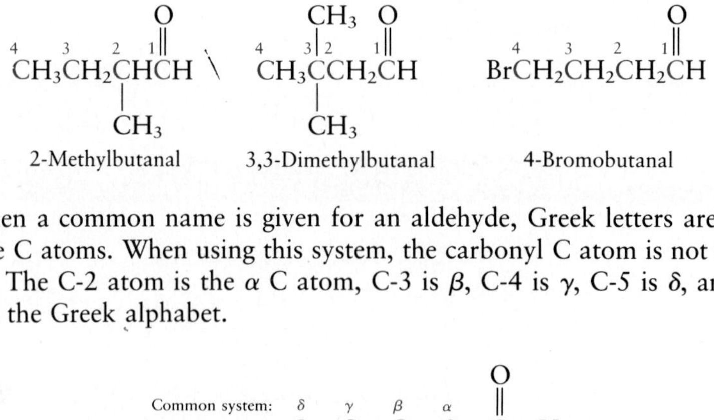

$$\overset{4}{C}H_3\overset{3}{C}H_2\underset{\underset{\displaystyle CH_3}{|}}{\overset{2}{C}}H\overset{\overset{\displaystyle O}{\|}}{\overset{1}{C}}H \qquad CH_3\underset{\underset{\displaystyle CH_3}{|}}{\overset{\overset{\displaystyle CH_3}{|}}{\overset{3}{C}}}\overset{2}{C}H_2\overset{\overset{\displaystyle O}{\|}}{\overset{1}{C}}H \qquad Br\overset{4}{C}H_2\overset{3}{C}H_2\overset{2}{C}H_2\overset{\overset{\displaystyle O}{\|}}{\overset{1}{C}}H$$

2-Methylbutanal   3,3-Dimethylbutanal   4-Bromobutanal

When a common name is given for an aldehyde, Greek letters are used to label the C atoms. When using this system, the carbonyl C atom is not assigned a letter. The C-2 atom is the α C atom, C-3 is β, C-4 is γ, C-5 is δ, and so on through the Greek alphabet.

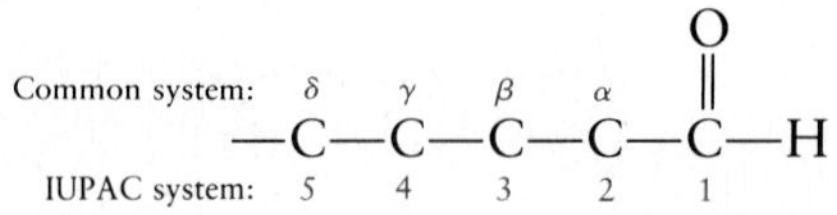

$$\begin{array}{lcccccc} \text{Common system:} & \delta & \gamma & \beta & \alpha & & \\ & -C- & C- & C- & C- & \overset{\overset{\displaystyle O}{\|}}{C} & -H \\ \text{IUPAC system:} & 5 & 4 & 3 & 2 & 1 & \end{array}$$

The Greek letters are used to locate substituents in the same way that numbers are. Thus Greek letters appear in the names of the compounds below when they are named as *butyr*aldehydes (see Table 16.1) according to the common system.

TABLE 16.1 **NAMES AND FORMULAS OF ALIPHATIC ALDEHYDES**

Formula	IUPAC name	Common name (derived from name of carboxylic acid)
$HC(=O)H$	Methanal	Formaldehyde (*form*ic acid)
$HC(=O)CH_3$	Ethanal	Acetaldehyde (*acet*ic acid)
$HC(=O)CH_2CH_3$	Propanal	Propionaldehyde (*propion*ic acid)
$HC(=O)CH_2CH_2CH_3$	Butanal	Butyraldehyde (*butyr*ic acid)
$HC(=O)CH_2CH_2CH_2CH_3$	Pentanal	
$HC(=O)CH_2CH_2CH_2CH_2CH_3$	Hexanal	
$HC(=O)CH_2CH_2CH_2CH_2CH_2CH_3$	Heptanal	
$HC(=O)CH_2CH_2CH_2CH_2CH_2CH_2CH_3$	Octanal	
$HC(=O)CH_2CH_2CH_2CH_2CH_2CH_2CH_2CH_3$	Nonanal	
$HC(=O)CH_2CH_2CH_2CH_2CH_2CH_2CH_2CH_2CH_3$	Decanal	

$CH_3CH_2CH(CH_3)CH(=O)$
α-Methylbutyraldehyde

$CH_3C(CH_3)_2CH_2CH(=O)$
β,β-Dimethylbutyraldehyde

$BrCH_2CH_2CH_2CH(=O)$
γ-Bromobutyraldehyde

The two naming systems should not be mixed. For instance, the name α-methylbutanal is unacceptable.

Aromatic Aldehydes

The simplest aromatic aldehyde, in which the R group is phenyl, is always called by its common name, benzaldehyde (derived from *benz*oic acid).

$C_6H_5-C(=O)-H$ *Benz*aldehyde

Aldehydes whose aromatic ring also has a different substituent(s) are named according to the priority system we discussed in Section 14.5. The compound below is named as an aldehyde instead of a phenol since the aldehyde group is higher in the priority list than the hydroxyl group (see Table 14.4).

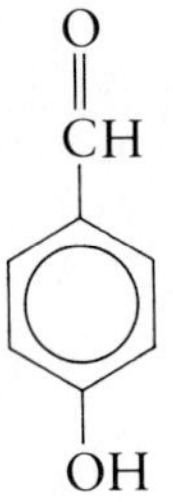

p-Hydroxybenzaldehyde (4-hydroxybenzaldehyde)

Note that several of the examples of aromatic compounds with pleasant aromas shown in Figure 14.2 are aldehydes. In fact, many derivatives of benzaldehyde appear in nature as flavoring ingredients in spices. Vanillin is an aromatic aldehyde which also includes alcohol and ether functional groups. Since these groups are both lower in priority than the aldehyde group, vanillin is named as an aldehyde:

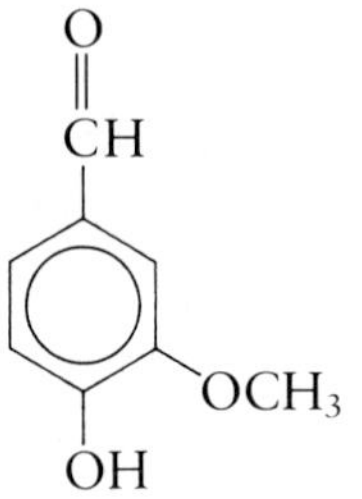

4-Hydroxy-3-methoxybenzaldehyde (vanillin)

Vanilla beans contain 2 to 3% vanillin.

Vanillin is a major component of vanilla flavoring, which is extracted from vanilla beans. In Color Plate 18 you can see the white needlelike crystals of vanillin taken from a chemical reagent bottle, the same vanillin that is found in the vanilla bean pod.

Nitrobenzene is "artificial oil of bitter almonds" (Section 14.7).

Figure 16.3 presents some other aromatic aldehydes, including cinnamaldehyde, a major component of oil of cinnamon, and anisaldehyde, a compound with a floral odor used as a perfume ingredient. The parent compound benzaldehyde is present in the oils derived from distillation of seeds of almond and apricot trees and is known as "oil of bitter almonds." Another component present in the distillate is hydrocyanic acid (HCN), a highly toxic substance that can account for as much as 2 to 11 percent of the bitter almond oil. Almond extract

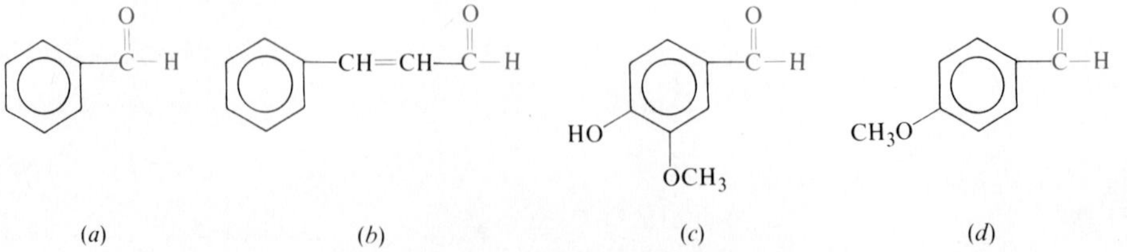

FIGURE 16.3
Aromatic aldehydes: (*a*) Benzaldehyde (colorless liquid in almond oil); (*b*) cinnamaldehyde (yellowish liquid in cinnamon oil); (*c*) vanillin (white crystals in vanilla bean): (*d*) anisaldehyde (liquid used in perfumery).

(*a*) (*b*) (*c*) (*d*)

flavoring is safe to consume since it is made from almond oil prepared by *squeezing* the oil out of the almonds, a process that produces "sweet" almond oil containing no hydrocyanic acid.

SAMPLE EXERCISE 16.1

Name the aldehydes below:

(a) $ClCH_2CH_2\overset{O}{\overset{\|}{C}}H$

(b) 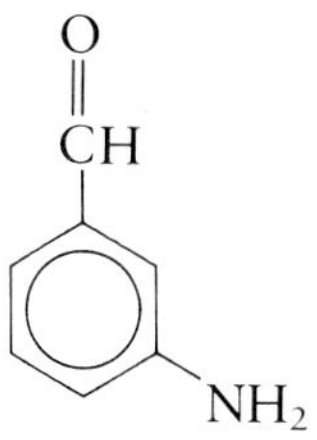 m-$H_2N-C_6H_4-\overset{O}{\overset{\|}{C}}H$ (benzene ring with CHO at top and NH_2 at the meta position)

Solution:

(a) $\underset{3}{\overset{\beta}{Cl\,C}}H_2\underset{2}{\overset{\alpha}{C}}H_2\underset{1}{\overset{O}{\overset{\|}{C}}}H$

This compound is derived from the three-carbon aldehyde named either propanal (IUPAC) or propionaldehyde (common). Its full name is 3-chloropropanal or β-chloropropionaldehyde.

(b) 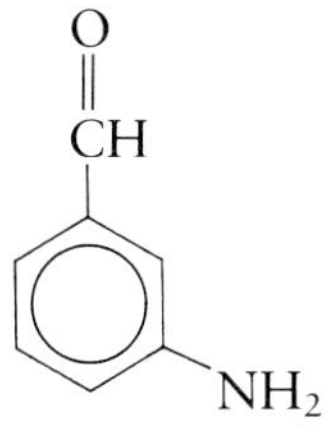 m-$H_2N-C_6H_4-\overset{O}{\overset{\|}{C}}H$ (benzene ring with CHO at top and NH_2 at the meta position)

This aromatic compound is named as a benzaldehyde derivative since the amino group is lower in priority. Thus it is called either *m*-aminobenzaldehyde or 3-aminobenzaldehyde.

EXERCISE 16.1

One of the first hypnotic or sedative (sleep-producing) drugs used was prepared by combining the compound below, called chloral, with water. Give both the IUPAC and common names for this aldehyde.

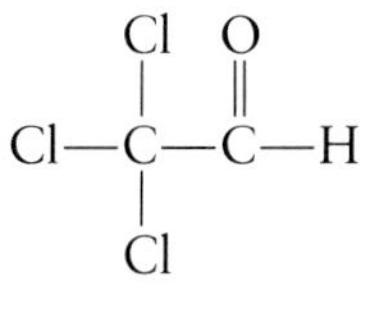

$$Cl-\underset{Cl}{\overset{Cl}{C}}-\overset{O}{\overset{\|}{C}}-H$$

16.4 NAMING KETONES

In the IUPAC system ketone names are derived from the names of alkanes which have the same number of C atoms (including the carbonyl C atom) by dropping the *-e* from alkan*e* and adding *-one* to form the name alkan*one*. The name of the ketone having three C atoms is derived from propane.

$$\overset{\displaystyle O}{\overset{\|}{CH_3CCH_3}}$$

Propan***one***

For ketones which have more than three C atoms, it is also necessary to specify which C atom belongs to the carbonyl group. To number the ketone C atoms we start from the end of the molecule which is closest to the carbonyl. For instance, to name the two possible pentanones,

$$\underset{1\ \ 2\ 3\ \ \ 4\ \ \ 5}{CH_3\overset{O}{\overset{\|}{C}}CH_2CH_2CH_3} \qquad \underset{1\ \ \ 2\ \ \ 3\ 4\ \ \ 5}{CH_3CH_2\overset{O}{\overset{\|}{C}}CH_2CH_3}$$

2-Pentanone 3-Pentanone

The numbers are also used to locate substituents. For example,

$$\underset{6\ \ 5\ \ 4\ \ \ 3\ \ \ 2\ 1}{CH_3\overset{Cl}{\overset{|}{C}}HCH_2CH_2\overset{O}{\overset{\|}{C}}CH_3} \qquad \underset{8\ \ 7\ \ 6\ \ \ 5\ \ 4\ 3\ \ 2\ \ 1}{CH_3\overset{CH_3}{\overset{|}{C}}HCH_2CH_2\overset{O}{\overset{\|}{C}}CH_2CH_2CH_3}$$

5-Chloro-2-hexanone 7-Methyl-4-octanone

Note that the location of the C=O group (not of substituents) controls the numbering.

In the common naming system the hydrocarbon groups attached to the carbonyl are named in alphabetical order followed by the word ketone. According to this method the ketones below are ethyl methyl ketone and dimethyl ketone (or simply methyl ketone):

$$CH_3\overset{O}{\overset{\|}{C}}CH_2CH_3 \qquad CH_3\overset{O}{\overset{\|}{C}}CH_3$$

Ethyl methyl ketone (2-butanone) Dimethyl ketone or methyl ketone (propanone)

You must be careful not to spill acetone on clothing, since it dissolves many synthetic fabrics.

Ethyl methyl ketone is often referred to as MEK (for methyl ethyl ketone) in industry, where it is an important solvent. The trivial name acetone is almost always used instead of the names given above (propanone or dimethyl ketone or methyl ketone). Acetone is also an excellent solvent and is an ingredient in many nail polish removers.

We can name an aromatic ketone by using the phenyl group as a substituent or as a *-phenone*, the name for a carbonyl group attached to a benzene ring:

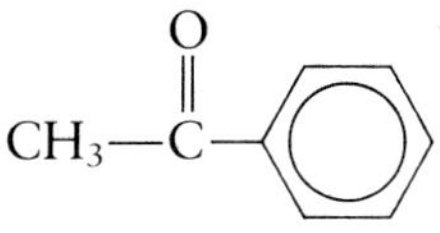

$$CH_3-\overset{O}{\overset{\|}{C}}-C_6H_5 \qquad C_6H_5-\overset{O}{\overset{\|}{C}}-C_6H_5$$

Methyl phenyl ketone (acetophenone) — Diphenyl ketone (benzophenone)

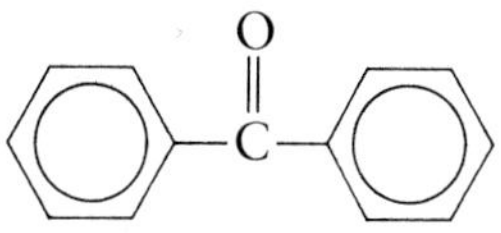

Compounds which have names ending in the suffix *-one* are likely to be ketones. For example, the hormone called progester*one*, essential for the maintenance of pregnancy, includes two ketone functional groups.

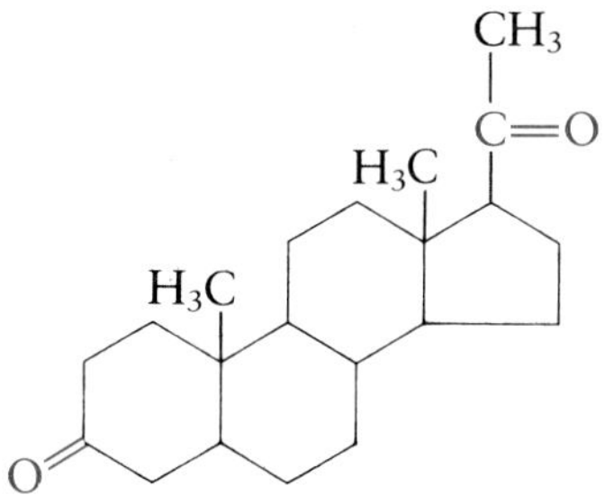

progester***one***

SAMPLE EXERCISE 16.2

Give two possible names for the ketone shown below:

$$CH_3CH_2\overset{O}{\overset{\|}{C}}CH_2CH_2CH_2CH_3$$

Solution:

In the IUPAC system this seven-carbon ketone is named as a derivative of heptane. We number from the left, so the full name is 3-heptanone.

$$\underset{1}{CH_3}\underset{2}{CH_2}\underset{3}{\overset{O}{\overset{\|}{C}}}\underset{4}{CH_2}\underset{5}{CH_2}\underset{6}{CH_2}\underset{7}{CH_3}$$

The common name for 3-heptanone is butyl ethyl ketone.

EXERCISE 16.2

A spray product used to keep cats away from a place contains methyl nonyl ketone as an active ingredient. Give the formula and the IUPAC name for this compound.

16.5 PHYSICAL PROPERTIES OF ALDEHYDES AND KETONES

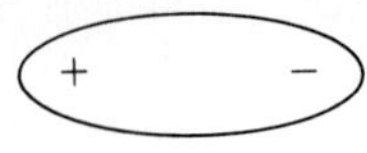

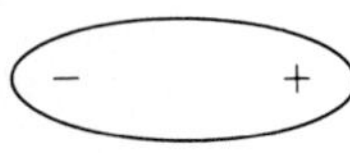

FIGURE 16.4
Attraction between two polar molecules. The positive end of one polar molecule is attracted to the negative end of another.

The boiling points of aldehydes and ketones are higher than would be expected from simply considering their formula weights. Butane (formula weight 58) is a gas boiling at −0.5°C, as compared with propanal (formula weight 58), which is a liquid boiling at 49°C, and acetone (formula weight 58), which boils at 56°C. As mentioned previously, the carbonyl group is polar and thus ketone and aldehyde molecules are polar. The forces of attraction between two polar molecules is much greater than that between two nonpolar molecules, as shown in Figure 16.4. Here you can see that the positive end of one polar molecule is attracted to the negative end of a neighboring molecule. The greater the forces of attraction among the molecules of a substance, the greater the amount of energy needed to separate them from each other and thus the higher the boiling point of the substance. This explains the fact that aldehydes and ketones have higher boiling points than the nonpolar alkanes with the same formula weights.

Aldehydes and ketones contain C to O bonds but no H to O bonds.

On the other hand, the boiling points of alcohols are higher than those of corresponding aldehydes and ketones because of the even stronger attractive forces due to hydrogen bonding. Molecules of aldehydes or ketones do not contain O to H bonds; hence they cannot form hydrogen bonds with each other as alcohol molecules can. Thus propanol, with a formula weight (FW) of 60, just slightly higher than that of propanal and acetone, has a much higher boiling point.

TABLE 16.2 PHYSICAL PROPERTIES OF ALDEHYDES

Name	Formula	bp, °C	Solubility (g/100 g H_2O)
Methanal (formaldehyde)	$HC(=O)H$	−21 (gas)	Very soluble
Ethanal (acetaldehyde)	$HC(=O)CH_3$	21	Infinite
Propanal	$HC(=O)CH_2CH_3$	49	16
Butanal	$HC(=O)CH_2CH_2CH_3$	76	7
Pentanal	$HC(=O)CH_2CH_2CH_2CH_3$	103	4
Hexanal	$HC(=O)CH_2CH_2CH_2CH_2CH_3$	128	1
Heptanal	$HC(=O)CH_2CH_2CH_2CH_2CH_2CH_3$	153	0.1
Octanal	$HC(=O)CH_2CH_2CH_2CH_2CH_2CH_2CH_3$	171	Insoluble

TABLE 16.3 **PHYSICAL PROPERTIES OF KETONES**

Propanone (acetone)	$CH_3\overset{O}{\overset{\|}{C}}CH_3$	56	Infinite
2-Butanone	$CH_3\overset{O}{\overset{\|}{C}}CH_2CH_3$	80	26
2-Pentanone	$CH_3\overset{O}{\overset{\|}{C}}CH_2CH_2CH_3$	102	5
2-Hexanone	$CH_3\overset{O}{\overset{\|}{C}}CH_2CH_2CH_2CH_3$	128	1.6
2-Heptanone	$CH_3\overset{O}{\overset{\|}{C}}CH_2CH_2CH_2CH_2CH_3$	149	0.4
2-Octanone	$CH_3\overset{O}{\overset{\|}{C}}CH_2CH_2CH_2CH_2CH_2CH_3$	173	Insoluble

$CH_3CH_2CH_2CH_3$	$CH_3CH_2\overset{O}{\overset{\|}{C}}—H$	$CH_3\overset{O}{\overset{\|}{C}}CH_3$	$CH_3CH_2CH_2OH$
Butane (FW 58): nonpolar, bp −0.5°C	Propanal (FW 58): polar, bp 49°C	Acetone (FW 58): polar, bp 56°C	1-Propanol (FW 60) highly polar, bp 97°C

The boiling points of some aldehydes and ketones are listed in Tables 16.2 and 16.3.

Like ether molecules, it is possible for aldehyde or ketone molecules to form hydrogen bonds with water molecules (see Section 15.12). Because of this the lower-molecular-weight aldehydes and ketones are soluble in water. The rule of thumb which says that alcohols with less than five C atoms are water-soluble holds for aldehydes and ketones as well, as you can see from Tables 16.2 and 16.3.

16.6 OXIDATION OF ALDEHYDES AND KETONES

Because they both contain carbonyl groups, we would expect the reactions of aldehydes and ketones to be similar. Although this is generally true, there are some differences. In most of their reactions ketones react more slowly and with greater difficulty than do aldehydes. This is because ketones have a bulky hydrocarbon group in place of the H atom of an aldehyde, which restricts access to the reactive carbonyl group. The greatest difference in their reactivity occurs in reactions with oxidizing agents. Aldehydes are *much* more easily oxidized than ketones. As you saw when we discussed the oxidation of alcohols to aldehydes, a further oxidation can take place in which the aldehyde product is oxidized to produce a carboxylic acid.

$$\underset{\text{Aldehyde}}{\mathrm{R{-}\overset{\overset{\displaystyle O}{\|}}{C}{-}H}} \quad + \quad \underset{\text{Oxidizing agent}}{[\mathrm{O}]} \quad \longrightarrow \quad \underset{\text{Carboxylic acid}}{\mathrm{R{-}\overset{\overset{\displaystyle O}{\|}}{C}{-}OH}}$$

For ketones to be oxidized, very strenuous conditions, such as prolonged treatment with hot solutions of oxidizing agents, are required. If and when the oxidation does occur, a mixture of products results which may include fragments of the original ketone molecule. This outstanding difference in their ability to be oxidized is the basis of two important tests used to distinguish between aldehydes and ketones.

Tollens' Silver Mirror Test

In **Tollens' test** a silver compound, $Ag(NH_3)_2OH$, is the oxidizing agent [O]. When this substance, called Tollens' reagent, reacts with an aldehyde, the products include the ammonium salt of the carboxylic acid and metallic silver, Ag. The complete reaction is

$$\mathrm{R{-}\overset{\overset{\displaystyle O}{\|}}{C}{-}H} + 2\mathrm{Ag(NH_3)_2OH} \longrightarrow \mathrm{R{-}\overset{\overset{\displaystyle O}{\|}}{C}{-}ONH_4} + 2\mathrm{Ag} + \mathrm{H_2O} + 3\mathrm{NH_3}$$

When the test is performed, the silver metal appears dramatically as a shiny mirrorlike surface, which coats the inside of the test tube, as shown in Color Plate 19. Ketones do not react with Tollens' reagent. Thus a substance which is known to be either an aldehyde or a ketone is readily identified by this test.

Benedict's and Fehling's Tests

Benedict's and Fehling's reagents both contain the same oxidizing agent, the Cu^{2+} ion, which is dissolved in aqueous NaOH to form a blue solution. Only aliphatic aldehydes react with Benedict's or Fehling's reagents. As the reaction takes place, a brick red precipitate, copper(I) oxide, Cu_2O, appears.

$$\underset{\text{Aliphatic aldehyde}}{\mathrm{RCH_2{-}\overset{\overset{\displaystyle O}{\|}}{C}{-}H}} + \mathrm{Cu^{2+}} + \mathrm{NaOH} \longrightarrow \mathrm{RCH_2{-}\overset{\overset{\displaystyle O}{\|}}{C}{-}ONa} + \underline{\mathrm{Cu_2O}}$$

(unbalanced)

Neither ketones nor aromatic aldehydes react with Benedict's or Fehling's solutions. However, there is one exception to this. Ketones (such as fructose, Fig. 16.1) which have hydroxyl groups on the C adjacent to the carbonyl group *are* oxidized by Benedict's or Fehling's solution.

Further discussion of diabetes can be found in Chapter 26, Section 26.9.

The **Benedict's test** is used in the diagnosis of ***diabetes mellitus.*** In this form of diabetes, the pancreas fails to produce enough *insulin,* a hormone which is involved in the metabolism of carbohydrates. Without insulin, body tissues are unable to utilize the glucose. The result is a condition called *hyperglycemia* in which the level of blood glucose is elevated from a normal value of 80 to 100 mg/dl to as high as 500 mg/dl. As the blood glucose level rises above normal, the kidneys begin to excrete glucose, thus increasing the glucose levels in the urine. Since glucose is an aldehyde, it reacts readily with Benedict's reagent.

$$\underset{\text{Glucose}}{\underset{\substack{| \\ OH}}{CH_2}\underset{\substack{| \\ OH}}{CH}\underset{\substack{| \\ OH}}{CH}\underset{\substack{| \\ OH}}{CH}\underset{\substack{| \\ OH}}{CH}\overset{\substack{O \\ \|}}{C}H} + \underset{\text{Blue test solution}}{Cu^{2+}} + NaOH \longrightarrow \underset{\substack{| \\ OH}}{CH_2}\underset{\substack{| \\ OH}}{CH}\underset{\substack{| \\ OH}}{CH}\underset{\substack{| \\ OH}}{CH}\underset{\substack{| \\ OH}}{CH}\overset{\substack{O \\ \|}}{C}ONa + \underset{\text{Reddish solid}}{\underline{Cu_2O}}$$

The Benedict's test may give a false positive in the presence of other substances that can be oxidized, such as drug metabolites.

The coloration that appears in a positive Benedict's test can be used to estimate the amount of glucose in a urine sample. The test solution is blue and the reaction mixture turns greenish as the oxidation begins, then yellow, orange, and finally red. A yellowish green color indicates about 0.5% glucose and a red color means that the level of glucose is greater than 2% (see test results in Color Plate 1).

SAMPLE EXERCISE 16.3

A substance known to be an aldehyde or ketone dissolves readily in water and reacts with Benedict's solution to form a red precipitate. Which of the following compounds could it be?

(a) $C_6H_5\overset{\substack{O \\ \|}}{C}H$ (benzene ring attached to CH=O)

(b) $CH_3(CH_2)_6\overset{\substack{O \\ \|}}{C}H$

(c) $CH_3\overset{\substack{O \\ \|}}{C}CH_2CH_3$

(d) $CH_3CH_2\overset{\substack{O \\ \|}}{C}H$

Solution:

Compounds **a** and **c** are eliminated because Benedict's solution does not react with aromatic aldehydes or with unsubstituted ketones such as ethyl methyl ketone. Aldehyde **b** has eight C atoms and is not water-soluble. The unknown substance could be compound **d**, propanal, a water-soluble aliphatic aldehyde.

EXERCISE 16.3

A urine sample to be tested for glucose contains fructose. Will the fructose interfere with the Benedict's test for glucose? Why or why not?

16.7 ADDITION TO THE CARBONYL GROUP

In Chapter 13 you saw that a variety of substances could be added across the C to C multiple bonds of alkenes and alkynes (Sections 13.9 and 13.14). The carbonyl C to O double bond also participates in addition reactions and because the C=O bond is polar, it reacts with even more compounds than the nonpolar C=C and C≡C bonds. In this section we will discuss the addition of hydrogen, water, and alcohols to aldehydes and ketones.

Addition of H_2: Reduction

When alcohols are *oxidized,* they *lose H atoms* to form aldehydes or ketones. When aldehydes or ketones are *reduced,* the reverse happens—they *gain H atoms* to produce alcohols. Hydrogen, H_2, is one reducing agent that can be used to reduce aldehydes or ketones. Like the addition of H_2 to alkenes and alkynes, this reaction is called a hydrogenation and must be carried out in the presence of a metal catalyst (Ni, Pt, or Pd). When H_2 is added across the double bond of an aldehyde, a primary alcohol is the product. For instance, acetaldehyde is reduced to ethanol as one H atom adds to the carbonyl C atom and the other to the carbonyl O atom. The H atoms added are shown in color.

$$\underset{\text{Acetaldehyde (ethanal)}}{CH_3\overset{\overset{\displaystyle O}{\|}}{C}H} + H{-}H \xrightarrow{Ni} \underset{\text{Ethanol}}{CH_3\overset{\overset{\displaystyle OH}{|}}{\underset{\underset{\displaystyle H}{|}}{C}}H} \quad (CH_3CH_2OH)$$

When acetone is reduced by H_2, the product is the secondary alcohol 2-propanol (isopropyl alcohol).

$$\underset{\text{Acetone}}{CH_3\overset{\overset{\displaystyle O}{\|}}{C}CH_3} + H \quad H \xrightarrow{Ni} \underset{\text{2-Propanol}}{CH_3\overset{\overset{\displaystyle OH}{|}}{\underset{\underset{\displaystyle H}{|}}{C}}CH_3} \quad (CH_3\overset{\overset{\displaystyle OH}{|}}{C}HCH_3)$$

Using hydrogen gas for reductions is inconvenient because the pressurized H_2 gas which must be used is explosive and has to be handled very carefully. For this reason metal hydrides such as sodium borohydride ($NaBH_4$) or lithium aluminum hydride ($LiAlH_4$) rather than H_2 gas are used for laboratory reductions. In the reaction below $LiAlH_4$ supplies the H atoms in a reaction with propanal to form 1-propanol.

$$\underset{\text{Propanal}}{CH_3CH_2\overset{\overset{\displaystyle O}{\|}}{C}H} + LiAlH_4 \longrightarrow \underset{\text{1-Propanol}}{CH_3CH_2CH_2OH} \qquad \text{(unbalanced)}$$

Many alcohols which are less available than the corresponding carbonyl compounds are prepared in the laboratory by reduction reactions such as the ones above.

SAMPLE EXERCISE 16.4

Write a reaction for the reduction of ethyl methyl ketone to produce a secondary alcohol. Name the product.

Solution:

To do this we can add H_2 to ethyl methyl ketone in the presence of a catalyst such as nickel.

$$CH_3CH_2\overset{\overset{\displaystyle O}{\|}}{C}CH_3 + H{-}H \xrightarrow{Ni} CH_3CH_2\underset{\underset{\displaystyle H}{|}}{\overset{\overset{\displaystyle OH}{|}}{C}}CH_3$$

The product, $CH_3CH_2\overset{\overset{\displaystyle OH}{|}}{C}HCH_3$, is 2-butanol.

EXERCISE 16.4

The reduction of an aldehyde with $NaBH_4$ is one reaction used to prepare 1-butanol. Which aldehyde is used?

Addition of Water

The addition of water to aldehydes or ketones produces products called aldehyde hydrates or ketone hydrates (even though they do not contain intact H_2O molecules). In a hydration reaction an H atom from water adds to the carbonyl oxygen and the OH group from water adds to the carbonyl carbon. Most of these hydrates, such as the acetaldehyde hydrate shown below, are unstable and readily regenerate the aldehyde and water reactants.

$$\underset{\text{Acetaldehyde}}{CH_3\overset{\overset{\displaystyle O}{\|}}{C}H} + H{-}OH \rightleftharpoons \underset{\substack{\text{Acetaldehyde hydrate}\\ \text{(unstable)}}}{CH_3\underset{\underset{\displaystyle OH}{|}}{\overset{\overset{\displaystyle OH}{|}}{C}}H}$$

"Knock-out drops" are chloral hydrate.

One exception is chloral hydrate, a compound used as a sedative (see Exercise 16.1). Chloral hydrate is a stable product of the addition of water to the aldehyde chloral.

$$\underset{\text{Chloral}}{Cl{-}\underset{\underset{\displaystyle Cl}{|}}{\overset{\overset{\displaystyle Cl}{|}}{C}}{-}\overset{\overset{\displaystyle O}{\|}}{C}{-}H} + H{-}OH \longrightarrow \underset{\text{Chloral hydrate}}{Cl{-}\underset{\underset{\displaystyle Cl}{|}}{\overset{\overset{\displaystyle Cl}{|}}{C}}{-}\underset{\underset{\displaystyle OH}{|}}{\overset{\overset{\displaystyle OH}{|}}{C}}{-}H}$$

Addition of Alcohols

Under acidic conditions two molecules of alcohol can react with one molecule of aldehyde or ketone to produce compounds called **acetals** (with aldehydes) and **ketals** (with ketones). We can write the reactions in two steps, adding first one alcohol molecule to produce either a **hemiacetal** or a **hemiketal**. For instance, the reaction of acetaldehyde with one molecule of methanol produces a hemiacetal

Note that the electropositive H of methanol adds to the negative O atom of the carbonyl group.

and that of acetone with methanol produces a hemiketal. The methanol hydroxyl H atom is added to the O end of the carbonyl and the rest of the alcohol molecule (OCH_3) to the C atom of the carbonyl. The product hemiacetals and hemiketals are generally unstable.

$$\underset{\text{Acetaldehyde}}{CH_3\overset{\overset{\delta-}{O}}{\overset{\|}{C}}H}_{\delta+} + \underset{\text{Methanol}}{HOCH_3} \underset{}{\overset{H^+}{\rightleftharpoons}} \underset{\text{Hemiacetal (unstable)}}{CH_3\overset{OH}{\overset{|}{\underset{\underset{OCH_3}{|}}{C}}}H}$$

$$\underset{\text{Acetone}}{CH_3\overset{\overset{\delta-}{O}}{\overset{\|}{C}}CH_3}_{\delta+} + \underset{\text{Methanol}}{HOCH_3} \overset{H^+}{\rightleftharpoons} \underset{\text{Hemiketal (unstable)}}{CH_3\overset{OH}{\overset{|}{\underset{\underset{OCH_3}{|}}{C}}}CH_3}$$

The hemiacetals and hemiketals can then react with another molecule of alcohol to produce acetals or ketals. In this reaction the hydroxyl group in the hemiacetal or hemiketal is converted to a methoxy group. We can write the reactions describing this by splitting out a molecule of water, as shown below.

$$\underset{\text{Hemiacetal}}{CH_3-\overset{OH}{\overset{|}{\underset{\underset{OCH_3}{|}}{C}}}-H} + HOCH_3 \overset{H^+}{\rightleftharpoons} \underset{\text{Acetal}}{CH_3-\overset{OCH_3}{\overset{|}{\underset{\underset{OCH_3}{|}}{C}}}-H} + H_2O$$

$$\underset{\text{Hemiketal}}{CH_3-\overset{OH}{\overset{|}{\underset{\underset{OCH_3}{|}}{C}}}-CH_3} + HOCH_3 \overset{H^+}{\rightleftharpoons} \underset{\text{Ketal}}{CH_3-\overset{OCH_3}{\overset{|}{\underset{\underset{OCH_3}{|}}{C}}}-CH_3} + H_2O$$

You can recognize a hemiacetal by noting that its formula includes a C atom bonded to an OH and OR, whereas in an acetal the C atom is bonded to two OR groups.

$$\underset{\text{Hemiacetal}}{R'-\overset{OH}{\overset{|}{\underset{\underset{OR}{|}}{C}}}-H} \qquad \underset{\text{Acetal}}{R'-\overset{OR}{\overset{|}{\underset{\underset{OR}{|}}{C}}}-H}$$

Likewise, hemiketals have an OH and OR bonded to a C atom, and ketals have two OR groups.

```
     OH            OR
     |             |
R′—C—R′      R′—C—R′
     |             |
     OR            OR
 Hemiketal        Ketal
```

Even though *most* hemiacetals and hemiketals are unstable, exceptions to this are the *cyclic* hemiacetals and hemiketals. For instance, sugar molecules such as glucose exist primarily in the form of cyclic hemiacetals even though we often draw them as open chains.

```
     O
     ‖
  H—C
     |
  H—C—OH
     |
  H—C—OH
     |
  H—C—OH
     |
  H—C—OH
     |
    CH2OH
Open-chain glucose
```

The hydroxyl group shown in color below reacts with the aldehyde group within the same glucose molecule to form a hemiacetal. The H atom of the hydroxyl group of glucose adds to the carbonyl O atom of the same molecule. The hydroxyl O atom then forms a new bond with the carbonyl C atom. The product molecule is the hemiacetal form of glucose, which exists in equilibrium with the open-chain glucose and in fact is the predominant form in which glucose exists.

Cyclic hemiacetals such as cyclic glucose *are* stable.

```
     O                     OH
     ‖                     |
  H—C                  H—C——┐
     |                     |     |
  H—C—OH               H—C—OH |
     |                     |     |
  H—C—OH      ⇌        H—C—OH |
     |                     |     |
  H—C—OH               H—C—OH |
     |                     |     |
  H—C—OH               H—C—O——┘
     |                     |
    CH2OH                 CH2OH
Open-chain glucose    Hemiacetal glucose
```

In Chapter 21, when we discuss carbohydrates in detail, we will refine the picture of the hemiacetal structure shown above so that the O to carbonyl C bond length is not so exaggerated.

SAMPLE EXERCISE 16.5

Write the reaction for the formation of an acetal from the reaction of two molecules of ethanol with one molecule of propanal.

Solution:

Write the reaction in two steps. First one molecule of ethanol is added across the carbonyl double bond, with the hydroxyl H atom placed on the carbonyl O atom and the OCH_2CH_3 portion of the ethanol molecule placed on the carbonyl C atom.

$$\underset{\text{Propanal}}{CH_3CH_2\overset{\overset{\displaystyle O}{\|}}{C}H} + HOCH_2CH_3 \xrightarrow{H^+} \underset{\text{Hemiacetal}}{CH_3CH_2\overset{\overset{\displaystyle OH}{|}}{\underset{\underset{\displaystyle OCH_2CH_3}{|}}{C}}H}$$

Then another molecule of ethanol reacts to split out a water molecule formed from the hydroxyl OH and an ethanol H atom.

$$\underset{\text{Hemiacetal}}{CH_3CH_2\overset{\overset{\displaystyle OH}{|}}{\underset{\underset{\displaystyle OCH_2CH_3}{|}}{C}}H} + HOCH_2CH_3 \xrightarrow{H^+} \underset{\text{Acetal}}{CH_3CH_2\overset{\overset{\displaystyle OCH_2CH_3}{|}}{\underset{\underset{\displaystyle OCH_2CH_3}{|}}{C}}H} + H_2O$$

EXERCISE 16.5

What reactant has combined with two molecules of methanol to produce the compound shown below? What general type of compound is this?

$$CH_3CH_2\overset{\overset{\displaystyle OCH_3}{|}}{\underset{\underset{\displaystyle OCH_3}{|}}{C}}CH_3$$

Table 16.4 summarizes the reactions of aldehydes and ketones that we have covered.

16.8 IMPORTANT ALDEHYDES AND KETONES

Aldehydes and ketones are versatile intermediates in laboratory syntheses because they undergo so many reactions. In this section we will look at a few of the aldehydes and ketones which are used in medicine and industry.

TABLE 16.4 REACTIONS OF ALDEHYDES AND KETONES

Oxidation

Tollens':

$$2Ag(NH_3)_2OH + R{-}\overset{\overset{\displaystyle O}{\|}}{C}{-}H \longrightarrow 2Ag + H_2O + 3NH_3 + R{-}\overset{\overset{\displaystyle O}{\|}}{C}{-}ONH_4$$

$$Ag(NH_3)_2OH + R{-}\overset{\overset{\displaystyle O}{\|}}{C}{-}R \longrightarrow \text{(no reaction)}$$

Benedict's:

$$Cu^{2+} + NaOH + RCH_2\overset{\overset{\displaystyle O}{\|}}{C}{-}H \longrightarrow \underline{Cu_2O} + RCH_2\overset{\overset{\displaystyle O}{\|}}{C}{-}ONa \text{ (unbalanced)}$$

$$Cu^{2+} + NaOH + R{-}\overset{\overset{\displaystyle O}{\|}}{C}{-}R \longrightarrow \text{(no reaction)}$$

$$Cu^{2+} + NaOH + C_6H_5{-}\overset{\overset{\displaystyle O}{\|}}{C}{-}H \longrightarrow \text{(no reaction)}$$

Hydrogenation

$$H_2 + R{-}\overset{\overset{\displaystyle O}{\|}}{C}{-}H \xrightarrow{Ni} \underset{\text{Primary alcohol}}{RCH_2OH}$$

$$H_2 + R{-}\overset{\overset{\displaystyle O}{\|}}{C}{-}R' \xrightarrow{Ni} \underset{\text{Secondary alcohol}}{\overset{\overset{\displaystyle OH}{|}}{RCHR}}$$

Reaction with alcohol addition

$$R'OH + R{-}\overset{\overset{\displaystyle O}{\|}}{C}{-}H \overset{H^+}{\rightleftharpoons} \underset{\text{Hemiacetal}}{R{-}\underset{\underset{\displaystyle OR'}{|}}{\overset{\overset{\displaystyle OH}{|}}{C}}{-}H} + R'OH \overset{H^+}{\rightleftharpoons} \underset{\text{Acetal}}{R{-}\underset{\underset{\displaystyle OR'}{|}}{\overset{\overset{\displaystyle OR'}{|}}{C}}{-}H} + H_2O$$

$$R'OH + R{-}\overset{\overset{\displaystyle O}{\|}}{C}{-}R \overset{H^+}{\rightleftharpoons} \underset{\text{Hemiketal}}{R{-}\underset{\underset{\displaystyle OR'}{|}}{\overset{\overset{\displaystyle OH}{|}}{C}}{-}R} + R'OH \overset{H^+}{\rightleftharpoons} \underset{\text{Ketal}}{R{-}\underset{\underset{\displaystyle OR'}{|}}{\overset{\overset{\displaystyle OR'}{|}}{C}}{-}R} + H_2O$$

Formaldehyde

Formaldehyde is prepared by the oxidation of methanol.

$$CH_3OH + [O] \longrightarrow H{-}\overset{\overset{\displaystyle O}{\|}}{C}{-}H + H_2O$$

Pure gaseous formaldehyde is too reactive to be stored in its pure form. Available in an aqueous solution is *formalin,* which is 37% formaldehyde. Formaldehyde is also sold in the form of a solid formaldehyde polymer called paraformaldehyde, which is produced by concentrating formaldehyde solutions. Formalin or paraformaldehyde can be heated to obtain formaldehyde for performing reactions in the laboratory.

A major industrial use for formaldehyde is that of the synthesis of polymers by the reaction of formaldehyde with other compounds. Earlier we said that Bakelite was a polymer made from phenol (Section 15.10)); the other ingredient is formaldehyde. The structure of a segment of phenol-formaldehyde polymer is shown in Figure 16.5, which shows the phenol components joined to each other by CH_2 linkages derived from formaldehyde molecules. Formaldehyde also forms polymers with itself, which is one reason that it is so difficult to store pure formaldehyde gas.

Formaldehyde is a component of smog resulting from the incomplete combustion of carbon-containing fuels and is irritating to the eye and to the respiratory tract. The air quality limit for formaldehyde in the United States is 0.1 ppm, compared with 2 ppm over an 8-h workday for industrial workers. The reason that the allowed level for workers is so much higher than for the general public (typical for many pollutants) is that the workers are all supposedly healthy, resistant individuals. The general population, especially in urban areas, always includes some people who suffer from respiratory difficulties and would thus be particularly sensitive to pollutants such as formaldehyde. Acrolein, another aldehyde present in smog, is also a known eye irritant.

$$CH_2{=}CH{-}\overset{\overset{\displaystyle O}{\|}}{C}{-}H$$

Acrolein

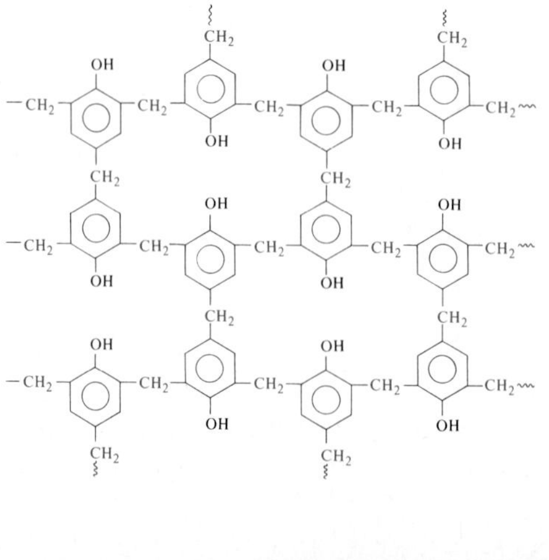

FIGURE 16.5
Phenol-formaldehyde polymer. The CH_2 linkages (in color) are derived from formaldehyde.

Exposure to formaldehyde can result in contact dermatitus of a long duration.

Formaldehyde also has medical uses. All aldehydes can function as bactericides because they are able to bind to bacterial cell proteins, thereby causing the death of the bacteria. In the form of a 1 to 2% solution, formaldehyde is useful as a disinfectant. Because formaldehyde solutions have pungent, unpleasant odors and are irritating to skin and tissues, they are usually used only on inanimate objects. Formalin can be heated to release formaldehyde gas in order to disinfect dwellings exposed to contagious diseases. A 4% aqueous solution of formaldehyde is used as embalming fluid to preserve tissues.

Acetaldehyde

The oxidation of ethanol produces acetaldehyde, as we saw in Section 15.5. Upon heating with an acid, acetaldehyde forms a cyclic compound called paraldehyde.

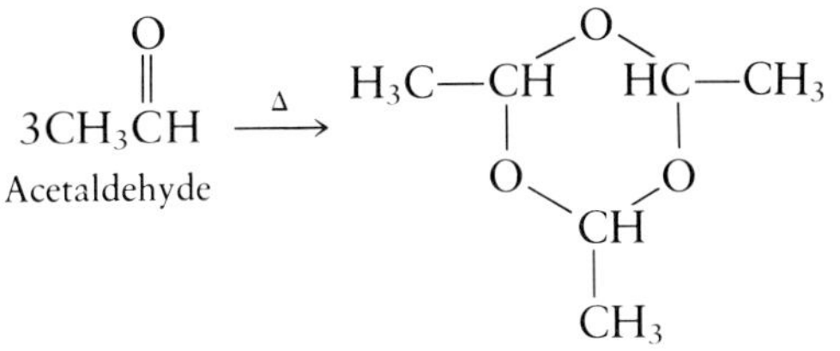

$$3CH_3\overset{\overset{\displaystyle O}{\|}}{C}H \xrightarrow{\Delta} \text{(cyclic trimer: ring of three O and three CH; substituents } H_3C\text{—CH, HC—}CH_3\text{, CH—}CH_3)$$

Acetaldehyde   Paraldehyde

Paraldehyde acts as a sedative hypnotic. Over a prolonged period of time it can be oxidized by air and sunlight to form acetic acid. To prevent this, the drug is dispensed in amber-colored bottles to protect it from the sun. One drawback to its use is the unpleasant odor of acetaldehyde, which remains upon the breath of the patient, thus restricting the use of paraldehyde.

Glutaraldehyde

Glutaraldehyde, a dialdehyde, is an excellent disinfectant. It is used in the form of a 2% solution.

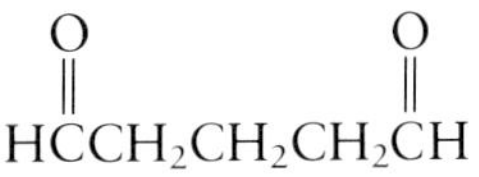

$$H\overset{\overset{\displaystyle O}{\|}}{C}CH_2CH_2CH_2\overset{\overset{\displaystyle O}{\|}}{C}H$$

Glutaraldehyde

Glutaraldehyde is useful for items that cannot be sterilized by treatment with heat. When used for periods of 7 h or more, glutaraldehyde can serve as a sterilizing agent, that is, it can cause complete destruction of all microbial forms, including viruses. Because glutaraldehyde is an eye and skin irritant, it cannot be applied to living tissue. Instruments immersed in glutaraldehyde must be carefully washed with water or alcohol before they are used.

Glutaraldehyde is used to sterilize surgical instruments.

Acetone

When isopropyl alcohol is oxidized, the product is acetone (Secton 15.5). In living things acetone is a by-product of lipid metabolism and in small amounts, it is a normal component of blood and urine. These amounts may be greatly increased in diabetics or in persons suffering from starvation, a subject that we will pursue further in the chapters on metabolism. In some cases acetone is even detectable on the breath.

Acetone and methyl ethyl ketone (MEK) are both important industrial solvents. Because they contain polar carbonyl groups and nonpolar hydrocarbon groups, they dissolve a wide variety of organic compounds.

SUMMARY

Aldehydes and ketones are compounds produced by the oxidation of primary and secondary alcohols, respectively. Aldehydes are represented by the general formula $R—\overset{\overset{\Large O}{\|}}{C}—H$ (R is H or a hydrocarbon group) and ketones by $R—\overset{\overset{\Large O}{\|}}{C}—R'$ (R and R′ are hydrocarbon groups). Their common structural feature is the carbonyl group, C=O.

According to the IUPAC system aldehydes are named as alkanals, the name being derived from that of the alkane with the same number of C atoms (including the carbonyl C atom). In substituted aldehydes the carbonyl C atom is assigned the number 1. Common names for aldehydes, derived from the names of the corresponding carboxylic acids, indicate the location of substituents by assigning the Greek letter α to the C-2 atom, β to C-3, and so on. Ketones are named as alkanones in the IUPAC system, with the lowest possible number used to locate the carbonyl group. Common names for ketones are derived by naming the two hydrocarbon groups attached to the carbonyl.

Aldehydes and ketones both can form hydrogen bonds with water and are thus soluble in water provided their molecules include less than five C atoms. The boiling points of aldehydes and ketones are higher than those of the corresponding nonpolar alkanes but lower than those of the hydrogen-bonded alcohols of similar formula weight.

In general ketones are less reactive than aldehydes. Aldehydes are so much more easily oxidized than ketones that oxidizing agents can be used to distinguish them from ketones. Two oxidizing agents used to test for aldehydes are Tollens' reagent [$Ag(NH_3)_2OH$] and Benedict's reagent (Cu^{2+}).

More substances can be added across the polar carbonyl double bond than across the double or triple C to C bonds. Aldehydes and ketones can be reduced to alcohols by the action of gaseous hydrogen or metal hydrides. The addition of one molecule of alcohol to an aldehyde or ketone produces a hemiacetal or a hemiketal as the H of the alcohol adds to the carbonyl O and the OR to the carbonyl C atom. Only cyclic hemiacetals and hemiketals are stable. Reaction with a second alcohol molecule causes the formation of a stable acetal or ketal as the alcohol OR replaces the hydroxyl group of the hemiacetal or hemiketal.

Aldehydes and ketones are very useful in synthetic chemistry because they can react with a large number of substances. In medicine aldehydes serve as disinfectants. Low-molecular-weight ketones are excellent solvents, widely used in industry.

KEY WORDS

aldehyde
ketone
carbonyl group
Tollens' test
Benedict's test
dehydrogenation
acetal
hemiacetal
ketal
hemiketal

EXERCISES

16.6 Give the general formulas for an aldehyde and a ketone, being careful to specify the nature of any R group you include.

16.7 What are the IUPAC names for the aldehydes below?

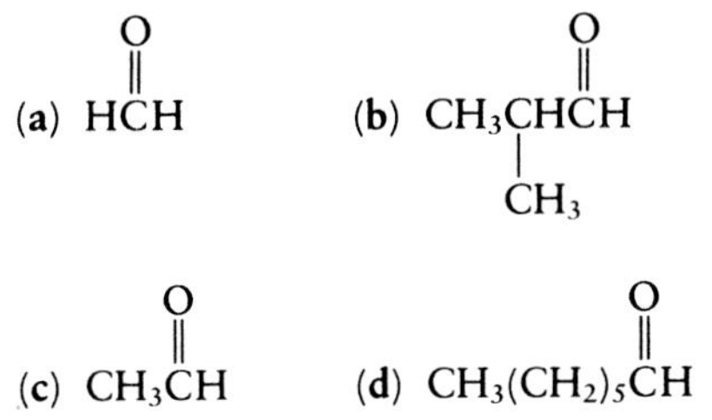

(a) HCH (with C=O) (b) CH_3CHCH (with C=O, CH_3 on second C)

(c) CH_3CH (with C=O) (d) $CH_3(CH_2)_5CH$ (with C=O)

16.8 Give IUPAC names for the following aldehydes:

(a) CH_3CCH_2CH (CH_3 and Cl on C-2; C=O at end) (b) $CH_3CHCH_2CH_2CH_2CH$ (Br on C-2; C=O at end)

(c) $ClCH_2CH_2CH$ (C=O at end) (d) $HCCH_2CHCH_2CH_2CH_3$ (C=O on first C; OH on C-3)

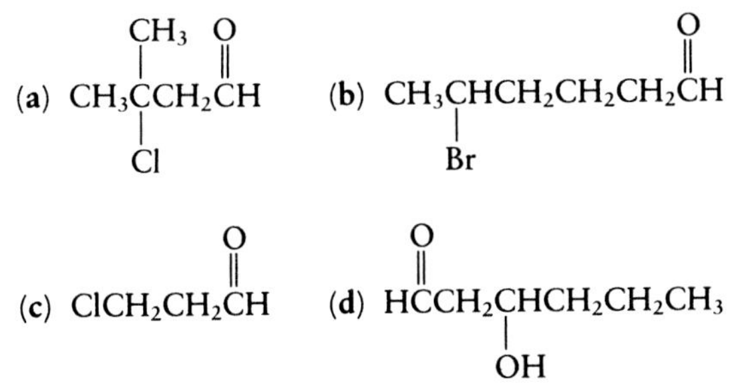

16.9 Name the aldehydes in Exercise 16.7*a*, *b* and *c*, using the common naming system (and Greek letters instead of numbers).

16.10 Name the aldehydes in Exercise 16.8*a* and *c*, using the common naming system (and Greek letters instead of numbers).

16.11 The trivial name valeraldehyde is used for pentanal. What carboxylic acid name was it derived from?

16.12 Name the aromatic aldehydes below:

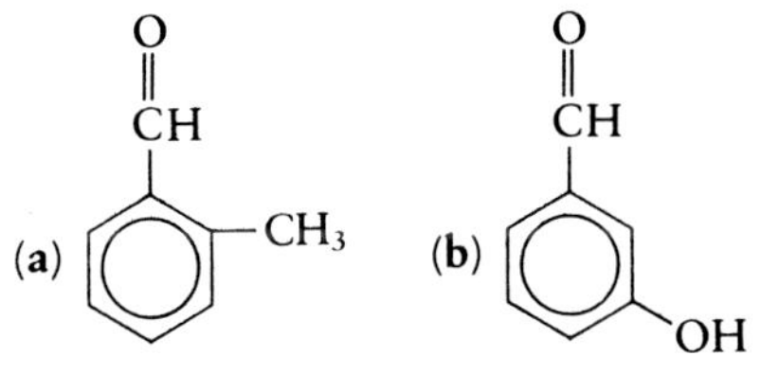

(a) benzene ring with CH=O and ortho CH_3 (b) benzene ring with CH=O and meta OH

16.13 What is another name for anisaldehyde (shown below)?

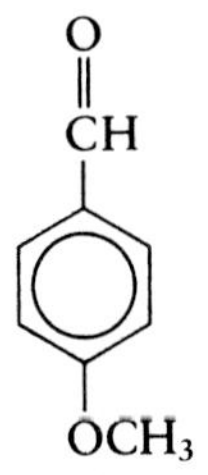

benzene ring with CH=O and para OCH_3

16.14 Give formulas for the following aldehydes: (a) Ethanal; (b) formaldehyde; (c) decanal.

16.15 Give formulas for these substituted aldehydes:
(a) 2-Chloropropanal
(b) α-Chlorobutyraldehyde
(c) 3-Chloro-4-methylpentanal

16.16 Draw the structures for the aromatic aldehydes:
(a) *o*-Bromobenzaldehyde
(b) *m*-Hydroxybenzaldehyde.

16.17 Name the ketones below:

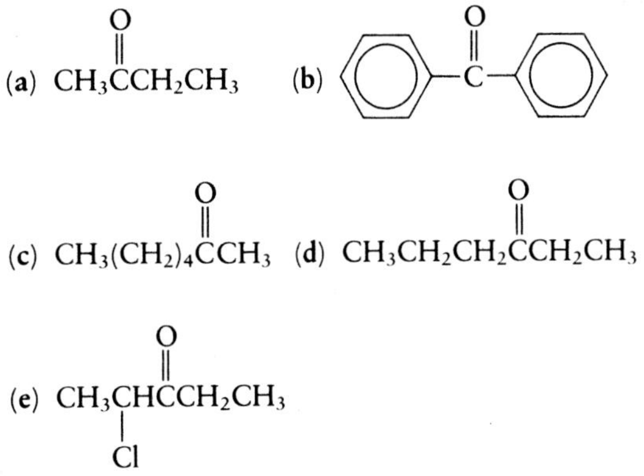

(a) $CH_3CCH_2CH_3$ (C=O on C-2) (b) two benzene rings joined by C=O

(c) $CH_3(CH_2)_4CCH_3$ (C=O) (d) $CH_3CH_2CH_2CCH_2CH_3$ (C=O)

(e) $CH_3CHCCH_2CH_3$ (Cl on C-2; C=O on C-3)

16.18 Give formulas for the following ketones.
(a) Isopropyl methyl ketone (b) 2-Heptanone
(c) Acetone (d) 3-Heptanone

16.19 What formulas correspond to the following ketones: (a) 1-Chloro-2-pentanone; (b) ethyl phenyl ketone?

16.20 The compound dihydroxyacetone is a metabolism product of glucose. Give its formula, assuming that the hydroxyl groups are not attached to the same C atom.

16.21 A series of major tranquilizers are derivatives of the aromatic ketone butyrophenone. Give the formula for butyrophenone. What other name can be used for butyrophenone?

16.22 How many *straight-chain* heptanones are possible? Give their names and formulas.

16.23 Write the formulas and names for all possible *straight-chain* octanones.

16.24 What is wrong with each of the following ketone and aldehyde names: (a) Ethanone; (b) 4-hexanone; (c) α-methylbutanal; (d) 1-chloropropanal?

16.25 In what way is the bonding in the carbonyl group similar to that in the alkene double bond? How is it different?

16.26 Which of the formulas below is most likely to represent cortisone, a therapeutic substance used to reduce inflammation?

(a) [structure: CH_3CH_2 and 4-hydroxyphenyl (HO) on one carbon, C=C, phenyl and CH_2CH_3 on the other]

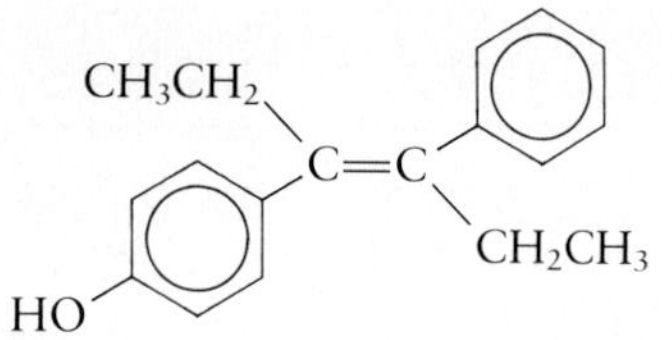

(b) [steroid structure with $\overset{O}{\parallel}CCH_2OH$, OH, H_3C, H_3C, O, O]

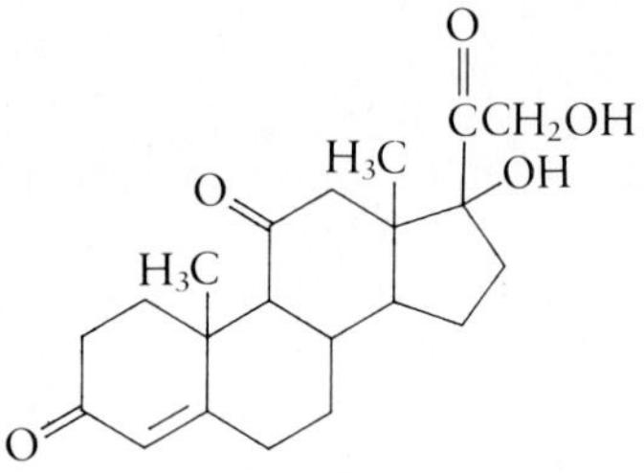

16.27 A compound (aldehyde or ketone) produces a silver mirror when mixed with Tollens' reagent. Which of the following could it be?

(a) $CH_3\overset{O}{\overset{\parallel}{C}}CH_3$ (b) $CH_3CH_2CH_2\overset{O}{\overset{\parallel}{C}}H$

(c) $CH_3\underset{CH_3}{\underset{|}{C}}H\overset{O}{\overset{\parallel}{C}}CH_2CH_3$

16.28 A compound known to be an aldehyde or ketone forms a brick red precipitate on reaction with Benedict's solution and is only slightly soluble in water. Which of the compounds below is it?

(a) $CH_3\overset{O}{\overset{\parallel}{C}}CH_3$ (b) $CH_3\overset{O}{\overset{\parallel}{C}}H$

(c) 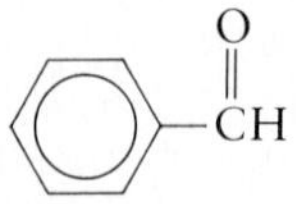 $C_6H_5\overset{O}{\overset{\parallel}{C}}H$ (d) $CH_3(CH_2)_3\overset{O}{\overset{\parallel}{C}}H$

16.29 Match the following compounds with their correct boiling points (without looking them up in tables) and give your reasoning: (a) 1-Pentanol; (b) diethyl ketone; (c) hexane; (1) 69; (2) 102; (3) 138.

16.30 Why would you expect the disinfectant glutaraldehyde (Section 16.8) to be infinitely soluble in water (which it is) although its formula contains five C atoms?

16.31 A substance known to be an aldehyde or ketone has a boiling point between 170 and 180°C and reacts with Benedict's or Fehling's solution and with the Tollens' reagent. What compound in Table 16.2 or Table 16.3 could this be? Benzaldehyde boils at 178°C. Could this compound be benzaldehyde? Explain.

16.32 Why do chemists prefer to use metal hydrides such as $NaBH_4$ or $LiAlH_4$ instead of H_2 gas for hydrogenation of aldehydes or ketones?

16.33 What compounds could undergo hydrogenation to produce 1-pentanol and 2-pentanol? Write the equations for these two reactions.

16.34 A chemist is preparing a compound called porphin, which is a component of biological molecules such as hemoglobin, chlorophyll, and vitamin B-12 (see Section 18.9). The starting material is an alcohol which is not commercially available. However, the corresponding aldehyde, 2-pyrrolecarboxaldehyde, (shown below) can be purchased. How could the alcohol be prepared?

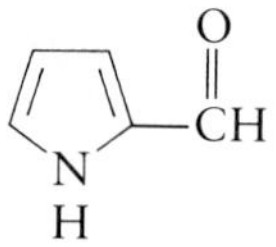

[structure: pyrrole ring (N–H) with $-\overset{O}{\overset{\parallel}{C}}H$]

2-Pyrrolecarboxaldehyde

16.35 Write equations for the reaction of acetaldehyde with ethanol to form a(n): (a) Hemiacetal; (b) acetal.

16.36 What kinds of hemiacetals and hemiketals are stable? What important biological compounds exist as hemiacetals or hemiketals?

16.37 Match the compounds below with their correct classifications: (a) Acetal; (b) hemiacetal; (c) ketal; (d) hemiketal.

(1) $CH_3CH_2CH_2—\overset{OCH_3}{\underset{OCH_3}{C}}—H$

(2) $CH_3—\overset{OCH_2CH_2CH_3}{\underset{OCH_2CH_2CH_3}{C}}—CH_2CH_3$

(3) $CH_3CH_2CH_2—\overset{OH}{\underset{OCH_3}{C}}—H$

(4) $CH_3—\overset{OCH_2CH_2CH_3}{\underset{OH}{C}}—CH_2CH_3$

16.38 Two of the compounds shown in Exercise 16.37 were derived from the reaction of an alcohol with a ketone and the other two from the reaction of a different alcohol with an aldehyde. Give the formulas and names of the two alcohols, the ketone, and the aldehyde.

16.39 How is chloral hydrate different from other aldehyde hydrates? What is it used for?

16.40 The compound acetone is known as a *ketone body* and is produced from the metabolism of fats in persons suffering from starvation or untreated diabetes. Could the Benedict's or Fehling's tests be used to detect acetone in a urine sample?

16.41 A diabetic is required to take a Breathalyzer test (see Section 15.10). Should acetone on the breath of this person interfere with the test?

16.42 Paraldehyde is contraindicated (inadvisable) in persons being treated with the drug disulfiram (Section 15.10). Why?

16.43 Why is it difficult to store pure formaldehyde gas?

16.44 What aldehydes are used as disinfectants? Why are they not used directly on the skin?

17 CARBOXYLIC ACIDS AND DERIVATIVES

17.1 INTRODUCTION

In the discussion of acids and bases you learned that the organic compound acetic acid behaves as a weak acid (Section 11.5). Acetic acid is an example of a *carboxylic acid.* In Chapter 11 we used an abbreviated formula HAc to represent acetic acid, where the H stands for the proton that is released and the Ac for the rest of the molecule. Here we will look at the complete structures of acetic acid and the other carboxylic acids and of several derivative compounds, including the *esters, salts, amides, acyl halides,* and *acid anhydrides* that are products of their chemical reactions.

We have already encountered two reactions that give carboxylic acids as products. Aldehydes are oxidized to form carboxylic acids (Section 16.6)

$$\underset{\text{Aldehyde}}{\text{R}-\overset{\overset{\displaystyle\text{O}}{\|}}{\text{C}}-\text{H}} + [\text{O}] \longrightarrow \underset{\text{Carboxylic acid}}{\text{R}-\overset{\overset{\displaystyle\text{O}}{\|}}{\text{C}}-\text{OH}}$$

and alkylbenzenes (arenes) form benzoic acid upon oxidation (Section 14.8).

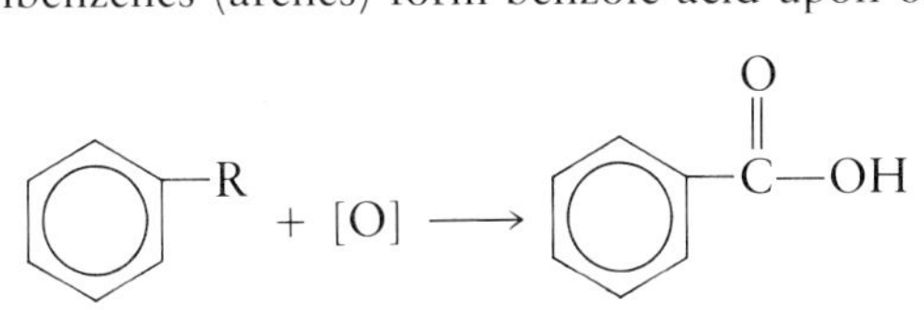

$$\text{C}_6\text{H}_5-\text{R} + [\text{O}] \longrightarrow \text{C}_6\text{H}_5-\overset{\overset{\displaystyle\text{O}}{\|}}{\text{C}}-\text{OH} \qquad \text{(unbalanced)}$$

The functional group of a carboxylic acid is the carboxyl group, $-\overset{\overset{\displaystyle\text{O}}{\|}}{\text{C}}-\text{OH}$.

Figure 17.1 gives the structures of a number of carboxylic acids. You can see that the common feature present in all of them is the **carboxyl group,** which consists of a carbonyl group bonded to a hydroxyl group.

$$\underset{\text{Carboxyl group}}{-\overset{\overset{\displaystyle\text{O}}{\|}}{\text{C}}-\text{O}-\text{H}}$$

In the general formula for a **carboxylic acid,** the R stands for a hydrocarbon group or a hydrogen atom.

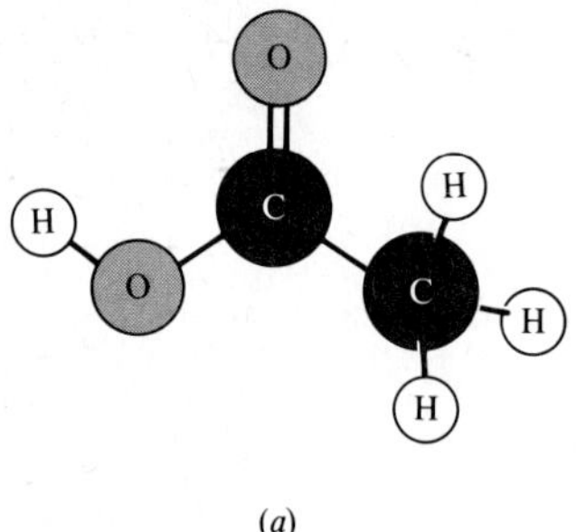

(a)

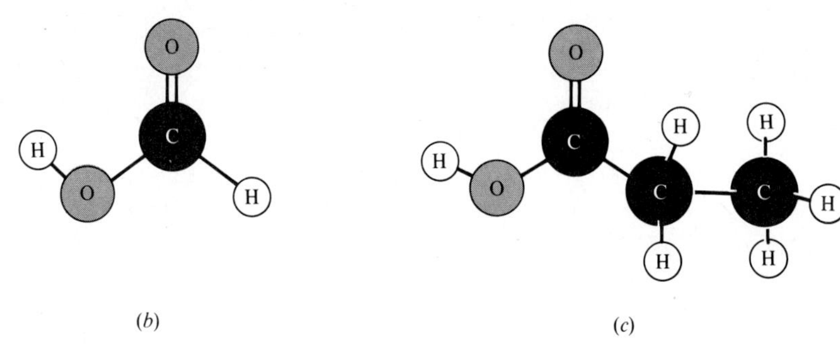

(b) (c)

FIGURE 17.1
Structures of carboxylic acids. (*a*) Ethanoic acid (acetic acid). (*b*) Methanoic acid (formic acid). (*c*) Propanoic acid (propionic acid).

$$R-\overset{\overset{\displaystyle O}{\|}}{C}-OH$$

general carboxylic acid;
R = hydrocarbon or H

The hydroxyl H atom indicated (in color) in the formula above is the one donated in the acid-base reactions of carboxylic acids.

Carboxylic acid formulas are sometimes written in a condensed form designed to save space. In these formulas the carbonyl is written as CO instead of C=O. For instance, the formula for acetic acid, in which the R group is methyl, can be written CH_3COOH or CH_3CO_2H instead of $CH_3\overset{\overset{\displaystyle O}{\|}}{C}OH$.

In the sections that follow we will see how the physical and chemical properties of carboxylic acids are related to their structures, and we will discuss some carboxylic acids of special importance in living systems.

17.2 NAMING CARBOXYLIC ACIDS

Unsubstituted carboxylic acid names are derived from the name of the alkane with the same number of C atoms (including the carboxyl C atom). The IUPAC name for a carboxylic acid is obtained by dropping the *-e* from alkane and adding *-oic acid*. For instance, the name of the five-carbon carboxylic acid shown below is derived from the five-carbon alkane pentane

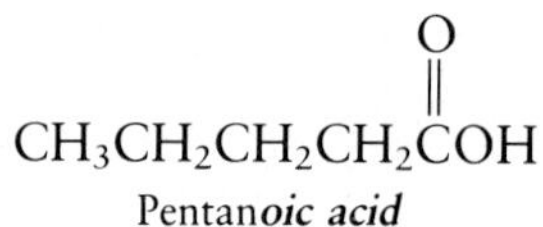

$$CH_3CH_2CH_2CH_2\overset{\overset{\displaystyle O}{\|}}{C}OH$$

Pentan***oic acid***

Common names are very frequently used instead of IUPAC names for carboxylic acids. The common names are derived from the names of the materials from which the carboxylic acids were first isolated. For example, the common name of methanoic acid, the one-carbon carboxylic acid (HCOOH), is formic acid because it was first found in *formicae,* Latin for "ants." At one time formic acid was actually prepared by boiling ants! Ethanoic acid, the two-carbon carboxylic acid present in vinegar, is nearly always called acetic acid from the Latin word *acetum,* "vinegar." Table 17.1 gives the formulas and the IUPAC and common names for the first 18 straight-chain carboxylic acids. You will notice

TABLE 17.1 CARBOXYLIC ACID NAMES

Formula	IUPAC name	Common name
*$HOC(=O)H$	Methanoic acid	Formic acid
$HOC(=O)CH_3$	Ethanoic acid	Acetic acid
$HOC(=O)CH_2CH_3$	Propanoic acid	Propionic acid
$HOC(=O)(CH_2)_2CH_3$	Butanoic acid	Butyric acid
$HOC(=O)(CH_2)_3CH_3$	Pentanoic acid	Valeric acid
$HOC(=O)(CH_2)_4CH_3$	Hexanoic acid	Caproic acid
$HOC(=O)(CH_2)_5CH_3$	Heptanoic acid	Enanthic acid
$HOC(=O)(CH_2)_6CH_3$	Octanoic acid	Caprylic acid
$HOC(=O)(CH_2)_7CH_3$	Nonanoic acid	Pelargonic acid
$HOC(=O)(CH_2)_8CH_3$	Decanoic acid	Capric acid
$HOC(=O)(CH_2)_9CH_3$	Undecanoic acid	
$HOC(=O)(CH_2)_{10}CH_3$	Dodecanoic acid	Lauric acid
$HOC(=O)(CH_2)_{11}CH_3$	Tridecanoic acid	
$HOC(=O)(CH_2)_{12}CH_3$	Tetradecanoic acid	Myristic acid
$HOC(=O)(CH_2)_{13}CH_3$	Pentadecanoic acid	
$HOC(=O)(CH_2)_{14}CH_3$	Hexadecanoic acid	Palmitic acid
$HOC(=O)(CH_2)_{15}CH_3$	Heptadecanoic acid	Margaric acid
$HOC(=O)(CH_2)_{16}CH_3$	Octadecanoic acid	Stearic acid

*The carboxylic acid functional groups are shown in color.

that common names are listed for all the acids having an even number of carbon atoms but not for all the odd-numbered acids. That is because odd-numbered carboxylic acids with more than 10 C atoms are rare in nature and, except for margaric acid, $CH_3(CH_2)_{15}COOH$, are always called by their IUPAC names. The reason for this is that living systems synthesize long-chain carboxylic acids (components of fats) by using two-carbon building blocks, as we shall learn in Chapter 27 (Metabolism of Lipids).

Recall that common names of aldehydes (see Table 16.1) are derived from those of the corresponding carboxylic acids. Formaldehyde, the common name of the one-carbon aldehyde (methanal), comes from formic acid and the name acetaldehyde (ethanal) from acetic acid.

Substituted Carboxylic Acids

To name substituted carboxylic acids the C atoms of the main chain are labeled in the same way that they are for aldehydes (Section 16.3): thus, according to the IUPAC system the carboxyl C atom is assigned the number 1, and according to the common system the C atom adjacent to the carbonyl is the α C atom.

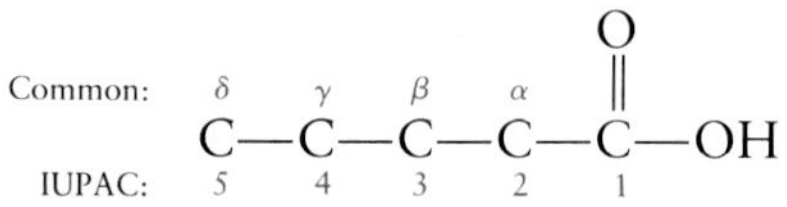

$$\begin{array}{lcccccl} \text{Common:} & \delta & \gamma & \beta & \alpha & \overset{\text{O}}{\|} & \\ & \text{C}- & \text{C}- & \text{C}- & \text{C}- & \text{C} & -\text{OH} \\ \text{IUPAC:} & 5 & 4 & 3 & 2 & 1 & \end{array}$$

For example, the compounds below can be named by using either system.

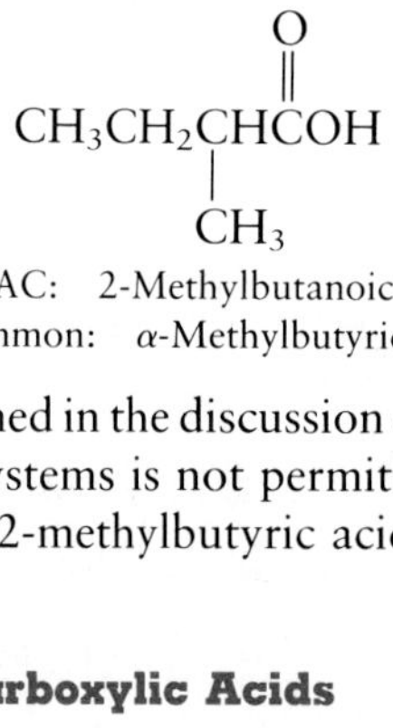

$$CH_3CH_2\underset{\underset{CH_3}{|}}{CH}\overset{\overset{O}{\|}}{C}OH \qquad CH_3CH_2CH_2\underset{\underset{OH}{|}}{CH}CH_2\overset{\overset{O}{\|}}{C}OH$$

IUPAC: 2-Methylbutanoic acid — 3-Hydroxyhexanoic acid
Common: α-Methylbutyric acid — β-Hydroxycaproic acid

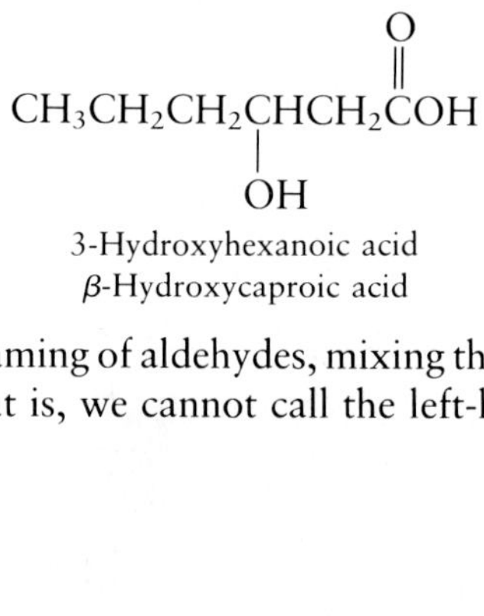

As we mentioned in the discussion of the naming of aldehydes, mixing the common and IUPAC systems is not permitted. That is, we cannot call the left-hand compound above 2-methylbutyric acid.

Aromatic Carboxylic Acids

Most of the aromatic carboxylic acids in which the carboxyl group is attached directly to the benzene ring are named as derivatives of benzoic acid, since the carboxyl group is very high on the priority list given in Table 14.4. For example:

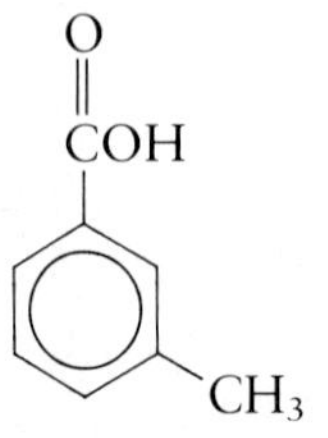

[Structures: benzene rings each bearing $\overset{O}{\|}COH$, with CH_3 (meta), NH_2 (para), OH (ortho)]

m-Methylbenzoic acid (3-methylbenzoic acid) — *p*-Aminobenzoic acid (4-aminobenzoic acid) — *o*-Hydroxybenzoic acid (2-hydroxybenzoic acid)

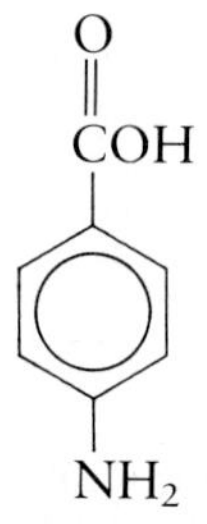

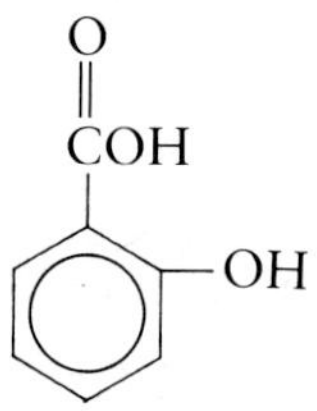

The compound *para*-aminobenzoic acid, also called PABA, is used in suntan lotions (see Exercise 14.1). Instead of *o*-hydroxybenzoic acid, the right-hand compound just given is almost always known by its common name, *salicylic acid.* Aspirin, other related pain-killers, and wintergreen are all derivatives of salicylic acid.

SAMPLE EXERCISE 17.1

Name the carboxylic acids below.

(a)

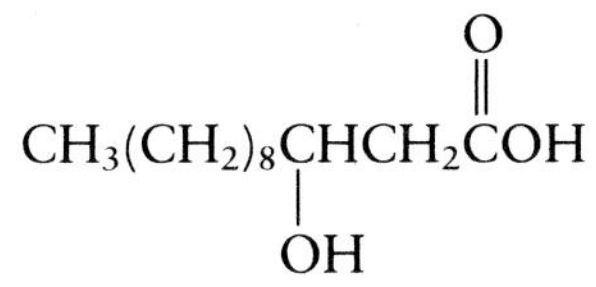

$$CH_3(CH_2)_8\underset{\displaystyle OH}{\underset{|}{C}}HCH_2\overset{\displaystyle O}{\overset{\|}{C}}OH$$

(b)

$$C_6H_5{-}CH_2\overset{\displaystyle O}{\overset{\|}{C}}OH$$

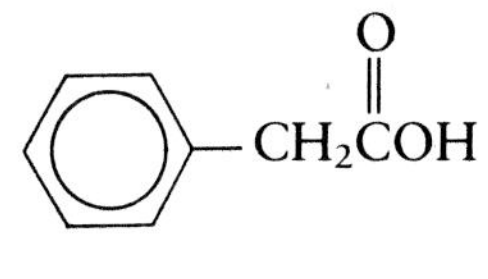

Solution:

(a) We can name this 12-carbon acid as a derivative of lauric (dodecanoic) acid (see Table 17.1).

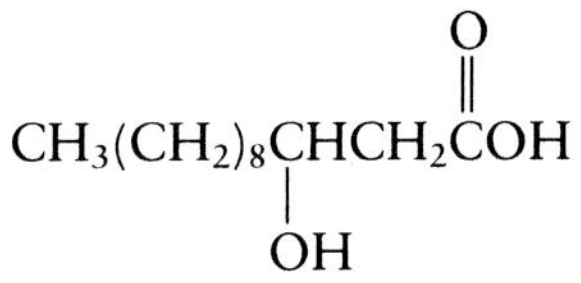

$$CH_3(CH_2)_8\underset{\displaystyle OH}{\underset{|}{C}}HCH_2\overset{\displaystyle O}{\overset{\|}{C}}OH$$

3-Hydroxydodecanoic acid (β-hydroxylauric acid)

(b) This carboxylic acid is named as a derivative of ethanoic or acetic acid with a phenyl substituent.

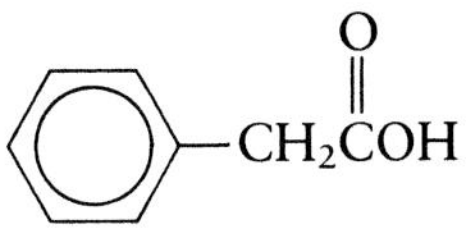

$$C_6H_5{-}CH_2\overset{\displaystyle O}{\overset{\|}{C}}OH$$

Phenylethanoic acid (phenylacetic acid)

EXERCISE 17.1

The compound below, called glycine, is a building block for proteins in living organisms. Give its IUPAC and common names. (Recall from Table 14.2 that the NH_2 group is called amino.)

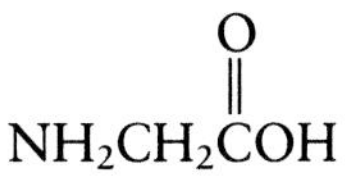

$$NH_2CH_2\overset{\displaystyle O}{\overset{\|}{C}}OH$$

Dicarboxylic Acids

Dicarboxylic acids contain two carboxyl groups. In the IUPAC system they are named as alkanedioic acids from the name of the alkane with the same number of C atoms (including both carboxyl carbons). For instance, the name of the four-carbon dicarboxylic acid is based upon butane.

$$\overset{O}{\overset{\|}{HOC}}CH_2CH_2\overset{O}{\overset{\|}{C}}OH$$

Butanedioic acid

However, the common names for dicarboxylic acids are used more often than the IUPAC ones, particularly for the lower-formula weight acids, in which n in the general formula below is 0 to 6.

$$HO\overset{O}{\overset{\|}{C}}(CH_2)_n\overset{O}{\overset{\|}{C}}OH$$

The common names are oxalic ($n = 0$), malonic ($n = 1$), succinic ($n = 2$), glutaric ($n = 3$), adipic ($n = 4$), pimelic ($n = 5$), and suberic ($n = 6$). (One way to remember this is to use the acronym OMSGAPS to suggest the first letter of each name.) The IUPAC and common names of the dicarboxylic acids are listed in Table 17.2.

TABLE 17.2 **NAMES AND FORMULAS OF DICARBOXYLIC ACIDS**

Formula	IUPAC name	Common name
$HO\overset{O}{\overset{\|}{C}}-\overset{O}{\overset{\|}{C}}OH$	Ethanedioic acid	Oxalic acid
$HO\overset{O}{\overset{\|}{C}}CH_2\overset{O}{\overset{\|}{C}}OH$	Propanedioic acid	Malonic acid
$HO\overset{O}{\overset{\|}{C}}CH_2CH_2\overset{O}{\overset{\|}{C}}OH$	Butanedioic acid	Succinic acid
$HO\overset{O}{\overset{\|}{C}}CH_2CH_2CH_2\overset{O}{\overset{\|}{C}}OH$	Pentanedioic acid	Glutaric acid
$HO\overset{O}{\overset{\|}{C}}CH_2CH_2CH_2CH_2\overset{O}{\overset{\|}{C}}OH$	Hexanedioic acid	Adipic acid
$HO\overset{O}{\overset{\|}{C}}CH_2CH_2CH_2CH_2CH_2\overset{O}{\overset{\|}{C}}OH$	Heptanedioic acid	Pimelic acid
$HO\overset{O}{\overset{\|}{C}}CH_2CH_2CH_2CH_2CH_2CH_2\overset{O}{\overset{\|}{C}}OH$	Octanedioic acid	Suberic acid

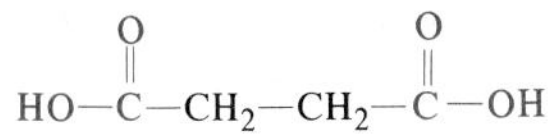

$$HO-\overset{O}{\overset{\|}{C}}-CH_2-CH_2-\overset{O}{\overset{\|}{C}}-OH$$

Succinic acid

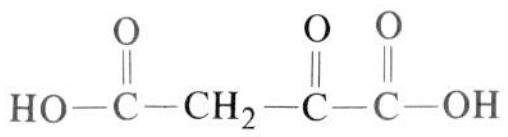

$$HO-\overset{O}{\overset{\|}{C}}-CH_2-\overset{O}{\overset{\|}{C}}-\overset{O}{\overset{\|}{C}}-OH$$

Oxaloacetic acid

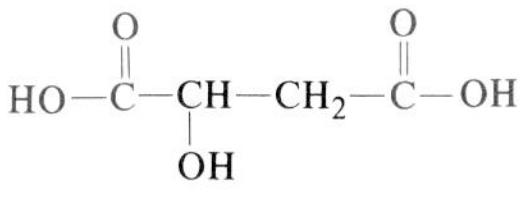

$$HO-\overset{O}{\overset{\|}{C}}-\underset{OH}{\underset{|}{CH}}-CH_2-\overset{O}{\overset{\|}{C}}-OH$$

Malic acid

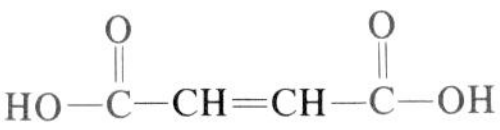

$$HO-\overset{O}{\overset{\|}{C}}-CH=CH-\overset{O}{\overset{\|}{C}}-OH$$

Fumaric acid

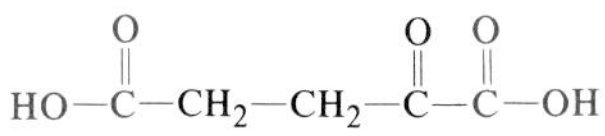

$$HO-\overset{O}{\overset{\|}{C}}-CH_2-CH_2-\overset{O}{\overset{\|}{C}}-\overset{O}{\overset{\|}{C}}-OH$$

α-Ketoglutaric acid

$$\begin{array}{l} CH_2-\overset{O}{\overset{\|}{C}}-OH \\ \quad | \\ HO-C-\overset{O}{\overset{\|}{C}}-OH \\ \quad | \\ CH_2-\overset{O}{\overset{\|}{C}}-OH \end{array}$$

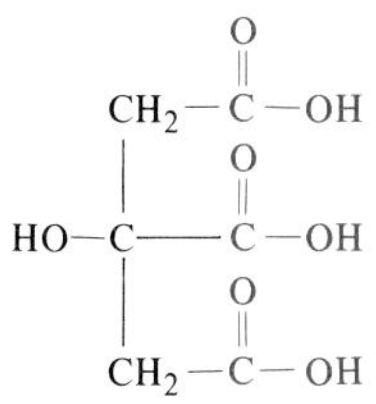

Citric acid

FIGURE 17.2
These acids and derivatives are metabolic intermediates in the tricarboxylic acid cycle.

Dicarboxylic acids and their derivatives appear as intermediate compounds in metabolic cycles. For instance, the compounds shown in Figure 17.2 are part of the *tricarboxylic acid cycle,* also known as the *citric acid cycle,* or *Krebs cycle.* This metabolic pathway is the sequence of reactions by which food molecules are oxidized to produce energy. In the final four chapters of this text we will see how various food molecules break down to form metabolites such as those in the Krebs cycle.

Another important use for dicarboxylic acids is in the area of polymer synthesis. Because they have two functional groups and thus two reactive ends, dicarboxylic acids can combine with other compounds that also have two reactive ends to make long-chain polymer molecules, many of which are used to make synthetic fibers such as nylon and polyester (we will discuss these in Chapter 19.)

The unsaturated dicarboxylic acid butenedioic acid exhibits cis-trans isomerism (see Section 13.7) and thus represents two different compounds. The two isomers of butenedioic acid are known by the common names fumaric acid (trans isomer) and maleic acid (cis isomer).

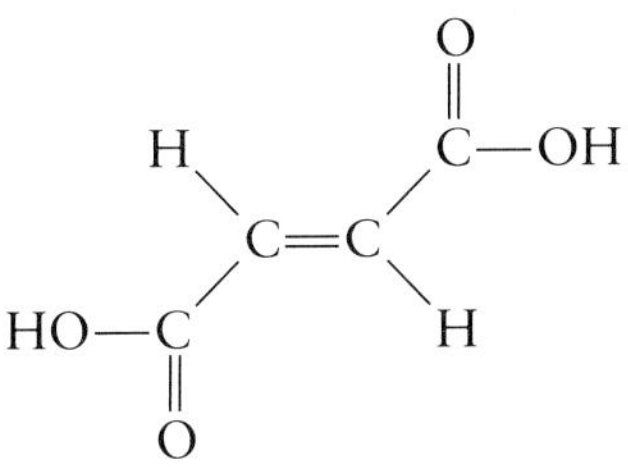

$$\begin{array}{ccc} H & & \overset{O}{\overset{\|}{C}}-OH \\ & C=C & \\ HO-\underset{O}{\underset{\|}{C}} & & H \end{array} \qquad \begin{array}{ccc} HO-\overset{O}{\overset{\|}{C}} & & \overset{O}{\overset{\|}{C}}-OH \\ & C=C & \\ H & & H \end{array}$$

trans-Butenedioic acid (fumaric acid) *cis*-Butenedioic acid (maleic acid)

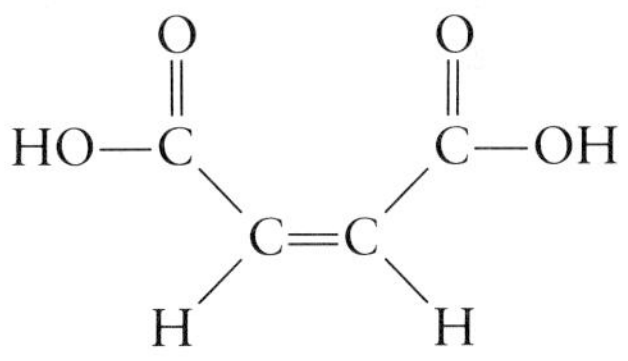

Note that the trans isomer, fumaric acid, is one of the metabolic intermediates shown in Figure 17.2.

Figure 17.3 shows the formulas of the three possible dicarboxyl derivatives of benzene. The para-substituted benzene, called terephthalic acid, is used in the synthesis of polymers such as polyester fibers.

Citric acid is a **tricarboxylic acid** in which three carboxyl groups are attached to the three C atoms of propane (see Figure 17.2). Citric acid is also an intermediate in the Krebs cycle and is responsible for giving the cycle its two other names, citric acid cycle and tricarboxylic acid cycle.

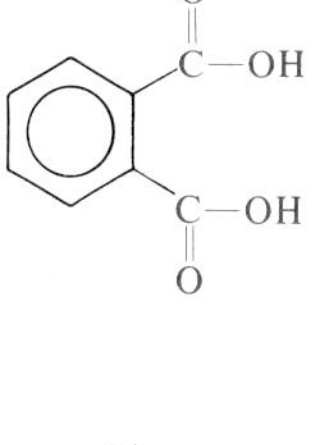

(a) 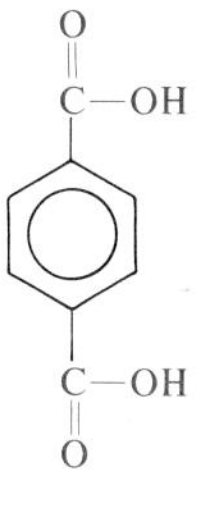 (b) 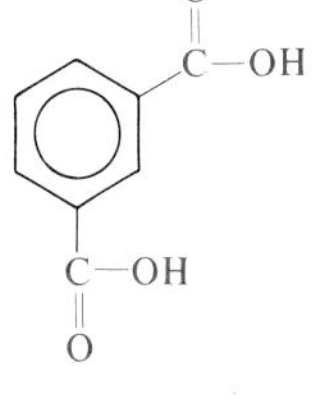 (c)

FIGURE 17.3
Dicarboxyl benzenes:
(*a*) phthalic acid;
(*b*) terephthalic acid (isomer used in polymer synthesis to make polyesters);
(*c*) isophthalic acid.

17.3 PHYSICAL PROPERTIES OF CARBOXYLIC ACIDS

Looking at the structures in Figure 17.1 you can see that carboxylic acids all have a hydrogen atom bonded to an oxygen atom in the hydroxyl group attached to the carbonyl. Thus they can participate in hydrogen bonding, as water and alcohol molecules do. However, the hydrogen bonding is a little different for carboxylic acids. Suppose we have two carboxylic acid molecules, molecule A and molecule B. The hydroxyl H atom of carboxylic acid molecule A is attracted to the carbonyl O of the neighboring molecule B, and the hydroxyl H atom of B is attracted to the carbonyl O of molecule A. As a result of this mutual attraction, in which two H bonds form between two molecules, pairs of carboxylic acid molecules form relatively stable double molecules, as shown in Figure 17.4. These carboxylic acid *dimers* tend to behave as though they were single molecules. We say that two or more molecules which behave as though they were one molecule are *associated;* thus carboxylic acids are associated. One way to detect association is to use a colligative property to measure the formula weight of a compound. Recall that colligative properties depend upon the number of "particles" in solution (see Section 9.8). A carboxylic acid dimer behaves as though it were one particle and thus the formula weight determined by a colligative property measurement will correspond to that of the dimer, not that of the monomer. For instance, the formula weight for benzoic acid ($C_7H_6O_2$) is 122. However, the formula weight determined from freezing point depression data is 242, which is very close to the formula weight of the benzoic acid dimer (244).

Benzoic acid, $C_7H_6O_2$
(formula weight 122)

Benzoic acid dimer, $C_{14}H_{12}O_4$
(formula weight 244)

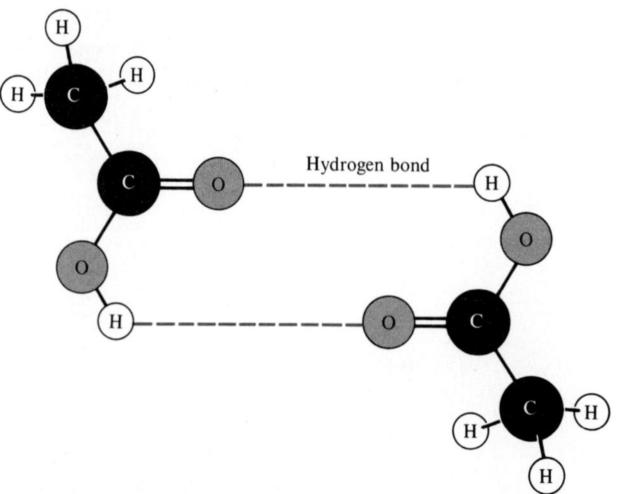

FIGURE 17.4
Hydrogen bonding in acetic acid dimer.

Boiling Points

The hydrogen-bonded carboxylic acids have unusually high boiling points, even higher than those of alcohols with the same formula weights. For instance, the boiling point of formic acid (methanoic acid) is higher than that of ethanol.

$$\underset{\substack{\text{Formic acid} \\ \text{(formula weight 46; bp 101°C)}}}{\overset{\overset{\displaystyle O}{\|}}{HCOH}} \qquad \underset{\substack{\text{Ethanol} \\ \text{(formula weight 46; bp 78°C)}}}{CH_3CH_2OH}$$

Carboxylic acids with more than nine C atoms are solids at 25°C, as you can see from Table 17.3, where the physical properties of some carboxylic acids are listed.

Solubility in Water

Like alcohols, carboxylic acids can form hydrogen bonds with water as well as with each other and therefore exhibit solubility behavior similar to that of the alcohols. Carboxylic acids with less than five C atoms in their formulas are infinitely water-soluble (see Table 17.3). However, the polar carboxyl ends of all

TABLE 17.3 PHYSICAL PROPERTIES OF CARBOXYLIC ACIDS

Formula	Name	Boiling point, °C	Melting point, °C	Physical state, 25°	Water solubility (g/100 g)
$HCOOH$	Formic	101*		L	Infinite
CH_3COOH	Acetic	118		L	Infinite
CH_3CH_2COOH	Propanoic	141		L	Infinite
$CH_3(CH_2)_2COOH$	Butanoic	164		L	Infinite
$CH_3(CH_2)_3COOH$	Pentanoic	187		L	5
$CH_3(CH_2)_4COOH$	Hexanoic	205		L	1
$CH_3(CH_2)_6COOH$	Octanoic	237		L	0.7
$CH_3(CH_2)_8COOH$	Decanoic		31	S	0.2
$CH_3(CH_2)_{10}COOH$	Dodecanoic		44	S	Insoluble
$CH_3(CH_2)_{12}COOH$	Tetradecanoic		54	S	Insoluble
$CH_3(CH_2)_{14}COOH$	Hexadecanoic		63	S	Insoluble
$CH_3(CH_2)_{16}COOH$	Octadecanoic		70	S	Insoluble
C_6H_5—COOH (benzene ring)	Benzoic		122	S	0.34
C_6H_4(—COOH)(—OH) (benzene ring, ortho)	Salicylic		159	S	0.22

*In this table the boiling points only are listed for the liquids and melting points only for the solids.

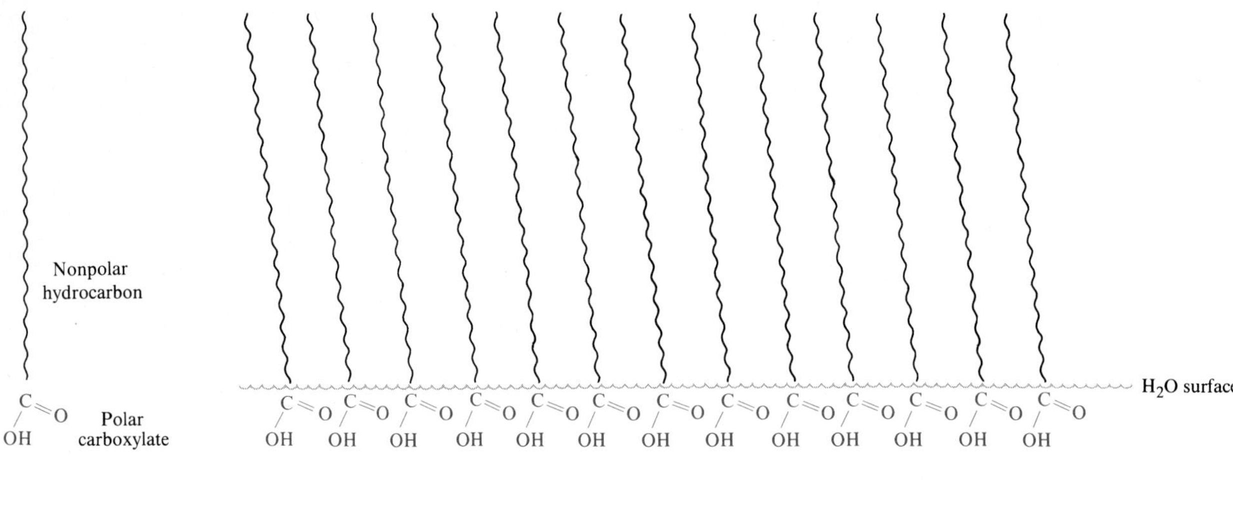

FIGURE 17.5
(*a*) Carboxylic acid.
(*b*) Monolayer.

carboxylic acids, even those with more than five C atoms, are water-soluble (see Figure 17.5*a*). Thus it is possible for the polar end of a long-chain carboxylic acid molecule to be dissolved in water while the nonpolar hydrocarbon end of the molecule is not dissolved. This allows long-chain carboxylic acids such as stearic acid (octadecanoic acid) to form monomolecular films called *monolayers* on a water surface, in which only the polar ends of the molecules are dissolved while the nonpolar chains are not (see Figure 17.5*b*). Monolayers of stearic acid can be prepared in the laboratory by carefully spreading a solution of stearic acid onto a water surface. One practical use for monolayers of nontoxic substances such as stearic acid is that of preventing evaporation of water from reservoirs.

Other long-chain polar organic compounds such as octadecanol ($CH_3(CH_2)_{17}OH$) also form monolayers.

Odor

The odor of rancid butter is due to butyric acid.

When they are pure or in very concentrated solutions, the low-formula-weight carboxylic acids have a powerful sour odor. You can imagine how strong this odor must be by comparison with that of vinegar, which is only a 5% solution of acetic acid in water. The higher-formula-weight acids, which are liquids (see Table 17.3), have disagreeable odors responsible for the rancid smell of spoiled fats. The solid carboxylic acids, such as stearic acid, are nonvolatile and odorless.

17.4 ACIDITY OF CARBOXYLIC ACIDS

We can explain the acidity of the carboxyl H atom of carboxylic acids in much the same way that we explained the acidity of the hydroxyl H atom of phenol (Section 15.8). Like the phenoxide anion, the **carboxylate anion** that forms when the carboxylic acid donates its hydroxyl proton is especially stable.

$$\underset{\text{Carboxylic acid}}{\overset{\overset{\displaystyle O}{\|}}{RCOH}} + H_2O \rightleftharpoons \underset{\text{Carboxylate anion}}{\overset{\overset{\displaystyle O}{\|}}{RCO^-}} + \underset{\text{Hydronium ion}}{H_3O^+}$$

The negative charge of the carboxylate anion can be delocalized, or "spread," onto the carboxyl group, thereby imparting extra stability to the anion and thus encouraging the ionization.

The ionization of acetic acid (ethanoic acid) produces acetate (ethanoate) and hydronium ions.

$$\underset{\text{Acetic acid}}{\overset{\overset{\displaystyle O}{\|}}{CH_3COH}} + H_2O \rightleftharpoons \underset{\text{Acetate ion}}{\overset{\overset{\displaystyle O}{\|}}{CH_3CO^-}} + \underset{\text{Hydronium ion}}{H_3O^+}$$

This same ionization equation appears in Table 11.5 (where K_a values for weak acids are listed), but there acetic acid is written in the abbreviated form HAc. To write the K_a expression we put the acetate and hydronium ion concentrations in the numerator and the acetic acid concentration in the denominator.

$$K_a = \frac{[CH_3COO^-][H_3O^+]}{[CH_3COOH]}$$

The values of K_a for some carboxylic acids are given in Table 17.4.

Carboxyl*ate* ion names are derived from the carboxylic acid name by substituting *-ate ion* for *-ic acid*. Thus acetic acid produces acetate ion, butanoic acid produces butanoate ion, and so on.

TABLE 17.4 **K_a VALUES FOR WEAK CARBOXYLIC ACIDS**

Ionization	K_a at 25°C
$HCOOH + H_2O \rightleftharpoons HCOO^- + H_3O^+$ (Formic acid → Formate ion)	1.8×10^{-4}
$CH_3COOH + H_2O \rightleftharpoons CH_3COO^- + H_3O^+$ (Acetic acid → Acetate ion)	1.8×10^{-5}
$CH_3CH_2COOH + H_2O \rightleftharpoons CH_3CH_2COO^- + H_3O^+$ (Propionic acid → Propionate ion)	1.3×10^{-5}
$CH_3CH_2CH_2COOH + H_2O \rightleftharpoons CH_3CH_2CH_2COO^- + H_3O^+$ (Butyric acid → Butyrate ion)	1.5×10^{-5}
$C_6H_5COOH + H_2O \rightleftharpoons C_6H_5COO^- + H_3O^+$ (Benzoic acid → Benzoate ion)	6.5×10^{-5}
$C_6H_4(OH)COOH + H_2O \rightleftharpoons C_6H_4(OH)COO^- + H_3O^+$ (Salicylic acid → Salicylate ion)	1.1×10^{-3}

SAMPLE EXERCISE 17.2

Write the ionization equation for propanoic acid and name the product anion using the IUPAC and common system.

Solution:

Propanoic acid, also called propionic acid, $CH_3CH_2\overset{\overset{\displaystyle O}{\|}}{C}OH$, donates a proton to H_2O to form a hydronium and a propanoate (or propionate) ion.

$$\underset{\substack{\text{Propanoic acid}\\\text{(propionic acid)}}}{CH_3CH_2\overset{\overset{\displaystyle O}{\|}}{C}OH} + H_2O \rightleftharpoons \underset{\substack{\text{Propanoate ion}\\\text{(propionate ion)}}}{CH_3CH_2\overset{\overset{\displaystyle O}{\|}}{C}O^-} + H_3O^+$$

EXERCISE 17.2

Name the ion that forms when $CH_3CH_2CH_2CH_2\overset{\overset{\displaystyle O}{\|}}{C}OH$ ionizes and write the ionization reaction.

17.5 SALTS OF CARBOXYLIC ACIDS

The name acetate is usually used rather than ethanoate.

Carboxylic acids are neutralized by bases to form salts. To name the salts we use the same method that we learned for inorganic ionic compounds in Chapter 4, in which the name of the cation is followed by the name of the anion. For instance, acetic acid reacts with sodium hydroxide to produce sodium acetate.

$$\underset{\text{Acetic acid}}{CH_3\overset{\overset{\displaystyle O}{\|}}{C}OH} + \underset{\text{Sodium hydroxide}}{NaOH} \longrightarrow \underset{\text{Sodium acetate}}{CH_3\overset{\overset{\displaystyle O}{\|}}{C}ONa} + H_2O$$

We write the cation on the right of the salt formula instead of on the left as we did for inorganic compounds such as NaCl. When a doubly charged cation such as Ca^{2+} appears in the formula, the formula must also include two acetate ions to balance the 2+ charge. Parentheses are used to enclose the organic anion and the subscript 2 is placed outside the parentheses. Thus we write the formula for calcium acetate as $(CH_3\overset{\overset{\displaystyle O}{\|}}{C}O)_2Ca$.

Salts of carboxylic acids are ionic compounds and so we could rewrite the formula for sodium acetate to show that it includes two ions.

$$CH_3\overset{\overset{O}{\|}}{C}O^-Na^+$$

Sodium acetate

The sodium and potassium salts of even the longer-chain carboxylic acids are soluble in water, but the Ca, Mg, and Fe salts are not. In the next section we will see the importance of these solubility characteristics for salts such as sodium stearate, $CH_3(CH_2)_{16}\overset{\overset{O}{\|}}{C}ONa$, which are used as soaps.

You may see "soda of benzoate" instead of sodium benzoate on labels.

Because some carboxylate salts are able to stop the growth of bacteria and fungi, they are added to foods to prevent mold formation and spoilage. For instance, sodium benzoate may be found in pickles, olives, and relishes.

$$C_6H_5\overset{\overset{O}{\|}}{C}ONa$$

Sodium benzoate

The Ca salt of undecylenic acid is also used in medicated powders.

The zinc salt of undecylenic acid, an unsaturated carboxylic acid, is used in foot powders for the treatment of ***athlete's foot.***

$$(CH_2{=}CH(CH_2)_8\overset{\overset{O}{\|}}{C}O)_2Zn$$

Zinc undecylenate

SAMPLE EXERCISE 17.3

Write a reaction for the formation of calcium propionate, a preservative listed on bread labels. What is its IUPAC name?

Solution:

Calcium propionate can be produced by the reaction of calcium hydroxide with propionic (propanoic) acid.

$$\underset{\text{Propionic acid}}{CH_3CH_2\overset{\overset{O}{\|}}{C}OH} + \underset{\text{Calcium hydroxide}}{Ca(OH)_2} \longrightarrow \underset{\text{Calcium propionate}}{(CH_3CH_2\overset{\overset{O}{\|}}{C}O)_2Ca} + H_2O$$

Its IUPAC name is calcium propanoate.

EXERCISE 17.3

Write the reaction for the formation of sodium benzoate.

17.6 SOAPS AND DETERGENTS

Soaps are the sodium or potassium salts of long-chain carboxylic acids such as sodium stearate (octadecanoate), written in full below.

$$CH_3CH_2CH_2CH_2CH_2CH_2CH_2CH_2CH_2CH_2CH_2CH_2CH_2CH_2CH_2CH_2CH_2\overset{\overset{\large O}{\|}}{C}O^-Na^+$$

We can explain the cleaning power of sodium stearate and other soaps by looking at its structure. The polar carboxylate end of the molecule dissolves in water and the long hydrocarbon chain (17 C atoms exclusive of the carboxyl group in sodium stearate) does not. However, the nonpolar hydrocarbon chain *is* soluble in nonpolar fat and grease, which are among the substances we know as "dirt." When soap, water, and dirt are mixed, the polar carboxyl ends of the soap molecules dissolve in the water and the hydrocarbon chains dissolve in the dirt, as shown in Figure 17.6*a*. A collection of soap molecules is able to trap the dirt by forming a spherical structure called a **micelle** (see Figure 17.6*b*). In the form of micelles the dirt is broken up by the soap so that it can be washed away.

Hand soaps contain sodium stearate and shaving creams contain potassium stearate, a very soft soap. When soaps are mixed with hard water, that is, water containing ions such as Ca^{2+}, Mg^{2+}, and Fe^{2+}, water-insoluble calcium, magnesium and iron salts of stearic acid form. These salts are responsible for the "ring around the bathtub." If shampoos and dish washing liquids were made of soap, using them in hard water would leave a film of insoluble salts on hair and dishes.

Synthetic detergents are often called *syndets*.

Detergents are used for cleaning hair, dishes, and clothing because their salts are much more water-soluble than are those of stearic acid (see Table 17.5). The detergents we will discuss here are those which are salts of sulfur-containing organic acids called **sulfonic acids.** In the general formula for a sulfonic acid the R refers to a long-chain hydrocarbon group, which may include a benzene ring.

FIGURE 17.6
(*a*) The nonpolar end of the soap molecule dissolves in dirt. The polar end of the soap molecule dissolves in H_2O. (*b*) A micelle. R represents the long nonpolar chain of the soap molecules.

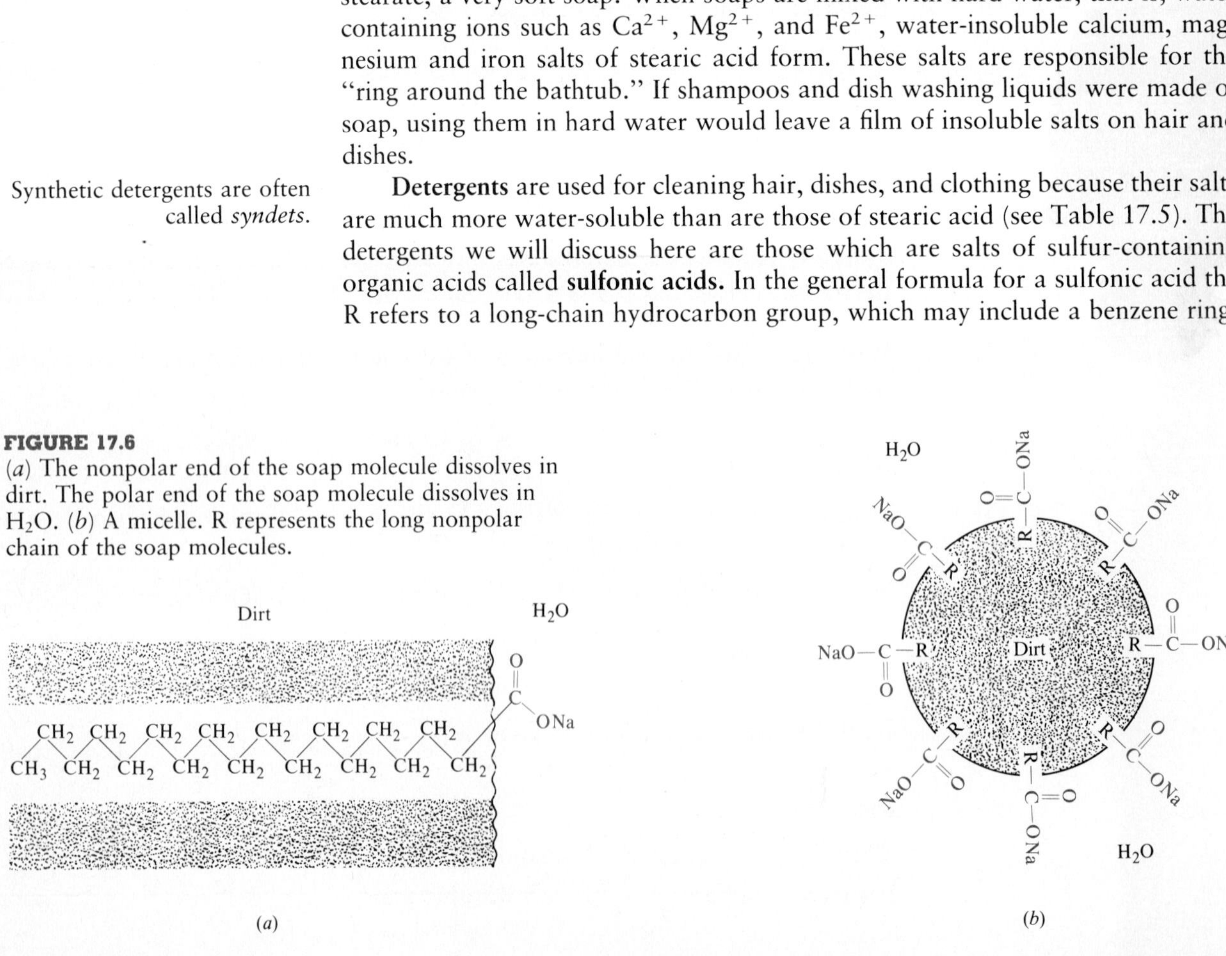

TABLE 17.5 **COMPARING SOLUBILITIES OF SOAPS AND DETERGENTS**

Formula	Solubility in hot water
Stearate soaps*	
RCOONa	Soluble
RCOOK	Soluble
$(RCOO)_2Mg$	Insoluble
$(RCOO)_2Ca$	Insoluble
$(RCOO)_2Fe$	Insoluble
Alkylbenzenesulfonate detergents†	
$R-C_6H_4-SO_3Na$	Soluble
$R-C_6H_4-SO_3K$	Soluble
$(R-C_6H_4-SO_3)_2Mg$	Soluble
$(R-C_6H_4-SO_3)_2Ca$	Soluble
$(R-C_6H_4-SO_3)_2Fe$	Soluble

*R = $CH_3(CH_2)_{16}$.
†R contains 12 to 15 C atoms.

$$R-\overset{\overset{\displaystyle O}{\|}}{\underset{\underset{\displaystyle O}{\|}}{S}}-OH$$

General sulfonic acid

To name sulfonic acids we name the parent hydrocarbon group corresponding to R and add the term *-sulfonic acid*. For example,

$$CH_3-\overset{\overset{\displaystyle O}{\|}}{\underset{\underset{\displaystyle O}{\|}}{S}}-OH \qquad CH_3CH_2CH_2CH_2-C_6H_4-\overset{\overset{\displaystyle O}{\|}}{\underset{\underset{\displaystyle O}{\|}}{S}}-OH$$

Methanesulfonic acid — Butylbenzenesulfonic acid

The salts of sulfonic acids are called *sulfonates*.

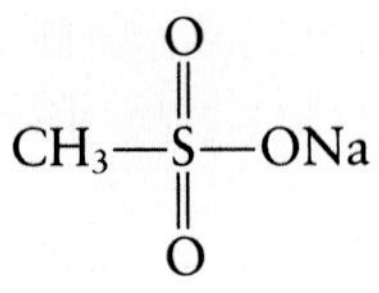

$$CH_3{-}\overset{\overset{\displaystyle O}{\|}}{\underset{\underset{\displaystyle O}{\|}}{S}}{-}ONa \qquad CH_3CH_2CH_2CH_2{-}C_6H_4{-}\overset{\overset{\displaystyle O}{\|}}{\underset{\underset{\displaystyle O}{\|}}{S}}{-}ONa$$

Sodium methanesulfonate 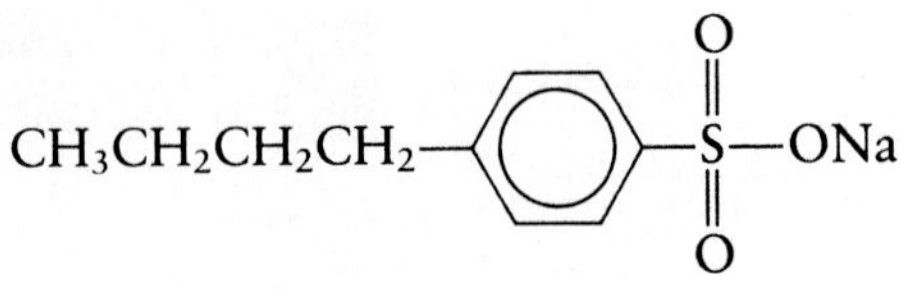 — Sodium butylbenzenesulfonate

Alkylbenzenesulfonates, abbreviated ABS, are common ingredients in detergent products.

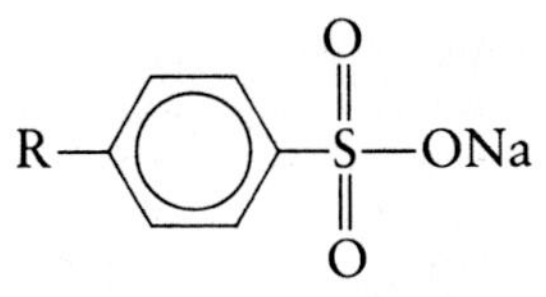

$$R{-}C_6H_4{-}\overset{\overset{\displaystyle O}{\|}}{\underset{\underset{\displaystyle O}{\|}}{S}}{-}ONa$$

Alkylbenzenesulfonate

The general mechanism by which sulfonate detergents are able to clean involves forming micelles in the same way that carboxylate soaps do. What distinguishes the sulfonates (in which R is a long-chain hydrocarbon) from the carboxylates is that their Ca^{2+}, Mg^{2+}, and Fe^{2+} salts *are* soluble in water (see Table 17.5). Thus, objects washed with detergents are not coated with insoluble residues caused by the ions present in hard water. Detergents and soaps possess antigermicidal properties which make them useful as mild disinfectants.

Microorganisms become enmeshed in lather and are removed in rinse water.

Biodegradable detergents are those which can be consumed by bacteria. What they all have in common is a straight- (or almost straight-) chain hydrocarbon group in their structures. Bacteria are able to "eat" these linear hydrocarbon fragments because they are similar to the straight-chain hydrocarbon groups found in natural fats (see Figure 17.7). One example of a biodegradable detergent is the alkylbenzenesulfonate shown below:

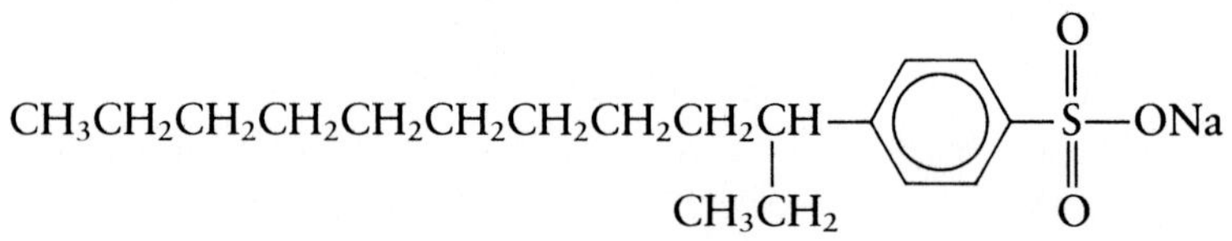

$$CH_3CH_2CH_2CH_2CH_2CH_2CH_2CH_2CH_2\underset{\underset{\displaystyle CH_3CH_2}{|}}{CH}{-}C_6H_4{-}\overset{\overset{\displaystyle O}{\|}}{\underset{\underset{\displaystyle O}{\|}}{S}}{-}ONa$$

Biodegradable ABS detergent

Some of the first synthetic detergents used were not biodegradable. One example is the ABS compound below, which contains a highly branched R group.

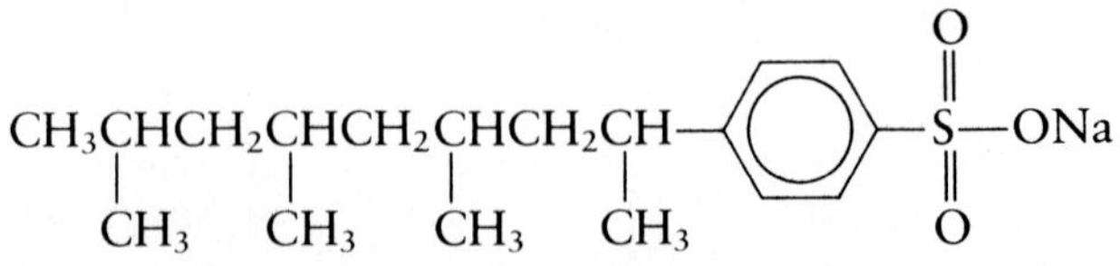

$$CH_3\underset{\underset{\displaystyle CH_3}{|}}{CH}CH_2\underset{\underset{\displaystyle CH_3}{|}}{CH}CH_2\underset{\underset{\displaystyle CH_3}{|}}{CH}CH_2\underset{\underset{\displaystyle CH_3}{|}}{CH}{-}C_6H_4{-}\overset{\overset{\displaystyle O}{\|}}{\underset{\underset{\displaystyle O}{\|}}{S}}{-}ONa$$

Nonbiodegradable ABS detergent

An undesirable consequence of the use of nonbiodegradable detergents is that they cannot easily be removed from water sources. Foam and suds collect upon the surfaces of lakes and rivers, producing pollution which is not only unsightly but also harmful to the creatures living in the waters.

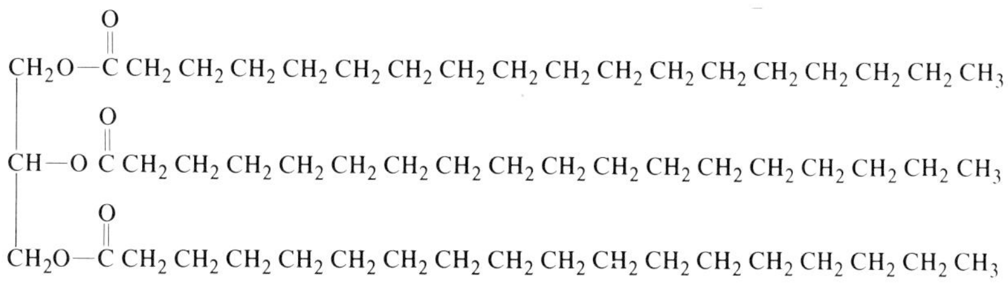

$$\begin{array}{l} CH_2O-\overset{O}{\overset{\|}{C}}CH_2CH_2CH_2CH_2CH_2CH_2CH_2CH_2CH_2CH_2CH_2CH_2CH_2CH_2CH_2CH_2CH_3 \\ |\\ CH-O\overset{O}{\overset{\|}{C}}CH_2CH_2CH_2CH_2CH_2CH_2CH_2CH_2CH_2CH_2CH_2CH_2CH_2CH_2CH_2CH_2CH_3 \\ | \\ CH_2O-\overset{O}{\overset{\|}{C}}CH_2CH_2CH_2CH_2CH_2CH_2CH_2CH_2CH_2CH_2CH_2CH_2CH_2CH_2CH_2CH_2CH_3 \end{array}$$

FIGURE 17.7
Structure of a typical fat.

SAMPLE EXERCISE 17.4

Name the compound below. Is it a soap, a biodegradable detergent, or a non-biodegradable detergent?

$$CH_3CH_2CH_2CH_2CH_2CH_2CH_2CH_2CH_2CH_2-C_6H_4-\overset{O}{\overset{\|}{\underset{\underset{O}{\|}}{S}}}-OK$$

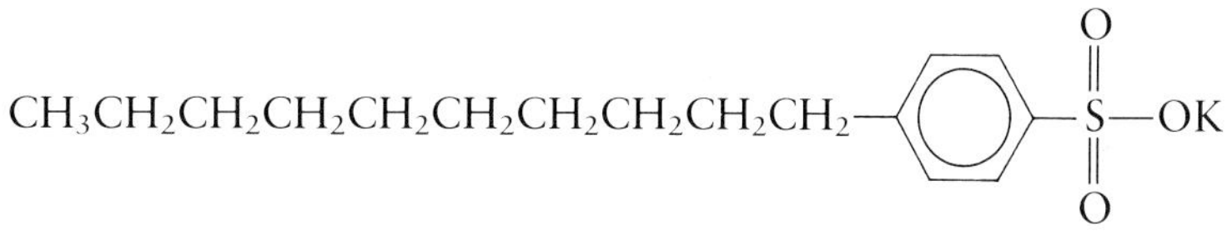

Solution:

This compound is a potassium alkylbenzenesulfonate. The alkyl group is $C_{10}H_{21}$ (decyl) and the full name is potassium decylbenzenesulfonate. It is a biodegradable detergent because the hydrocarbon chain is linear.

EXERCISE 17.4

Many shampoos contain the detergent sodium laurylbenzenesulfonate. If the lauryl group is a straight-chain alkyl group with 12 C atoms, draw the structure of this shampoo ingredient.

17.7 ESTERS

Other acids such as sulfonic acids and phosphoric acid also form esters.

Carboxylic acids react with alcohols in the presence of an acid catalyst to form compounds called **esters.** Let us write the product of the reaction for the ester that forms when an alcohol R′OH is allowed to react with an acid RCOOH. To write an esterification reaction it is helpful to draw the reactant formulas so that their reactive ends are pointing toward each other. To visualize the products that form we can "lasso out" a molecule of water, as shown below.

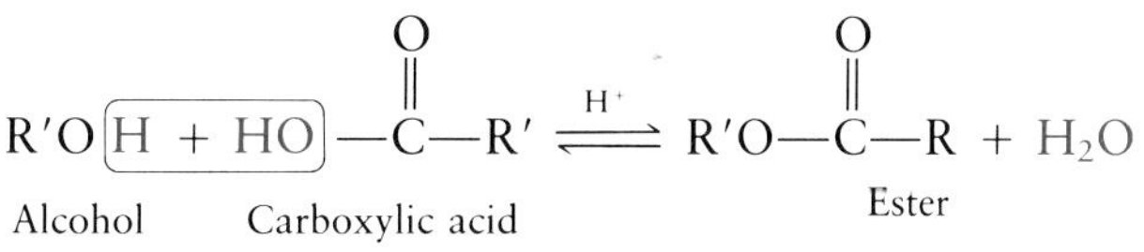

$$\underset{\text{Alcohol}}{R'O}\boxed{H + HO}\underset{\text{Carboxylic acid}}{-\overset{O}{\overset{\|}{C}}-R'} \overset{H^+}{\rightleftharpoons} \underset{\text{Ester}}{R'O-\overset{O}{\overset{\|}{C}}-R} + H_2O$$

The alkoxy group (R′O) then bonds to the $\overset{O}{\overset{\|}{C}}$—R group to form the ester product. A reaction such as this, in which two reactant molecule combine and a small molecule (such as water) splits out, is known as a **condensation reaction.** The ester formation reaction is a reversible one and can be driven to the right to form the ester product by removal of water, according to LeChatelier's principle (Section 10.9).

Natural O contains 99.76% O-16, 0.20% O-18, and 0.04% 0-17. (Table 3.4)

Note that we removed the O atom from the acid molecule rather than from the alcohol. An experiment using O-18 atoms has been used to confirm the source of the O in the water product. Suppose we use an alcohol reactant in which all the O atoms are O-18 atoms instead of the natural mixture of O atoms normally present. It is possible to detect the presence of O-18. If the O-18 turns up in the water, that means that the O atoms must have come from the alcohol and not the acid; and conversely if the O-18 is detected in the ester, it means that the water O atoms must have come from the carboxylic acid. The O-18 is found to be in the ester (not in the water) and therefore must have come from the labeled alcohol:

$$RO^{18}\boxed{H + HO}—\overset{O}{\overset{\|}{C}}—R' \overset{H^+}{\rightleftharpoons} RO^{18}—\overset{O}{\overset{\|}{C}}—R' + H_2O$$

Note that the RO portion of the ester molecule in color below comes from the alcohol and the $\overset{O}{\overset{\|}{C}}R'$ part from the acid.

from the alcohol from the acid

$$\underset{\text{Alcohol}}{RO}\boxed{H + HO}\underset{\text{Acid}}{\overset{O}{\overset{\|}{C}}R'} \overset{H^+}{\rightleftharpoons} \underset{\text{Ester}}{RO\overset{O}{\overset{\|}{C}}R'} + H_2O$$

Naming Esters

Esters are named as *alkylcarboxylates*. The alkyl part of the name is derived from the alcohol reactant (named as an alkyl alcohol) and the carboxylate part from the carboxylic acid reactant. For instance, the reaction between acetic acid and ethanol yields the following ester:

from ethyl alcohol from acetic acid

$$\underset{\text{Ethyl alcohol}}{CH_3CH_2OH} + \underset{\substack{\text{Acetic acid} \\ \text{(ethanoic acid)}}}{HO\overset{O}{\overset{\|}{C}}CH_3} \overset{H^+}{\rightleftharpoons} \underset{\substack{\text{Ethyl acetate} \\ \text{(ethyl ethanoate)}}}{CH_3CH_2O\overset{O}{\overset{\|}{C}}CH_3} + H_2O$$

The first part of the name is ethyl from *ethyl* alcohol and the last part is *acetate* from acetic acid. This compound is nearly always called ethyl acetate, even though the IUPAC name is ethyl ethanoate.

We can name esters without seeing the chemical equation by noting what alkyl group is attached to an oxygen atom and identifying the acid that contributes the remaining hydrocarbon portion of the molecule. For instance, the ester below is named propyl butanoate (or propyl butyrate) since a propyl group is bonded to the ester oxygen atom, which means that that portion in color is from propyl alcohol. Butanoic acid is the source of the remaining hydrocarbon fragment.

from propyl alcohol — from butanoic acid

$$CH_3CH_2CH_2O\overset{\overset{\displaystyle O}{\|}}{C}CH_2CH_2CH_3$$

Propyl butanoate

SAMPLE EXERCISE 17.5

Write the reaction for the formation of octyl acetate, one of many substances responsible for the flavor of an orange.

Solution:

Write the reaction of octyl alcohol (from octyl) with acetic acid (from acetate).

$$\underset{\text{Octyl alcohol}}{CH_3(CH_2)_6CH_2O}\boxed{H + HO}\underset{\text{Acetic acid}}{\overset{\overset{\displaystyle O}{\|}}{C}CH_3} \overset{H^+}{\rightleftharpoons} \underset{\text{Octyl acetate}}{CH_3(CH_2)_6CH_2O\overset{\overset{\displaystyle O}{\|}}{C}CH_3} + H_2O$$

EXERCISE 17.5

Give the formula and name of the ester compound (occurring in peaches and apricots) formed from the reaction of ethanol with butanoic acid.

Physical Properties of Esters

In the examples above we have mentioned some esters that are components of flavorings in fruits. In general, esters have pleasant fruity odors and are used in artificial flavorings and perfumes. Table 17.6 lists the names, formulas, and odors of some of these. Like ketones, esters, which have both polar and nonpolar groups, are excellent solvents. In Section 16.4 we said that acetone (a ketone) is an ingredient in nail polish removers. In fact, ethyl acetate is even more commonly used for such products.

TABLE 17.6 **FORMULAS, NAMES, AND SOURCES OF ESTERS**

Formula	Name	Source
* $CH_3CH_2OC(=O)CH_3$	Ethyl acetate	Apples and other fruits
$CH_3CH_2OC(=O)CH_2CH_2CH_3$	Ethyl butanoate	Peaches and apricots
$CH_3CH_2OC(=O)(CH_2)_5CH_3$	Ethyl heptanoate	Wine bouquet
$CH_3CH(CH_3)CH_2CH_2OC(=O)CH_3$	Isopentyl acetate (isoamyl acetate)	Bananas
$CH_3CH_2OC(=O)H$	Ethyl formate	Rum
$CH_3OC(=O)C_6H_4OH$ (HO ortho on ring)	Methyl salicylate	Wintergreen
$CH_3(CH_2)_7OC(=O)CH_3$	Octyl acetate	Orange

*The colored part of each ester is derived from an alcohol.

Chemical Properties of Esters

An ester can be converted back into the original alcohol and carboxylic acid (or its salt) from which it was formed by reaction with water. This type of reaction, in which water acts to break down a compound into its original components, is known as **hydrolysis.** If we start with an ester, $R\overset{O}{\overset{\|}{C}}OR'$, the products are the acid $R\overset{O}{\overset{\|}{C}}OH$ and the alcohol R′OH.

$$R\overset{O}{\overset{\|}{C}}OR' + H_2O \rightleftharpoons R\overset{O}{\overset{\|}{C}}OH + R'OH$$

The hydrolysis of esters requires an acid or a base as catalyst, along with the water reactant. If the catalyst is a base, one product will be the sodium salt of the carboxylic acid instead of the acid itself, and the reaction will be irreversible.

The reaction shown below describes the hydrolysis of ethyl acetate by aqueous sodium hydroxide to form the products ethanol and sodium acetate.

$$\underset{\text{Ethyl acetate}}{CH_3\overset{\overset{\displaystyle O}{\|}}{C}OCH_2CH_3} + H_2O \xrightarrow{NaOH} \underset{\text{Sodium acetate}}{CH_3\overset{\overset{\displaystyle O}{\|}}{C}ONa} + \underset{\text{Ethanol}}{CH_3CH_2OH}$$

In Latin *sapo* means soap.

Base-catalyzed ester hydrolysis is called **saponification,** because such reactions are "soap-making" reactions. Soap compounds such as sodium stearate, $CH_3(CH_2)_{16}COONa$, are produced by the hydrolysis of fat molecules, which have three ester functional groups (see Figure 17.7). We will talk about fats and their hydrolysis in Chapter 22 (Lipids).

SAMPLE EXERCISE 17.6

Give the reaction for the formation and the base-catalyzed hydrolysis of methyl salicylate, oil of wintergreen.

Solution:

Methyl salicylate forms from salicylic acid and methanol.

$$\underset{\text{Methanol}}{CH_3OH} + \underset{\text{Salicylic acid}}{HO\overset{\overset{\displaystyle O}{\|}}{C}-C_6H_4(OH)} \overset{H^+}{\rightleftharpoons} \underset{\text{Methyl salicylate}}{CH_3O\overset{\overset{\displaystyle O}{\|}}{C}-C_6H_4(OH)} + H_2O$$

The hydrolysis of methyl salicylate regenerates the methanol and produces the sodium salt of salicylic acid.

$$\underset{\text{Methyl salicylate}}{CH_3O\overset{\overset{\displaystyle O}{\|}}{C}-C_6H_4(OH)} + H_2O \xrightarrow{NaOH} \underset{\text{Sodium salicylate}}{NaO\overset{\overset{\displaystyle O}{\|}}{C}-C_6H_4(OH)} + \underset{\text{Methanol}}{CH_3OH}$$

EXERCISE 17.6

A base-catalyzed ester hydrolysis produces ethanol and potassium stearate, a very soft soap used in shaving creams. What was the original ester?

17.8 AMIDES

Carboxylic acids can react with ammonia (NH_3) to form nitrogen-containing organic compounds called **amides.** Since ammonia is a base (Section 11.3) and carboxylic acids are acidic, the first step in the amide preparation is an acid-base reaction. The carboxylic acid proton is accepted by the ammonia to form the ammonium ion and the product is the ammonium salt of the carboxylic acid.

$$\underset{\text{Acid}}{R-\overset{\overset{O}{\|}}{C}-OH} + \underset{\text{Base}}{NH_3} \longrightarrow \underset{\text{Ammonium carboxylate}}{R-\overset{\overset{O}{\|}}{C}-ONH_4}$$

When the ammonium carboxylate salt is heated, it dehydrates, a molecule of water is released, and the amide forms.

$$\underset{\text{Ammonium carboxylate}}{R-\overset{\overset{O}{\|}}{C}-ONH_4} \xrightarrow{\Delta} \underset{\text{Amide}}{R-\overset{\overset{O}{\|}}{C}-NH_2} + H_2O$$

We can also write the amide formation as though it occurred as a single-step condensation reaction in which the carboxylic acid and ammonia react with the loss of a molecule of water.

$$\underset{\text{Carboxylic acid}}{R-\overset{\overset{O}{\|}}{C}-\boxed{OH + H}}\underset{\text{Ammonia}}{-\underset{\underset{H}{|}}{N}-H} \xrightarrow{\Delta} \underset{\text{Amide}}{R-\overset{\overset{O}{\|}}{C}-\underset{\underset{H}{|}}{N}-H} + H_2O$$

For instance, when acetic acid reacts with ammonia, the product is the amide called acetamide.

$$\underset{\text{Acetic acid}}{CH_3-\overset{\overset{O}{\|}}{C}-\boxed{OH + H}}-\underset{\underset{H}{|}}{N}-H \xrightarrow{\Delta} \underset{\text{Acetamide}}{CH_3-\overset{\overset{O}{\|}}{C}-\underset{\underset{H}{|}}{N}-H} + H_2O$$

Amide names such as acetamide are derived by dropping the *-ic* from a common acid name or the *-oic* from an IUPAC acid name and then adding *-amide.* Thus acetic acid becomes acetamide and ethanoic acid becomes ethanamide.

Carboxylic acids can also react with an organic ammonia derivative called an *amine,* in which one or more ammonia H atoms are replaced by hydrocarbon groups. The products of reactions such as this are called *substituted amides.*

$$\underset{\text{Carboxylic acid}}{R-\overset{\overset{O}{\|}}{C}-\boxed{OH + H}}\underset{\text{Amine}}{-\underset{\underset{H}{|}}{N}-R} \xrightarrow{\Delta} \underset{\text{Substituted amide}}{R-\overset{\overset{O}{\|}}{C}-\underset{\underset{H}{|}}{N}-R} + H_2O$$

We will learn how to name substituted amides in Chapter 18, where the chemistry of amines is discussed.

Properties of Amides

Amines are weak bases and amides are neutral.

Amides are not particularly acidic or basic. Their structures appear to be similar to those of amines because both include an N atom bonded to two H atoms, called the *amino group*. In Chapter 11 you saw that methylamine, CH_3NH_2, behaves as a weak base. In general it is true that all amines, like ammonia, accept protons and are basic. The difference in the structures of amines and amides is that amides have a carbonyl group bonded to an N atom. The presence of the carbonyl group makes it very difficult for the amide N atom to accept a proton because the electronegative O atom of the carbonyl group attracts the nonbonding electron pair of the amide N. Because of this phenomenon, known as electron withdrawal, the electron pair is less available for bonding to a proton, as shown in Figure 17.8.

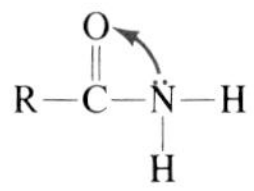

$$R-\overset{\overset{\large O}{\|}}{C}-\ddot{N}-H \quad (\text{N attached to H below; arrow from N lone pair toward O})$$

FIGURE 17.8

Since amides contain N to H bonds, they are thus able to participate in hydrogen bonding (see Section 4.16). A hydrogen bond between two amide molecules forms when an amide H atom of one molecule is attracted to the carboxyl O atom of a neighboring molecule.

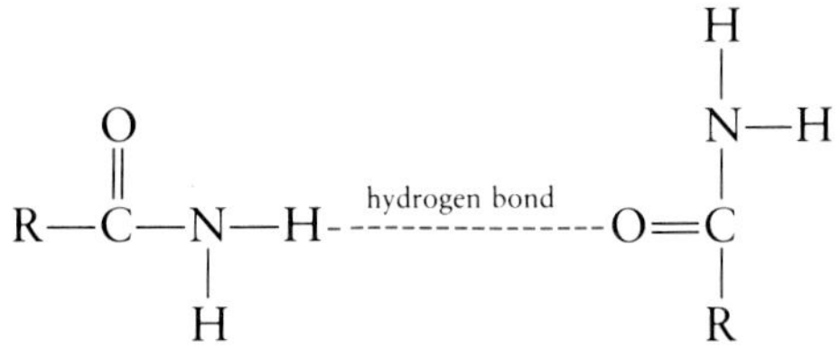

$$R-\overset{\overset{\large O}{\|}}{C}-\underset{\underset{\large H}{|}}{N}-H \cdots\cdots\overset{\text{hydrogen bond}}{\cdots\cdots} O=\underset{\underset{\large R}{|}}{\overset{\overset{\large H-N-H}{|}}{C}}$$

Because of hydrogen bonding amides have unusually high boiling points, and except for formamide ($H\overset{\overset{O}{\|}}{C}NH_2$) they are all solids. We will encounter hydrogen bonding among amide molecules again in Chapter 23 when we discuss *proteins*, polymer molecules in which the monomer units are joined by amide linkages.

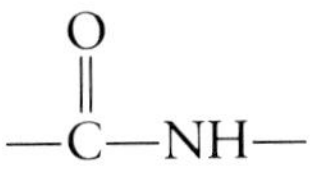

$$-\overset{\overset{\large O}{\|}}{C}-NH-$$

Amide linkage

Amides can be hydrolyzed upon vigorous heating in the presence of water and acidic or basic catalysts to regenerate the original acid and ammonia (or an amine). In the acid-catalyzed reactions below, the ammonia appears in the form of the ammonium ion, NH_4^+.

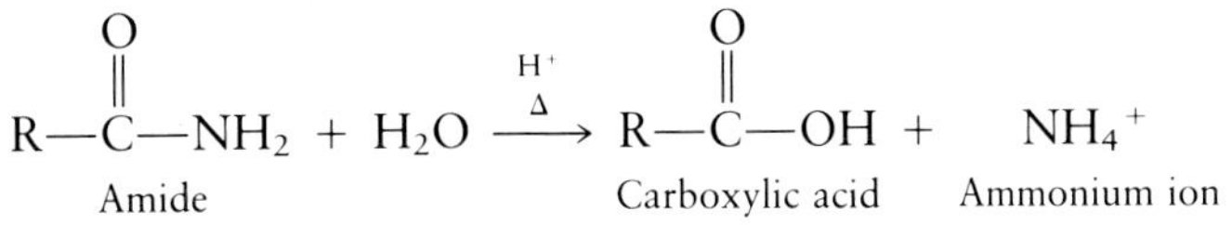

$$\underset{\text{Amide}}{R-\overset{\overset{\large O}{\|}}{C}-NH_2} + H_2O \xrightarrow[\Delta]{H^+} \underset{\text{Carboxylic acid}}{R-\overset{\overset{\large O}{\|}}{C}-OH} + \underset{\text{Ammonium ion}}{NH_4^+}$$

For instance, we can write the reaction for the hydrolysis of acetamide to produce acetic acid and ammonium ion.

$$\underset{\text{Acetamide}}{CH_3\overset{\overset{\displaystyle O}{\|}}{C}NH_2} + H_2O \xrightarrow[\Delta]{H^+} \underset{\text{Acetic acid}}{CH_3\overset{\overset{\displaystyle O}{\|}}{C}OH} + \underset{\text{Ammonium ion}}{NH_4^+}$$

In living systems protein molecules are broken down by hydrolysis of amide linkages with the assistance of enzymes present in the stomach and intestines.

SAMPLE EXERCISE 17.7

Write the reaction for the formation of propanamide from propanoic acid.

Solution:

The formula of propanoic acid is $CH_3CH_2\overset{\overset{\displaystyle O}{\|}}{C}OH$. The other reactant is NH_3. Writing the condensation reaction in one step,

$$\underset{\text{Propanoic acid}}{CH_3CH_2\overset{\overset{\displaystyle O}{\|}}{C}—}\boxed{OH + H}\underset{\text{Ammonia}}{—\underset{\underset{\displaystyle H}{|}}{N}—H} \xrightarrow{\Delta} \underset{\text{Propanamide}}{CH_3CH_2\overset{\overset{\displaystyle O}{\|}}{C}—\underset{\underset{\displaystyle H}{|}}{N}—H} + H_2O$$

EXERCISE 17.7

Write the reaction for the acid-catalyzed hydrolysis of butanamide.

17.9 ACYL CHLORIDES AND ACID ANHYDRIDES

The reactions of carboxylic acids with alcohols (to produce esters) and with ammonia (to give amides) are slow and impractical to perform in the laboratory. Instead, chemists use either of two more reactive carboxylic acid derivatives, *acyl chlorides* and *acid anhydrides*.

Acyl Chlorides

Acyl chlorides, in which the carboxyl OH group is replaced with a chlorine atom, are produced easily by reaction of carboxylic acids with phosphorus trichloride (PCl_3).

$$\mathrm{R{-}\overset{\overset{\displaystyle O}{\|}}{C}{-}OH + PCl_3 \longrightarrow \underset{\text{Acyl chloride}}{R{-}\overset{\overset{\displaystyle O}{\|}}{C}{-}Cl} + H_3PO_3} \qquad \text{(unbalanced)}$$

The acyl group name is derived by dropping the *-ic* from the carboxylic name and adding *-yl*. Thus the product of the reaction of acet*ic acid* and PCl_3 is acet*yl chloride*.

$$\mathrm{\underset{\text{Acetic acid}}{CH_3\overset{\overset{\displaystyle O}{\|}}{C}OH} + PCl_3 \longrightarrow \underset{\text{Acetyl chloride}}{CH_3\overset{\overset{\displaystyle O}{\|}}{C}Cl} + H_3PO_3} \qquad \text{(unbalanced)}$$

Acyl chlorides are liquids with irritating, unpleasant odors. Chemically they are quite reactive and are usually used in place of carboxylic acids to prepare esters and amides. In these reactions an HCl molecule (instead of a water molecule) is the product of the condensation.

$$\mathrm{\underset{\text{Alcohol}}{RO\boxed{H + Cl}}{-}\underset{\text{Acyl chloride}}{\overset{\overset{\displaystyle O}{\|}}{C}{-}R'} \longrightarrow \underset{\text{Ester}}{RO{-}\overset{\overset{\displaystyle O}{\|}}{C}{-}R'} + HCl}$$

$$\mathrm{\underset{\text{Ammonia}}{H{-}\overset{\overset{\displaystyle H}{|}}{N}{-}}\boxed{H + Cl}{-}\underset{\text{Acyl chloride}}{\overset{\overset{\displaystyle O}{\|}}{C}{-}R'} \longrightarrow \underset{\text{Amide}}{H{-}\overset{\overset{\displaystyle H}{|}}{N}{-}\overset{\overset{\displaystyle O}{\|}}{C}{-}R'} + HCl}$$

Acyl chlorides are so reactive that it is difficult to store them without decomposition. They are converted back into carboxylic acids by hydrolysis, a reaction which can occur spontaneously in moist air.

$$\mathrm{\underset{\text{Acyl chloride}}{R{-}\overset{\overset{\displaystyle O}{\|}}{C}{-}Cl} + H_2O \longrightarrow \underset{\text{Carboxylic acid}}{R{-}\overset{\overset{\displaystyle O}{\|}}{C}{-}OH} + HCl}$$

Acid Anhydrides

To draw the structure of a carboxylic acid anhydride we join two carboxylic acid molecules by removing a molecule of water:

$$\mathrm{R{-}\overset{\overset{\displaystyle O}{\|}}{C}{-}\boxed{OH \quad H}O{-}\overset{\overset{\displaystyle O}{\|}}{C}{-}R \longrightarrow \underset{\text{Acid anhydride}}{R{-}\overset{\overset{\displaystyle O}{\|}}{C}{-}O{-}\overset{\overset{\displaystyle O}{\|}}{C}{-}R} + HOH}$$

The name of the acid anhydride is the name of the carboxylic acid used to form it with the word *acid* replaced by *anhydride*. The most important acid anhydride is acetic anhydride.

$$\underset{\text{Acetic anhydride}}{CH_3\overset{O}{\overset{\|}{C}}O\overset{O}{\overset{\|}{C}}CH_3}$$

Like acetyl chloride, acetic anhydride reacts with alcohols to form esters. The products include a molecule of acetic acid instead of HCl (when using acetyl chloride) or H_2O (when using acetic acid). Unlike acetyl chloride, acetic anhydride is easy to handle. The reaction of acetic anhydride with the *hydroxyl group* of salicylic acid produces acetylsalicylic acid (*aspirin*) and acetic acid, a reaction conveniently done in student laboratories.

$$\underset{\text{Salicyclic acid}}{HO\text{-}C_6H_4\text{-}\overset{O}{\overset{\|}{C}}OH} + \underset{\text{Acetic anhydride}}{CH_3\overset{O}{\overset{\|}{C}}O\overset{O}{\overset{\|}{C}}CH_3} \longrightarrow \underset{\text{Acetylsalicylic acid}}{CH_3\overset{O}{\overset{\|}{C}}O\text{-}C_6H_4\text{-}\overset{O}{\overset{\|}{C}}OH} + \underset{\text{Acetic acid}}{CH_3\overset{O}{\overset{\|}{C}}OH}$$

Note that salicylic acid is the alcohol reactant in this ester formation reaction; its carboxyl group is not involved.

SAMPLE EXERCISE 17.8

Write the reaction for the formation of methyl propanoate using an acyl chloride as one reactant.

Solution:

We need to use propanoyl chloride (instead of propanoic acid) and methanol.

$$\underset{\text{Methanol}}{CH_3O\boxed{H\ +}} \underset{\text{Propanoyl chloride}}{\boxed{Cl}\overset{O}{\overset{\|}{C}}CH_2CH_3} \longrightarrow \underset{\text{Methyl propanoate}}{CH_3O\overset{O}{\overset{\|}{C}}CH_2CH_3} + HCl$$

EXERCISE 17.8

What acyl chloride and what alcohol would be needed to make ethyl pentanoate?

The structures of the carboxylic acid derivatives discussed thus far are shown in Figure 17.9.

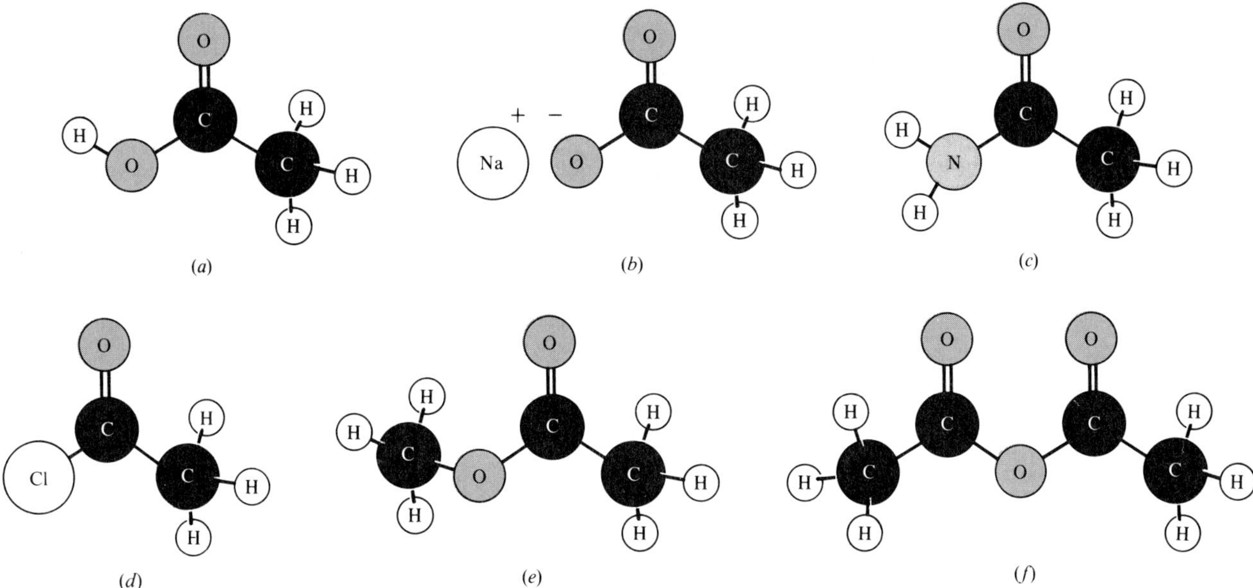

FIGURE 17.9
Carboxylic acid derivatives: (*a*) Ethanoic, or acetic, acid; (*b*) sodium ethanoate, or sodium acetate; (*c*) ethanamide, or acetamide; (*d*) ethanoyl chloride, or acetyl chloride; (*e*) methyl ethanoate, or methyl acetate; (*f*) ethanoyl anhydride, or acetic anhydride.

17.10 IMPORTANT CARBOXYLIC ACIDS AND DERIVATIVES

Here we will take a closer look at the properties of some carboxylic acids, including citric acid and salicylic acid and their derivatives, compounds which can be found in a variety of products used for therapeutic purposes.

Acetic Acid

One source of acetic acid is the oxidation of ethanol found in fermented fruit juices. In the presence of air and bacteria of the genus called *Acetobacter*, which contain the necessary enzymes, the ethanol is oxidized to acetic acid.

$$CH_3CH_2OH + O_2 \xrightarrow[\text{acetobacter}]{\text{air}} CH_3\overset{\overset{\displaystyle O}{\|}}{C}OH + H_2O$$

This reaction is responsible for the sour flavor of spoiled wine.

You are most familiar with acetic acid in 5% aqueous solutions as vinegar. In its pure form acetic acid is called *glacial* acetic acid because it looks like an icy solid on cold days (it melts at 16°C). Glacial acetic acid has an overpoweringly sour odor.

Formic Acid

Originally formic acid was actually prepared by distilling ants. Today it is made from sodium hydroxide and carbon monoxide, which under conditions of high pressure and temperature react to product sodium formate.

$$CO + NaOH \xrightarrow[6\text{–}10\ \text{atm}]{200°C} \underset{\text{Sodium formate}}{HC(=O)ONa}$$

Reaction of sodium formate with sulfuric acid gives formic acid.

$$\underset{\text{Sodium formate}}{HC(=O)ONa} + H_2SO_4 \longrightarrow \underset{\text{Formic acid}}{HC(=O)OH} + NaHSO_4$$

Formic acid is used to make esters such as ethyl formate, a flavoring listed in Table 17.6.

Citric Acid

One Alka-Seltzer effervescent antacid tablet contains 1.008 g $NaHCO_3$, 0.300 g $KHCO_3$, and 0.800 g citric acid.

Citric acid (Section 17.3) is a sour-tasting white solid which is a common component of plant and animal tissues. Particularly high concentrations of citric acid are found in citrus fruits. Citric acid is the ingredient added to create the fizzing action of some antacid tablets by releasing CO_2 from sodium bicarbonate, $NaHCO_3$.

$$3NaHCO_3 + \underset{\text{Citric acid}}{HO\text{—}C(CH_2C(=O)OH)_2\text{—}C(=O)OH} \longrightarrow \underset{\text{Sodium citrate}}{HO\text{—}C(CH_2C(=O)ONa)_2\text{—}C(=O)ONa} + 3CO_2 + 3H_2O$$

Some of the $NaHCO_3$ is left unneutralized to behave as an antacid. The bicarbonate ion, HCO_3^- accepts protons to neutralize the HCl in stomach acid. The sodium citrate that forms is also basic (see Table 11.2) and thus the citrate ion provides additional antacid action according to the neutralization reaction below:

The citrate ion accepts protons.

$$\underset{\text{Citrate ion}}{HO\text{—}C(CH_2C(=O)O^-)_2\text{—}C(=O)O^-} + 3HCl \longrightarrow \underset{\text{Citric acid}}{HO\text{—}C(CH_2C(=O)OH)_2\text{—}C(=O)OH} + 3Cl^-$$

As mentioned previously, citric acid is a metabolic intermediate in the path (tricarboxylic acid cycle) by which foodstuffs are converted into energy.

Salicylic Acid

Many derivatives of salicylic acid have analgesic (pain-killing) properties.

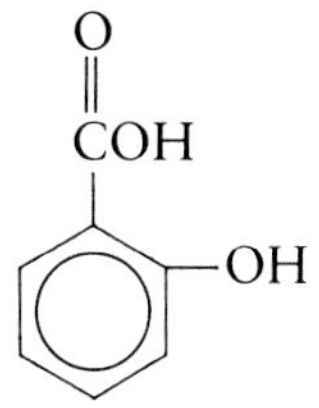

Salicylic acid

Some medicated acne creams contain salicylic acid to peel away dead skin tissue.

Salicylic acid itself is a pain-killer, but it cannot be taken internally because it is destructive to tissues. Salicylic acid is the active ingredient in medicated disks used to remove corns.

In the previous section you saw that the hydroxyl H atom of salicylic acid can be replaced by an acetyl group to form acetylsalicylic acid, the compound better known as aspirin.

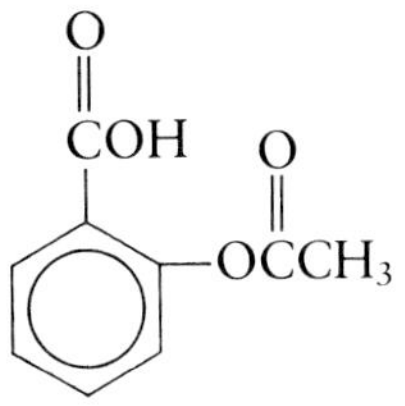

Acetylsalicylic acid (aspirin)

Aspirin is the most widely used of all analgesics. In body fluids aspirin undergoes hydrolysis to produce two carboxylic acids, salicylic acid and acetic acid.

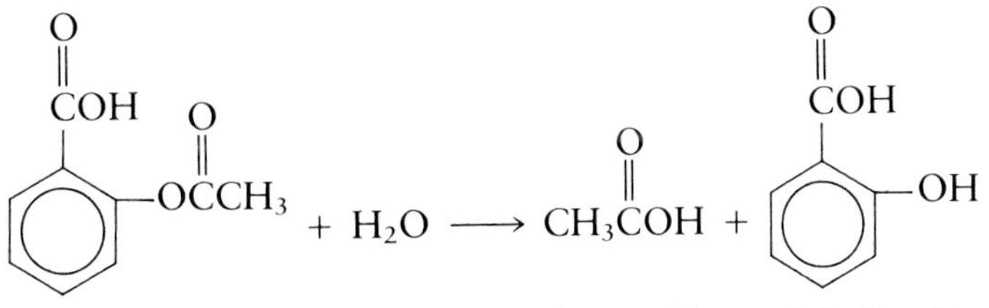

$$\text{Acetylsalicylic acid} + H_2O \longrightarrow CH_3\overset{O}{\overset{\|}{C}}OH + \text{Salicylic acid}$$

Acetylsalicylic acid Acetic acid Salicylic acid

Other basic substances added to aspirin products are $Mg(OH)_2$ and $Al(OH)_3$.

These acids can cause heartburn or stomach acidity. In the case of excessive aspirin use, ulcers can result from the action of salicylic acid. Some aspirin products are buffered with basic substances such as magnesium carbonate ($MgCO_3$) to help neutralize the acidic hydrolysis products and prevent stomach upset.

Another salicylic acid derivative which has analgesic action is salicylamide.

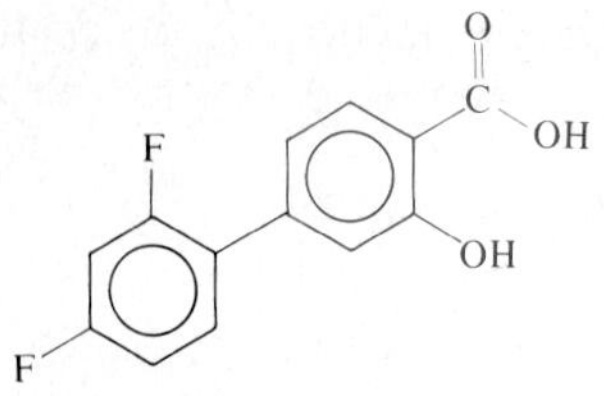

FIGURE 17.10
The structure of 4-(2,4-diflurophenyl)salicylic acid, a compound that exhibits potent analgesic action.

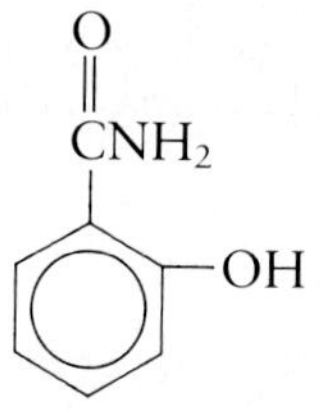

Salicylamide

Since salicylamide does not include the acetyl group as aspirin does, it does not produce acetic acid upon hydrolysis and may cause less stomach upset than aspirin.

The salicylic acid derivative shown in Figure 17.10, 4-(2,4-difluorophenyl)salicylic acid, called diflunisal, is supposed to be more potent and longer-lasting than aspirin.

Table 17.7 lists the ingredients present in some over-the-counter analgesic drugs. Persons who are allergic to salicylates must be particularly careful about which ones to use.

TABLE 17.7 **SOME INGREDIENTS IN OVER-THE-COUNTER ANALGESICS**

Product	Ingredients*
Bufferin	Acetylsalicylic acid, magnesium carbonate
Bayer aspirin	Acetylsalicylic acid
Excedrin	Acetylsalicylic acid, caffeine, acetominophen†
Excedrin P.M.	Acetylsalicylic acid, acetominophen†, pyrilamine maleate (an antihistamine)
Empirin	Acetylsalicylic acid, caffeine
Anacin	Acetylsalicylic acid, caffeine
Tylenol	Acetominophen†
Datril	Acetominophen†
Os-Cal-Gesic	Salicylamide, calcium (from oyster shell), vitamin D
Dolobid	4-(2,4-Difluorophenylsalicylic) acid

*Salicylic acid derivatives are in color.
†Acetominophen, which can be classified as a substituted amide, is another analgesic with the formula shown:

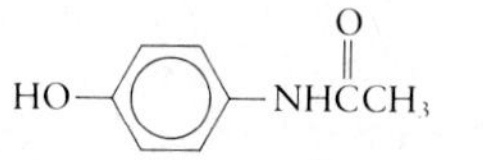

$$HO-C_6H_4-NHCCH_3$$

SUMMARY

A carboxylic acid has the formula $R\overset{\overset{O}{\|}}{C}OH$, in which R (a hydrogen atom or hydrocarbon group) is bonded to the carboxyl group, $\overset{\overset{O}{\|}}{C}OH$.

The IUPAC name for a carboxylic acid is derived by dropping the *-e* from the name of the alkane with the same total number of C atoms and adding *-oic acid.* Common names are frequently used for low-formula-weight acids and for those which have an even number of C atoms. Dicarboxylic acids are named as alkanedioic acids according to the IUPAC system but are more often referred to by a set of common names.

Carboxylic acids exist as dimers stabilized by two hydrogen bonds between each pair of molecules. Because of this they have unusually high boiling points. Carboxylic acids can form hydrogen bonds with water, and those with fewer than five C atoms are water-soluble.

Many of the reactions of carboxylic acids are related to the acidity of the carboxyl group H atom. On reaction with strong bases such as NaOH, carboxylic acids are neutralized to form salts. Salts are named by combining the name of the cation with that of the carboxylate anion, produced by dropping the *-ic acid* from the carboxylic acid name and adding *-ate.* Salts with very long hydrocarbon chains are soaps. The nonpolar hydrocarbon end dissolves in the dirt while the polar carboxylate end dissolves in water. Collections of soap molecules trap dirt in this way by forming spherical micelles, which can be washed away.

Detergents are salts of sulfonic acids ($R\overset{\overset{O}{\|}}{\underset{\underset{O}{\|}}{S}}OH$) which work in the same way that soaps do, with one difference. Detergent salts are much more water-soluble than soaps and will not leave a film on objects washed in hard water.

When a carboxylic acid reacts with ammonia, the ammonium salt forms first and upon heating is dehydrated to form an amide, $R\overset{\overset{O}{\|}}{C}NH_2$. Amides, which are named as alkanamides, are not particularly basic or acidic. Most are solids because of hydrogen bonding between H atoms of one molecule and carboxyl O atoms of a neighboring molecule. Amides can be hydrolyzed to produce ammonia and a carboxylic acid.

The reaction of a carboxylic acid ($R\overset{\overset{O}{\|}}{C}OH$) and an alcohol (R′OH) in the presence of an acid catalyst gives an ester with the formula $R\overset{\overset{O}{\|}}{C}OR'$. The ester is named as an alkyl (from the name of the alcohol reactant) carboxylate (from the name of the acid). Esters have a pleasant fruity odor and are used in flavorings and perfumes. Upon hydrolysis esters can be broken down to produce the original alcohol and the carboxylic acid (or its salt).

An acyl chloride, $R\overset{\overset{O}{\|}}{C}Cl$, forms when PCl_3 reacts with a carboxylic acid. These very reactive compounds are used in place of carboxylic acids to prepare esters or amides, yielding an HCl molecule instead of H_2O. Acid anhydrides consist of two carboxylic acid molecules joined with the loss of a water molecule. Acetic anhydride reacts with an alcohol to give an ester and acetic acid.

KEY WORDS

carboxylic acid
carboxyl group
dicarboxylic acid
tricarboxylic acid
carboxylate anion
soap
detergent
sulfonic acid
micelle
ester
condensation reaction
amide
hydrolysis reaction
saponification
acyl chloride
acid anhydride

EXERCISES

17.9 Write the general formula for a carboxylic acid, making sure to specify the identity of any R group that you include.

17.10 Name the following carboxylic acids, using both common and IUPAC names:

(a) 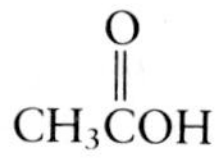 $CH_3\overset{O}{\overset{\|}{C}}OH$ (b) $CH_3(CH_2)_{10}\overset{O}{\overset{\|}{C}}OH$

(c) $CH_3\underset{OH}{\underset{|}{C}}HCH_2\overset{O}{\overset{\|}{C}}OH$ (d) 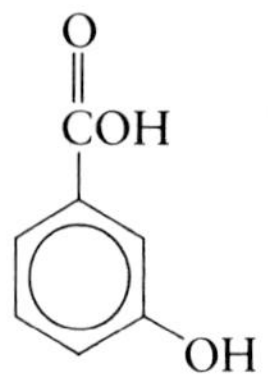 $\overset{O}{\overset{\|}{C}}OH$ attached to a benzene ring bearing OH (meta)

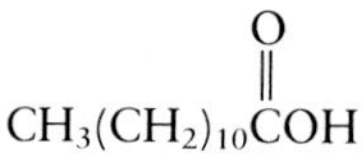

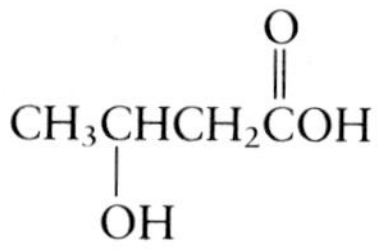

(e) 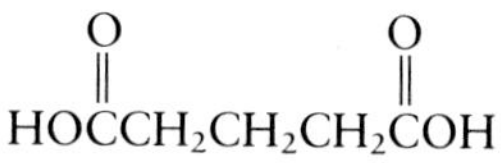 $HO\overset{O}{\overset{\|}{C}}CH_2CH_2CH_2\overset{O}{\overset{\|}{C}}OH$

17.11 Name the following carboxylic acids, using both common and IUPAC names:

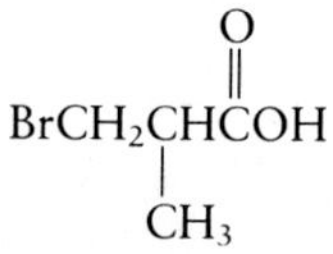

(a) 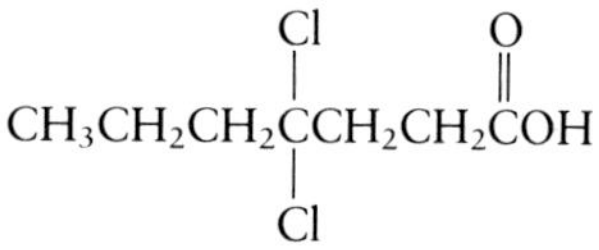 $CH_3CH_2CH_2\underset{Cl}{\underset{|}{\overset{Cl}{\overset{|}{C}}}}CH_2CH_2\overset{O}{\overset{\|}{C}}OH$

(b) $BrCH_2\underset{CH_3}{\underset{|}{C}}H\overset{O}{\overset{\|}{C}}OH$ (c) $\overset{O}{\overset{\|}{C}}OH$ attached to a benzene ring bearing CH_3 (ortho)

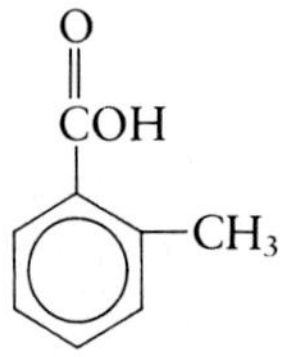

(d) 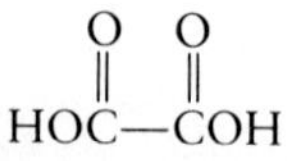 $HO\overset{O}{\overset{\|}{C}}-\overset{O}{\overset{\|}{C}}OH$

17.12 The compound below is sometimes abbreviated TFA. From what name is this abbreviation derived?

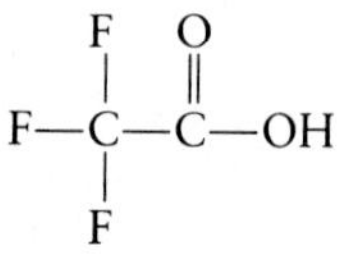

$$F-\underset{F}{\underset{|}{\overset{F}{\overset{|}{C}}}}-\overset{O}{\overset{\|}{C}}-OH$$

17.13 The following compounds are all building blocks for proteins in living things. Give their common and IUPAC names. (Recall from Table 14.2 that the NH_2-group is called amino.) What structural features do they all have in common?

(a) 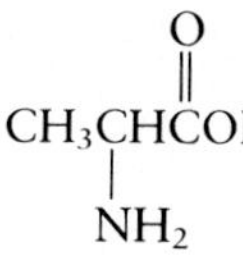 $CH_3\underset{NH_2}{\underset{|}{C}}H\overset{O}{\overset{\|}{C}}OH$ (alanine)

(b) 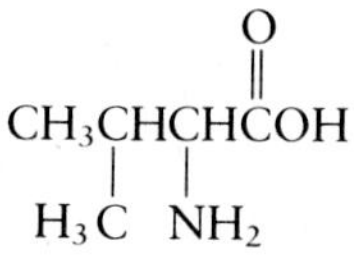 $CH_3\underset{H_3C}{\underset{|}{C}}H\underset{NH_2}{\underset{|}{C}}H\overset{O}{\overset{\|}{C}}OH$ (valine)

(c) 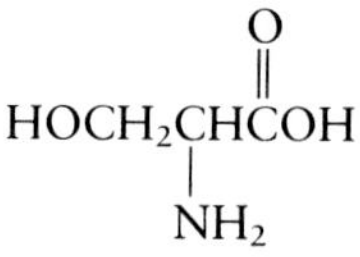 $HOCH_2\underset{NH_2}{\underset{|}{C}}H\overset{O}{\overset{\|}{C}}OH$ (serine)

(d) 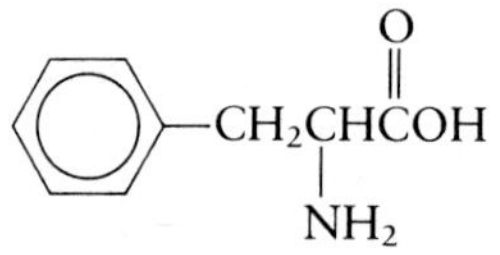 $C_6H_5-CH_2\underset{NH_2}{\underset{|}{C}}H\overset{O}{\overset{\|}{C}}OH$ (phenylalanine)

17.14 Write structural formulas that correspond to the following names:
(a) Methanoic acid
(b) Trichloroacetic acid
(c) Stearic acid
(d) Tetradecanoic acid

17.15 Give structural formulas for
(a) β-Chlorobutyric acid
(b) 3-Hydroxypentanoic acid
(c) Adipic acid
(d) 3,4-Dichlorobenzoic acid

17.16 The formula below represents ascorbic acid (vitamin C). Is this a carboxylic acid? Why or why not?

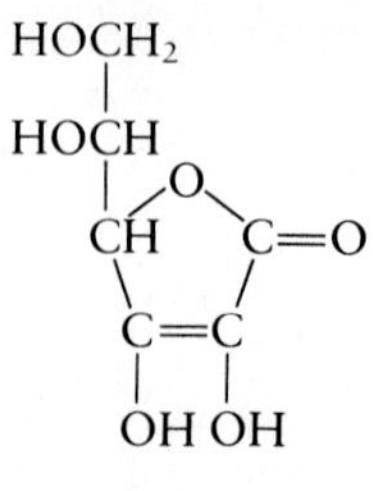

HOCH₂–HOCH–CH (ring O) C=O; C=C with OH OH

17.17 Sketch the dimer that forms from two molecules of propanoic acid. Be sure to include the hydrogen bonds.

17.18 Write the ionization equation and the K_a expression for aqueous formic acid. What is the name of the anion that forms?

17.19 One ingredient in a cervical cream is sodium propionate, added to halt the growth of bacteria. Give the formula for sodium propionate and write an equation for its formation from propionic acid.

17.20 Name the compound below, an ingredient in a solution used to treat potassium deficiency.

$$CH_3\overset{\overset{O}{\|}}{C}OK$$

17.21 The formula for the unsaturated acid called sorbic acid is given below. Write the reaction for the formation of potassium sorbate, a compound used as a food preservative.

$$CH_3CH{=}CH{-}CH{=}CH\overset{\overset{O}{\|}}{C}OH$$

Sorbic acid

17.22 Give the formula for magnesium salicylate, used to treat arthritic pain.

17.23 Give the formula and name for the calcium salt of undecylenic acid, a substance found in powders used to treat diaper rash. (The formula for the zinc salt of undecylenic acid is given in Section 17.5.)

17.24 Make a sketch that illustrates how soaps and detergents clean.

17.25 What is the difference between a soap and a detergent?

17.26 Decide whether the compounds below could be classified as soaps or detergents. Are any of them nonbiodegradable?

(a) $CH_3(CH_2)_{14}\overset{\overset{O}{\|}}{C}ONa$

(b) 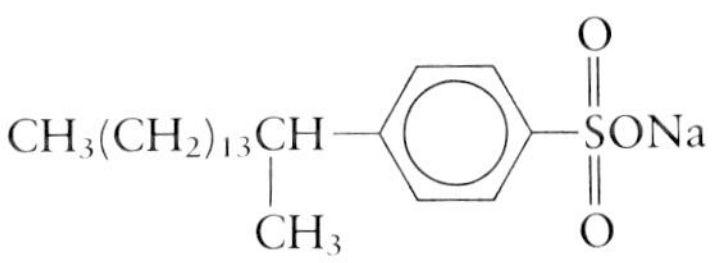 $CH_3(CH_2)_{13}\underset{\underset{CH_3}{|}}{CH}{-}C_6H_4{-}\overset{\overset{O}{\|}}{\underset{\underset{O}{\|}}{S}}ONa$

(c) $CH_3\overset{\overset{O}{\|}}{C}ONa$

(d) 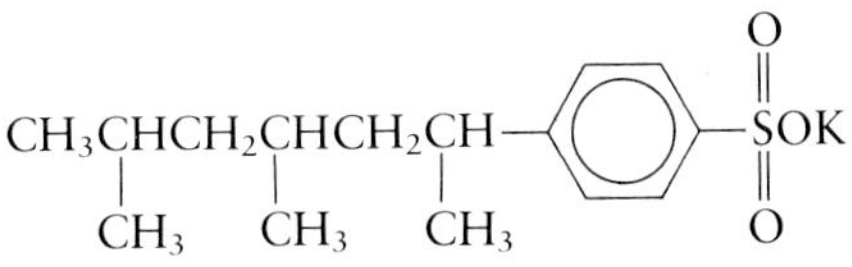 $CH_3\underset{\underset{CH_3}{|}}{C}HCH_2\underset{\underset{CH_3}{|}}{C}HCH_2\underset{\underset{CH_3}{|}}{C}H{-}C_6H_4{-}\overset{\overset{O}{\|}}{\underset{\underset{O}{\|}}{S}}OK$

17.27 What type of compound is represented by the abbreviation ABS? Are any of these shown in Exercise 17.26?

17.28 Give the general formulas for esters and amides, being careful to specify whether or not the R groups that you include could be H atoms.

17.29 Name the esters below:

(a) $CH_3O\overset{\overset{O}{\|}}{C}CH_2CH_3$

(b) $CH_3(CH_2)_5\overset{\overset{O}{\|}}{C}OCH_3$

(c) $CH_3\underset{\underset{CH_3}{|}}{C}HO\overset{\overset{O}{\|}}{C}CH_3$

(d) $H\overset{\overset{O}{\|}}{C}OCH_2CH_2CH_3$

(e) $CH_3(CH_2)_7O\overset{\overset{O}{\|}}{C}CH_2CH_3$

(f) 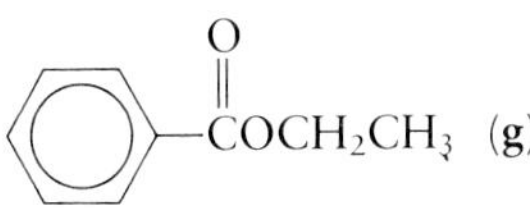 $C_6H_5{-}\overset{\overset{O}{\|}}{C}OCH_2CH_3$

(g) 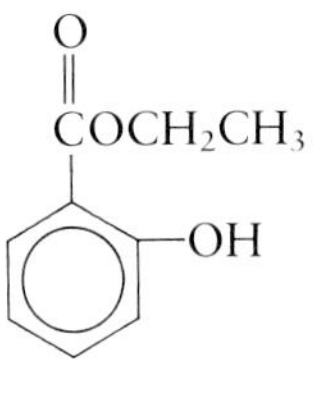 $\overset{\overset{O}{\|}}{C}OCH_2CH_3$ on a benzene ring bearing an ortho $-OH$

17.30 For each ester in Exercise 17.29 provide the formula and name of the alcohol and carboxylic acid needed for its synthesis.

17.31 Give the formula for isopropyl myristate, an ingredient in a perfume oil (see Table 17.1).

17.32 Heptanoic acid is present in grape skins and slowly reacts with ethanol to produce an ester which is partly responsible for the flavor of aged wine. Give the name and formula for the ester.

17.33 Name the following amides;

(a) $CH_3CH_2CH_2\overset{\overset{O}{\|}}{C}NH_2$

(b) $CH_3(CH_2)_{10}\overset{\overset{O}{\|}}{C}NH_2$

17.34 Write the reaction for the formation of the analgesic salicylamide from salicylic acid.

17.35 What is the general formula for an acyl chloride? Why are acyl halides sometimes used instead of carboxylic acids to prepare esters and amides? Write the reaction for the preparation of salicylamide, starting with an acyl chloride.

17.36 Write the reaction for the formation of methyl butyrate (butter rum flavoring) starting with methanol and (a) a carboxylic acid and (b) an acyl chloride.

17.37 Complete the following reactions by supplying the missing reactant(s) or product(s).

(a) $CH_3OH + HO\overset{O}{\overset{\|}{C}}CH_2CH_2CH_3 \xrightarrow{H^+}$

(b) $? + ? \xrightarrow{H^+} CH_3\underset{CH_3}{\underset{|}{C}}HO\overset{O}{\overset{\|}{C}}CH_2CH_3 + H_2O$

(c) 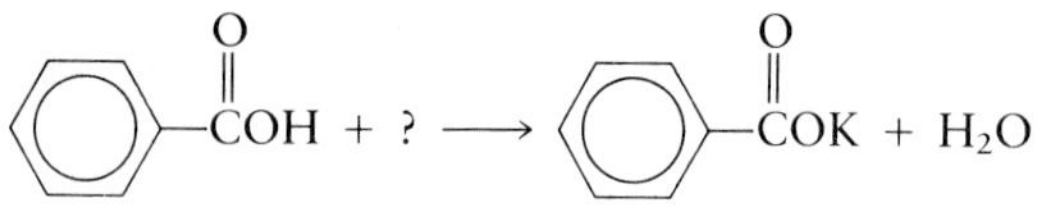 $C_6H_5\overset{O}{\overset{\|}{C}}OH + ? \longrightarrow C_6H_5\overset{O}{\overset{\|}{C}}OK + H_2O$

(d) $CH_3CH_2CH_2CH_2CH_2\overset{O}{\overset{\|}{C}}OH + NH_3 \xrightarrow{\Delta}$

(e) $CH_3\overset{O}{\overset{\|}{C}}Cl + CH_3OH \longrightarrow CH_3\overset{O}{\overset{\|}{C}}OCH_3 + ?$

(f) $CH_3CH_2\overset{O}{\overset{\|}{C}}OCH_2CH_3 + H_2O \xrightarrow{NaOH}$

(g) $H{-}\overset{O}{\overset{\|}{C}}{-}NH_2 + H_2O \xrightarrow{H^+} ? + NH_4^+$

17.38 Supply the missing reactant(s) or product(s) in the reactions below.

(a) $? + ? \xrightarrow{H^+}$ hexyl acetate + water

(b) Benzoic acid + ? $\xrightarrow{\Delta}$ benzamide + water

(c) Salicylic acid + ? $\longrightarrow$ sodium salicylate + water

(d) ? + water $\xrightarrow{NaOH}$ ethanol + sodium octanoate

(e) ? + methanol $\longrightarrow$ hydrogen chloride + methylpropanoate

17.39 The compound below is a useful organic reagent but is unpleasant to handle because it is a lachrymator, that is, an agent that produces tears. What kind of compound is this? Name it.

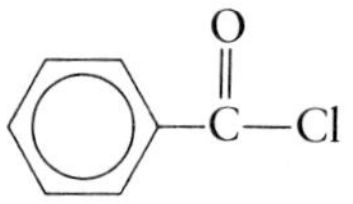

$C_6H_5{-}\overset{O}{\overset{\|}{C}}{-}Cl$

17.40 Why do chemists prepare esters and amides by using acyl halides instead of carboxylic acids?

17.41 A student laboratory experiment involves the synthesis of aspirin from salicylic acid and acetic anhydride.

(a) Why must students be very careful in handling the salicylic acid?

(b) Why doesn't the procedure call for acetyl chloride (rather than acetic anhydride)?

17.42 How did chemists prove that the oxygen atom in the water product of an ester formation reaction was *not* derived from the alcohol reactant?

17.43 Why does the removal of water in an esterification reaction improve the yield of ester product?

18 AMINES, OTHER NITROGEN COMPOUNDS, AND ORGANIC SULFUR COMPOUNDS

18.1 INTRODUCTION

In the first half of this chapter we will turn our attention to the properties of the *amines*, the organic derivatives of ammonia, NH_3. Later in the chapter we will study a miscellaneous group of organic compounds which have not fallen into any of the categories studied so far. These include other nitrogen-containing compounds and the organic sulfur compounds.

Amid*es* contain a C═O group bonded to N; ami*nes* do not.

Amines are organic derivatives of ammonia in which one, two, or all three ammonia H atoms are replaced by hydrocarbon groups. Figure 18.1 shows the structures of ammonia and of some amine compounds. The amines in which one H atom is replaced by a hydrocarbon group are known as **primary amines.**

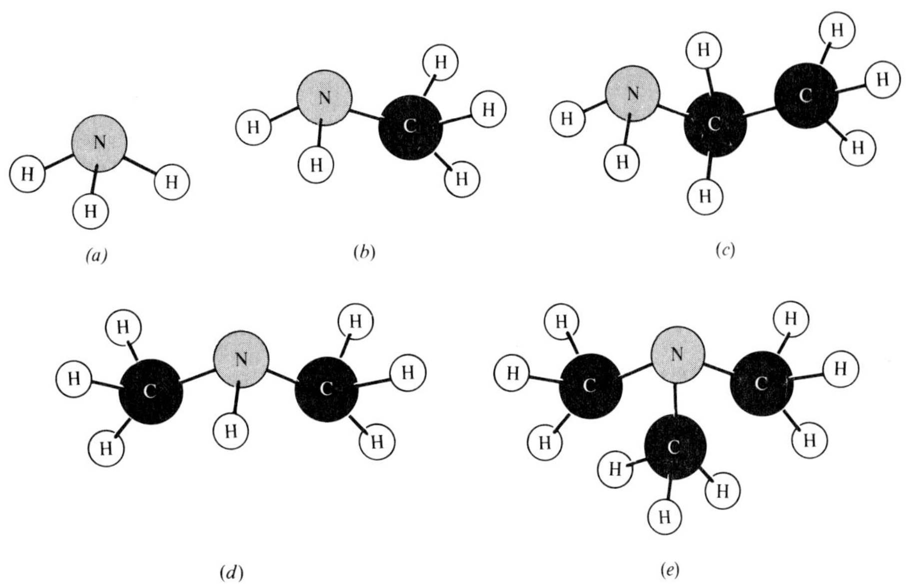

FIGURE 18.1
(*a*) Ammonia; (*b*) methyl amine; (*c*) ethyl amine; (*d*) dimethyl amine; (*e*) trimethyl amine.

$$\begin{array}{c} \text{H} \\ | \\ \text{R—N—H} \end{array}$$
Primary amine

Secondary amines are those in which two ammonia H atoms are replaced by hydrocarbon groups.

$$\begin{array}{c} \text{H} \\ | \\ \text{R—N—R}' \end{array}$$
Secondary amine

In **tertiary amines** all three H atoms of ammonia are replaced by hydrocarbon groups.

$$\begin{array}{c} \text{R}'' \\ | \\ \text{R—N—R}' \end{array}$$
Tertiary amine

In living systems amines serve as protein building blocks and as neurotransmitters. A variety of drug compounds which act as local anesthetics, analgesics, stimulants, and antibacterial agents are amines. We will discuss all these in the following sections, where our study of the properties of the amino group will help to give us some insight into how these substances perform their functions.

18.2 NAMING AMINES

Amine names are formed by naming the alkyl groups attached to the amine N atom (in alphabetical order or according to complexity) and then adding the suffix *-amine*. For example,

$$CH_3NH_2 \qquad CH_3NHCH_3 \qquad \begin{array}{c} CH_3NCH_2CH_3 \\ | \\ CH_3 \end{array}$$
Methylamine   Dimethylamine   Ethyldimethylamine

Note when using the alphabetical system that ethyl is written before dimethyl, since dimethyl is considered to start with m (not d).

It is also permissible to name amines as derivatives of hydrocarbons, a method which is especially convenient when the attached hydrocarbon groups are complex. For instance, we can name the amine shown below as a derivative of hexane.

$$\begin{array}{l} \overset{6}{C}H_3\overset{5}{C}H\overset{4}{C}H_2\overset{3}{C}H_2\overset{2}{C}H\overset{1}{C}H_2NH_2 \\ \quad\;\; | \qquad\qquad\quad | \\ \quad CH_3 \qquad\quad\; CH_3 \end{array}$$
1-Amino-2,5-dimethylhexane

Aromatic amines are named as derivatives of aniline provided the amino group has a higher priority than any other benzene ring substituents (see Table

14.4). For instance, the left-hand compound below is named as an aniline. The compound on the right is named as a phenol since hydroxy takes priority over amino.

Aromatic amines are toxic. Serious poisoning can result from ingestion of only 0.25 ml of aniline.

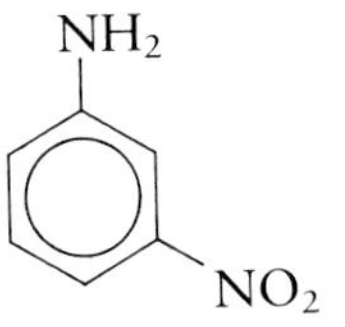

NH_2 / NO_2

m-Nitroaniline

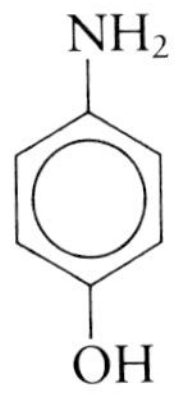

NH_2 / OH

p-Aminophenol

Secondary or tertiary aromatic amines can be named by beginning their names with a capital *N* followed by the names of the alkyl groups that are bonded to the amine N atom. For example, suppose one of the H atoms bonded to the N atom in aniline is replaced with a methyl group:

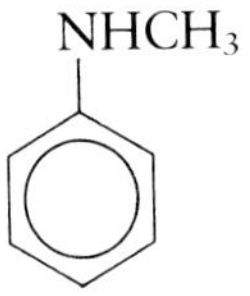

$NHCH_3$

N-Methylaniline

When there are two alkyl groups attached, the letter *N* is repeated, as in the tertiary amine shown below:

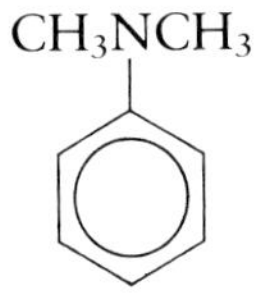

CH_3NCH_3

N,*N*-Dimethylaniline

When the amino group is not the principal functional group in any compound in which it appears, it is named as a substituent. The compounds below are known as *amino acids* since the carboxylic acid group is of higher priority than the amino group.

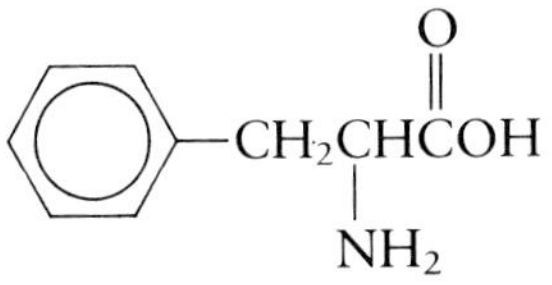

$C_6H_5-CH_2CH(NH_2)C(=O)OH$

2-Amino-3-phenylpropanoic acid
(α-amino-β-phenylpropionic acid)

$NH_2CH_2CH_2CH_2C(=O)OH$

4-Aminobutanoic acid
(γ-aminobutyric acid)

α-Amino acids are components of proteins.

There are a group of about two dozen α-amino acids (including the one shown above, known as phenylalanine) that serve as building blocks for the protein molecules of living organisms.

Compounds which have common names ending in *-ine* are likely to be amines. In fact, "vitamine" was the original spelling for the organic compounds present in foodstuffs and required for normal growth and maintenance of animals. The final *-e* was dropped when it was discovered that many vitamins were not amines.

Phenylethylamines

Norepinephrine is also called noradrenaline.

Norepinephr*ine,* epinephr*ine,* and dopam*ine* are three naturally occurring amines known as catecholamines because their formulas, shown in Figure 18.2, include the structure of 1,2-dihydroxybenzene, or catechol (see Section 15.2). The compound norepinephrine (abbreviated NE), when released from storage granules in nerve endings, assists in the transmission of nerve impulses. Figure 18.3 illustrates how NE behaves as a *neurotransmitter.* Dopamine, also found in nerve endings, is a precursor of both NE and epinephrine. Secretion of epinephrine (Adrenaline) into the blood prepares the body for emergencies by increasing cardiac output and blood pressure and by causing certain muscles to contract. Several synthetic compounds with structures and actions similar to those of these biogenic amines include amphetam*ine,* methamphetam*ine* ("speed"), and ephedr*ine* (see Figure 18.4).

Note that the amines mentioned above are derived from the compound below, known as phenylethylamine.

C_6H_5—$CH_2CH_2NH_2$

Phenylethylamine

HO, OH

(*a*)

—$CHCH_2NH_2$ (OH); HO, OH

(*b*)

—$CHCH_2NHCH_3$ (OH); HO, OH

(*c*)

—$CH_2CH_2NH_2$; HO, OH

(*d*)

FIGURE 18.2
Catechol amines: (*a*) Catechol; (*b*) norepinephr*ine* (NE) (noraderenal*ine*); (*c*) epinephr*ine* (aderenal*ine*); (*d*) dopam*ine.*

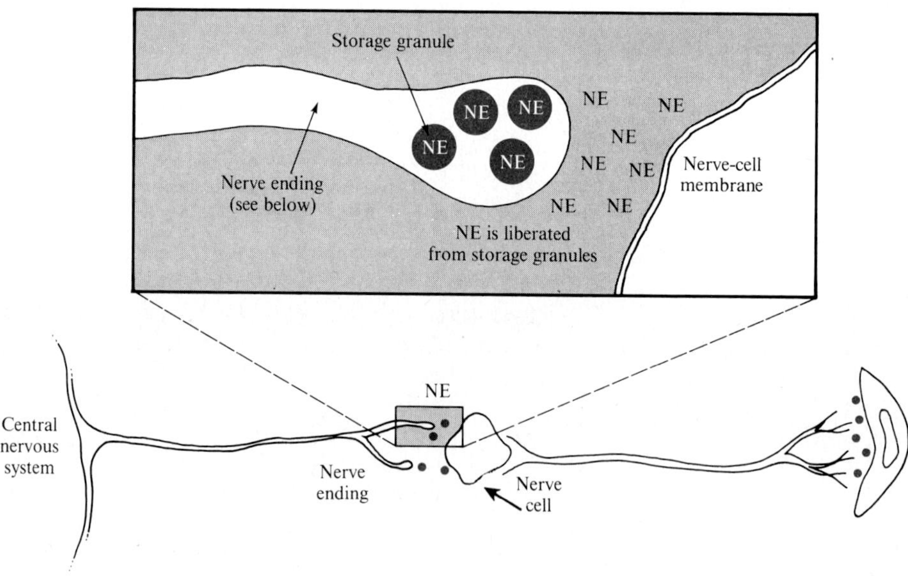

FIGURE 18.3
Norepinephrine as a neurotransmitter.

—CH_2CHNH_2 (CH_3)

(*a*)

—$CH_2CHNHCH_3$ (CH_3)

(*b*)

—$CHCHNHCH_3$ (OH, CH_3)

(*c*)

FIGURE 18.4
Synthetic neurotransmitters: (*a*) amphetam*ine*; (*b*) methamphetam*ine*; (*c*) ephedr*ine.*

Adrenergic is derived from *adren-* (adrenaline or noradrenaline) and *ergon*, the Greek word for "work."

Table 18.1 gives the major therapeutic uses for some naturally occurring and synthetic phenylethylamines. Although their primary uses vary, all these drugs, natural and synthetic, evoke physiological responses similar to those of norepinephrine. Nerve fibers that synthesize and secrete norepinephrine are called *adrenergic nerves*. Hence the drugs in Table 18.1 all belong to a class of drugs known as the **adrenergic drugs.**

TABLE 18.1 USES OF PHENYLETHYLAMINES

Formula	Name	Major therapeutic use
3,4-$(HO)_2C_6H_3$–$CH(OH)CH_2NH_2$	Norepinephrine	To support blood pressure in acute hypotension (shock, spinal anesthesia)
3,4-$(HO)_2C_6H_3$–$CH(OH)CH_2NHCH_3$	Epinephrine (Adrenalin)	Vasoconstrictor (to prolong effect of local anesthetics), for relief of allergic symptoms, cardiac stimulant
3,4-$(HO)_2C_6H_3$–$CH(OH)CH_2N(CH_3)_2$	Isoproterenol	Bronchodilation
3,4-$(HO)_2C_6H_3$–$CH_2CH_2NH_2$	Dopamine	To treat shock (from kidney or heart failure)
3-$(OH)C_6H_4$–$CH(OH)CH(CH_3)NH_2$	Metaraminol	To treat acute hypotension
3-$(HO)C_6H_4$–$CH(OH)CH_2NHCH_3$	Phenylephrine	Nasal decongestant
C_6H_5–$CH(OH)CH(CH_3)NHCH_3$	Ephedrine	Nasal decongestant
C_6H_5–$CH(OH)CH(CH_3)NH_2$	Phenylpropanolamine	Nasal decongestant
C_6H_5–$CH_2CH(CH_3)NH_2$	Amphetamine	To treat hyperactivity (in children), narcolepsy, and obesity
C_6H_5–$CH_2CH(CH_3)NHCH_3$	Methamphetamine	To treat hyperactivity (in children) and obesity

Name the compound amphetamine as a hydrocarbon derivative (see Figure 18.4). Is amphetamine a primary, secondary, or tertiary amine?

Solution:

$$C_6H_5\text{—}CH_2\underset{\displaystyle CH_3}{\underset{|}{C}}HNH_2$$

Rewriting this formula, we see that the longest hydrocarbon chain has three C atoms. Numbering starts from the left to give the substituents the lowest possible numbers.

$$C_6H_5\text{—}\overset{1}{C}H_2\overset{2}{\underset{\displaystyle NH_2}{\underset{|}{C}}}H\overset{3}{C}H_3$$

The name is 2-amino-1-phenylpropane. Amphetamine is a primary amine, since only one H atom of NH_3 is replaced by a hydrocarbon group.

EXERCISE 18.1

Name the compound called phenylethylamine as a hydrocarbon derivative.

18.3 PHYSICAL PROPERTIES OF AMINES

Amines, like ammonia, exhibit hydrogen bonding because their structures include nitrogen atom bonded to a hydrogen atom. Intermolecular hydrogen bonding in methylamine (CH_3NH_2) is shown in Figure 18.5. Because of hydrogen bonding the boiling points of amines are unusually high. For instance, ethane and methylamine have similar formula weights but very different boiling points.

CH_3CH_3	CH_3NH_2
Ethane	Methyl amine
Formula weight 30	Formula weight 31
Boiling point $-88.6°C$	Boiling point $-6.3°C$

The hydrogen bonds that attract amine molecules to each other are not as strong as those among alcohol molecules because the electronegativity of nitrogen (3.0) is lower than that of oxygen (3.5), and therefore N—H bonds are less polar than O—H bonds. Thus amines boil at lower temperatures than the corresponding alcohols.

FIGURE 18.5
Hydrogen bonding in amines. The hydrogen bond (in color) forms a bridge between the H atom of one methyl amine molecule and the N atom of a neighboring methyl amine molecule.

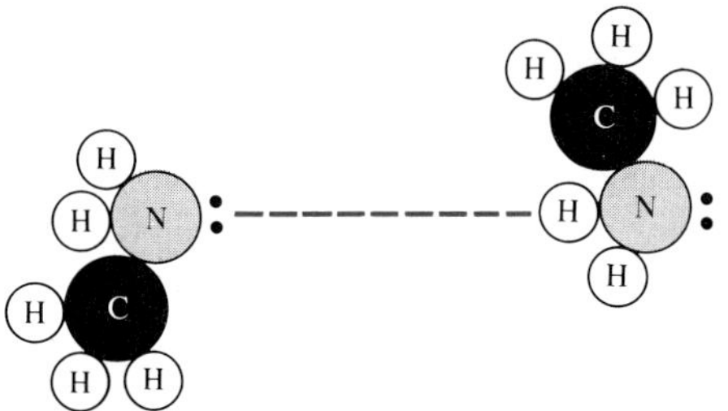

CH_3NH_2	CH_3OH
Methylamine	Methanol
Formula weight 31	Formula weight 32
Boiling point −6.3°C	Boiling point 65°C

Amines can form hydrogen bonds to water and are very soluble in water as long as their hydrocarbon chains have fewer than five C atoms.

The lower-formula-weight amines have unpleasant, fishy odors. Methyl-, dimethyl-, and trimethylamine all contribute to the odor of stale fish. Malodorous diamines are produced when proteins decompose in decaying animal tissues. Two of these are the diamines below, known as putrescine and cadaverine:

$NH_2CH_2CH_2CH_2CH_2NH_2$	$NH_2CH_2CH_2CH_2CH_2CH_2NH_2$
Putrescine (1,4-diaminobutane)	Cadaverine (1,5-diaminopentane)

18.4 AMINES: ORGANIC BASES

In Chapter 11 you saw that ammonia behaves as a weak base, accepting protons to produce ammonium ions.

$$\underset{\text{Ammonia}}{NH_3} + H_2O \rightleftharpoons \underset{\text{Ammonium}}{NH_4^+} + OH^-$$

Primary, secondary, and tertiary alkylamines also behave as weak bases. The ions they produce are derivatives of the ammonium ion and are called **alkylammonium ions.** For instance, methylamine accepts a proton to form the *methyl*ammonium ion.

$$\underset{\text{Methylamine}}{CH_3NH_2} + H_2O \rightleftharpoons \underset{\text{Methylammonium ion}}{CH_3NH_3^+} + OH^-$$

The ionization constant for methylamine is 3.7×10^{-4} (see Table 11.6, where weak bases are listed). Dimethylamine produces the dimethylammonium ion

$$\underset{\text{Dimethylamine}}{(CH_3)_2NH} + H_2O \rightleftharpoons \underset{\text{Dimethylammonium ion}}{(CH_3)_2NH_2^+} + OH^-$$

and trimethylamine accepts a proton to form the trimethylammonium ion

$$(CH_3)_3N + H_2O \rightleftharpoons (CH_3)_3NH^+ + OH^-$$

Trimethylamine — Trimethylammonium ion

When ammonia (a base) reacts with HCl (an acid), the salt ammonium chloride forms.

$$NH_3 + HCl \longrightarrow NH_4Cl$$

Amines are also neutralized by HCl to produce alkylammonium chloride salts. For instance, methylamine gives methylammonium chloride.

$$CH_3NH_2 + HCl \longrightarrow CH_3NH_3Cl$$

Methylamine — Methylammonium chloride

To remind us that CH_3NH_3Cl is a salt, we can write its formula as $CH_3NH_3{}^+Cl^-$, so that we can see the ion components. Salts such as $RNH_3{}^+Cl^-$ are often called **amine hydrochlorides** and their formulas may also be written $RNH_2 \cdot HCl$. Thus methylammonium chloride is also known as methylamine hydrochloride, $CH_3NH_2 \cdot HCl$.

Most amine hydrochlorides are water-soluble. For instance, hexylamine is only slightly soluble in water but its hexylammonium chloride salt is very soluble.

$$CH_3CH_2CH_2CH_2CH_2CH_2NH_2 + HCl \longrightarrow CH_3CH_2CH_2CH_2CH_2CH_2NH_3{}^+Cl^-$$

Hexylamine: slightly soluble in water — Hexylammonium chloride (hexylamine hydrochloride): very soluble in water

Thus, adding HCl to amines is a useful way to increase their solubility in water. Amines used as therapeutic drugs are often administered in the form of their hydrochloride salts. For example, the tertiary amine procaine (Novocain) is a local anesthetic which is injected in the form of its hydrochloride salt, procaine hydrochloride.

$$CH_3CH_2OC(=O)\text{—}C_6H_4\text{—}N(CH_2CH_3)_2 + HCl \longrightarrow CH_3CH_2OC(=O)\text{—}C_6H_4\text{—}NH^+(CH_2CH_3)_2\,Cl^-$$

Procaine: insoluble in water — Procaine hydrochloride: soluble in water

Besides chlorides certain amine drugs are also available as sulfates, phosphates or other salts.

The amine forms of compounds such as procaine are sometimes called *free-base* amines to distinguish them from their hydrochloride salts.

SAMPLE EXERCISES 18.2

Write the equation for the reaction of ethylmethylamine with HCl and name the product.

Solution:

Ethylmethylamine, $CH_3CH_2\underset{\displaystyle CH_3}{\underset{|}{N}}H$, reacts with HCl to form a salt.

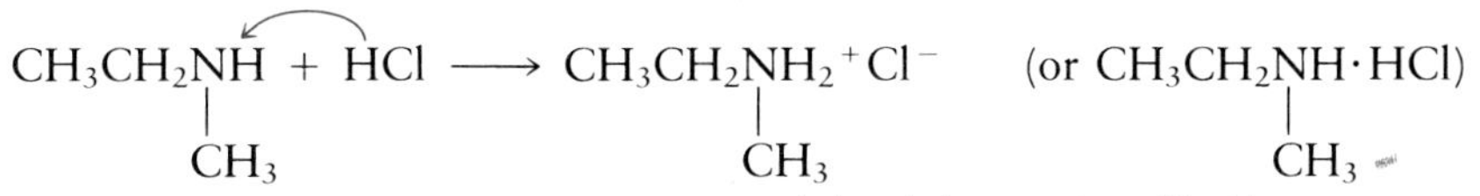

$$CH_3CH_2\underset{\displaystyle CH_3}{\underset{|}{N}}H + HCl \longrightarrow CH_3CH_2\underset{\displaystyle CH_3}{\underset{|}{N}}H_2{}^+Cl^- \qquad (\text{or } CH_3CH_2\underset{\displaystyle CH_3}{\underset{|}{N}}H\cdot HCl)$$

Ethylmethylammonium chloride
(ethylmethylamine hydrochloride)

EXERCISE 18.2

Write the reaction for the formation of dopamine hydrochloride, the form in which it appears in the drug Intropin. (See Table 18.1.)

18.5 LOCAL ANESTHETICS

Local anesthetics are compounds (most of them amines) which temporarily block nerve conduction, as shown in Figure 18.6. Some drugs which produce this effect are procaine, benzocaine, lidocaine, and cocaine. You can see by looking at their formulas in Figure 18.7 (and can surmise from their names) that they are all amines. In addition, they all include a benzene ring and an intermediate chain which links the aromatic portion of the molecule to the amine. Benzocaine is an ingredient in creams and lotions used as topical anesthetics to relieve minor skin irritations. Cocaine is sometimes used for eye surgery. Besides its local anesthetic action, cocaine causes powerful central nervous system stimulation and euphoria and can produce a psychological dependence in chronic users. Dentists inject procaine hydrochloride in mixtures with epinephrine (see Figure 18.2). Epineph-

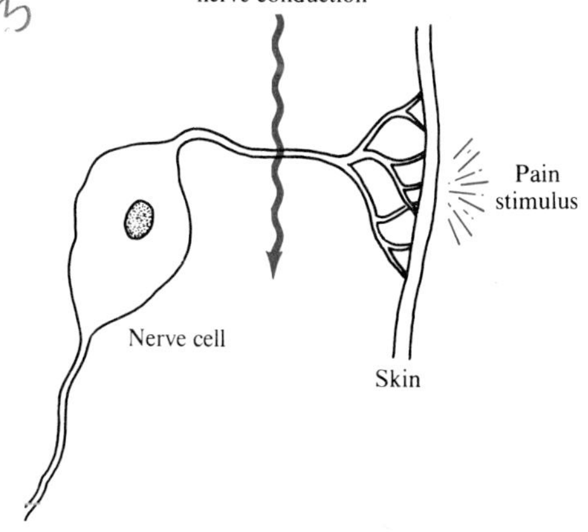

FIGURE 18.6
Action of local anesthetics.

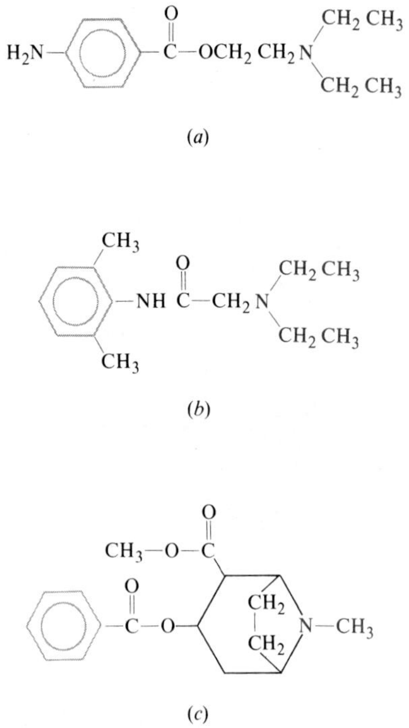

FIGURE 18.7
Local anesthetics: (*a*) Procaine (Novacain); (*b*) lidocaine (Xylocaine); (*c*) cocaine. The local anesthetics contain an aromatic ring (shown in light color), an intermediate chain, and a tertiary amino group (shown in darker color). The aromatic ring is needed for lipid solubility. The amino group is needed so that the local anesthetic can be made water-soluble by formation of its salt.

Lidocaine is more than twice as potent as procaine.

rine, a vasoconstrictor, causes constriction of the blood vessels, thus preventing the rapid removal of the local anesthetic from the site of injection (see Table 18.1). Lidocaine is commonly used by injection around the spinal cord (epidural anesthesia) because it has the ability to diffuse easily through the tissue that surrounds the spinal cord (the dura mater). This is a technique often used in obstetrics.

As mentioned previously, local anesthetics are administered in the form of their water-soluble hydrochloride salts. Suppose we represent a local anesthetic as a general tertiary amine, R_3N. Its hydrochloride salt, $R_3NH^+Cl^-$, contains the trialkylammonium cation R_3NH^+. For the local anesthetic to reach the nerves on which it acts, it must cross membranes composed of nonpolar fatty substances called lipids. The cation R_3NH^+ cannot cross such a membrane easily because it is charged, but the free base amine, R_3N, can. Local anesthetics work because in body tissues some of the R_3NH^+ cation is converted to the free base R_3N. Like the ammonium ion (see Table 11.5), the R_3NH^+ ion is acidic and thus donates a proton to water.

$$\underset{\text{Cation}}{R_3NH^+} + H_2O \rightleftharpoons \underset{\text{Free base}}{R_3N} + H_3O^+$$

The free-base amine that forms is able to cross the lipid membranes and thus to produce local anesthesia.

Suppose the tissues at the site of injection are acidic, which means that $[H_3O^+] > [OH^-]$. According to Le Chatelier's principle (Section 10.9), extra H_3O^+ shifts the equilibrium reaction above to the left, thus reducing the amount of free base available to cross membranes. Infected tissues are acidic, which means that local anesthesia may not be achieved if the anesthetic is injected into an infected area (see Figure 18.8).

FIGURE 18.8
Transport of local anesthetics. (*a*) Normal tissue. There is free base present to cross nonpolar lipid membrane. (*b*) Infected tissue. There may be not enough R_3N. The polar R_3NH^+Cl salt cannot cross the lipid membrane.

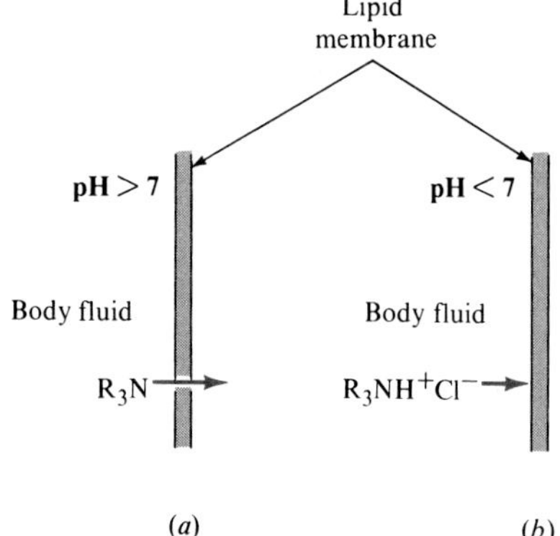

18.6 REACTIONS OF AMINES

Above we discussed the reaction of amines with HCl to produce chloride salts. In this section we will consider the reaction of amines with carboxylic acids and alkyl halides and the metabolic fate of the biogenic amines such as norepinephrine.

Reaction with Carboxylic Acids

In Chapter 17 you saw that the reaction of ammonia with a carboxylic acid produces an ammonium salt. Upon heating, the salt dehydrates to form an amide. We used a single-step reaction to describe this.

An acyl chloride can be used in place of the carboxylic acid.

$$\underset{\text{Carboxylic acid}}{R{-}\overset{\overset{\displaystyle O}{\|}}{C}{-}\boxed{OH + H}}{-}\underset{\underset{\displaystyle H}{|}}{N}{-}H \xrightarrow{\Delta} \underset{\text{Amide}}{R{-}\overset{\overset{\displaystyle O}{\|}}{C}{-}\underset{\underset{\displaystyle H}{|}}{N}{-}H} + H_2O$$

Amines also react with acids to form salts which lose water, only in this case the products are **substituted amides,** in which one or both amide H atoms are replaced by hydrocarbon groups. If a primary amine is a reactant, the product is a monosubstituted amide

$$\underset{\text{Carboxylic acid}}{R{-}\overset{\overset{\displaystyle O}{\|}}{C}{-}\boxed{OH + H}}\underset{\text{Primary amine}}{{-}\underset{\underset{\displaystyle H}{|}}{N}{-}R'} \xrightarrow{\Delta} \underset{\text{Monosubstituted amide}}{R{-}\overset{\overset{\displaystyle O}{\|}}{C}{-}\underset{\underset{\displaystyle H}{|}}{N}{-}R'} + H_2O$$

and the reaction of a secondary amine with a carboxylic acid gives a disubstituted amide

$$\underset{\text{Carboxylic acid}}{R{-}\overset{\overset{\displaystyle O}{\|}}{C}{-}\boxed{OH + H}}\underset{\text{Secondary amine}}{{-}\underset{\underset{\displaystyle R''}{|}}{N}{-}R'} \xrightarrow{\Delta} \underset{\text{Disubstituted amide}}{R{-}\overset{\overset{\displaystyle O}{\|}}{C}{-}\underset{\underset{\displaystyle R''}{|}}{N}{-}R'} + H_2O$$

The names of substituted amides begin with the capital letter *N* (for monosubstituted amides) or *N,N* (for disubstituted amides), followed by the names of the alkyl groups attached to the amide N atom. When acetic acid reacts with methylamine, the product is called *N*-methylacetamide:

$$\underset{\text{Acetic acid}}{CH_3-\overset{\overset{\displaystyle O}{\|}}{C}-\boxed{OH + H}}\underset{\text{Methylamine}}{-\underset{\underset{\displaystyle H}{|}}{N}-CH_3} \xrightarrow{\Delta} \underset{N\text{-Methylacetamide}}{CH_3-\overset{\overset{\displaystyle O}{\|}}{C}-\underset{\underset{\displaystyle H}{|}}{N}-CH_3} + H_2O$$

The reaction of formic acid with dimethylamide gives *N,N*-dimethylformamide (*N,N*-dimethylmethanamide).

$$\underset{\text{Formic acid}}{H-\overset{\overset{\displaystyle O}{\|}}{C}-\boxed{OH + H}}\underset{\text{Dimethylamine}}{-\underset{\underset{\displaystyle CH_3}{|}}{N}-CH_3} \xrightarrow{\Delta} \underset{N,N\text{-Dimethylformamide}}{H-\overset{\overset{\displaystyle O}{\|}}{C}-\underset{\underset{\displaystyle CH_3}{|}}{N}-CH_3} + H_2O$$

The product *N,N*-dimethylformamide, a liquid known by the abbreviation DMF, is an excellent solvent for polar organic compounds.

SAMPLE EXERCISES 18.3

What is the name and formula of the product that forms when ethylamine is heated with propanoic acid?

Solution:

The primary amine, $CH_3CH_2NH_2$, reacts with the carboxylic acid, $CH_3CH_2\overset{\overset{\displaystyle O}{\|}}{C}OH$, to form a monosubstituted amide.

$$\underset{\text{Propanoic acid}}{CH_3CH_2\overset{\overset{\displaystyle O}{\|}}{C}-\boxed{OH + H}}\underset{\text{Ethylamine}}{-\underset{\underset{\displaystyle H}{|}}{N}CH_2CH_3} \xrightarrow{\Delta} \underset{N\text{-Ethylpropanamide}}{CH_3CH_2\overset{\overset{\displaystyle O}{\|}}{C}-\underset{\underset{\displaystyle H}{|}}{N}CH_2CH_3} + H_2O$$

EXERCISE 18.3

What is the name of the amide shown below? What two reactants can be combined to form this compound?

$$CH_3\overset{\overset{\displaystyle O}{\|}}{C}\underset{\underset{\displaystyle CH_2CH_3}{|}}{N}CH_2CH_3$$

Reaction with Alkyl Halides

When a tertiary alkylamine reacts with an alkyl halide, the products are tetraalkylammonium halides. The alkyl group of the halide bonds to the amine through its nonbonding pair of electrons on the N atom.

$$\underset{\text{Tertiary amine}}{R{-}\overset{\displaystyle R}{\underset{\displaystyle R}{N}}{:}} \;+\; \underset{\text{Alkyl halide}}{R{-}X} \;\longrightarrow\; \underset{\text{Tetraalkylammonium salt}}{[R{-}\overset{\displaystyle R}{\underset{\displaystyle R}{N}}{-}R]^{+}X^{-}}$$

The cation R_4N^+ is called *tetraalkylammonium,* since it is derived from NH_4^+ with all four H atoms replaced by alkyl groups. Salts containing R_4N^+ are known as **quaternary ammonium salts.** The term *quaternary* is used because the N atom in the cation is bonded to four C atoms of the four hydrocarbon R groups.

Quaternary ammonium salts in which one of the R groups is a long alkyl chain are detergents. One example is the following chloride salt, which contains a hexadecyl group:

$$[CH_3(CH_2)_{15}{-}\overset{\displaystyle CH_3}{\underset{\displaystyle CH_3}{N}}{-}CH_3]^{+}Cl^{-}$$

Hexadecyltrimethylammonium chloride

The polar end of this molecule, where the detergent action lies, is in the cation instead of in the anion (as it is for sulfonate detergents or carboxylic acid soaps). Thus quaternary ammonium salt detergents are known as **cationic detergents,** or "invert soaps." The action of a typical cationic detergent is compared with that of anionic detergents in Figure 18.9.

Quaternary ammonium salt solutions (1:750) are used for preoperative hand and arm soaks.

In Chapter 17 we said that all soaps and detergents have some antimicrobial action (Section 17.7). Cationic detergents are much more germicidal than anionic detergents. In addition to their significant germicidal properties, quaternary am-

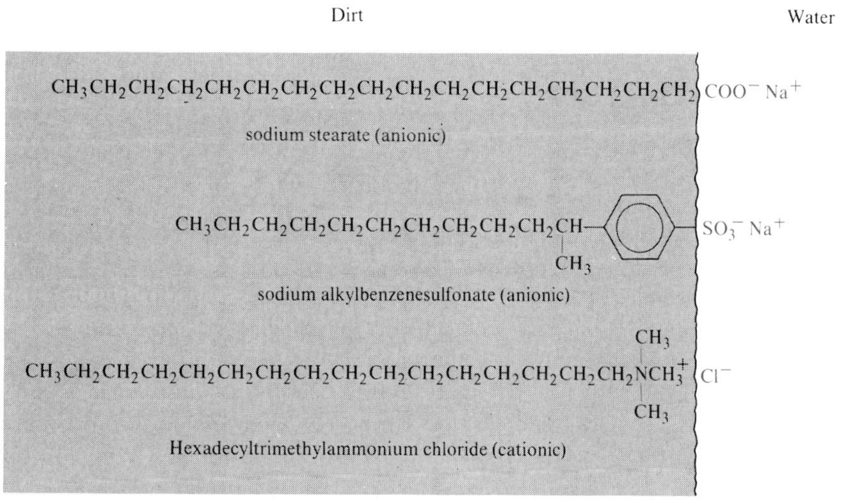

Dirt | Water

$CH_3CH_2CH_2CH_2CH_2CH_2CH_2CH_2CH_2CH_2CH_2CH_2CH_2CH_2CH_2CH_2CH_2COO^-\ Na^+$

sodium stearate (anionic)

$CH_3CH_2CH_2CH_2CH_2CH_2CH_2CH_2CH_2CH_2\underset{\displaystyle CH_3}{CH}{-}C_6H_4{-}SO_3^-\ Na^+$

sodium alkylbenzenesulfonate (anionic)

$CH_3CH_2CH_2CH_2CH_2CH_2CH_2CH_2CH_2CH_2CH_2CH_2CH_2CH_2CH_2CH_2\overset{\displaystyle CH_3}{\underset{\displaystyle CH_3}{N}}CH_3^+\ Cl^-$

Hexadecyltrimethylammonium chloride (cationic)

FIGURE 18.9
Activity of anionic and cationic detergents. The nonpolar hydrocarbon chain is part of the negative anion of the carboxylate soap and the anionic sulfonate detergent. The nonpolar hydrocarbon chain is part of the positive cation of the quaternary ammonium salt detergent.

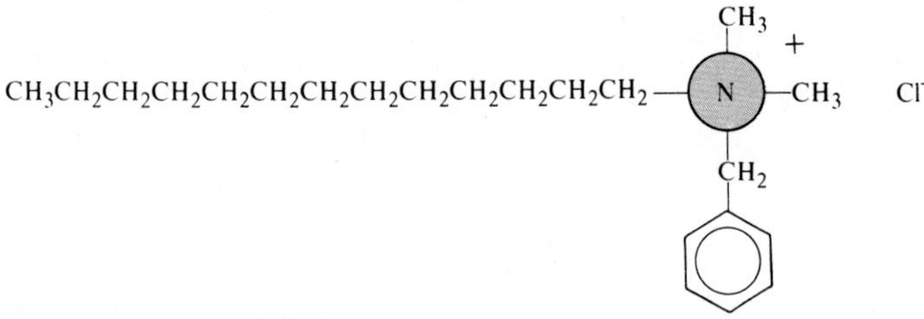

FIGURE 18.10
Zephiran, a surface antiseptic, is a mixture of alkylbenzyldimethylammonium chlorides, such as this one. The alkyl groups range from C_8H_{17} to $C_{18}H_{37}$.

monium salt detergents are highly soluble, nontoxic, noncorrosive, and stable. Quaternary ammonium salts such as the one shown above are used extensively as skin antiseptics and as sanitizing agents in eating establishments and food processing plants. Zephiran chloride is a cationic detergent used in surgical preparation (see Figure 18.10).

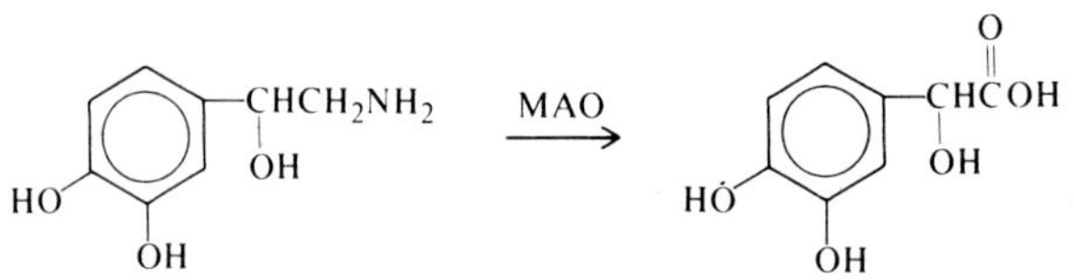

FIGURE 18.11
Degradation of norepinephrine. Metabolic pathway for degradation of NE with the assistance of monamine oxidase, MAO. MAOI drugs, the monamine oxidase inhibitors interfere with this.

Metabolism of Amines

The enzyme MAO is needed to degrade amines such as norepinephrine.

Biogenic amines are metabolized with the assistance of an enzyme system known as *monamine oxidase* (MAO). In Figure 18.11, where a part of the degradation pathway for norepinephrine is shown, you can see that the amino group is first converted to a carboxyl group.

The decreased availability of neurotransmitter amines such as NE is thought to be a cause of depression. One type of drug used to fight depression acts by inhibiting MAO and thus increasing the store of NE in the nerve endings. The structures of some of these drugs, known as monamine oxidase inhibitors (MAOI), are shown in Figure 18.12. Prescriptions for other amine drugs such as antihis-

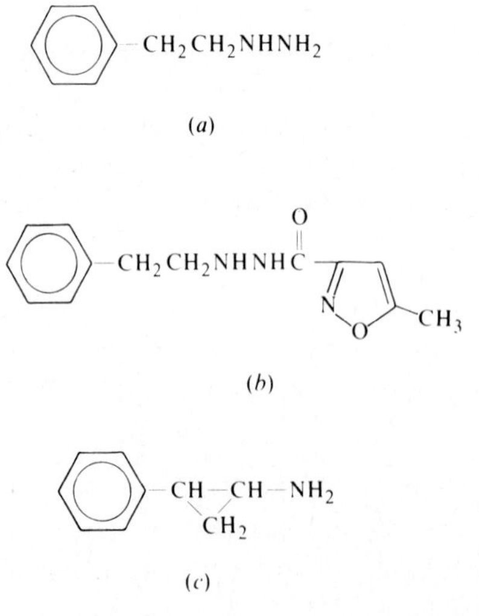

FIGURE 18.12
Structures of some MAOI drugs. (*a*) Phenelzine (Nardil); (*b*) isocarboxazid (Marplan); (*c*) tranylcypromine (Parnate). These drugs, used as antidepressants, deactivate the enzyme monamine oxidase, MAO.

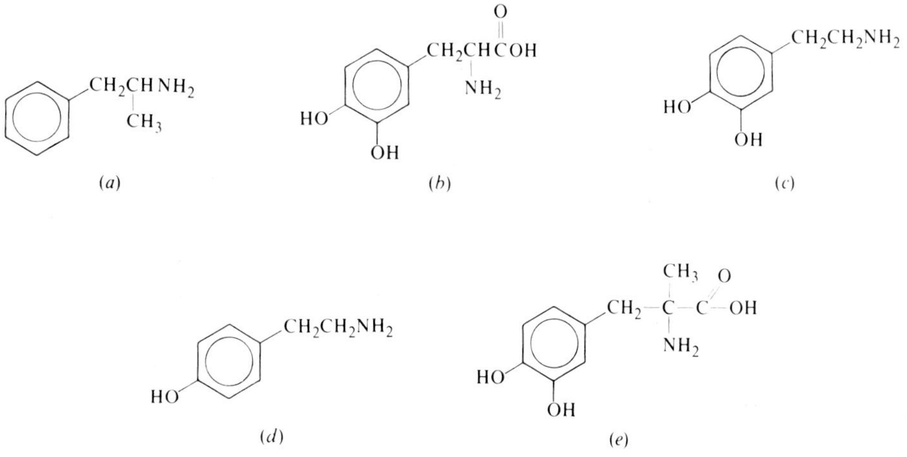

FIGURE 18.13
Some substances to avoid when taking MAOI drugs. (*a*) amphetamine; (*b*) levodopa; (*c*) dopamine; (*d*) tyramine (in aged cheese and wine); (*e*) methyldopa. Taking any of these in combination with MAOI drugs can cause hypertensive crises.

Acute hypertensive crises occur when MAOI drugs are taken with amphetamines or antihistamines.

tamines or amphetamines warn the user not to mix them with MAOI, since there will be no MAO to participate in their breakdown. The effect of amine drugs such as the ones shown in Figure 18.13 may be prolonged and intensified when taken in combination with MAOI.

18.7 SULFA DRUGS

In Chapter 17 we encountered benzenesulfonic acids as components of many detergent compounds. Sulfonic acids also react with ammonia (or amines) to form amides (or substituted amides).

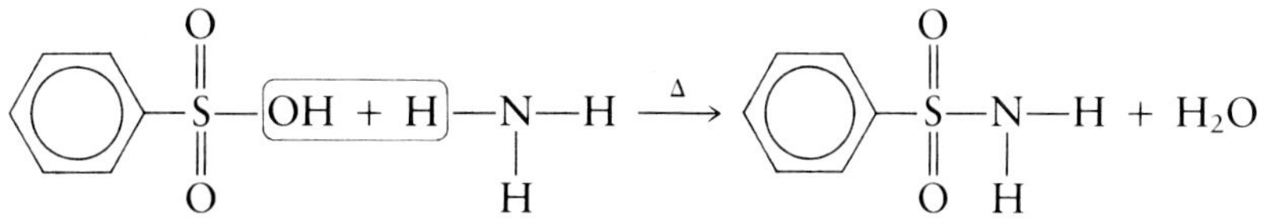

$$C_6H_5{-}SO_2{-}OH + H{-}NH_2 \xrightarrow{\Delta} C_6H_5{-}SO_2{-}NH_2 + H_2O$$

Benzenesulfonic acid → Benzenesulfonamide

One group of sulfonamides includes the **sulfa drugs**, which are used in the treatment of bacterial infections because of their ability to arrest or hinder the growth of bacteria. The parent compound for all the sulfonamide drugs is called sulfanilamide, which is the *p*-aminobenzenesulfonamide shown below.

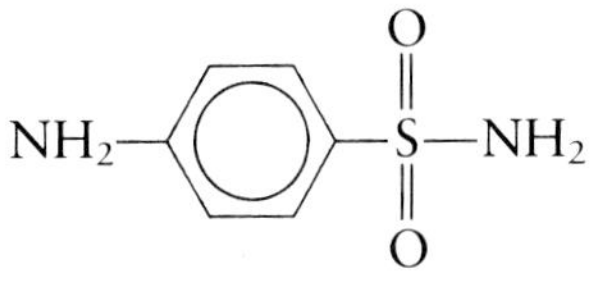

$$NH_2{-}C_6H_4{-}SO_2{-}NH_2$$

Sulfanilamide

However, sulfanilamide is more toxic and less effective than many of its derivatives. The sulfonamides actually used have one of the amide H atoms of sulfanilamide replaced by a substituent, R:

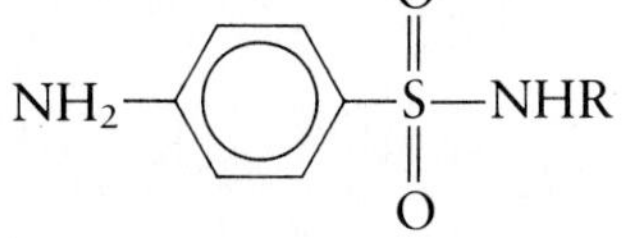

$$NH_2-C_6H_4-\overset{O}{\underset{O}{\overset{\|}{\underset{\|}{S}}}}-NHR$$

Sulfanilamide derivative

For instance, the sulfa drug called sulfacetamide has the acyl group acetyl ($\overset{O}{\overset{\|}{C}}CH_3$) as a substituent.

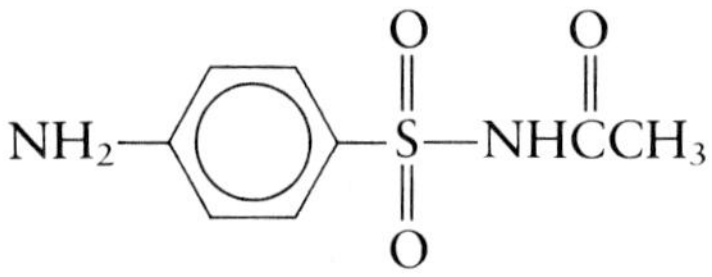

$$NH_2-C_6H_4-\overset{O}{\underset{O}{\overset{\|}{\underset{\|}{S}}}}-NH\overset{O}{\overset{\|}{C}}CH_3$$

Sulfacetamide

Administering PABA was found to destroy the effect of sulfonamide drugs.

The nature of the R group affects the activity of the sulfonamides in ways that are not entirely clear. However, the way in which sulfonamides are able to kill bacteria is understood. Folic acid is required by bacteria to allow them to metabolize single-carbon-atom sections of hydrocarbons. Sulfonamide drugs kill bacteria by preventing the formation of folic acid. In Figure 18.14 you can see that one segment of the folic acid molecule comes from *p*-aminobenzoic acid (PABA); for folic acid to form, the *p*-aminobenzoic acid must first combine with an enzyme. The role of the sulfonamide is to bind to this enzyme, thus preventing the PABA from binding to it, as shown in Figure 18.15. Sulfonamides are able to do this because they are similar in structure to PABA.

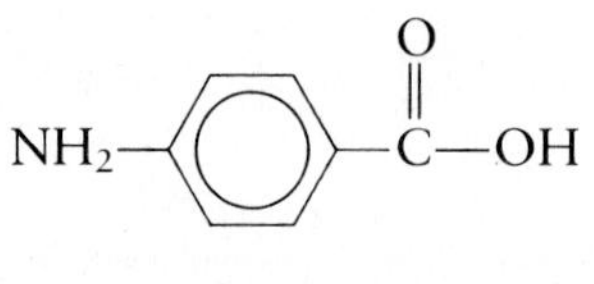

$$NH_2-C_6H_4-\overset{O}{\overset{\|}{C}}-OH \qquad NH_2-C_6H_4-\overset{O}{\underset{O}{\overset{\|}{\underset{\|}{S}}}}-NHR$$

p-Aminobenzoic acid (PABA) 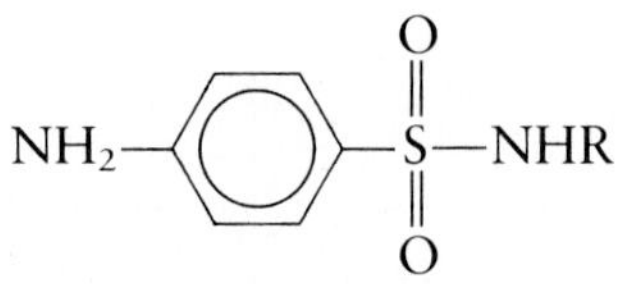 Sulfonamide

Folic acid is a vitamin for humans.

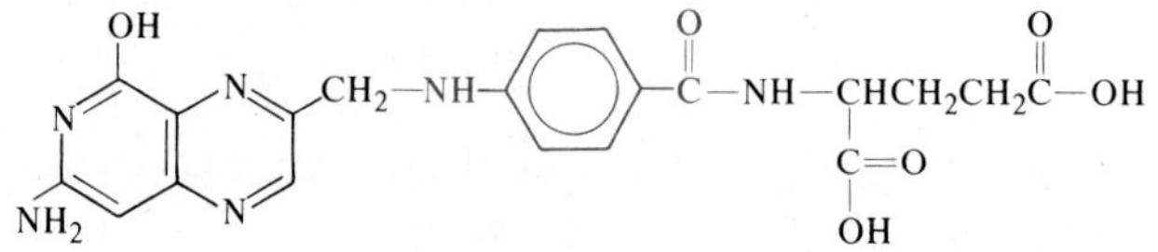

The bacteria cannot complete the biochemical synthesis of folic acid needed for their survival. The sulfonamides are not harmful to humans who receive ample amounts of folic acid in their diets and thus do not depend upon folic acid biosynthesis.

FIGURE 18.14
Folic acid structure. The part of the folic acid structure derived from *p*-aminobenzoic acid is shown in color.

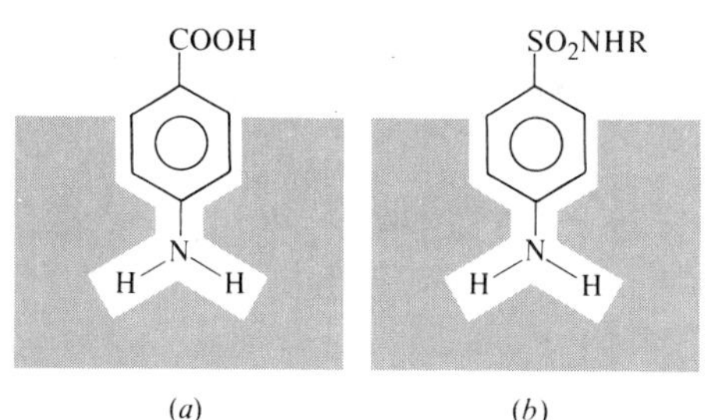

FIGURE 18.15 Activity of sulfonamides. (*a*) Enzyme (in color) bound to *p*-aminobenzoic acid (PABA). (*b*) Enzyme bound to a sulfonamide. The sulfonamide molecule prevents PABA from forming folic acid by binding to the necessary enzyme.

18.8 NITRILES

Nitriles are organic compounds in which a hydrocarbon group (R in the formula below) is bonded to a cyanide group, C≡N.

$$R{-}C{\equiv}N$$
Nitrile

When we write CN, it means C≡N.

At the beginning of our discussion of organic chemistry (Section 12.1) we said that there were some C-containing compounds that were not considered to be organic and among these we listed hydrogen cyanide, HCN. Thus in the formula above, R is taken to be a hydrocarbon group and not a hydrogen atom. We usually write the cyanide part of the formula as CN, with the triple bond understood.

In the IUPAC system alkyl nitriles are named as alkanenitriles, the alkane part of the name indicating the total number of C atoms, including the cyanide carbon. According to the common system the nitrile name is derived from the corresponding carboxylic acid minus *-ic acid* plus *-nitrile*. For example,

CH_3CN	CH_3CH_2CN
Methanenitrile (acetonitrile)	Ethanenitrile (propionitrile)

When the cyanide group appears as a substituent (CN), it is called *cyano-*.

Nitriles are considerably less toxic than their inorganic relative hydrogen cyanide, HCN. A highly toxic gas with an almondy odor, HCN deactivates the respiration process by combining with iron ions in certain respiratory enzymes. Nitriles cannot do this.

Nitriles are useful intermediates in synthesis pathways. Adding a cyanide group to a compound is one way to increase the total number of C atoms in its formula by one. The extra C atom is introduced as a cyanide group, which can then be converted to some other organic group. Thus, reduction of a cyanide gives an amine because two H_2 molecules add across the cyanide triple bond.

$$RC{\equiv}N + 2H_2 \rightarrow RCH_2NH_2$$

Alternatively, addition of water can convert the cyanide group to a carboxyl group.

$$R{-}C{\equiv}N + 2H_2O \longrightarrow R{-}\overset{\overset{\displaystyle O}{\|}}{C}{-}OH + NH_3$$

SAMPLE EXERCISES 18.4

The name of the unsaturated carboxylic acid below is acrylic acid. Give the formula and the name of the corresponding nitrile.

$$CH_2{=}CH{-}\overset{\overset{\displaystyle O}{\|}}{C}{-}OH$$

Acrylic acid

Solution:

The nitrile formula also contains three C atoms, including the cyanide C atom.

$$CH_2{=}CH{-}CN$$

The name is acrylonitrile. This monomer is used to prepare a polymer used in plastics and fibers (Orlon).

EXERCISE 18.4

Name the aromatic compound below.

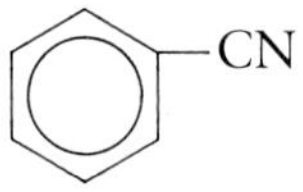

$$C_6H_5{-}CN$$

18.9 HETEROCYCLIC NITROGEN COMPOUNDS

In general, the term *heterocyclic* refers to ring compounds in which one of the ring atoms is not a carbon atom. We have already encountered heterocyclic oxygen compounds in the discussion of cyclic ethers (Section 15.11). **Heterocyclic nitrogen compounds** are ring compounds in which one or more ring atoms are nitrogen atoms.

Pyrrole is a five-membered heterocyclic N compound, a liquid called "bone oil" because it is derived from tars which remain upon distillation of waste animal bones.

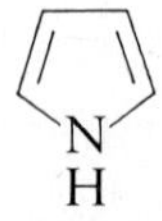

$$C_4H_4NH$$

Pyrrole

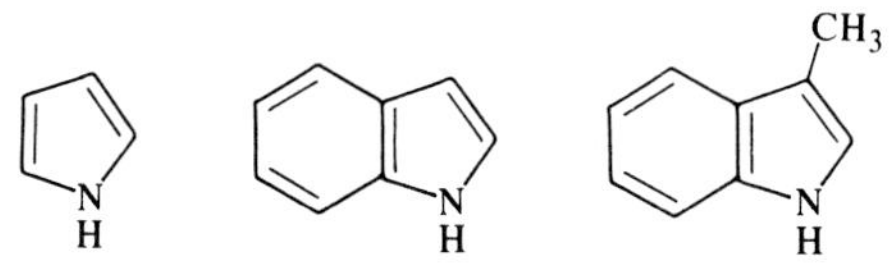

Pyrrole Indole Skatole

FIGURE 18.16
Structures of indole and skatole. Pyrrole derivatives with intense fecal odor. In highly dilute solutions, the indole has a pleasant odor and has actually been used in perfumery.

Two derivatives of pyrrole, indole and skatole, shown in Figure 18.16, contribute to the odor of feces.

The pyrrole ring system is also present in the group of heterocyclic N compounds known as the **porphyrins.** The simplest porphyrin molecule is porphin, a heterocyclic N compound which includes four pyrrole rings:

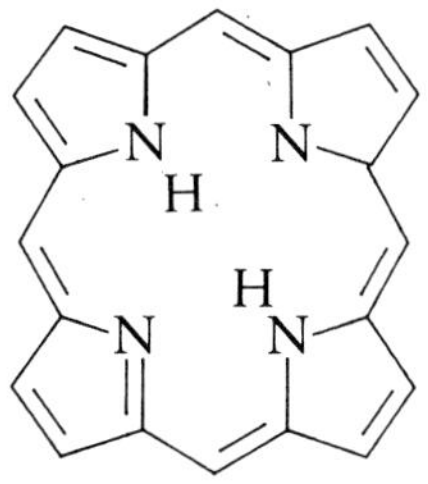

Porphin

Porphyrin molecules may have metals bonded to the central N atom, as shown in Figure 18.17, where the natural porphin derivatives chlorophyll, vitamin B_{12}, and heme (an integral part of the hemoglobin molecule) are presented.

Two six-membered heterocyclic N compounds are pyridine, an obnoxious-smelling liquid used as a solvent, and pyrimidine, a building block of the nucleic acid molecules DNA and RNA:

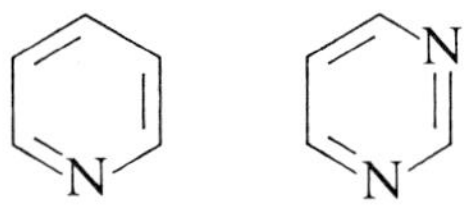

Pyridine Pyrimidine

In addition to pyrimidine, the fused-ring (see Section 14.9) heterocyclic N compound purine is a component of DNA and RNA molecules.

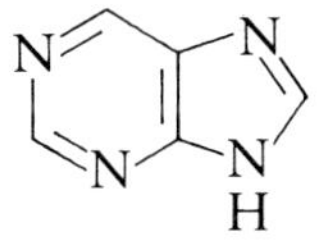

Purine

A cup of coffee or one No-Doz tablet contains about 100 mg of caffeine.

The central nervous system stimulants caffeine, theophylline, and theobromine are all purine derivatives known as *xanthines.* From their formulas in Figure 18.18 you can see that the structural differences among them are small even though they vary widely in potency, caffeine being a much stronger stimulant than either theophylline or theobromine. The natural xanthines are all mild *diuretics,* i.e., substances used to increase the flow of urine. Theophylline is the one preferred for this purpose since caffeine and theobromine cause restlessness and insomnia.

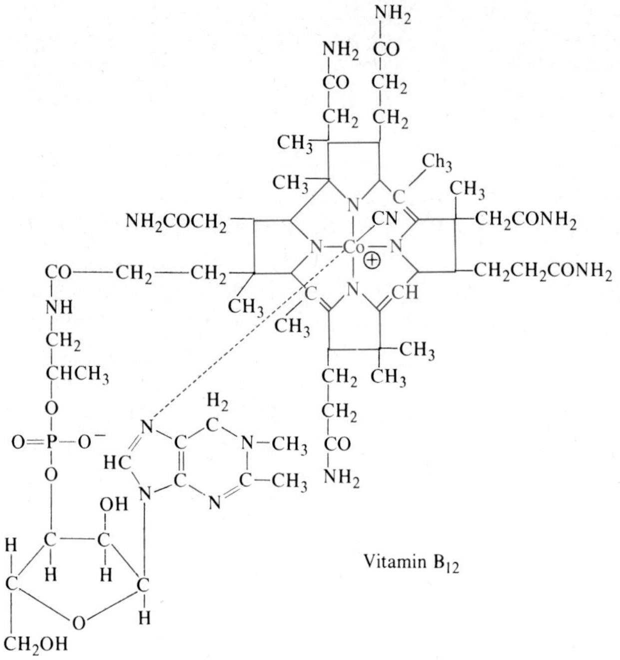

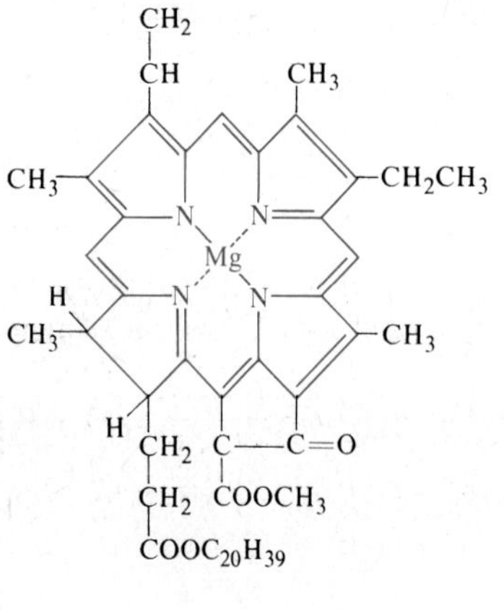

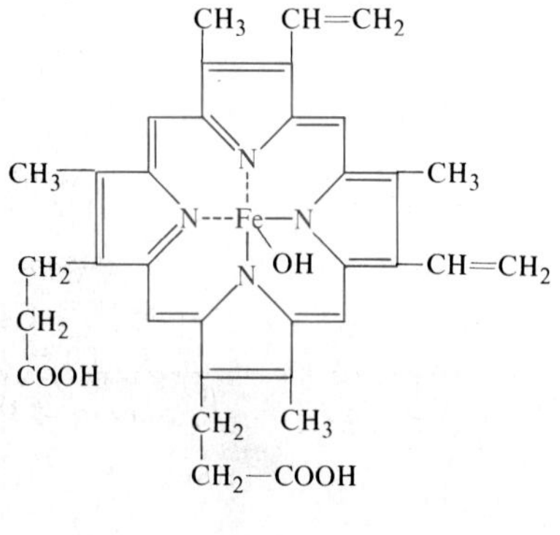

FIGURE 18.17
The porphin ring structures are shown in color. (Most of the carbonyl groups in these formulas are written as CO instead of C=O.)

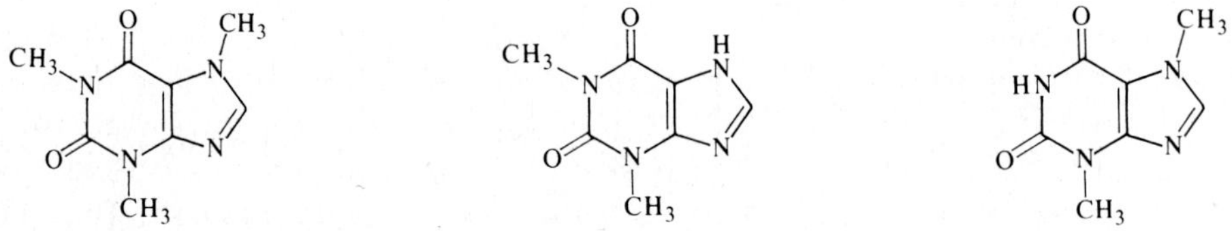

FIGURE 18.18
Xanthines: (*a*) caffeine (in coffee, tea, cola nuts); (*b*) theophylline (in tea); (*c*) theobromine (in cocoa).

18.10 BARBITURATES

The **barbiturates** are derivatives of *barbituric acid*, a pyrimidine derivative in which three of the ring C atoms are double-bonded to oxygen atoms. In barbituric acid the R and R′ in the structure below are both hydrogen atoms.

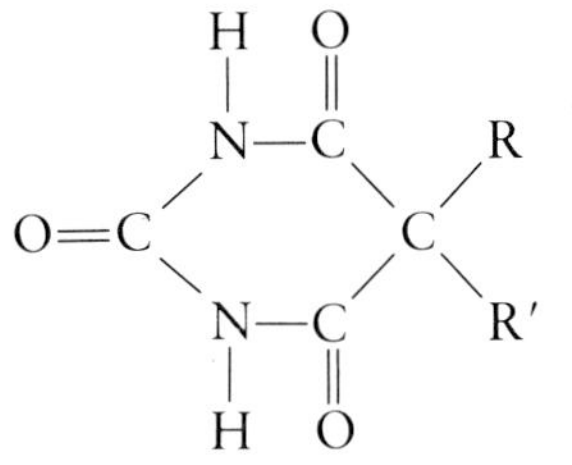

```
          H  O
          |  ||
          N—C     R
        /     \  /
   O=C         C
        \     /  \
          N—C     R′
          |  ||
          H  O
```

General structure of a barbiturate

Hypnotics are sleep-producing and sedatives are calming. The difference in effect depends on the dose.

Barbituric acid derivatives are central-nervous-system depressants, used as sedatives, hypnotics, or anticonvulsants. Their structures always include hydrocarbon substituents at the positions labeled R and R′ above. The activity of the barbituric acid derivatives depends upon the nature of the R and R′ substituents. Those in which R or R′ is a phenyl group have enhanced anticonvulsant effects and are used to prevent seizures. Barbiturates that include an ethyl group and a longer-chain group are more effective than is the one with two ethyl substituents (barbital). When the total number of C atoms (in R and R′) exceeds eight, the compounds become too toxic to be effective. Branched side chains produce stronger hypnotic effects than do straight chains. Table 18.2 lists the substituents present in some commonly used barbiturates and their major therapeutic uses, including their duration of action.

TABLE 18.2 STRUCTURE AND USE OF BARBITURATES

Name	R	R′	Major therapeutic use
Barbituric acid	H	H	None
Barbital (Veronal)	CH_3CH_2—	CH_3CH_2—	Long-acting weak sedative
Phenobarbital (Luminal)	CH_3CH_2—	 C_6H_5— (phenyl ring)	Anticonvulsant, long-acting sedative
Amobarbital (Amytal)	CH_3CH_2—	$CH_3CHCH_2CH_2$— with CH_3 on the second C	Intermediate-acting sedative
Secobarbital (Seconal)	CH_2=$CHCH_2$—	$CH_3CH_2CHCH_2CH_3$ with a bond down from the third C	Short-acting sedative
Pentobarbital (Nembutal)	CH_3CH_2—	$CH_3CHCH_2CH_2CH_3$ with a bond down from the second C	Short-acting sedative

18.11 ORGANIC SULFUR COMPOUNDS

Sulfur is a group VIA element which has bonding characteristics similar to those of oxygen and forms a number of organic compounds that are analogous to those of oxygen. Here we will undertake a brief survey of the chemistry of organic sulfur compounds.

Thiols

Thiols are sulfur alcohols in which the hydroxyl oxygen atom is replaced by a sulfur atom, as in the general formula below.

$$R—S—H \qquad \text{A thiol}$$

Thiols are also called *mercapt*ans because they can react with mercury and thus are known as "*mer*cury *capt*urers." In Chapter 8 we discussed the effectiveness of the thiol compound called dimercaprol in the treatment of mercury poisoning. The sulfur alcohols are named as alkanethiols in the IUPAC system but they are commonly referred to as alkyl mercaptans. For example,

$$CH_3SH \qquad\qquad \begin{array}{c} CH_3CHSH \\ | \\ CH_3 \end{array}$$

Methanethiol (methyl mercaptan) — 2-Propanethiol (isopropyl mercaptan)

Because the electronegativity of the S atom (2.4) is not very different from that of H (2.1), the S—H bond is not polar enough for hydrogen bonding to take place between thiol molecules. Thus thiols boil at lower temperatures than alcohols or amines of similar formula weight.

One distinctive characteristic of thiols is their disagreeable odors. The substance responsible for the odor emitted by a skunk is 2-butanethiol:

$$\begin{array}{c} \overset{4}{C}H_3\overset{3}{C}H_2\overset{2}{C}H\overset{1}{C}H_3 \\ | \\ SH \end{array}$$

2-Butanethiol

The impurities added to natural gas, which by itself is odorless, are thiols such as the ones below, which we have named as mercaptans:

$$CH_3SH \qquad\qquad \begin{array}{c} CH_3 \\ | \\ CH_3—C—SH \\ | \\ CH_3 \end{array}$$

Methyl mercaptan — *tert*-Butyl mercaptan

Propanethiol is one of many organic compounds identified in the vapor from raw onions.

Sulfides

Organic **sulfides** are analogous to ethers (R—O—R′) in which the O atom is replaced by an S atom.

$$R{-}S{-}R' \qquad \text{Sulfide}$$

Sulfides can be oxidized to form compounds known as **sulfoxides.**

$$\underset{\text{Sulfide}}{R{-}S{-}R} + [O] \longrightarrow \underset{\text{Sulfoxide}}{R{-}\overset{\overset{\displaystyle O}{\|}}{S}{-}R}$$

For instance, the oxidation of dimethyl sulfide produces dimethyl sulfoxide.

$$\underset{\text{Dimethyl sulfide}}{CH_3{-}S{-}CH_3} + [O] \longrightarrow \underset{\text{Dimethyl sulfoxide}}{CH_3{-}\overset{\overset{\displaystyle O}{\|}}{S}{-}CH_3}$$

The product of this reaction, *dimethyl sulfoxide,* abbreviated DMSO, has a very interesting pharmaceutical application. DMSO, a liquid miscible with water and with a variety of organic solvents, is capable of increasing the penetration of ionized drugs into the deeper layers of the skin. Whether DMSO will be able to find use in dermatology or in administration of drugs through the skin remains to be seen. First the toxicity of DMSO and its ability to cause tissue damage must be thoroughly studied.

Disulfides have the formula R—S—S—R′. They can be produced by the oxidation of mercaptans, as shown in the reaction below.

$$\underset{\text{Mercaptan}}{R{-}S{-}H + H{-}S{-}R} + [O] \longrightarrow \underset{\text{Disulfide}}{R{-}S{-}S{-}R} + H_2O$$

The Latin word for "garlic" is *allium.*

Allyl disulfide and allyl propyl disulfide are the chief constituents of garlic oil.

$$\underset{\text{Allyl disulfide}}{CH_2{=}CHCH_2S{-}SCH_2CH{=}CH_2} \qquad \underset{\text{Allyl propyl disulfide}}{CH_3CH_2CH_2S{-}SCH_2CH{=}CH_2}$$

In our study of proteins in Chapter 23, we will see that disulfide bonds (S—S) form links between different protein molecules and between parts of the same protein chain.

Heterocyclic Sulfur Compounds

Thiophene is a five-membered heterocyclic sulfur compound found along with benzene in coal tars. Thiophene has an odor and a boiling point (84°C) so close to those of benzene (80°C) that it was originally thought to be benzene. Thiophene is always present as an impurity in technical grade (impure) benzene.

Thiophene

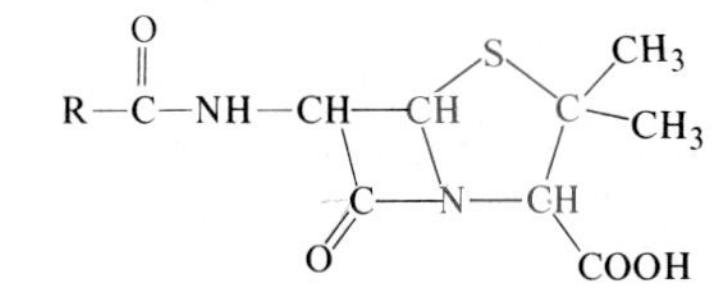

FIGURE 18.19
Penicillin formula. The thiazole ring system (in color) is present in penicillins.

$$\mathrm{R{-}\overset{\overset{\displaystyle O}{\|}}{C}{-}NH{-}CH{-}CH{<}\ ring:\ S,\ C(CH_3)_2,\ CH(COOH),\ N,\ C{=}O}$$

The compound below is an N- and S-containing heterocyclic called thiazole.

Thiazole

The thiazole ring system is present in the natural penicillins, the first antibiotics ever used in medicine (Figure 18.19).

SUMMARY

Amines are organic derivatives of ammonia, NH_3. In primary amines, RNH_2, one of the H atoms is replaced by a hydrocarbon group; in secondary amines, R_2NH, two H atoms are replaced; and in tertiary amines, R_3N, all three H atoms are replaced.

Amines are named as alkylamines or as amino (NH_2) derivatives of hydrocarbons. Aminobenzene is called aniline. The phenylethylamines include the naturally occurring neurotransmitters norepinephrine (NE), epinephrine, and dopamine, as well as the synthetic amphetamines.

Amines are hydrogen-bonded to each other and thus have unusually high boiling points. They also form hydrogen bonds with water, and those with less than five C atoms are very soluble in water. Low-molecular-weight amines have unpleasant, fishy odors.

Like ammonia, amines are basic and accept protons to form alkylammonium ions, RNH_3^+, R_2NH^+, and R_3N^+, from primary, secondary, and tertiary amines, respectively. Amines are neutralized by acids such as HCl to form water-soluble salts known as alkylammonium chlorides or amine hydrochlorides. Many drugs, such as the local anesthetics, are administered in the form of their hydrochloride salts. When heated with carboxylic acids, ($\mathrm{R{-}\overset{\overset{O}{\|}}{C}{-}OH}$), primary amines ($RNH_2$) form monosubstituted amides ($\mathrm{R{-}\overset{\overset{O}{\|}}{C}{-}NHR}$) and secondary amines ($R_2NH$) form disubstituted amides, ($\mathrm{R{-}\overset{\overset{O}{\|}}{C}{-}NR_2}$). The reaction of a tertiary amine (R_3N) with an alkyl halide (RX) produces a quaternary ammonium salt ($R_4N^+X^-$). Quaternary ammonium salts with a long-chain R group are cationic detergents. They have good germicidal properties and are used as disinfectants.

Amines also react with sulfonic acids to form sulfonamides, $\mathrm{R{-}\overset{\overset{O}{\|}}{\underset{\underset{O}{\|}}{S}}{-}NH_2}$. The sulfa drugs are derivatives of a sulfonamide called sulfanilamide. They kill bacteria by binding to an enzyme required by PABA, a nutrient that is essential for bacterial survival.

Nitriles are organic cyanide compounds, $\mathrm{R{-}C{\equiv}N}$, named as alkanenitriles. The group CN is called cyano. Nitriles can be used in synthetic schemes to introduce an extra C atom into a hydrocarbon chain.

In heterocyclic N compounds N atoms replace one or more ring C atoms. Two of these, purine and pyrimidine, are components of the nucleic acids, DNA and RNA. Central-nervous-system stimulants such as caffeine are derivatives of purine known as xanthines.

Barbiturates are derivatives of barbituric acid, a compound related to pyrimidine. The nature of the hydrocarbon substituents in the structure of a barbiturate determines its activity as a sedative or anticonvulsant.

Alcohols in which the hydroxyl O atom is replaced by an S atom, R—S—H, are called thiols or mercaptans, compounds characterized by their unpleasant odors. Thiols can be oxidized to produce disulfides, R—S—S—R. Organic sulfides, R—S—R, are analogous to ethers, R—O—R. Upon oxidation they are converted to sulfoxides, $\mathrm{R{-}\overset{\overset{O}{\|}}{S}{-}R}$. One of these, dimethyl sulfoxide, known as DMSO, is able to enhance the absorption of drugs through the skin.

KEY WORDS

amine	amine hydrochloride	sulfonamide	mercaptan
primary amine	local anesthetic	nitrile	sulfide
secondary amine	substituted amide	heterocyclic nitrogen compounds	disulfide
tertiary amine	quaternary ammonium salt	barbiturate	sulfoxide
adrenergic drug	cationic detergent	porphyrin	
alkylammonium ion	sulfa drug	thiol	

EXERCISES

18.5 Name the amines below.

(a) $CH_3CH_2NH_2$; (b) $CH_3CH_2\underset{\displaystyle CH_3}{\underset{|}{C}}HNH_2$.

(c) 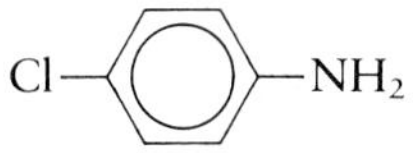 $Cl-\langle\bigcirc\rangle-NH_2$

(d) 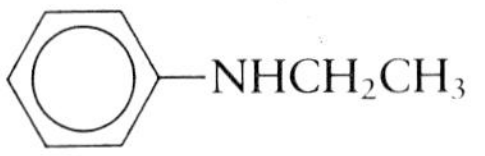 $\langle\bigcirc\rangle-NHCH_2CH_3$

18.6 Name the following amines:

(a) $CH_3NHCH_2CH_2CH_3$

(b) $CH_3CH_2CH_2CH_2CH_2\underset{\displaystyle CH_3}{\underset{|}{N}}CH_3$

(c) $CH_3CH_2\underset{\displaystyle CH_2CH_3}{\underset{|}{N}}CH_2CH_3$

(d) $CH_3(CH_2)_5NH_2$

(e) 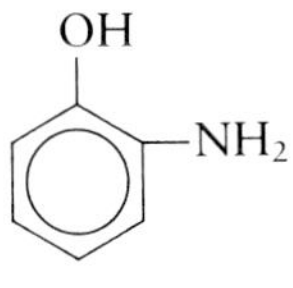 $\langle\bigcirc\rangle$ with OH and NH_2 on adjacent ring carbons (OH, NH_2)

18.7 Classify the amines in Exercises 18.5 and 18.6 according to whether they are primary, secondary, or tertiary.

18.8 The compound below, used to synthesize nylon, is called hexamethylenediamine. Give another name for it.

$$NH_2CH_2CH_2CH_2CH_2CH_2CH_2NH_2$$

18.9 Give formulas for the following amines and decide whether they are primary, secondary or tertiary:
(a) Isopropylamine
(b) *o*-Bromoaniline
(c) Butyldimethylamine
(d) Ethylpropylamine
(e) 2-Amino-3-methylbutane
(f) *N,N*-Dimethylaniline
(g) Decylamine
(h) Triphenylamine
(i) 1,3-Diaminopropane

18.10 What abbreviation analogous to PABA could be used for the compound below?

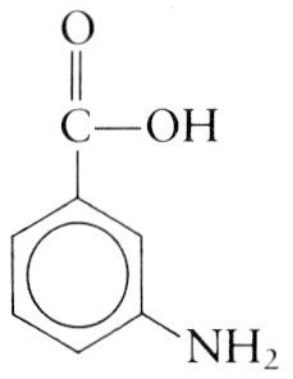

$\langle\bigcirc\rangle$ bearing $\overset{\displaystyle O}{\overset{\|}{C}}-OH$ and, in the meta position, NH_2

18.11 The compound below is called leucine. What two functional groups does it contain? Which one has a higher priority? Give another name for it.

$$CH_3\underset{\displaystyle CH_3}{\underset{|}{C}}HCH_2\underset{\displaystyle NH_2}{\underset{|}{C}}H\overset{\displaystyle O}{\overset{\|}{C}}OH$$

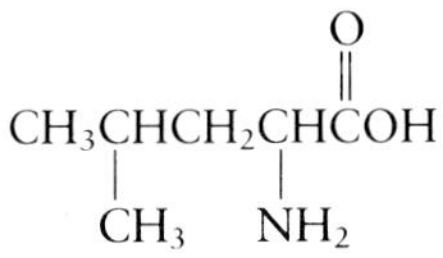

18.12 The boiling point of dimethylamine (formula weight 45) is 7°C, higher than that of trimethylamine (formula weight 59), which has a boiling point of 4°C. Can you explain this?

18.13 What is meant by the terms *amine hydrochloride* and *free base*?

18.14 Why are local anesthetic compounds such as procaine administered as hydrochlorides instead of as free bases?

18.15 Write the reaction for the formation of the salt butylamine hydrochloride. What is the formula of the cation it contains?

18.16 Which of the following compounds should be most soluble in water? Why?
(a) $CH_3(CH_2)_6NH_2$ (b) $CH_3(CH_2)_9NH_3Cl$

18.17 The hydrochloride of phenylpropanolamine (see Table 18.1) is used as a bronchodilator, a drug which increases the diameter of pulmonary air passages. Write the reaction for its formation.

18.18 Compare the structures of epinephrine and phenylephrine. To what general class of drugs do they belong?

18.19 Name the following substituted amides:

(a) $CH_3CH_2\overset{\overset{O}{\|}}{C}NHCH_3$

(b) $H\overset{\overset{O}{\|}}{C}\underset{\underset{CH_3}{|}}{N}CH_2CH_2CH_3$

(c) 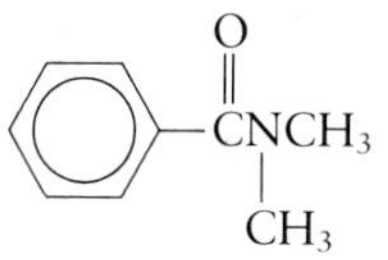 $C_6H_5-\overset{\overset{O}{\|}}{C}\underset{\underset{CH_3}{|}}{N}CH_3$

18.20 The potent hallucinogen called LSD is lysergic acid diethylamide. Given the formula below for lysergic acid, what is the formula for LSD?

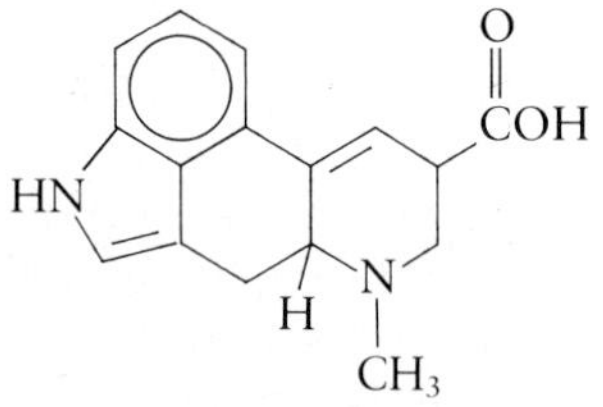

HN, $\overset{\overset{O}{\|}}{C}OH$, H, N, CH_3

18.21 Write the reaction for the formation of *N*-methylpropanamide from propanoic acid. How would you prepare *N*,*N*-dimethylpropanamide?

18.22 What is meant by the term monamine oxidase inhibitor (MAOI)? What condition is treated by such drugs? Why should MAOI not be used in combination with drugs such as amphetamines?

18.23 What are sulfa drugs? Describe the mechanism by which sulfa drugs are able to kill bacteria.

18.24 A cream used to treat vaginal infections contains the three sulfa drugs sulfacetamide, sulfabenzamide, and sulfathiazole.
(a) Give the formula for sulfabenzamide.
(b) In sulfathiazole, the R substituent in the general sulfanilamide formula is a thiazole ring. The ring is attached to the amide N atom through the C atom between the S and N atoms of the thiazole ring. Give its formula.

18.25 The compound shown below is used to block nerve impulses. What general type of compound is this? Name the compound.

$$[CH_3CH_2\overset{\overset{CH_2CH_3}{|}}{\underset{\underset{CH_2CH_3}{|}}{N}}CH_2CH_3]^+Br^-$$

18.26 How does a quaternary ammonium ion differ from an alkylammonium ion derived from an amine hydrochloride salt?

18.27 Write the ionization reaction for ethylamine in water.

18.28 Name the following nitriles:

(a) $CH_3CH_2CH_2CN$ (b) 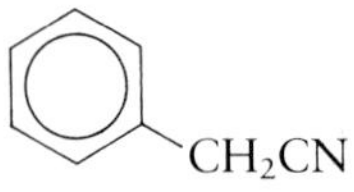 $C_6H_5-CH_2CN$

18.29 A dental patient who suffers from infected gums is given a shot of procaine to have a cavity filled but still feels pain when the tooth is drilled. Assuming that the dentist waited the required time to allow the local anesthetic to take effect, explain what could have happened.

18.30 Give formulas for the following sulfur compounds: (a) Isopropyl mercaptan; (b) Diethyl sulfide; (c) Ethanethiol; (d) Benzenethiol.

18.31 Lemon juice is used to flavor fish. Can you think of a chemical reason for this?

18.32 The compound below, called sodium thiopental (Pentothal) is administered intravenously as an anesthetic. To what class of compounds is it related? Other than the fact that it is shown as the sodium salt, what is the main difference in its structure as compared with other members of this group of drug compounds?

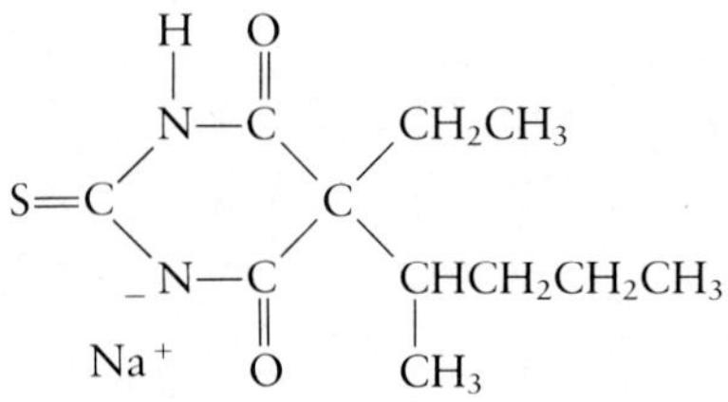

H, O, N—C, CH_2CH_3, S=C, C, N—C, $CHCH_2CH_2CH_3$, Na^+, O, CH_3

19 SYNTHETIC POLYMERS AND PROSTHESES

19.1 INTRODUCTION

You have already encountered polymers several times in this text. In Chapter 13 you learned that **polymers** are giant molecules made up of many parts (*poly-*, "many," plus *-mer*, "part") and that the small molecules that are used to build up the large polymer chains are called **monomers**. We discussed the addition of ethene monomer molecules to each other to form the polymer molecule polyethylene (Section 13.9) and the formation of synthetic "natural rubber" from isoprene (Section 13.11). We saw also that compounds such as dicarboxylic acids are used in industry to produce polymers (Section 17.3). Here we will classify and study polymers in enough detail to understand how and why they play such an important role in every area of our society.

To realize the extent to which synthetic polymers have become an integral part of modern living you can imagine an ordinary room filled with familiar objects. Now imagine that every synthetic polymer is somehow magically removed from the room. Clothing made from polyester threads would vanish, along with nylon hosiery and the soles of "rubber-soled" shoes. Record albums, tape cassettes, and other plastic objects would disappear. The insulation covering electric wires, the glue holding books and furniture together, and even the paint covering the walls would no longer be there.

Few fields have been influenced more by the development of polymers than that of medicine, where objects as elaborate as artificial organs and as simple as syringes are made of plastic. A study of the structures and properties of polymer molecules will help you to understand the possible benefits and the special limitations of synthetic polymers used as substitutes for natural materials.

19.2 TEMPERATURE TRANSITIONS

We have defined the melting point of a compound as the temperature at which the compound changes from the solid state to the liquid state. The melting temperatures of polymers are labeled as T_m.

$$\text{Polymer(s)} \xrightarrow{\Delta} \text{polymer(l)} \qquad \text{at } T_m$$

Polymers soften first at T_g and then melt at a higher temperature, T_m.

However, at temperatures considerably lower than the melting point polymer samples undergo another important temperature transition, which is not seen in monomeric compounds. At a temperature known as the **glass transition temperature** T_g, polymers begin to soften and as they do so they lose their rigidity and become more flexible.

TABLE 19.1 **TEMPERATURE TRANSITIONS OF SOME POLYMERS**

Name of polymer	Repeating unit	T_g, °C*	T_m, °C†
Polyethylene	$+CH_2CH_2+_n$	−120	110–137‡
Polypropylene	$+CH_2CH(CH_3)+_n$	−18	176
Polystyrene	$+CH_2CH(C_6H_5)+_n$	100	240
Polyvinylchloride	$+CH_2CH(Cl)+_n$	81	212
Polymethylmethacrylate	$+CH_2C(CH_3)(C{=}O\,OCH_3)+_n$	100	About 200
Teflon	$+CF_2CF_2+_n$	126	327
Polyacrylonitrile	$+CH_2CH(CN)+_n$	104	317
Nylon-6,6	$+NH(CH_2)_6NHC(=O)(CH_2)_4C(=O)+_n$	50	265
Dacron	$+OCH_2CH_2OC(=O)-C_6H_4-C(=O)+_n$	69	267
Poly(ethylene adipate)	$+OCH_2CH_2OC(=O)(CH_2)_4C(=O)+_n$	−70	50
Poly(tetramethylene suberate)	$+O(CH_2)_4OC(=O)(CH_2)_6C(=O)+_n$	−57	64

*At T_g the polymers soften, but some deform *much* more than others.
†At T_m the polymers melt or decompose.
‡Branched polyethylene melts at a a lower temperature than does linear polyethylene.

$$\text{Polymer (hard, inflexible)} \xrightarrow{\Delta} \text{polymer (soft, flexible)} \qquad \text{at } T_g$$

Different polymers behave differently at these two temperatures. Some polymers decompose at their melting temperatures, and some polymers deform much more than others at the glass transition temperature. This is of concern when polymers are used in medical devices, many of which need sterilization by heat. Table 19.1 lists the melting and glass transition temperatures for some of the polymers that we will discuss in the next sections. Most of these transitions occur over a range of several degrees, and the temperatures listed in the table lie in the middle of the range.

19.3 POLYALKENES

We will begin our discussion of structure with polymers that form when one alkene molecule adds to another. Polymers that form by addition reactions are known as **addition polymers.**

Polyethylene

We have already discussed (Section 13.9) the addition of ethene to itself to form the dimer 1-butene, as shown below:

$$H_2C{=}CH_2 + H_2C{=}CH_2 \longrightarrow H{-}CH_2{-}CH_2{-}CH{=}CH_2$$

Another ethene molecule can now be added to 1-butene to form a longer molecule and so on until a very long chain is formed. The chain consists of $-CH_2-CH_2-$ **repeating units.** Polymer structures are much too large to be represented by full formulas. Instead, we place the repeating unit in parentheses and use the subscript n to represent the number of repeating units in the chain.

$$\left(CH_2-CH_2\right)_n$$

Repeating unit

In writing a repeating unit such as the one above, we do not indicate what is attached to the end of the polymer molecule. We do this because the properties of the polymer molecule depend upon the long chain, not upon its ends. Furthermore, we cannot always be sure exactly what group is on a polymer chain end. (Possible attachments include H atoms, a double-bonded group, or even some other functional group from a catalyst present in the reaction mixture.) Repeating units shown in condensed form may be linear or branched, i.e., they may include side chains. Thus the formula $\left(CH_2-CH_2\right)_n$ may stand for either of the structures shown in Figure 13.8.

We can write the reaction in which polyethylene forms from n moles of ethylene:

The atoms present in the repeating unit are the same as those in the monomer.

$$n\mathrm{CH_2{=}CH_2} \longrightarrow \mathrm{+CH_2{-}CH_2+_{\mathit{n}}}$$
$$\text{Ethylene} \qquad\qquad \text{Polyethylene}$$

The name of an addition polymer is formed by following the prefix *poly-* with the name of the monomer—hence the name polyethylene. For this particular polymer the common name ethylene (instead of ethene) is almost always used to form the polymer name.

Useful polymers generally have molecular weights greater than 10,000.

The physical properties of polyethylene are influenced by the value of n, that is, the molecular weight of its molecules. The term molecular weight does not mean the same thing for a polymer as it does for a monomer molecule. Because a polymer sample usually contains molecules of varying lengths, we must speak of the *average molecular weight* of a polymer. A general rule of thumb is that the average molecular weight of a polymer must be about 10,000 for the polymer to have useful mechanical properties. Before polyethylene can be molded into a hard plastic, it must include about 400 repeating units so that its molecular weight will be greater than 10,000.

Polyethylene is one of the most useful of all polymers. Because of its alkanelike structure it is chemically unreactive. Its relatively low melting point (see Table 19.1) makes polyethylene one of the easiest of all polymers to process. Polyethylene is molded into plastic toys, housewares, and bottles.

Unfortunately most synthetic polymers trigger rejection mechanisms by the body.

The excellent chemical inertness of polyethylene allows it to be used for **prostheses,** devices used to replace missing body parts. Polyethylene is used in catheters, tubing, and drains. A diagram of a polyethylene device used to establish adequate drainage of the aqueous humor of the eye in cases of glaucoma is shown in Figure 19.1.

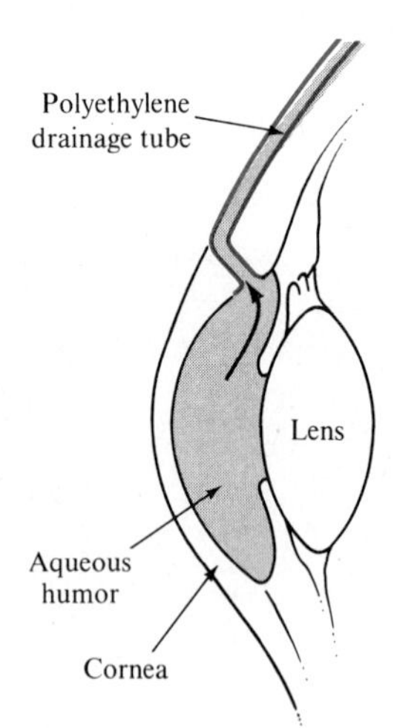

FIGURE 19.1

Polypropylene

When propene (propylene) polymerizes, the product is polypropylene. To visualize the structure of the repeating units of substituted ethenes, it is easiest to draw full structures.

$$n\ \overset{\mathrm{H}\quad\ \mathrm{H}}{\underset{\mathrm{H}\quad\ \mathrm{CH_3}}{\mathrm{C{=}C}}} \longrightarrow \overset{\mathrm{H}\quad\ \mathrm{H}}{\underset{\mathrm{H}\quad\ \mathrm{CH_3}}{\mathrm{+C{-}C+_{\mathit{n}}}}}$$
$$\text{Propylene} \qquad\qquad \text{Polypropylene}$$

The C to C backbone (the main chain) of an alkene polymer is formed from the double-bonded C atoms only. The methyl group of propylene (in color above) is attached to the main chain of polypropylene but is not a part of it. We can think of the methyl groups as if they were pendants hanging from a necklace of C atoms, as shown in Figure 19.2. Groups attached to the main C to C chain of a polymer molecule, such as the methyl groups shown in the diagram, are known as **pendant groups.**

Polypropylene is superior to polyethylene in some ways. It is more rigid and has a higher melting point (176°C) than polyethylene. Thus it is the polymer of choice over polyethylene whenever strength, rigidity, and heat stability are im-

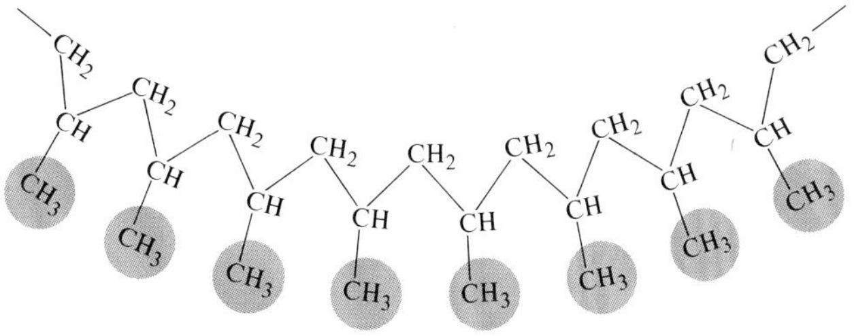

FIGURE 19.2 Polypropylene "necklace" with methyl pendants.

portant requirements. Polypropylene is used for carpet fibers, toys, and packing films. For medical purposes it has the advantage of being more conveniently sterilized by heat treatment.

SAMPLE EXERCISE 19.1

Write the reaction for the polymerization of 1-butene. Name the product and identify the pendant group.

Solution:

We begin by writing a full structure of 1-butene in which the group attached to the C to C double bond is shown as a pendant.

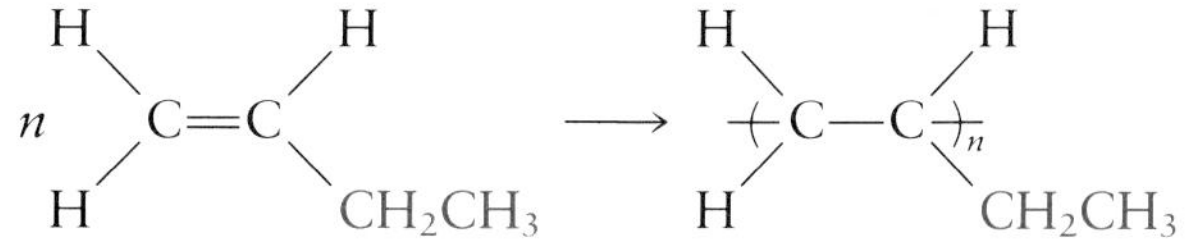

$$n\ \overset{H}{\underset{H}{>}}C{=}C\overset{H}{\underset{CH_2CH_3}{<}} \longrightarrow \left(\overset{H}{\underset{H}{|}}C{-}\overset{H}{\underset{CH_2CH_3}{|}}C\right)_n$$

The name of the product is poly-1-butene. The pendant group is $—CH_2CH_3$, ethyl.

EXERCISE 19.1

Write the reaction for the formation of poly-1-pentene. What is the pendant group?

19.4 POLYMERS OF SUBSTITUTED ALKENES

Above you saw that derivatives of ethene such as propene, in which an ethene H is replaced with a methyl group, add to themselves to form polymers. In this section we will discuss the polymerization of alkene monomers in which one or more ethene H atoms are replaced with other substituents, including halogen atoms, and the phenyl, carboxylate, and cyano groups.

Polyvinylchloride

Halogenated alkenes polymerize to form a useful class of polymers. For instance, polyvinylchloride (PVC) is made from vinyl chloride.

$$n\ \begin{matrix} H & & H \\ & C{=}C & \\ H & & Cl \end{matrix} \longrightarrow \left[\begin{matrix} H & & H \\ & C{-}C & \\ H & & Cl \end{matrix}\right]_n$$

Vinyl chloride — Polyvinylchloride (PVC)

The group of polymers derived from simple vinyl compounds is known as the *vinyls*.

You saw that halogenated alkanes tend to be nonflammable (see Section 12.15). Likewise, polyvinylchloride is nonflammable.

Additives must be mixed with PVC to avoid discoloration when the polymer is exposed to heat or sunlight. Substances called *plasticizers* must also be added to PVC, a rigid plastic, to make it flexible enough for its use in upholstery, rainwear, floor covering, and tubing and as a leather substitute in shoes. One brand of polyvinylchloride tubing is known by the trade name of Tygon.

PVC can be used to make an artificial leg, but should not be used in any device that must be placed inside the body.

Polyvinylchloride is not a good polymer to use in body implants. Its chemical composition varies too much because of the additives that must be combined with it. Furthermore, some of the formulations have been shown to be toxic.

SAMPLE EXERCISE 19.2

Give the name (common and IUPAC) and the repeating unit for the polymerization product of the compound shown below.

$$CH_2{=}CH{-}F$$

Solution:

The name of the monomer is vinyl fluoride or fluoroethene.

$$n\ \begin{matrix} H & & H \\ & C{=}C & \\ H & & F \end{matrix} \longrightarrow \left[\begin{matrix} H & & H \\ & C{-}C & \\ H & & F \end{matrix}\right]_n$$

Vinyl fluoride (fluoroethene) — Polyvinylfluoride (polyfluoroethene)

Polyvinylfluoride is easier to process but less resistant to corrosive substances than is Teflon, a polymer with four F atoms per repeating unit (see next subsection).

EXERCISE 19.2

Give the formula for the monomer needed to produce poly-1,1-dichloroethene (polyvinylidenechloride), used to make the food wrapping film called Saran.

Teflon

It is possible to polymerize the compound tetrafluoroethene to form a fluorinated polymer.

$$n\ F_2C{=}CF_2 \longrightarrow \text{+}CF_2{-}CF_2\text{+}_n$$

Tetrafluoroethene   Polytetrafluoroethene (Teflon)

Among the many useful properties of Teflon are its flame resistance, chemical inertness, and remarkably low friction and adhesion. Some nonstick cookware is Teflon-lined. Hoses and valves which must resist chemical action are made of Teflon. Because of its very high melting point (327°C) and its lack of solubility, Teflon is very difficult to process and is thus quite expensive. Its inertness, low adhesion, and resistance to temperature changes are qualities which have encouraged investigations of Teflon for use in making various prosthetic devices.

Polystyrene

Polystyrene is prepared by polymerizing the substituted alkene phenylethene, a compound known by its common name *styrene*.

$$C_6H_5{-}CH{=}CH_2$$

Styrene

The product of the polymerization of styrene consists of a C to C backbone with phenyl pendants on every other C atom.

$$n\ H_2C{=}CH(C_6H_5) \longrightarrow \text{+}CH_2{-}CH(C_6H_5)\text{+}_n$$

Styrene   Polystyrene

Polystyrene has many properties which make it useful. It is rigid and strong and can be easily colored. Because it includes C to C single bonds and an inert benzene ring, polystyrene is chemically inert. However, there are drawbacks. Polystyrene is very brittle and has a poor resistance to organic solvents. In Section 19.2 we mentioned that some polymers deform more than others at their glass transition temperatures; polystyrene (T_g 100°C) is one of these. In the 1940s and 1950s polystyrene was widely used in spite of its brittleness and sensitivity to heat. This early exposure to an inferior plastic gave rise to the popular opinion of the day that plastics were cheap substitutes for "real" materials. Today polystyrene is used in the form of a rigid foam (air plus polymer) to provide good thermal insulation for use in drinking cups and in construction. Since heating above 100°C causes severe distortion of molded polystyrene objects, sterilization by heat is impossible. Their surfaces can be sterilized with liquid bactericidal agents.

Polyacrylonitrile (PAN)

The monomer molecule used to make polyacrylonitrile is cyano- (C≡N or CN) substituted ethene, a compound known as acrylonitrile (see Sample Exercise 18.4):

$$CH_2{=}CH{-}CN$$

Cyanoethene (acrylonitrile)

Polyacrylonitrile consists of a carbon to carbon backbone with cyano groups as pendants.

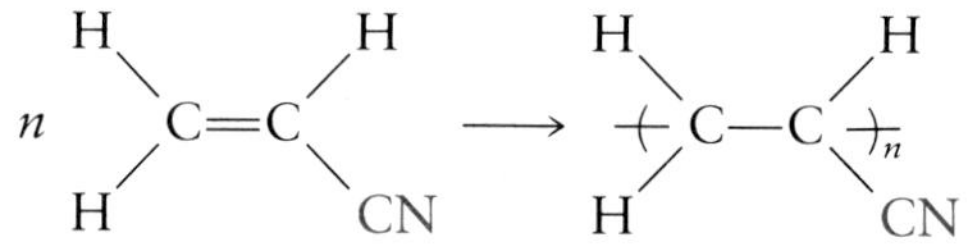

$$n\ \mathrm{(H)_2C{=}C(H)(CN)} \longrightarrow \mathrm{\left[-CH_2{-}CH(CN)-\right]_n}$$

Acrylonitrile → Polyacrylonitrile

Polyacrylonitrile is used to make acrylic fibers known by the trade name Orlon. Orlon fibers, which are strong, stiff, and resistant to chemicals and moisture, are used to make sweaters, blankets, and carpeting.

Polymethylmethacrylate (PMMA)

Methyl methacrylate, the methyl ester of the unsaturated methacrylic acid, is the monomer used to make polymethylmethacrylate.

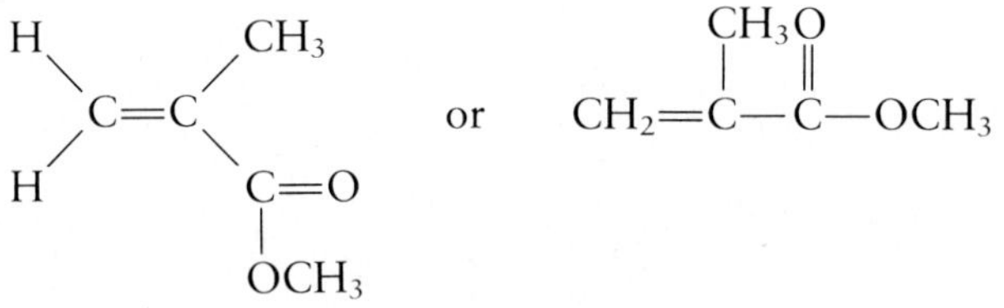

$$\mathrm{(H)_2C{=}C(CH_3)(C{=}O)OCH_3} \quad \text{or} \quad CH_2{=}C(CH_3){-}C(=O){-}OCH_3$$

Methyl methacrylate

The reaction for the polymerization of methyl methacrylate is

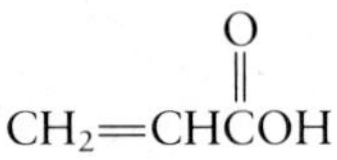

$$n\ \mathrm{(H)_2C{=}C(CH_3)(C{=}O)OCH_3} \longrightarrow \mathrm{\left[-CH_2{-}C(CH_3)(C{=}O\,OCH_3)-\right]_n}$$

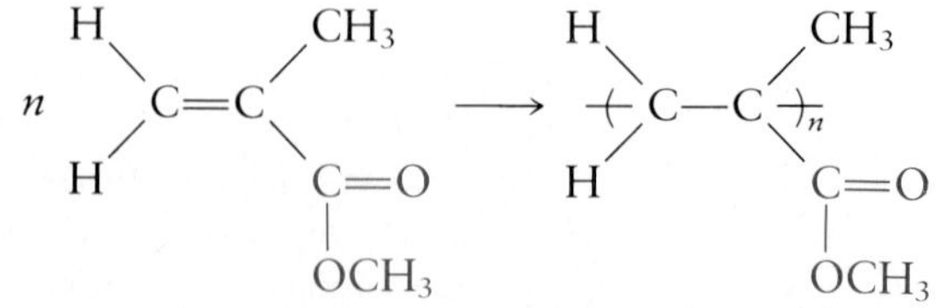

Methyl methacrylate → Polymethylmethacrylate

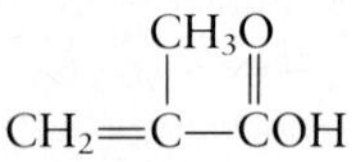

$CH_2{=}CHC(=O)OH$

Acrylic acid

$CH_2{=}C(CH_3){-}C(=O)OH$

Methacrylic acid

Polymethylmethacrylate is remarkably transparent and resistant to color changes.

Because of its excellent optical properties polymethylmethacrylate is especially useful in products in which light transmission is important. Lucite and Plexiglas are both trade names for polymethylmethacrylate used as a substitute for glass. Contact lenses are made from polymethylmethacrylate. This acrylic is particularly resistant to attack by aqueous solutions and is thus used in dentures, which must be able to withstand the rapid pH changes that occur upon the ingestion of certain foods.

19.5 POLYESTERS

Thus far the reactions used to produce polymers have been addition reactions and the monomers have been alkenes or derivatives of alkenes. Polymers known as **condensation polymers** can also be made by condensation reactions, in which monomer molecules combine to lose some small molecule such as H_2O or HCl. In Chapter 17 you saw that esters are produced when alcohols react with carboxylic acids.

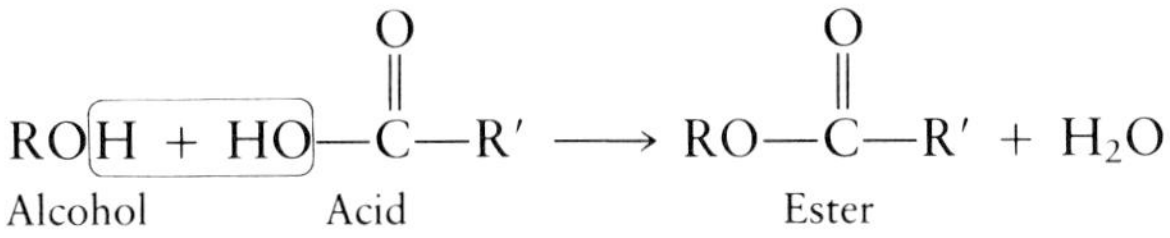

$$\underset{\text{Alcohol}}{\mathrm{RO\boxed{H + HO}}}\underset{\text{Acid}}{-\overset{\overset{\displaystyle O}{\|}}{C}-R'} \longrightarrow \underset{\text{Ester}}{\mathrm{RO}-\overset{\overset{\displaystyle O}{\|}}{C}-R'} + H_2O$$

In order to make giant molecules we must use a diol and a dicarboxylic acid which are able to link together repeatedly to make long chains. In the general formulas below we have used the script R ($\mathcal{R}$) to indicate the hydrocarbon portion of the diol or diacid. Four water molecules are removed from the monomers below to form the polymer segment shown.

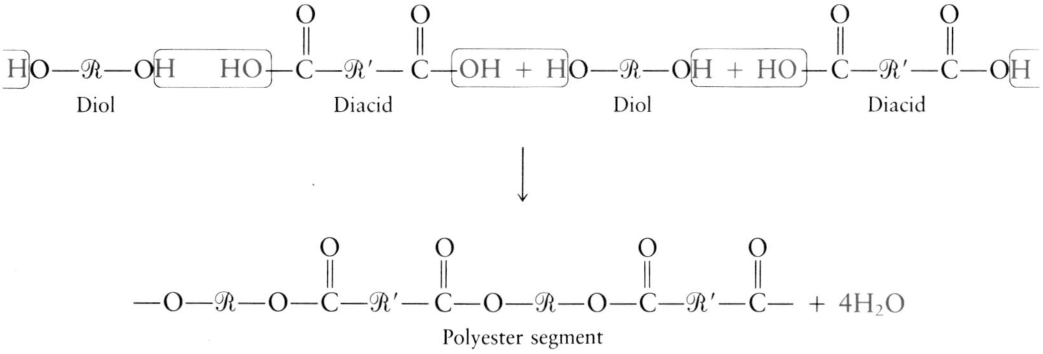

$$\underset{\text{Diol}}{\mathrm{\boxed{H}O-\mathcal{R}-O\boxed{H\quad HO}}}\underset{\text{Diacid}}{-\overset{\overset{\displaystyle O}{\|}}{C}-\mathcal{R}'-\overset{\overset{\displaystyle O}{\|}}{C}}\mathrm{\boxed{-OH + H}}\underset{\text{Diol}}{\mathrm{O-\mathcal{R}-O}}\boxed{\mathrm{H + HO}}\underset{\text{Diacid}}{-\overset{\overset{\displaystyle O}{\|}}{C}-\mathcal{R}'-\overset{\overset{\displaystyle O}{\|}}{C}-\mathrm{O\boxed{H}}}$$

$$\downarrow$$

$$\underset{\text{Polyester segment}}{-O-\mathcal{R}-O-\overset{\overset{\displaystyle O}{\|}}{C}-\mathcal{R}'-\overset{\overset{\displaystyle O}{\|}}{C}-O-\mathcal{R}-O-\overset{\overset{\displaystyle O}{\|}}{C}-\mathcal{R}'-\overset{\overset{\displaystyle O}{\|}}{C}-} + 4H_2O$$

We also use a repeating unit to describe polymers like this. The repeating unit includes the fragment of the molecule that is repeated throughout the chain.

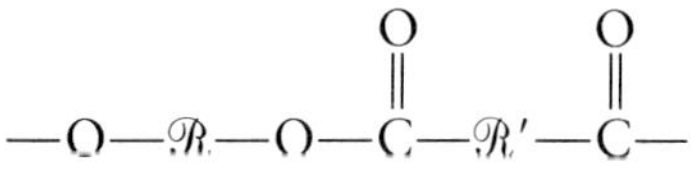

$$\underset{\text{Repeating unit of polyester}}{-O-\mathcal{R}-O-\overset{\overset{\displaystyle O}{\|}}{C}-\mathcal{R}'-\overset{\overset{\displaystyle O}{\|}}{C}-}$$

If we start with n molecules of diol and n molecules of diacid, the number of repeating units is n:

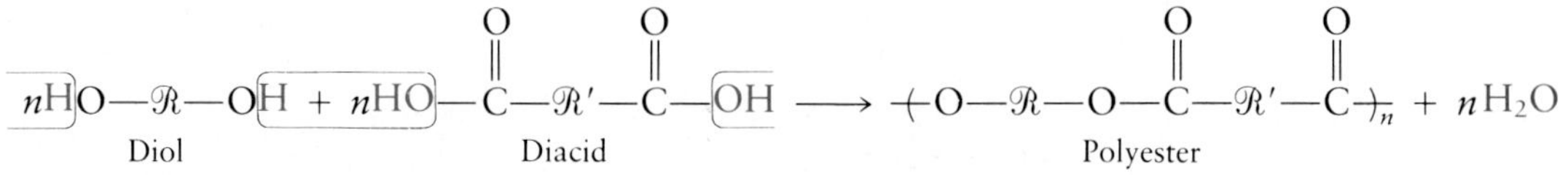

$$n\mathrm{HO{-}}\mathcal{R}\mathrm{{-}OH} + n\mathrm{HO{-}\overset{O}{\overset{\|}{C}}{-}}\mathcal{R}'\mathrm{{-}\overset{O}{\overset{\|}{C}}{-}OH} \longrightarrow \mathrm{+O{-}}\mathcal{R}\mathrm{{-}O{-}\overset{O}{\overset{\|}{C}}{-}}\mathcal{R}'\mathrm{{-}\overset{O}{\overset{\|}{C}}+_{\mathit{n}}} + n\mathrm{H_2O}$$

Diol Diacid Polyester

The polyester called polyethylene adipate is made from ethylene glycol ($\mathcal{R}$ is CH_2CH_2) and adipic acid ($\mathcal{R}'$ is $CH_2CH_2CH_2CH_2$):

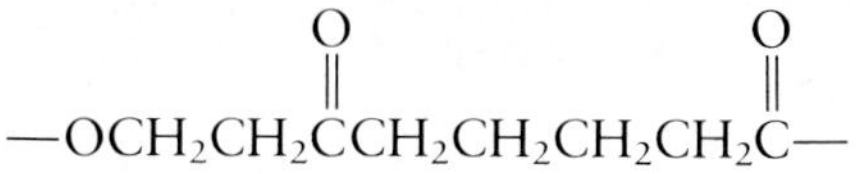

$$\mathrm{{-}OCH_2CH_2\overset{O}{\overset{\|}{C}}CH_2CH_2CH_2CH_2\overset{O}{\overset{\|}{C}}{-}}$$

repeating unit of polyethyleneadipate

Polyesters and other condensation polymers tend to polymerize in long straight chains which are particularly useful in making fibers. The polyester formed in the reaction above would be of little use as a synthetic fiber because it melts at 50°C (see Table 19.1), a temperature much too low to permit safe washing and ironing. A dramatic increase in the melting point of a polyester such as the one above is produced by substituting a benzene ring for the $CH_2CH_2CH_2CH_2$ between the two carboxyl groups in adipic acid. The carboxylic acid is called terephthalic acid (see Figure 17.3) and the polymer produced is polyethylene terephthalate (known as Dacron in the United States), which melts at 267°C.

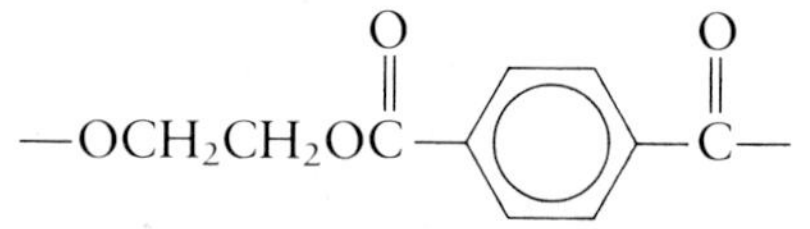

$$\mathrm{{-}OCH_2CH_2O\overset{O}{\overset{\|}{C}}{-}C_6H_4{-}\overset{O}{\overset{\|}{C}}{-}}$$

repeating unit of Dacron

Dacron is used to repair damaged blood vessels.

The development of Dacron is one example of how polymer chemists are able to adjust polymer properties by varying chemical structure. The widest use for Dacron fabrics in surgery is in arterial prostheses to replace sections of damaged arteries. Dacron is also used as a nonabsorbable suture material.

19.6 POLYAMIDES: NYLONS

Amides are produced when amines react with carboxylic acids.

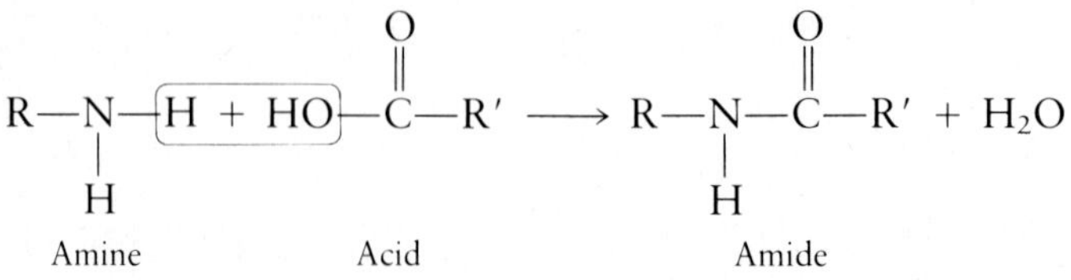

$$\mathrm{R{-}\underset{H}{\underset{|}{N}}{-}H + HO{-}\overset{O}{\overset{\|}{C}}{-}R'} \longrightarrow \mathrm{R{-}\underset{H}{\underset{|}{N}}{-}\overset{O}{\overset{\|}{C}}{-}R' + H_2O}$$

Amine Acid Amide

To make polyamide molecules, the monomers must each have two reactive ends. In the reaction shown below, n diamine molecules react with n diacid molecules to form a polyamide, with the loss of n molecules of water.

$$\underset{\text{Diamine}}{n\,\mathrm{H{-}N(H){-}\mathcal{R}{-}N(H){-}H}} + \underset{\text{Diacid}}{n\,\mathrm{HO{-}C(=O){-}\mathcal{R}'{-}C(=O){-}OH}} \longrightarrow \underset{\text{Polyamide}}{\mathrm{+\!\!\!-N(H){-}\mathcal{R}{-}N(H){-}C(=O){-}\mathcal{R}'{-}C(=O)\!\!-\!\!+_{n}}} + n\,\mathrm{H_2O}$$

In 1938 the first polyamide was synthesized by the reaction of 1,6-diaminohexane ($\mathcal{R}$ is $CH_2CH_2CH_2CH_2CH_2CH_2$) with adipic acid ($\mathcal{R}'$ is $CH_2CH_2CH_2CH_2$).

$$\underset{\text{1,6-Diaminohexane}}{n\,\mathrm{H{-}N(H)(CH_2)_6N(H){-}H}} + \underset{\text{Adipic acid}}{n\,\mathrm{HO{-}C(=O)(CH_2)_4C(=O){-}OH}} \longrightarrow \underset{\text{Polyamide (nylon-6,6)}}{\mathrm{+\!\!\!-N(H)(CH_2)_6N(H){-}C(=O)(CH_2)_4C(=O)\!\!-\!\!+_{n}}} + n\,\mathrm{H_2O}$$

Polyamides such as the one above, which include hydrocarbon segments composed of CH_2 units, are called **nylons.** Numbers follow the name nylon to indicate the number of C atoms in each monomer; the first number is the number of C atoms in the diamine and the second the number of C atoms (including the carboxyl groups) in the diacid. Thus the nylon above is called nylon-6,6, since both reactant monomers contain six C atoms.

Polyamides have unusually high melting points because of hydrogen bonds that form between molecules. The carbonyl O atom of one polyamide molecule is hydrogen-bonded to the amide H atom of another, as shown in Figure 19.3. The melting point of nylon-6,6 is 265°C, which makes this polyamide a good candidate for use in fibers.

It is also possible to make a polyamide by starting with a single monomer molecule that includes an amine functional group at one end and a carboxyl group at the other, that is, an amino acid.

$$\underset{\text{Amino acid}}{n\,\mathrm{H{-}N(H){-}\mathcal{R}{-}C(=O){-}OH}} \longrightarrow \underset{\text{Nylon}}{\mathrm{+\!\!\!-N(H){-}\mathcal{R}{-}C(=O)\!\!-\!\!+_{n}}} + n\,\mathrm{H_2O}$$

FIGURE 19.3 Hydrogen bonding in polyamides

Suppose the $\mathcal{R}$ group shown is $(CH_2)_5$, which means that the amino acid reactant is 6-aminohexanoic acid ($NH_2CH_2CH_2CH_2CH_2CH_2\overset{O}{\overset{\|}{C}}OH$).

$$n\,\boxed{H}\!-\!\underset{\displaystyle H}{\underset{|}{N}}(CH_2)_5\overset{O}{\overset{\|}{C}}\!-\!\boxed{OH} \longrightarrow +\!\underset{\displaystyle H}{\underset{|}{N}}(CH_2)_5\overset{O}{\overset{\|}{C}}\!+_n + n\,H_2O$$

6-Aminohexanoic acid Nylon-6

The amino acid components of proteins have the amino group on the α (C-2).

The name of the product of this reaction, nylon-6, includes only one number since there is only one hydrocarbon chain present. This type of nylon bears a close resemblance to the natural polyamides, proteins (see Chapter 23). The difference is that proteins are made up of about 20 to 24 different α-amino acids.

SAMPLE EXERCISE 19.3

Give the formulas for the two monomers which would be needed to make nylon-4,4.

Solution:

A diamine with four C atoms and a dicarboxylic acid with four C atoms are needed:

$$NH_2CH_2CH_2CH_2CH_2NH_2 \quad \text{and} \quad HO\overset{O}{\overset{\|}{C}}CH_2CH_2\overset{O}{\overset{\|}{C}}OH$$

EXERCISE 19.3

What amino acid would be needed to prepare nylon-4?

19.7 SILICON POLYMERS

The backbone of a silicon polymer is —O—Si—O—Si—O—Si—.

In Chapter 12, when we first introduced the subject of organic chemistry, we found that Si could form short chains of six atoms. Thus it would be impossible to make a polymer molecule in which the backbone is made of Si atoms only. However, it is possible to make Si to O to Si chains of unlimited length, and in fact the backbone of a silicon polymer, called a **siloxane** chain, is made up of Si to O bonds.

The monomer molecules used to make silicon polymers are organic dihydroxyl derivatives of silane (SiH_4) in which two H atoms are replaced with hydroxyl groups and two H atoms are replaced with alkyl groups. For instance, the compound dihydroxydimethylsilane polymerizes by losing water molecules to form chains such as the one below:

$$\mathrm{HO{-}Si(CH_3)_2{-}OH + HO{-}Si(CH_3)_2{-}OH + HO{-}Si(CH_3)_2{-}OH \longrightarrow {-}O{-}Si(CH_3)_2{-}O{-}Si(CH_3)_2{-}O{-}Si(CH_3)_2{-} + 3H_2O}$$

Dihydroxydimethylsilane — Silicone polymer

For n monomer molecules,

$$n\,\mathrm{HO{-}Si(CH_3)_2{-}OH \longrightarrow {+}O{-}Si(CH_3)_2{+}_n + n\,H_2O}$$

These polymers, called **silicone polymers,** are used because of their remarkable resistance to decomposition by heat and to the action of chemicals.

In Chapter 13 you saw that natural rubber could be strengthened by cross-linking polyisoprene chains with sulfide bonds (Section 13.11). In general, cross-linked polymers are unusually strong and chemically inert. **Silicone rubber** is formed by cross-linking silicone polymer chains such as the ones above by adding a trihydroxy monomer to the reaction mixture. This allows cross links to form along the polymer chain as the additional hydroxyl groups react to split out a molecule of water. The reaction below shows the formation of one cross link.

$$\begin{array}{l} \mathrm{HO{-}Si(CH_3)(OH){-}OH + HO{-}Si(CH_3)_2{-}OH} \\ \mathrm{HO{-}Si(CH_3)(OH){-}OH + HO{-}Si(CH_3)_2{-}OH} \end{array} \longrightarrow \begin{array}{l} \mathrm{{-}O{-}Si(CH_3){-}O{-}Si(CH_3)_2{-}} \\ \quad\ \ | \\ \quad\ \ \mathrm{O} \\ \quad\ \ | \\ \mathrm{{-}O{-}Si(CH_3){-}O{-}Si(CH_3)_2{-}} \end{array}$$

Trihydroxymethylsilane — Dihydroxydimethylsilane — Cross-linked silicone (silicone rubber)

Silicone rubber is strong and resistant to heat and chemicals and causes little or no tissue reaction.

The substance called Silly Putty (a silicone rubber) undergoes interesting and reversible shape changes. Other less frivolous uses for silicone rubbers depend upon their tremendous strength and inertness. It has been said that the "body almost ignores the presence of silicone rubber." It is true that the silicone polymer causes little or no tissue reaction; because of this it is one of the most widely

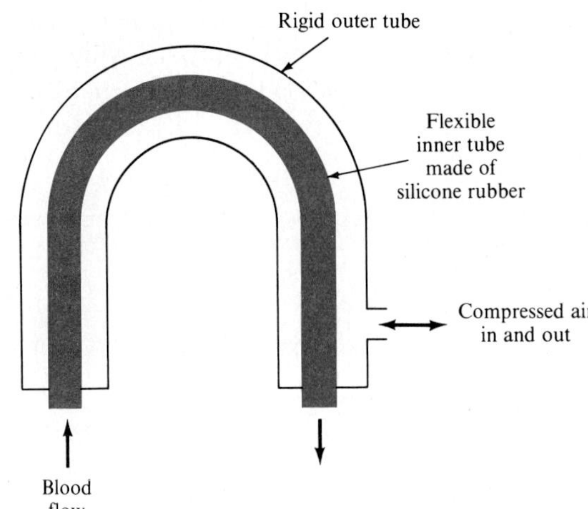

FIGURE 19.4
Simple "artificial heart" device designed for implanting in the body. Air pulses compress the silicon rubber inner tube, which is connected to the aorta.

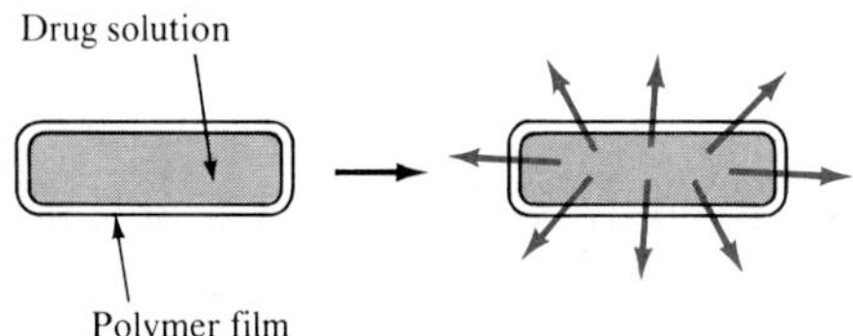

FIGURE 19.5
Drug released slowly through the polymer film.

used polymers for body implants. Silicone rubber is used for various prostheses, including those involved in the reconstruction of breasts. Artificial heart valves can be constructed from balls of silicone rubber, and many artificial heart pumps include an internal tube of silicone rubber (see Figure 19.4). Pacemakers are encased in silicone rubber packages.

One other interesting use for silicone rubber is in films for the encapsulation of drug compounds. The drug compound, placed in a capsule made of silicone rubber, is slowly released as it diffuses through the polymer covering, as shown in Figure 19.5. In this way continuous controlled release of a drug can be maintained for weeks or even months, which makes regular injections or oral dosages unnecessary. In addition, the capsule can be placed at a site in the body where the drug will have its maximal effect.

SUMMARY

Polymers are giant molecules formed by linking together small molecules called monomers. Many synthetic polymers are used in prostheses, which are devices that replace missing body parts. The most useful polymers in medical applications are chemically inert and able to withstand enough heat to permit sterilization. Polymers soften at the glass transition temperature (T_g) and melt at the melting temperature (T_m). The mechanical properties of a polymer are best when its average molecular weight is 10,000 or more.

Addition polymers form when alkenes (or substituted alkenes) add to themselves. Polymer formulas are shown by giving the structure of the repeating unit; polymer names are derived by following the prefix *poly-* with the name of the monomer. The backbone of an addition polymer includes the C atoms that were double-bonded. The attached groups which branch off from the main chain are called pendant groups.

Polyalkenes include polyethylene, one of the most useful polymers because it is so inert and easy to process. Chloroethene (vinyl chloride) polymerizes to form polyvinylchloride. Polystyrene, a brittle substance, was one of the first polymers produced. Because of its excellent optical properties polymethylmethacrylate is chosen for glass substitutes and contact lenses. Polyacrylonitrile is used in Orlon.

When two monomer molecules react with the loss of a small molecule, they link together to form condensation polymers. Many condensation polymers are used in the production of fibers. The reaction of a diol with a diacid gives a polyester. One of the most important polyesters is polyethylene terephthalate (Dacron), which is used in surgery to repair blood vessels. Polyamides, called nylons, are produced when diamines react with diacids.

Silicone polymers, made from dihydroxysilane monomers, are inert and heat-resistant. The backbone of these polymers consists of an Si to O to Si siloxane chain. Two silicone polymers can be cross-linked to produce silicone rubber, a strong, chemically inert polymer that can withstand conditions within the body. Silicone rubber is used for a variety of prosthetic devices.

KEY WORDS

polymer	addition polymer	pendant group	nylon
monomer	repeating unit	condensation polymer	siloxane
glass transition	prostheses	polyester	silicone rubber

EXERCISES

19.4 What is the difference between the glass transition temperature and the melting point of a polymer?

19.5 Which of the following can be sterilized by autoclaving at 120°C with little or no risk of deformation?
(**a**) Teflon-coated Dacron sutures
(**b**) Polymethylmethacrylate contact lenses
(**c**) Polyethylene mesh

19.6 What is meant by an addition polymer?

19.7 For polypropylene, which of the following range values for n should give a polymer with the most useful properties? Explain your choice.
(**a**) 5–10; (**b**) 50–100; (**c**) 250–300.

19.8 For the polymerization of 1-hexene,
(**a**) Write the polymerization reaction, giving the repeating unit for the product.
(**b**) Name the polymer.
(**c**) Identify the pendant group.
(**d**) Draw a segment of the polymer backbone which includes four pendant groups.

19.9 Give the repeating units and the names of the polymers which are formed from the polymerization of
(**a**) 1,1-Difluoroethene (also known as vinylidene fluoride)
(**b**) 1-Heptene

19.10 Give the structures of the monomers needed to produce the following addition polymers:
(**a**) Polyvinylchloride
(**b**) Polyacrylic acid
(**c**) Poly-2-methylpropene (also called polyisobutylene)

19.11 Name the polymer below and give the structure for the monomer that produced it.

$$\left(\begin{array}{c}\text{CHCH}_2 \\ | \\ \text{CH}_2 \\ | \\ \text{CH}_2 \\ | \\ \text{CH}_2 \\ | \\ \text{CH}_2 \\ | \\ \text{CH}_2 \\ | \\ \text{CH}_3\end{array}\right)_n$$

19.12 Draw the structure of the repeating unit of polyacrylamide. Give the structure of the monomer which produces it.

19.13 Name the polymer below, using the common name for the double-bonded compound which produced it. (*Hint:* This polymer is called PVA.)

$$-\!\!\left[CH_2\underset{\underset{OH}{|}}{C}H \right]\!\!-_n$$

19.14 What monomers are needed to make nylon-8,8?

19.15 What monomers produce nylon-6,10?

19.16 A polyester forms when 1,4-dihydroxybutane reacts with octanedioic acid (suberic acid).
- (a) Give the structures for the two monomers.
- (b) Give the repeating unit for the polymer.
- (c) Do you think this polyester would make a useful fiber? (See Table 19.1.) Why?

19.17 An interesting way to prepare nylon is to mix a CCl_4 solution of adipyl chloride (the dichloride of hexanedioic acid) with 1,6-diaminohexane dissolved in water. The nylon forms at the interface of the two immiscible solvents CCl_4 and H_2O and can be drawn off the interface as a long continuous "rope." Draw the structures for the monomers used in this experiment, known as the "nylon rope trick." What is the small molecule that is eliminated upon polymerization?

19.18 Why is it not possible to make giant molecules containing an Si to Si bonded backbone? What is the chemical structure of the backbone of a silicone polymer?

19.19 What is the formula of the monomer used to produce the silicone polymer below?

$$-\!\!\left[O-\overset{\overset{CH_3}{|}}{\underset{\underset{C_6H_5}{|}}{Si}} \right]\!\!-_n$$

19.20 Which of the following pairs of monomers could be used to produce a condensation polymer? Which are nylons and which are polyesters?
- (a) 1,4-Dihydroxybutane and 1,6-diaminohexane
- (b) Ethylene glycol and succinic acid
- (c) 1,4-Diaminobutane and adipic acid
- (d) Ethene and propene

19.21 What monomer is needed to make nylon-11,

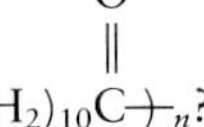

$$-\!\!\left[NH(CH_2)_{10}\overset{\overset{O}{\|}}{C} \right]\!\!-_n?$$

19.22 Compare the pairs of polymers below with respect to the property indicated:
- (a) Flame resistance: polyethylene and polyvinylchloride
- (b) Color stability: polyvinylchloride and polymethylmethacrylate
- (c) Heat resistance: polyethylene adipate and polyethylene terephthalate

19.23 What is silicone rubber? Why is it so useful in making artificial body parts?

19.24 Why do polyamides have such high melting points?

20 . . . . OPTICAL ISOMERS

20.1 INTRODUCTION

Thus far two types of isomerism have been introduced. In Chapter 12 you found that structural isomers are compounds which have the same molecular formulas but different structural formulas; then in Chapter 13 you encountered geometric (cis-trans) isomers, compounds which have the same molecular formula and the same structural formula but a different arrangement of their atoms in space. In general, isomers such as cis-trans isomers, which differ only in their spatial arrangements, are called **stereoisomers**. In this chapter we will find out about another kind of stereoisomerism, **optical isomerism**.

As you study biochemistry, you will discover the importance of optical isomerism. Many biochemical reactions take place for one member of a pair of optical isomers but not for the other. For instance, nearly all amino acids used in the biosynthesis of protein molecules exhibit optical isomerism, but only one of a pair of amino acid stereoisomers can be incorporated into a protein molecule of a living organism. Certain drugs, such as the amphetamines (Section 18.2) and narcotic analgesics, exhibit optical isomerism, but only one of each pair of isomers has a significant pharmacological effect. We will begin our study by learning the criterion necessary for optical isomerism to exist.

20.2 CHIRALITY

Two compounds that are optical isomers of one another are always mirror images of one another. (In Section 20.4 we will see why the term "optical" was chosen for these isomers.) What makes the two compounds different is that it is impossible to *superimpose* one upon the other, that is, to place one compound on top of the other so that all parts coincide. A compound that *cannot* be superimposed upon its mirror image is said to be **chiral**. An **achiral** compound *can* be superimposed upon its mirror image.

We can use our two hands to understand what is meant by nonsuperimposable isomers. Your right hand and left hand are composed of the same parts,

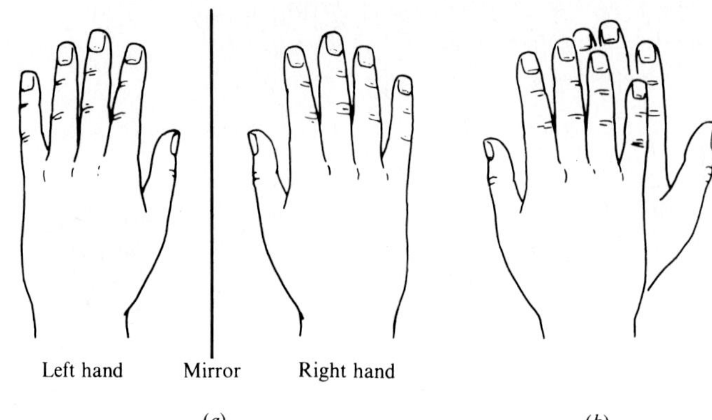

FIGURE 20.1
Chiral pair of hands. (*a*) The mirror image of a left hand is a right hand. (*b*) Left and right hands cannot be superimposed.

Chiro comes from the Greek word for "hand," and "handedness" is a synonym for chirality.

connected to each other in the same way. If you place your two hands palm down in front of you, you can see that your two hands are mirror images of each other. You can also see that it is impossible to superimpose one upon the other so that the thumb, fingers, and palm all coincide (see Figure 20.1). Thus a hand is a chiral object.

SAMPLE EXERCISE 20.1

Decide whether or not the following objects are chiral.

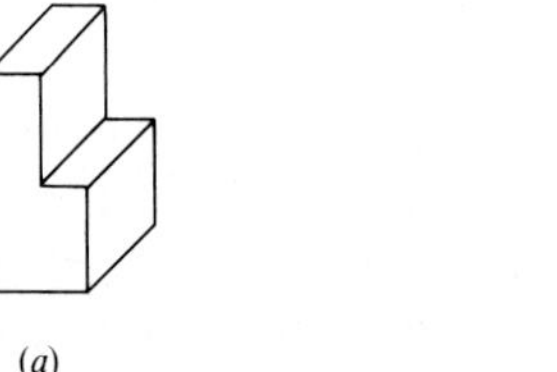
(*a*)

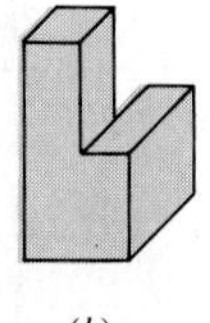
(*b*)

Solution:

(a) First construct the mirror image of the object.

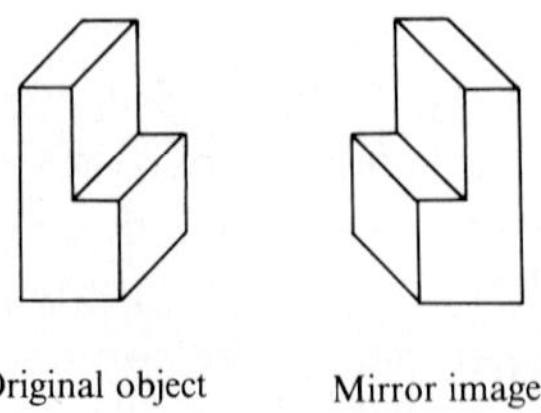

Then see if the mirror image can be superimposed upon the original object.

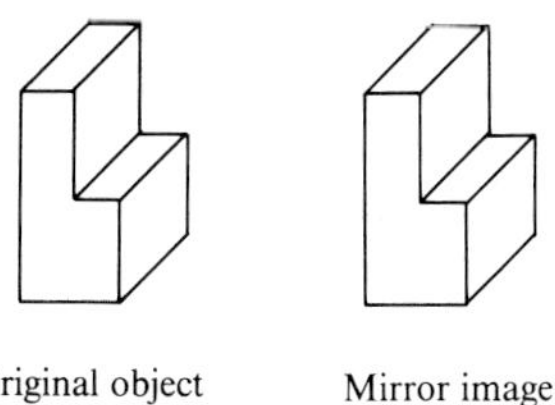

They can be superimposed. Hence the object is achiral.

(**b**) This time you see that the mirror image and original object cannot be superimposed.

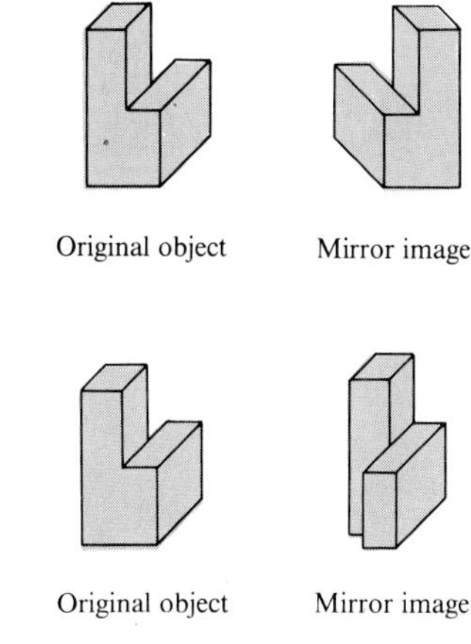

Thus this object is chiral.

EXERCISE 20.1

Is the object shown below chiral or achiral?

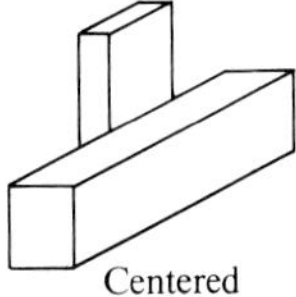

20.3 CHIRAL CENTERS AND ASYMMETRIC CARBON ATOMS

Most molecules which contain a carbon atom attached to *four different atoms or groups* are chiral. This kind of C atom represents a **chiral center** and is known as a **chiral C atom** or an **asymmetric C atom.** Figure 20.2 shows a chiral molecule and its mirror image. These structures contain a central C atom attached to four different groups, indicated in the figure as four different spheres. Notice that the

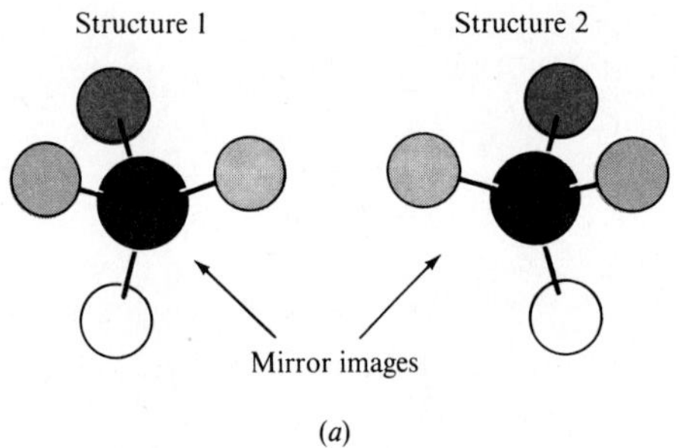

(*a*)

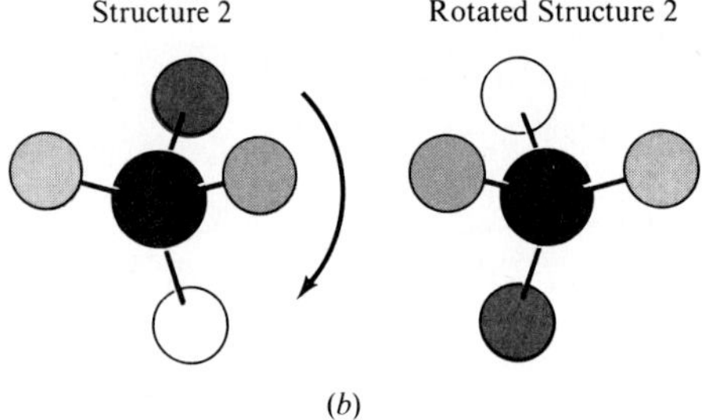

(*b*)

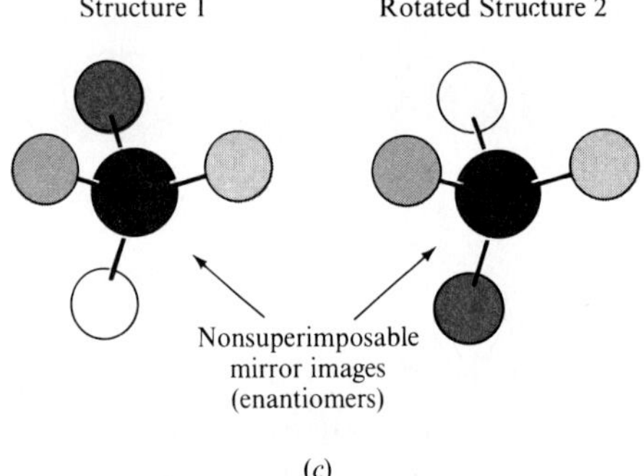

(*c*)

FIGURE 20.2
An asymmetric C compound cannot be superimposed on its mirror image. (*a*) The four different groups attached to the central C are represented by four different spheres. The central C is asymmetric. (*b*) Rotating structure 2 around so that the gray and light colored spheres can be superimposed upon those of structure 1 is possible. (*c*) But now the dark colored and white spheres do not coincide. These mirror images cannot be superimposed. They are enantiomers.

In Greek *enantias* means "opposite."

Asymmetric C atoms are bonded to four different groups.

two compounds cannot be superimposed. The chiral molecule and its mirror image are called **enantiomers**.

To see whether or not a given compound is chiral we inspect its formula to see if it includes an asymmetric C atom. This is easiest to do when using full formulas. For instance, the formula below represents 2-chlorobutane:

$$
\begin{array}{c}
\mathrm{H} \\
| \\
\mathrm{CH_3CH_2{-}C^*{-}CH_3} \\
| \\
\mathrm{Cl}
\end{array}
$$

An asterisk is sometimes used to indicate an asymmetric carbon, C*.

You can readily see that the C-2 atom of 2-chlorobutane (C* in the formula) is attached to four different atoms or groups of atoms:

1. A hydrogen atom H
2. A chlorine atom Cl

3. A methyl group CH_3
4. An ethyl group CH_3CH_2

Thus the C-2 atom is an asymmetric C atom, and 2-chlorobutane is chiral.

If any two of the four groups attached to the C atom in a compound are the same, the C atom is no longer asymmetric. Enough symmetry is introduced in this way to destroy the chirality of the molecule. For instance, suppose we replace the H atom on the C-2 atom of 2-chlorobutane with another Cl atom to form 2,2-dichlorobutane.

$$CH_3CH_2-\overset{\displaystyle Cl}{\underset{\displaystyle Cl}{\overset{|}{\underset{|}{C}}}}-CH_3$$

Since the formula for 2,2-dichlorobutane does not include an asymmetric C atom, this compound is not chiral. You can see this in Figure 20.3, where two of the

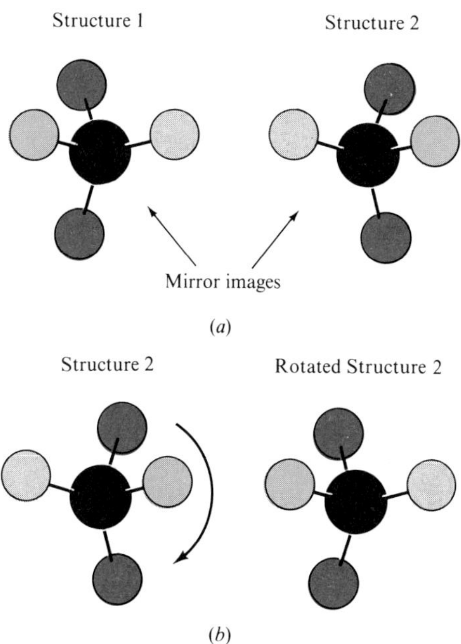

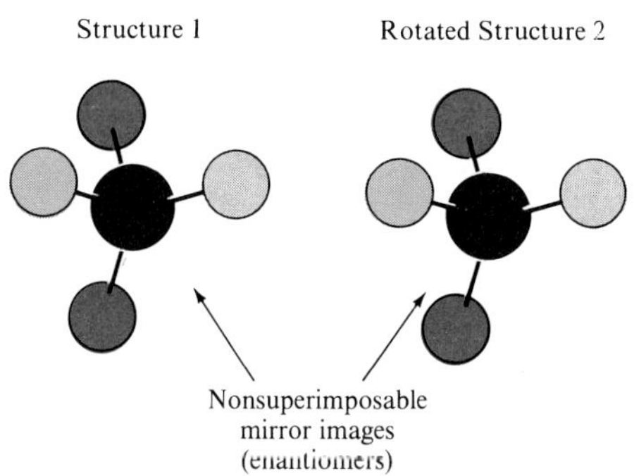

FIGURE 20.3
A carbon compound without an asymmetric carbon can be superimposed on its mirror image. (*a*) Two of the groups attached to the central C are the same. The C atom is not asymmetric. (*b*) Rotating structure 2 around so that the gray and light-colored spheres can be superimposed is possible. (*c*) Now the identical dark-colored spheres do coincide. The mirror images can easily be superimposed. They are identical compounds, not enantiomers

spheres attached to a central C atom are identical, producing a structure which *can* be superimposed upon its mirror image.

SAMPLE EXERCISE 20.2

Decide whether the following amino acids, which are components of protein molecules, are chiral.

(a) $NH_2CH(CH_3)C(=O)OH$

2-Aminopropanoic acid (alanine)

(b) $NH_2CH_2C(=O)OH$

2-Aminoethanoic acid (glycine)

Solution:

(a) In looking at the formula for alanine we see that it does contain a carbon atom attached to four different atoms or groups of atoms.

$$NH_2—C^*H(CH_3)—C(=O)OH$$

Alanine contains an asymmetric C atom and so is chiral.

(b) We examine the full formula for glycine.

$$NH_2—CH(H)—C(=O)OH$$

The C-2 atom (in color) is attached to an amino group, a carboxyl group, and *two* hydrogen atoms. Thus glycine is not chiral; in fact of all the amino acids used to build protein molecules, it is the *only* one that is achiral.

EXERCISE 20.2

Show that amphetamine (Section 18.2) exhibits optical isomerism.

$$C_6H_5—CH_2CH(CH_3)NH_2$$

20.4 PROPERTIES OF OPTICAL ISOMERS; ROTATION OF POLARIZED LIGHT

You have seen that the physical and chemical properties of structural isomers can vary widely. Some of them, ethanol and methyl ether, for instance, do not even contain the same functional groups. The properties of a pair of cis-trans isomers are also markedly different (see Section 13.7 and Table 13.2). Optical isomers are not so conspicuously different; in fact, most of the physical properties (such as melting point) of a pair of enantiomers are the same. However, there is a striking difference in one particular physical property, that is, the ability to rotate the plane of polarized light. It was because of this special optical property that the term *optical isomer* was originally chosen. To describe this phenomenon, let us first see what is meant by the term *polarized light*.

Polarized Light

"Ordinary," that is, *unpolarized,* light consists of waves aligned in all possible directions. Viewing the ray of unpolarized light in Figure 20.4*a* head on and peering down the direction of light movement, you would see that the light ray consists of waves (shown as arrows) pointing in all directions. Substances called *polarizers* are able to absorb all but a single plane of light, as shown in Figure 20.4*b*, where only one plane, represented by one of the directional arrows, remains. The light which passes through the polarizer is called **plane-polarized light**.

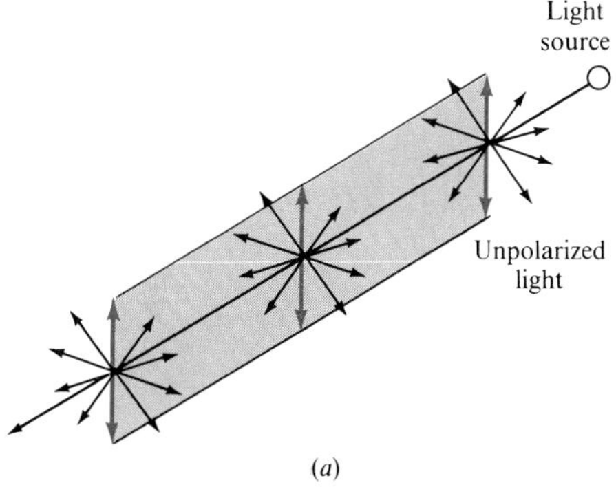

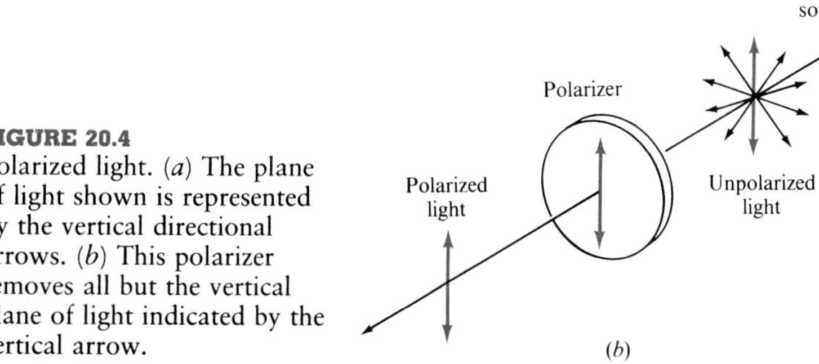

FIGURE 20.4
Polarized light. (*a*) The plane of light shown is represented by the vertical directional arrows. (*b*) This polarizer removes all but the vertical plane of light indicated by the vertical arrow.

The polarizing lenses in sunglasses are set to cut out horizontally polarized light because the glare-producing light reflected from road or water surfaces is partially polarized in the horizontal direction. When two polarizing lenses are *crossed,* that is, placed at right angles to one another, no light (or very little light) passes through, as shown in Color Plate 20.

Rotation of Polarized Light

Behavior of an optically active chiral compound when illuminated with plane-polarized light is shown in Figure 20.5, where you can see that the optically active compound rotates the plane of the light. This is also shown in Color Plate 21*a*, where two different compounds (one active and one inactive) are placed between two sets of crossed polarizers. The parts shown in Figure 20.5, the light source, polarizer, and sample compartment, are housed in a device called a *polarimeter,* a device used to make quantitative rotation measurements.

The **rotation angle** α can be used as an identifying property of a compound. The value of α for a particular optical isomer depends on:

1. The length of the sample cell l, dm
2. The concentration of the sample solution c, g/100 ml
3. The temperature t
4. The nature of the light source

$$[\alpha] = \frac{\alpha \times 100}{c \times l}$$

You can see the D line at 589 nm in the sodium vapor spectrum shown in Color Plate 3*a*.

For rotation angles to be useful, each of these conditions must be specified. The rotation angle is multiplied by 100 and divided by the sample concentration and the length of the sample cell to produce the **specific rotation angle**, written $[\alpha]$. The temperature t and light source D are indicated as shown in the symbol below. The D refers to a line from the atomic emission spectrum (Section 3.15) produced by a sodium vapor lamp such as the lamp pictured in Color Plate 6*c*.

$$[\alpha]_{\mathrm{D}}^{t}$$

A pair of enantiomers, two compounds which differ only in handedness, rotate the plane of polarized light *through the same angles but in opposite directions,* as shown in Figure 20.6 for the enantiomers of amphetamine (Exercise

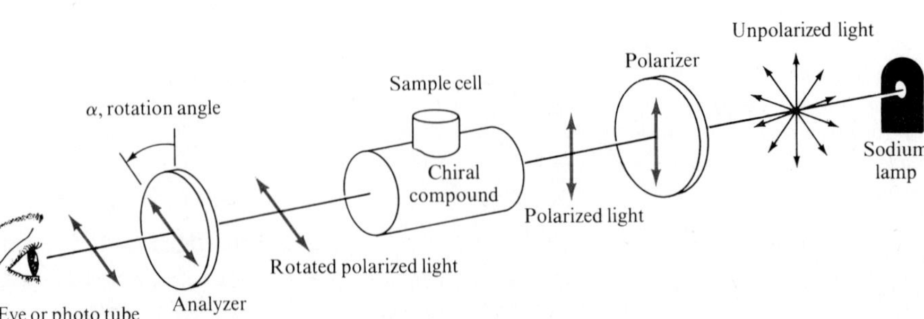

FIGURE 20.5
Polarimeter. The analyzer is a second polarizer that also passes only vertical polarized light. By rotating this polarizer, the rotated light can pass through. The angle by which it must be rotated is α.

Compound: amphetamine
Solvent: benzene
Concentration: 8 g/100 cm^3
Sample cell length: 1 dm

C_6H_5—CH_2CHNH_2 with CH_3 on the CH carbon

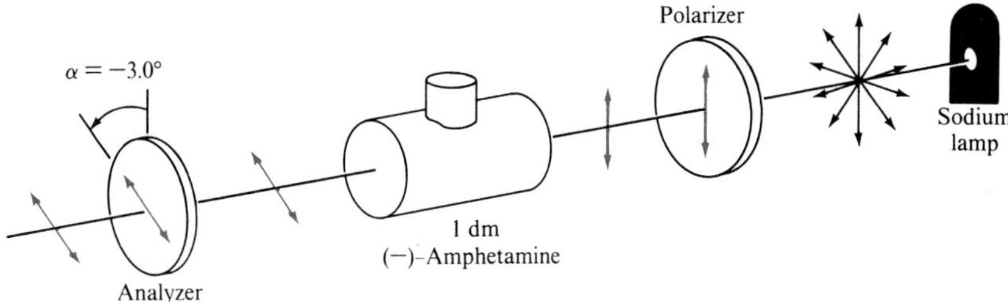

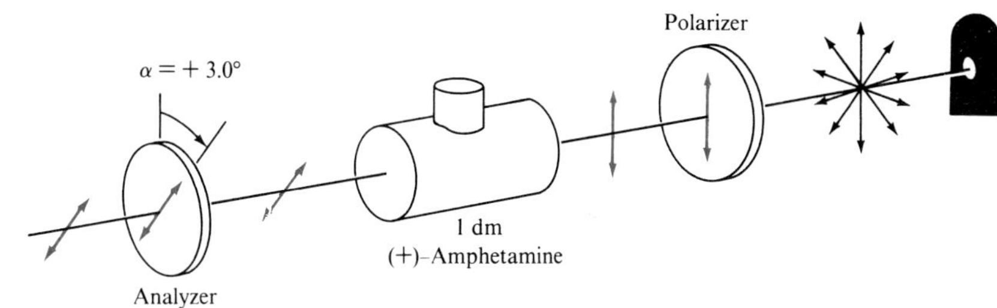

FIGURE 20.6
Optical rotation of (+)- and (−)-amphetamines. The rotation angle α for levorotatory (−)-amphetamine is −3.0° and that for dextrorotatory (+)-amphetamine is +3.0°. The specific rotations are −37.5° and +37.5° for the conditions specified. $(\alpha \times 100)/(8 \times 1) = 300/8 = 37.5$.

The difference in the rotation of polarized light for a pair of enantiomers is shown in Color Plates 21*b* and 21*c*.

20.2). The isomers which rotate polarized light in the clockwise direction are called **dextrorotatory**, or (+), and those which rotate light in a counterclockwise direction are **levorotatory**, or (−). The names of enantiomers are often preceded by a (+) or (−) to indicate the direction of rotation. Note in the figure that the value of the rotation angle α is 3.0° for the conditions specified, and that of the specific rotation $[\alpha]$ is 37.5°.

20.5 WRITING FORMULAS FOR OPTICAL ISOMERS

The structures of a pair of enantiomers could be represented by three-dimensional drawings such as the ones shown in Figure 20.2, but for persons without considerable artistic skills such pictures are too difficult to draw, and furthermore they are confusing to look at. There are two ways commonly used to represent a pair of optical isomers using two-dimensional figures.

Wedge and Dash Structures

In **wedge and dash structures** wedges (►) are used to indicate groups which come forward out of the plane of the paper and dashes (≡) the groups that extend back from the plane of the paper. For instance, consider a molecule in which an

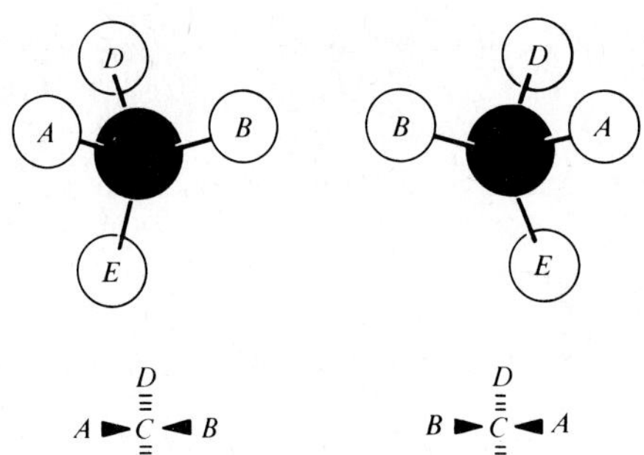

FIGURE 20.7
Models that correspond to wedge and dash structures. The *A* and *B* are coming out of the plane of the paper. The *D* and *E* are extending back from the plane of the paper.

asymmetric C atom is bonded to four different groups *A*, *B*, *D*, and *E*. Suppose *A* and *B* are in front of the plane of the paper and *D* and *E* are behind it. The wedge and dash drawings below represent the two optical isomers.

Atoms A and B, attached to wedges, are pointing out of the paper at you.

Figure 20.7 shows the models that correspond to these drawings. You can duplicate these with a ball-and-stick model set or by creating your own models with four toothpicks stuck in an orange, the two horizontal ones (*A* and *B*) pointing toward you and the two vertical ones (*D* and *E*) away from you. Note that the *D*'s and *E*'s are oriented the same way in both enantiomers but the *A*'s and *B*'s are not.

Suppose we try to mentally superimpose the two structures above by rotating enantiomer 1 so that the *A* and *B* are interchanged. Now we can superimpose the *A*'s and *B*'s of both enantiomers. But when we do that, the *D*'s and *E*'s can no longer be superimposed. The rotated structure is not the same as enantiomer 2.

D *A*—C—*B* *E*	*E* *B*—C—*A* *D*	*D* *B*—C—*A* *E*
Enantiomer 1	Rotated enantiomer 1	Enantiomer 2

With practice you can begin to visualize three-dimensional structures with the aid of wedge and dash drawings.

Fischer Projections

The German chemist Emil Fischer (1852–1919) won a second Nobel prize in chemistry in 1902.

Fischer projections are more convenient to draw even though they do not give nearly as good a perspective as the wedge and dash drawings above. In a **Fischer projection** the intersection of a vertical and a horizontal line represents the asymmetric C atom. By convention the groups attached to the horizontal lines extend in front of the plane of the paper (as the wedges do), and those connected to the vertical lines extend behind the paper (as the dashes do). We can now draw Fischer projections that correspond to the wedge and dash drawings above.

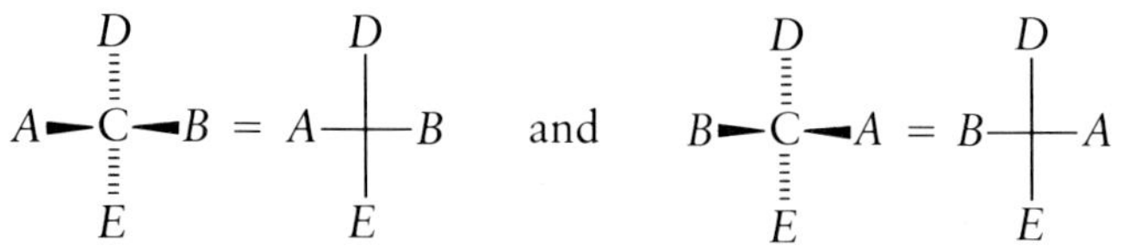

$$A\!-\!\underset{E}{\overset{D}{C}}\!-\!B = A\!-\!\underset{E}{\overset{D}{+}}\!-\!B \quad \text{and} \quad B\!-\!\underset{E}{\overset{D}{C}}\!-\!A = B\!-\!\underset{E}{\overset{D}{+}}\!-\!A$$

If the compound to be represented includes more than one C atom, the longest C chain is drawn vertically with C-1 at the top. For instance, suppose we wish to draw the Fischer projection for 2-bromobutane.

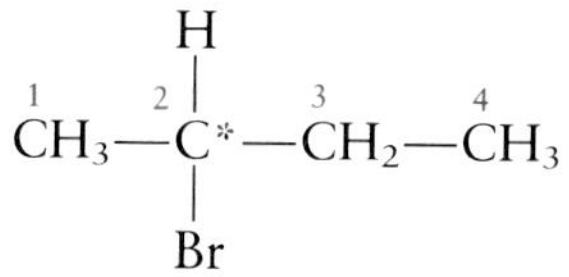

$$\overset{1}{CH_3}-\underset{Br}{\overset{H}{\overset{2}{C^*}}}-\overset{3}{CH_2}-\overset{4}{CH_3}$$

The C-2 atom is the asymmetric C atom and is thus the intersection point. The methyl and ethyl groups are attached to the vertical line with the methyl at the top since it is C-1. The Br and H atoms are attached to the horizontal line.

$$Br\!-\!\underset{CH_2CH_3}{\overset{CH_3}{+}}\!-\!H \quad \text{and} \quad H\!-\!\underset{CH_2CH_3}{\overset{CH_3}{+}}\!-\!Br$$

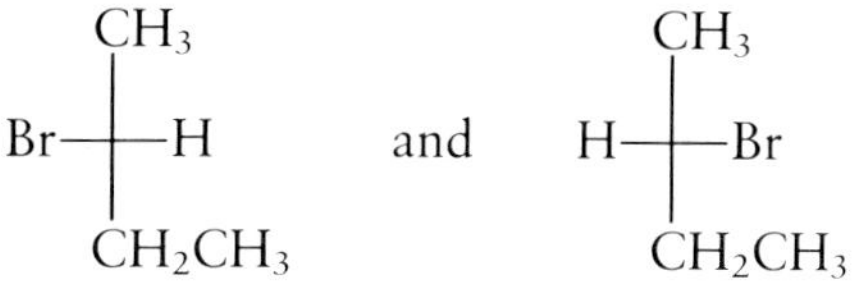

The corresponding wedge and dash structures are

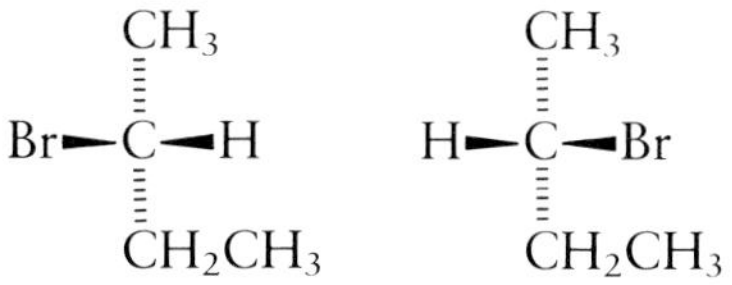

$$Br\!-\!\underset{CH_2CH_3}{\overset{CH_3}{C}}\!-\!H \qquad H\!-\!\underset{CH_2CH_3}{\overset{CH_3}{C}}\!-\!Br$$

SAMPLE EXERCISE 20.3

Represent the enantiomers of the amino acid serine using both Fischer projection and wedge and dash drawings.

$$HO\overset{3}{C}H_2\underset{NH_2}{\overset{2}{C}}H\overset{\overset{O}{\|}}{\overset{1}{C}}-OH$$

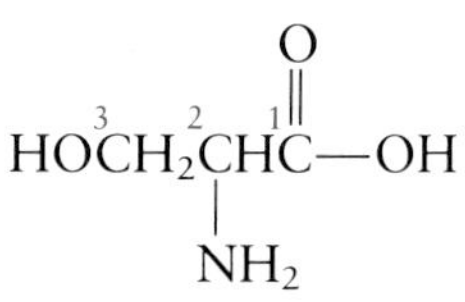

Serine

Solution:

To draw the Fischer projection take the C-2 atom (the asymmetric C) as the intersection of the horizontal and vertical lines. The three-carbon-atom chain is vertical, with the C-1 atom (the carboxyl carbon) at the top. The NH_2 group and the H atom on the C-2 atom are attached to the horizontal line.

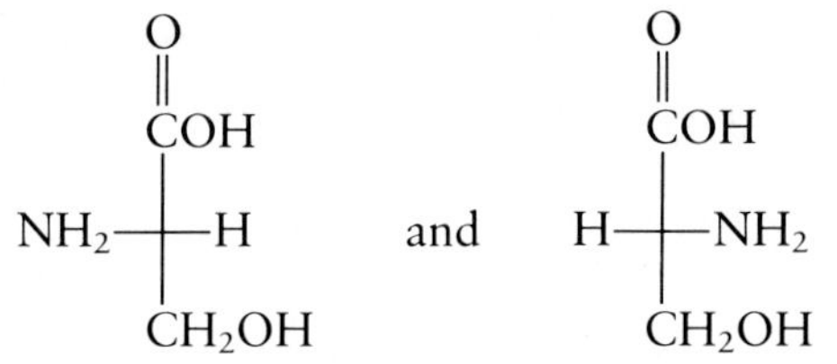

$$\begin{array}{c}O\\\|\\COH\\|\\NH_2-\!\!+\!\!-H\\|\\CH_2OH\end{array}\qquad\text{and}\qquad\begin{array}{c}O\\\|\\COH\\|\\H-\!\!+\!\!-NH_2\\|\\CH_2OH\end{array}$$

In the corresponding wedge and dash structures the horizontal groups (H and NH_2) are attached to the asymmetric C with wedges and the vertical groups (CH_2OH and COOH) are attached with dashes.

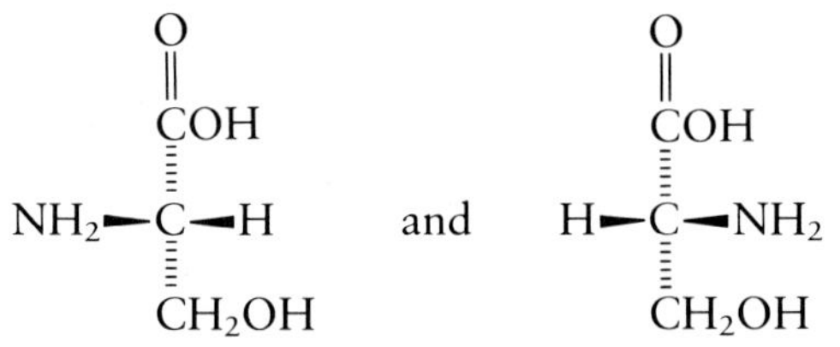

$$\begin{array}{c}O\\\|\\COH\\\vdots\\NH_2\blacktriangleright C\blacktriangleleft H\\\vdots\\CH_2OH\end{array}\qquad\text{and}\qquad\begin{array}{c}O\\\|\\COH\\\vdots\\H\blacktriangleright C\blacktriangleleft NH_2\\\vdots\\CH_2OH\end{array}$$

EXERCISE 20.3

Draw the enantiomers of alanine (2-aminopropanoic acid) using both Fischer projections and wedge and dash structures.

$$\begin{array}{ccccc} & & H & & O\\ & & | & & \|\\ CH_3 & - & C & - & COH\\ & & | & & \\ & & NH_2 & & \end{array}$$

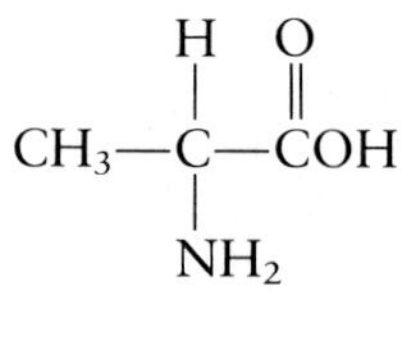

20.6 NAMING ENANTIOMERS

Since a pair of enantiomers is two different compounds, these compounds must have different names. Emil Fischer first suggested the **D-L system** for specifying the absolute configuration of an optical isomer, that is, the arrangement of its atoms in space. According to this sytem all optical isomers are compared with the isomers of glyceraldehyde (glycerol in which one hydroxyl group is oxidized to an aldehyde), an optically active compound with the formula

$$\mathrm{HOCH_2\overset{*}{C}H(OH)CH{=}O}$$

Glyceraldehyde

The structure corresponding to the Fischer projection formula in which the OH group (in color) attached to the asymmetric C points to the right was arbitratily given the name D-glyceraldehyde, and the other isomer was called L-glyceraldehyde.

$$\begin{array}{ccc} \mathrm{O} & & \mathrm{O} \\ \| & & \| \\ \mathrm{CH} & & \mathrm{CH} \\ \mathrm{H{-}\!\!\!+\!\!\!-OH} & & \mathrm{HO{-}\!\!\!+\!\!\!-H} \\ \mathrm{CH_2OH} & & \mathrm{CH_2OH} \end{array}$$

D-Glyceraldehyde L-Glyceraldehyde

When the names were first assigned it was not known whether D-glyceraldehyde was dextrorotatory or levorotatory. Not until 1951 was it discovered that the D-glyceraldehyde isomer rotates plane-polarized light in the clockwise direction. Thus Fischer's arbitrary choice for D-glyceraldehyde also happened to correspond to (+)-glyceraldehyde. The names can be written as D-(+)-glyceraldehyde and L-(−)-glyceraldehyde. It is possible for compounds with the D structure to be levorotatory, that is, there are D-(−)-compounds, and vice versa. The letters D and L have nothing to do with the rotation directions, dextrorotatory and levorotatory; that is

The direction in which the isomer happens to rotate plane-polarized light has no direct correlation with the arrangement of its atoms in space.

It is incorrect to use the lowercase letters d and l instead of (+) and (−) since they are easily confused with the capital D and L used to denote arrangement in space.

Optical isomers which have the general formula $\mathrm{R{-}\underset{}{\overset{X}{\overset{|}{C}}}H{-}R'}$ can be compared directly with glyceraldehyde. In the formula the R and R′ refer to any C-containing groups and the X (attached to the asymmetric C atom) refers to some other functional group, usually a halogen, amino, or hydroxyl. Recall that the Fischer projection formulas are drawn so that the C-1 atom is at the top of the vertical line. The optical isomers having structures like those of D-glyceraldehyde, in which the X group points toward the right, are D isomers.

$$\begin{array}{ccc} \mathrm{R'} & & \mathrm{R'} \\ \mathrm{H{-}\!\!\!+\!\!\!-X} & & \mathrm{X{-}\!\!\!+\!\!\!-H} \\ \mathrm{R} & & \mathrm{R} \end{array}$$

D Isomer L Isomer

A D isomer can be (+) or (−) but must have a formula comparable with that of D-glyceraldehyde.

For instance, suppose we wish to assign names to the two enantiomers of alanine, $CH_3\underset{\underset{NH_2}{|}}{C}H\overset{\overset{O}{\|}}{C}OH$. We draw their Fischer projection formulas, putting the C-1 atom (the carboxyl C) at the top of the vertical line. The structure in which the amino group points to the right is D-alanine and the other one is L-alanine.

$$\begin{array}{ccc} & O & \\ & \| & \\ & COH & \\ & | & \\ H- & + & -NH_2 \\ & | & \\ & CH_3 & \end{array} \qquad \begin{array}{ccc} & O & \\ & \| & \\ & COH & \\ & | & \\ NH_2- & + & -H \\ & | & \\ & CH_3 & \end{array}$$

D-Alanine L-Alanine

Figure 20.8 shows the Fischer projection drawings, names, and three-dimensional structures for the enantiomers of alanine so that you can see how they correspond to one another.

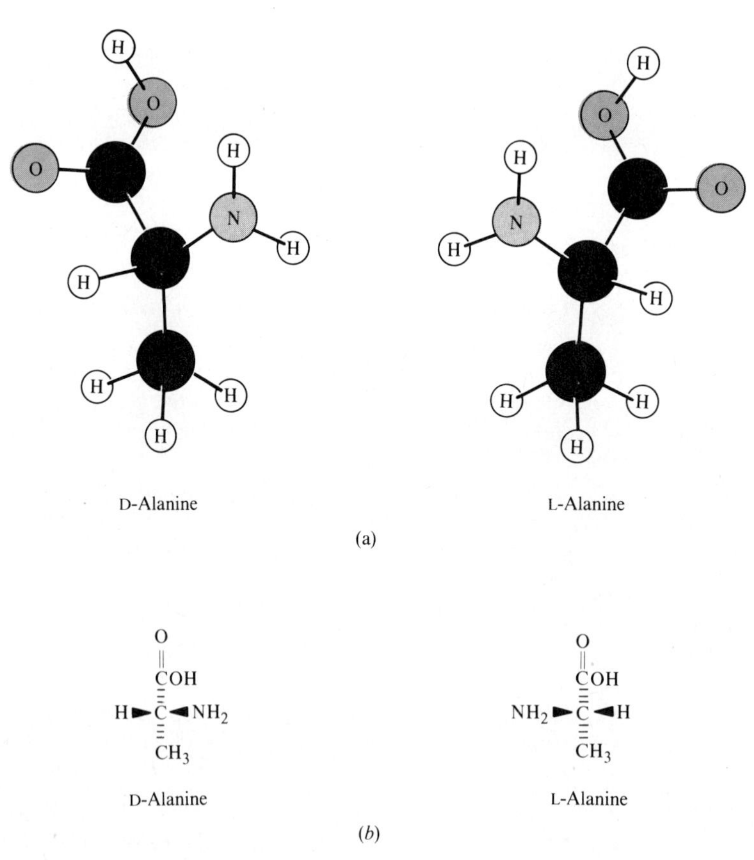

$$\begin{array}{ccc} & O & \\ & \| & \\ & COH & \\ H- & + & -NH_2 \\ & CH_3 & \end{array} \qquad \begin{array}{ccc} & O & \\ & \| & \\ & COH & \\ NH_2- & + & -H \\ & CH_3 & \end{array}$$

FIGURE 20.8
Alanine enantiomers. (*a*) Models. (*b*) Wedge and dash structures. (*c*) Fischer projection formulas.

SAMPLE EXERCISE 20.4

Draw the Fischer projection formulas for lactic acid (2-hydroxypropanoic acid) the product of a set of reactions (called glycolysis) involved in the metabolism of glucose. Which is the D isomer and which is the L isomer? Can you identify the (+) isomer, the one that is actually present in blood and muscle tissue?

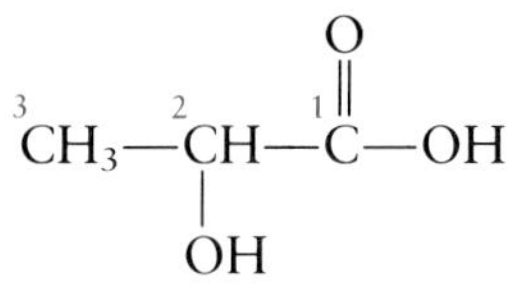

$$\overset{3}{C}H_3—\overset{2}{C}H(OH)—\overset{1}{C}(=O)—OH$$

Solution:

We put the C-1 atom at the top of the vertical line. The hydroxyl group (in color) attached to the asymmetric C atom (C-2) projects to the right or to the left. The one in which the hydroxyl points to the right is the D isomer.

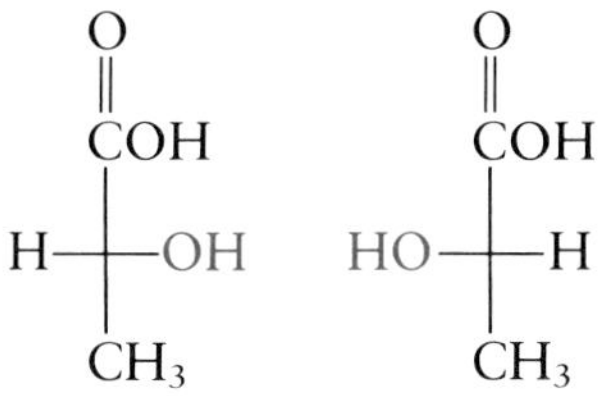

$\overset{O}{\overset{\|\|}{C}}OH$	$\overset{O}{\overset{\|\|}{C}}OH$
H—┼—OH	HO—┼—H
CH_3	CH_3
D-Lactic acid	L-Lactic acid

We cannot say which one is (+) without experimental evidence.

EXERCISE 20.4

Draw Fischer projection formulas for the amino acid below, called valine (2-amino-3-methylbutanoic acid). Which is D-valine and which is L-valine?

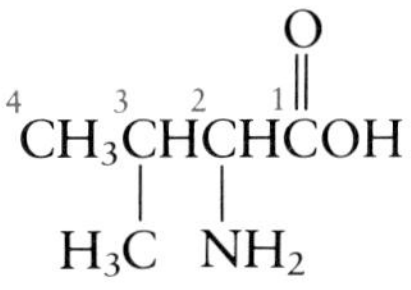

$$\overset{4}{C}H_3\overset{3}{C}H(CH_3)\overset{2}{C}H(NH_2)\overset{1}{C}(=O)OH$$

20.7 DIASTEREOISOMERS

Compounds which have more than one asymmetric C atom have more than two stereoisomers. The maximum number of stereoisomers possible is given by the formula 2^n, where n is the number of asymmetric carbon atoms. For instance, the five-carbon *sugar* (Chapter 21) compound shown below has three asymmetric C atoms and thus could have as many as 2^3, or eight stereoisomers.

One of the eight stereoisomers of this five-carbon sugar is D-ribose, a component of the nucleic acid RNA (Chapter 24).

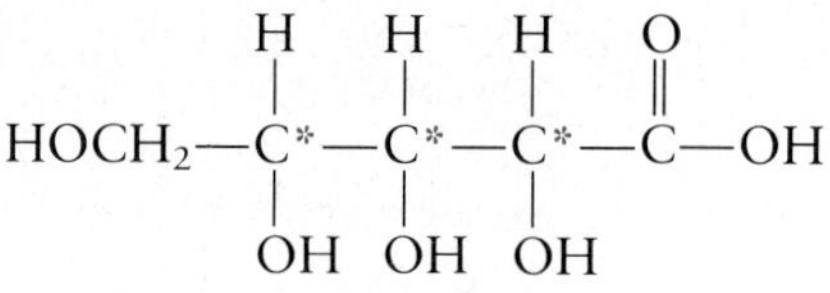

$$
\begin{array}{ccccccccc}
 & & H & & H & & H & & O \\
 & & | & & | & & | & & \| \\
HOCH_2 & — & C^* & — & C^* & — & C^* & — & C—OH \\
 & & | & & | & & | & & \\
 & & OH & & OH & & OH & &
\end{array}
$$

Five-carbon sugar compound

Not all the stereoisomers for a given optically active compound are mirror images of one another. Enantiomers are the stereoisomers which *are* mirror images of one another; **diastereoisomers** are optical isomers of a compound which *are not* mirror images of one another.

For instance, suppose we draw the four Fischer projection formulas for the following four-carbon sugar, which has two asymmetric carbons and therefore four (2^2) stereoisomers.

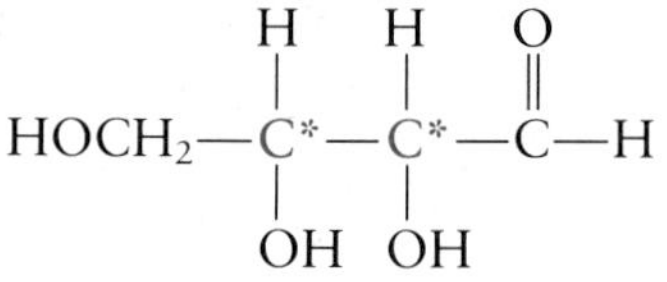

$$
\begin{array}{ccccccc}
 & & H & & H & & O \\
 & & | & & | & & \| \\
HOCH_2 & — & C^* & — & C^* & — & C—H \\
 & & | & & | & & \\
 & & OH & & OH & &
\end{array}
$$

The hydrogen atoms and hydroxyl groups point to the left or right in four possible ways to produce structures 1 through 4 below.

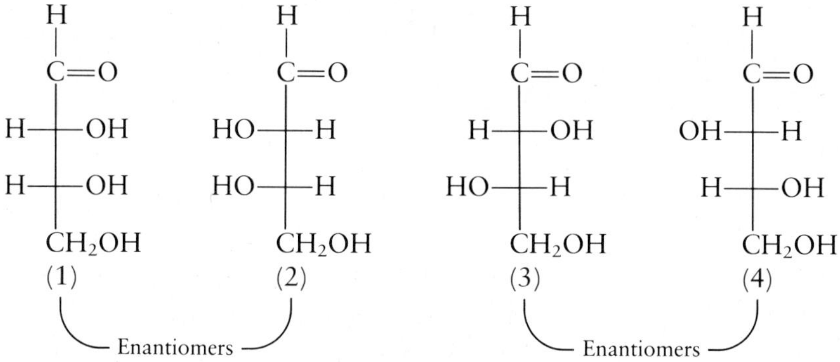

$$
\begin{array}{ccc}
 & H & \\
 & | & \\
 & C{=}O & \\
H & — & OH \\
H & — & OH \\
 & CH_2OH & \\
 & (1) &
\end{array}
\qquad
\begin{array}{ccc}
 & H & \\
 & | & \\
 & C{=}O & \\
HO & — & H \\
HO & — & H \\
 & CH_2OH & \\
 & (2) &
\end{array}
\qquad
\begin{array}{ccc}
 & H & \\
 & | & \\
 & C{=}O & \\
H & — & OH \\
HO & — & H \\
 & CH_2OH & \\
 & (3) &
\end{array}
\qquad
\begin{array}{ccc}
 & H & \\
 & | & \\
 & C{=}O & \\
OH & — & H \\
H & — & OH \\
 & CH_2OH & \\
 & (4) &
\end{array}
$$

Enantiomers (1 and 2) Enantiomers (3 and 4)

Structures 1 and 2 and structures 3 and 4 are mirror images of one another and are thus enantiomers, but the relationship is different between the other possible pairs of compounds, namely, 1 and 3, 1 and 4, 2 and 3, or 2 and 4. These pairs are the diastereoisomers, the stereoisomers which are not mirror images of one another. Unlike enantiomers, which have the same physical properties except for the direction in which they rotate plane-polarized light, diastereoisomers generally have different physical properties.

Stereoisomers of compounds with more than one chiral center can also be compared with glyceraldehyde in order to identify them as D or L isomers. Before making the comparison we must decide which asymmetric C atom to inspect. By convention we designate *sugar compounds* as D isomers or L isomers by comparing the *highest-numbered* asymmetric C atom in their structures with the single asymmetric C atom of glyceraldehyde. Since the C-1 atom is at the top of the vertical line, the highest-numbered C would be closest to the bottom, that is, the lowest chiral center in the Fischer projection drawing (for a sugar). Thus structures 1 and 4 are D isomers since the OH groups (in color) on the bottom asymmetric carbons point to the right and structures 2 and 3 are L isomers because the OH groups point to the left. Diastereoisomers often have different names. Structures 1 and 2, which are enantiomers, are called D-erythrose and L-erythrose and structures 3 and 4 are named D-threose and L-threose.

Diastereoisomers may have different names as well as different physical properties.

```
     H              H              H              H
     |              |              |              |
    C=O            C=O            C=O            C=O
     |              |              |              |
H ───┼── OH   HO ───┼── H     H ───┼── OH   HO ───┼── H
     |              |              |              |
H ───┼── OH   HO ───┼── H    HO ───┼── H     H ───┼── OH
     |              |              |              |
   CH2OH          CH2OH          CH2OH          CH2OH
    (1)            (2)            (3)            (4)
 D Isomer       L Isomer       L Isomer       D Isomer
(D-erythrose)  (L-erythrose)  (L-threose)    (D-threose)
```

Unlike glucose (blood sugar), fructose (fruit sugar), sucrose (table sugar), and ribose (in RNA), the erythroses and threoses are not very abundant in nature. In Chapter 21, where carbohydrate chemistry is covered, you will learn much more about naming sugars.

There are two amino acid components of protein molecules which also have two asymmetric C atoms. By convention *2-amino acids* (often called α-amino acids) are compared with glyceraldehyde by looking at the *C-2 atom* (the α C atom), the one to which the amino group is attached (see Sample Exercise 20.5).

SAMPLE EXERCISE 20.5

Draw the Fischer projections for the four stereoisomers of the amino acid below, called threonine (one of the two amino acids mentioned above). Label the ones that are enantiomers. Which are D isomers and which are L isomers?

```
                           O
  4      3      2       1  ‖
 CH3 ── CH ── CH ── C ── OH
         |      |
         OH     NH2
```

Solution:

We put C-1 at the top. The D isomers have NH_2 groups on the top asymmetric C atom (C-2) pointing to the right.

```
      OH                  OH                  OH                  OH
      |                   |                   |                   |
     C=O                 C=O                 C=O                 C=O
      |                   |                   |                   |
H ────┼── NH2     NH2 ────┼── H       H ──────┼── NH2     NH2 ────┼── H
      |                   |                   |                   |
H ────┼── OH       HO ────┼── H      HO ──────┼── H         H ────┼── OH
      |                   |                   |                   |
     CH3                 CH3                 CH3                 CH3
   D Isomer            L Isomer            D Isomer            L Isomer
(D-allo-threonine)  (L-allo-threonine)   (D-threonine)       (L-threonine)
              Enantiomers                             Enantiomers
```

The prefix *allo-* is Greek for "other."

One of the stereoisomers above, L-threonine, is an essential nutrient for humans because it is a component of protein molecules that is not synthesized in the body. Its mirror image is D-threonine. The *other* diastereoisomers are called the *allo* forms.

EXERCISE 20.5

The Fischer projections given represent the possible structures of the sugar compound below. Identify the pairs which are enantiomers and those which are diastereoisomers.

The names ribulose and xylulose correspond to the structures as indicated. Give the complete names of all four structures, and state whether they are D or L.

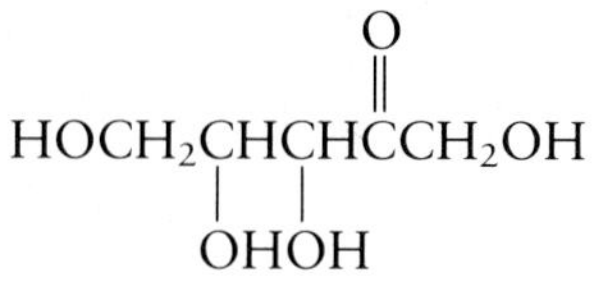

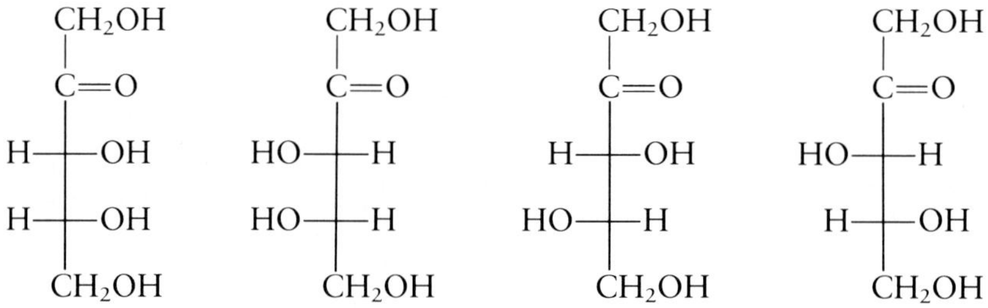

$$HOCH_2\underset{OH}{CH}\underset{OH}{CH}\overset{O}{\overset{\|}{C}}CH_2OH$$

CH_2OH	CH_2OH	CH_2OH	CH_2OH
C=O	C=O	C=O	C=O
H—+—OH	HO—+—H	H—+—OH	HO—+—H
H—+—OH	HO—+—H	HO—+—H	H—+—OH
CH_2OH	CH_2OH	CH_2OH	CH_2OH

Ribulose Xylulose

20.8 MESO COMPOUNDS

We have said that the *maximum* number of stereoisomers for a given compound is 2^n. Some optically active compounds have fewer stereoisomers than predicted by this formula because their structures have an extra element of symmetry. For a molecule containing two or more asymmetric C atoms, the extra symmetry is introduced if the molecule can be divided into two identical halves. Tartaric acid is one example of such a compound. The formula for tartaric acid includes two asymmetric C atoms and two identical halves.

$$HO-\overset{O}{\overset{\|}{C}}-\underset{OH}{\overset{H}{C^*}}-\underset{OH}{\overset{H}{C^*}}-\overset{O}{\overset{\|}{C}}-OH$$

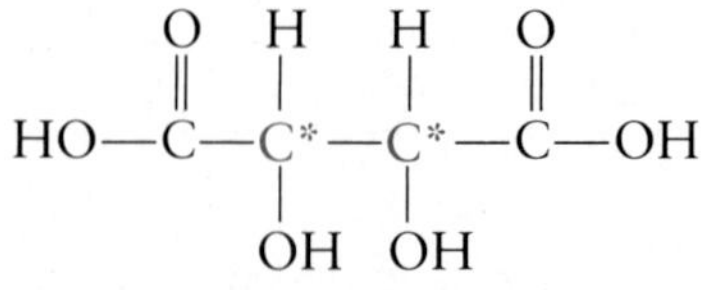

Tartaric acid

Compounds such as tartaric acid, which have two asymmetric C atoms and two identical halves, have only three stereoisomers. Two of the isomers are enan-

TABLE 20.1 **PROPERTIES OF TARTARIC ACID STEREOISOMERS**

Name	Melting point, °C	Density, g/ml	$[\alpha]_D^{20}$	Other common names
L-(+)-Tartaric acid	168–170	1.76	+12°	Natural tartaric acid
D-(−)-Tartaric acid	168–170	1.76	−12°	Unusual or unnatural tartaric acid
meso-Tartaric acid	146	1.67	0	
DL-Tartaric acid*	206	1.79	0	Racemic tartaric acid

*A 50-50 mixture of D and L isomers; see Section 20.9.

Meso is pronounced "meezo."

tiomers and the third is the *meso* form. We can show that two of the possible stereoisomers of tartaric acid are identical by looking carefully at the four Fischer projection formulas that can be drawn.

(1)	(2)	(3)	(4)
OH	OH	OH	OH
C=O	C=O	C=O	C=O
H—OH	HO—H	HO—H	H—OH
H—OH	HO—H	H—OH	HO—H
C=O	C=O	C=O	C=O
OH	OH	OH	OH
meso-Tartaric acid	meso-Tartaric acid	D-Tartaric acid	L-Tartaric acid

(3) and (4): Enantiomers

Structures 1 and 2 are mirror images, but they *can* be superimposed upon one another; they are identical and so represent only one stereoisomer. The compound represented by structures 1 and 2 is called a **meso isomer** and is named *meso*-tartaric acid. Meso isomers are not optically active, that is, they do not rotate plane-polarized light. They also have different physical properties from the other optically active isomers, as you can see in Table 20.1, where the physical properties of the stereoisomers of tartaric acid are compared.

20.9 RACEMIC MIXTURES

A 50-50 mixture of two enantiomers is called a **racemic mixture** or a **racemate.** Racemic mixtures are named by prefixing DL to the name of the compound. For instance, the name of the racemic mixture containing equal amounts of D-glyceraldehyde and L-glyceraldehyde is DL-glyceraldehyde. Racemic mixtures are also named by using the prefix (±); thus, DL-glyceraldehyde may also be called (±)-glyceraldehyde.

TABLE 20.2 PROPERTIES OF LACTIC ACID STEREOISOMERS

Compound	Melting point, °C	$[\alpha]_D^{22}$	Physical appearance	Source and/or use
L-(+)-Lactic acid	53	+2.6°	Crystalline solid	Blood and muscle of humans and animals, especially after vigorous exercise
D-(−)-Lactic acid	53	−2.6°	Crystalline solid	
DL-Lactic acid	18	0	Syrupy liquid	Sour milk; ingredient in infant formulas, acidifying agent

The properties of racemic mixtures are different from those of the pure isomers. Since one enantiomer is dextrorotatory and the other is levorotatory, the optical activity of the mixture cancels out and is thus zero. Physical properties of racemic mixtures tend to be different from those of either pure isomer. For instance, DL-lactic acid (found in sour milk) is a colorless syrupy liquid (mp 18°C), and the individual enantiomers are white solids melting at 53°C (see Table 20.2). Note also in Table 20.1 that the melting point and density of DL-tartaric acid are different from those of the three pure stereoisomers of tartaric acid.

Racemic is derived from the Latin *racemus,* meaning "bunch of grapes," because (±)-tartaric acid is found in grapes.

The first separation of a racemic mixture into two enantiomers was accomplished by Louis Pasteur in 1848. Pasteur noticed that a sample of sodium ammonium tartrate (a salt of tartaric acid) included two different types of crystals, "left-handed" and "right-handed" ones.

$$\mathrm{NaO-\overset{\overset{\displaystyle O}{\|}}{C}-\underset{\underset{\displaystyle OH}{|}}{\overset{\overset{\displaystyle H}{|}}{C^*}}-\underset{\underset{\displaystyle OH}{|}}{\overset{\overset{\displaystyle H}{|}}{C^*}}-\overset{\overset{\displaystyle O}{\|}}{C}-ONH_4}$$

Sodium ammonium tartrate

With tweezers Pasteur separated the two kinds of crystals and went on to discover that a solution of one set of crystals was dextrorotatory and a solution of the other was levorotatory.

Physical methods of separation such as the one used by Pasteur are tedious and often impossible since many enantiomers do not form two kinds of crystals that look different. Other separation techniques take advantage of chemical and biological properties which may differ between two enantiomers. One interesting separation draws upon the ability of a particular species of bacteria to consume one of a pair of isomers, leaving the other. A serious drawback of this method is the inability to recover the isomer consumed by the bacteria.

20.10 OPTICALLY ACTIVE COMPOUNDS IN LIVING SYSTEMS

The optically active compounds of nature most often exist in only one enantiomeric form. For instance, the amino acid building blocks which join together to form giant protein molecules are L amino acids. Plants tend to form only the D isomers of carbohydrate molecules, because the enzymes (Section 10.7) which act as catalysts for biological syntheses have a specific stereochemistry. That is, the shape of the enzyme must complement the shape of the compound, or *substrate* with which it interacts. In this chapter we will pay attention to only one feature of the shape of enzymes and substrates—their handedness. The handedness of the substrate compound must complement the handedness of the enzyme. A right-handed compound will fit on a right-handed enzyme, just as a right glove fits on a right hand (see Figure 20.9).

Different physical properties of enantiomers may depend upon a biochemical reaction as well. For instance, the odor of a compound is thought to depend upon interaction of its molecules with nasal receptor sites (see Section 8.2). According to this theory the shape of the molecule influences the interaction; thus enantiomers may have different odors. The cyclic compound (−)-carvone (see Figure

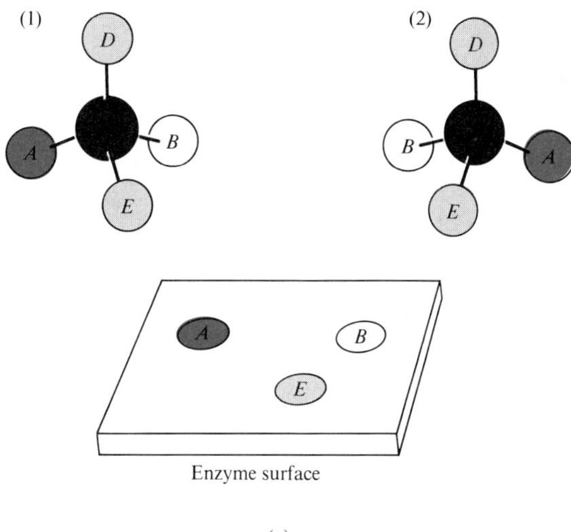

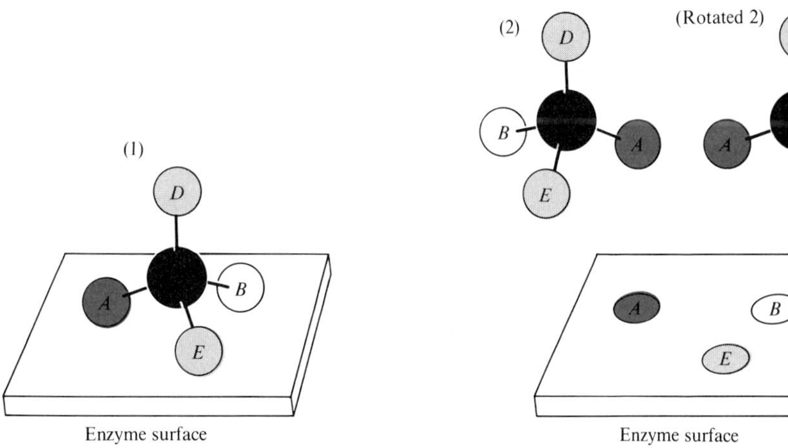

FIGURE 20.9
(*a*) Enantiomers and enzyme surface. (*b*) Enantiomer 1 fits onto the enzyme surface. (*c*) Enantiomer 2 does not fit onto the enzyme surface. If we rotate the molecule so that the *A* and *B* do fit, then the *E* does not fit.

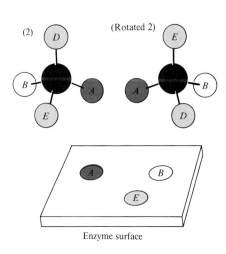

13.10) is the chief component of oil of spearmint, while (+)-carvone smells more like caraway.

The pharmacological activity of many drug compounds depends upon their stereochemistry.

In the introduction to this chapter we said that many drugs are much more potent in one particular enantiomeric form. This is true because the sites with which drugs must interact to produce an effect also have specific stereochemistries. Dextrorotatory (+)-amphetamine is more than 10 times more potent than (−)-amphetamine. Amphetamine drug products contain (±)-amphetamine, (+)-amphetamine, or a mixture of these. The relationship between molecular shape and drug activity has been examined in great detail for one group of drug compounds, the narcotic analgesics.

Narcotic Analgesics

Narcosis is Greek for "sleep" or "stupor."

Narcotic analgesics are pain-killers (analgesics) which also cause central nervous system depression, even to the point of sleep. Their action is thought to depend upon interaction with **receptor sites** located in the brain. The stereochemistry of the optically active narcotic analgesic compounds determines whether or not they will have any biological activity; only their D-isomers are active, whereas the L-isomers are pharmacologically inert.

The D isomers of the narcotic analgesics are the more active ones.

The original narcotic analgesic was opium (derived from the opium poppy), which is a mixture of many compounds. Two of them, morphine and codeine, are pharmacologically active. In Figure 20.10 you can see that morphine has two hydroxyl groups, whereas the much less potent codeine has one methoxy group. The even more potent (but shorter-acting) drug heroin, a synthetic compound, is derived from morphine by replacing the two hydroxyl groups with acetyl groups. Opiates are not the only narcotic analgesics; methadone, a compound which is not a morphine derivative, is also active. The formulas of morphine, codeine, methadone, and heroin are shown in Figure 20.10. According to theory,

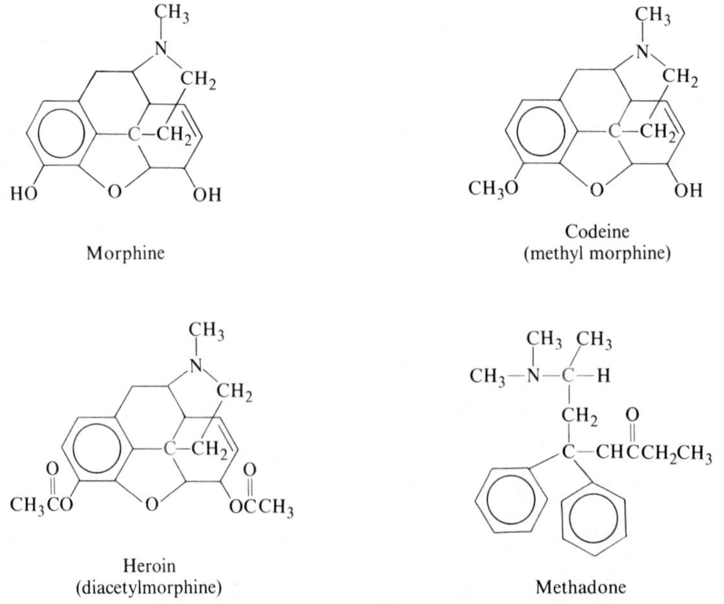

FIGURE 20.10
Structures of morphine, codeine, heroin, and methadone. The asymmetric C atoms used to compare these structures with glyceraldehyde enantiomers are shown in color. In each case, it is the D isomer that is a potent narcotic analgesic.

the receptor site has a shape into which only D-morphine, D-codeine, D-methadone, and D-heroin can fit in order to make the contact necessary for drug activity to occur. In Chapter 23 we will return to the structure of narcotic analgesic compounds when we discuss the pentapeptides.

SUMMARY

Optical isomers are examples of stereoisomers, compounds that differ only in the spatial arrangement of their atoms. A compound that exhibits optical isomerism is chiral, that is, it cannot be superimposed upon its mirror image. A chiral molecule and its mirror image are called enantiomers. Chiral organic compounds contain one or more asymmetric carbon atoms, that is, carbon atoms bonded to four different groups or atoms.

Optical isomers are called "optical" because they rotate plane-polarized light. A pair of enantiomers rotate polarized light through the same angles but in opposite directions. Dextrorotatory isomers rotate polarized light in the clockwise direction (+) and levorotatory isomers in the counterclockwise direction (−).

One way to represent the absolute configurations of a pair of optical isomers is by using wedges and dashes. The wedges (► and ◄) indicate groups facing out of the plane of the paper toward the reader and dashes (≡) represent groups extending behind the plane. Another way is to use Fischer projections, in which the interaction of a vertical and horizontal line is the asymmetric C atom. Groups attached to the horizontal line extend forward out of the paper and those on the vertical lines extend behind it.

Enantiomers are sometimes named by preceding the compound name with (+) or (−) to give the rotation direction. However, the direction in which an isomer rotates polarized light has no direct correlation with the arrangement of its atoms in space. One nomenclature system based on spatial arrangements of atoms (especially for amino acids and sugars) is the D-L system, in which optical isomers are compared with the isomers of glyceraldehyde. To use the system the vertical line of a Fischer projection represents the longest C chain, with the C-1 atom at the top. The D isomer is the one in which the functional group on the horizontal line points to the right, as the OH group does in D-glyceraldehyde. When compounds have more than one asymmetric C atom, the one to compare must be specified. For sugars it is the highest-number asymmetric C atom (the lowest chiral center in the Fischer projection formula) and for amino acids it is the C-2 atom (the α C atom).

Compounds with more than one asymmetric C atom can have as many as 2^n stereoisomers, where n is the number of asymmetric C atoms in the formula. Diastereoisomers are optical isomers of such a compound which are not mirror images of each other. Diastereoisomers tend to have different properties as well as different rotational directions. Enantiomers have the same physical properties except that their optical rotations are of opposite sign.

Molecules having more than one asymmetric C atom and consisting of two identical halves have a meso isomer. Meso compounds have different properties from the other optically active stereoisomers and do not rotate the plane of polarized light.

A 50-50 mixture of two enantiomers is a racemic mixture or a racemate and is named by prefixing DL or (±) to the compound name. Racemic mixtures do not rotate the plane of polarized light.

The stereochemistry of biochemicals and drug compounds is important in determining their reactivity, because biochemical reactions require enzymes or receptor sites which must complement the shape of the reactant compound.

KEY WORDS

stereoisomers
optical isomers
chiral
achiral
chiral center
asymmetric C atom
enantiomer
plane-polarized light
rotation angle
specific rotation
dextrorotatory
levorotatory
wedge and dash structure
Fischer projection
D-L system
diastereoisomers
meso isomer
racemic mixture
racemate
receptor site
narcotic analgesic

EXERCISES

20.6 What kind of isomerism is exhibited by each of the following pairs of compounds? Which pair would be expected to have the most similar set of physical properties?

(a) $CH_3CH_2(H)C{=}C(H)CH_2CH_3$ (both CH_3CH_2 groups on the same side) and $CH_3CH_2(H)C{=}C(H)CH_2CH_3$ (CH_3CH_2 groups on opposite sides)

(b) $CH_3CH_2CH_2OH$ and $CH_3CH_2OCH_3$

(c) $CH_3CH_2CH_2CH_2CH_2CH_2CH_3$ and $CH_3CH(CH_3)CH_2CH(CH_3)CH_3$

(d) CH_3—C(Cl)(Br)—H and H—C(Cl)(Br)—CH_3 (Cl and Br on hashed bonds; CH_3 and H on wedged bonds)

20.7 A cube is placed upon a rectangular box to create the following solid shapes. Which ones are chiral?

(a) In this one the cube is located in the center of the box.

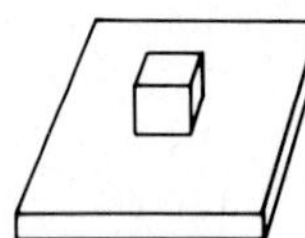

(b) Here the cube is placed in one corner of the box.

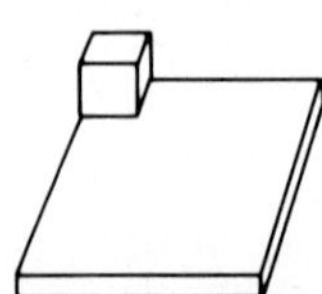

(c) This time the cube is placed in the middle of one side of the box.

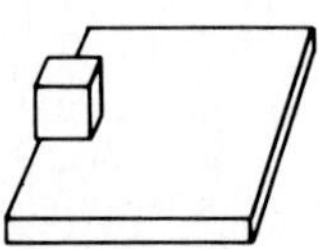

20.8 Decide whether the following body parts are chiral: (a) Foot; (b) ear; (c) nose.

20.9 Of the compounds below, which ones exhibit optical isomerism?

(a) $CH_2{=}CH{-}Cl$ (b) $CH_3CH(OH)CH_2CH_2CH_2CH_3$

(c) $CH_3C(Cl){=}C(Cl)CH_2CH_3$ (d) $C_6H_5{-}CH(NH_2)CH_2CH_3$

(e) Br—CH(Cl)—F (f) $HOOCCH_2CH(CH_3)CH_2COOH$ (HOCCH₂CHCH₂COH with C=O groups)

(g) $HOOC{-}CH(NH_2){-}CH(CH_3)_2$ (h) $CH_2{=}CHCH(Cl)CH_3$

20.10 Which of the following compounds exhibit optical isomerism: (a) Chloroform; (b) 2-bromopentane; (c) 2-aminobutanoic acid. For each one that does, give the wedge and dash formula and the Fischer projection formula.

20.11 What must R be in the general α-amino acid formula below so that the compound will *not* be optically active?

$$R{-}CH(NH_2){-}C(=O){-}OH$$

20.12 There are two possible phenylethanols (1-phenylethanol and 2-phenylethanol). Which one is optically active?

20.13 Give the structural formula for 2-bromohexane and indicate the asymmetric C atom. List the four groups attached to the asymmetric carbon. Draw Fischer projection formulas for the stereoisomers of 2-bromohexane.

20.14 What is the difference between unpolarized and polarized light?

20.15 What is meant by the terms levorotatory and dextrorotatory? How is the rotation direction shown in a formula name?

20.16 What is meant by the capital D and L in the names D-glyceraldehyde and L-glyceraldehyde?

20.17 Is it always true that D isomers are dextrorotatory and that L isomers are levorotatory? Explain your answer.

20.18 The drug L-dopa (levodopa), used in the treatment of Parkinson's disease, is L-dihydroxyphenylalanine. Given the structural formula below, draw a wedge and dash diagram and a Fischer projection formula to correspond to the L isomer. What information given above allows you to specify the direction in which this compound rotates the plane of polarized light?

HO–(ring)(HO)–$CH_2CH(NH_2)COOH$ [ring bearing two HO groups; CH_2CHCOH with C=O and NH_2 on the CH]

20.19 Levodopa is the precursor of dopamine, a compound deficient in patients suffering from Parkinsonism. Does dopamine exhibit optical isomerism?

HO–(ring)(HO)–$CH_2CH_2NH_2$

20.20 Name the compounds shown below, including the D and L.

	CH_2CH_3	
H	—	I
	CH_3	

	CH_2CH_3	
I	—	H
	CH_3	

20.21 Suppose the $[\alpha]_D$ of the L isomer in Exercise 20.20 is $-15.9°$ and its boiling point is 118°C. Can you specify the value of $[\alpha]_D$ and the boiling point of the other isomer?

20.22 How many stereoisomers are possible for the following compounds?

(a) $CH_3CHCHCH_2CH_3$ (Cl on C-2, Br on C-3)

(b) $HOCCHCHCHCHCH_3$ (C=O on C-1; OH, OH, OH, OH on C-2 to C-5)

20.23 The structures below represent the four possible stereoisomers of 2,3-dihydroxybutanal, $CH_3CHCHCH$ (with OH, OH on the two CH groups and =O on the terminal CH).

(1)

	H–C=O	
HO	—	H
HO	—	H
	CH_3	

(2)

	H–C=O	
HO	—	H
H	—	OH
	CH_3	

(3)

	H–C=O	
H	—	OH
HO	—	H
	CH_3	

(4)

	H–C=O	
H	—	OH
H	—	OH
	CH_3	

(a) Which pairs of structures are enantiomers?
(b) Which pairs of structures are diastereoisomers?
(c) Using the C-3 atom (lowest chiral center) for comparison with D- and L-glyceraldehyde, label the D isomers and the L isomers.

20.24 Fill in the values of $[\alpha]_D$ for the isomers shown below, starting with the one that is given.

	CH_2OH	
HO	—	H
H	—	OH
	CH_2OH	

$[\alpha]_D^{20} = -11.1°$

	CH_2OH	
H	—	OH
HO	—	H
	CH_2OH	

$[\alpha]_D^{20} = ?$

	CH_2OH	
H	—	OH
H	—	OH
	CH_2OH	

$[\alpha]_D^{20} = ?$

	CH_2OH	
HO	—	H
HO	—	H
	CH_2OH	

$[\alpha]_D^{20} = ?$

20.25 Meso compounds and racemic mixtures are alike in that neither produce any rotation of plane-polarized light. How are they different?

20.26 Give the name, composition, and physical appearance of the racemic mixture of 2-hydroxypropanoic acid (lactic acid), used as an ingredient in infant formula preparations. How does this form of lactic acid differ from the lactic acid that is present in the muscle and blood?

20.27 Dexedrine consists of (+)-amphetamine. Why is there no corresponding product called "Levedrine" containing only (−)-amphetamine?

20.28 For the amino acid below, called leucine, answer the following questions:

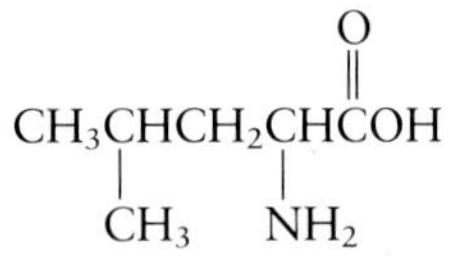

$$\mathrm{CH_3\underset{\displaystyle CH_3}{\underset{|}{C}}HCH_2\underset{\displaystyle NH_2}{\underset{|}{C}}H\overset{\displaystyle O}{\overset{\|}{C}}OH}$$

(a) How many stereoisomers should exist?
(b) What are their Fischer projection formulas?
(c) Which form is used to construct proteins in living systems?

20.29 The compound below is a rare amino acid, 5-hydroxylysine.

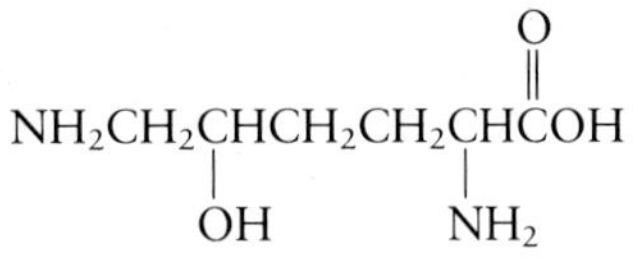

$$\mathrm{NH_2CH_2\underset{\displaystyle OH}{\underset{|}{C}}HCH_2CH_2\underset{\displaystyle NH_2}{\underset{|}{C}}H\overset{\displaystyle O}{\overset{\|}{C}}OH}$$

(a) How many stereoisomers are possible?
(b) What are their Fischer projection formulas?
(c) Which isomer (or isomers) are D and which are L? (Remember to use the C-2 atom to make the L and D assignments.)

20.30 Isoleucine, like threonine (Sample Exercise 20.5), is an amino acid component of living protein which has two asymmetric C atoms.

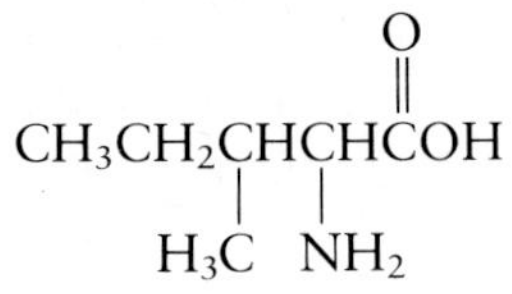

$$\mathrm{CH_3CH_2\underset{\displaystyle H_3C}{\underset{|}{C}}H\underset{\displaystyle NH_2}{\underset{|}{C}}H\overset{\displaystyle O}{\overset{\|}{C}}OH}$$

(a) How many stereoisomers of isoleucine are there?
(b) Give their Fischer projections.
(c) Which ones are D and which are L?

20.31 Label the asymmetric C atom(s) in the compound propoxyphene (Darvon).

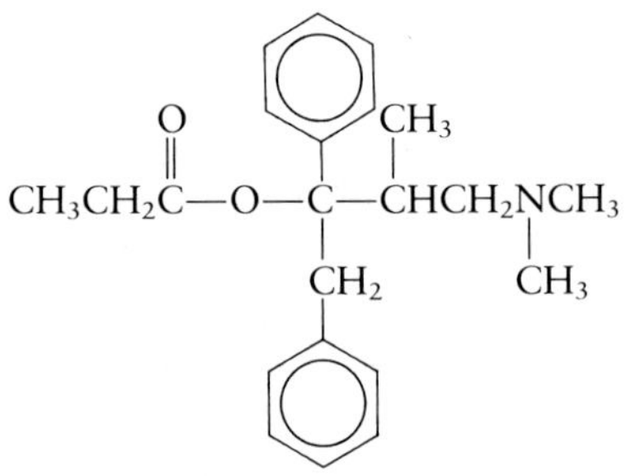

$$\mathrm{CH_3CH_2\overset{\displaystyle O}{\overset{\|}{C}}{-}O{-}\underset{\displaystyle \underset{|}{CH_2}\text{—}C_6H_5}{\underset{|}{\overset{\displaystyle C_6H_5}{\overset{|}{C}}}}{-}\overset{\displaystyle CH_3}{\overset{|}{C}}HCH_2NCH_3}$$

(with CH_3 on the N; the phenyl rings are drawn as benzene rings)

What compound discussed in this chapter does propoxyphene closely resemble?

21 CARBOHYDRATES

21.1 INTRODUCTION

The molecular formulas of many sugars and starches can be written as $C_x(H_2O)_x$. For instance, the formula for glucose is $C_6H_{12}O_6$, which can be rearranged to read $C_6(H_2O)_6$. Early chemists concluded from this that sugar and starch molecules were actually hydrated carbon atoms and thus called them **carbohydrates.** It *is* true that most carbohydrates do have molecular formulas that follow the formula above, but it is *not* true that carbohydrates are hydrates of carbon, because the chemical properties of carbohydrates do not support such structures. We now know that simple carbohydrates are really polyhydroxy aldehydes or polyhydroxy ketones. The name *carbohydrate* remains even though the idea which gave birth to it has become obsolete.

In Latin *saccharum* means "sugar."

To study the large number of possible carbohydrate compounds, we first divide them into classes called *saccharides.* The simplest carbohydrates are the **monosaccharides,** which cannot be broken down into smaller carbohydrate molecules. **Disaccharides** contain two monosaccharide units. The term sugar is loosely used to refer to any monosaccharide or disaccharide, not restricted to sucrose, the disaccharide you know as "table sugar." *Starch* and *cellulose* are two familiar **polysaccharides,** giant polymers made of *many* monosaccharide monomers. Our study of carbohydrate chemistry begins with the monosaccharides, sometimes called the "simple sugars."

21.2 MONOSACCHARIDES

Recall that the general formula for an aldehyde is $R-\overset{\overset{\displaystyle O}{\|}}{C}-H$ and that for a ketone is $R-\overset{\overset{\displaystyle O}{\|}}{C}-R$.

The structural formulas of several monosaccharides are shown in Figure 21.1, where you can see that they all include an aldehyde or a ketone group. Hydroxyl groups are attached to each C atom except that of the carbonyl group. Monosaccharides are classified to indicate the number of carbon atoms in their formulas and whether they are aldehydes or ketones. These and all other sugar names end in the suffix *-ose.*

$$\begin{array}{c}
\mathrm{H} \\
| \\
\mathrm{C{=}O} \\
| \\
\mathrm{H{-}C{-}OH} \\
| \\
\mathrm{H{-}C{-}OH} \\
| \\
\mathrm{H{-}C{-}OH} \\
| \\
\mathrm{CH_2OH} \\
(a)
\end{array}
\qquad
\begin{array}{c}
\mathrm{CH_2OH} \\
| \\
\mathrm{C{=}O} \\
| \\
\mathrm{HO{-}C{-}H} \\
| \\
\mathrm{H{-}C{-}OH} \\
| \\
\mathrm{H{-}C{-}OH} \\
| \\
\mathrm{CH_2OH} \\
(b)
\end{array}
\qquad
\begin{array}{c}
\mathrm{H} \\
| \\
\mathrm{C{=}O} \\
| \\
\mathrm{H{-}C{-}OH} \\
| \\
\mathrm{HO{-}C{-}H} \\
| \\
\mathrm{H{-}C{-}OH} \\
| \\
\mathrm{H{-}C{-}OH} \\
| \\
\mathrm{CH_2OH} \\
(c)
\end{array}$$

FIGURE 21.1 Monosaccharide formulas: (*a*) ribose; (*b*) fructose; (*c*) glucose. Ribose and glucose are aldehydes. Fructose is a ketone.

To give the number of C atoms in a monosaccharide formula, the numerical prefixes tri-, tetr-, pent-, hex-, hept-, and oct- are used. For instance, ribose contains a total of five C atoms (see Figure 21.1*a*) and thus is known as a *pent*ose. The terms **aldose** for hydroxyaldehydes and **ketose** for hydroxyketones specify the functional group of a monosaccharide. Ribose is an aldose as well as a pentose. Fructose (Figure 21.1*b*) is a hexose as well as a ketose. Useful general names for monosaccharides are created by combining the prefixes aldo- or keto- with the name that gives C number content. For instance, the five-carbon aldose ribose is an aldopentose and the six-carbon ketose fructose is a ketohexose.

In the sections that follow we will give the formulas of the aldoses and ketoses from trioses to hexoses and their stereoisomers. The aldohexoses, ketohexoses, and aldopentoses will receive special attention since they include the most important monosaccharides in living systems.

SAMPLE EXERCISE 21.1

To what general class of monosaccharides does glucose belong?

Solution:

From Figure 21.1*c* we see that glucose contains six C atoms and an aldehyde group. Thus glucose is both an aldose and a hexose and so is called an aldohexose.

EXERCISE 21.1

What general name can be given to the carbohydrate shown below?

$$\begin{array}{l}
\qquad\qquad\qquad\qquad\qquad\quad\ \mathrm{O} \\
\qquad\qquad\qquad\qquad\qquad\quad\ \| \\
\mathrm{HOCH_2\underset{|}{C}H\ \underset{|}{C}H\ \underset{|}{C}H\ \underset{|}{C}H\ \underset{|}{C}HCCH_2OH} \\
\qquad\quad\ \mathrm{OH\ OH\ OH\ OH\ OH}
\end{array}$$

21.3 IMPORTANT ALDOSES

Aldose formulas can be constructed by starting from the simplest of all aldoses, the aldotriose called glyceraldehyde. To write the formula for an aldotetrose we insert one H—C—OH unit in the formula of an aldotriose (see Figure 21.2). Aldopentose and aldohexose formulas are constructed in a similar way, as shown in the figure. The aldoses all include asymmetric C atoms in their formulas and thus all have stereoisomers.

Aldotrioses and Aldotetroses

Recall that the aldotriose glyceraldehyde is the compound upon which the D-L naming system is based (see Section 20.6). One reason that biochemists like to use the D-L system to name stereoisomers is that it is convenient to compare other carbohydrate compounds with the D and L isomers of glyceraldehyde.

Glyceraldehyde can be produced from the breakdown of larger monosaccharides. A phosphate derivative of D-glyceraldehyde, D-glyceraldehyde-3-phosphate, is an intermediate in the metabolic pathway of glycolysis, in which glucose is converted into lactic acid (Chapter 26).

Because an aldotetrose has two asymmetric carbon atoms, it must have 2^2, or four stereoisomers (Section 20.7). These include two pairs of enantiomers (mirror images), the D and L erythroses and the D and L threoses. Neither the erythroses nor the threoses are abundant in nature. The compound D-erythrose-4-phosphate, found in minute amounts in the muscles of all animals, is involved in the biosynthesis of certain amino acids. In fact, nearly all the sugars in nature are D isomers and are the only isomers included in Fig. 21.3, where D-glyceraldehyde, D-erythrose, D-threose, and the other D aldoses are shown.

Most natural sugars are D isomers.

Aldopentoses

Along with the aldohexoses, the aldopentoses are the most widely distributed sugars in living systems. Because an aldopentose has three asymmetric carbon

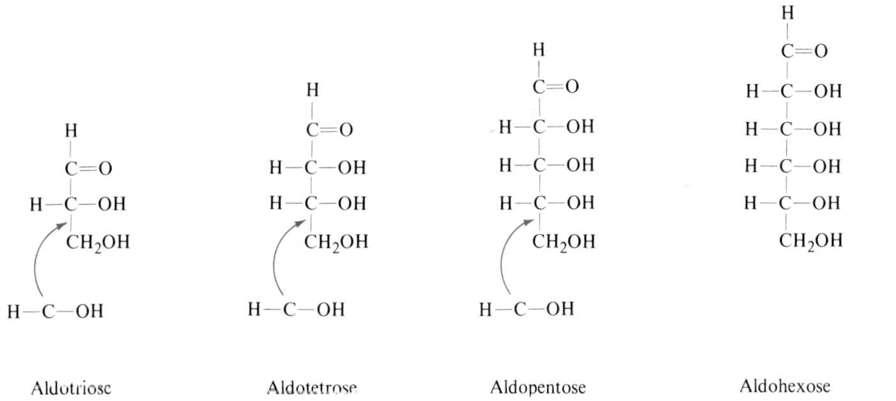

FIGURE 21.2
From an aldotriose to an aldohexose. Inserting one H—C—OH unit into an aldotriose produces an aldotetrose. Adding one H—C—OH to an aldeotetrose gives an aldopentose, and so on.

FIGURE 21.3
D-Aldoses: (*a*) D-aldotriose; (*b*) D-aldotetroses; (*c*) D-aldopentose; (*d*) D-aldohexoses The sugars shown in color (ribose, glucose, and galactose) are the ones that are most important in nature.

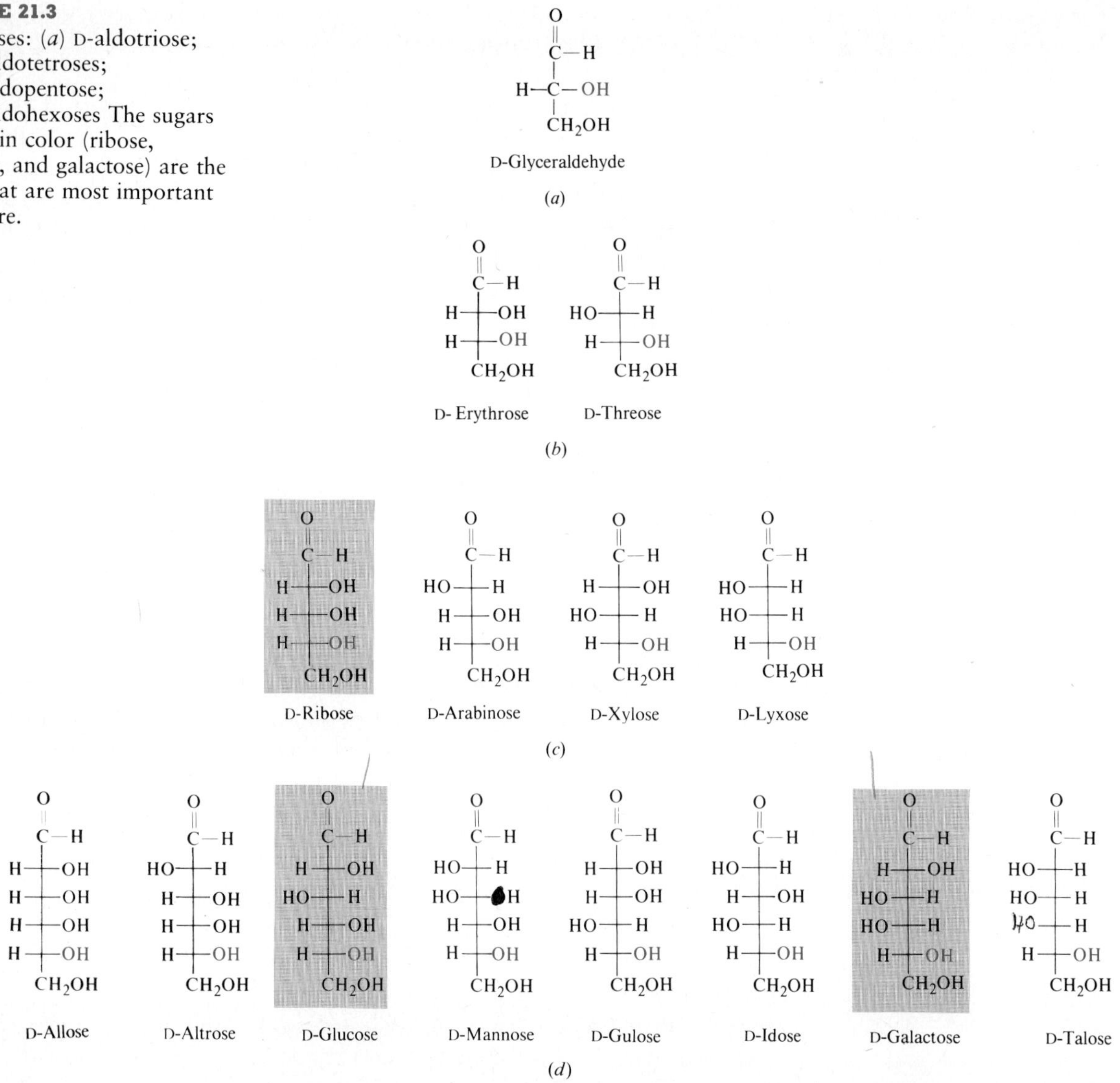

D-Glyceraldehyde

(*a*)

D-Erythrose D-Threose

(*b*)

D-Ribose D-Arabinose D-Xylose D-Lyxose

(*c*)

D-Allose D-Altrose D-Glucose D-Mannose D-Gulose D-Idose D-Galactose D-Talose

(*d*)

atoms, there must be 2^3, or eight, possible stereoisomers. The Fischer projection formulas shown in Figure 21.3*c* represent the four aldopentoses with structures comparable with that of D-glyceraldehyde (OH groups on highest-numbered chiral C atom point to the right). The analagous set of aldopentoses, the L isomers, in which the same OH groups all point to the left, are not shown.

Ribose appears in RNA.

The sugar **D-ribose** appears as a component of ribonucleic acid (RNA), a polymeric compound that plays a major role in the synthesis of protein molecules.

The xylose excretion test is used to diagnose intestinal disease which would cause carbohydrate malabsorption.

Both D-xylose and D-arabinose are found in nuts. Xylose, a sugar that is normally not metabolized, is used to detect carbohydrate malabsorption in the *xylose excretion test*. After a known amount of D-xylose has been given to a patient, its appearance in the urine is observed. In normal individuals 65 percent of the xylose should be absorbed intact and excreted in the urine in 5 h. A decreased amount of the D-xylose in the urine indicates malabsorption, due usually to intestinal disease.

Deoxyribose is present in DNA.

$$
\begin{array}{c}
\mathrm{H} \\
| \\
{}^{1}\mathrm{C{=}O} \\
\mathrm{H}\overset{2}{-}\!\!\!|\!\!\!-\mathrm{H} \\
\mathrm{H}\overset{3}{-}\!\!\!|\!\!\!-\mathrm{OH} \\
\mathrm{H}\overset{4}{-}\!\!\!|\!\!\!-\mathrm{OH} \\
{}^{5}\mathrm{CH_2OH}
\end{array}
$$

D-2-Deoxyribose

Another aldopentose with a structure similar to that of ribose is called **2-deoxyribose.**

Note that the structure of D-ribose and D-2-deoxyribose are identical except that there is a hydrogen atom instead of a hydroxyl group on the C-2 atom of D-2-deoxyribose; hence the prefix *deoxy-*. Deoxyribose is a component of deoxyribonucleic acid (DNA), a compound which transmits genetic information from parent to offspring by directing the synthesis of protein molecules.

Aldohexoses

The name glucose is derived from the Greek word *glykys*, meaning "sweet."

The sugar D-**glucose** is one of the 16 (2^4) possible stereoisomers of an aldohexose (see Figure 21.3*d*). Glucose, either alone or linked to itself or to other monosaccharides, is not only the most abundant carbohydrate on earth, it is the most abundant *organic compound* on earth. The polysaccharides starch and cellulose are built up from glucose monomers. Glucose itself, a white crystalline solid found in fruit juice and honey and in the blood of mammals, where a normal level is about 0.1 percent, is sometimes called "grape sugar" or "blood sugar." Glucose does not taste as sweet as sucrose, as you can see from looking at Table 21.1,

TABLE 21.1 **RELATIVE SWEETNESS OF SUGARS COMPARED WITH SUCROSE**

Sugar	Relative sweetness (sucrose = 1)	Type of compound
Fructose	1.5	Monosaccharide
Sucrose	1	Disaccharide
Glucose	0.7	Monosaccharide
Galactose	0.6	Monosaccharide
Mannose	0.6	Monosaccharide
Maltose	0.5	Disaccharide
Lactose	0.4	Disaccharide
Calcium cyclamate*	30	Sulfamic acid derivative
Aspartame*	200	Dipeptide ester
Saccharin*	300	Benzoic acid derivative

*These noncarbohydrate compounds are (or have been) used as artificial sweeteners.

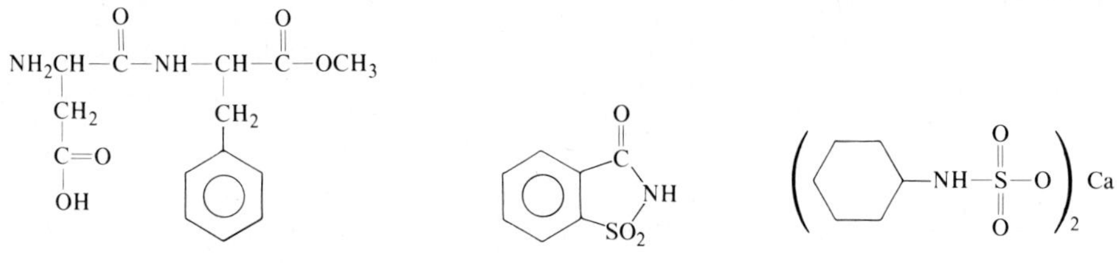

$$\begin{array}{l} \text{NH}_2\text{CH}-\overset{\overset{\text{O}}{\|}}{\text{C}}-\text{NH}-\text{CH}-\overset{\overset{\text{O}}{\|}}{\text{C}}-\text{OCH}_3 \\ \quad | \qquad\qquad\qquad | \\ \quad \text{CH}_2 \qquad\qquad \text{CH}_2 \\ \quad | \qquad\qquad\qquad | \\ \quad \text{C}{=}\text{O} \qquad\quad \text{C}_6\text{H}_5 \\ \quad | \\ \quad \text{OH} \end{array}$$

Aspartame

Saccharin

Calcium cyclamate

FIGURE 21.4
Noncarbohydrate sweeteners. Many sweet-tasting compounds, such as these three, are not carbohydrates.

which lists the relative sweetness of seven sugars and three artificial sweeteners (the formulas of these compounds are given in Figure 21.4).

Dextrose is a special name used for D-glucose.

The compound D-glucose is also called *dextrose*, since D-glucose happens to be D-(+)-glucose. Solutions consisting mainly of dextrose and water are made commercially by the hydrolysis of starches (such as cornstarch) to form a product known as corn syrup or "liquid glucose." Dextrose is added to cow's milk to prepare infant formulas and along with electrolytes (Section 9.11) is an ingredient in intravenous feeding solutions.

Galactose is derived from the Greek *galact* meaning "milk."

Individuals with galactosemia must avoid milk products.

In nature **galactose** is found combined with glucose in the disaccharide *lactose,* also called "milk sugar." Persons who suffer from the congenital disorder known as ***galactosemia*** are unable to metabolize galactose because they lack the enzyme that degrades galactose. Infants suffering from this disease (occurring about once in 25,000 births) do not thrive and without treatment are subject to severe liver disorders and eventually to mental retardation. Normal health is often restored when all dietary sources of galactose, including milk products as well as peas and organ meats (both of which may contain free galactose), are eliminated from the diet.

21.4 IMPORTANT KETOSES

In ketoses the carbonyl C atom is bonded to two C atoms. The simplest one is a ketotriose, dihydroxyacetone, which can be derived by placing a hydroxyl group on each methyl C atom of acetone itself.

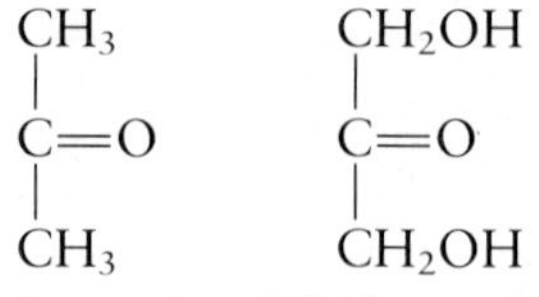

$$\begin{array}{cc} \text{CH}_3 & \text{CH}_2\text{OH} \\ | & | \\ \text{C}{=}\text{O} & \text{C}{=}\text{O} \\ | & | \\ \text{CH}_3 & \text{CH}_2\text{OH} \\ \text{Acetone} & \text{Dihydroxyacetone} \end{array}$$

There is no asymmetric C atom in the structure of dihydroxyacetone, and thus it is not optically active. In the body the phosphate of dihydroxyacetone is produced in the breakdown of glucose and is utilized in the biosynthesis of glycerol, a component of fats.

We will continue our discussion of ketoses by jumping ahead to the ketohexoses, bypassing the ketotetroses and ketopentoses, which are not abundant in nature. For the structures and names of all the D ketoses, see Figure 21.5.

$$\begin{array}{c} CH_2OH \\ | \\ C{=}O \\ | \\ CH_2OH \end{array}$$

Dihydroxyacetone

(*a*)

$$\begin{array}{c} CH_2OH \\ | \\ C{=}O \\ H-\!\!\!\!-\!\!\!\!-OH \\ CH_2OH \end{array}$$

D-Erythrulose

(*b*)

$$\begin{array}{c} CH_2OH \\ | \\ C{=}O \\ H-\!\!\!\!-OH \\ H-\!\!\!\!-OH \\ CH_2OH \end{array} \qquad \begin{array}{c} CH_2OH \\ | \\ C{=}O \\ HO-\!\!\!\!-H \\ H-\!\!\!\!-OH \\ CH_2OH \end{array}$$

D-Ribulose D-Xylulose

(*c*)

$$\begin{array}{c} CH_2OH \\ | \\ C{=}O \\ H-\!\!\!\!-OH \\ H-\!\!\!\!-OH \\ H-\!\!\!\!-OH \\ CH_2OH \end{array} \quad \begin{array}{c} CH_2OH \\ | \\ C{=}O \\ HO-\!\!\!\!-H \\ H-\!\!\!\!-OH \\ H-\!\!\!\!-OH \\ CH_2OH \end{array} \quad \begin{array}{c} CH_2OH \\ | \\ C{=}O \\ HO-\!\!\!\!-OH \\ HO-\!\!\!\!-H \\ H-\!\!\!\!-OH \\ CH_2OH \end{array} \quad \begin{array}{c} CH_2OH \\ | \\ C{=}O \\ HO-\!\!\!\!-H \\ HO-\!\!\!\!-H \\ H-\!\!\!\!-OH \\ CH_2OH \end{array}$$

D-Psicose D-Fructose D-Sorbose D-Tagatose

(*d*)

FIGURE 21.5
D-ketoses: (*a*) ketotriose; (*b*) D-ketotetrose; (*c*) D-ketopentoses; (*d*) D-ketohexoses. The ketohexose D-fructose (in color) is abundant in nature.

SAMPLE EXERCISE 21.2

Draw the structure of a ketotetrose and give the Fischer projection formulas for its stereoisomers. Try this without looking at Figure 21.5.

Solution:

To write the formula for a general ketotetrose, we insert one HCOH unit into the formula for dihydroxyacetone.

$$\begin{array}{c} CH_2OH \\ | \\ C{=}O \\ |^{*} \\ HCOH \\ | \\ CH_2OH \end{array}$$

Only one C atom is chiral and hence there are only 2^1, or two, stereoisomers.

These two enantiomers are named erythr*ul*ose, derived by inserting the letters -ul- into the aldotetrose name erythrose, a system used to name some ketoses.

$$\begin{array}{c} CH_2OH \\ | \\ C{=}O \\ | \\ H-\!\!\!\!-OH \\ | \\ CH_2OH \end{array} \qquad \begin{array}{c} CH_2OH \\ | \\ C{=}O \\ | \\ HO-\!\!\!\!-H \\ | \\ CH_2OH \end{array}$$

D-Erythrulose L-Erythrulose

EXERCISE 21.2

Again without looking at Figure 21.5, give the Fischer formulas for the stereoisomers of a ketopentose.

Ketohexoses

By far the most abundant ketose in nature is D-**fructose**, one of the four D stereoisomers of a ketohexose (see Figure 21.5*d*).

Honey is particularly sweet because of the large amount of fructose it contains.

Fructose, also known as "fruit sugar," is the sweetest of all sugars (see Table 21.1) and is found in fruit juices and in honey. The composition and flavor of honey depend upon the plant source of the nectar used to make it, but a typical sample might contain 41 percent fructose, 34 percent glucose, 2.4 percent sucrose, and 18.3 percent water. Sucrose (table sugar) is a disaccharide formed by the combination of glucose and fructose. Fructose in polymer form is also the chief component of a starch called inulin, found in Jerusalem artichokes and in some other plants. Because it happens to be levorotatory, the compound D-fructose is sometimes referred to as *levulose*.

21.5 CYCLIC MONOSACCHARIDES

In Chapter 16 you saw that hemiacetals and hemiketals form when alcohols are added to aldehydes or ketones (Section 16.7):

$$\underset{\text{Aldehyde}}{R-\overset{\overset{\displaystyle O}{\|}}{C}-H} + \underset{\text{Alcohol}}{R'OH} \longrightarrow \underset{\text{Hemiacetal}}{R-\underset{\underset{\displaystyle OR'}{|}}{\overset{\overset{\displaystyle OH}{|}}{C}}-H}$$

$$\underset{\text{Ketone}}{R-\overset{\overset{\displaystyle O}{\|}}{C}-R} + \underset{\text{Alcohol}}{R'OH} \longrightarrow \underset{\text{Hemiketal}}{R-\underset{\underset{\displaystyle OR'}{|}}{\overset{\overset{\displaystyle OH}{|}}{C}}-R}$$

Most hemiacetals and hemiketals are unstable (Section 16.7). However, as we mentioned before, cyclic hemiacetals and cyclic hemiketals are exceptions to this rule. In fact, you will see that the cyclic hemiacetal or hemiketal forms of many monosaccharides are much more stable than their open-chain counterparts.

Aldohexoses: Pyranoses

Open-chain monosaccharides form cyclic hemiacetals or hemiketals when an H atom from a hydroxyl group (the one shown below in color) adds to the carbonyl group. A new single bond forms between the hydroxyl O and the carbonyl C. For instance, to draw the hemiacetal structure for an aldohexose,

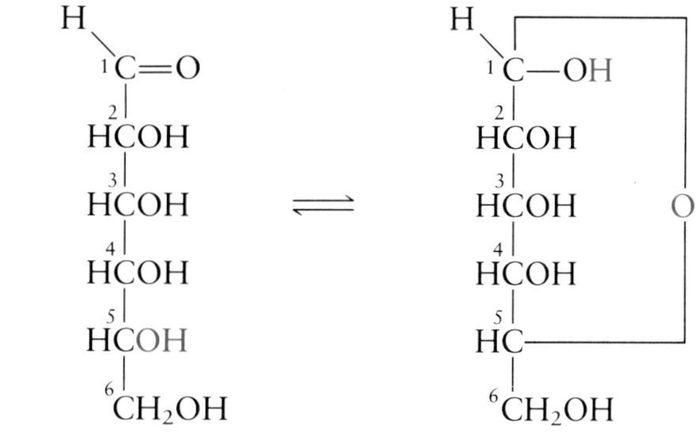

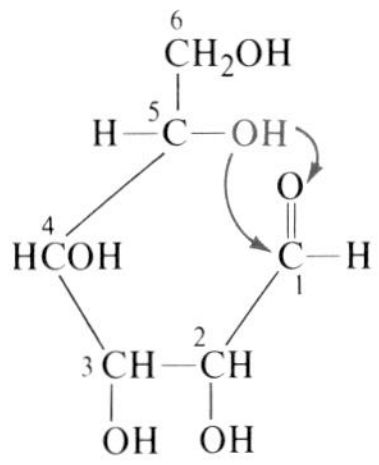

FIGURE 21.6
In this "bent" aldohexose structure, you can see that the OH group on C-5 comes close to the carbonyl.

Open-chain aldohexose ⇌ Cyclic hemiacetal aldohexose

The open-chain and cyclic forms of monosaccharides such as aldohexoses exist in equilibrium with each other.

By starting with a three-dimensional "bent" figure of an open-chain aldohexose, it is much easier to see how hemiacetal formation takes place. This is shown in Figure 21.6, where you can see that the H atom to be added (the one from the hydroxyl attached to the C-5 atom) does come close to the O atom of the carbonyl group.

We usually draw cyclic hemiacetal structures so that the atoms making up the cyclic ring of an aldohexose form a hexagon with five C atoms and one O atom, as shown below. In our discussion of cyclic ethers (see Figure 15.10) we encountered a similar ring structure, also containing five C atoms and one O atom, in the molecule pyran, a six-membered cyclic ether.

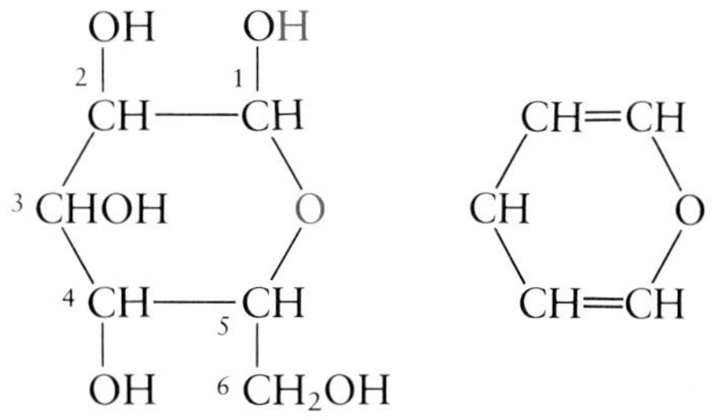

Cyclic aldohexose

Pyran

Glucopyranose refers to the cyclic form of glucose.

Glucose exists mainly in the cyclic hemiacetal form.

Since the hemiacetal form of all aldohexoses include pyranlike ring structures, they are called **pyranoses**, and their names are sometimes modified with the ending *-pyranose*. Thus, the hemiacetal form of glucose may be called *glucopyranose*.

Hemiacetals that form from pentoses and hexoses such as the one above are particularly stable. In fact, monosaccharides with five or six C atoms are so stable in the hemiacetal or hemiketal form that only a small percentage of their molecules exist in the open-chain form. For instance, more than 99 percent of D-glucose molecules are in the hemiacetal form while less than 1 percent are in the open-chain form. The same reasoning that we used to explain the stability of cyclohexane rings (Section 12.16) can be used to explain the stability of pyranose rings. The pyranose ring can pucker to form a chairlike structure with tetrahedral bond angles (109.5°), as shown in Figure 21.7. This eliminates any ring strain that would detract from the stability of the six-membered ring.

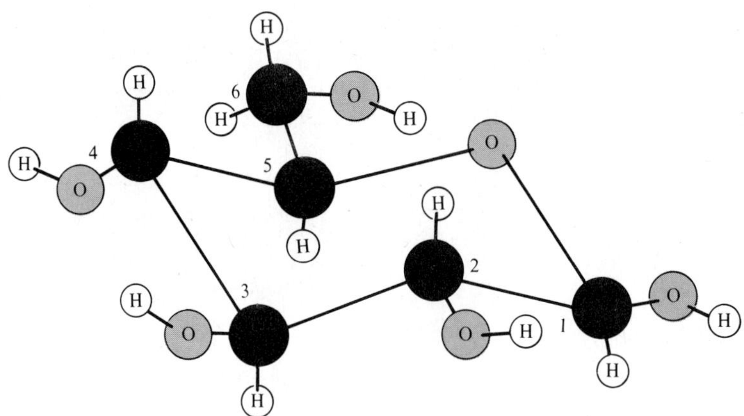

FIGURE 21.7
The chair form of the pyranose ring formed by an aldohexose is similar to the chair form of the cyclohexane ring.

$^{5}CH_2OH$
H—^{4}C—OH
O
^{3}HCOH
C—H ^{1}
^{2}CH
OH

FIGURE 21.8
In this "bent" aldopentose formula, note that the reacting OH group on C-4 approaches the carbonyl.

Aldopentoses and Ketohexoses: Furanoses

The cyclic forms of aldopentoses and ketohexoses both contain five-membered rings that include four C atoms and one O atom. To produce the hemiacetal form of an aldopentose, the hydroxyl H atom on the C-4 atom adds to the carbonyl. Again, the bent-chain structure brings the OH (in color) close to the carbonyl O atom, as shown in Figure 21.8.

Open-chain aldopentose		Cyclic hemiacetal aldopentose
H		H
^{1}C=O		^{1}C—OH
^{2}HCOH	⇌	^{2}HCOH O
^{3}HCOH		^{3}HCOH
^{4}HCOH		^{4}HC—
$^{5}CH_2OH$		$^{5}CH_2OH$

You can see that the hemiacetal ring structure for any aldopentose includes four C atoms and one O atom.

Ketohexoses such as fructose form hemiketal structures, which also contain five-membered rings.

Open-chain ketohexose		Cyclic hemiacetal ketohexose
$^{1}CH_2OH$		$^{1}CH_2OH$
^{2}C=O		^{2}C—OH
^{3}HCOH		^{3}HCOH
^{4}HCOH	⇌	^{4}HCOH O
^{5}HCOH		^{5}HC—
$^{6}CH_2OH$		$^{6}CH_2OH$

You can recognize cyclic sugars that come from ketoses (hemiketals) because they have a hydroxymethyl (CH_2OH) group instead of a hydrogen atom on the carbonyl C atom (C-2). Like cyclopentane (Section 12.16), the five-membered rings in the structures of aldopentoses and ketohexoses are especially stable because they involve very little ring strain.

We usually draw the cyclic aldopentose and ketohexose structures so that the atoms in the ring form a pentagon, as shown below. The rings present in these cyclic forms of aldopentoses and ketohexoses resemble furan, another cyclic ether (see Figure 15.10).

The O and H derived from the hemiacetal OH are in color.

^{1}CHOH, ^{2}HOCH, ^{3}HOCH, ^{4}CH, O, $^{5}CH_2OH$
Cyclic aldopentose

$^{1}CH_2OH$, ^{2}COH, ^{3}HOCH, ^{4}HOCH, ^{5}CH, O, $^{6}CH_2OH$
Cyclic ketohexose

CH, CH, O, CH, CH
Furan

Because of this the cyclic forms of aldopentoses such as ribose and ketohexoses such as fructose are called **furanoses**, and the ending *-furanose* is sometimes tacked onto their names. For instance, the cyclic form of fructose would be *fructofuranose* and that of ribose *ribofuranose*.

SAMPLE EXERCISE 21.3

The 2-deoxyaldopentoses also exist mainly as cyclic hemiacetals. Show how they form.

Solution:

Draw the structure of a 2-deoxyaldopentose and add the hydroxyl H atom on C-4 to the carbonyl C atom to form the hemiacetal.

H, ^{1}C=O, $^{2}CH_2$, ^{3}HCOH, ^{4}HCOH, $^{5}CH_2OH$ $\rightleftharpoons$ H, ^{1}C—OH, $^{2}CH_2$, ^{3}HCOH, ^{4}HC—O, $^{5}CH_2OH$ or ^{1}CHOH, $^{2}CH_2$, ^{3}HOHC, ^{4}CH, O, $^{5}CH_2OH$

Cyclic hemiacetal form of 2-deoxyaldopentose

EXERCISE 21.3

Should the cyclic form of 2-deoxyribose (a deoxyaldopentose) be called 2-deoxyribofuranose or 2-deoxyribopyranose? Why?

Although the pyran and furan style figures we have constructed for cyclic sugars are more accurate representations than the straight chains were, they are not yet complete. We will find that cyclic monosaccharides have more stereoisomers than corresponding open-chain ones. In the next sections we will discuss these additional stereoisomers and introduce a conventional method for showing the stereochemistry of cyclic sugars.

21.6 α and β FORMS OF CYCLIC SUGARS

A careful look at the formula of a cyclic sugar reveals that a new chiral center has appeared, one that was not there in the open-chain ones. In cyclic sugars the carbonyl C atom, previously nonchiral, becomes chiral. The cyclic forms of monosaccharides thus have twice as many stereoisomers as the corresponding open-chain forms. For instance, in an open-chain aldohexose there are four asymmetric C atoms (C*), but in a cyclic aldohexose there are five:

Open chain		Cyclic hemiacetal
H—^{1}C=O		H—^{1}C*—OH (bonded to ring O)
^{2}HC*OH		^{2}HC*OH
^{3}HC*OH	⇌	^{3}HC*OH
^{4}HC*OH		^{4}HC*OH
^{5}HC*OH		^{5}HC*— (bonded to ring O)
$^6CH_2OH$		$^6CH_2OH$

That is, cyclic forms of aldohexoses have 2^5, or 32, stereoisomers instead of only 2^4, or 16. For every possible open-chain aldohexose there are two cyclic ones. For instance, there are two D-glucoses, two L-glucoses, two D-galactoses, two L-galactoses, and so on.

The new stereoisomers are distinguished from each other by noting which of the two possible orientations is adopted by the hydroxyl group on the C-1 atom. To see this we can draw Fischer projection formulas for the two stereoisomers of cyclic D-glucose. The hydroxyl groups of D-glucose are oriented as shown in Figure 21.5*d*. The OH group (in color below) on C-1 of the hemiacetal can point to the right or to the left. The stereoisomer in which the OH group on

Originally the α isomer was arbitrarily said to be the more dextrorotatory member of a pair of anomers. Later it was found that all α isomers have the same configuration about the anomeric C.

C-1 points to the right is the α *isomer* and the one in which it points to the left is the β *isomer.*

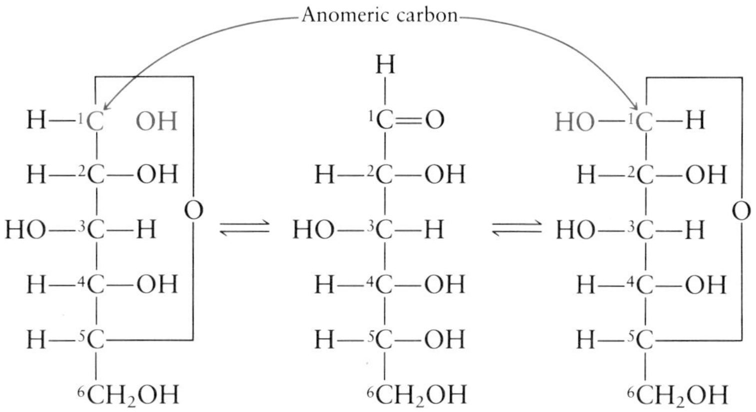

```
                               Anomeric carbon
                                      H
                                      |
   H—¹C  OH   ┐                     ¹C=O                  HO—¹C—H   ┐
      |       |                       |                       |     |
   H—²C—OH    |                   H—²C—OH                  H—²C—OH  |
      |       O   ⇌                   |             ⇌         |     O
  HO—³C—H     |                  HO—³C—H                  HO—³C—H   |
      |       |                       |                       |     |
   H—⁴C—OH    |                   H—⁴C—OH                  H—⁴C—OH  |
      |       |                       |                       |     |
   H—⁵C———————┘                   H—⁵C—OH                  H—⁵C—————┘
      |                               |                       |
     ⁶CH₂OH                          ⁶CH₂OH                  ⁶CH₂OH
```

α-D-Glucose (36%) $[\alpha]_D^{20}$ 112° | Open-chain D-glucose (<1%) | β-D-Glucose (64%) $[\alpha]_D^{20}$ 19°

Note that the anomeric C is the only C in the formula that is bonded to two O atoms.

A pair of cyclic sugars, one α and the other β, that differ only in their orientations about the **anomeric carbon atom,** that is, the C atom that was originally part of the carbonyl group, are called **anomers**. For aldoses the anomeric C atom is C-1 and for ketoses it is C-2. The compounds shown above, α-D-glucose and β-D-glucose, represent a pair of anomers.

Aqueous solutions of glucose contain about 0.02 percent of the open-chain isomer.

When either anomer is dissolved in water, its ring opens up to form the open-chain sugar, which then converts into the other anomer. For D-glucose the result is an equilibrium mixture that contains about 36 percent of the α-isomer, 64 percent of the β-isomer (the most stable one), and much less than 1 percent of open-chain D-glucose.

The physical and chemical properties of a pair of anomers are generally different (see Table 21.2). A pure crystal of α-D-glucose has an optical rotation of +112°, different from a crystal of β-D-glucose, which has an optical rotation of +19°. As the equilibrium mixture forms, the rotation angle changes gradually until it reaches the equilibrium value of 52.7° for D-glucose. This phenomenon is known as **mutarotation.**

TABLE 21.2 **COMPARING α-D-GLUCOSE AND β-D-GLUCOSE**

Property	α-D-Glucose	β-D-Glucose
Melting point, °C	146	150
Specific rotation $[\alpha]_D^{20}$	+112	+19
Water solubility, g/100 ml	83	180
Relative rate of oxidation by the enzyme glucose oxidase	<1	100

SAMPLE EXERCISE 21.4

What pair of anomers corresponds to the formulas below?

I	II
H—^{1}C—OH	HO—^{1}C—H
H—^{2}C—OH	H—^{2}C—OH
H—^{3}C—OH	H—^{3}C—OH
H—^{4}C—	H—^{4}C—
$^5CH_2OH$	$^5CH_2OH$

(In each formula, an O bridges C-1 and C-4.)

Solution:

First we must find out what monosaccharide this is. Because it has five C atoms, it is a pentose. Since the topmost C atom is attached to an H and an OH (and not to CH_2OH and an OH) it must have come from an aldose.

The OH groups on C-2 and C-3 point to the right and the one that was on C-4 also pointed to the right. From looking at Figure 21.5*c* we see that this corresponds to D-ribose. To distinguish the α and β forms, examine the anomeric C-1 atom (in color). Compound I must be α-D-ribose since the OH on C-1 points to the right. Compound II, then, is β-D-ribose.

EXERCISE 21.4

Identify the anomeric pair shown below:

I	II
HO—C—CH_2OH	$HOCH_2$—C—OH
HO—C—H	HO—C—H
H—C—OH	H—C—OH
H—C—	H—C—
CH_2OH	CH_2OH

(In each formula, an O bridges the top C and the fourth C.)

21.7 HAWORTH FORMULAS

Walter Haworth (1883–1950) won a Nobel prize in 1937 for his work in carbohydrate chemistry.

We must now find a way to indicate the orientation of all the groups attached to the ring C atoms of cyclic sugars by using hexagonal and pentagonal structures. One way to depict the stereochemistry of cyclic sugars is by using *Haworth projection formulas*. To construct the Haworth formula for a given cyclic sugar, follow the rules below:

1. Place the ring O at the top of a pentagon and the upper right of a hexagon as shown below. Number the C atoms, putting the anomeric C to the lower right of the O atom. For aldoses that will be the C-1 atom and for ketoses the C-2 atom.

The anomeric C atoms are indicated with a colored dot and colored numbers.

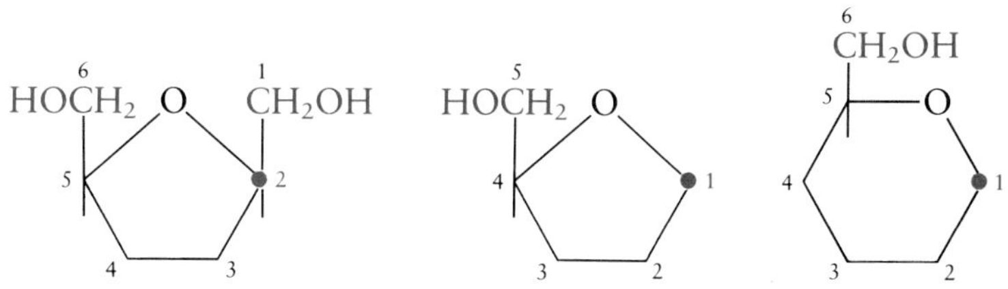

Furanose ring (ketohexose) — Furanose ring (aldopentose) — Pyranose ring (aldohexose)

The CH_2OH groups on C-4 or C-5 point up by convention.

Use the word DOWNRIGHT to help you remember how to convert Fischer formulas to Haworth formulas.

2. Place attached groups or atoms on the ring with vertical lines. Hydrogen atoms are usually not written in, just understood. Groups that point to the *right* in Fischer projection formulas point *down* in Haworth projection formulas.

H—C—OH is shown as —|— OH

Suppose we wish to draw Haworth formulas for α-D-glucose and β-D-glucose. Follow the rules above:

In aldoses the anomeric C is C-1.

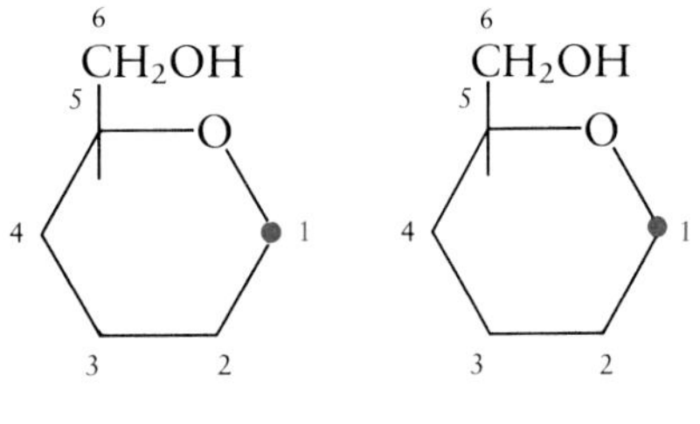

1. Glucose is an aldohexose and forms a six-membered ring in its hemiacetal form. Thus we draw hexagons for the pyranose rings and number them.

2. Next attach the OH and H atoms using the Fischer drawings to guide their orientation.

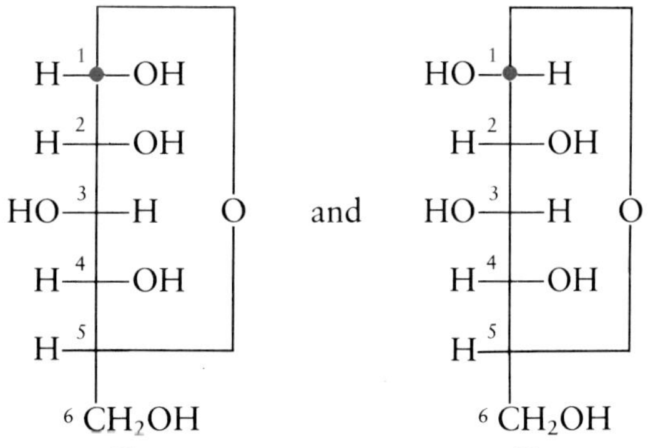

α-D-Glucose and β-D-Glucose

To help recall the orientation of OH groups on C-2, C-3, and C-4 of glucose, use the word DUD for down (right), up (left), and down (right).

The OH groups that point right in the Fischer projection formula point down in the Haworth formulas:

α-D-Glucose

β-D-Glucose

We will use Haworth formulas such as these to represent the sugar components of larger molecules such as disaccharides, polysaccharides, and nucleic acids (Chapter 24).

SAMPLE EXERCISE 21.5

Draw Haworth formulas to represent the anomers α-D-ribose and β-D-ribose.

Solution:

Ribose is an aldopentose with the Fischer formula below (see Figure 21.5*c*). To form the α and β forms add the H atom shown at the left in color to the carbonyl. Point the newly formed OH to the right in the α form and to the left in the β form.

D-Ribose

α-D-Ribose

β-D-Ribose

To construct Haworth formulas begin with numbered pentagons (furanose rings) and the attached CH_2OH group.

Now attach the OH groups and H atoms to complete the structures.

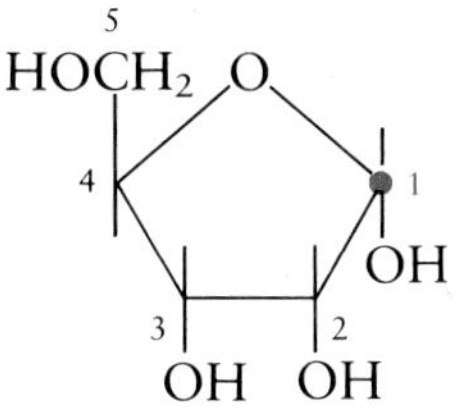

α-D-Ribose

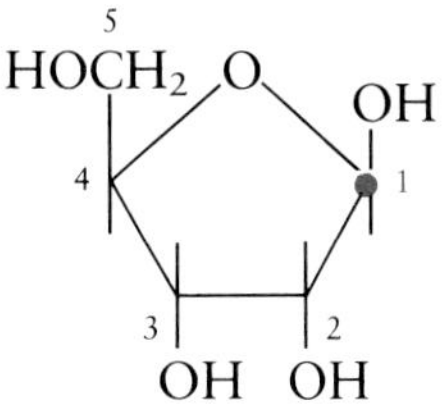

β-D-Ribose

EXERCISE 21.5

What is the name of the compound below? Draw its Fischer projection formula.

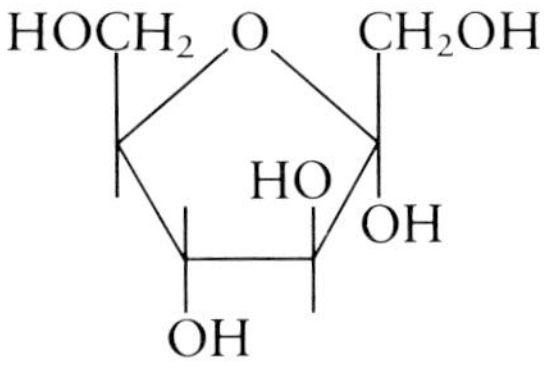

21.8 REACTIONS OF MONOSACCHARIDES

Monosaccharides undergo reactions typical of hydroxy aldehydes and hydroxy ketones. We will discuss two of these—oxidation and the formation of acetals (or ketals). You can review these reactions by turning back to Sections 16.6 and 16.7, where they were first introduced for aldehydes and ketones.

Oxidation of Aldoses and Ketoses

The Benedict's and Fehling's tests are both copper reduction tests, in which $Cu^{2+} \rightarrow Cu^{+}$.

In Section 16.6 you saw that all aliphatic aldehydes can be oxidized by Tollens' reagent, $Ag(NH_3)_2OH$, or Benedict's or Fehling's reagent, both Cu^{2+} in aqueous alkaline solution. Under basic conditions the aldoses are oxidized to the corresonding carboxylic acid salt when treated with either reagent. For instance, the open-chain form of D-glucose is oxidized to salts of D-gluconic acid, as shown in the equations below.

The silver mirror on a test tube is shown in Color Plate 19.

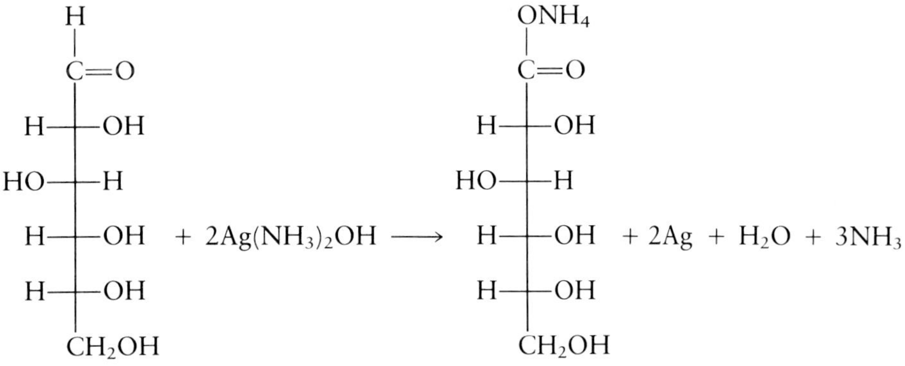

$$\text{D-Glucose} + 2Ag(NH_3)_2OH \longrightarrow \text{Ammonium D-gluconate} + 2Ag + H_2O + 3NH_3$$

D-Glucose — Tollens' reagent — Ammonium D-gluconate — Silver mirror

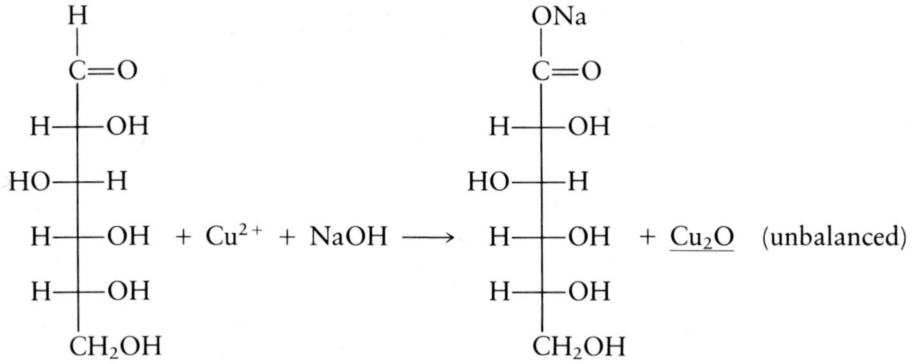

$$\begin{array}{c} \text{H} \\ | \\ \text{C}{=}\text{O} \\ \text{H}{-}\text{C}{-}\text{OH} \\ \text{HO}{-}\text{C}{-}\text{H} \\ \text{H}{-}\text{C}{-}\text{OH} \\ \text{H}{-}\text{C}{-}\text{OH} \\ | \\ \text{CH}_2\text{OH} \\ \text{D-Glucose} \end{array} + \underset{\text{Benedict's reagent}}{Cu^{2+} + \text{NaOH}} \longrightarrow \begin{array}{c} \text{ONa} \\ | \\ \text{C}{=}\text{O} \\ \text{H}{-}\text{C}{-}\text{OH} \\ \text{HO}{-}\text{C}{-}\text{H} \\ \text{H}{-}\text{C}{-}\text{OH} \\ \text{H}{-}\text{C}{-}\text{OH} \\ | \\ \text{CH}_2\text{OH} \\ \text{Sodium D-gluconate} \end{array} + \underset{\text{Reddish copper(I) oxide}}{\underline{Cu_2O}} \quad \text{(unbalanced)}$$

The use of Benedict's reagent to test for abnormal levels of glucose in urine is also described in Section 16.6 and illustrated in Color Plate 1.

Only the open-chain aldoses are oxidized in this way, because their structures include aldehyde groups, called **free aldehydes**, that are available to react. In cyclic sugars the carbonyl groups have been converted to hydroxyl groups, leaving no free aldehydes. However, eventually all the glucose molecules *do* become oxidized. As the small amount (less than 1 percent of molecules) of the open-chain glucose present reacts, the equilibrium mixture shifts to produce more open-chain glucose by the opening of glucopyranose rings. (See Le Chatelier's principle in Section 10.9 to recall how equilibrium systems shift to compensate for stresses put upon them.) More free aldehyde groups are now available to react and when they have reacted, more rings open up. This continues until all the glucose molecules have been oxidized.

We mentioned that hydroxy ketones are one exception to the rule that ketones cannot easily be oxidized (Section 16.6). Ketones with hydroxyl groups on a C atom adjacent to the carbonyl do react with oxidizing agents because they are in equilibrium with an aldehyde form. The hydroxy ketone $R\overset{O}{\overset{\|}{C}}CH_2OH$ is partially converted to the hydroxy aldehyde $R\underset{OH}{\underset{|}{C}}H\overset{O}{\overset{\|}{C}}H$ through an intermediate *enediol,* so called because it has both a double bond (ene) and two hydroxyl groups (diol).

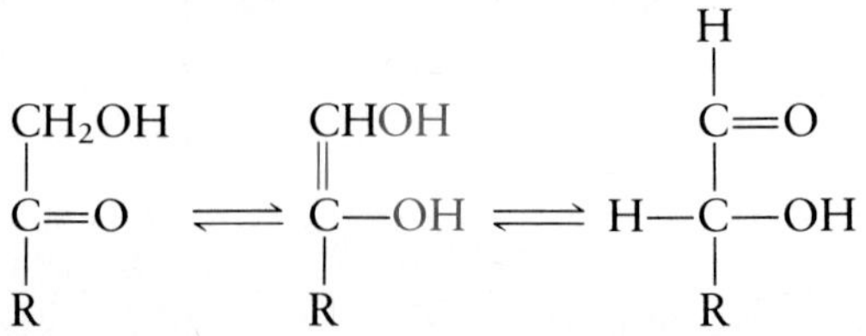

$$\underset{\text{Hydroxy ketone}}{\begin{array}{c} \text{CH}_2\text{OH} \\ | \\ \text{C}{=}\text{O} \\ | \\ \text{R} \end{array}} \rightleftharpoons \underset{\text{Enediol}}{\begin{array}{c} \text{CHOH} \\ \| \\ \text{C}{-}\text{OH} \\ | \\ \text{R} \end{array}} \rightleftharpoons \underset{\text{Hydroxy aldehyde}}{\begin{array}{c} \text{H} \\ | \\ \text{C}{=}\text{O} \\ | \\ \text{H}{-}\text{C}{-}\text{OH} \\ | \\ \text{R} \end{array}}$$

Ketoses, such as fructose, all have structures that can undergo the conversion above. In fact, ketoses are oxidized (slowly compared with aldoses) by Benedict's, Fehling's, and Tollens' reagents.

Copper reduction tests for glucose in urine also detect galactose, fructose, and any other monosaccharide.

Thus all monosaccharide sugars can be oxidized by Tollens', Benedict's or Fehling's solutions. There is another way of putting this: since the sugars are oxidized, they are the reducing agents. For instance, if the oxidizing solution is Benedict's reagent, the oxidizing agent is Cu^{2+} and the reducing agent is the sugar. A sugar that can be oxidized is a **reducing sugar**.

All monosaccharides are classified as reducing sugars.

Glucose Oxidase Reaction

In the presence of the enzyme *glucose oxidase* glucose reacts with molecular oxygen O_2 to form hydrogen peroxide and gluconic acid.

$$\text{Glucose} + O_2 \xrightarrow{\text{glucose oxidase}} \text{gluconic acid} + H_2O_2$$

This reaction is used to measure the amount of glucose in urine by the *glucose enzymatic test*. When paper test strips (such as Tes-Tape) impregnated with glucose oxidase are dipped into a sample of urine containing glucose, the glucose oxidase catalyzes the reaction of glucose with O_2. The amount of glucose present is determined by measuring the amount of hydrogen peroxide that forms. This is done by allowing the H_2O_2 product to react with another substance called *o*-tolidine in the presence of the enzyme peroxidase (derived from horseradish) to produce a blue color. Both the peroxidase and *o*-tolidine are also contained in the paper test strips.

Glucose enzymatic test strips contain glucose oxidase, peroxidase, *o*-tolidine, and food color.

$$H_2O_2 + NH_2\text{—C}_6\text{H}_3(\text{CH}_3)\text{—C}_6\text{H}_3(\text{CH}_3)\text{—}NH_2 \xrightarrow{\text{peroxidase}} \text{blue color}$$

o-tolidine

Other reducing sugars will not interfere with the enzyme test for glucose in urine.

Yellow food dye is added to the paper strips to extend the color range of the test from yellow (no glucose) to deep blue (see Color Plate 22). Since the glucose oxidase does not react with other sugars it is more specific for glucose than the Benedict's test. The disadvantages of the enzyme test is that it is more difficult to read the colors.

Formation of Glucoside Ethers

In Chapter 16 you saw that the addition of alcohol to aldehydes first produces a hemiacetal, which then reacts with more alcohol to form an acetal (Section 16.7).

$$\underset{\text{Hemiacetal}}{\underset{|\atop OR'}{RCH}OH} + \underset{\text{Alcohol}}{HOR'} \longrightarrow \underset{\text{Acetal}}{\underset{|\atop OR'}{RCH}OR'} + H_2O$$

A cyclic sugar reacts with an alcohol to form a glycoside.

The hemiacetal or hemiketal sugars also react with alkyl alcohols in the presence of a mineral acid catalyst to produce acetals or ketals, called alkyl **glycosides**.

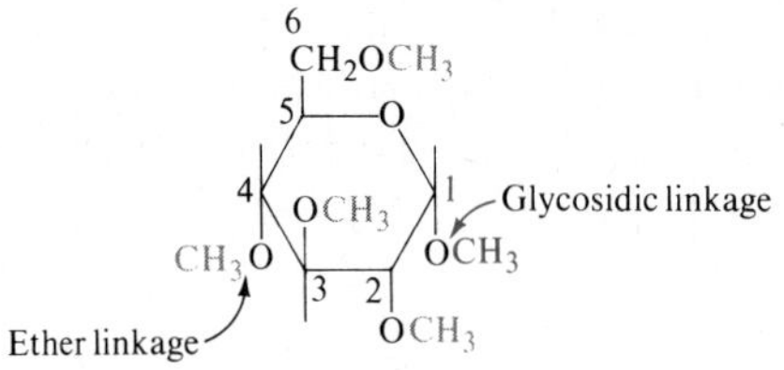

FIGURE 21.9
The methyl joined by the glycosidic linkage (in color) is more easily attached and more easily removed than are those joined by ether linkages (shaded)

The name of a particular glycoside is formed by dropping the *-e* from the sugar name and adding the suffix *-ide*. A glycoside that forms from the reaction of methanol with *glucose* is called a methyl *glucos*ide.

Glycosides of monosaccharides form by splitting out a molecule of water from the alcohol and the hydroxyl group attached to the anomeric C atom, that is, the *hemiacetal hydroxyl* group. For instance, α-D-glucose reacts with methanol to form the corresponding methylglycoside.

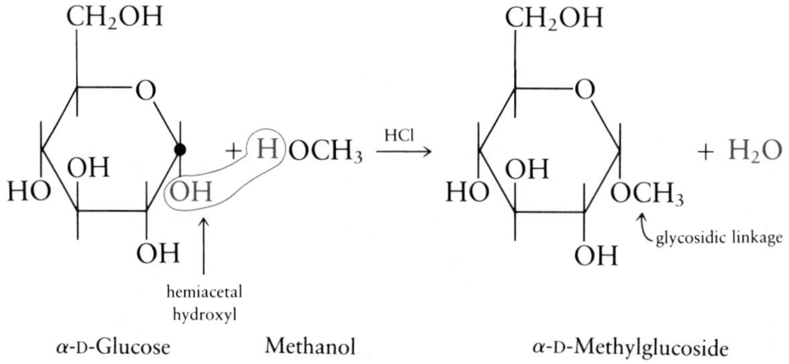

Notice that the stereochemistry about the anomeric C atom is retained; the OCH_3 group attached to the C-1 atom points down, as the OH group did. Thus α-D-glucose produces α-D-methylglucoside. The bond between the anomeric C and the O of the acetal group is called a **glycosidic linkage**. Although the glycosidic linkage appears to be similar to the ether linkage, it is much more easily hydrolyzed than the latter, which is relatively unreactive (Section 15.13). Other hydroxyl H atoms in sugar molecules can also be replaced with alkyl groups to produce ether linkages (see Figure 21.9). These are much more stable than the glycosidic linkages.

The reaction in which a glycosidic linkage is formed is a very important one in living organisms because this is the way in which monosaccharides are joined together to form disaccharides and polysaccharides.

SAMPLE EXERCISE 21.6

Complete the reaction below between D-fructose and methanol. What is the name of the product?

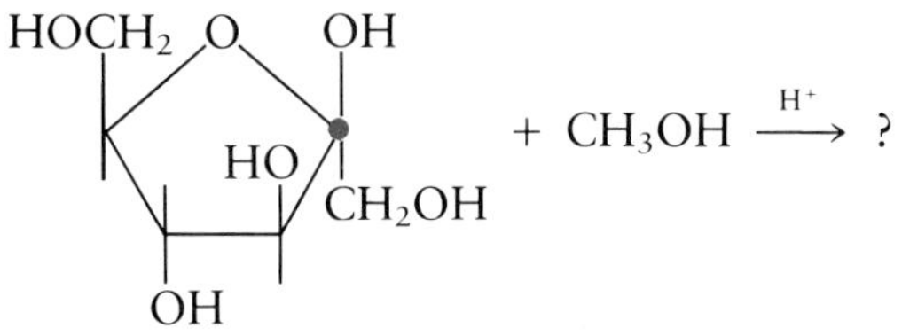

HOCH₂ O OH

HO CH₂OH

OH

$+ CH_3OH \xrightarrow{H^+} ?$

Solution:

A glycoside forms with the removal of a water molecule. It is the C-2 OH group that participates:

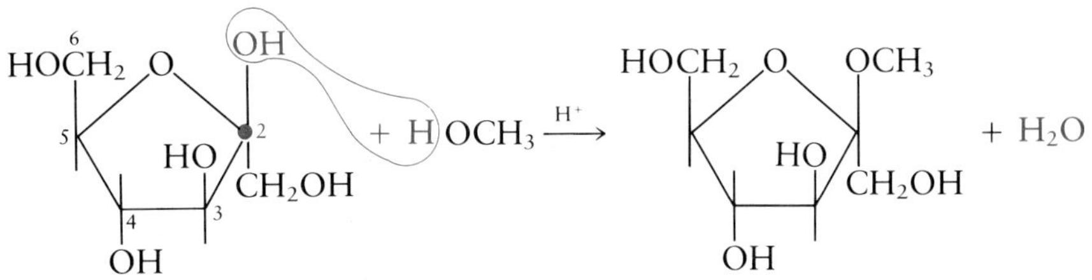

$+ HOCH_3 \xrightarrow{H^+}$ $+ H_2O$

Since the OH on C-2 points up, the starting sugar is β-D-fructose. The product name is thus β-D-methylfructoside.

EXERCISE 21.6

Complete the reaction below and name the product.

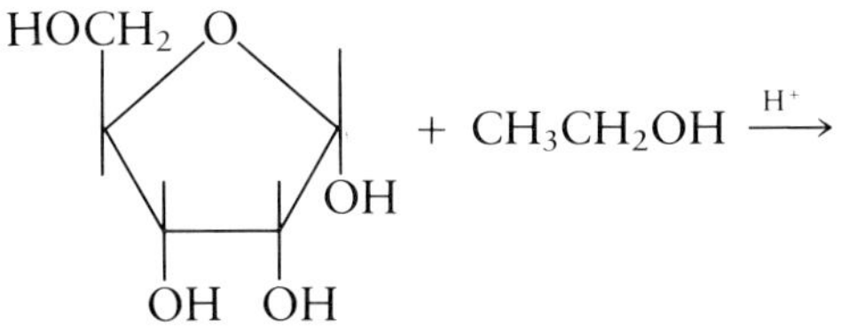

$+ CH_3CH_2OH \xrightarrow{H^+}$

D-Ribose

21.9 DISACCHARIDES

A **disaccharide** forms when two monosaccharide molecules combine by splitting out a molecule of water. The glycosidic linkage that joins the two sugars always involves the hemiacetal hydroxyl group of one sugar and one of the hydroxyl groups of the other monosaccharide. We will look at the structures of four disaccharides, maltose, cellobiose, lactose, and sucrose, the last being the substance that most nonchemists are thinking about when they say "sugar."

Maltose

The hemiacetal hydroxyl groups, drawn ∿OH, can be either α or β.

Maltose can be broken down into two molecules of glucose. It forms when one α-D-glucose molecule reacts with another D-glucose molecule to give an α-1,4 linkage.

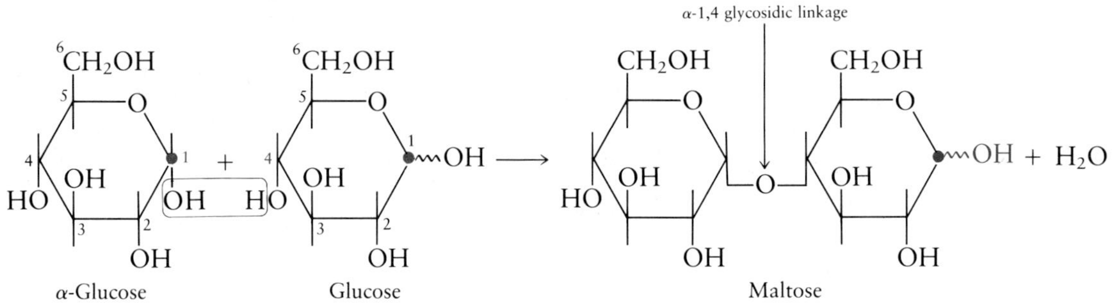

α-1,4 glycosidic linkage

α-Glucose + Glucose → Maltose + H_2O

You can see that the linkage between them is labeled with the numbers of the C atoms to which the reacting hydroxyl groups are attached. The number of the anomeric C comes first. For glucose as for all aldoses, the hemiacetals hydroxyl group is on C-1. The reaction takes place with the hydroxyl group on C-4 of a second glucose molecule to form a *1,4 linkage. Note that the stereochemistry of the glycosidic linkage is also indicated with an α since the sugar that supplied the hemiacetal OH is an α-glucose.* Thus the linkage is called an α-1,4 linkage.

You will see that the stereochemistry of the linkage between monosaccharides determines whether or not a disaccharide or polysaccharide formed from them can be degraded by enzymes present in animals.

Note that there is an unreacted hemiacetal hydroxyl group on maltose (in color above). Thus, the ring can "open up" at that point to form a free aldehyde group available to react with oxidizing agents.

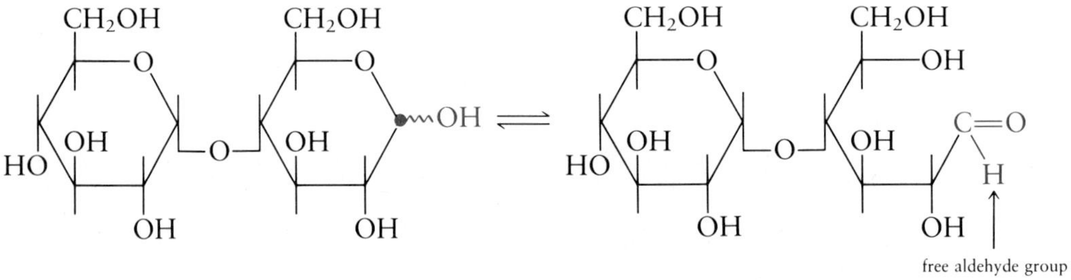

free aldehyde group

Thus maltose is classified as a reducing sugar.

Nearly all natural maltose or "malt sugar" is found in combined form as starch and is one of the intermediate products in the digestion of starch (Section 21.10). Maltose is also derived from "malting," that is, soaking, germinating, and drying of grains such as barley, a step in beer making. The *malt* produced includes malt starch and enzymes that are able to convert the malt starch into maltose, which is then fermented to produce alcohol.

Cellobiose

Cellobiose is also composed of glucose molecules, but this molecule is formed by reaction of a hemiacetal that is part of a β sugar (the hydroxyl group on C-1 points up), and thus the linkage formed is a β-1,4 linkage.

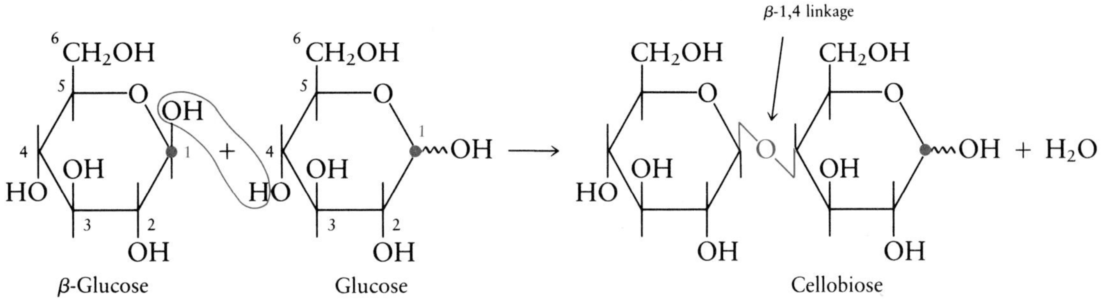

β-1,4 linkage

β-Glucose + Glucose ⟶ Cellobiose + H_2O

A glycosidic linkage is α if an α sugar supplies the hemiacetal OH and β if the OH is supplied by a β sugar.

Cellobiose is a reducing sugar since its hemiacetal OH can open up.

You can see that maltose and cellobiose are identical except for the fact that cellobiose has a β-1,4 linkage. This apparently tiny structural difference has a gigantic effect on the properties of the two sugars. Maltose (see Table 21.1) is sweet and cellobiose is not, and the compounds have different optical rotations, melting points, and solubilities. Most striking of all is their biochemical difference. Cellobiose, produced from the breakdown of the polysaccharide cellulose, cannot be used as a source of nutrition for mammals, as mammalian digestive tracts do not secrete enzymes that can break β-1,4 linkages between the two glucose molecules.

Lactose

When a β-D-galactose molecule combines with D-glucose, a β-1,4 linkage and the sugar **lactose**, or "milk sugar," is formed.

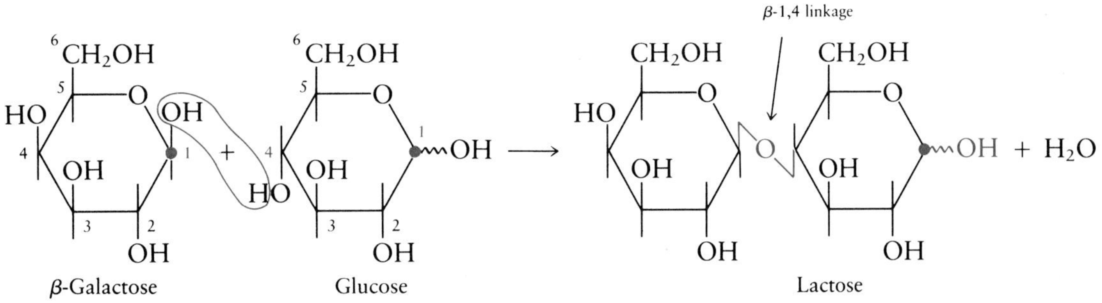

β-1,4 linkage

β-Galactose + Glucose ⟶ Lactose + H_2O

Persons with lactose intolerance are deficient in lactase, the enzyme that breaks the linkage between glucose and galactose.

Lactose is a reducing sugar since the hemiacetal hydroxyl (in color) of the second glucose molecule is retained, which permits the ring to open up to form a free aldehyde group. In the body the lactose molecule is broken down by the action of an enzyme known as *lactase,* which cleaves the β-1,4 linkages between galactose and glucose. In some children this enzyme is not synthesized in the intestine as it should be; as a result the lactose is never properly metabolized, thereby causing diarrhea and eventually dehydration. The inability to absorb lactose, called ***lactase deficiency syndrome*** or ***lactose intolerance***, is also present in some adults, particularly those of African and Far Eastern origins. It is controlled by eliminating all dietary sources of lactose, including all dairy products and even certain medications. Lactose is sometimes mixed with drugs because it has excellent tablet-forming properties.

Sucrose

Sucrose is table sugar. In nature sucrose occurs in a number of plants, including sugar cane and sugar beets, its two main sources.

To form **sucrose** an α-D-glucose combines with a β-D-fructose molecule. What is different about the acetal linkage in sucrose as compared with the others we have covered so far is that it joins *both* anomeric C atoms, C-1 of glucose and C-2 of fructose. This type of bond is called an α,β linkage.

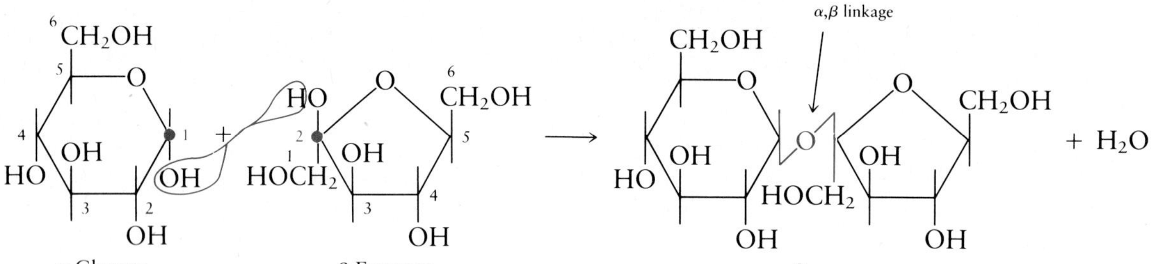

α-Glucose + β-Fructose $\longrightarrow$ Sucrose + H_2O

Since both C atoms that once were part of the hemiacetal or hemiketal groups have reacted, there is no potential aldehyde or ketone group possible; neither ring can reopen, which means that sucrose is a **nonreducing sugar**, that is, a sugar which does not react with Tollens' or Benedict's reagent and cannot be easily oxidized.

When sucrose undergoes hydrolysis, it produces an equimolar mixture of glucose and fructose called *invert sugar.*

The enzyme is called sucrase or invertase.

$$\text{Sucrose} + H_2O \xrightarrow{\text{acid or enzyme}} \underbrace{\text{glucose} + \text{fructose}}_{\text{Invert sugar}}$$

Invert sugar is used in candy making because it is as sweet as sucrose but does not crystallize as easily.

Why the name invert sugar? The optical rotation of sucrose is $+66°$. The optical rotation of an equimolar mixture of glucose ($[\alpha]$ $+52°$) and fructose ($[\alpha]$ $-92°$) is the average of $+52°$ and $-92°$, $-40°/2$, or $-20°$. The name was chosen because the optical rotation of sucrose "inverts" from plus to minus when it is hydrolyzed to form invert sugar.

SAMPLE EXERCISE 21.7

What is the linkage that joins the two D-glucose units of trehalose, a disaccharide found in young mushrooms and in other fungi?

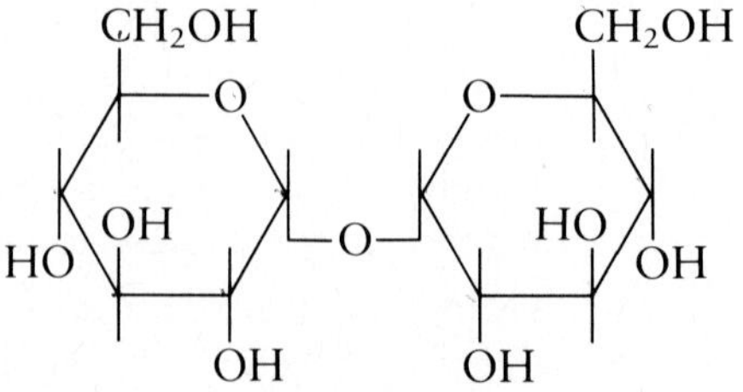

Solution:

First number the C atoms in the Haworth formulas above.

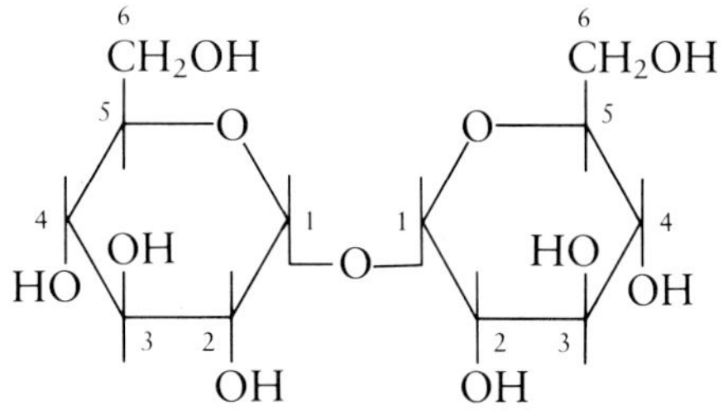

The linkage is between C-1 of one D-glucose and C-1 of the other. Since the OH group that reacted (in the leftmost sugar) point down, the linkage is α-1,1.

EXERCISE 21.7

Is trehalose (see example above) a reducing sugar or a nonreducing sugar?

21.10 POLYSACCHARIDES

In this section we will discuss several polysaccharides, including starch, glycogen, and cellulose. Of these the first two are food reserves while the third, cellulose, is primarily a structural component of plants.

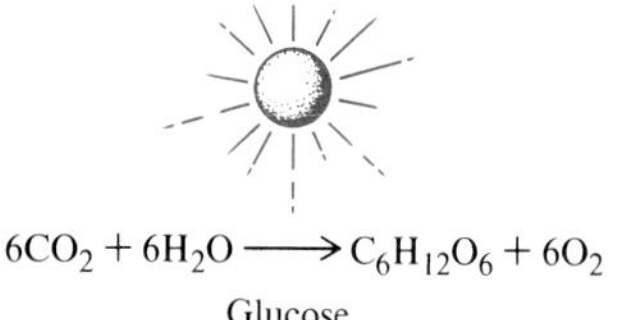

$$6CO_2 + 6H_2O \longrightarrow \underset{\text{Glucose}}{C_6H_{12}O_6} + 6O_2$$

FIGURE 21.10
In this reaction, usually used to represent photosynthesis, plants utilize solar energy to synthesize glucose from carbon dioxide and water. Starch is composed of glucose monomers.

Starch

In the process of photosynthesis plants utilize CO_2 and H_2O to produce carbohydrate molecules (see Figure 21.10). **Starch** is the form in which plants store the carbohydrates they synthesize. In one form or another starch represents a principal source of nourishment for a large portion of the people of the world. Starch from wheat, rice, corn, potatoes, taro root, and legumes (beans and peas) can be ground into flour, used in its native forms or isolated and added to other foods for texture.

Starch is a polymer of D-glucose.

The term *starch* refers to two different polysaccharide molecules, the linear polymer **amylose** and the branched polymer **amylopectin**. The general structures of these two polysaccharides are shown in Figure 21.11, where you can see that the monomer unit of both is D-glucose. Starch molecules contain anywhere from 250 to 1000 glucose units, and most starch is a mixture containing about 20 percent amylose and 80 percent amylopectin.

The linear starch polymer, amylose, is composed of D-glucose monomer molecules joined by α-1,4 linkages, as they are in maltose. Amylose molecules exist in the form of coiled structures, as shown in Figure 21.12. The channel within this spiral structure provides just enough space to accommodate I_2 molecules, which react to form a blue amylose-iodine complex. The appearance of this deep blue color is the basis of the *starch-iodine test,* which can be used to test for the presence of starch (see Color Plate 23). The starch-iodine test can also be used to follow the hydrolysis of starch. The blue color of the complex disappears when the starch is degraded to glucose.

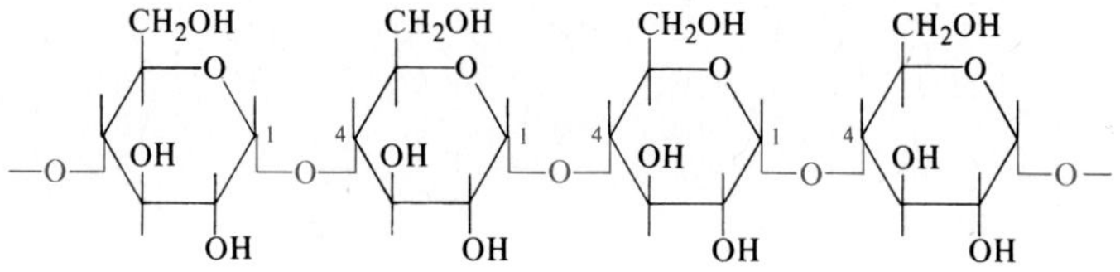

FIGURE 21.11
Starch. (*a*) Amylose segment. D-glucose units are joined by α-1,4 linkages.
(*b*) Amylopectin segment. D-glucose units branch off the main chain through α-1,6 linkages.

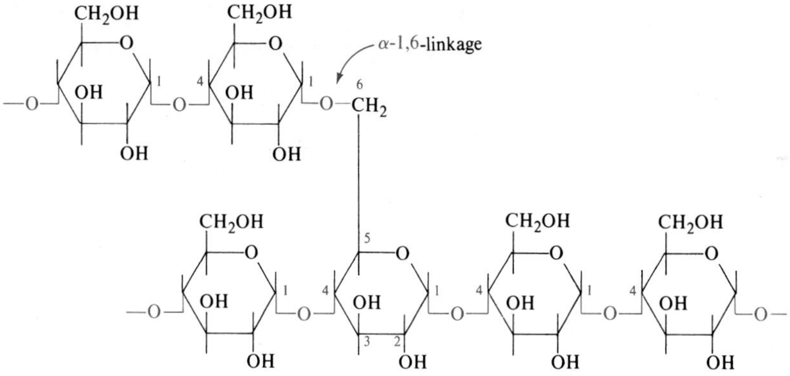

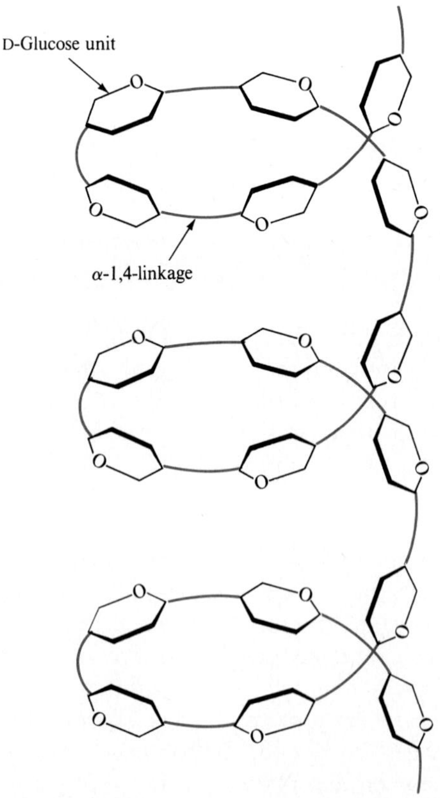

FIGURE 21.12
Coiled amylose segment. The amylose molecule is linear but shaped like a coil. The α-1,4 linkages are shown in color.

$$\underset{\text{Blue}}{\text{starch-}I_2} \xrightarrow{\text{hydrolysis}} \text{glucose} + I_2$$

The main chain of the branched polymer molecule amylopectin consists of D-glucose units joined by α-1,4 linkages, as in amylose. But as you can see in the structure shown in Figure 21.11, branching in amylopectin occurs off the main chain through α-1,6 linkages.

Glycogen

Our bodies store excess carbohydrates as glycogen, also a polymer of D-glucose.

Glycogen is the form in which animals store carbohydrates and is thus the animal equivalent of starch. Carbohydrate molecules not required for immediate nourishment are converted into glycogen molecules, which are stored in the liver or muscle tissue. In structure glycogen resembles amylopectin but is even more highly branched, as shown in Figure 21.13. The human body draws upon its glycogen reserves to provide energy or to maintain a normal blood level of glucose, a topic that we will have more to say about in Chapter 26, Metabolism of Carbohydrates.

Cellulose

Cellulose, the most abundant organic compound on earth, forms the supporting structure of plants. (When we said earlier that glucose was the most abundant compound on earth, we meant in free *or* combined form.) About 25 percent of the weight of trees and more than 90 percent of cotton is cellulose.

Structurally cellulose is related to cellobiose in the same way that starch is related to maltose. The monosaccharide units of cellulose are β-glucose molecules connected by β-1,4 linkages into cellobiose units, as in the cellulose segment shown in Figure 21.14.

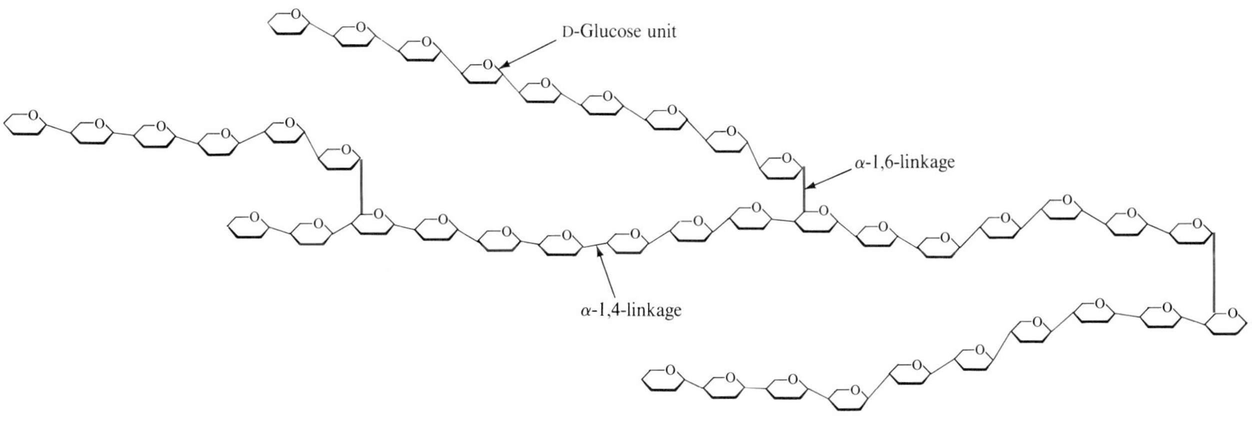

FIGURE 21.13
Segment of glycogen. The structure is similar to that of amylopectin except that the branching (via α-1,6 linkages shown in color) occurs about every 8 to 12 glucose units in glycogen and about every twenty-four to thirty glucose units in amylopectin.

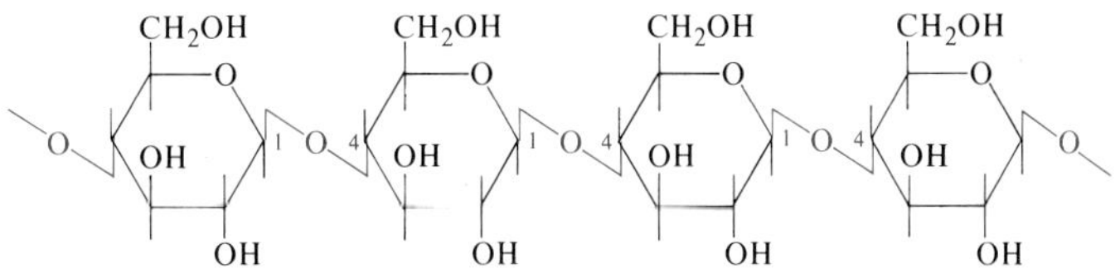

FIGURE 21.14
Cellulose segment. D-glucose monomers are joined by β-1,4 linkages.

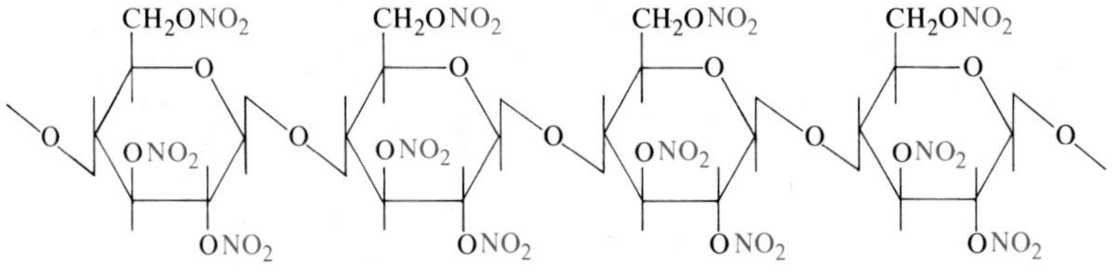

FIGURE 21.15
Cellulose nitrate. The hydroxyl groups of cellulose react with a mixture of HNO_3 and H_2SO_4 to form cellulose nitrate or nitrocellulose.

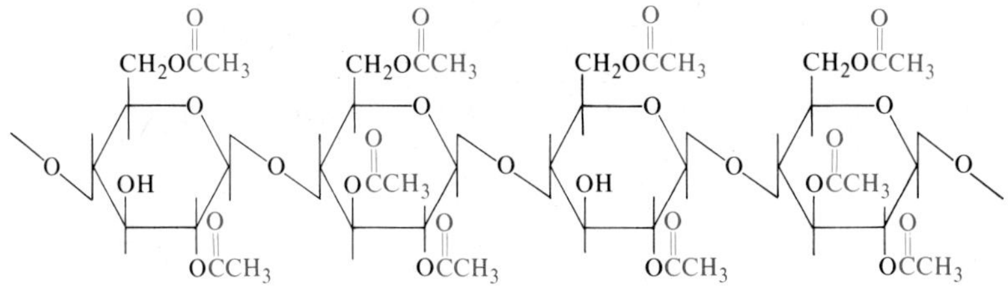

FIGURE 21.16
Cellulose acetate. About 80 percent of the hydroxyl groups are converted to acetates.

Humans cannot digest cellulose.

Cellulose in foods provides the roughage needed for optimal functioning of the lower intestine.

Cellulose molecules are linear, but unlike amylose (also linear) are insoluble in water. Because most animals do not have the enzyme needed to cleave β-1,4 linkages, they cannot use cellulose for nourishment. Exceptions include cattle and termites, whose alimentary canals house bacteria which are capable of digesting cellulose. The cattle and termites can then absorb the sugars produced as a result of this preliminary digestion.

Cellulose and its derivatives have many commercial uses. *Rayon* is a fiber made from cellulose. Transparent cellulose sheeting is called *cellophane*. When treated with nitric acid and sulfuric acid, cellulose is converted to *cellulose nitrate* (Figure 21.15), a polymer with various uses depending upon the number of hydroxyl groups that are nitrated. Cellulose nitrate with 12.5 to 13.4 percent nitrogen is known as guncotton and is highly explosive. Cellulose nitrate containing 11 to 12 percent nitrogen is in celluloid, a product once used in plastics and photographic film but since replaced by other more stable polymers. The acetate ester of cellulose (see Figure 21.16), *cellulose acetate,* made by reaction of cellulose with acetic acid or acetic anhydride (Section 17.10), is one polymer that is used as a substitute for Celluloid. Cellulose acetate (Celanese acetate) is used in fabrics, upholstery, and cigarette filters. It is possible to make the corresponding derivatives of starches, but these are not commercially useful.

SUMMARY

Carbohydrates are polyhydroxy aldehydes or polyhydroxy ketones. Monosaccharides, sometimes known as simple sugars, cannot be broken down into simpler carbohydrate molecules. Aldoses are monosaccharides with aldehyde functional groups. The simplest of these is glyceraldehyde, the compound upon which the D-L naming system is based. The most important natural aldoses are the aldopentoses D-ribose (in RNA) and D-deoxyribose (in DNA) and the aldohexoses D-glucose and D-galactose. Ketoses have ketone functional groups in their formulas. Of all the ketoses, D-fructose, a ketohexose, is the one that is most abundant in nature.

Aldoses and ketoses form stable cyclic hemiacetals, which exist in equilibrium with the straight-chain monosaccharide molecules. Aldohexoses tend to form six-membered rings called pyranoses, while most aldopentoses and ketohexoses form five-membered rings known as furanoses.

Each cyclic sugar has two more stereoisomers than the corresponding open-chain form. In the cyclic form the C atom derived from the carbonyl group becomes asymmetric and is called the anomeric C atom. The additional stereoisomers are said to be anomers of each other and are named by placing an α or β in front of the name of the open-chain sugar. Monosaccharides exist in the form of an equilibrium mixture containing the open-chain molecule and both the α and β anomeric forms, which convert from one to another by a process known as mutarotation.

Haworth projection formulas are very useful for representing the complete stereochemistry of the cyclic monosaccharides. Groups that point to the right in Fischer projection formulas point down in Haworth formulas.

Reducing sugars have free aldehyde or ketone groups and can be oxidized by Tollens' or Benedict's reagent. All monosaccharides are reducing sugars.

The hemiacetal (or hemiketal) hydroxyl group reacts with a molecule of alcohol to form acetal compounds called glycosides. The glycosidic linkage that forms is typical of those that join monosaccharide molecules together to form disaccharides ("two sugars") and polysaccharides ("many sugars"). The linkage is named by giving the stereochemistry of the hemiacetal OH group (α or β) and the numbers of the C atoms linked.

The disaccharides maltose (α-D-glucose + D-glucose), cellobiose (β-D-glucose + D-glucose), and lactose (β-D-galactose + D-glucose) are all reducing sugars. Sucrose (α-D-glucose + β-D-fructose), or table sugar, is a nonreducing sugar since it is formed by an α,β linkage that ties up both anomeric C atoms.

Starch is a mixture of two polysaccharides formed from α-D-glucose monomers. One component is amylose, a linear polymer molecule containing α-1,4 linkages, and the other is amylopectin, a branched polymer of D-glucose including some α-1,6 linkages. Glycogen, a highly branched starch molecule, is also composed of α-D-glucose monomers and is the form in which animals store starch.

Cellulose is a polymer of β-D-glucose. The β-1,4 linkages in cellulose cannot be cleaved by enzymes secreted by the digestive tracts of most animals, and hence cellulose cannot provide a source of nourishment. Cellulose (rayon and cellophane) and its derivatives (such as cellulose nitrate and cellulose acetate) have many household and industrial uses.

KEY WORDS

carbohydrate	fructose	free aldehyde	sucrose
monosaccharide	open-chain sugar	reducing sugar	nonreducing sugar
aldose	cyclic sugar	glycoside	polysaccharide
ketose	pyranose	glycosidic linkage	starch
ribose	furanose	disaccharide	amylose
deoxyribose	anomers	lactose	amylopectin
glucose	anomeric carbon	galactosemia	glycogen
galactose	mutarotation	lactose intolerance	cellulose

EXERCISES

21.8 Classify the carbohydrates below according to their functional groups and carbon content.

(a)
$$\begin{array}{c} CH_2OH \\ | \\ C{=}O \\ | \\ HCOH \\ | \\ HCOH \\ | \\ HCOH \\ | \\ CH_2OH \end{array}$$

(b)
$$\begin{array}{c} H \\ | \\ C{=}O \\ | \\ HCOH \\ | \\ HCOH \\ | \\ HCOH \\ | \\ HCOH \\ | \\ HCOH \\ | \\ HCOH \\ | \\ CH_2OH \end{array}$$

(c)
$$\begin{array}{c} H \\ | \\ C{=}O \\ | \\ HCOH \\ | \\ HCOH \\ | \\ CH_2OH \end{array}$$

(d)
$$\begin{array}{c} CH_2OH \\ | \\ HCOH \\ | \\ HCOH \\ | \\ C{=}O \\ | \\ CH_2OH \end{array}$$

21.9 For each monosaccharide shown above, how many stereoisomers are possible? (Consider only the open chain forms as shown.)

21.10 The formula for a deoxy aldopentose is

$$\begin{array}{c} H \\ | \\ C{=}O \\ | \\ HCH \\ | \\ HCOH \\ | \\ HCOH \\ | \\ CH_2OH \end{array}$$

(a) How many stereoisomers are possible for this compound?

(b) Write Fischer projection formulas for the D isomers only.
(c) Which isomer is D-deoxyribose?

21.11 Write general formulas for an aldoheptose and for a ketoheptose (open-chain forms). How many stereoisomers are possible for each one? Is it generally true that aldoses have twice as many stereoisomers as do ketoses with the same C content?

21.12 One of the formulas below represents D-glucosamine, a compound present in chitin, a polysaccharide found in insect skeletons. Which is it?

```
(a)      H           (b)      H
         |                    |
        C=O                  C=O
         |                    |
     H---+---NH2          H---+---NH2
    HO---+---H           HO---+---H
     H---+---OH          HO---+---H
    HO---+---H            H---+---OH
         |                    |
       CH2OH                CH2OH

(c)      H           (d)    CH2OH
         |                    |
        C=O                  C=O
         |                    |
     H---+---NH2          H---+---NH2
    HO---+---H           HO---+---H
     H---+---OH           H---+---OH
     H---+---OH           H---+---OH
         |                    |
       CH2OH                CH2OH
```

21.13 The sugar below, used in the manufacture of L-ascorbic acid (vitamin C), is one of the most abundant of the L sugars in nature.

```
       CH2OH
         |
        C=O
         |
    HO---+---H
     H---+---OH
    HO---+---H
         |
       CH2OH
```

(a) Classify this monosaccharide according to its functional group and carbon content.
(b) What is the name of the sugar?

21.14 The compound L-fucose is an important component of some bacterial cell walls. Give the Fischer projection formula for this compound, also known as 6-deoxy-L-galactose.

21.15 For open-chain D-galactose do the following:
(a) Draw the Fischer projection formula.
(b) Using an arrow that originates from the H that is added, show how the hemiacetal forms.

21.16 Starting with Fischer formulas draw the hemiacetal structures for α-D-galactose and β-D-galactose. Indicate clearly what differentiates the α and β forms. Draw the Haworth formulas for α- and β-galactose. Are α- and β-galactoses classified as galactofuranoses or galactopyranoses?

21.17 Why are furanose and pyranose rings particularly stable?

21.18 Of the formulas shown below, which ones could represent glucose?

(a) $C_6H_{12}O_6$

(b)
```
CH2CHCHCHC=O
|  |  |  |  |
OH OHOHOHH
```

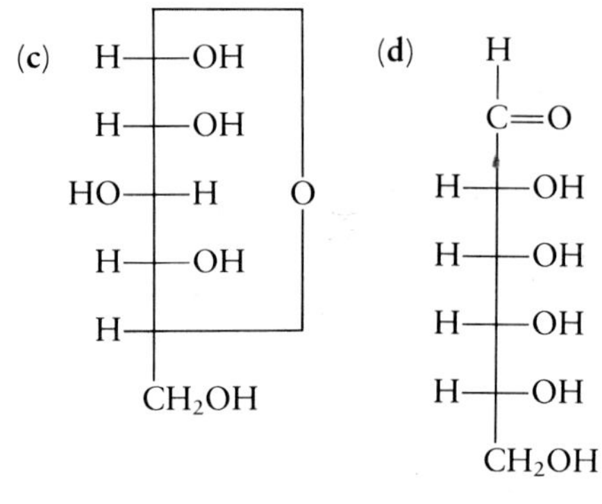

(e) [Haworth ring: CH₂OH, O, OH, OH, HO, OH]

(f) [Haworth ring: CH₂OH, O, OH, HO, OH, OH]

21.19 Of the formulas shown below, which ones could represent fructose?

(a) $C_6H_{12}O_6$

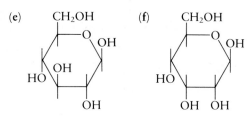

(b)
```
          O
          ||
CH2CHCHCHCCH2OH
|  |  |  |
OH OHOHOH
```

(c)

CH_2OH
H—OH
HO—H
H—OH
H—OH
CH_2OH

(d)

$HOCH_2$—OH
HO—H
H—OH
H—
CH_2OH
O

(e) $HOCH_2$ O OH HO CH_2OH OH

(f) $HOCH_2$ O CH_2OH HO HO OH OH

21.20 The ketose shown is sometimes referred to as "pseudofructose."

CH_2OH
C=O
H—OH
H—OH
H—OH
CH_2OH

(a) How does its structure differ from that of fructose?
(b) Using Figure 21.5, name this compound.
(c) Indicate all asymmetric C atoms in its open-chain formula. How many stereoisomers are possible?
(d) Starting with the formula above, draw the hemiketal form. How many stereoisomers does it have?

21.21 Draw Haworth formulas for the two hemiacetal stereoisomers of the aldose below:

H
C=O
H—OH
HO—H
H—OH
H—OH
CH_2OH

Name the isomers as aldopyranoses.

21.22 Draw the Haworth formulas for the α and β forms of D-sorbose, a ketohexose (see Figure 21.5*d*).

21.23 The disaccharide below is called gentobiose.

CH_2OH O OH HO OH O CH_2 O OH OH HO OH

(a) What monosaccharide(s) are produced upon the hydrolysis of gentobiose?
(b) What is the linkage that joins them?
(c) Is gentobiose a reducing sugar? Why?

21.24 Most ketones do not react with chemical oxidizing agents. Why are ketoses an exception?

21.25 Raffinose is a sugar present in small amounts in many plants:

CH_2OH HO O OH OH O CH_2 O OH HO OH O $HOCH_2$ O H HO CH_2OH OH

(a) To what general class of saccharides does raffinose belong?
(b) What monosaccharide(s) are produced upon the hydrolysis of raffinose?
(c) Is raffinose a reducing or a nonreducing sugar? Explain.

21.26 What is the disorder called galactosemia? How is it treated?

21.27 What is meant by lactase deficiency syndrome? What dietary precautions must be taken by someone suffering from this disorder?

21.28 Organ meats and peas contain some free galactose and are thus prohibited for persons with galactosemia. May individuals suffering from lactose deficiency syndrome have peas or organ meats in their diets? Explain.

21.29 Oriental foods are generally not prepared with milk, cream, or cheese. Can you give a reason for this?

21.30 Which of the following sugars would interfere with a Benedict's test for glucose in urine: (a) Fructose; (b) maltose; (c) sucrose?

21.31 What are the products of the reaction of glucose with O_2 in the presence of glucose oxidase?

21.32 How are glucose enzymatic test strips used to measure the amount of glucose in urine?

21.33 Suppose a urine sample contained lactose. What result would be obtained by the (**a**) copper reduction method (such as Benedict's test); (**b**) enzyme method?

21.34 Explain how the xylose excretion test works.

21.35 What two reactants are needed to make α-D-methylribofuranoside?

21.36 Write the reaction for the production of α-D-methylribofuranoside. Use Haworth formulas.

21.37 Of the following carbohydrates, which are composed of glucose units only: (**a**) Sucrose; (**b**) lactose; (**c**) amylose; (**d**) starch; (**e**) cellulose; (**f**) maltose; (**g**) cellobiose?

21.38 What are the two molecular components of starch? How are they different structurally? How are they the same?

21.39 Would it be possible for mammals to derive nourishment from cellobiose? Why?

21.40 A segment of inulin, a polymer of D-fructose used as a diagnostic agent to detect kidney malfunction, is shown below. What label should be given to the glycosidic linkage?

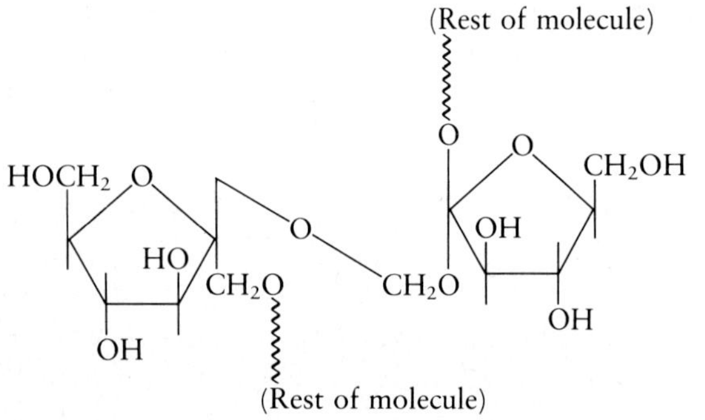

(Rest of molecule)
O
$HOCH_2$ O — HO — OH — CH_2O — O — CH_2O — O — OH — CH_2OH — OH
(Rest of molecule)

21.41 Is mutarotation possible for sucrose? Why?

21.42 What is invert sugar? How is the name derived?

21.43 The product called Emetrol, used to relieve nausea and vomiting, is described as "an oral solution containing balanced amounts of levulose and dextrose." To prepare Emetrol which of the following substances is added to water: (**a**) Sucrose; (**b**) invert sugar; (**c**) lactose; (**d**) honey; (**e**) corn syrup?

21.44 One of the compounds below represents the sugar alcohol D-mannitol (Section 15.2), a diuretic substance used in diagnostic tests of kidney function (diuretics increase urine flow). Which one is it? (See Figure 21.3.)

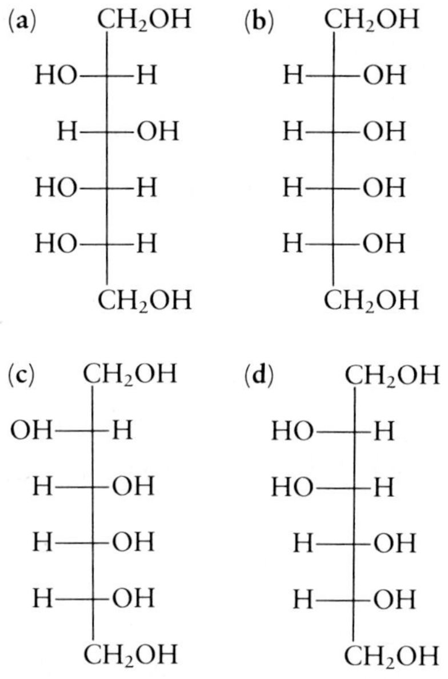

(a)	(b)	(c)	(d)
CH_2OH	CH_2OH	CH_2OH	CH_2OH
HO—H	H—OH	OH—H	HO—H
H—OH	H—OH	H—OH	HO—H
HO—H	H—OH	H—OH	H—OH
HO—H	H—OH	H—OH	H—OH
CH_2OH	CH_2OH	CH_2OH	CH_2OH

21.45 An infant who is not growing properly is brought into a clinic for examination. Suppose you suspect galactosemia. What tests using enzyme and copper reduction test strips could you perform to strengthen your diagnosis? Suppose the diagnosis of galactosemia is confirmed. How would you describe the dietary treatment to the parents?

22 LIPIDS

22.1 INTRODUCTION

If we mix a sample of plant or animal tissue with benzene or another nonpolar solvent, some components of the tissue will dissolve, while others will not. The compounds in living tissue that *are* soluble in nonpolar solvents are known as **lipids**. A variety of lipids are shown in Figure 22.1, where you can see that their structures cannot be described by a single general formula. A triacylglycerol fat, for instance, looks nothing like a steroid. However, there is one feature that they do have in common: all the compounds in the figure are nonpolar or contain long nonpolar hydrocarbon chains, which explains their solubility in nonpolar solvents (see Section 9.4).

Lipids function in a number of ways in living systems. The most nonpolar of them (such as the fat shown in Figure 22.1*a*) are stored in the body, where they serve as energy reservoirs that are metabolized when needed. These fats are constantly replenished as excess food is ingested because all excess foods, even carbohydrates and proteins, are converted by the body into fats. That is why overeating produces large amounts of fatty tissue. Other lipids, including the phosphoglycerides, are much more polar than the glyceride fats. Lipids such as these are structural components of the membranes which enclose cells, the microscopic compartments of living matter.

By using chromatographic techniques (Section 2.5) it is possible to separate the complex mixture of lipids isolated from tissues.

Seven general types of lipids isolated are triacylglycerol fats, prostaglandins, phosphoglycerides, sphingolipids (and glycolipids), waxes, terpenes, and steroids.

In the following sections we will describe all of these. Our discussion begins with the fatty acids which are constituents of all the lipids mentioned above except for terpenes and steroids.

$CH_2OC(=O)(CH_2)_7CH{=}CH(CH_2)_7CH_3$
$CH{-}OC(=O)(CH_2)_{14}CH_3$
$CH_2OC(=O)(CH_2)_{14}CH_3$

(a)

CH_3 CH_3 $CHCH_2CH_2CH_2CH$ CH_3 CH_3 CH_3 HO

(b)

$CH_2OP(=O)(O^-)OCH_2CH_2NH_3^+$
$CH_3(CH_2)_7CH{=}CH(CH_2)_7C(=O)OCH$
$CH_2OC(=O)(CH_2)_{16}CH_3$

(c)

$CH_3(CH_2)_{18}C(=O)O(CH_2)_{21}CH_3$

(d)

$CH_3(CH_2)_{12}CH{=}CHCH{-}OH$
$CH_3(CH_2)_{22}C(=O)NHCH$
CH_2
$HOCH_2$, HO, O, O, OH, OH

(e)

$CH_3C(CH_3){=}CHCH_2CH_2C(CH_3){=}CHCH_2CH_2C(CH_3){=}CHCH_2OH$

(f)

$C(=O)$—$CHCH_2CH{=}CHCH_2CH_2CH_2C(=O){-}OH$
CH_2 $CHCH{=}CHCH(OH)CH_2CH_2CH_2CH_2CH_3$
CH—OH

(g)

FIGURE 22.1
A variety of lipids:
(*a*) triacylglycerol fat;
(*b*) steroid; (*c*) phosphoglyceride; (*d*) wax;
(*e*) glycolipid;
(*f*) terpene; (*g*) prostaglandin.

22.2 FATTY ACIDS

Recall that carboxylic acids have the general formula $R{-}C(=O){-}OH$.

Fatty acids are carboxylic acids in which the R group in the general formula is a hydrocarbon chain, which is almost always long and unbranched. Fatty acids do not ordinarily appear uncombined in nature; more often they are components of larger lipid molecules. Figure 22.2 shows the products of the breakdown of lipids that do include fatty acids.

Nearly all fatty acids have an even number of C atoms in their formulas (including the carboxyl C), because the fats from which they are derived are synthesized in living things by the addition of two C atom fragments to one another (see Chapter 27 on the metabolism of lipids). Fatty acids may or may not have double bonds in their hydrocarbon chains.

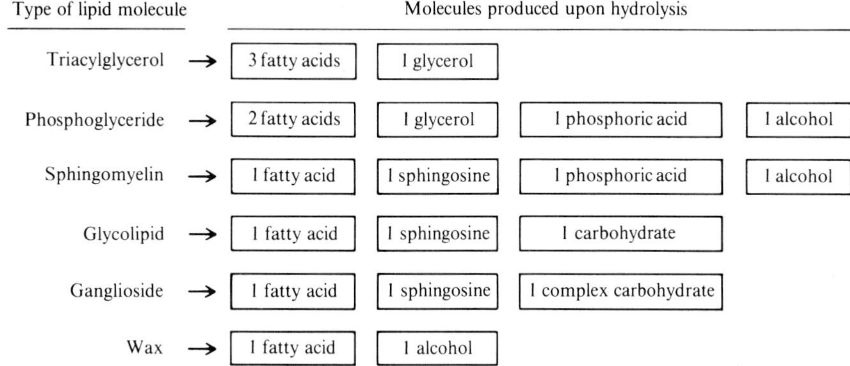

FIGURE 22.2
Lipids that contain fatty acids.

TABLE 22.1 **SATURATED FATTY ACIDS**

No. of C atoms	Formula	Common name	Source	Melting point, °C
4	$CH_3(CH_2)_2COOH$	Butyric	Butter (*butyrum*)	−6
6	$CH_3(CH_2)_4COOH$	Caproic	Goat (*caper*)	−4
8	$CH_3(CH_2)_6COOH$	Caprylic	Goat (*caper*)	16
10	$CH_3(CH_2)_8COOH$	Capric	Goat (*caper*)	31
12	$CH_3(CH_2)_{10}COOH$	Lauric	Laurel	43
14	$CH_3(CH_2)_{12}COOH$	Myristic	Nutmeg (*myristica*)	54
16	$CH_3(CH_2)_{14}COOH$	Palmitic	Palm oil	63
18	$CH_3(CH_2)_{16}COOH$	Stearic	Tallow (*stear*)	70
20	$CH_3(CH_2)_{18}COOH$	Arachidic	Peanuts (*arachis*)	75

Saturated Fatty Acids

Even-numbered fatty acids are abundant in nature and are usually referred to by common names.

In saturated fatty acids the hydrocarbon chain contains no C to C double bonds. Some saturated fatty acids that appear in lipids are listed in Table 22.1, where their names, melting points, and natural sources are given. The most abundant fatty acid of all is palmitic acid (hexadecanoic acid), a compound found in nearly all fats. Note from the table that saturated fatty acids which have 10 or more C atoms are all solids.

Unsaturated Fatty Acids

Unsaturated fatty acids have at least one double bond in their hydrocarbon chains (see Table 22.2). The most abundant of them is oleic acid, the cis isomer of the 18-carbon acid in which there is a double bond between the C-9 and C-10 atoms.

TABLE 22.2 UNSATURATED FATTY ACIDS

No. of atoms	Formula	Names	Melting point, °C
16	$CH_3(CH_2)_5CH{=}CH(CH_2)_7COOH$	Palmitoleic	−0.5
18	$CH_3(CH_2)_7CH{=}CH(CH_2)_7COOH$	Oleic	13
18	$CH_3(CH_2)_4CH{=}CHCH_2CH{=}CH(CH_2)_7COOH$	Linoleic	−5
18	$CH_3CH_2CH{=}CHCH_2CH{=}CHCH_2CH{=}CH(CH_2)_7COOH$	Linolenic	−11
20	$CH_3(CH_2)_4CH{=}CHCH_2CH{=}CHCH_2CH{=}CHCH_2CH{=}CH(CH_2)_3COOH$	Arachidonic	−49

$$\underset{18}{CH_3}\underset{17}{CH_2}\underset{16}{CH_2}\underset{15}{CH_2}\underset{14}{CH_2}\underset{13}{CH_2}\underset{12}{CH_2}\underset{11}{CH_2}-\underset{H}{\overset{10}{C}}{=}\underset{H}{\overset{9}{C}}-\underset{8}{CH_2}\underset{7}{CH_2}\underset{6}{CH_2}\underset{5}{CH_2}\underset{4}{CH_2}\underset{3}{CH_2}\underset{2}{CH_2}\underset{1}{\overset{\overset{O}{\|}}{C}}OH$$

Oleic acid

Some common unsaturated fatty acids that have two or more double bonds are linoleic acid, linolenic acid, and arachidonic acid (see Table 22.2).

Essential fatty acids (abbreviated EFA) are those that cannot be synthesized in the human body and must be supplied by the diet. The most abundant EFA in mammals is the multiply unsaturated fatty acid linoleic acid, shown below.

$$CH_3CH_2CH_2CH_2CH_2CH{=}CHCH_2CH{=}CHCH_2CH_2CH_2CH_2CH_2CH_2CH_2\overset{\overset{O}{\|}}{C}OH$$

Linoleic acid, an EFA

The absence of linoleic acid in the diet produces symptoms of EFA deficiency, such as sparse hair, scaly skin, and poor healing of wounds. Arachidonic acid (Table 22.2) is also classified as an essential fatty acid, although the body can synthesize this substance from linoleic acid. In young animals arachidonic acid alone or both linoleic and arachidonic acids must be present for normal skin structure to be maintained. Adults can depend on accumulated body reserves of EFA and thus have lower daily requirements.

The required amount of EFA in the diet is 2 percent of total caloric intake for adults, and 3 to 4 percent for infants.

Prostaglandins

Prostaglandins are lipids that contain 20 C atoms including a five-membered ring structure. The prostaglandin first isolated from seminal fluid and from the prostate gland was originally thought to be the only prostaglandin, a single substance secreted by the male genital tract. Later many different prostaglandins, including the typical one shown below, were found to be present in almost all animal tissues.

FIGURE 22.3
According to one theory, aspirin kills pain by inhibiting the synthesis of prostaglandins, PG. (The labels in parentheses indicate specific types of prostaglandins.) Linoleic acid leads to PG (E_1), a potent fever-producing agent, via a similar pathway.

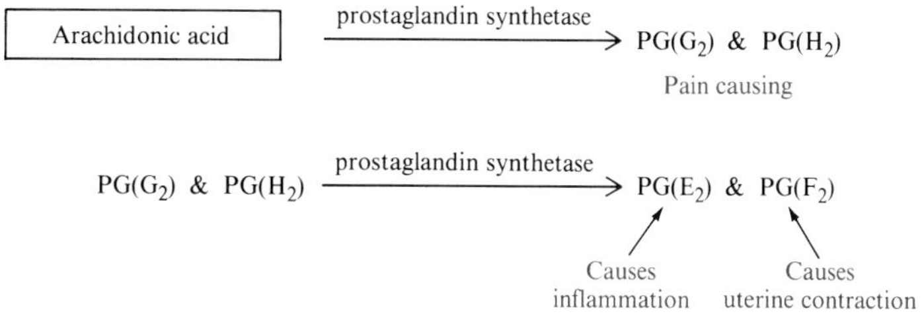

$$\boxed{\text{Arachidonic acid}} \xrightarrow{\text{prostaglandin synthetase}} PG(G_2)\ \&\ PG(H_2)$$

Pain causing

$$PG(G_2)\ \&\ PG(H_2) \xrightarrow{\text{prostaglandin synthetase}} PG(E_2)\ \&\ PG(F_2)$$

Causes inflammation — Causes uterine contraction

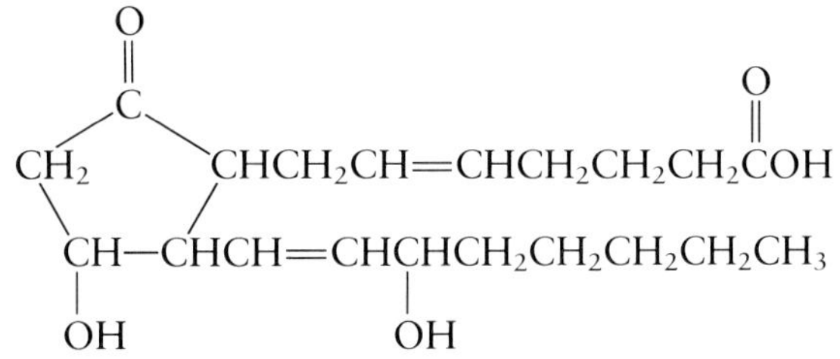

```
        O
        ‖
       .C.                                         O
     /     \                                       ‖
  CH2       CHCH2CH=CHCH2CH2CH2COH
     \      /
      CH—CHCH=CHCHCH2CH2CH2CH2CH3
      |          |
      OH         OH
```

Typical prostaglandin

In tissues prostaglandins are synthesized from arachidonic acid, drawn below in such a way that you can see their structural similarities:

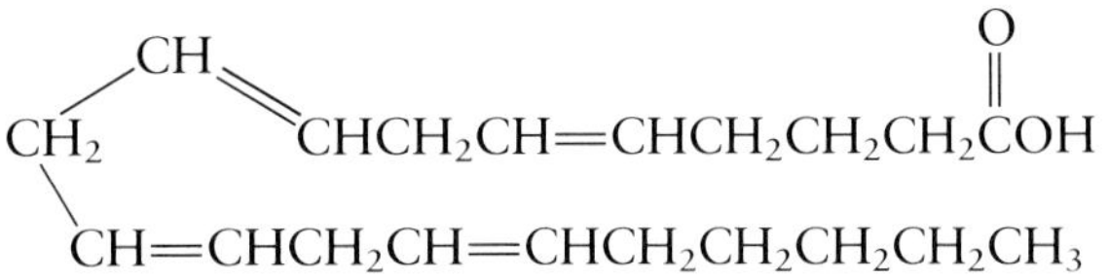

```
       .CH.                                        O
     /      \\                                     ‖
  CH2        CHCH2CH=CHCH2CH2CH2COH
     \
      CH=CHCH2CH=CHCH2CH2CH2CH2CH3
```

Arachidonic acid (the precursor of prostaglandins)

Prostaglandins regulate a number of biological activities and thus exhibit hormonal behavior. For instance, they are known to cause smooth muscle to contract. A clinical use for some prostaglandins is to induce labor. Prostaglandins and some of their precursors are also thought to cause inflammation, vasoconstriction, and pain sensation. The anti-inflammatory, antipyretic (fever-reducing), and analgesic actions of aspirin and other nonnarcotic analgesics are believed to result from their ability to interfere with the synthesis of prostaglandins, as outlined in Figure 22.3. According to this theory, the nonnarcotic analgesics inhibit the action of the enzyme prostaglandin synthetase, thus reducing the formation of excess prostaglandins and the pain, fever, and inflammation caused by them.

It is thought that aspirin reduces pain by inhibiting prostaglandin biosynthesis.

22.3 TRIACYLGLYCEROLS

Recall that the formula for an ester is $R—\overset{\overset{\displaystyle O}{\|}}{C}—OR$.

Triacylglycerols (also known as *triglycerides*), the most abundant lipids in nature, are the triesters of glycerol (1,2,3-propanetriol). They are formed when one molecule of glycerol reacts with three fatty acid molecules to form a triester, as shown in the reaction below.

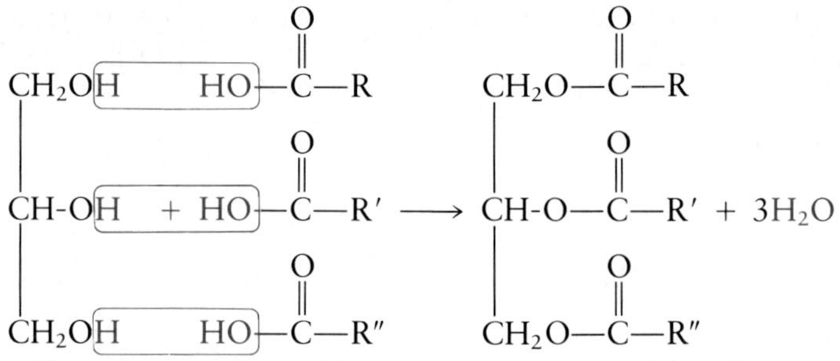

$$\begin{array}{l} \text{CH}_2\text{OH} \quad \text{HO}-\overset{\overset{\text{O}}{\|}}{\text{C}}-\text{R} \\ | \\ \text{CH-OH} \; + \; \text{HO}-\overset{\overset{\text{O}}{\|}}{\text{C}}-\text{R}' \longrightarrow \\ | \\ \text{CH}_2\text{OH} \quad \text{HO}-\overset{\overset{\text{O}}{\|}}{\text{C}}-\text{R}'' \end{array} \quad \begin{array}{l} \text{CH}_2\text{O}-\overset{\overset{\text{O}}{\|}}{\text{C}}-\text{R} \\ | \\ \text{CH-O}-\overset{\overset{\text{O}}{\|}}{\text{C}}-\text{R}' + 3\text{H}_2\text{O} \\ | \\ \text{CH}_2\text{O}-\overset{\overset{\text{O}}{\|}}{\text{C}}-\text{R}'' \end{array}$$

Glycerol Fatty acids Triacylglycerol

The group $R-\overset{\overset{O}{\|}}{C}$ is called acyl and is shown in color in the triacylglycerol formulas below.

The R groups (R, R′, and R″) in the reactant fatty acids may be the same or different. *Simple fats* are those formed from three identical fatty acids. Two examples of simple fats are tristearin, a triacylglycerol in which all three reactant fatty acid molecules are stearic acid, and triolein, the fat produced from oleic acid only.

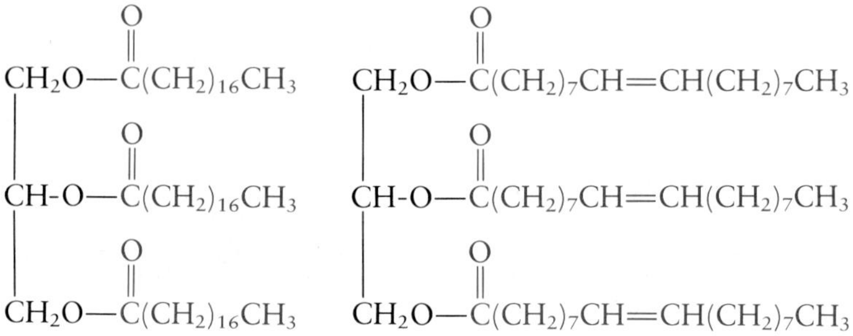

$$\begin{array}{l} \text{CH}_2\text{O}-\overset{\overset{\text{O}}{\|}}{\text{C}}(\text{CH}_2)_{16}\text{CH}_3 \\ | \\ \text{CH-O}-\overset{\overset{\text{O}}{\|}}{\text{C}}(\text{CH}_2)_{16}\text{CH}_3 \\ | \\ \text{CH}_2\text{O}-\overset{\overset{\text{O}}{\|}}{\text{C}}(\text{CH}_2)_{16}\text{CH}_3 \end{array} \qquad \begin{array}{l} \text{CH}_2\text{O}-\overset{\overset{\text{O}}{\|}}{\text{C}}(\text{CH}_2)_7\text{CH}{=}\text{CH}(\text{CH}_2)_7\text{CH}_3 \\ | \\ \text{CH-O}-\overset{\overset{\text{O}}{\|}}{\text{C}}(\text{CH}_2)_7\text{CH}{=}\text{CH}(\text{CH}_2)_7\text{CH}_3 \\ | \\ \text{CH}_2\text{O}-\overset{\overset{\text{O}}{\|}}{\text{C}}(\text{CH}_2)_7\text{CH}{=}\text{CH}(\text{CH}_2)_7\text{CH}_3 \end{array}$$

Tristearin Triolein

Most natural fats are *mixed fats* formed from more than one kind of fatty acid, such as the one below that includes acyl groups derived from two molecules of palmitic acid and one of oleic acid:

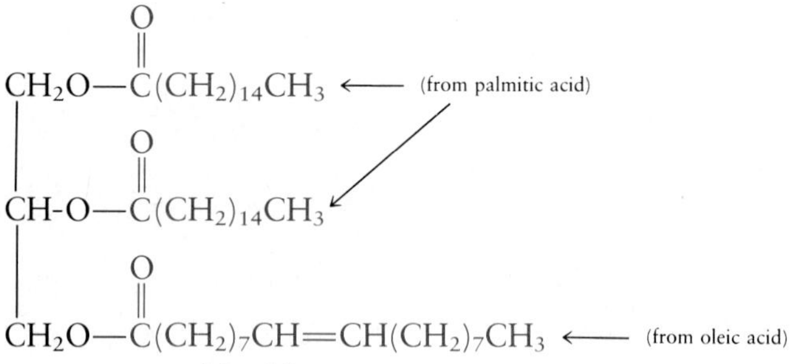

$$\begin{array}{l} \text{CH}_2\text{O}-\overset{\overset{\text{O}}{\|}}{\text{C}}(\text{CH}_2)_{14}\text{CH}_3 \longleftarrow \text{(from palmitic acid)} \\ | \\ \text{CH-O}-\overset{\overset{\text{O}}{\|}}{\text{C}}(\text{CH}_2)_{14}\text{CH}_3 \\ | \\ \text{CH}_2\text{O}-\overset{\overset{\text{O}}{\|}}{\text{C}}(\text{CH}_2)_7\text{CH}{=}\text{CH}(\text{CH}_2)_7\text{CH}_3 \longleftarrow \text{(from oleic acid)} \end{array}$$

Mixed fat

Fats that come from natural sources, such as butter fat, are complex mixtures of simple and mixed triacylglycerols. Table 22.3 gives the fatty acid composition of butter, lard, corn oil, peanut oil, olive oil, and soybean oil. Note that all the fats listed contain significant amounts of the saturated fatty acid palmitic acid and the unsaturated fatty acid oleic acid.

Saturated and Unsaturated Fats

Fats are classified according to the amount of unsaturation present in their hy-

TABLE 22.3 COMPOSITION OF SOME FATS AND OILS

Fatty acid	R in RCOOH formula	Fatty acid content, mole %					
		Butter	Lard	Corn oil	Peanut oil	Olive oil	Soybean oil
		Saturated fatty acids					
Butyric	C_3H_7	3–4					
Myristic	$C_{13}H_{27}$	7–9	1–2	0–2		0–1	
Palmitic	$C_{15}H_{31}$	23–26	28–30	7–11	6–9	5–15	10–13
Stearic	$C_{17}H_{35}$	10–13	12–18	3–4	2–6	1–4	
		Unsaturated fatty acids					
Palmitoleic	$C_6H_{13}CH{=}CH(CH_2)_7$	5	1–3	0–2	0–1	0–1	
Oleic	$C_8H_{18}CH{=}CH(CH_2)_7$	30–40	41–48	43–49	50–70	69–84	21–29
Linoleic	$C_5H_{11}CH{=}CHCH_2CH{=}CH(CH_2)_7$	4–5	6–7	34–42	13–26	4–12	50–59
Total saturated acids		43–52	41–50	10–17	8–15	6–20	10–13
Total unsaturated acids		39–50	48–58	77–93	63–97	73–97	71–88

drocarbon chains. As you can see from Table 22.3, all the fats listed contain *both* saturated and unsaturated fatty acids.

All fats, even unsaturated ones, contain some saturated fatty acids.

Thus, strictly speaking, all fats are unsaturated since they all contain at least some oleic acid. But the term **unsaturated fat** refers only to fats that have a large percentage (usually more than 80 percent) of unsaturated fatty acids in their formulas compared with saturated fats. **Saturated fats** are those which have a smaller amount of unsaturated fats (about 50 percent) compared with saturated ones. According to these definitions, butter and lard are classified as saturated fats and the oils from corn, peanuts, olives, and soybeans as unsaturated fats (see Table 22.3).

In general, saturated fats such as butter and lard come from animals and are usually solids at room temperature. Unsaturated fats come from vegetables and most are liquids at room temperatures. Liquid fats, such as those derived from corn, peanuts, olives, and soybeans, are often called *oils*. Vegetable oils contain much more linoleic acid than do the animal fats. The higher the degree of unsaturation, the lower the melting point of the fat, that is, the more fluid it is. For instance, an average sample of soybean oil, which contains about 50 percent linoleic acid, starts to solidify at $-10°C$, compared with 5°C for olive oil, which is much lower in linoleic acid (see Table 22.3).

22.4 REACTIONS OF FATS AND OILS

Triacylglycerol fats are esters and thus undergo the reactions of esters. Those with unsaturated hydrocarbon chains also participate in reactions involving their double bonds.

Hydrolysis

Hydrolysis of fats by lipase is what happens when your body digests fats.

In Section 17.8 you saw that hydrolysis of an ester regenerates the reactants that produced it, an alcohol and a carboxylic acid. Likewise, the hydrolysis of a fat molecule generates three molecules of fatty acid and a glycerol molecule. Hydrolysis of fats does not proceed rapidly without a catalyst. Boiling fat in water when cooking (soups, for instance) does not cause the fat to decompose. In the body, where fats are an important source of energy, enzymes called *lipases* speed up the hydrolysis of fats (Chapter 27). In the laboratory we use acids or bases as catalysts.

Saponification

The base-catalyzed hydrolysis of a fat belongs to the class of reactions known as saponifications (Section 17.8). When the base is NaOH, the sodium salts of the fatty acids are produced.

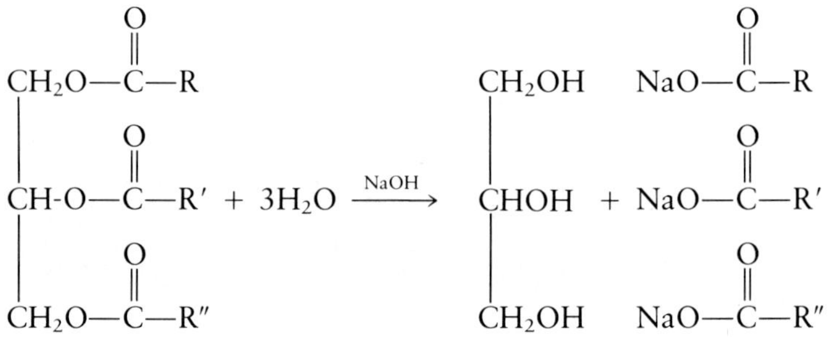

$$\begin{array}{l} CH_2O\!-\!\overset{\overset{\displaystyle O}{\|}}{C}\!-\!R \\ | \\ CH\text{-}O\!-\!\overset{\overset{\displaystyle O}{\|}}{C}\!-\!R' \\ | \\ CH_2O\!-\!\overset{\overset{\displaystyle O}{\|}}{C}\!-\!R'' \end{array} + 3H_2O \xrightarrow{NaOH} \begin{array}{l} CH_2OH \\ | \\ CHOH \\ | \\ CH_2OH \end{array} + \begin{array}{l} NaO\!-\!\overset{\overset{\displaystyle O}{\|}}{C}\!-\!R \\ \\ NaO\!-\!\overset{\overset{\displaystyle O}{\|}}{C}\!-\!R' \\ \\ NaO\!-\!\overset{\overset{\displaystyle O}{\|}}{C}\!-\!R'' \end{array}$$

Triacylglycerol Glycerol Salts of fatty acids

These sodium salts behave as soaps, since they have long nonpolar hydrocarbon chains, which can dissolve fats, grease, and other nonpolar "dirt" substances, and polar carboxylate ends, which dissolve in water (Section 17.7).

Hydrogenation

We said that unsaturated fats (oils) are generally liquids. It is possible to obtain solid, saturated fats by catalytic hydrogenation of oils. Like alkenes, the unsaturated fatty acid components of fats can be hydrogenated when treated with H_2 gas in the presence of a suitable catalyst (Section 13.9), as shown in the reaction below.

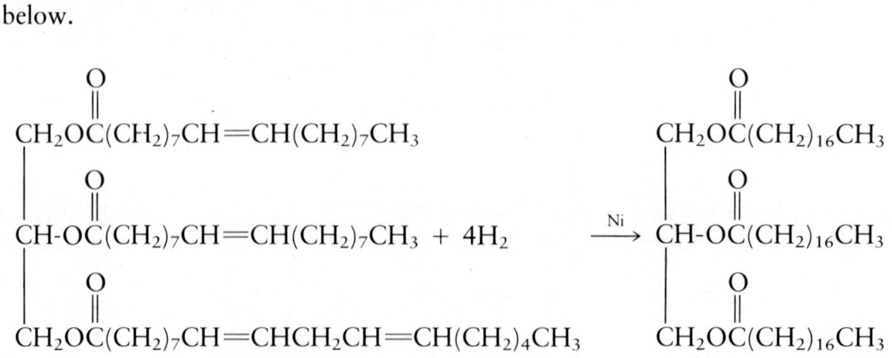

$$\begin{array}{l} CH_2O\overset{\overset{\displaystyle O}{\|}}{C}(CH_2)_7CH{=}CH(CH_2)_7CH_3 \\ | \\ CH\text{-}O\overset{\overset{\displaystyle O}{\|}}{C}(CH_2)_7CH{=}CH(CH_2)_7CH_3 \\ | \\ CH_2O\overset{\overset{\displaystyle O}{\|}}{C}(CH_2)_7CH{=}CHCH_2CH{=}CH(CH_2)_4CH_3 \end{array} + 4H_2 \xrightarrow{Ni} \begin{array}{l} CH_2O\overset{\overset{\displaystyle O}{\|}}{C}(CH_2)_{16}CH_3 \\ | \\ CH\text{-}O\overset{\overset{\displaystyle O}{\|}}{C}(CH_2)_{16}CH_3 \\ | \\ CH_2O\overset{\overset{\displaystyle O}{\|}}{C}(CH_2)_{16}CH_3 \end{array}$$

Unsaturated fat (liquid) Saturated fat (solid)

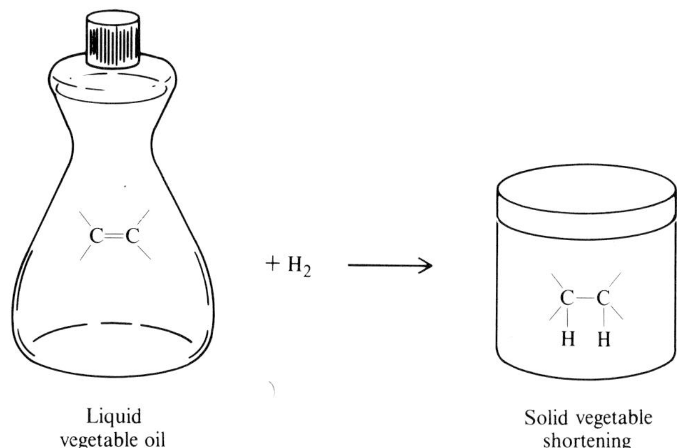

FIGURE 22.4
Hydrogenation of oils. Liquid vegetable oils can be solidified by the addition of hydrogen, which adds across fatty acid double bonds.

Vegetable shortening (used to make pie crusts) is made by partial hydrogenation of the double bonds in liquid unsaturated oils (see Figure 22.4).

Rancidification

In Section 13.8 you saw that double-bonded compounds are oxidized to form diols. In air the C to C double bonds of unsaturated fats also undergo oxidation to produce aldehydes, ketones, or acids. The equation below shows such a reaction in which the products are carboxylic acids.

$$
\begin{array}{lcl}
CH_2O\overset{\overset{O}{\|}}{C}(CH_2)_7CH{=}CH(CH_2)_7CH_3 & & CH_2O\overset{\overset{O}{\|}}{C}(CH_2)_7\overset{\overset{O}{\|}}{C}OH \\
| & & | \\
CH\text{-}O\overset{\overset{O}{\|}}{C}(CH_2)_7CH{=}CH(CH_2)_7CH_3 & \xrightarrow{O_2} & CH\text{-}O\overset{\overset{O}{\|}}{C}(CH_2)_7\overset{\overset{O}{\|}}{C}OH + 2CH_3(CH_2)_7\overset{\overset{O}{\|}}{C}OH \\
| & & | \\
CH_2O\overset{\overset{O}{\|}}{C}(CH_2)_{14}CH_3 & & CH_2O\overset{\overset{O}{\|}}{C}(CH_2)_{14}CH_3
\end{array}
$$

Unsaturated fat — Carboxylic acids

The phenols BHT and BHA extend the shelf life of unsaturated fats (oils) by preventing their oxidation.

The oxidation of the fatty acid chains of a fat is called **rancidification.** Rancid fats have unpleasant odors and tastes because of compounds such as the sour-tasting carboxylic acids produced in the reaction above. To prevent rancidity in products containing unsaturated fats, phenolic compounds are added to serve as antioxidants. See Figure 15.5, which shows the antioxidant food additives known as BHT and BHA.

Halogenation

The halogens Cl_2 or Br_2 readily add across the double bonds of unsaturated fatty acids.

$$CH_3(CH_2)_7CH{=}CH(CH_2)_7\overset{\overset{\displaystyle O}{\|}}{C}{-}OH + Br_2 \longrightarrow CH_3(CH_2)_7\underset{\underset{\displaystyle Br}{|}}{C}H{-}\underset{\underset{\displaystyle Br}{|}}{C}H(CH_2)_7\overset{\overset{\displaystyle O}{\|}}{C}{-}OH$$

Oleic acid 9,10-Dibromostearic acid

The iodine number for corn oil is 123 compared with only 59 for lard.

Halogenation of an unsaturated fat is used to estimate its degree of unsaturation. The **iodine number** is expressed in terms of the number of grams of I_2 that would be absorbed by 100 g of fat. In actual practice compounds such as ICl or IBr are used because I_2 does not easily add across the double bond (see Section 13.9).

SAMPLE EXERCISE 22.1

Give the formulas and names of the fatty acids produced upon the hydrolysis of the fat below:

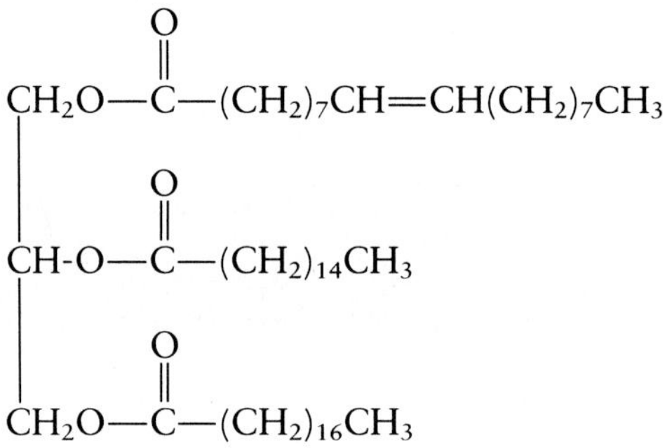

$$\begin{array}{l} CH_2O{-}\overset{\overset{\displaystyle O}{\|}}{C}{-}(CH_2)_7CH{=}CH(CH_2)_7CH_3 \\ | \\ CH{-}O{-}\overset{\overset{\displaystyle O}{\|}}{C}{-}(CH_2)_{14}CH_3 \\ | \\ CH_2O{-}\overset{\overset{\displaystyle O}{\|}}{C}{-}(CH_2)_{16}CH_3 \end{array}$$

Solution:

There are three fatty acids produced:

$$(1)\ HO{-}\overset{\overset{\displaystyle O}{\|}}{C}{-}(CH_2)_7CH{=}CH(CH_2)_7CH_3$$

$$(2)\ HO{-}\overset{\overset{\displaystyle O}{\|}}{C}{-}(CH_2)_{14}CH_3$$

$$(3)\ HO{-}\overset{\overset{\displaystyle O}{\|}}{C}{-}(CH_2)_{16}CH_3$$

From Table 22.2 we find that acid 1 is oleic acid. From Table 22.1 we see that acid 2 is palmitic acid and acid 3 is stearic acid.

EXERCISE 22.1

Give the structure of linolein, a triacylglycerol fat that is a constituent of linseed oil and produces glycerol and linoleic acid upon hydrolysis.

SAMPLE EXERCISE 22.2

How many moles of H_2 are needed to accomplish complete hydrogenation of the oil below? Give the structure of the product.

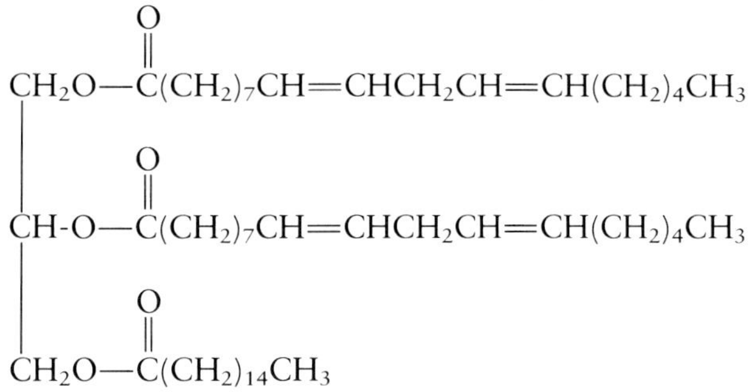

$$\begin{array}{l} \overset{O}{\overset{\|}{}} \\ CH_2O—C(CH_2)_7CH{=}CHCH_2CH{=}CH(CH_2)_4CH_3 \\ | \qquad\quad O \\ | \qquad\quad \| \\ CH\text{-}O—C(CH_2)_7CH{=}CHCH_2CH{=}CH(CH_2)_4CH_3 \\ | \qquad\quad O \\ | \qquad\quad \| \\ CH_2O—C(CH_2)_{14}CH_3 \end{array}$$

Solution:

The oil structure contains four C to C double bonds requiring 4 mol H_2

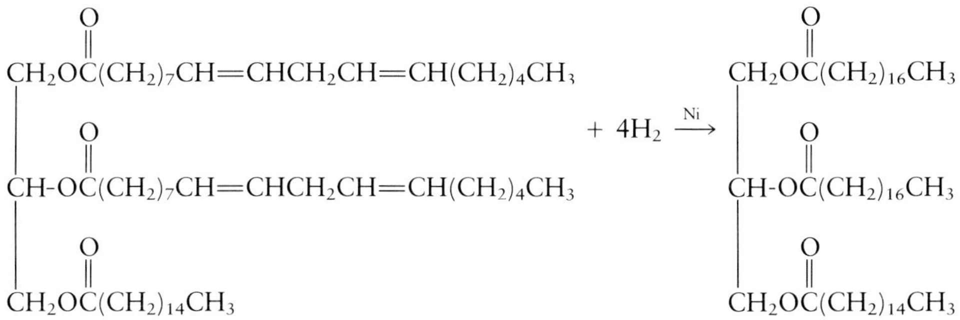

$$\begin{array}{l} \quad O \\ \quad \| \\ CH_2OC(CH_2)_7CH{=}CHCH_2CH{=}CH(CH_2)_4CH_3 \\ | \quad O \\ | \quad \| \\ CH\text{-}OC(CH_2)_7CH{=}CHCH_2CH{=}CH(CH_2)_4CH_3 \\ | \quad O \\ | \quad \| \\ CH_2OC(CH_2)_{14}CH_3 \end{array} + 4H_2 \xrightarrow{Ni} \begin{array}{l} \quad O \\ \quad \| \\ CH_2OC(CH_2)_{16}CH_3 \\ | \quad O \\ | \quad \| \\ CH\text{-}OC(CH_2)_{16}CH_3 \\ | \quad O \\ | \quad \| \\ CH_2OC(CH_2)_{14}CH_3 \end{array}$$

EXERCISE 22.2

Write the formula for the product of the compound that forms when the oil in Sample Exercise 22.2 reacts with 4 mol of bromine (Br_2).

22.5 PHOSPHOGLYCERIDES

Phosphoglycerides are one type of lipid found in all biological membranes. From Figure 22.2 you can see that a **phosphoglyceride** molecule can be broken down into two fatty acid molecules, one glycerol molecule, one phosphoric acid molecule, and one alcohol molecule (A). These different components are indicated in the structure of the general phosphoglyceride shown below.

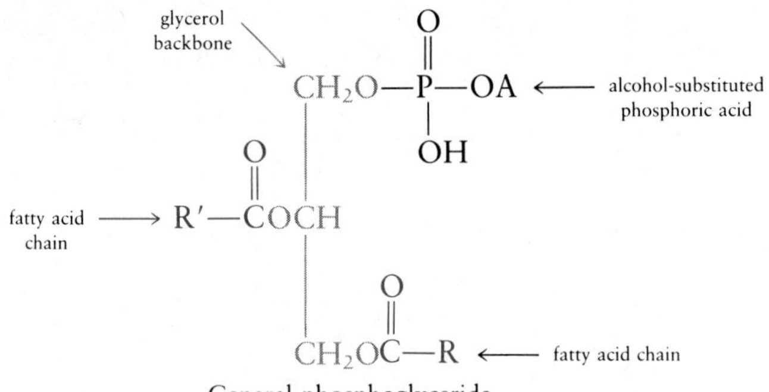

$$
\begin{array}{l}
\text{glycerol backbone} \searrow \quad \overset{\displaystyle O}{\|} \\
\quad CH_2O{-}P{-}OA \leftarrow \text{alcohol-substituted phosphoric acid} \\
\qquad\qquad\ | \\
\qquad\qquad OH \\
\text{fatty acid chain} \rightarrow R'{-}\overset{\displaystyle O}{\overset{\|}{C}}OCH \\
\qquad CH_2O\overset{\displaystyle O}{\overset{\|}{C}}{-}R \leftarrow \text{fatty acid chain}
\end{array}
$$

General phosphoglyceride

Figure 22.5 shows the step-by-step buildup of a general phosphoglyceride. Usually, R is a saturated fatty acid chain and R′ is unsaturated. Phosphoglycerides are also called *alcohol phosphoglycerides*. Below we will look at the structures of two of them.

Important Phosphoglycerides

There are two types of phosphoglycerides that are major components of most animal cell membranes. In one of them, ethanolamine phosphoglyceride, the A group in the formula above is derived from ethanolamine, $HOCH_2CH_2NH_2$.

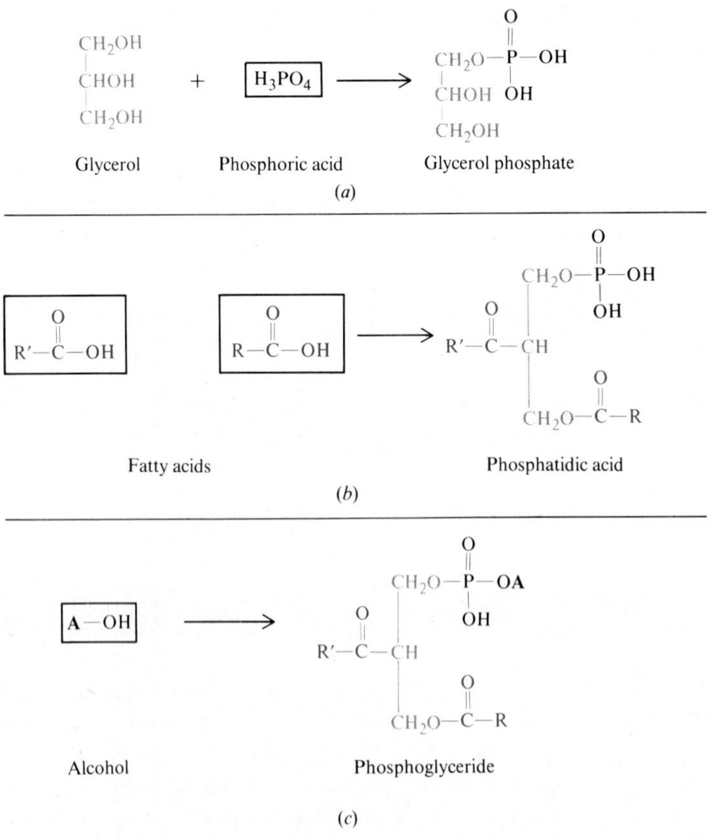

$$
\begin{array}{c} CH_2OH \\ | \\ CHOH \\ | \\ CH_2OH \end{array} + \boxed{H_3PO_4} \longrightarrow \begin{array}{l} \qquad\quad O \\ \qquad\quad \| \\ CH_2O{-}P{-}OH \\ |\qquad\quad | \\ CHOH\ \ OH \\ | \\ CH_2OH \end{array}
$$

Glycerol Phosphoric acid Glycerol phosphate

(*a*)

$$
\boxed{R'{-}\overset{\displaystyle O}{\overset{\|}{C}}{-}OH} \quad \boxed{R{-}\overset{\displaystyle O}{\overset{\|}{C}}{-}OH} \longrightarrow \begin{array}{l} \qquad\qquad CH_2O{-}\overset{\displaystyle O}{\overset{\|}{P}}{-}OH \\ \qquad\qquad |\qquad\quad | \\ \qquad\qquad |\qquad\quad OH \\ R'{-}\overset{\displaystyle O}{\overset{\|}{C}}{-}CH \\ \qquad\qquad | \\ \qquad\qquad CH_2O{-}\overset{\displaystyle O}{\overset{\|}{C}}{-}R \end{array}
$$

Fatty acids Phosphatidic acid

(*b*)

$$
\boxed{A{-}OH} \longrightarrow \begin{array}{l} \qquad\qquad CH_2O{-}\overset{\displaystyle O}{\overset{\|}{P}}{-}OA \\ \qquad\qquad |\qquad\quad | \\ \qquad\qquad |\qquad\quad OH \\ R'{-}\overset{\displaystyle O}{\overset{\|}{C}}{-}CH \\ \qquad\qquad | \\ \qquad\qquad CH_2O{-}\overset{\displaystyle O}{\overset{\|}{C}}{-}R \end{array}
$$

Alcohol Phosphoglyceride

(*c*)

FIGURE 22.5
Building up a phosphoglyceride.
(*a*) Phosphoric acid adds to glycerol.
(*b*) Two fatty acids combine with glyerol phosphate.
(*c*) The phosphate group is esterified with an alcohol.

In Greek, *kephalos* means "head."

Because it is found in brain tissues, this type of phosphoglyceride is more often called **cephalin.** A typical cephalin is shown below.

```
                   O
                   ‖
         CH2O—P—OCH2CH2NH2
          |        |
   O      |        OH
   ‖      |
R′—C—OCH
          |
          |        O
          |        ‖
         CH2O—C—R
```

Cephalin (ethanolamine phosphoglyceride)

At physiological pH the cephalin exists as a doubly charged ion. The amino group accepts a proton and the remaining phosphoric acid proton is donated to form the species shown below:

```
                   O
                   ‖
         CH2O—P—OCH2CH2NH3+
          |        |
   O      |        O−
   ‖      |
R′—C—OCH
          |
          |        O
          |        ‖
         CH2O—C—R
```

Charged form of a cephalin

The other kind of phosphoglyceride in cell membranes is called a **lecithin** and has a structure in which the A residue is derived from the cation of choline, $[HOCH_2CH_2N^+(CH_3)_3]OH^-$, a quaternary ammonium compound (Section 18.6).

```
                   O              CH3
                   ‖               |
         CH2O—P—OCH2CH2N+CH3
          |        |               |
   O      |        O−             CH3
   ‖      |
R′—C—OCH
          |
          |        O
          |        ‖
         CH2O—C—R
```

Lecithin (choline phosphoglyceride)

In Greek, *lekithos* means "yolk of an egg."

In the food industry lecithins are used as *emulsifiers,* that is, agents that break up mixtures of oil and water into an *emulsion* of tiny droplets of oil suspended in water. In Chapter 17 you saw how soaps act as emulsifiers by forming micelles to break up dirt. Like soap molecules, lecithin (and other phosphoglycerides) have both polar heads and nonpolar tails (see Figure 22.6). The lecithins naturally present in egg yolk are responsible for stabilizing the oil and water suspensions in products such as mayonnaise and salad dressings. Later we will see that the

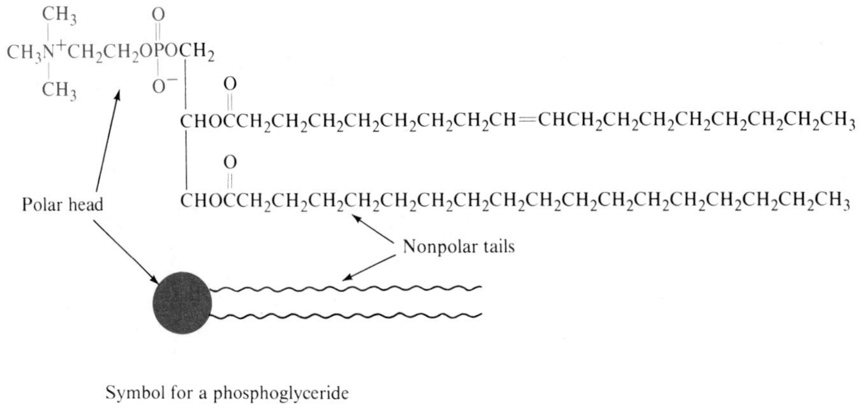

$$\begin{array}{l} \quad CH_3 \qquad\quad O \\ \quad | \qquad\qquad\ \| \\ CH_3N^+CH_2CH_2OPOCH_2 \\ \quad | \qquad\qquad\ | \quad | \qquad O \\ \quad CH_3 \qquad\quad O^- \ | \qquad \| \\ \qquad\qquad\qquad\quad CHOCCH_2CH_2CH_2CH_2CH_2CH_2CH_2CH{=}CHCH_2CH_2CH_2CH_2CH_2CH_2CH_2CH_3 \\ \qquad\qquad\qquad\quad | \qquad O \\ \qquad\qquad\qquad\quad | \qquad \| \\ \qquad\qquad\qquad\quad CHOCCH_2CH_2CH_2CH_2CH_2CH_2CH_2CH_2CH_2CH_2CH_2CH_2CH_2CH_2CH_2CH_2CH_3 \end{array}$$

Polar head

Nonpolar tails

Symbol for a phosphoglyceride

FIGURE 22.6 Dual nature of phosphoglycerides.

dual nature (polar as well as nonpolar) of lipids such as these is the property that allows them to serve as components of cell membranes.

When only the unsaturated acid chain R′ is removed (by hydrolysis) from a lecithin such as the one above, a lecithin derivative known as *lysolecithin* forms.

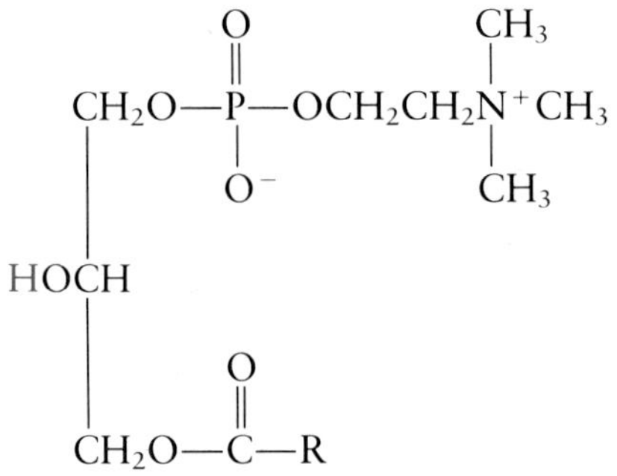

$$\begin{array}{l} \qquad\qquad O \qquad\qquad\qquad CH_3 \\ \qquad\qquad \| \qquad\qquad\qquad\ | \\ CH_2O{-}P{-}OCH_2CH_2N^+CH_3 \\ | \qquad\quad | \qquad\qquad\qquad\ | \\ | \qquad\quad O^- \qquad\qquad\quad CH_3 \\ HOCH \\ | \qquad\quad O \\ | \qquad\quad \| \\ CH_2O{-}C{-}R \end{array}$$

Lysolecithin

Lysolecithin is a toxin that destroys red blood cells.

Lysolecithin is a toxic substance that causes the destruction of red blood cells (hemolysis). Some snake venoms and insect poisons are toxic because they contain enzymes capable of catalyzing the hydrolysis of lecithin to lysolecithin.

SAMPLE EXERCISE 22.3

What is the name of the phosphoglyceride shown below?

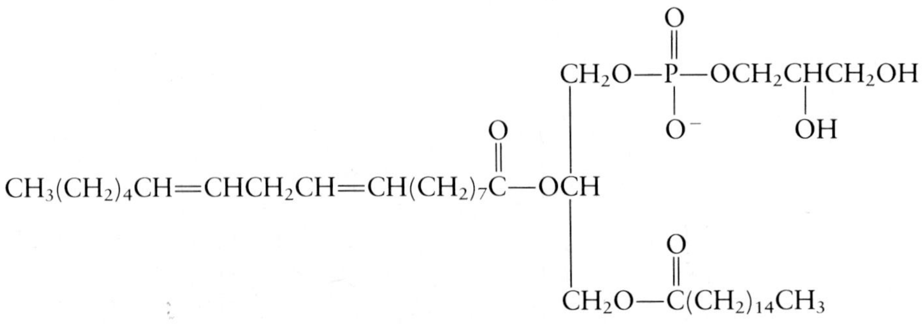

$$\begin{array}{l} \qquad\qquad\qquad\qquad\qquad\qquad\qquad\qquad\qquad\qquad O \\ \qquad\qquad\qquad\qquad\qquad\qquad\qquad\qquad\qquad\qquad \| \\ \qquad\qquad\qquad\qquad\qquad\qquad\qquad\qquad CH_2O{-}P{-}OCH_2CHCH_2OH \\ \qquad\qquad\qquad\qquad\qquad\qquad\qquad O \qquad | \qquad\ | \qquad\qquad | \\ \qquad\qquad\qquad\qquad\qquad\qquad\qquad \| \qquad | \qquad O^- \qquad\quad OH \\ CH_3(CH_2)_4CH{=}CHCH_2CH{=}CH(CH_2)_7C{-}OCH \\ \qquad\qquad\qquad\qquad\qquad\qquad\qquad\qquad\ | \qquad O \\ \qquad\qquad\qquad\qquad\qquad\qquad\qquad\qquad\ | \qquad \| \\ \qquad\qquad\qquad\qquad\qquad\qquad\qquad\qquad CH_2O{-}C(CH_2)_{14}CH_3 \end{array}$$

Solution:

To name this phosphoglyceride note that the group attached to the phosphate ($CH_2\underset{\displaystyle OH}{\underset{|}{C}}HCH_2OH$) is derived from glycerol, $HOCH_2\underset{\displaystyle OH}{\underset{|}{C}}HCH_2OH$. Thus it is called a glycerol phosphoglyceride.

EXERCISE 22.3

Name the two fatty acids shown in the phosphoglyceride in Sample Exercise 22.3.

22.6 SPHINGOLIPIDS

Sphingolipids are also found in cell membranes and are particularly abundant in brain and nerve tissue. As you can see from Figure 22.2, glycerol is not shown as a breakdown product for sphingomyelins or glycolipids. These lipids are both classified as **sphingolipids** because they include a backbone of **sphingosine**, an amino alcohol.

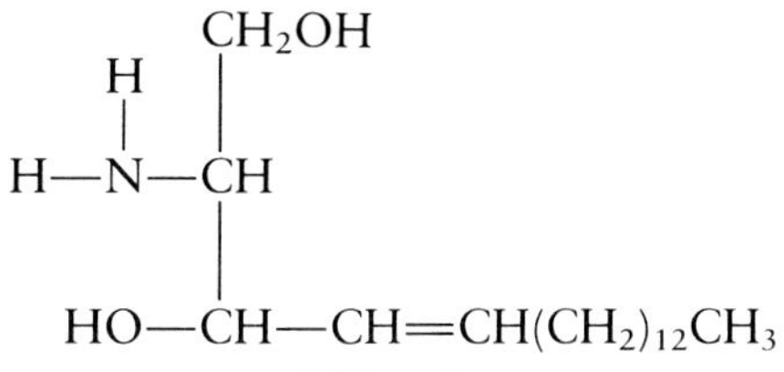

$$\begin{array}{l} \qquad\qquad\;\; CH_2OH \\ \quad\;\; H \qquad | \\ \quad\;\; | \qquad\;\; | \\ H{-}N{-}CH \\ \qquad\quad\;\; | \\ \quad HO{-}CH{-}CH{=}CH(CH_2)_{12}CH_3 \end{array}$$

Sphingosine

Replacing one of the amino H atoms with a fatty acid acyl group $R{-}\overset{\overset{\displaystyle O}{\|}}{C}$ produces an amide of sphingosine known as a **ceramide**. You will see shortly that ceramides are the basic structural units of all sphingolipids.

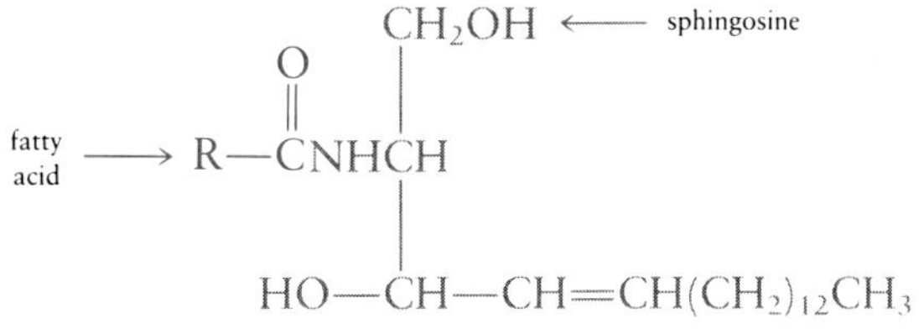

$$\begin{array}{l} \qquad\qquad\qquad\qquad\quad CH_2OH \longleftarrow \text{sphingosine} \\ \qquad\qquad\qquad\;\; O \qquad | \\ \qquad\qquad\qquad\;\; \| \qquad\; | \\ \text{fatty acid} \longrightarrow R{-}CNHCH \\ \qquad\qquad\qquad\qquad\quad\; | \\ \qquad\qquad\qquad\quad HO{-}CH{-}CH{=}CH(CH_2)_{12}CH_3 \end{array}$$

Ceramide

Sphingomyelins

The myelin sheath that wraps nerve fibers contains phospholipids and sphingolipids.

Sphingomyelins are the most abundant sphingolipids found in the tissues of higher animals. Like phosphoglycerides, sphingomyelins contain phosphate groups. Thus they have polar as well as nonpolar segments and properties that are similar to

$$\begin{array}{l} \text{Choline: } CH_3N^+(CH_3)_2CH_2CH_2O-P(=O)(O^-)-OCH_2 \\ \quad CH_2-CHNHC(=O)CH_2CH_2CH_2CH_2CH_2CH_2CH_2CH{=}CHCH_2CH_2CH_2CH_2CH_2CH_2CH_2CH_3 \ (\text{Oleic acid}) \\ \quad HO-CHCH{=}CHCH_2CH_2CH_2CH_2CH_2CH_2CH_2CH_2CH_2CH_2CH_2CH_2CH_3 \end{array}$$

FIGURE 22.7
A sphingomyelin, in which the alcohol is choline and the fatty acid is oleic acid.

In multiple sclerosis lipids are lost from the myelin sheath, which leads to nerve damage.

those of the cephalin and lecithin phosphoglycerides. To complete the structure of a sphingomyelin, a phosphate esterified with an alcohol (A) is attached to the ceramide structure, as shown below.

$$\begin{array}{l} CH_2O-P(=O)(O^-)-OA \leftarrow \text{alcohol-substituted phosphoric acid} \\ \text{Fatty acid} \rightarrow R-C(=O)\ HCH \leftarrow \text{sphingosine} \\ HO-CH-CH{=}CH(CH_2)_{12}CH_3 \end{array}$$

Sphingomyelin

In Figure 22.7 you can see that the A group in sphingomyelins comes from choline, the same group that is present in lecithin.

Glycolipids

The **glycolipids**, or "sugar lipids," also include the ceramide (sphingosine + fatty acid) structure, but their polar heads are composed of carbohydrate groups in place of the phosphate esters of sphingomyelins. A **cerebroside** is a glycolipid found in the membranes of brain tissue, as its name suggests. The structure of the cerebroside shown below includes a galactose molecule attached to ceramide:

$$\begin{array}{l} \text{galactose} \rightarrow \text{(ring with } CH_2OH, HO, OH, HO) \\ CH_2O \\ R-C(=O)NHCH \\ HO-CH-CH{=}CH(CH_2)_{12}CH_3 \end{array} \quad \text{ceramide}$$

Cerebroside

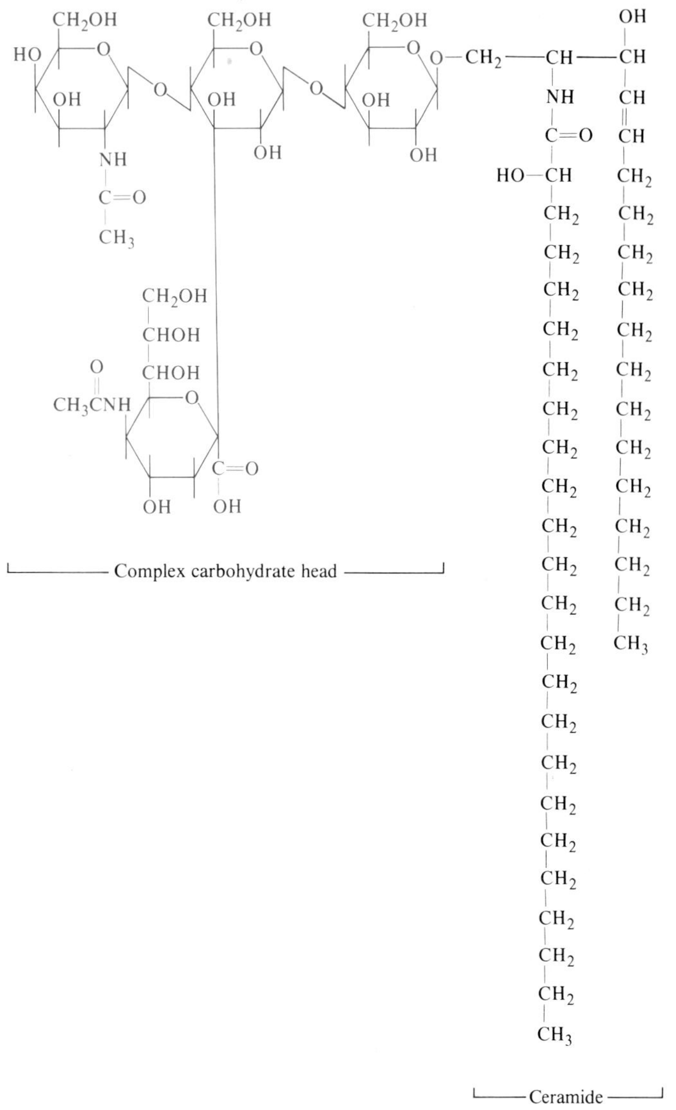

CH₂OH CH₂OH CH₂OH OH HO O O O O O—CH₂—CH—CH OH OH OH NH CH C=O CH NH OH OH HO—CH CH₂ C=O CH₃ CH₂OH CHOH O CHOH CH₃CNH O C=O OH OH

Complex carbohydrate head

Ceramide

FIGURE 22.8
Ganglioside (G_{M2}) accumulating in Tay-Sachs.

In Tay-Sachs disease the enzyme needed to break down a ganglioside is deficient.

Gangliosides, found on the outer surface of nerve cells, are glycolipids in which the carbohydrate that is attached to ceramide is much more complex than a monosaccharide. The ganglioside shown in Figure 22.8 accumulates in the brain and spleen of individuals suffering from ***Tay-Sachs*** disease because they lack an enzyme called hexosaminidase A needed to break it down. This accumulation leads to neurological deterioration, which occurs after the first month of life and leads to death within 5 years. Tay-Sachs, a hereditary disorder, is one of many genetic disorders in lipid metabolism that have been discovered in humans.

SAMPLE EXERCISE 22.4

Of the structures below which one is a sphingolipid and which is a phosphoglyceride?

(I)

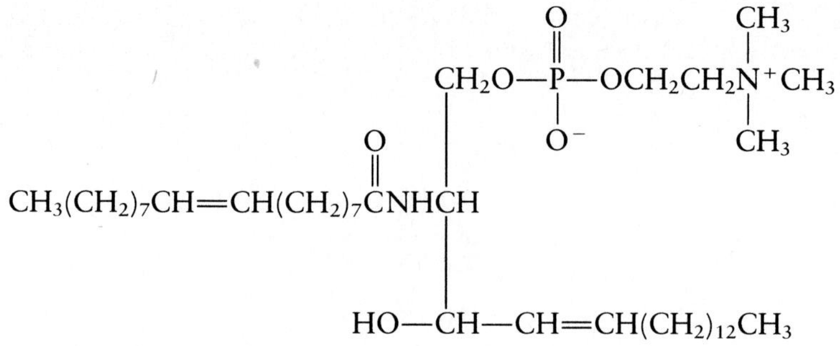

$$\begin{array}{l} CH_3(CH_2)_7CH{=}CH(CH_2)_7\overset{O}{\overset{\|}{C}}NHCH \\ \quad | \; CH_2O{-}\overset{O}{\overset{\|}{P}}(O^-){-}OCH_2CH_2N^+(CH_3)_3 \\ \quad | \; HO{-}CH{-}CH{=}CH(CH_2)_{12}CH_3 \end{array}$$

(II)

$$\begin{array}{l} CH_3(CH_2)_7CH{=}CH(CH_2)_7\overset{O}{\overset{\|}{C}}{-}OCH \\ \quad | \; CH_2O{-}\overset{O}{\overset{\|}{P}}(O^-){-}OCH_2CH_2N^+(CH_3)_3 \\ \quad | \; CH_2O{-}\overset{O}{\overset{\|}{C}}(CH_2)_{16}CH_3 \end{array}$$

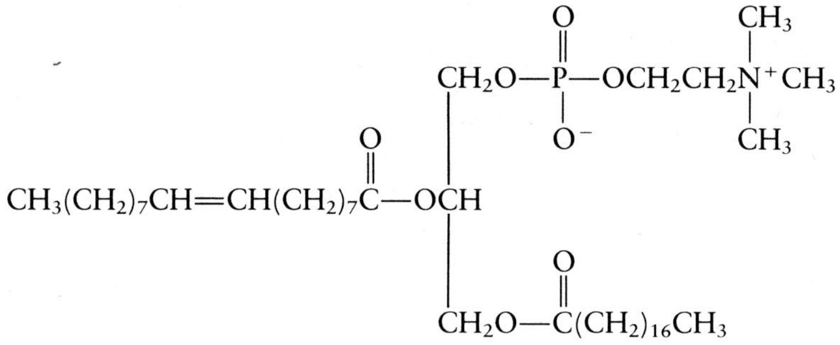

Solution:

Structure I is a sphingolipid because it contains sphingosine (note the amide linkage derived from the amino group of sphingosine). Structure II is a phosphoglyceride; it has a glycerol backbone with no amide linkage.

EXERCISE 22.4

Accumulation of the compound below in nerve tissue leads to an enzyme deficiency disorder known as ***Gaucher's disease***, characterized by spleen and liver malfunction. What type of lipid is this?

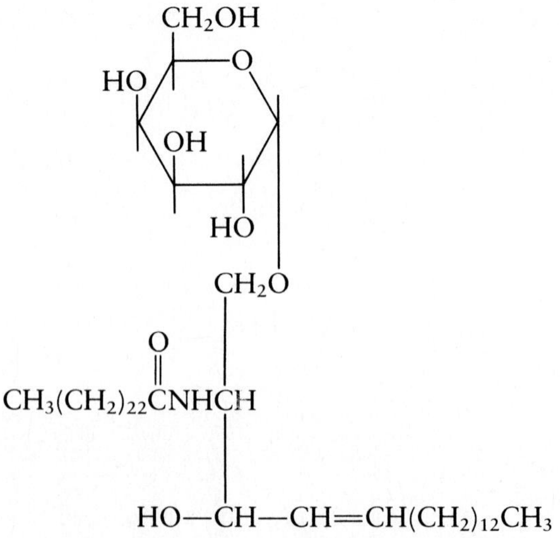

CH₂OH, HO, OH, HO (glucose ring, O) — CH_2O

$$\begin{array}{l} CH_3(CH_2)_{22}\overset{O}{\overset{\|}{C}}NHCH \\ \quad | \; CH_2O{-}(\text{glucose}) \\ \quad | \; HO{-}CH{-}CH{=}CH(CH_2)_{12}CH_3 \end{array}$$

22.7 WAXES AND TERPENES

Lipid waxes are esters and paraffin waxes are alkanes.

Lipid **waxes** are esters formed from long-chain fatty acids and high-molecular-weight alcohols. Lipid waxes are not the same as paraffin waxes, which are high-molecular-weight alkanes derived from petroleum.

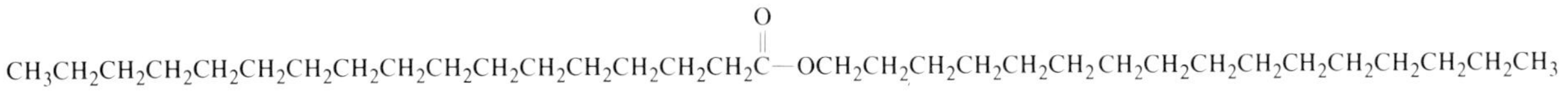

(*a*)

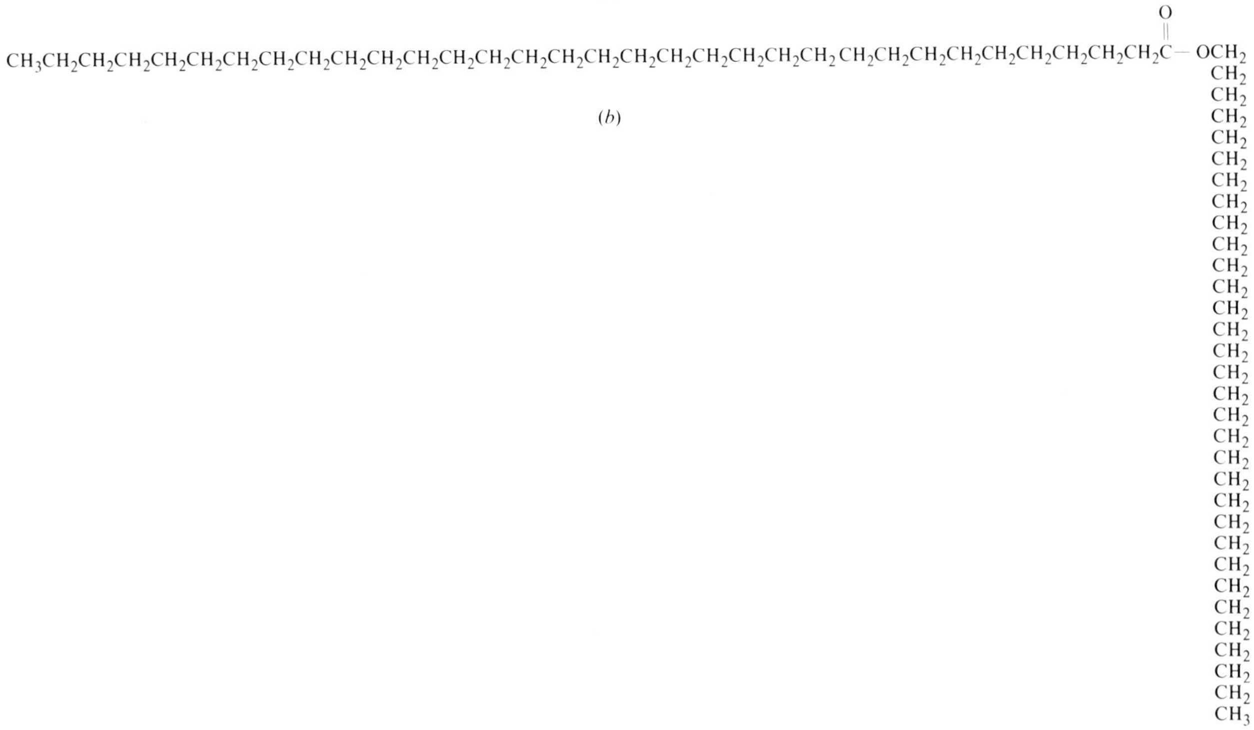

(*b*)

FIGURE 22.9
Lipid waxes. (*a*) Spermaceti wax, found in the head of the sperm whale, is a soft wax used in ointments.
(*b*) Caranuba wax, found on Brazilian palm leaves, is used in polishes and mimeograph stencils. The one shown is an ester with 32 C atoms in its component acid and alcohol.

In nature, waxes serve as protective coatings on leaves, skin, feathers, fur, and the outer skeletons of some insects. The lipid wax below, derived from palmitic acid and a 26-carbon alcohol, is a component of beeswax, the material from which bees build the cells of the honeycomb.

$$CH_3(CH_2)_{14}\overset{\overset{\displaystyle O}{\|}}{C}\text{—}\boxed{OH + H}O(CH_2)_{25}CH_3 \longrightarrow \underset{\text{Wax}}{CH_3(CH_2)_{14}\overset{\overset{\displaystyle O}{\|}}{C}\text{—}O(CH_2)_{25}CH_3} + H_2O$$

The word lanolin is derived from *lana*, meaning "wool" in Latin.

The formulas for two other natural waxes are shown in Figure 22.9. Lanolin, a substance used as a base for ointments, salves, and creams, is a mixture of waxes derived from wool.

Terpenes, compounds containing isoprene fragments (section 13.11), are also classified as lipids because they are biological molecules that dissolve in nonpolar solvents. Unlike the lipids that we have discussed so far, terpenes have no fatty acid residues in their structures. The formulas for a variety of cyclic and straight chain terpenes are shown in Figure 13.10. Recall that vitamin A and its precursor, β-carotene, are terpenes (Figure 13.11).

22.8 STEROIDS

Steroids are all derivatives of the hydrocarbon ring system below:

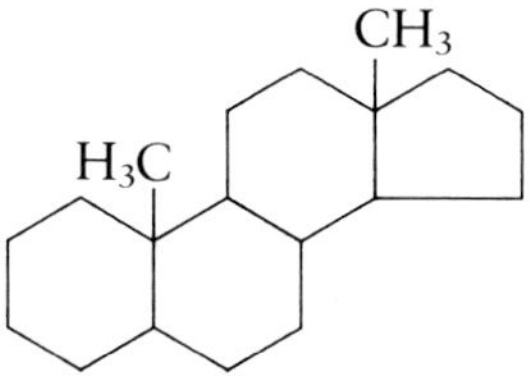

CH_3

H_3C

One type of steroid found in living cells is a **sterol**, a compound in which a hydroxyl group is attached to the steroid ring system. The most abundant sterol in animal tissues is **cholesterol**, the steroid shown in color in Fig. 22.10.

Cholesterol in animals is present in nerve tissue, blood, and bile, the greenish fluid secreted by the liver that aids in the digestion of fat. In fact, the name cholesterol comes from the Greek *chole* for bile and *stereos* for solid. Gallstones are nearly pure (80 to 98 percent) cholesterol.

In the body cholesterol is the precursor of biological steroids which perform crucial body functions. Among these are the salts of the bile acids, one of which is shown below.

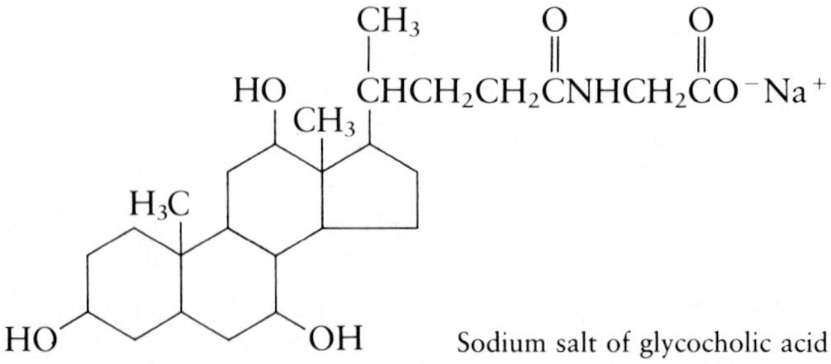

$$\overset{\displaystyle CH_3}{|}\!\!\!CHCH_2CH_2\overset{\overset{\displaystyle O}{\|}}{C}NHCH_2\overset{\overset{\displaystyle O}{\|}}{C}O^-Na^+$$

HO CH_3

H_3C

HO OH

Sodium salt of glycocholic acid

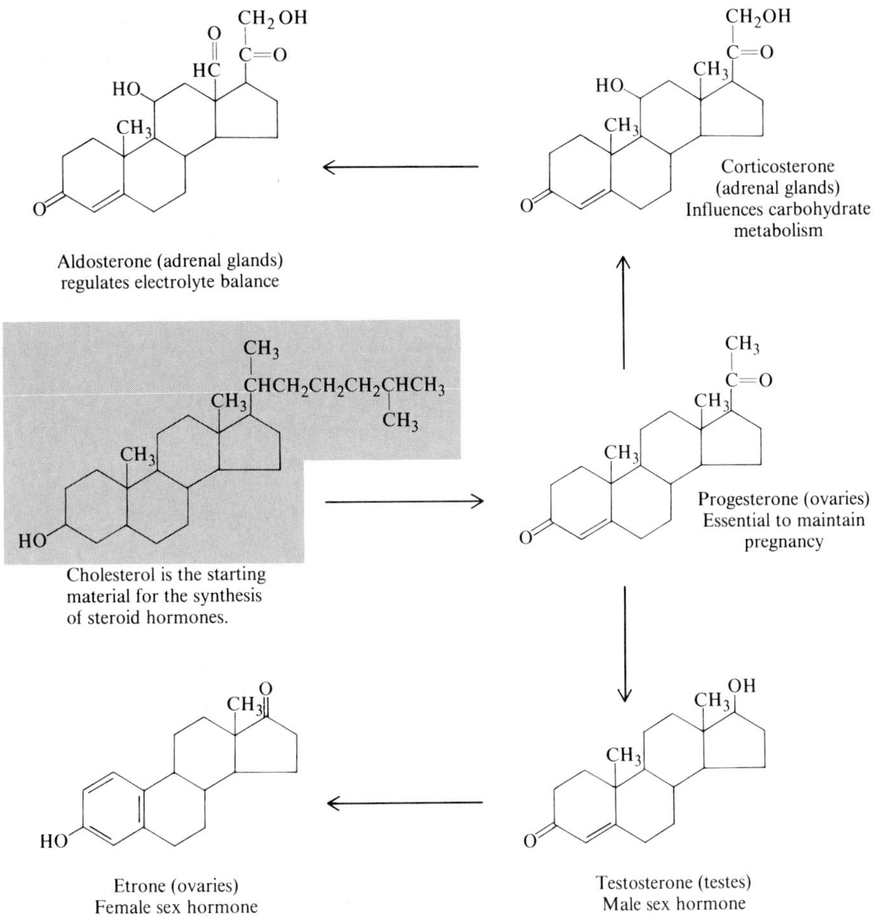

FIGURE 22.10
Steroid hormones derived from cholesterol.

The emulsifying action of a bile salt is shown in Figure 27.3.

A bile salt includes both polar and nonpolar structural features and behaves as a powerful detergent, breaking up lipid deposits so that they can be absorbed and digested.

Vitamin D deficiency causes hypocalcemia (low Ca^{2+} levels) and hypophosphatemia (low levels of PO_4^{3-}).

Another necessary cholesterol derivative is the compound 7-dehydrocholesterol, which is converted to one active form of vitamin D (known as *vitamin* D_3, or *cholecalciferol*) when the skin is exposed to sunlight (see Figure 22.11). Vitamin D increases the utilization and retention of the elements calcium and phosphorus obtained in the diet. Without it, bones must deteriorate to provide the calcium needed to maintain normal blood levels. In children vitamin D deficiency leads to a disease called ***rickets,*** characterized by defective bone growth. Vitamin D is a component of fish liver oils, one natural source of the vitamin.

The glands that secrete hormones are called *endocrine* glands.

Cholesterol is also the starting material for the biosynthesis of all steroid hormones, which include the male and female sex hormones, the *androgens* and *estrogens,* respectively, along with some other important hormones. The biosynthetic pathways from cholesterol to the major steroid hormones and the glands or organs in which each hormone is produced are shown in Figure 22.10.

Your body needs some cholesterol.

We will return to the subject of cholesterol and its role in living systems in Chapter 27, where the metabolism of lipids is discussed. Thus far, we have seen that cholesterol and its derivatives do perform vital functions in the body.

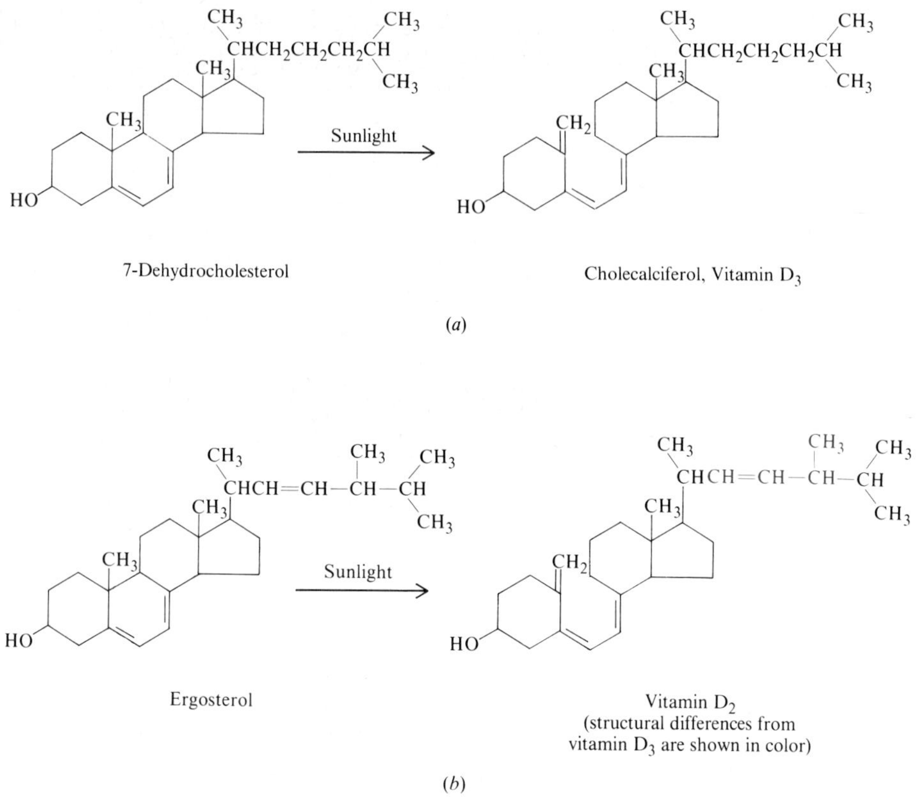

7-Dehydrocholesterol

Cholecalciferol, Vitamin D_3

(*a*)

Ergosterol

Vitamin D_2
(structural differences from vitamin D_3 are shown in color)

(*b*)

FIGURE 22.11
Formation of vitamins D_2 and D_3

22.9 FAT-SOLUBLE VITAMINS

Vitamins, the organic compounds needed for normal growth and maintainance, are divided into two major classes based upon their solubility. Vitamins that are soluble in water belong to the group called **water-soluble vitamins.** In general, these vitamins can be excreted in the urine, are not stored in the body in appreciable amounts, and must be constantly supplied in the diet. We will return to the water-soluble vitamins in Chapter 25. The vitamins that are soluble in fats are known as **fat-soluble vitamins.** These vitamins are absorbed along with dietary fats and are not excreted in the urine. The body can store fat-soluble vitamins in moderate amounts and is thus not so dependent upon a daily supply of them in the diet.

The fat-soluble vitamins are A, D, E, and K.

We have already encountered three fat-soluble vitamins, A, D, and E, in previous sections. Below we will complete our earlier discussions of their functions and activities and introduce the other fat-soluble vitamin, vitamin K. The proposed biological functions of the four fat-soluble vitamins, vitamins A, D, E, and K, are summarized in Table 22.4. For the dietary sources of the fat-soluble vitamins and their RDA (recommended daily allowance) values, refer to the nutrition table on the inside cover. The units for the RDA of fat-soluble vitamins are sometimes expressed in *international units* (IU), which are specifically defined for each vitamin (see Table 22.5).

TABLE 22.4 **BIOCHEMICAL FUNCITONS OF THE FAT-SOLUBLE VITAMINS**

Vitamin	Biochemical function
A (retinal form)	Visual cycle
D	Calcium and phosphate metabolism
E	Biologic antioxidant
K	Clotting process (biosynthesis of prothrombin)

TABLE 22.5 **MEANING OF IU FOR AMOUNTS OF FAT-SOLUBLE VITAMINS**

Vitamin	Meaning of 1 international unit (IU)
A	0.3 μg retinol or 0.6 μg β-carotene*
D	0.025 μg
E	1 mg

*Although as shown in Figure 13.11, two vitamin A molecules can form from one β-carotene, the process is actually much less efficient. Allowances of vitamin A are also expressed in terms of retinol equivalents (RE), where 1RE = 1 μg retinol and 1RE = 6 μg β-carotene.

Vitamin D

In the previous section the structure and function of vitamin D was discussed. There you saw that one active form of vitamin D is vitamin D_3, a derivative of cholesterol. The other active form of vitamin D is vitamin D_2, a derivative of a plant sterol called ergosterol, which is different from vitamin D_3 (Figure 22.11*b*) only in the part of the side chain shown in color in the figure. Both forms have equal biological value. Humans can derive vitamin D both from the diet and from exposure to sunlight.

Vitamin E

Vitamin E is an oily yellow liquid.

In our coverage of alcohol compounds we discussed the structure and activity of vitamin E, or α-tocopherol, a derivative of phenol (Section 15.8). There you saw that vitamin E, like other phenol derivatives, behaves as an antioxidant. Vitamin E is known to serve as an antioxidant in naturally occurring fats, where it inhibits the oxidation both of unsaturated fats and of vitamin A, which also has double bonds in its structure. So far the only function of vitamin E that has been established is its role as an antioxidant. Symptoms of vitamin E deficiency, a vitamin that is widely distributed in foods, have been clearly noted only in individuals suffering from fat malabsorption or malnutrition.

Vitamin A

Recall from Section 13.11 that carotene forms vitamin A.

Earlier you saw that vitamin A is classified as a terpene. Its structure also contains an alcohol group, which can be oxidized first to the aldehyde and then to the acid (see Figure 22.12). The alcohol form of vitamin A is called *retinol,* the aldehyde form is *retinal,* and the acid form is *retanoic acid.*

```
CH3 CH3
   \ /
    C
  /   \
CH2    C—CH=CHC=CHCH=CHC=CH—CH2OH
|      ||     |         |
CH2    C      CH3       CH3
  \  /  \
  CH2    CH3
```

(*a*)

```
CH3 CH3                                    O
   \ /                                     ||
    C
  /   \
CH2    C—CH=CHC=CHCH=CHC=CH—C—H
|      ||     |         |
CH2    C      CH3       CH3
  \  /  \
  CH2    CH3
```

(*b*)

```
CH3 CH3                                    O
   \ /                                     ||
    C
  /   \
CH2    C—CH=CHC=CHCH=CHC=CH—C—OH
|      ||     |         |
CH2    C      CH3       CH3
  \  /  \
  CH2    CH3
```

(*c*)

FIGURE 22.12
Forms of vitamin A: (*a*) retinol; (*b*) retinal; (*c*) retinoic acid.

Vitamin A is involved in the visual cycle.

In the form of retinal, vitamin A is known to play a role in the visual cycle, as shown in Figure 22.13. *Rhodopsin* is a complex formed from retinal and opsin, a protein that is present in the rods of the eye. Bright light degrades the rhodopsin complex into its constituents, retinal and opsin. When this happens, calcium ions in the rod cells trigger a nerve impulse that allows light to be perceived by the brain. Although the retinal and opsin produced do combine again to re-form rhodopsin, the restoration is only partially complete. To allow complete regeneration of rhodopsin after exposure to bright light, an ample supply of vitamin A must be available. If there is not enough vitamin A present, vision will be impaired when the eye is exposed first to bright light and then to subdued light. The inability of the eye to adapt to the dark is known as ***night blindness,*** an initial symptom of vitamin A deficiency. Later a disease called ***xerophthalmia*** can develop, in which the eyes and eyelids become inflamed and then infected, a condition which can result in loss of sight. Prolonged excessive intake of vitamin A (usually in the form of vitamin A supplements) leads to a serious toxicity syndrome, which can be cured completely by withdrawal of the excess vitamin A.

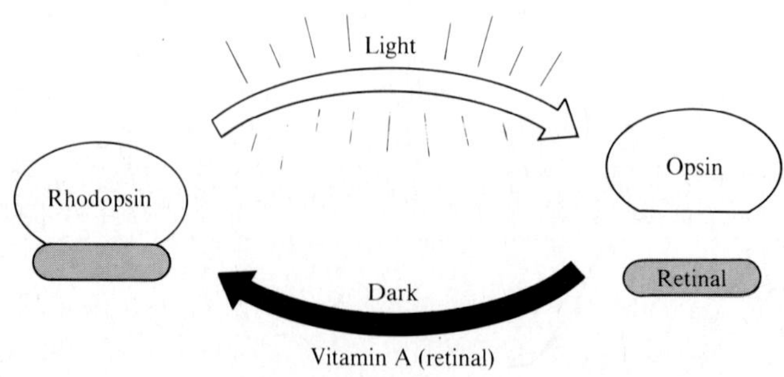

FIGURE 22.13
Visual cycle and vitamin A. In this simplified version of the visual cycle, rhodopsin is degraded by bright light. Some of the retinal product is also degraded by this process. Additional retinal in the form of vitamin A must be supplied to regenerate the rhodopsin complex.

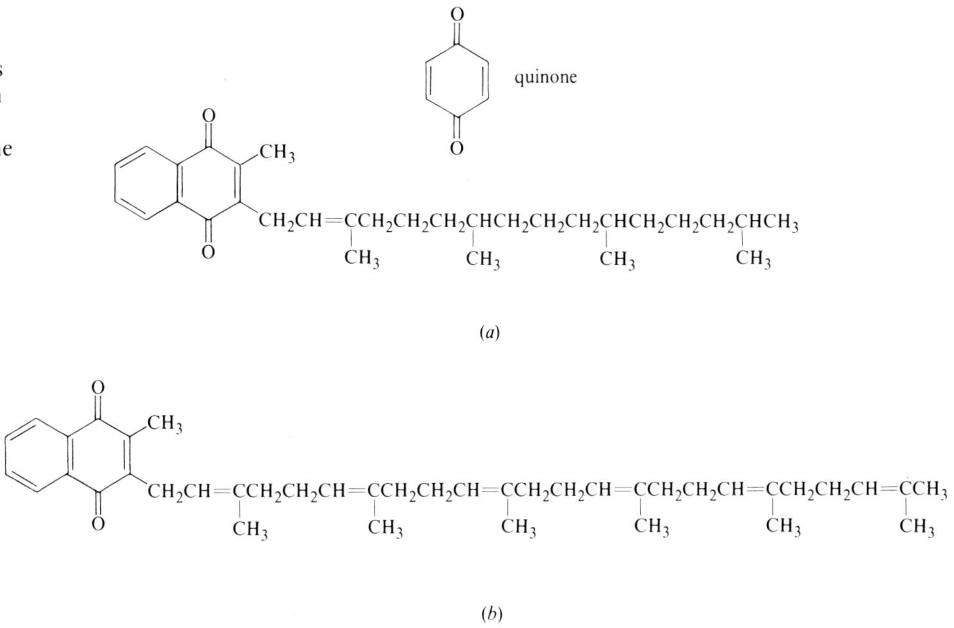

FIGURE 22.14
Vitamin K. (*a*) Vitamin K_1, found in plant foods such as leafy vegetables. (*b*) Vitamin K_2, the form of vitamin K synthesized by bacteria in the human intestinal tract.

quinone

CH_3

$CH_2CH{=}\underset{CH_3}{C}CH_2CH_2CH_2\underset{CH_3}{C}HCH_2CH_2CH_2\underset{CH_3}{C}HCH_2CH_2CH_2\underset{CH_3}{C}HCH_3$

(*a*)

CH_3

$CH_2CH{=}\underset{CH_3}{C}CH_2CH_2CH{=}\underset{CH_3}{C}CH_2CH_2CH{=}\underset{CH_3}{C}CH_2CH_2CH{=}\underset{CH_3}{C}CH_2CH_2CH{=}\underset{CH_3}{C}CH_2CH_2CH{=}\underset{CH_3}{C}CH_3$

(*b*)

Vitamin K

Vitamin K plays a role in blood clotting—hence the name *K* from the Danish form of the word *koagulation*.

Vitamin K is a derivative of quinone, as shown in Figure 22.14. Vitamin K deficiency can cause an increase in the clotting time of blood, thus producing hemorrhages under the skin and in muscle tissue. This happens because vitamin K is needed to synthesize prothrombin, which is then converted to thrombin, an enzyme required in the clotting process. We will return to the discussion of thrombin (a protein) in Chapter 23.

Vitamin K is widely distributed in nature. No definite dietary requirements for vitamin K have been set and deficiency of vitamin K in humans due to dietary restriction has not been observed.

Excess vitamin intake is called hypervitaminosis.

To help you answer questions about the pros and cons of vitamin supplements, a list of some common vitamin supplement products is given in one of the tables on the inside cover. The amounts of each fat-soluble vitamin that they contain are given so that you can compare them with the RDA values. Other tables list common foods and their content of vitamins A, D, E, and K as well as furnish information on the toxic effects of ingesting amounts of these vitamins that far exceed the RDA.

22.10 CELL MEMBRANES

Cells of mammals contain *protoplasm*, the living substance present within the cell. The protoplasm is surrounded by walls called **plasma membranes**, about 6 to 10 nm in thickness, that give shape to the cell. The typical animal cell shown

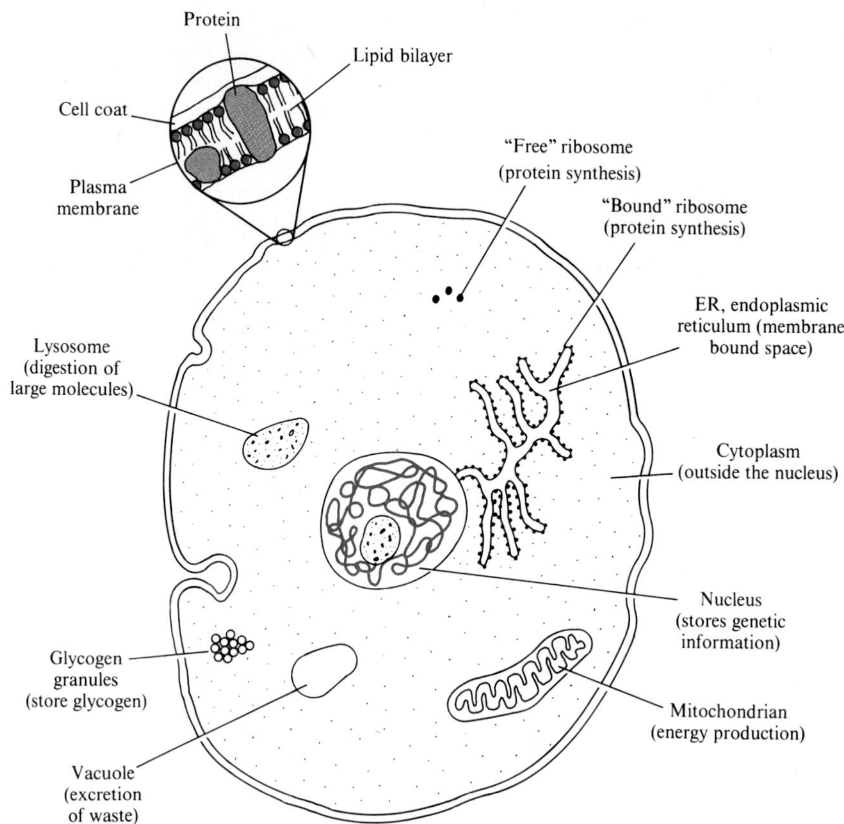

FIGURE 22.15
Typical animal cell showing some major structures and their functions. Only one diagram of each structure is shown, even though there may be many per cell (one nucleus, many mitochondria).

in Figure 22.15 is round, which is only one of many possible shapes that a cell can have. Within the cell other membranes surround the nucleus of the cell and its *organelles*, the smaller structural components of the cell.

Cell membranes contain lipids and proteins.

All cell membranes are made of two components, proteins and lipids, present in roughly equal amounts. Some protein molecules (Chapter 23) lend structure to the cell and others regulate the transport of substances such as metabolites or ions across cell membranes. The major lipids present in the membranes are phosphoglycerides, glycolipids, and cholesterol. How the proteins and lipids are arranged to form membranes is not completely understood; however, there is one leading theory of membrane structure called the *fluid mosaic model.*

According to the **fluid mosaic model** of cell membranes, the lipid molecules form a *bilayer* structure in which protein molecules are embedded like the colored stones stuck onto a mosaic background. The ability of membrane lipids to exist as bimolecular layers comes from the same dual nature that allows them to form micelle structures. The **bilayer** forms as the nonpolar tails of two lipid molecules are attracted to each other while their polar heads face outward toward the aqueous medium. The nonpolar tail of the molecule is called the **hydrophobic** (water-hating) end and the polar head is the **hydrophilic** (water-loving) end. See Figure 22.16, which is a bilayer structure composed of phosphoglyceride molecules. In Figure 22.17 the round protein molecules are added to complete the fluid mosaic cell membrane.

Cell membranes can undergo shape changes. The proteins in some cell membranes are known to move at rather high rates and others are stabilized so that

FIGURE 22.16
Phosphoglyceride bilayer. (*a*) The polar heads of the phosphoglycerides face toward the aqueous medium and the nonpolar tails face inward toward each other. (*b*) The lipid bilayer portion of a section of cell membrane.

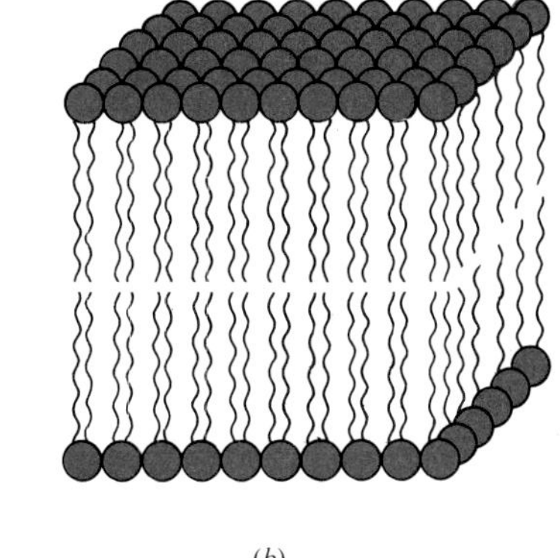

FIGURE 22.17
Fluid mosaic model of cell membrane. The shaded areas are protein molecules embedded in the lipid bilayer.

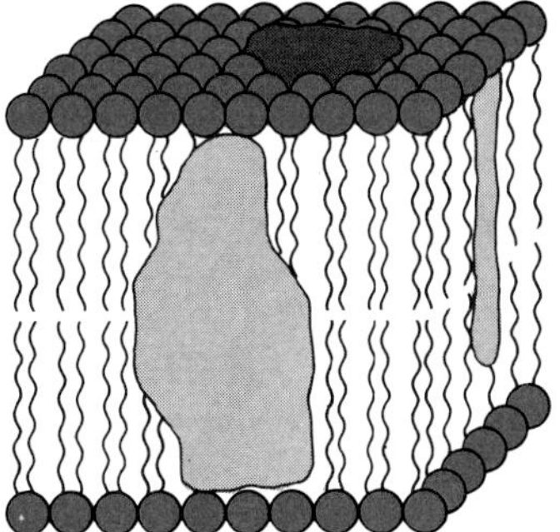

they always occupy the same region of the cell surface. These phenomena are related to the *fluidity* of cell membranes. The lipids that form bilayers include some unsaturation in their hydrocarbon chains. The greater the amount of unsaturation, the greater the fluidity of the cell membrane. Recall that the fluidity of triglyceride fats also becomes greater when the unsaturation increases (Section 22.3). Thus protein molecules can move more freely within very fluid cell membranes and are restricted in cell membranes with saturated hydrocarbon chains.

In Chapter 9 you saw that the process of osmosis depends upon the selective permeability of the cell membrane (Section 9.10). Cell membranes behave as if they had pores about 0.8 nm in diameter (Section 9.11), although the pores have never actually been seen. However, some nutrients, such as glucose and amino acids, that are too large to pass readily through the pores must cross cell membranes for the cell to survive. The protein molecules embedded in the cell membranes bind to these nutrients to carry them across the membranes and into the interior of the cell where they are needed. Transport of Na^+ and K^+ ions, the basis of processes such as nerve conduction and muscle contraction, is also regulated by membrane proteins. Potassium ion can be moved or "pumped" into cells even though the concentration of K^+ within most animal cells is much higher than it is outside the cell (see Figure 8.12). Likewise, Na^+ ions can be pumped out of the cell even though the concentration of Na^+ outside the cell is much higher than that inside the cell (see Figure 8.12). This movement is possible because membrane protein molecules with special affinities for extracellular K^+ and intracellular Na^+ behave as pumps to transport the ions across the plasma membrane.

SUMMARY

Lipids are nonpolar compounds found in living systems.

Fatty acids, components of many classes of lipids, are carboxylic acids with straight hydrocarbon chains. Unsaturated fatty acids have one or more C to C double bonds in their hydrocarbon chains, while in saturated fatty acids all C to C bonds are single. Essential fatty acids (EFA) such as linoleic acid cannot be synthesized in the body. The EFA arachidonic acid is a precursor of prostaglandin, a lipid compound which causes smooth muscle to contract and is thought to be responsible for pain sensation.

Body fat is composed of triacylglycerols, which are the triesters of glycerol. Unsaturated fats (oils), which come from vegetable sources, are defined as fats containing at least 80 percent unsaturated fatty acids. Saturated fats are derived from animals, contain only about 50 percent unsaturated fatty acids, and tend to be solids at room temperature. Hydrolysis of fats to form fatty acids and glycerol is an important step in lipid metabolism. The double bonds in unsaturated fats can be oxidized (rancidification), hydrogenated, or halogenated.

Phosphoglycerides include glycerol, two fatty acids, phosphoric acid, and an alcohol. Phosphoglycerides have both polar and nonpolar character, which allows them to form micelles, as well as the bilayers present in cell membranes. Their nonpolar, or hydrophobic, ends are attracted to each other and their polar, or hydrophilic, ends are attracted to the aqueous environment.

The backbone of sphingolipids, abundant in brain and nerve tissue, is not glycerol but an amino alcohol called sphingosine. Sphingosine combined with a fatty acid is called ceramide. In sphingomyelins phosphoric acid and an alcohol are attached to the ceramide. Glycolipids contain a sugar molecule in place of the phosphoric acid and alcohol and gangliosides contain complex carbohydrates.

Other classes of lipids include waxes, which are esters of fatty acids and high-molecular-weight alcohols, and terpenes, compounds containing the isoprene structure. Steroids are derivatives of a particular hydrocarbon ring structure, the steroid ring system. The most abundant is cholesterol, the precursor of vitamin D, bile acids, and the sex hormones. There are four fat-soluble vitamins, including vitamin A (involved in vision), vitamin D (assists in calcium and phosphorus metabolism), vitamin E (biologic antioxidant), and vitamin K (involved in blood clotting).

Cell membranes contain lipids and protein. According to the fluid mosaic model of membranes, the lipids appear as bimolecular layers, with protein molecules embedded throughout the structure. The membranes behave as though they had 0.8-nm pores, which allow only very small molecules such as water to pass through. The proteins assist in the transport of other, larger nutrients across the cell membranes.

KEY WORDS

lipid
fatty acid
essential fatty acid
prostaglandin
triacylglycerol
unsaturated fat
saturated fat
rancidification
iodine number
phosphoglyceride
cephalin
lecithin
ceramide
cerebroside
sphingosine
ganglioside
sphingolipid
glycolipid
wax
terpene
steroid
cholesterol
fat-soluble vitamins
vitamin D
vitamin A
vitamin E
vitamin K
plasma membrane
fluid mosaic model
bilayer
hydrophobic
hydrophilic

EXERCISES

22.5 What physical property do lipids have in common?

22.6 Lipids are very soluble in which of the following solvents: (**a**) Ethanol; (**b**) benzene; (**c**) carbon tetrachloride; (**d**) water?

22.7 Of the following compounds, which are lipids? To what general class of lipids does each one belong? Identify the compounds that are not lipids.

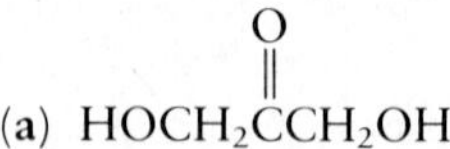

(a) $HOCH_2C(=O)CH_2OH$

(b) $HOCH_2CH(OH)CH(OH)CH(OH)CH(OH)C(=O)CH_2OH$

(c) $CH_3(CH_2)_{18}C(=O)O(CH_2)_{17}CH_3$

(d) $HOCH_2CH(OH)CH_2OH$

(e)

$CH_2OC(=O)(CH_2)_{12}CH_3$

$CH\text{-}OC(=O)(CH_2)_7CH{=}CH(CH_2)_7CH_3$

$CH_2OC(=O)(CH_2)_{16}CH_3$

(f) [steroid structure: HO on ring, CH_3 groups, side chain $CH(CH_3)CH_2CH_2CH_2CH(CH_3)CH_3$]

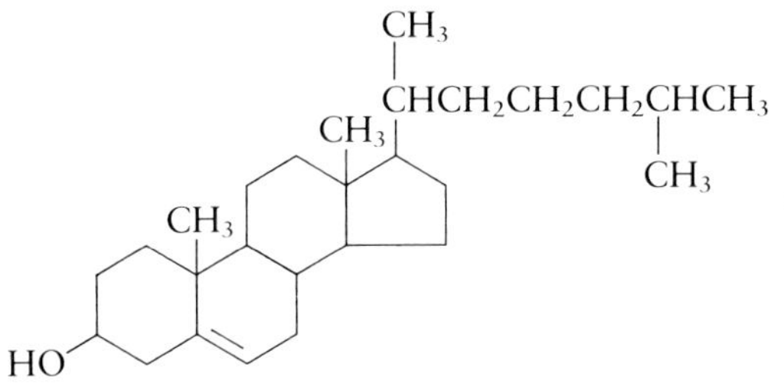

22.8 Which of the carboxylic acids shown below occur in natural animal fats?

(a) $C_6H_5C(=O)OH$ (b) $CH_3(CH_2)_{14}C(=O)OH$

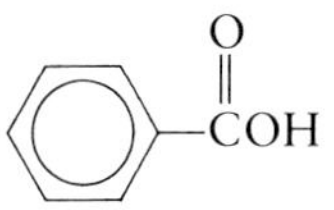

(c) $CH_3CH(CH_3)(CH_2)_5CH(CH_3)CH_2CH(CH_3)CH_2C(=O)OH$

22.9 For the triacylglycerol below,
(a) Identify the fatty acids.
(b) Write the reaction for the compound's formation from glycerol.

$CH_2OC(=O)(CH_2)_{12}CH_3$

$CH\text{-}OC(=O)(CH_2)_{16}CH_3$

$CH_2OC(=O)(CH_2)_7CH{=}CH(CH_2)_7CH_3$

22.10 Complete the reactons below for the formation of triglycerides by supplying formulas for the missing products or reactants (use Tables 22.1 and 22.2).
(a) Glycerol + 3 palmitic acid → ? + $3H_2O$
(b) ? + 3 oleic acid → triolein + $3H_2O$

(c) Glycerol + 2? + ? →

$CH_2OC(=O)(CH_2)_{12}CH_3$

$CH\text{-}OC(=O)(CH_2)_{12}CH_3$

$CH_2OC(=O)(CH_2)_7CH{=}CH(CH_2)_7CH_3$

22.11 For the three hydrogenation reactions below supply the formula for the missing reactant or product. (Choose fatty acids from those listed in Tables 22.1 and 22.2.)
(a) Linolenic acid + ? → stearic acid
(b) Palmitoleic acid + H_2 → ?
(c) ? + $2H_2$ → stearic acid

22.12 Decide whether the following statements are true or false. For each one that is false give a reason.
(a) Saturated fats do not contain any C to C double bonds.
(b) Animal fats may contain both saturated and unsaturated fatty acids.
(c) Vegetable fats may contain both saturated and unsaturated fatty acids.
(d) Vegetable fats contain a higher percentage of saturated fats than do animal fats.

22.13 Of the common animal and vegetable fats listed in Table 22.3 which is the most unsaturated? Why?

22.14 The following table gives the amounts of important fatty acids present in the fats isolated from walnuts and lamb meat. Which is which? Upon what is your decision based?

Fat	Palmitic	Stearic	Oleic	Linoleic	Linolenic
?	5	2	35	48	7
?	29	25	36	3	1

22.15 Medium-chain triglycerides (abbreviated MCT) are used in the treatment of patients with impaired absorption or digestion of fats. A natural source for MCT is coconut oil, which contains octanoic and decanoic acids. Write the formulas for all the possible MCT triglyceride fats which can be produced from these two acids. (*Hint:* There are six possible triglycerides.)

22.16 What is meant by the term *essential fatty acid?* Give an example of one.

22.17 Which one of the fats and oils listed in Table 22.3 is likely to be present in Intralipid, a product used to prevent EFA deficiency in patients whose total nutritional requirements must be met by IV feedings?

22.18 Suppose you have two test tubes, one containing a solution of stearic acid and the other a solution of linoleic acid. How can you tell which is which? Give any chemical reactions involved.

22.19 The iodine values for two different fats are 95 and 36. Which one is peanut oil and which is butter? Explain how you made your choice.

22.20 For the reaction shown below,
(a) Give the formulas and names of the products.
(b) What is this special type of hydrolysis reaction called?

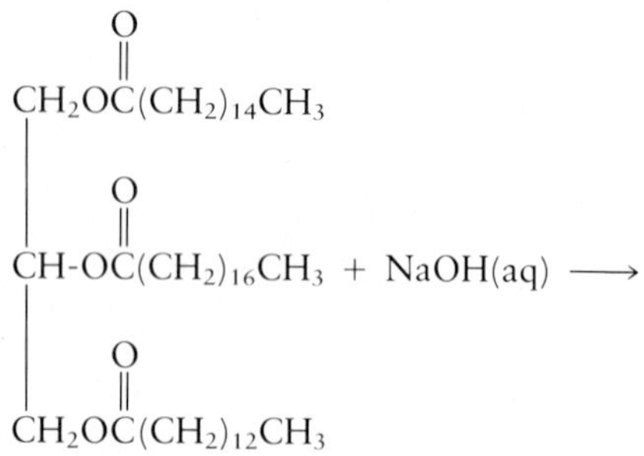

$$\begin{array}{l} CH_2OC(=O)(CH_2)_{14}CH_3 \\ | \\ CH\text{-}OC(=O)(CH_2)_{16}CH_3 + NaOH(aq) \longrightarrow \\ | \\ CH_2OC(=O)(CH_2)_{12}CH_3 \end{array}$$

22.21 In the food industry the term *rancidity* refers to off flavors and odors in fats. How are these produced? How are they prevented?

22.22 Give the formulas for the reactants needed to produce the fatty acid ester below, a typical wax found as a protective coating on leaves.

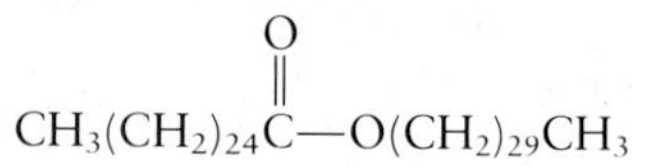

$$CH_3(CH_2)_{24}\overset{O}{\overset{\|}{C}}\text{—}O(CH_2)_{29}CH_3$$

22.23 What fatty acid is the precursor for a prostaglandin?

22.24 How is the mechanism of action of aspirin related to prostaglandin synthesis?

22.25 Of the following lipid compounds, which ones could be broken down to produce glycerol: (a) A prostaglandin; (b) a cephalin; (c) cholesterol; (d) a lecithin; (e) a ganglioside; (f) triolein?

22.26 For the compound shown below answer the following questions:

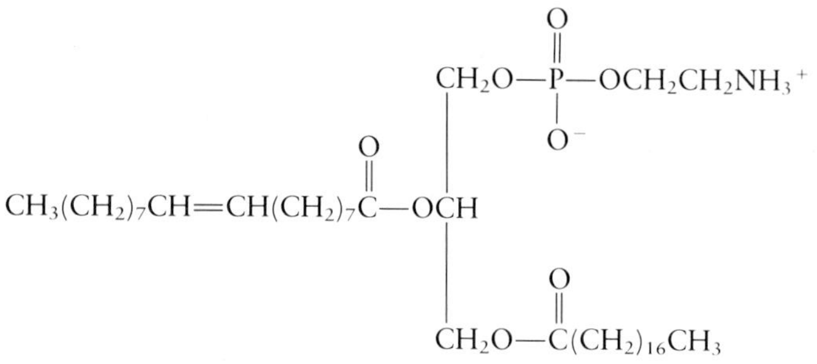

$$\begin{array}{l} \qquad\qquad\qquad\qquad CH_2O\text{—}P(=O)(O^-)\text{—}OCH_2CH_2NH_3^+ \\ \qquad\qquad\qquad\qquad | \\ CH_3(CH_2)_7CH{=}CH(CH_2)_7C(=O)\text{—}OCH \\ \qquad\qquad\qquad\qquad | \\ \qquad\qquad\qquad\qquad CH_2O\text{—}C(=O)(CH_2)_{16}CH_3 \end{array}$$

(a) To what class of lipids does this compound belong?
(b) What fatty acids are part of this compound?
(c) What amino alcohol is attached to the phosphate?
(d) What is the name of this compound?

22.27 To what general lipid class does the compound shown below belong?

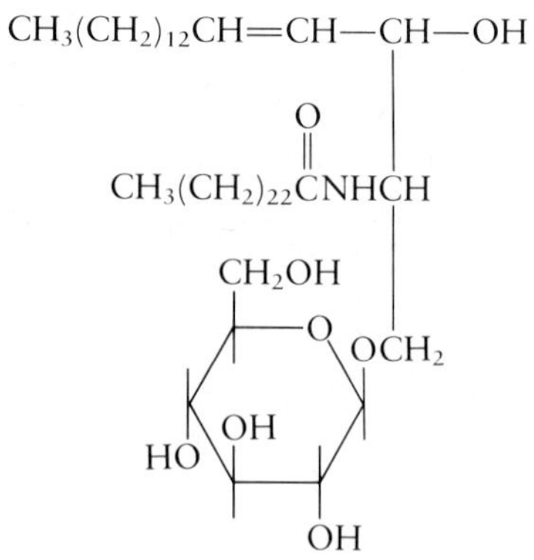

$$\begin{array}{l} CH_3(CH_2)_{12}CH{=}CH\text{—}CH\text{—}OH \\ \qquad\qquad\qquad\qquad | \\ CH_3(CH_2)_{22}C(=O)NHCH \\ \qquad\qquad\qquad\qquad | \\ \qquad\qquad\qquad\qquad OCH_2 \end{array}$$

(OCH₂ attached to a pyranose ring bearing CH_2OH, HO, OH, and OH groups)

22.28 What is the name of the attached ring structure in the formula of the compound in Exercise 22.27? (See Section 21.7.)

22.29 ***Niemann-Pick*** disease is a fatal childhood disorder which is due to the lack of an enzyme needed to cause the breakdown of the compound below.

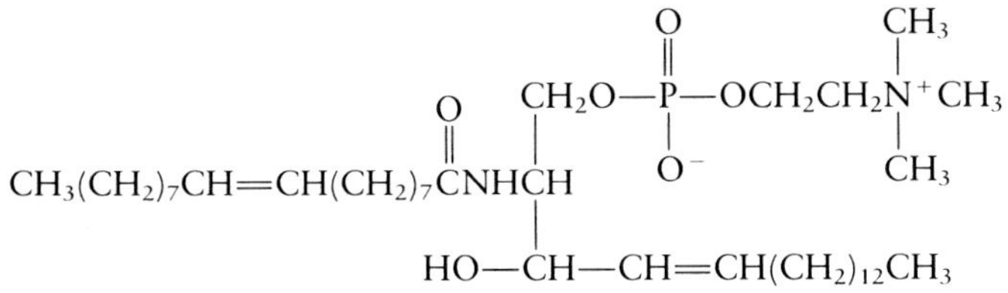

$$CH_3(CH_2)_7CH{=}CH(CH_2)_7\overset{O}{\overset{\|}{C}}NH\underset{HO-CH-CH=CH(CH_2)_{12}CH_3}{\underset{|}{\overset{CH_2O-\overset{O}{\overset{\|}{P}}(O^-)-OCH_2CH_2N^+(CH_3)_3}{\overset{|}{CH}}}}$$

The name of the enzyme is *most* likely to be (**a**) amylase; (**b**) cholesterase; (**c**) sphingomyelinase; or (**d**) hexosaminidase.

22.30 What is the cause of Tay-Sachs disease?

22.31 One hormone secreted in urine in increased amounts during pregnancy is estradiol:

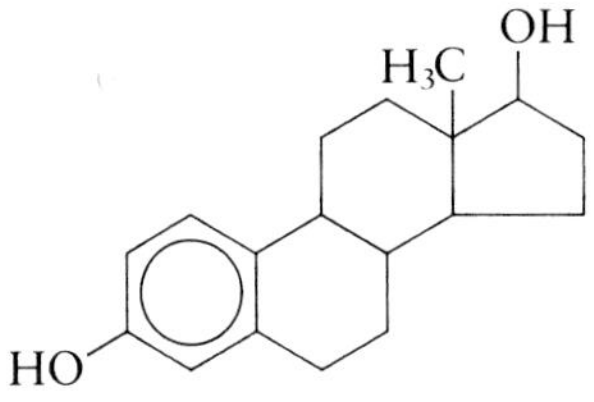

HO, H_3C, OH

(**a**) To what general class of compounds does estradiol belong?
(**b**) Give the molecular formula for estradiol.

22.32 What two general components are present in all cell membranes?

22.33 Why is water able to pass through biological membranes?

22.34 Why are triacylglycerols not major components of lipid bilayers?

22.35 The following are some of the lipid ingredients in a typical nondairy creamer product: partially hydrogenated vegetable oils (including coconut oil, cottonseed oil, soybean oil, palm kernel oil); lecithin; mono- and diglycerides.
(**a**) To which general class of lipid does each ingredient belong?
(**b**) Give the structures of some possible mono- and diglycerides.
(**c**) What function could the lecithin have?
(**d**) Why are the vegetable oils partially hydrogenated?

22.36 What is meant by fat-soluble vitamins?

22.37 In what two ways can your body obtain vitamin D?

22.38 Which food processing technique listed below is more likely to destroy the vitamin A present in a food? Why?
(**a**) Heating in an open pot where air is present.
(**b**) Cooking in water in a closed pot.

22.39 Spinach and carrots are rich sources of vitamin A even though they do not contain any vitamin A. Explain.

22.40 Give a brief description of the functions of each of the fat-soluble vitamins.

22.41 In order to receive the RDA of vitamin D how much milk fortified with vitamin D would you have to drink?

22.42 Is the body more dependent on a daily supply of water-soluble or of fat-soluble vitamins? Explain.

23 PROTEINS

23.1 INTRODUCTION

The word *protein* comes from the Greek word *proteios,* meaning "primary." In this chapter you will see how appropriate that name is when we discover the extent to which the nature of a living organism is determined by its protein molecules. Proteins are the "stuff" of which much of the body is composed. Hair, muscles, skin, and nails are all protein. In fact, more than half the dry weight of a person weighing 60 kg (132 lb) is contributed by protein (see Figure 23.1, which illustrates the chemical composition of the human body). Proteins are also "working" molecules, which perform operational functions in living systems. The enzymes that catalyze biochemical reactions are proteins, as are the antibodies that interact with invading species to prevent disease and many of the hormones that regulate biochemical processes. In fact, we can say that the proteins of a living organism determine what type of organism it will be.

Despite the varied functions of proteins, there are similarities in their chemical structures.

Proteins all contain the elements C, H, O, N, and usually S, and they are all polyamide polymers.

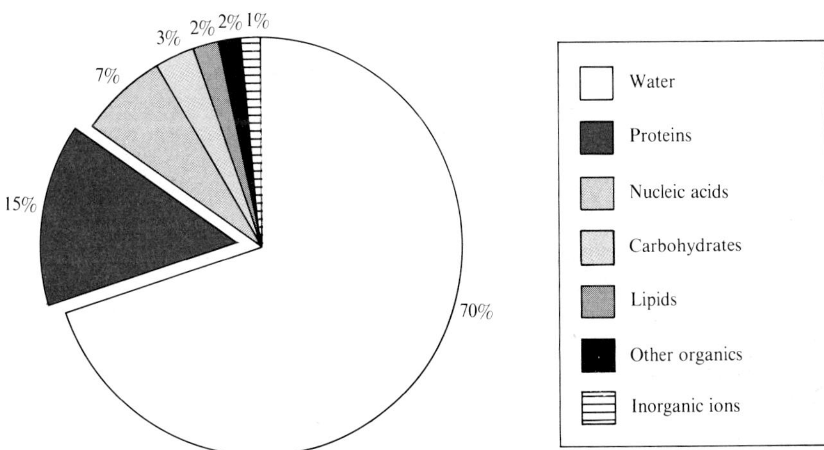

FIGURE 23.1
Body components. Proteins make up 15 percent of the total body weight and half the dry weight.

We will begin out study of proteins by looking at the structures of the building blocks from which they are constructed, that is, the amino acid monomers.

23.2 AMINO ACIDS

Amino acids are carboxylic acids which include an amino group in their structures (Section 18.2). The amino acids which are used to make up the proteins of living matter are those in which the amino group is bonded to the α (alpha) carbon atom (the C-2 carbon). In the general formula below for an α-amino acid the R represents an organic side chain or an H atom.

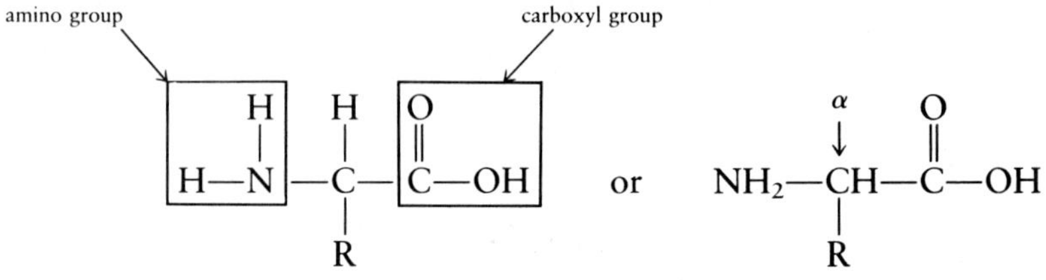

amino group → $\boxed{H-\underset{}{\overset{H}{\overset{|}{N}}}}-\underset{R}{\underset{|}{\overset{H}{\overset{|}{C}}}}-\boxed{\overset{O}{\overset{\|}{C}}-OH}$ ← carboxyl group or $NH_2-\underset{R}{\underset{|}{\overset{\alpha\downarrow}{CH}}}-\overset{O}{\overset{\|}{C}}-OH$

General α-amino acid

There are 20 common R groups and thus 20 common amino acids in the proteins commonly found in living things. For instance, when the R group is a hydrogen atom, the amino acid becomes α-aminoacetic acid (or 2-aminoethanoic acid), known by the trivial name of glycine (abbreviated Gly when part of an amino acid sequence or formed as a degradation residue).

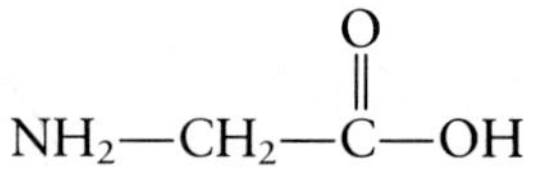

$$NH_2-CH_2-\overset{O}{\overset{\|}{C}}-OH$$ Glycine (Gly)

When the R side chain is $CH_2CH_2\overset{O}{\overset{\|}{C}}OH$, the amino acid is glutamic acid (Glu).

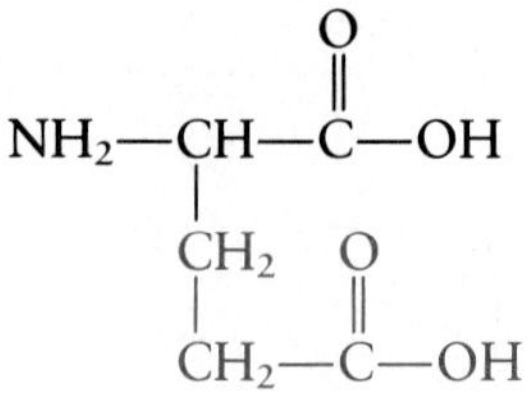

$$NH_2-\underset{\underset{CH_2-\overset{O}{\overset{\|}{C}}-OH}{\underset{|}{CH_2}}}{\underset{|}{CH}}-\overset{O}{\overset{\|}{C}}-OH$$ Glutamic acid

The sodium salt of this compound, monosodium glutamate (MSG), is shown below.

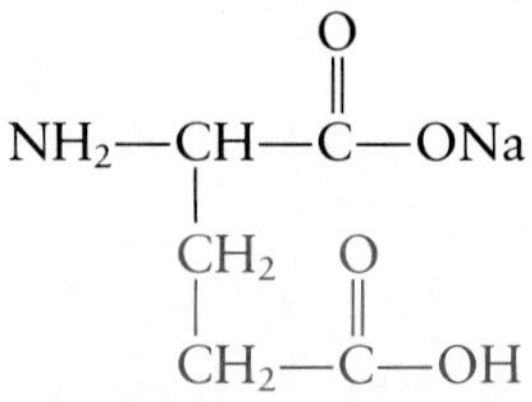

$$NH_2-\underset{\underset{CH_2-\overset{O}{\overset{\|}{C}}-OH}{\underset{|}{CH_2}}}{\underset{|}{CH}}-\overset{O}{\overset{\|}{C}}-ONa$$ Monosodium glutamate

Chinese restaurant syndrome is caused by the sodium salt of glutamic acid.

Monosodium glutamate enhances the flavors of foods and is often used in cooking, especially in Chinese dishes. Some individuals who are especially sensitive to MSG suffer from a disorder known as ***Chinese restaurant syndrome.*** Upon ingestion

TABLE 23.1 THE TWENTY COMMON AMINO ACIDS*

Formula	Name	Formula	Name
$\mathrm{H\underset{NH_2}{C}HCOOH}$	Glycine (Gly)	$\mathrm{NH_2\overset{O}{\overset{\Vert}{C}}CH_2\underset{NH_2}{C}HCOOH}$	Asparagine (Asn)
$\mathrm{CH_3\underset{NH_2}{C}HCOOH}$	Alanine (Ala)	$\mathrm{HOOCCH_2CH_2\underset{NH_2}{C}HCOOH}$	Glutamic acid (Glu)
$\mathrm{CH_3\underset{H_3C}{C}H\underset{NH_2}{C}HCOOH}$	Valine (Val)	$\mathrm{NH_2\overset{O}{\overset{\Vert}{C}}CH_2CH_2\underset{NH_2}{C}HCOOH}$	Glutamine (Gln)
$\mathrm{CH_3\underset{CH_3}{C}HCH_2\underset{NH_2}{C}HCOOH}$	Leucine (Leu)	$\mathrm{HSCH_2\underset{NH_2}{C}HCOOH}$	Cysteine (Cys)
$\mathrm{CH_3CH_2\underset{H_3C}{C}H\underset{NH_2}{C}HCOOH}$	Isoleucine (Ile)	$\mathrm{CH_3SCH_2CH_2\underset{NH_2}{C}HCOOH}$	Methionine (Met)
$\mathrm{HOCH_2\underset{NH_2}{C}HCOOH}$	Serine (Ser)	$\mathrm{HO{-}C_6H_4{-}CH_2\underset{NH_2}{C}HCOOH}$	Tyrosine (Tyr)
$\mathrm{HO\underset{H_3C}{C}H\underset{NH_2}{C}HCOOH}$	Threonine (Thr)	$\mathrm{C_6H_5{-}CH_2\underset{NH_2}{C}HCOOH}$	Phenylalanine (Phe)
$\mathrm{NH_2(CH_2)_4\underset{NH_2}{C}HCOOH}$	Lysine (Lys)	indol-3-yl$\mathrm{{-}CH_2\underset{NH_2}{C}HCOOH}$ (ring N–H)	Tryptophan (Trp)
$\mathrm{NH_2\overset{NH}{\overset{\Vert}{C}}NH(CH_2)_3\underset{NH_2}{C}HCOOH}$	Arginine (Arg)	$\mathrm{NH{-}CHCOOH}$ ring: $\mathrm{CH_2}$, $\mathrm{CH_2}$, $\mathrm{CH_2}$	Proline (Pro)
$\mathrm{HOOCCH_2\underset{NH_2}{C}HCOOH}$	Aspartic acid (Asp)	imidazolyl (N, N–H)$\mathrm{{-}CH_2\underset{NH_2}{C}HCOOH}$	Histidine (His)

*The R side chains in $\mathrm{R\underset{NH_2}{C}HCOOH}$ are in color.

of a large amount of MSG they may experience a temporary increase in blood pressure, producing dizziness, headache, facial flushing, and chest pain.

For the formulas, names, and abbreviations of the other common amino acids see Table 23.1.

SAMPLE EXERCISE 23.1

Give the formula and the IUPAC and trivial names for the amino acid in which the side chain is isopropyl.

Solution:

To write the formula for the amino acid replace the R in the general formula with an isopropyl group.

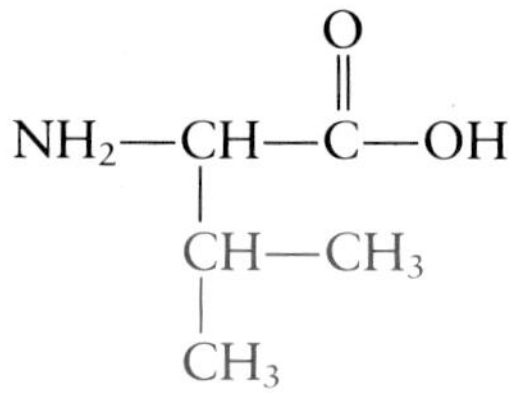

$$NH_2-\underset{\underset{\underset{\displaystyle CH_3}{|}}{\displaystyle CH-CH_3}}{\underset{|}{CH}}-\overset{\overset{\displaystyle O}{\|}}{C}-OH$$

Isopropyl group

To devise the IUPAC name we must first find the longest hydrocarbon chain, number it, and name the substituents.

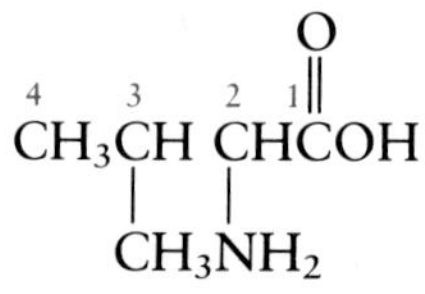

$$\overset{4}{C}H_3\underset{\underset{\displaystyle CH_3}{|}}{\overset{3}{C}H}\;\underset{\underset{\displaystyle NH_2}{|}}{\overset{2}{C}H}\overset{\overset{\displaystyle O}{\|}}{\overset{1}{C}}OH$$

The IUPAC name is thus 2-amino-3-methylbutanoic acid. From Table 23.1 we see that the common name is valine (Val), the name that is almost always used.

EXERCISE 23.1

Give the formula and the IUPAC and trivial names for the amino acid in which the side chain is isobutyl, $CH_2\underset{\underset{\displaystyle CH_3}{|}}{C}HCH_3$.

23.3 OPTICAL ACTIVITY OF AMINO ACIDS

The four groups attached to the α C atom, NH_2, R, $\overset{\overset{O}{\|}}{C}OH$, and H, are different in all the α-amino acids used to create living protein, except for glycine, in which R is a hydrogen atom.

$$\begin{array}{c} \quad\ \ \text{H}\quad\ \text{O} \\ \quad\ \ |\quad\ \ \| \\ \text{NH}_2\text{—C*—C—OH} \\ \quad\ \ | \\ \quad\ \ \text{R} \end{array}$$

Hence, these amino acid molecules (except for glycine) are chiral and so exhibit optical activity. It is convenient to name amino acid isomers by comparing their structures with those of glyceraldehyde by use of the D-L naming system (Section 20.6). Various ways to represent the structures of D- and L-alanine (R is CH_3) are shown in Figure 20.8. In Section 20.10 you saw that biological reactions often take place with only one of a pair of enantiomers. *It is the* L *amino acids that are used in the biochemical synthesis of proteins.*

SAMPLE EXERCISE 23.2

Give the Fischer projection formula for the optical isomer of phenylalanine found in the proteins of living organisms.

Solution:

From Table 23.1 we see that the R group for phenylalanine is CH_2—C_6H_5 (benzene ring).

$$\begin{array}{c} \qquad\qquad\ \ \text{O} \\ \qquad\qquad\ \ \| \\ \text{NH}_2\text{—CH—C—OH} \\ \quad\ | \\ \quad\ \text{CH}_2 \\ \quad\ | \\ \quad\ \text{C}_6\text{H}_5 \end{array}$$

Phenylalanine

To draw the Fischer projection for L-phenylalanine put the carboxyl C atom at the top of the C chain. The asymmetric C atom is the intersection of a horizontal line and the amino acid substituent points to the left.

$$\begin{array}{c} \text{O} \\ \| \\ \text{C—OH} \\ | \\ \text{NH}_2\text{—}\!\!+\!\!\text{—H} \\ | \\ \text{CH}_2 \\ | \\ \text{C}_6\text{H}_5 \end{array}$$

L-Phenylalanine

EXERCISE 23.2

The Fischer projection formulas shown represent amino acids. Which one of them is a common component of proteins?

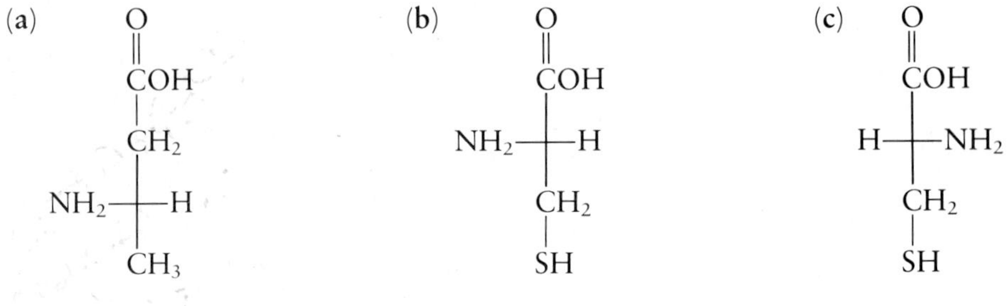

(a)
$$\begin{array}{c} O \\ \| \\ COH \\ | \\ CH_2 \\ NH_2 - \!\!\!+\!\!\! - H \\ CH_3 \end{array}$$

(b)
$$\begin{array}{c} O \\ \| \\ COH \\ NH_2 - \!\!\!+\!\!\! - H \\ CH_2 \\ | \\ SH \end{array}$$

(c)
$$\begin{array}{c} O \\ \| \\ COH \\ H - \!\!\!+\!\!\! - NH_2 \\ CH_2 \\ | \\ SH \end{array}$$

23.4 ACID-BASE PROPERTIES OF AMINO ACIDS

When dissolved in water an amino acid can behave as either an acid or a base because its formula contains an acidic (proton-donating) carboxyl group and a basic (proton-accepting) amino group.

$$-\overset{\overset{\displaystyle O}{\|}}{C}-OH + HOH \longrightarrow -\overset{\overset{\displaystyle O}{\|}}{C}-O^- + H_3O^+$$

$$-NH_2 + HOH \longrightarrow -NH_3^+ + OH^-$$

Zwitter in German means "hybrid" or "cross-breed."

In neutral solutions or solutions at intermediate pH values, the carboxyl proton of an amino acid donates a proton *and* the amino group accepts a proton. The ion that forms is called a **dipolar ion** or, more often, a **zwitterion.** Because it has both a negative and a positive charge, the zwitterion is electrically neutral.

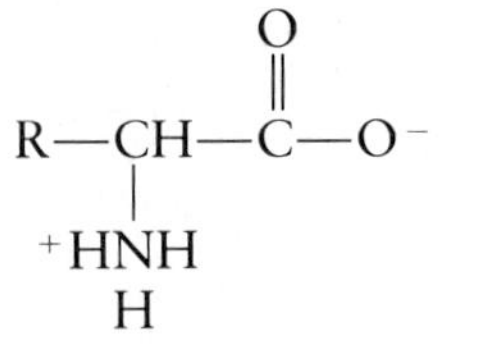

$$\begin{array}{l} R-\underset{\underset{\displaystyle {}^{+}HNH \atop H}{|}}{CH}-\overset{\overset{\displaystyle O}{\|}}{C}-O^- \end{array}$$

Zwitterion

In aqueous solution amino acids exist largely as zwitterions. In fact, amino acids never exist in an uncharged form. However, for convenience we will continue to write amino acid formulas in terms of the uncharged molecule, as we did for all the formulas given in Table 23.1.

Solid, crystalline amino acids also exist as zwitterions rather than uncharged molecules. Zwitterions are attracted to one another because of the charges they carry. Hence, like ionic compounds, in which cations and anions are attracted to each other, amino acids have unusually high melting points. For instance, the melting point of alanine (shown on the next page in its zwitterion form) is much greater than that of lactic acid, a compound with a similar structure and nearly the same formula weight.

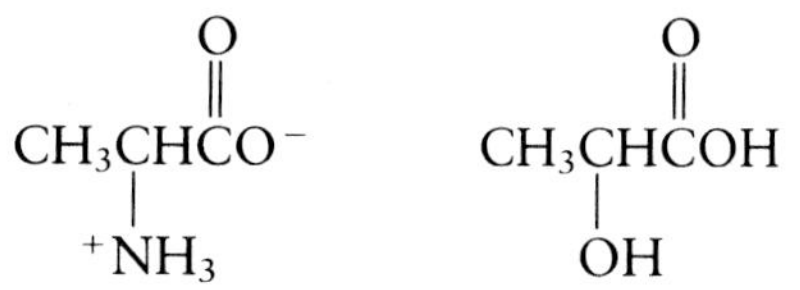

$$\underset{\substack{\text{Alanine, mp 314°C}\\\text{(formula weight 89)}}}{CH_3\underset{|}{C}H\overset{\overset{O}{\|}}{C}O^- \atop \quad {}^+NH_3} \qquad \underset{\substack{\text{Lactic acid, mp 53°C}\\\text{(formula weight 90)}}}{CH_3\underset{|}{C}H\overset{\overset{O}{\|}}{C}OH \atop \quad OH}$$

Ampho is Greek for "both."

When dissolved in water, the zwitterion can behave as an acid, with the NH_3^+ group donating a proton, or as a base, with the $\overset{\overset{O}{\|}}{C}O^-$ group accepting a proton. Compounds, such as amino acids in their zwitterion forms, that can exhibit the properties of both acids and bases are known as **amphoteric** compounds. Whether the zwitterion acts as an acid or as a base depends upon the acidity of the aqueous medium.

A zwitterion acts as a base in highly acidic solutions.

First let us look at the behavior of the zwitterion when the pH is very low, the medium is acidic, and $[H^+] > [OH^-]$. Because this solution already contains excess protons, the charged NH_3^+ group does not donate its proton. Under acidic conditions the $\overset{\overset{O}{\|}}{C}O^-$ group of an amino acid zwitterion accepts a proton to form a positively charged ion.

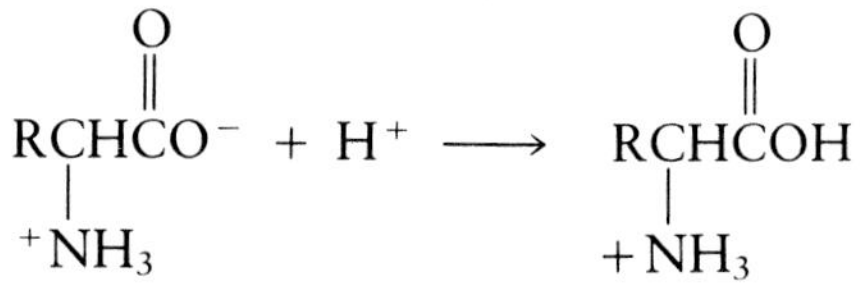

$$\underset{\text{Zwitterion}}{\overset{\overset{O}{\|}}{RCHCO^-} \atop {}^+NH_3} + H^+ \longrightarrow \underset{\text{Cation}}{\overset{\overset{O}{\|}}{RCHCOH} \atop {}^+NH_3} \qquad \text{very acidic, low pH medium}$$

A zwitterion acts as an acid in highly basic solutions.

When the medium is basic, at high pH, $[H^+] < [OH^-]$. Under these conditions the NH_3^+ group donates a proton to form the anion shown below.

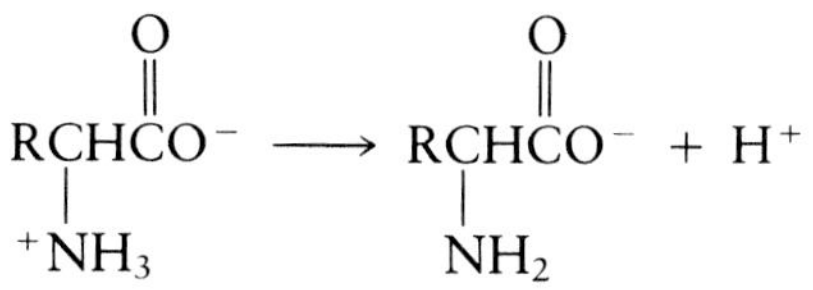

$$\underset{\text{Zwitterion}}{\overset{\overset{O}{\|}}{RCHCO^-} \atop {}^+NH_3} \longrightarrow \underset{\text{Anion}}{\overset{\overset{O}{\|}}{RCHCO^-} \atop NH_2} + H^+ \qquad \text{very basic, high pH medium}$$

Thus we see that there are two singly charged forms for an amino acid with an uncharged side group. The three possible charged species of an amino acid (in which R is not acidic or basic), namely, cation, anion, and neutral zwitterion, are shown below:

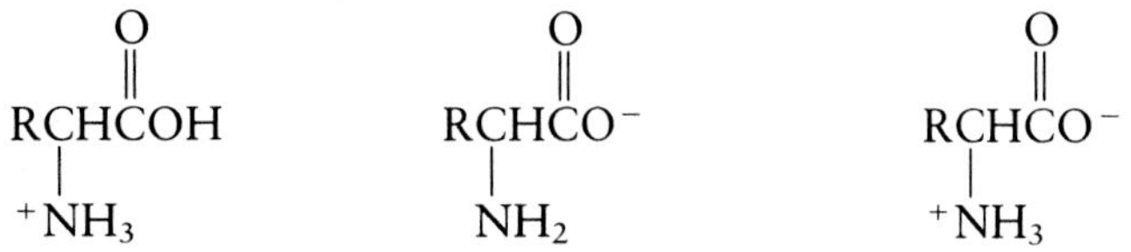

$$\underset{\text{Very low pH: cation}}{\overset{\overset{O}{\|}}{RCHCOH} \atop {}^+NH_3} \qquad \underset{\text{Very high pH; anion}}{\overset{\overset{O}{\|}}{RCHCO^-} \atop NH_2} \qquad \underset{\text{Intermediate pH: zwitterion}}{\overset{\overset{O}{\|}}{RCHCO^-} \atop {}^+NH_3}$$

Amino acids which have basic side chains (such as lysine), in which R is

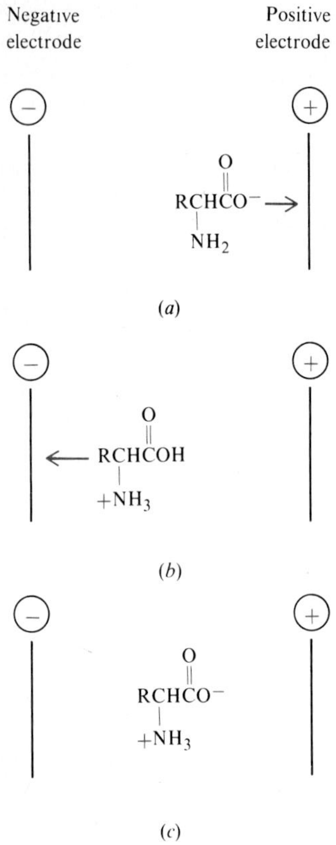

Negative electrode | Positive electrode

(a) $RCH(NH_2)CO_2^-$ → toward positive electrode

(b) ← $RCH(^+NH_3)COOH$ toward negative electrode

(c) $RCH(^+NH_3)CO_2^-$

FIGURE 23.2
Electrophoresis. (*a*) The negative species migrate to the positive electrode. (*b*) The positive species migrate to the negative electrode. (*c*) The zwitterion does not migrate.

$CH_2CH_2CH_2CH_2NH_2$ or acidic side chains (such as glutamic acid), where R is CH_2CH_2COOH, have additional charged species.

The acid-base behavior of amino acids is the basis of **electrophoresis**, one method used to separate and identify amino acids in a mixture. The amino acid mixture is placed in an electric field, as shown in Figure 23.2. Any positive species present will move, or *migrate,* to the negative electrode, and negative species will migrate to the positive electrode. Exactly neutral species will not migrate at all.

For each amino acid there is one pH value at which the number of positive charges is equal to the number of negative charges, a point known as the **isoelectric point**, or **pI**. At this point the amino acid exists primarily as the zwitterion, and the number of cations present is equal to the number of anions. For instance, alanine is essentially all zwitterion at its pI (6.00), with only very small amounts of the singly charged species present.

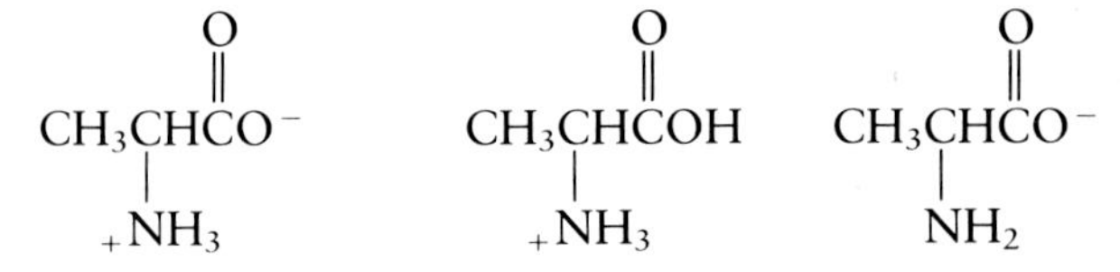

$CH_3CH(^+NH_3)CO_2^-$

Nearly all zwitterion at pI (6.00)

$CH_3CH(^+NH_3)COOH$ $CH_3CH(NH_2)CO_2^-$

Very small equal amounts of cation and anion at pI

Table 23.2 gives pI's for the common amino acids. The pI values for the amino acids with uncharged side chains are close to 6. They are not 7 because there are more anionic species than cationic species present in exactly neutral solutions. This is true because the NH_3^+ group has a slightly greater tendency to donate protons than the $\overset{O}{\overset{\|}{C}}O^-$ has to accept them. A little acid (and hence a slightly lower pH) is needed to donate protons to neutralize these extra anions. Note that the pI values for the acidic amino acids (glutamic and aspartic acid) are much lower. At neutral pH values these amino acids have a high concentration of anionic side chains ($\overset{O}{\overset{\|}{C}}O^-$). Thus, extra acid ($H^+$) must be added to neutralize them, as shown in Figure 23.3*a*. The basic amino acids have higher pI values. At neutral pH values their side chains are positively charged (NH_3^+). To counteract the excess cations, base (OH^-) must be added (Figure 23.3*b*).

At its pI an amino acid does not migrate in an electric field. Since each amino acid has a different value for pI, finding the pH at which an amino acid fails to migrate identifies it. For instance, suppose the isoelectric point for an amino acid is found to be 6.00. From Table 23.2 we see that it must be alanine (R is CH_3). Similar methods are used to separate and identify protein molecules, for which pI values are also tabulated. A conspicuous property of amino acids (and proteins) at their isoelectric points is a marked decrease in solubility, causing them to precipitate from solution. That is why sour milk curdles. When acids derived from lemon juice or bacterial action are added to milk, its pH dips to below 5, the pI value for the milk protein *casein*.

The protein fraction remaining after the caseins are removed from milk is called *whey*.

TABLE 23.2 **pI VALUES FOR AMINO ACIDS**

Amino acid	pI	Side chain (at pH of 6–7)
Acidic amino acids with negatively charged side chains		
Aspartic acid	2.77	CH_2COO^-
Glutamic acid	3.22	$CH_2CH_2COO^-$
Amino acids with uncharged side chains		
Cysteine	5.07	CH_2SH
Asparagine	5.41	CH_2CONH_2
Phenylalanine	5.48	CH_2—C_6H_5 (benzene ring)
Threonine	5.60	$CH(OH)CH_3$
Glutamine	5.65	$CH_2CH_2CONH_2$
Tyrosine	5.66	CH_2—C_6H_4—OH
Serine	5.68	CH_2OH
Methionine	5.74	$CH_2CH_2SCH_3$
Tryptophan	5.89	CH_2—(indole ring, N—H)
Valine	5.96	$CH(CH_3)CH_3$
Glycine	5.97	H
Leucine	5.98	$CH_2CH(CH_3)CH_3$
Alanine	6.00	CH_3
Isoleucine	6.02	$CH(CH_3)CH_2CH_3$
Proline	6.30	(See Table 23.1)
Basic amino acids with positively charged side chains		
Histidine	7.59	CH_2—(imidazole ring, NH^+, N—H)
Lysine	9.74	$CH_2CH_2CH_2CH_2NH_3^+$
Arginine	10.76	$CH_2CH_2CH_2NH—C(=NH)—NH_3^+$

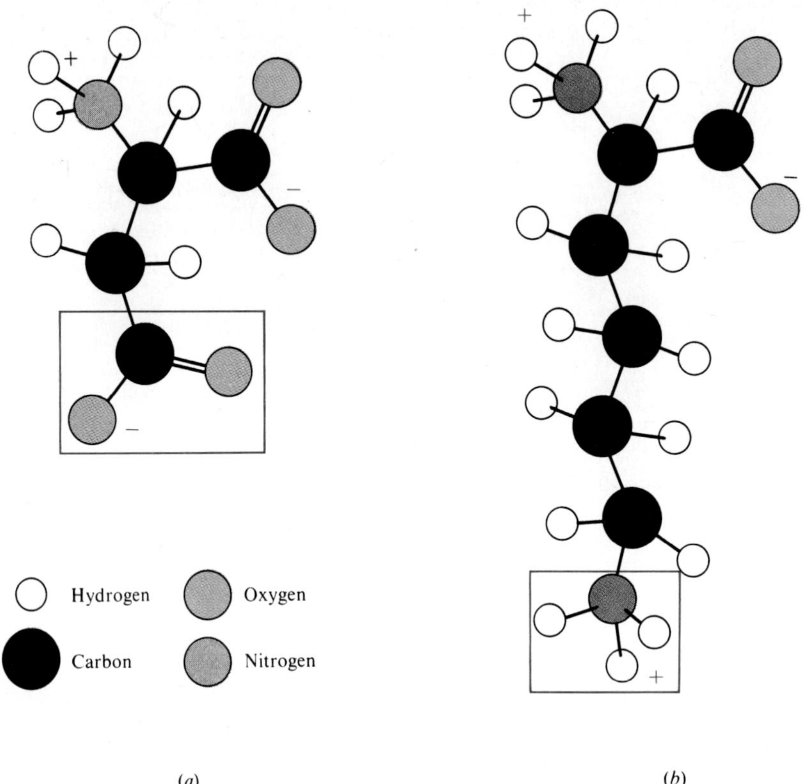

FIGURE 23.3
pI values for amino acids with charged side chains. (*a*) Aspartic acid. Acid is needed to neutralize extra anions. pI = 2.77. (*b*) Lysine. Base is needed to neutralize extra cations. pI = 9.74.

SAMPLE EXERCISE 23.3

Give the zwitterion structure and name of the amino acid that fails to migrate in an electric field at a pH of 5.07.

Solution:

From Table 23.2 we see that cysteine has a pI of 5.07. Table 23.1 gives its formula (R is CH_2SH).

$$HSCH_2CH(NH_2)C(=O)OH$$

Cysteine as a neutral molecule

$$HSCH_2CH(^{+}NH_3)C(=O)O^{-}$$

Cysteine as a zwitterion

EXERCISE 23.3

What is the name and zwitterion form for the amino acid which precipitates at a pH of 5.48?

23.5 FORMATION OF PEPTIDES

The formation of a dipeptide is an example of a condensation reaction.

You saw in Section 17.9 that amides form when carboxylic acids react with amines. Since amino acids contain both amino and carboxyl groups, they combine with each other to form amides, called **peptides**. The linkage that joins them is known as a **peptide linkage**. For instance, suppose two molecules of an amino acid are combined as in the reaction shown below. A molecule of water splits out to form a **dipeptide**.

$$\mathrm{H{-}N(H){-}CH(R){-}C({=}O){-}\boxed{OH + H}{-}N(H){-}CH(R){-}C({=}O){-}OH \longrightarrow H{-}N(H){-}CH(R){-}\underbrace{C({=}O){-}N(H)}_{\text{peptide linkage}}{-}CH(R){-}C({=}O){-}OH + H_2O}$$

Dipeptide

By convention, peptide formulas are written with the free amino group on the left and the carboxyl on the right.

Peptides are named as derivatives of the terminal amino acid, that is, the one on the right that contains the free carboxyl group. The names of the other amino acids are modified to end in -yl. For instance, suppose a dipeptide forms from two molecules of alanine (R is CH_3). The name of the product is alanylalanine.

$$\underset{\text{Alanine}}{\mathrm{H{-}N(H){-}CH(CH_3){-}C({=}O){-}\boxed{OH}}} + \underset{\text{Alanine}}{\mathrm{\boxed{H}{-}N(H){-}CH(CH_3){-}C({=}O){-}OH}} \longrightarrow \underset{\text{Alanylalanine (Ala—Ala)}}{\mathrm{H{-}N(H){-}CH(CH_3){-}C({=}O){-}N(H){-}CH(CH_3){-}C({=}O){-}OH}} + \mathrm{H_2O}$$

Using names such as alanylalanine becomes very awkward for peptides with more than two or three amino acid components. Instead, the names are abbreviated by using the three-letter abbreviations for each amino acid. Thus alanylalanine is written Ala—Ala.

When two different amino acids react, two different dipeptides can form. For instance, suppose alanine combines with serine. Alanylserine, Ala—Ser, is one possible product.

$$\underset{\text{Alanine}}{\mathrm{H{-}N(H){-}CH(CH_3){-}C({=}O){-}\boxed{OH}}} + \underset{\text{Serine}}{\mathrm{\boxed{H}{-}N(H){-}CH(CH_2OH){-}C({=}O){-}OH}} \longrightarrow \underset{\text{Alanylserine (Ala—Ser)}}{\mathrm{H{-}N(H){-}CH(CH_3){-}C({=}O){-}N(H){-}CH(CH_2OH){-}C({=}O){-}OH}} + \mathrm{H_2O}$$

The other product is serylalanine, Ser—Ala.

$$\underset{\text{Serine}}{\mathrm{H{-}N(H){-}CH(CH_2OH){-}C({=}O){-}\boxed{OH}}} + \underset{\text{Alanine}}{\mathrm{\boxed{H}{-}N(H){-}CH(CH_3){-}C({=}O){-}OH}} \longrightarrow \underset{\text{Serylalanine (Ser—Ala)}}{\mathrm{H{-}N(H){-}CH(CH_2OH){-}C({=}O){-}N(H){-}CH(CH_3){-}C({=}O){-}OH}} + \mathrm{H_2O}$$

When more than two amino acids are joined, the number of possible combinations increases dramatically. Three different amino acids form 3! (3 factorial), that is, $3 \times 2 \times 1$, or six different peptides; four different amino acids form 4!, or 24 combinations. If we combined the 20 common amino acids, 2.43×10^{18} different molecules could be produced!

Peptides formed from more than two amino acids, called **polypeptides**, are named with a prefix that indicates the number of amino acid monomer units joined together, e.g., tripeptide (three), tetrapeptide (four), pentapeptide (five), and so on. **Proteins** are polypeptides containing from 40 amino acid components (also known as amino acid *residues*) up to thousands. Insulin, for instance, required for proper metabolism of carbohydrates, is a comparatively small protein molecule, containing 51 amino acid residues and having a molecular weight of 5733. Hemoglobin is a much larger protein, which has 574 amino acid residues and a molecular weight of about 65,000. These are only two of the approximately 100,000 different proteins in your body.

SAMPLE EXERCISE 23.4

The artificial sweetner called aspartame (see Table 21.1) is the methyl ester of the dipeptide Asp—Phe. Write the reaction for the formation of this dipeptide.

Solution:

From Table 23.1 we see that the R group for phenylalamine (Phe) is $CH_2—C_6H_5$ (phenyl ring) and that for aspartic acid (Asp) is $CH_2\overset{\overset{O}{\|}}{C}OH$ or CH_2COOH. To write the reaction place the Asp on the left:

$$H—\overset{\overset{H}{|}}{N}—\underset{\underset{CH_2COOH}{|}}{CH}—\overset{\overset{O}{\|}}{C}—OH + H—\overset{\overset{H}{|}}{N}—\underset{\underset{CH_2—C_6H_5}{|}}{CH}—\overset{\overset{O}{\|}}{C}—OH \longrightarrow$$

To form the dipeptide, a water molecule is removed:

$$H—\overset{\overset{H}{|}}{N}—\underset{\underset{CH_2COOH}{|}}{CH}—\overset{\overset{O}{\|}}{C}—\boxed{OH + H}—\overset{\overset{H}{|}}{N}—\underset{\underset{CH_2—C_6H_5}{|}}{CH}—\overset{\overset{O}{\|}}{C}—OH \longrightarrow H—\overset{\overset{H}{|}}{N}—\underset{\underset{CH_2COOH}{|}}{CH}—\overset{\overset{O}{\|}}{C}—\overset{\overset{H}{|}}{N}—\underset{\underset{CH_2—C_6H_5}{|}}{CH}—\overset{\overset{O}{\|}}{C}—OH + H_2O$$

Asp Phe Asp—Phe

EXERCISE 23.4

Write the reaction for the formation of Phe—Asp, the other dipeptide that can form from the combination of aspartic acid with phenylalanine.

23.6 IMPORTANT SHORT PEPTIDES

In this section we will look at the structures of some peptides containing fewer than 10 amino acid residues, molecules too small to be considered proteins.

Pentapeptides

Pentapeptides act as pain-killers.

Encephalin is from the Greek *enkephalos,* "brain."

Pentapeptides such as the typical one shown in Fig. 23.4 are known to produce effects similar to those of morphine and other narcotic analgesics (Section 20.10). These morphinelike substances have been discovered in the brain and so are called **encephalins.** The encephalins are derived from larger peptides (containing about 80 amino acid residues) called **endorphins** from "endogeneous morphine," or morphine produced within. Pharmaceutical companies are testing the natural pentapeptides and other synthetic ones for use as pain-killers. So far, it appears that the body develops a tolerance for and becomes dependent upon pentapeptides as it does on morphine and the rest of the narcotic analgesics.

A sulfoxide is $R{-}\overset{\overset{O}{\|}}{S}{-}R$ (section 18.11) and a sulfone is $R{-}\overset{\overset{O}{\|}}{\underset{\underset{O}{\|}}{S}}{-}R$.

One theory for the action of pentapeptides is that they are capable of occupying opiate receptor sites (Section 20.10). There is some support for this idea in that particularly effective pentapeptides do share structural features (highlighted in Figure 23.4) common to all the narcotic analgesics. Among these are a phenyl ring and a tertiary N atom joined by a short hydrocarbon chain. These components are also highlighted in the structures of morphine and methadone, shown in Figure 23.5. The pentapeptide in Figure 23.4 is a synthetic compound in which a methyl group has been placed on the amide N atom of the phenylalanine residue and the disulfide in methionine has been oxidized to a sulfone. Note that the same features that appear in morphine and methadone are also present in the structure of this pentapeptide.

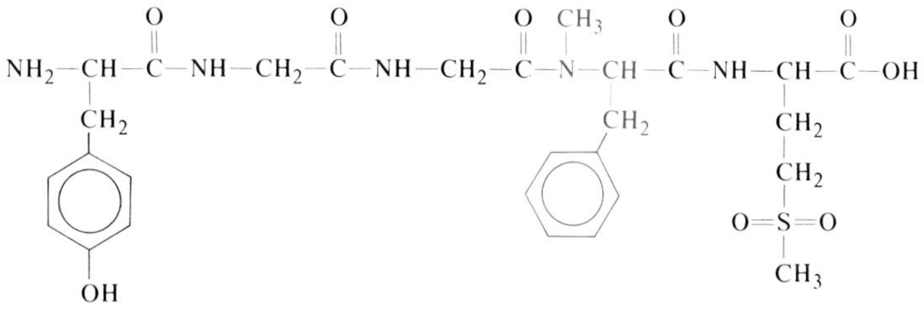

FIGURE 23.4
This derivative of the pentapeptide tyr-gly-gly-phe-met is a particularly potent narcotic analgesic. The structural features common to those of morphine and methadone are shown in color.

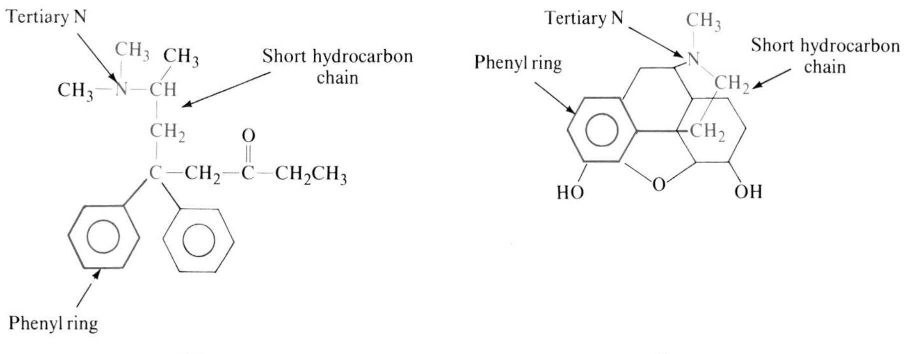

FIGURE 23.5
(*a*) Methadone and (*b*) morphine structures. Structural features common to the narcotic analgesics are shown in color.

Oxytocin: A Nonapeptide

One brand of synthetic oxytocin is Pitocin, a drug commonly used to induce labor.

Oxytocin, a hormone that regulates uterine contractions and lactation, was the first natural peptide ever to be synthesized in the laboratory. The nine amino acid residues in oxytocin include two Cys, one Tyr, one Ile, one Gln, one Asn, one Pro, one Leu, and one Gly. The terminal Gly is written as $GlyNH_2$ because the glycine on the free carboxyl end of the peptide is in the form of an amide, $—CH_2\overset{\overset{\displaystyle O}{\|}}{C}NH_2$, instead of an acid $—CH_2\overset{\overset{\displaystyle O}{\|}}{C}OH$.

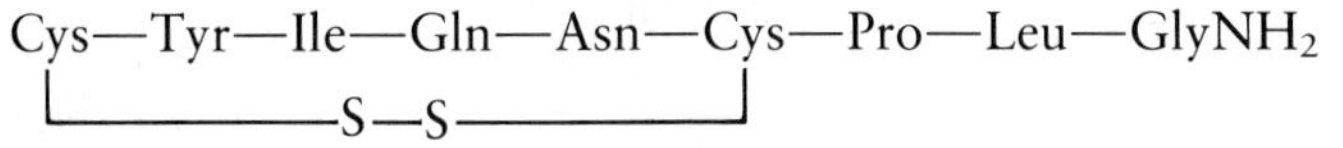

Cys—Tyr—Ile—Gln—Asn—Cys—Pro—Leu—$GlyNH_2$
(S—S linking the two Cys)

Oxytocin

In the structure of oxytocin the two cysteine (Cys) residues are joined by a **disulfide linkage**. The product of the combination of two cysteines, as in the reaction below, is a disulfide called **cystine**.

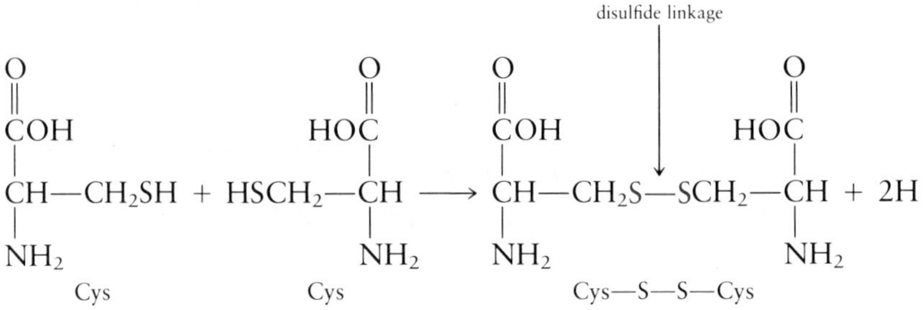

$$HO\overset{\overset{\displaystyle O}{\|}}{C}—CH(NH_2)—CH_2SH + HSCH_2—CH(NH_2)—\overset{\overset{\displaystyle O}{\|}}{C}OH \longrightarrow HO\overset{\overset{\displaystyle O}{\|}}{C}—CH(NH_2)—CH_2S—SCH_2—CH(NH_2)—\overset{\overset{\displaystyle O}{\|}}{C}OH + 2H$$

Cys Cys Cys—S—S—Cys (disulfide linkage)

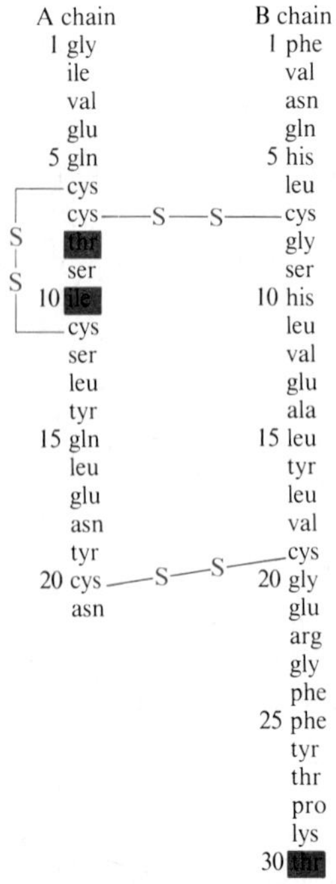

Disulfide bonds between cysteine residues are found in many protein molecules, including insulin, shown in Figure 23.6.

When oxytocin was first synthesized in the laboratory, it was tested by comparing its physiological action to that of the natural hormone and was found to have the same activity. It was also discovered that even seemingly minor structural changes profoundly affect hormonal activity. Replacing isoleucine (R is $CH(CH_3)CH_2CH_3$) with leucine (R is $CH_2CH(CH_3)CH_3$) reduced the potency of the hormone to one-tenth of its original value.

FIGURE 23.6
Human insulin. The disulfide linkages between cys residues are shown in color. The amino acids that are different for porcine and bovine insulin are shaded. In porcine insulin, the thirtieth residue in B is ala (B-30). In bovine insulin A-8 is ala. A-10 is val and B-30 is ala. Insulin preparations are from bovine and/or porcine sources.

A chain		B chain
1 gly		1 phe
ile		val
val		asn
glu		gln
5 gln		5 his
cys (S—S to A-11)		leu
cys	—S—S—	cys
thr		gly
ser		ser
10 ile		10 his
cys (S—S to A-6)		leu
ser		val
leu		glu
tyr		ala
15 gln		15 leu
leu		tyr
glu		leu
asn		val
tyr		cys
20 cys	—S—S—	20 gly
asn		glu
		arg
		gly
		phe
		25 phe
		tyr
		thr
		pro
		lys
		30 thr

Vasopressin

Another nonapeptide with a structure similar to that of oxytocin is **vasopressin**, a hormone that regulates water balance in the body.

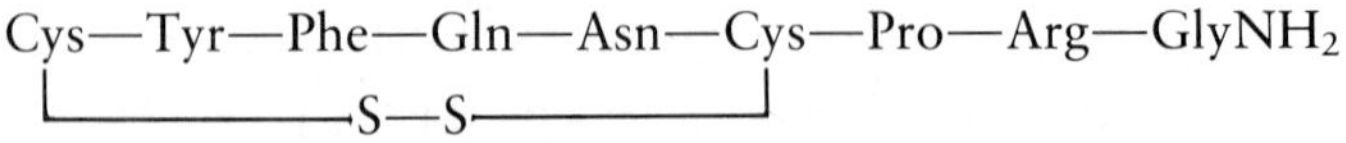

Cys—Tyr—Phe—Gln—Asn—Cys—Pro—Arg—$GlyNH_2$
(S—S linking the two Cys)

Vasopressin

You can see that replacement of Ile and Leu with Phe and Arg accounts for the only difference in the structures of oxytocin and vasopressin. It is not unusual for a change of even one amino acid residue in a peptide to have a drastic effect

TABLE 23.3 **PEPTIDE HORMONES**

Peptide	Number of amino acids	Source	Function
Oxytocin	9	Pituitary gland	Regulates uterine contractions and lactation
Vasopressin	9	Pituitary gland	Decreases urine flow
Bradykinin	9	Blood plasma	Regulates blood pressure
Gastrin	17	Stomach	Increases gastric acid secretion
Secretin	27	Duodenum (the first part of the small intestine)	Stimulates pancreatic juice secretion
Glucagon	29	Pancreas	Increases blood glucose level

on its properties, even if the peptide happens to be a giant protein molecule.

Antidiuretics decrease urine flow and thereby help the body to retain water.

Diabetes refers to conditions in which excess urine is excreted (polyuria).

Diabetes mellitus is discussed in Section 26.10.

Vasopressin is an example of an *antidiuretic hormone (ADH)*. A diuretic increases the flow of urine; an *anti*diuretic decreases urine flow by causing the kidneys to retain water. The osmotic pressure of the plasma (fluid portion of the blood) directs the increase or decrease of ADH. Suppose the osmotic pressure of the plasma rises above normal. The higher the concentration of solutes in the plasma, the higher will be the osmotic pressure, which you will recall is a colligative property (Section 9.8). To bring the osmotic pressure back to normal the plasma must be diluted with water. The body needs to retain water and so ADH is released. Conversely, when the osmotic pressure of the plasma is too low, ADH release is inhibited and urine is excreted to increase the solute concentration and osmotic pressure of the plasma. Alcohol has the ability to inhibit ADH, which probably accounts for the increased urine flow that occurs when alcohol is consumed. The disease ***diabetes insipidus*** (not the same as diabetes mellitus, or sugar diabetes) is caused by a deficiency of ADH. Those who suffer from this disorder excrete enormous volumes of urine, as much as 15 to 20 L a day, compared with the normal amount of about 1 to 1.5 L. The treatment for this is the administration of an ADH such as vasopressin. The functions and sources of various peptide hormones are listed in Table 23.3.

23.7 HYDROLYSIS OF PEPTIDES

As you have seen, the amino acid composition of a peptide is crucial in determining its properties. To find the amino acid content of polypeptides, they must first be broken down by hydrolysis. Hydrolysis of peptides is accomplished both in the laboratory and in the body, where it is a step in the digestion of proteins in food.

Laboratory Hydrolysis

In the laboratory strong solutions of hydrochloric acid (6*M* HCl) are used to break down polypeptides into amino acids. Heating with the acid converts the peptide linkages back into the component amino and carboxyl groups.

$$\underset{\text{Peptide}}{\sim\!\overset{\overset{\displaystyle O}{\|}}{C}\!-\!NH\!\sim} + H_2O \xrightarrow[\Delta]{6M\ HCl} \underset{\text{Carboxyl}}{\sim\!\overset{\overset{\displaystyle O}{\|}}{C}\!-\!OH} + \underset{\text{Amino}}{NH_2\!\sim}$$

Most of the amino acids emerge intact, that is, the strong acidic conditions do not cause them to decompose. There are a few exceptions. Tryptophan (R is CH_2–(3-indolyl), indole ring with N–H) is usually destroyed by the acid and thus does not appear as a product. The HCl also attacks the amide linkages in the side chains of the amino acids glutamine (Gln, R is $CH_2CH_2\overset{O}{\overset{\|}{C}}NH_2$) and asparagine (Asn, R is $CH_2\overset{O}{\overset{\|}{C}}NH_2$).

$$\underset{\text{Glutamine (Gln)}}{NH_2CH(CH_2CH_2\overset{O}{\overset{\|}{C}}\!-\!NH_2)\overset{O}{\overset{\|}{C}}\!-\!OH} + H_2O \xrightarrow[\Delta]{6M\ HCl} \underset{\text{Glutamic acid (Glu)}}{NH_2CH(CH_2CH_2\overset{O}{\overset{\|}{C}}\!-\!OH)\overset{O}{\overset{\|}{C}}\!-\!OH} + NH_4Cl$$

Thus Gln and Asn appear as the corresponding carboxylic acids, glutamic acid Glu, R is $CH_2CH_2\overset{O}{\overset{\|}{C}}OH$) and aspartic acid (Asp, R is $CH_2\overset{O}{\overset{\|}{C}}OH$).

For instance, suppose that the seven-amino-acid protein segment—Tyr—Gly—Trp—Ala—Ser—Gln—Ala—is subjected to acid hydrolysis.

$$\text{Tyr—Gly—Trp—Ala—Ser—Gln—Ala} \xrightarrow[\Delta]{6M\ HCl} \text{Tyr} + \text{Gly} + 2\text{Ala} + \text{Ser} + \text{Glu}$$

Note that there are only six amino acid residues in the product mixture because the tryptophan (Trp) did not survive and note also that the glutamine (Gln) appears in the product mixture as glutamic acid (Glu). There are other, independent methods, using spectroscopic techniques or some other set of hydrolysis conditions, to determine the presence of these amino acids and of cysteine, which is also partially destroyed in acid hydrolysis.

After hydrolysis the amino acid composition of the product mixture can be found by using a *chromatographic* method (Section 2.5). The chromatography column is packed with a polymeric substance, called a *resin,* which is bound to sodium ions. The amino acid mixture is made strongly acidic (pH 3) so that the amino acids will be present in their cationic form:

$$\text{R—}\underset{\substack{|\\ \text{NH}_2}}{\text{CH}}\text{—}\overset{\substack{\text{O}\\ \|}}{\text{C}}\text{—OH} + \text{H}^+ \longrightarrow \text{R—}\underset{\substack{|\\ {}^+\text{NH}_3}}{\text{CH}}\text{—}\overset{\substack{\text{O}\\ \|}}{\text{C}}\text{—OH}$$

When placed on the column the amino acid cations replace the Na^+ ions of the resin and are deposited on the resin. Each of the 20 common amino acids is bound to a different extent. They are collected one at a time by washing the column with NaCl solutions of varying pH. The pH at which each amino acid is removed is known and thus identifies the amino acid (see Figure 23.7). Because the amino acid cations are exchanged with sodium ions, the method is known as *ion-exchange chromatography*. Even very small samples of an amino acid mixture can be analyzed in only a few hours with an *amino acid analyzer*, which is an automated ion-exchange device. Table 23.4 gives the amino acid composition of the proteins insulin, hemoglobin, silk protein, wool protein, and collagen. We will refer to this table later to study the way in which the shapes and properties of these proteins depend upon their amino acid content.

Water softeners contribute Na^+ ions to water and thus cannot be used by individuals on sodium-restricted diets.

Ion-exchange chromatography is the principle upon which household water softeners work. The calcium, iron, and magnesium ions in hard water are exchanged with sodium ions as the hard water is poured through an ion-exchange resin containing sodium ions (see Figure 23.8).

$^+NH_3CHCOH$ (O, R_4) $^+NH_3CHCOH$ (O, R_1)

$^+NH_3CHCOH$ (O, R_3) $^+NH_3CHCOH$ (O, R_2)

$Polymer^- Na^+$

(*a*)

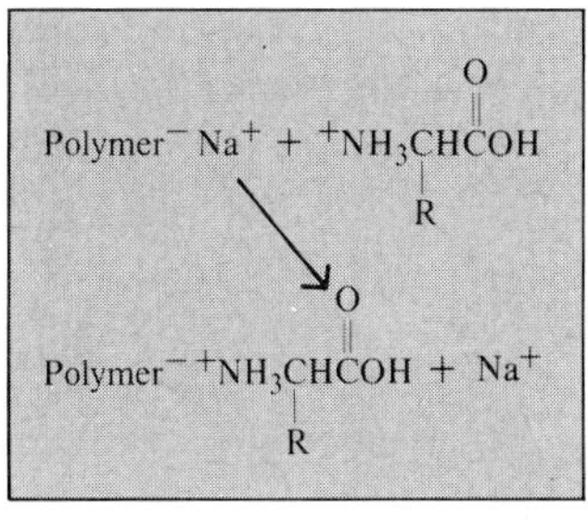

(*b*)

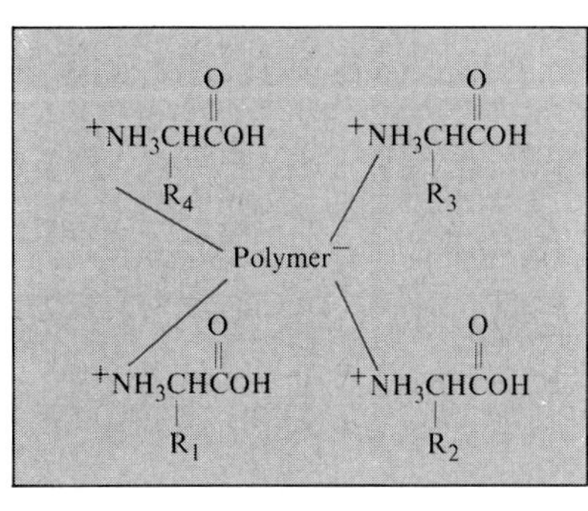

(*c*)

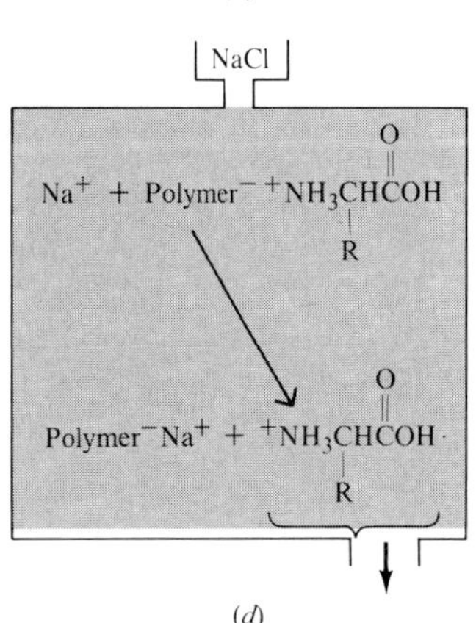

(*d*)

FIGURE 23.7
Diagram of an amino acid analyzer. (*a*) Mixture of cationic amino acids. (*b*) Sodium ions on the ion-exchange resin, polymer-Na^+, are swapped for amino acid cations. (*c*) Each amino acid cation is bound to a different extent, depending on R. (*d*) The amino acids are washed off the polymer by addition of Na^+. The pH of the NaCl solution determines which amino acid will come off.

TABLE 23.4 **AMINO ACID COMPOSITION OF SOME POLYPEPTIDES***

Amino acid residue	Insulin	Hemoglobin	Silk protein	Wool protein	Collagen
Nonpolar R groups					
Ala	5.9	12.5	29.4	5.0	10.7
Val	9.8	10.8	2.2	5.1	2.3
Leu	11.8	12.5	0.5	6.9	2.4
Ile	2.0	0	0.7	2.8	0.9
Pro†	2.0	4.9	0.3	7.5	21.6
Phe	5.9	5.2	0.5	2.5	1.2
Trp	0	1.0	0.2	1.2	0
Met	0	1.0	0	0.5	0.8
Polar R groups (uncharged)					
Gly	7.8	7.0	44.6	8.1	33
Ser	5.9	5.6	12.2	10.2	4.3
Thr	2.0	5.6	0.9	6.5	2.0
Cys	11.8	1.0	0	11.2	0
Tyr	7.8	2.1	5.2	4.2	0.4
Asn‡	5.9	5.2	0.3	—	—
Gln‡	5.9	1.4	0	—	—
Polar R groups (charged)					
Asp	0	3.5	1.0	6.0‡	4.5‡
Glu	7.8	4.2	1.0	12.1‡	7.1‡
Arg	2.0	2.1	0.5	7.2	5.0
His	3.9	6.6	0.2	0.7	0.4
Lys	2.0	7.7	0.3	2.3	3.4

*The amino acid content in the table is given in terms of mole percent.

†Refers to Pro + hydroxyproline.

‡The dashed entries (--) for Asn and Gln are there because they are included with the totals Asn + Asp or Gln + Glu (as listed for Asp and Glu).

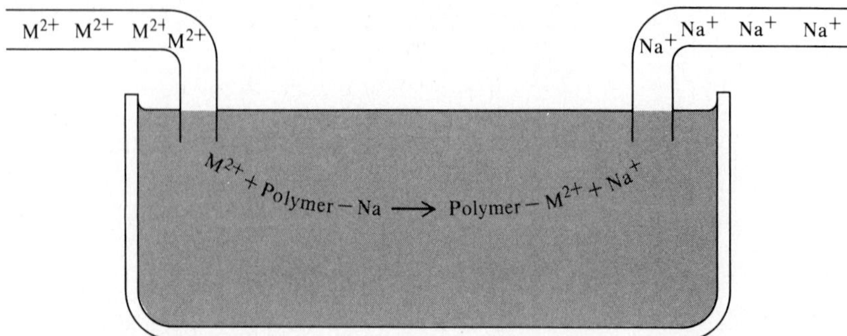

FIGURE 23.8
Ion-exchange water softener. The sodium ions replace the calcium and magnesium ions of the hard water in this diagram.

TABLE 23.5 **SOME ENZYMES AND THE PEPTIDE BONDS THEY CLEAVE**

Enzyme	Major sites of action*	Source
Trypsin	Arg, Lys	Pancreas
Chymotrypsin	Trp, Phe, Tyr	Pancreas
Pepsin	Trp, Phe, Tyr, Met, Leu	Stomach

*The enzymes cleave at the carbonyl of the amino acids given: $—\underset{\displaystyle R}{\underset{|}{CH}}—\overset{\displaystyle O}{\overset{\|}{C}}—NH—$

Protein Hydrolysis in the Body

In the laboratory hydrolysis discussed above, you saw that all the peptide linkages are broken. This is not the case in the body, where proteins are hydrolyzed by enzymes called *proteases*. Many different enzymes are involved, each of which is programmed to cleave the peptide chain between specific pairs of amino acid residues. For instance, the enzyme trypsin, found in the pancreas, breaks only those peptide bonds in which the carbonyl of the peptide is part of a lysine (Lys) or arginine (Arg) residue. Therefore, a Lys—Ala linkage can be cleaved by trypsin, but an Ala—Lys linkage cannot. Suppose the protein segment Gly—Lys—Ala—Ser—Glu—Arg—Val is hydrolyzed by trypsin:

$$\text{Gly—Lys—Ala—Ser—Glu—Arg—Val} \xrightarrow{\text{trypsin}} \text{Gly—Lys} + \text{Ala—Ser—Gly—Arg} + \text{Val}$$

Cleavage occurs at the two places indicated in color to produce a dipeptide, a tetrapeptide, and valine. Table 23.5 lists some enzymes and the specific peptide bonds that they can break.

Meat tenderizers contain proteases.

It is the partial breakdown of peptide bonds by moist heat that occurs when meat is cooked, thus aiding in its digestion. Enzymes similar to pepsin (see Table 23.5) are present in the natural substance *papain*, a major ingredient in meat tenderizers. Papain, isolated from the papaya, is able to catalyze the hydrolysis of proteins (particularly those in connective tissues) at room temperature. In this way a meat tenderizer shortens cooking time by "predigesting" the meat.

SAMPLE EXERCISE 23.5

Give the products of the hydrolysis of the peptide segment Ala—Arg—Asn—Ser—Phe—Tyr—Gly—Leu if the hydrolysis is done with

(**a**) 6*M* HCl (**b**) The enzyme trypsin

Solution:

(**a**) With 6*M* HCl, eight amino acid residues are produced and the asparagine (Asn) is converted to aspartic acid (Asp):

$$\text{Ala—Arg—Asn—Ser—Phe—Tyr—Gly—Leu} \xrightarrow[\Delta]{6M\ \text{HCl}} \text{Ala + Arg + Asp + Ser + Phe + Tyr + Gly + Leu}$$

(**b**) With trypsin, cleavage occurs only between arg and asn, producing a dipeptide and a hexapeptide.

$$\text{Ala—Arg—Asn—Ser—Phe—Tyr—Gly—Leu} \xrightarrow{\text{trypsin}} \text{Ala—Arg + Asn—Ser—Phe—Tyr—Gly—Leu}$$

EXERCISE 23.5

Give the products of the hydrolysis of the peptide chain Ala—Ala—Trp—Gly—Lys—Gly—Gln—Arg in the presence of:

(**a**) 6*M* HCl (**b**) Trypsin

23.8 PRIMARY STRUCTURES OF PROTEINS

You have just found out how the amino acid content of a particular protein is determined. However, not only the amino acid composition but also the order in which the amino acids are arranged determines the function of a peptide molecule. The sequence of amino acids which are joined together to form the polypeptide chain of a protein is known as the **primary structure** of the protein.

It took Frederick Sanger (1918–) and his colleagues at Cambridge University 10 years to determine the primary structure of insulin (Figure 23.6), a relatively small protein. In 1958 they received the Nobel prize for this landmark accomplishment.

23.9 SECONDARY STRUCTURE OF PROTEINS

The properties of proteins depend upon their *conformations*, or three-dimensional shapes, as well as upon their sequence of amino acids (their primary structures). The shape adopted by a protein molecule as a result of *hydrogen bonding* within polypeptide chains is called the **secondary structure** of the protein. Amide H atoms in peptide linkages in one part of the polypeptide chain are attracted to the carbonyl O atoms of peptide linkages at some other point in the chain.

$$\text{C=O} \cdots\cdots\cdots \text{H—N}$$

Hydrogen bond

Several different secondary structures are possible. Which one a given protein will adopt is largely dependent upon its amino acid content.

α Helix

The most common secondary shape for a protein molecule is the ***α* helix**, in which the polypeptide chain spirals in a clockwise direction, as shown in Figure 23.9. The *α*-helical shape is produced when an amide H atom forms a hydrogen bond with a carbonyl group that is three amino acid residues away.

The presence of the cyclic amino acid proline or its derivative hydroxyproline, found in some proteins, can prevent the formation of the *α* helix or produce "kinks" in it. Both proline and hydroxyproline form peptide linkages in which there are no H atoms available on their amide N atoms, as in the dipeptide sequence Ala-Pro, shown below.

$$\underset{\text{Ala}}{\mathrm{H{-}N(H){-}CH(CH_3){-}C(=O){-}OH}} + \underset{\text{Pro}}{\mathrm{H{-}N{-}CH{-}C(=O){-}OH}\ (\text{ring: } \mathrm{CH_2{-}CH_2{-}CH_2})} \longrightarrow \underset{\text{Ala—Pro}}{\mathrm{H{-}N(H){-}CH(CH_3){-}\overbrace{C(=O){-}N}^{\text{peptide linkage}}{-}CH{-}C(=O){-}OH}\ (\text{ring: } \mathrm{CH_2{-}CH_2{-}CH_2})} + \mathrm{H_2O}$$

Thus the hydrogen bonds needed to produce the *α*-helical structure cannot form in polypeptide chains containing large amounts of proline or hydroxyproline.

The *α* helix is found in ***α*-keratins**, the proteins that make up the hair, skin, and nails of humans and the fur, feathers, horns, and scales of animals. The *α*-helical secondary structure was first discovered by analyzing the interatomic dis-

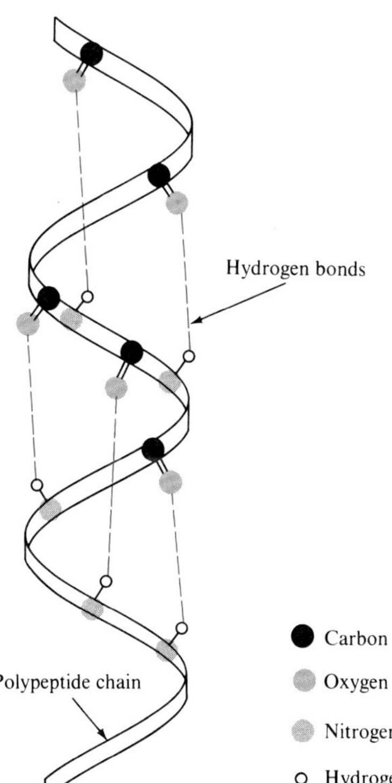

FIGURE 23.9
The *α*-helix secondary structure. Hydrogen bonds twist the polypeptide chain into an *α*-helix. (The R side groups are not shown.)

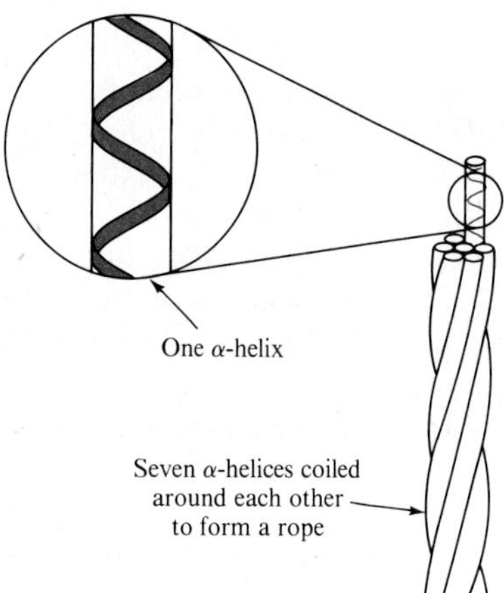

FIGURE 23.10
α-Keratin.

tances found in the α-keratin of wool. α-Keratin forms a rope containing anywhere from three to seven α-helical strands, wound around each other and held together by disulfide bonds between cysteine (R is CH_2SH) residues (see Figure 23.10). From Table 23.4 you can see that wool protein is 11.2 percent cysteine. Cysteine accounts for even more of the amino acids in the α-keratin of hair (16 to 18 percent) and is responsible for the sulfurous, unpleasant odor of burning hair.

α-Keratins in wool fibers and moistened hair can be stretched. Their α helices elongate as the hydrogen bonds among peptide chains break owing to the applied stress. However, when the stress is removed, both the hair and the wool return to their normal shapes, largely because of the restoring force of the disulfide linkages.

β-Pleated Sheet

A less common secondary structure is the **β-pleated sheet**, which forms when one long strand of a polypeptide chain forms hydrogen bonds with another neighboring strand, as shown in Figure 23.11. Many chain segments can form hydrogen bonds with each other to form this side-by-side arrangement. By viewing the

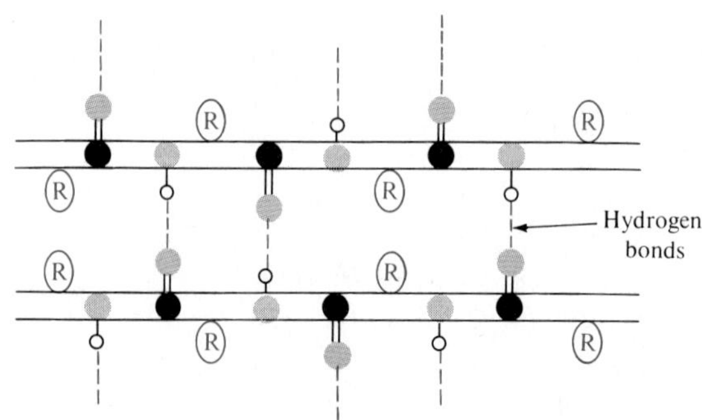

FIGURE 23.11
The β-pleated sheet secondary structure. Hydrogen bonds between neighboring segments of a polypeptide chain produces a β-pleated sheet. The R side chains must be small for this to be possible.

resulting structure in three dimensions, you would note that it actually does look like pleated material.

In general, pleated sheet structures are stable only in proteins which have a large percentage of small side chains, which allow the polypeptide strands to come close enough to each other to form the hydrogen bonds (see Figure 23.11). Proteins that exist as β-pleated sheets include the β-keratins found in the fibers spun by spiders and silkworms. Silk protein (called *fibroin*) is particularly rich in glycine (R is H) and alanine (R is CH_3). Of the amino acid residues in the silk protein listed in Table 23.4, 86.2 percent are the nonbulky groups glycine (R is H), alanine (R is CH_3), and serine (R is CH_2OH). The α-keratins contain many more bulky R groups and so cannot maintain a β-pleated sheet structure. Note that only 23.3 percent of wool protein is composed of alanine, glycine, and serine. Silk proteins are also low in cysteine residues and so cannot form S—S cross linkages.

Because of the many bonds that hold them together, the proteins in the β-pleated sheet conformation resist stretching. Thus, unlike wool and hair, silk does not stretch.

Triple Helix

Ligaments, largely collagen fibers, help to hold bones together at the joints.

Gelatin is *derived* by heating collagen.

Another possible conformation is the **triple helix**, in which three polypeptide chains are wrapped around each other, as shown in Figure 23.12. This is the conformation of the **collagens**, which are components of connective tissues and the most abundant of all proteins in the human body. Collagen forms a substantial portion of bones, tendons, cartilage, teeth, and skin. Collagens cannot form α-helices because of their high content of proline and hydroxyproline (see Table 23.4). A typical amino acid sequence in a collagen triple helix is Gly-X-Pro, where the X refers to some other residue and Pro to hydroxyproline or proline. The

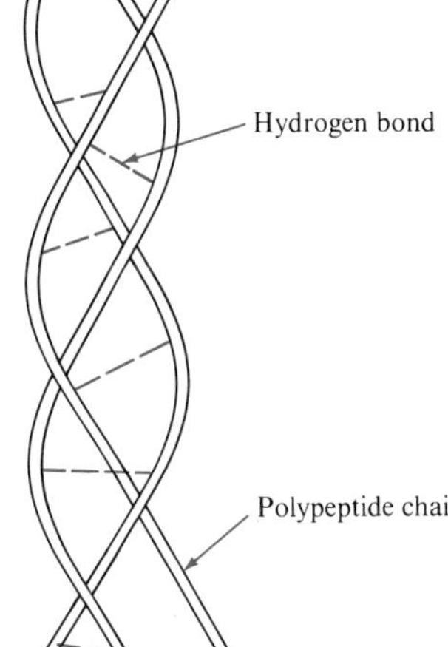

FIGURE 23.12
Triple helix secondary structure. Collagen consists of three helical polypeptide chains coiled around each other. The approximate location of the hydrogen bonds that hold them together are shown in color.

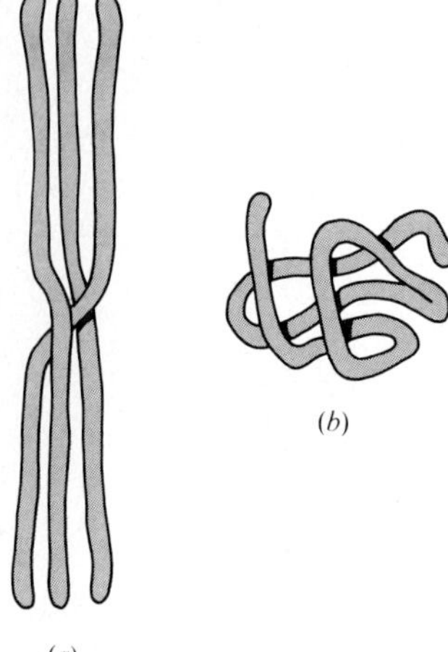

FIGURE 23.13
Fibrous and globular proteins. (*a*) In fibrous proteins, intertwined amino acid chains form long fibers. (*b*) In globular proteins, the amino acid chains bend and fold into spherical shapes.

three chains are hydrogen-bonded to each other through two out of every three amides and carbonyls, with one hydrogen bond lost for every proline side chain present. This interchain hydrogen bonding imparts strength and rigidity to the triple helix, making collagen proteins perfect components for connective ligaments, where mechanical strength is needed.

When collagen is boiled with water, it is converted into the water-soluble protein *gelatin.* The heat treatment causes the rupture of the hydrogen bonds that hold the triple helix together, as well as the collapse of the backbone polypeptide chains in regions where the proline (and hydroxyproline) concentration is high. Meats become more tender when heated because of the conversion of collagen to gelatin. This change begins to take place at about 60°C (140°F) or when the meat is considered to be "rare." Long, slow cooking in a moist atmosphere helps to degrade the collagen in less tender cuts of meat, cuts which contain larger amounts of connective tissue. Cooling of gelatin and water solutions produces a *gel* and is a technique used to thicken foods.

We have mentioned three classes of proteins in this section, α-keratins (wool and hair), β-keratins (silk), and the collagens. These three subclasses are known collectively as **fibrous proteins** because their polypeptide chains are arranged in a regular, parallel fashion to form long fibers or sheets (Figure 23.13*a*). Fibrous proteins are tough substances, which are generally insoluble in water and which make up the structural components of the body. In fibrous proteins there is a regular "straight" chain of amino acid residues with fixed distances between them. In fact, the polypeptide chains in many fibrous proteins contain segments of amino acids that repeat regularly. For instance, in silk protein the six-amino-acid residue Gly-Ser-Gly-Ala-Gly-Ala repeats over and over for long distances.

Conversion of fibrinogen to fibrin is involved in blood clotting.

Recall that vitamin K is needed for thrombin synthesis (Section 22.9).

Other examples of fibrous proteins include the *elastins* in blood vessel walls and the *myosins* in muscles. **Fibrinogen**, present in blood plasma, is a fibrous protein different from those we have mentioned so far because it is soluble in water. The final step in the coagulation of blood is the conversion of the soluble fibrinogen to fibrin, a protein that is insoluble in water and hence causes the blood to form a clot. The protein enzyme *thrombin* is the catalyst for this process.

$$\underset{\text{Soluble}}{\text{Fibrinogen}} \xrightarrow{\text{thrombin}} \underset{\text{Insoluble}}{\text{fibrin}}$$

When the reaction above takes place, the fibrinogen molecules (containing over 2500 amino acids) first release four smaller polypeptides (about 40 amino acids) called *fibrinopeptides,* as shown in Figure 23.14, leaving a smaller version of the original fibrinogen. The modified fibrinogen molecules, called *fibrin monomers,* are attracted to each other and join together to form *fibrin,* the insoluble protein which causes the blood to gel. Under normal circumstances the process described above happens *only* when the blood vessels are damaged, an event that triggers the production of thrombin, the necessary enzyme. This is the derivation of the terms *thrombus,* a clot of blood formed within the heart or blood vessels, and *thrombosis,* the formation of a clot.

Table 23.6 summarizes the fibrous proteins we have discussed. There is a second broad class of proteins into which the remaining proteins fall, *globular proteins*, the subject of the next section.

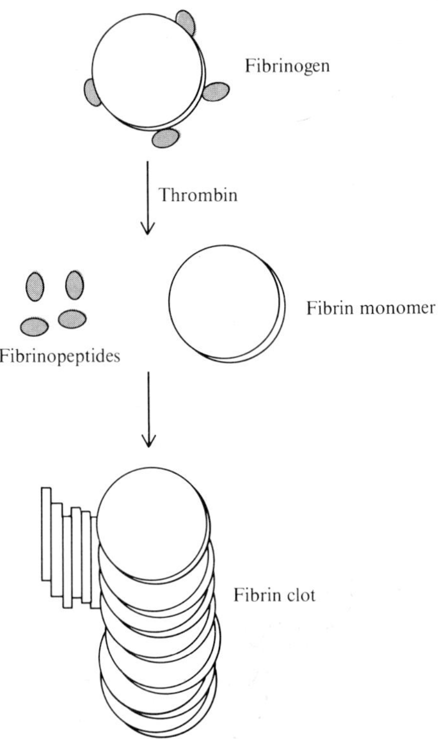

FIGURE 23.14
The fibrin monomers join together side by side and end to end to form the insoluble fibrin clot.

TABLE 23.6 **FIBROUS PROTEINS**

Fibrous protein	Source
α-Keratin	Hair, skin, nails, fur, feathers, horns, scales
β-Keratin	Silk
Collagen	Connective tissues, ligaments, bones, tendons, teeth, skin, cartilage
Elastins	Blood vessel walls
Myosins	Muscles
Fibrinogen	Blood plasma (0.3 g fibrinogen per 100 ml plasma)
Fibrin	Blood clot

23.10 TERTIARY AND QUATERNARY STRUCTURE OF PROTEINS

The **tertiary structure** of a protein arises from the interactions that take place among the side groups of polypeptide chains, interactions which cause bending and folding of the protein molecule. **Globular proteins** are named to describe the spherical shape into which their polypeptide chains are bent and folded as a result of tertiary structure (Figure 23.14*b*). Above we said the fibrous proteins are the structural components of living things. It is the globular proteins that perform

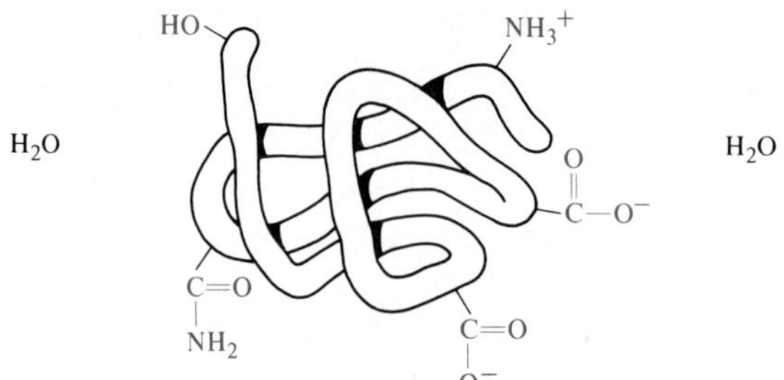

FIGURE 23.15 Polar side cha color extend i medium, maki proteins solub

the operational functions in the body by behaving as enzymes, hormones, antibodies, and transporters.

The terms *hydrophobic* (water-heating) and *hydrophilic* (water-loving) were introduced in Section 22.10.

The overall shape of the globular protein is formed by the clustering of nonpolar *hydrophobic* side groups toward the center of the globular structure and the polar *hydrophilic* side chains toward the aqueous surroundings (see Table 23.4, where the amino acids are classified according to the polarity of their side chains). Hydrogen bonds that form between these polar side chains and water make globular proteins soluble in water or in dilute salt solutions (see Figure 23.15). Below we will examine the different kinds of attractive forces operating between specific side chains that act to stabilize the typical spherical conformation of globular proteins.

Hydrophobic Interactions

We have mentioned hydrophobic interactions among nonpolar groups in our discussion of micelles (Section 17.7) and in connection with the formation of bilayers from lipid molecules (Section 22.9). Hydrophobic interactions are the forces operating among the nonpolar side chains of amino acids. For instance, nonpolar groups such as the methyl side chain of alanine and the isopropyl side chain of valine cluster together to form the interior of the globular protein molecules, a *hydrophobic pocket* from which water is excluded.

$$\mathrm{H{-}C{-}CH(CH_3)_2} \qquad \mathrm{CH_3{-}C{-}H}$$

Hydrophobic interaction

Hemeproteins contain the iron prophyrin heme and a protein.

You can see the hydrophobic pocket in the structures of *myoglobin* (Figure 23.16) and *hemoglobin* (Figure 23.17), two of the most important proteins in vertebrates. **Hemoglobin** is the blood protein responsible for transport of oxygen from the lungs and **myoglobin** is the protein that holds the oxygen in the muscles until it is needed for metabolism. Note that both include a nonprotein structure (shown in color). This part of the molecule is an iron porphyrin (see Section 18.9) called *heme*, and thus both myoglobin and hemoglobin are also known as **hemeproteins.** Hemoglobin contains four heme groups per molecule and myoglobin only one. It is the iron in heme that actually binds the oxygen molecules needed for metabolism.

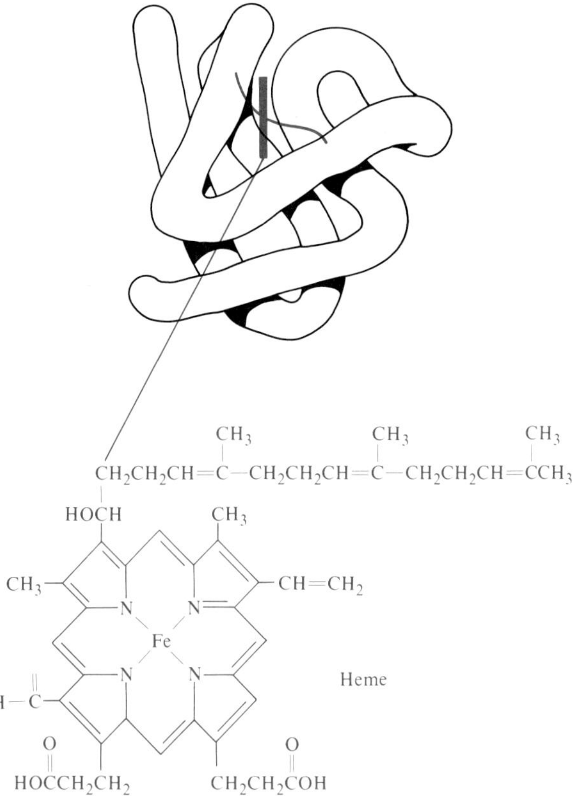

FIGURE 23.16
Myoglobin structure. Myoglobin contains one heme group (in color) and 153 amino acids. Most of the nonpolar side chains are located in the interior of the molecule.

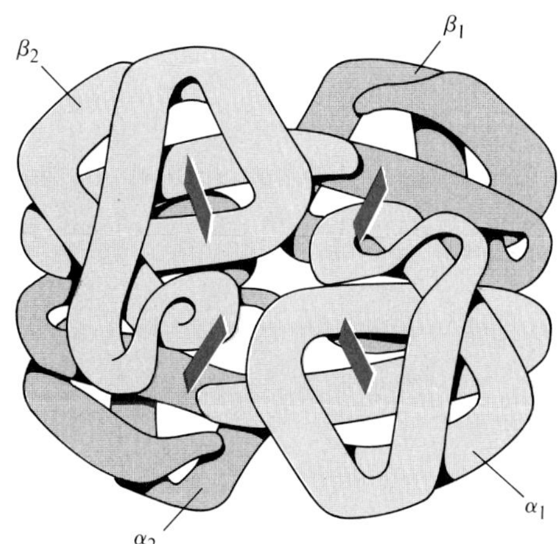

FIGURE 23.17
Structure of hemoglobin. The quaternary structure of hemoglobin includes four polypeptide chains (labeled α_1, α_2, β_1, β_2). The two chains in the front (α_2 and β_1) are in gray and the other two (α_1 and β_2) are in color. Each chain contains one heme group (in color) for a total of four. The entire molecule contains 574 amino acids.

Hydrogen Bonds between Side Chains

Hydrogen bonding between peptide groups, similar to that present in the α helix or β-pleated sheet, helps to stabilize the tertiary structure once it is formed.

Hydrogen bonding is also possible among side chains which include H—O or H—N bonds. For instance, two adjacent serines (R is CH_2OH) form a hydrogen bond between the O of one serine and the H of the other.

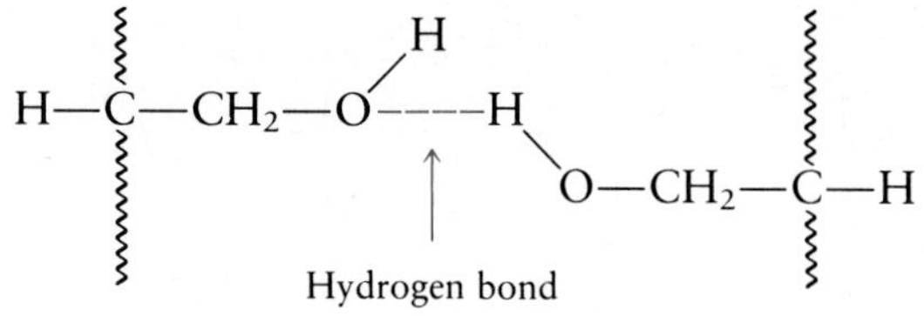

$$H-\overset{|}{\underset{|}{C}}-CH_2-\overset{\displaystyle H}{O}\cdots H\quad O-CH_2-\overset{|}{\underset{|}{C}}-H$$

Hydrogen bond

Ionic Bonding

Acidic side chains are negatively charged and basic side chains are positively charged (at intermediate pH's). Thus an acidic and a basic side chain can be attracted to each other by an electrostatic attractive force (plus to minus) that produces an ionic bond (Section 4.5). For instance, an ionic bond can form between the ionized side chains of glutamic acid (R is CH_2CH_2COOH) and lysine (R is $CH_2CH_2CH_2CH_2NH_2$):

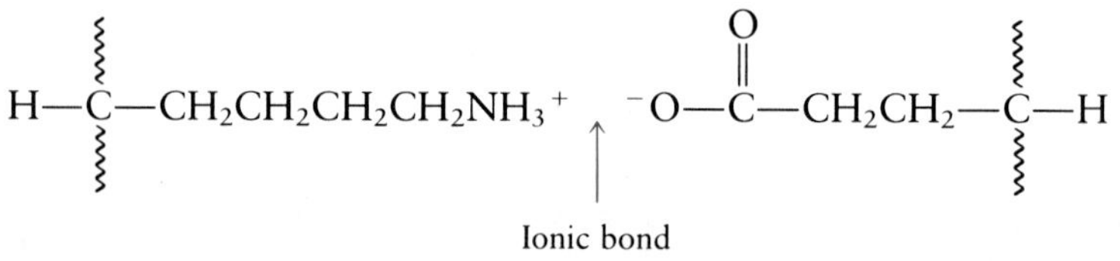

$$H-\overset{|}{\underset{|}{C}}-CH_2CH_2CH_2CH_2NH_3^+ \quad {}^-O-\overset{\displaystyle O}{\overset{\|}{C}}-CH_2CH_2-\overset{|}{\underset{|}{C}}-H$$

Ionic bond

SAMPLE EXERCISE 23.6

What type of interaction leading to tertiary structure is present between the side chains contributed by isoleucine and phenylalanine? (See Table 23.4.)

Solution:

Isoleucine (R is $\underset{\displaystyle CH_3}{\underset{|}{C}}HCH_2CH_3$) and phenylalanine $\left(\text{R is } CH_2-C_6H_5\right)$ have nonpolar hydrocarbon side chains. The interaction between them is hydrophobic.

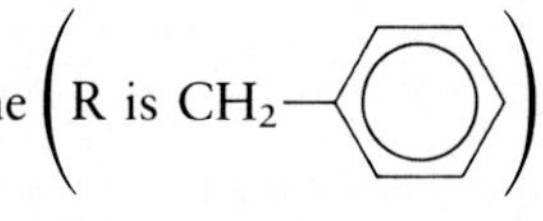

EXERCISE 23.6

How do two threonine side chains interact to contribute to the tertiary structure of a protein?

Some larger globular proteins exist in aggregates of more than one polypeptide chain. The chains are not usually joined by chemical bonds, but all the chains must be present for the protein to function properly. Proteins such as this are said to have a **quaternary structure.** For instance, hemoglobin exhibits a quaternary structure involving four hemoglobin chains, as shown in Figure 23.17. When we speak of a hemoglobin molecule, we mean the collection of these four subunit

TABLE 23.7 LEVELS OF PROTEIN STRUCTURE

Structure	Type of bonding
Primary	Covalent bonding linking amino acid residues
Secondary	Hydrogen bonding between peptide linkages
Tertiary	Bonding between side chains of amino acid residues
Quaternary	Association of more than one polypeptide chain

molecules, so tightly associated that they behave in solution as a single unit. (See Section 17.4, where the effects of association on colligative properties of carboxylic acids are discussed.) The meaning of the various levels of protein structure, namely, primary, secondary, tertiary, and quaternary, is summarized in Table 23.7.

23.11 DENATURING PROTEINS

We have seen that the properties of proteins depend upon their secondary or tertiary as well as their primary structures. **Denaturing** alters the secondary or tertiary structures of proteins, producing a dramatic change in their properties (see Figure 23.18). In general, globular proteins are more easily denatured than fibrous ones. The most visible change is decreased solubility, causing the protein to precipitate or coagulate so that it can no longer function properly. Proteins can be denatured by exposing them to heat (above 60 to 70°C), drastic changes in pH, heavy metals, detergents, certain organic reagents, radiation, or even violent shaking. Let us look at some specific examples.

Cooked egg white is denatured protein. Ovalalbumin is the globular protein in egg white which is transformed from a translucent, liquidy, water-soluble substance to an opaque white solid upon heating. Another way to denature the protein in egg white is by violent mixing to form a frothy solid.

The action of many disinfectants is due to their ability to denature proteins. Proteins in the cell walls of bacteria are denatured upon interaction with certain organic compounds such as the aldehydes, formaldehyde and glutaraldehyde (Section 16.8) and the phenols (Section 15.9). Proteins that behave as enzymes can be deactivated by reaction of their sulfhydryl groups with heavy metals (Ag, Hg, and Cu) or with compounds of heavy metals, as shown below for mercuric chloride, $HgCl_2$.

$$\text{Enzyme}\begin{matrix} \diagup \text{SH} \\ \diagdown \text{SH} \end{matrix} + HgCl_2 \longrightarrow \text{enzyme}\begin{matrix} \diagup \text{S} \diagdown \\ \diagdown \text{S} \diagup \end{matrix}\text{Hg} + 2HCl$$

Active enzyme — Inactive enzyme

Oxidizing agents such as potassium permanganate ($KMnO_4$) and sodium hypochlorite (NaClO) are also able to deactivate enzymes:

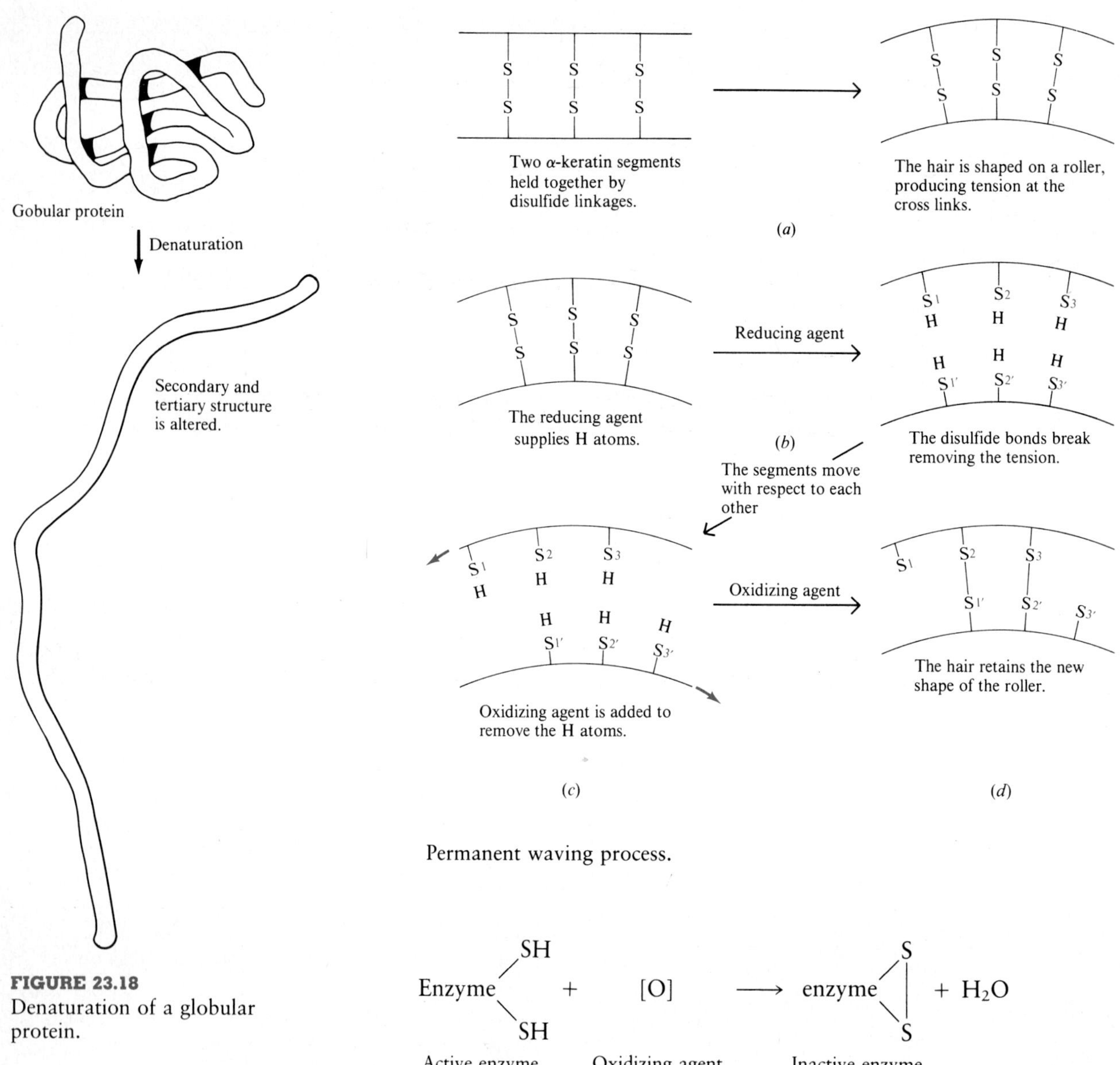
Gobular protein
Denaturation
Secondary and tertiary structure is altered.
Two α-keratin segments held together by disulfide linkages.
The hair is shaped on a roller, producing tension at the cross links.
(a)
Reducing agent
The reducing agent supplies H atoms.
The disulfide bonds break removing the tension.
(b)
The segments move with respect to each other
Oxidizing agent
Oxidizing agent is added to remove the H atoms.
The hair retains the new shape of the roller.
(c)
(d)
Enzyme(SH)(SH) + [O] ⟶ enzyme(S–S) + H_2O
Active enzyme
Oxidizing agent
Inactive enzyme

Permanent waving process.

FIGURE 23.18
Denaturation of a globular protein.

All the disinfectant compounds mentioned above are generally toxic to living matter and thus must be used in dilute solution and on the skin only.

The chemistry of hair revolves about the denaturation of the hair protein α-keratin. We can look at the changes in the properties of hair that occur upon disruption of two kinds of bonds among α-keratin molecules, ionic bonds and disulfide bonds. Ionic bonds form between the lysine (R is $CH_2CH_2CH_2CH_2NH_2$) and glutamic acid (R is CH_2CH_2COOH) residues on neighboring helices of α-keratin. In Section 23.9 we said that *wet* hair could be stretched, because the ionic bonds are weakened when hair is moistened.

The reducing agent is usually thioglycolic acid, $HSCH_2COOH$

In *permanent waving* the disulfide bonds of α-keratin are broken and then reformed. First the hair is shaped by winding around a roller, as shown in Figure 23.19*a*. The disulfide bonds are broken by the addition of a reducing agent that supplies H atoms to the S atoms involved in the disulfide bonds (Figure 23.19*b*).

$$—S—S— + \text{reducing agent} \longrightarrow —SH + HS—$$

Commonly used oxidizing agents are H_2O_2 (hydrogen peroxide) and $KBrO_3$ (potassium bromate).

Then an oxidizing agent (the "neutralizer" solution) is applied to the hair, removing the H atoms and reforming the disulfide bonds (Figure 23.19*c*).

$$—SH + HS + \text{ozidizing agent} \longrightarrow —S—S—$$

The hair retains the shape that it held on the roller (Figure 23.19*d*).

23.12 ESSENTIAL AMINO ACIDS

Your body needs both essential and nonessential amino acids.

In our discussion of lipids you saw that essential fatty acids (EFA) *cannot* be synthesized by the body and thus must be supplied in the diet (Section 22.2). There are also **essential amino acids** (EAA) that *cannot* be manufactured by humans (see Table 23.8). The other amino acids, the "nonessential" ones, are biologically just as important but *can* be synthesized in the body as the need for them arises.

$$BV = \frac{\text{N retained}}{\text{N absorbed}}$$

One source of EAA is ingested protein, but some proteins are much richer in EAA than others. A rating system assigns a **biologic value** (BV) to a given protein to indicate what percentage of nitrogen in that protein is retained by the body for maintenance and growth. In general, the BV value of a protein depends upon its EAA content. For instance, animal proteins tend to have higher amounts of EAA than plant proteins and thus have higher BV values. The most deficient amino acid in a poor-quality protein is known as the *limiting amino acid.*

TABLE 23.8

ESSENTIAL AMINO ACIDS

Phenylalanine	Isoleucine
Methionine	Threonine
Leucine	Tryptophan
Valine	Histidine*
Lysine	Arginine†

*Essential for children
†Probably essential for adults

Table 23.9 lists proteins in order of descending BV values and gives the amount of lysine and methionine (the limiting amino acids in many proteins) in each one. At the top of the BV list is egg protein, which is followed by milk protein. The BV values for the proteins in fish, meat, and poultry are also very high, while those of rice, wheat, corn, and bean proteins are much lower. Although you can see that animal proteins rate higher than those from plants, it is still possible for a vegetarian to be well nourished, especially if the diet includes some animal protein derived from eggs, and/or milk. Vegetarian diets can also consist of *complementary* proteins, that is, two low-quality proteins with different limiting amino acids. For instance, beans (low in methionine, high in lysine) can be eaten with corn (high in methionine and low in lysine) as in beans and corn flour tortillas. It is also possible to add a lysine supplement to diets in which cereal (particularly wheat) is the primary source of protein. Note from Table 23.9 that wheat is very low in lysine compared with egg and milk proteins.

Kwashiorkor is widely prevalent in underdeveloped tropical areas.

Proteins play such a vital role in fuctional and structural body processes that a diet with too little protein or poor-quality protein produces serious consequences. Some symptoms in children suffering from protein deprivation are weight loss, tiredness, decreased resistance to disease, and stunted growth. In underdeveloped countries a disease called ***kwashiorkor***, caused by protein deficiency, is common in young children. The name kwashiorkor is a word coined in Ghana, where the disease was first identified. It means literally "first-second" because of

TABLE 23.9 **BIOLOGIC VALUE (BV) TREND AND LYSINE AND METHIONINE CONTENT OF SELECTED PROTEIN FOODS**

Foods	BV	Lysine, %	Methionine, %
Egg, whole	Highest	6.1	3.2
Milk, whole	↓	6.2	2.8
Fish		9.0	3.2
Beef		8.6	2.7
Soybean		6.8	1.7
Rice, whole		3.2	3.4
Wheat, whole		2.7	2.5
Corn, whole		2.3	3.1
Beans, dried	Lowest	6.5	2.0

the incidence of the disease in the first child upon the birth of the second. This happens because the first infant is initially fed breast milk which has an adequate supply of protein, but upon the birth of the second infant the first is switched to a diet of cereal with very poor quality protein. Kwashiorkor then sets in. Recovery is possible and even common when proteins are introduced into the diet of the stricken child. One way in which the disease is detected is by analyzing the ratio of nonessential to essential amino acids in the urine. In normal persons the ratio should range between 1 to 1 and 2 to 1, but in individuals suffering form kwashiorkor the ratio of nonessential to essential amino acids is much higher, ranging from 2.5 to 1 up to 4 to 1.

SUMMARY

Proteins are polymer molecules in which the monomers are α-amino acids joined together by peptide linkages.

In the proteins of living organisms there are 20 common amino acids, named with three-letter abbreviations when a residue or part of a sequence. Except for glycine (Gly), they are all optically active, with only the L isomers found in natural protein. In solution at pH values of 6 to 7 amino acids exist primarily in the form of doubly charged ions called zwitterions. Amino acids in their zwitterion form are amphoteric, which means they can behave as acids or bases depending upon the pH of the medium. Amino acids with acidic or basic side chains (aspartic acid, glutamic acid, histidine, lysine, and arginine) carry an additional charge. For each amino acid there is a pH, called the pI or isoelectric point, at which the number of positive charges is equal to the number of negative charges.

When two amino acids are joined by a peptide linkage, the product is a dipeptide. Polypeptides include more than two amino acids and are named by giving first the name of the amino acid on the amino end (drawn on the left of the peptide structure) and last the one on the carboxyl end. Proteins are polypeptides containing more than 40 amino acid residues.

Some shorter polypeptides have important biological functions. Certain pentapeptides called encephalins possess pain-killing properties similar to those of morphine. Many hormones are peptides. The nonapeptide oxytocin regulates uterine contractions and lactation. The antidiuretic hormone vasopressin, also a nonapeptide, causes the kidneys to retain water.

Proteins can be broken down into their amino acid components by hydrolysis. In the laboratory all peptide linkages are cleaved by heating the protein with strong acid. In the body protein hydrolysis is catalyzed by enzymes, which break only specific peptide linkages.

The primary structure of a protein refers to its sequence of amino acids.

The secondary structure of a protein is the shape it adopts as a result of hydrogen bonding between peptide linkages. The protein α-keratin (in wool and hair) is α-helical, whereas the protein β-keratin (in silk) has a less common secondary structure, the β-pleated sheet. The collagens are arranged in a triple helix. When heated, collagen breaks down to form gelatin. These proteins, α-keratin, β-keratin, and the collagens, are all fibrous proteins, tough substances that are insoluble in water and make up the structural components of living organisms.

The tertiary structure of a protein refers to the bending and folding of its polypeptide chains as a result of interactions (hydrophobic, hydrogen bonding, and ionic bonding) among side chain groups. Globular proteins such as hemoglobin and myoglobin are formed into spherical shapes as a result of these interactions. Globular proteins are generally soluble in water or in dilute salt solutions and behave as enzymes, hormones, antibodies, and transporters. The quaternary structure of a protein refers to the aggregation of more than one protein molecule.

Denaturing, accomplished by heat, pH changes, chemical interactions, radiation, or even violent shaking, changes the secondary or tertiary structures of proteins. Denatured proteins have altered properties, including decreased water solubility.

Essential amino acids (EAA) cannot be manufactured in the body and so must be provided in the diet. Proteins are assigned a biologic value (BV) that reflects the quantity of EAA that they contain. In general, animal proteins contain more EAA than vegetable proteins.

KEY WORDS

α-amino acid	protein	α helix	globular proteins
amphoteric	encephalin	α-keratin	hemeprotein
zwitterion	endorphin	β-pleated sheet	hemoglobin
electrophoresis	oxytocin	triple helix	myoglobin
isoelectric point (pI)	disulfide linkage	collagen	quaternary structure
peptide linkage	vasopressin	fibrous proteins	denatured protein
dipeptide	primary structure	fibrinogen	essential amino acid
polypeptide	secondary structure	tertiary structure	biologic value

EXERCISES

23.7 Give the formulas and the common names for the α-amino acids in which the side chains are: (**a**) $\underset{\displaystyle CH_3}{\overset{}{\underset{|}{CHOH}}}$; (**b**) $CH_2CH_2SCH_3$.

23.8 Give the formula for 2-amino-3-methylpentanoic acid. Is this one of the 20 common amino acids?

23.9 Of all the amino acids listed in Table 23.1, which one does not exhibit optical activity? Why not?

23.10 Give the Fischer projection formulas for the optical isomers of serine. Which one is a building block for protein?

23.11 The amino acid shown is found in the cell walls of many bacteria. What is its name? Is it a component of proteins? Why?

$$\begin{array}{c} O \\ \| \\ COH \\ | \\ H-\!\!\!-\!\!\!\!\!\!\!\!\!\!\quad NH_2 \\ | \\ CH_2 \\ | \\ CH_2 \\ | \\ C=O \\ | \\ OH \end{array}$$

23.12 Give the formula for β-alanine, a building block of the B vitamin, pantothenic acid.

$$\begin{array}{l} \quad\quad\quad CH_3 \quad O \quad\quad\quad\quad\quad\quad O \\ \quad\quad\quad\; | \quad\;\; \| \quad\quad\quad\quad\quad\quad\; \| \\ HOCH_2{-}C{-}CHCNHCH_2CH_2COH \\ \quad\quad\quad\; | \quad | \\ \quad\quad\quad CH_3 OH \end{array}$$

23.13 Give the structure of β-cyanoalanine, an amino acid which is not a component of protein, but is found in some plants. (The cyano functional group is discussed in Secton 18.8.)

23.14 The formulas below represent some naturally occurring amino acids that are not found in proteins. Which ones are classified as α-amino acids (2-amino acids)? Give IUPAC names for each one.

(a) $NH_2CH_2CH_2CH_2\overset{\displaystyle O}{\overset{\|}{C}}OH$

(b) $HOCH_2CH_2\underset{\displaystyle NH_2}{\underset{|}{C}}H\overset{\displaystyle O}{\overset{\|}{C}}OH$

(c) $NH_2CH_2CH_2CH_2\underset{\displaystyle NH_2}{\underset{|}{C}}H\overset{\displaystyle O}{\overset{\|}{C}}OH$

(d) $HSCH_2CH_2\underset{\displaystyle NH_2}{\underset{|}{C}}H\overset{\displaystyle O}{\overset{\|}{C}}OH$

23.15 Write the reaction in which two lysine molecules combine to form a dipeptide. Name the product.

23.16 How many dipeptides are possible from the reaction of two different amino acids?

23.17 Give the formulas for the dipeptides which form when one serine molecule reacts with one glycine molecule. Name them, using the three-letter abbreviations.

23.18 The tripeptide glutathione, present in all animal tissue, appears to function in maintaining many enzymes in their active conformations. What are the names of the three amino acid components? What is unusual about the way in which the leftmost amino acid is linked to the others?

$$NH_2\underset{\displaystyle COOH}{\underset{|}{C}}HCH_2CH_2\overset{\displaystyle O}{\overset{\|}{C}}NH\underset{\displaystyle CH_2SH}{\underset{|}{C}}H\overset{\displaystyle O}{\overset{\|}{C}}NHCH_2\overset{\displaystyle O}{\overset{\|}{C}}OH \quad \text{Glutathione}$$

23.19 List the six possible tripeptides, using three-letter abbreviations, that could form when one molecule of serine, one molecule of leucine, and one molecule of valine link together.

23.20 Write the reaction for the formation of the tripeptide Gly-Phe-His.

23.21 Give the structures for the three possible charged forms of valine. Which one is the best description of valine in neutral solutions?

23.22 The melting point of glycine is 262°C, compared with that of glycolic acid (hydroxyglycine), which is only 80°C. Compare the formula weights of these two compounds. How do you explain the difference in their melting points?

23.23 In an electrophoresis experiment an amino acid (one of the 20 common ones) fails to migrate at a pH of 5.60. Which one is it? Give its zwitterion structure.

23.24 Which of the 20 common amino acids have more than two stereoisomers?

23.25 Give the products of the hydrolysis of the following polypeptides by 6*M* HCl: (**a**) Ala-Gly-Lys-Asn-Ala-Glu; (**b**) Phe-Arg-Thr-Leu-Trp-Ile-Trp.

23.26 Complete the following hydrolysis reactions, using Table 23.5.

(**a**) Ala-Lys-Gly-Gly-Arg-Trp $\xrightarrow{\text{trypsin}}$

(**b**) Gly-Tyr-Met-Ala-Phe-Lys-Ser-Gln $\xrightarrow{\text{chymotrypsin}}$

23.27 Suppose the reactions in Exercise 23.26 were carried out in the presence of 6*M* HCl. How would the products differ?

23.28 Mixing gelatin with raw papaya causes the gelatin to lose its characteristic gelling properties. Can you give a reason for this?

23.29 Give the names of the tripeptides that can form from one molecule each of isoleucine, glutamic acid, and phenylalanine. If the amino end of the tripeptide is identified as phenylalanine, which tripeptide structures are still possible?

23.30 The compound below is one encephalin discovered in the brain. How does it differ from Try-Gly-Gly-Phe-Met, the typical encephalin shown in Figure 23.4?

$$NH_2{-}\underset{\displaystyle \underset{\displaystyle C_6H_4OH}{|}}{\underset{\displaystyle CH_2}{\underset{|}{C}}}H{-}\overset{\displaystyle O}{\overset{\|}{C}}{-}NH{-}CH_2{-}\overset{\displaystyle O}{\overset{\|}{C}}{-}NH{-}CH_2{-}\overset{\displaystyle O}{\overset{\|}{C}}{-}NH{-}\underset{\displaystyle \underset{\displaystyle C_6H_5}{|}}{\underset{\displaystyle CH_2}{\underset{|}{C}}}H{-}\overset{\displaystyle O}{\overset{\|}{C}}{-}NH{-}\underset{\displaystyle CH_2{-}CH(CH_3){-}CH_3}{\underset{|}{C}}H{-}\overset{\displaystyle O}{\overset{\|}{C}}{-}OH$$

23.31 Give the formula for the dipeptide Gly-Pro. What is unusual about the peptide linkage in this compound. How does it differ from the peptide bond in Pro-Gly?
23.32 Why do proteins containing very large amounts of proline fail to form stable α helices?
23.33 Why are globular proteins more soluble in water than fibrous proteins?
23.34 Are trypsin, chymotrypsin, and pepsin classified as fibrous or globular proteins? Explain your answer.
23.35 A burning substance smells strongly of sulfur. Is it most likely to be silk or hair? Why?
23.36 The structure of which type of polymer (Chapter 19) most closely resembles that of a protein? How do they differ?
23.37 Explain what is meant by the primary, secondary, tertiary, and quaternary structures of a protein.
23.38 What type of interaction leading to tertiary structure is present between the side chains contributed by: (a) Thr and Ser; (b) Asp and Lys; (c) Val and Ile?
23.39 Why is it possible to stretch wet hair but not dry hair?
23.40 What is a hemeprotein? Given an example of one.
23.41 What is the secondary structure of collagen proteins? What function do they serve in the body?
23.42 Gelatin is said to be a derived protein because it does not occur naturally. From what protein is it derived?
23.43 Why is braising, that is, moist, slow cooking, recommended for tough cuts of beef?
23.44 What is meant by the term *essential amino acid?* Are nonessential amino acids of less biological importance than essential amino acids?
23.45 The percentages of essential amino acids in whole egg and in wheat gluten are listed below. Which set of percentages belongs to which protein? Which essential amino acid is particularly lacking in the wheat gluten compared with whole egg protein?

	Arg	**His**	**Thr**	**Val**	**Leu**	**Ile**	**Lys**	**Met**	**Phe**	**Trp**
Protein 1	3.7	2.0	2.8	4.3	7.7	4.6	2.0	1.7	5.0	0.5
Protein 2	6.2	2.1	4.9	7.0	9.0	6.2	6.1	3.2	5.6	1.1

23.46 What is the cause of kwashiorkor? What is the basis of the urine test used to diagnose this disease?
23.47 In what way is the protein fibrinogen different from most other fibrous proteins? How is fibrinogen involved in the formation of blood clots?
23.48 What is meant by the term *limiting amino acid?*
23.49 Would a vegetarian diet in which the primary sources of protein are rice and corn be adequate? Explain.

24 NUCLEIC ACIDS

24.1 INTRODUCTION

In the introduction to the first chapter of this test we said that chemists try to explain the visible macroscopic properties of matter by studying its invisible microscopic particles. One conspicuous property of living things is that offspring tend to resemble both their parents. In this chapter we will find out about a brilliant theory of heredity so detailed that the cause of some genetic diseases can be traced back to one functional group in one molecule. The theory began with Gregor Mendel's (1822–1884) breeding experiments, in which he was able to predict characteristics of plant offspring by postulating that traits were inherited in discrete units called **genes.** According to Mendel (who knew nothing of cell structure or molecules), each parent passes on one gene for each trait to its offspring, who thus inherits a *pair* of genes. One of the genes will determine which trait actually appears in the offspring.

The effort to find the molecular basis of heredity took a great leap forward around 1900, when it was found that genes were carried on **chromosomes,** bodies found in the *nuclei* of cells. The rod-shaped chromosomes are most easily observed in cells that are about to divide, as shown in Figure 24.1. Note from the figure that chromosomes, like the genes postulated by Mendel, occur in *pairs*. Each cell of a particular organism contains the same number of chromosomes, except for the reproductive cells, which have only half as many. For instance, in all human cells there are 46 chromosomes (23 pairs), except for egg and sperm cells, which

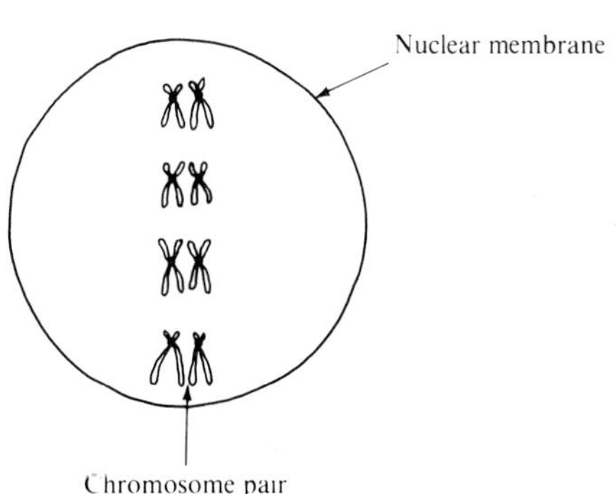

FIGURE 24.1
Chromosomes. In chromosome analysis, cells are allowed to grow. The growth is stopped before the cell divides at the point shown (called metaphase) when the chromosomes are most easily observed.

have only 23. The new individual produced when egg and sperm unite inherits a total of 46 chromosomes, 23 from one parent and 23 from the other. A typical set of human chromosomes is shown in Figure 24.2. We will see that the chromosomes of a cell behave as its "brain," containing all the information that the cell needs to function.

The modern theory of heredity is based upon the chemical makeup of the chromosome. In the last chapter you saw that the nature of an organism is in large part determined by its protein molecules. At one time it was thought that the information needed to pass on traits from cell to cell and from parent to offspring also resided in certain protein molecules. Scientists knew that proteins were sufficiently complex for this role because of the enormous number of possible combinations of the 20 amino acids used to construct them. However, this theory turned out to be wrong. The genetic information is now known to reside not in protein molecules but in another set of complex molecules called the *nucleic acids,* the chemical compounds found in chromosomes. They are called *nucleic* because they were first discovered in the nuclei of cells. A gene is a segment of a nucleic acid molecule.

We will study the structure and functions of the nucleic acids called *deoxyribonucleic acid* (*DNA*) and *ribonucleic acid* (*RNA*). DNA contains information in its chemical structure that is passed on to RNA to direct the synthesis of proteins. Since proteins determine the nature of an organism, DNA behaves as a hereditary "blueprint." DNA molecules can also make identical copies of

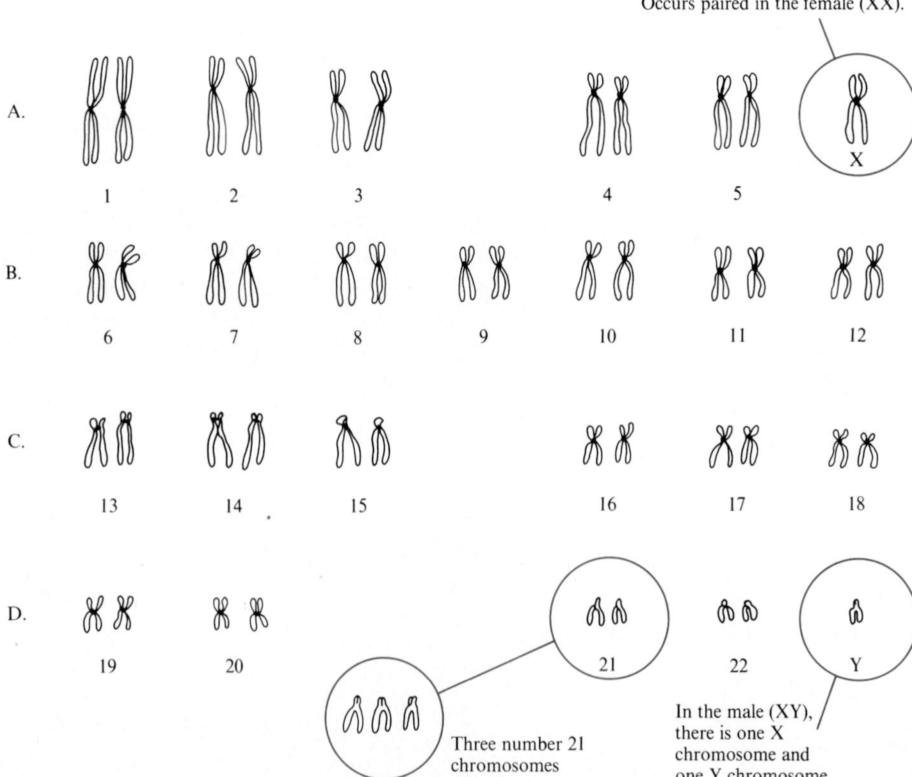

FIGURE 24.2
A normal set of human chromosomes. Three number 21 chromosomes (instead of two) cause ***Down's syndrome,*** a congenital defect characterized by some degree of mental retardation and cardiovascular and facial abnormalities.

themselves, thus producing a new cell that is identical to the original cell upon cell division. In this chapter we will see how these functions served by the nucleic acids depend upon the details of their chemical structures.

24.2 NUCLEOSIDES

A nucleic acid breaks down to produce nitrogen bases, sugars, and phosphoric acid.

Nucleic acids are polymers of monomer units called *nucleotides*. Each **nucleotide** is composed of three components, namely, phosphoric acid, a sugar, and a derivative of purine or pyrimidine (Section 18.9) called a **nitrogen base.** Two of the components, the sugar and the nitrogen base, combine to form a **nucleoside.** How nucleic acids break down into each of the above components is summarized in the diagram shown in Figure 24.3. The nucleic acids in living things contain nucleosides with two different sugars and five different nitrogen bases.

Sugars

The sugar present in RNA, or **ribonucleic acid,** is *ribose,* or to be more specific, β-D-ribose. As you will recall from Chapter 21, the β indicates the orientation of the hydroxyl groups on the C-1 atom (the anomeric carbon). In β isomers the OH group on C-1 points up, as shown in the Haworth formula below.

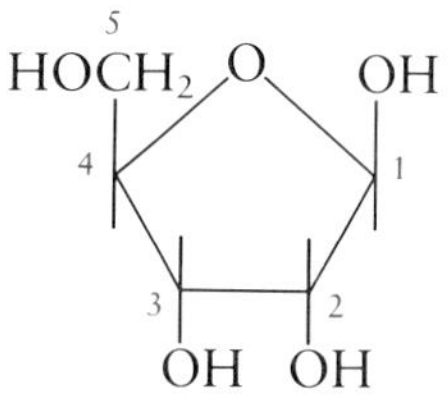

β-D-Ribose

The sugar present in DNA, or **deoxyribonucleic acid,** is β-D-*2-deoxyribose,* a

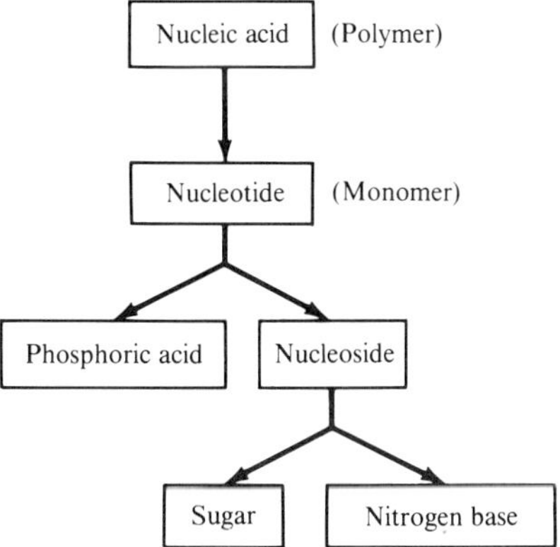

FIGURE 24.3
Components of nucleic acids.

close relative of β-D-ribose. The only difference in their structures is that the hydroxyl group on the C-2 atom of ribose is replaced with a hydrogen atom (in color below) in 2-deoxyribose.

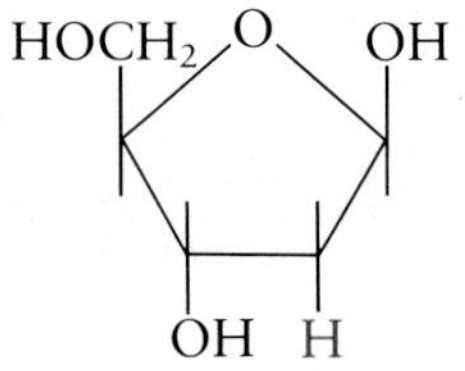

HOCH$_2$ O OH

OH H

β-D-2-Deoxyribose

Nitrogen Bases

There are two derivatives of the heterocyclic compound purine, *adenine* (A) and *guanine* (G), which appear in both DNA and in RNA.

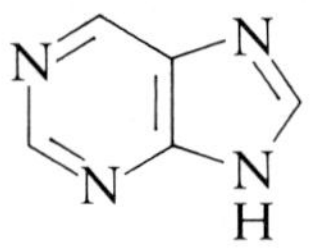

Purine

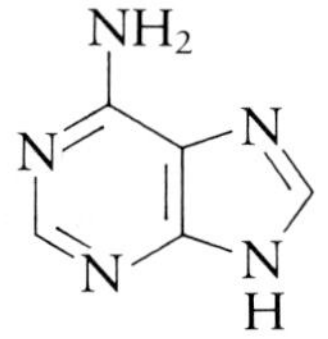

Adenine (A)
(in both DNA and RNA)

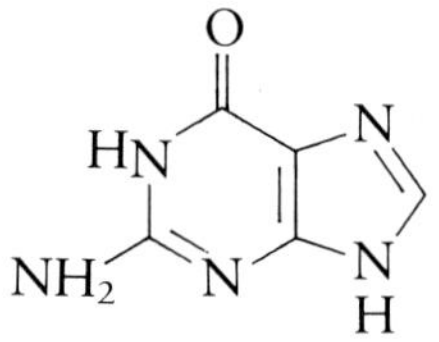

Guanine (G)
(in both DNA and RNA)

The other three N bases are derivatives of pyrimidine. One of them, *cytosine* (C), appears both in RNA and DNA. Of the other two, *thymine* (T) is in DNA only and *uracil* (U) is in RNA only.

The nitrogen bases A, G, C, T appear in DNA. The nitrogen bases A, G, C, U appear in RNA.

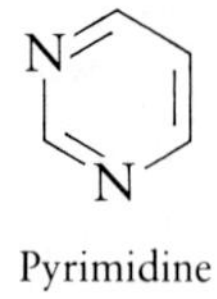

Pyrimidine

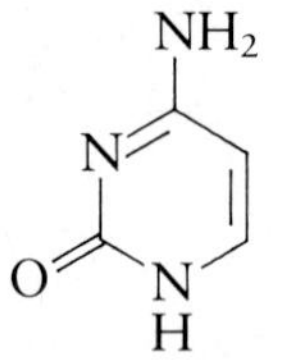

Cytosine (C)
(in both DNA and RNA)

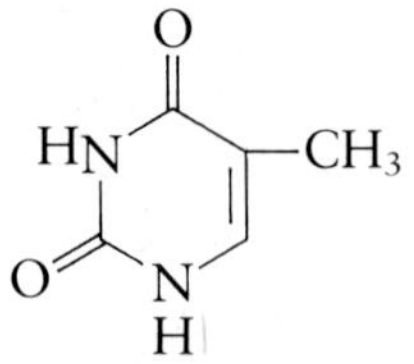

Thymine (T)
(in DNA only)

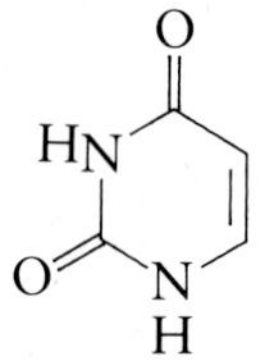

Uracil (U)
(in RNA only)

Nucleoside Structure

A **nucleoside** consists of a sugar bonded to a nitrogen base. These two components are joined by a bond between the C-1 atom of the sugar and a ring N atom of the base. For instance, the nucleoside shown below is composed of ribose and adenine.

The numbers of the sugar C atoms are primed (′) to distinguish them from ring positions of the nitrogen base.

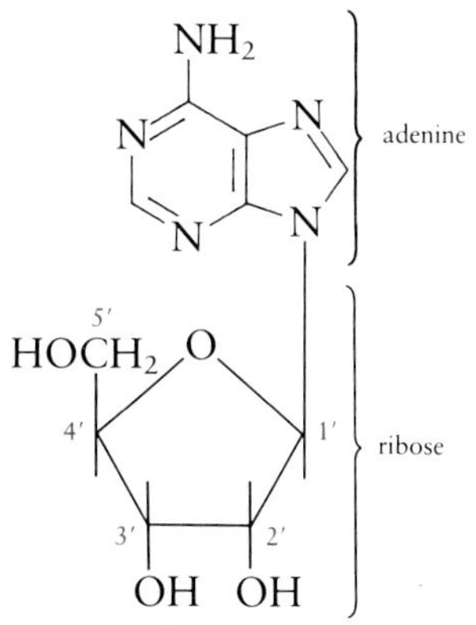

NH_2 (adenine) ... $HOCH_2$ (5′), O, 4′, 1′, 3′, 2′, OH OH (ribose)

Adenosine

Nucleosides made from ribose, **ribonucleosides,** are named by modifying the name of the nitrogen base, as shown in Table 24.1. You can see that ribonucleoside names derived from the purine derivatives adenine and guanine, have names that end in *-osine,* whereas the names of those derived from the pyrimidine bases cytosine, thymine, and uracil end in *-idine.* The corresponding **deoxyribonucleosides,** which contain deoxyribose and a nitrogen base, are named by adding the

TABLE 24.1 **COMMON NUCLEOSIDES AND THEIR COMPONENTS**

Nucleoside name	Nitrogen
Ribonucleosides*	
Adenosine	Adenine
Guanosine	Guanine
Cytidine	Cytosine
Uridine	Uracil
Deoxyribonucleosides*	
Deoxyadenosine	Adenine
Deoxyguanosine	Guanine
Deoxycytidine	Cytosine
Deoxythymidine	Thymine

*The sugar component is ribose in all ribonucleosides and deoxyribose in all deoxyribonucleosides.

prefix *-deoxy* to the ribonucleoside (see Table 24.1). The formula below stands for the deoxynucleoside deoxycytidine.

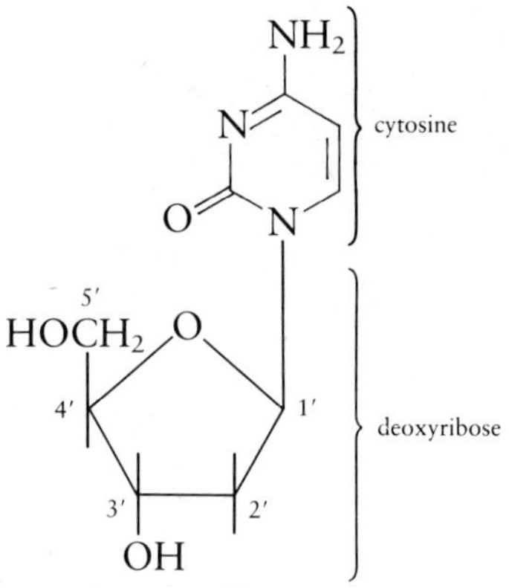

Deoxycytidine

SAMPLE EXERCISE 24.1

Name the nucleoside shown below.

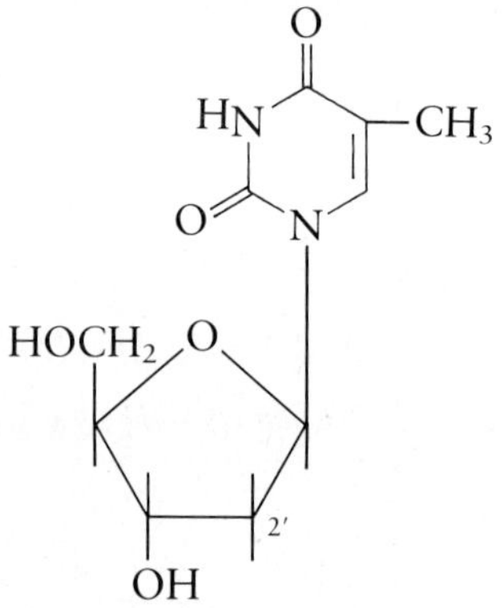

Solution:

Note that the components of the molecule above are deoxyribose (no OH on the C-2 atom) and the nitrogen base thymine.

Thus this deoxyribonucleoside is named deoxythymidine.

EXERCISE 24.1

What are the two components of the compound guanosine?

24.3 NUCLEOTIDES

The **nucleotide** components of nucleic acids are phosphates of nucleosides (see Figure 24.3). The phosphate group is linked to the nucleoside through the hydroxyl group on C-5 of the sugar molecule. For instance, the deoxynucleotide shown below forms when a phosphate group bonds to the hydroxyl group on C-5 of deoxyribose in deoxyadenosine.

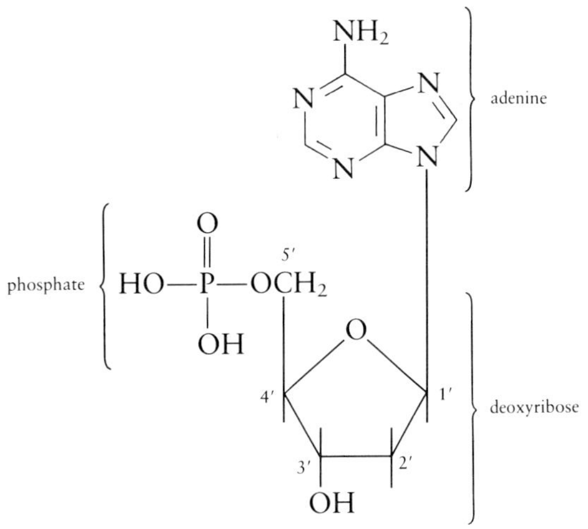

phosphate { HO—P(=O)(OH)—OCH_2 (5′) } — deoxyribose (1′, 2′, 3′, 4′; 3′-OH) — adenine (NH_2)

Deoxyadenosine-5′-phosphate (5′-dAMP or dAMP)

The nucleotides are named by giving the name of the nucleoside and the number of the sugar C atom to which the phosphate is attached, followed by the word *phosphate*. Thus the nucleotide above is called deoxyadenosine-5′-phosphate. Since names such as this are awkward to write and say, they are abbreviated. First the number of the sugar C atom that bears the phosphate group is given. Names of nucleotides formed by *d*eoxyribose begin with a lowercase d. Next the name of the nucleoside (here, adenosine) is indicated with the appropriate capital letter (A). This is followed by MP (for monophosphate). Thus the nucleotide above, deoxyadenosine-5′-phosphate, is called 5′-dAMP. There is another special rule about naming nucleotides: The number 5′ is understood when no number is given as part of the abbreviated name; thus 5′-dAMP becomes simply dAMP. The reason for this is that most of the nucleotides in living things are 5′-nucleotides. In the next section we will see how nucleotides join together to make giant polynucleotides, the nucleic acids.

SAMPLE EXERCISE 24.2

Give the abbreviated name for the nucleotide shown below.

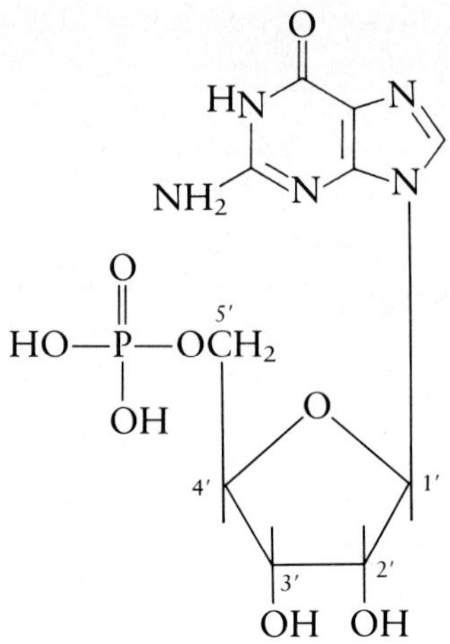

Solution:

The linkage between sugar and phosphate involves C-5′ of the sugar. The sugar is ribose (C-2′ is bonded to OH). The nitrogen base is guanine (G). Thus the name is 5′-GMP, or simply GMP.

EXERCISE 24.2

In the structure of UMP specify the: (**a**) Sugar; (**b**) nitrogen base; (**c**) C atom to which the phosphate is attached; (**d**) nucleic acid (DNA or RNA) in which it is found.

24.4 STRUCTURE OF DNA

DNA molecules are polynucleotides with formula weights of several billion. These enormous molecules break down to produce four different monomer nucleotides, dAMP, dGMP, dCMP, and dTMP (see Figure 24.4). To see how this

FIGURE 24.4
Nucleotide components of DNA.

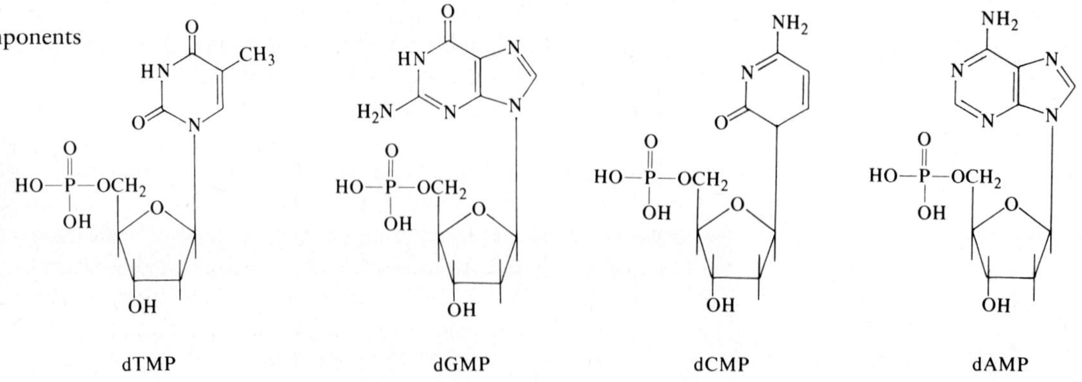

dTMP dGMP dCMP dAMP

happens, let us first join two of these to form a dinucleotide. The connection between them involves the phosphate group of one nucleotide and the C-3′ hydroxyl group on the other. The linkage that forms is called a *3′,5′ linkage* and is the only type found in DNA. For instance, the nucleotides dAMP and dGMP can be combined by splitting out a molecule of water to form the dinucleotide shown below. In the formulas given the nitrogen bases are indicated by letters (in color) only.

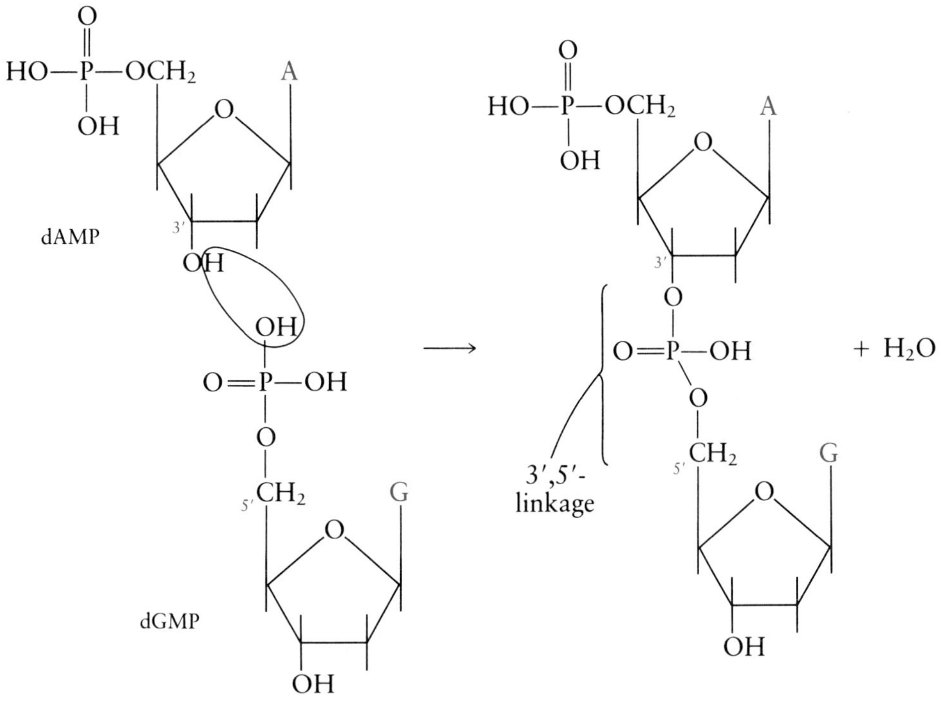

dAMP

dGMP

$\longrightarrow$

3′,5′-linkage

$+ H_2O$

Dinucleotide

All DNA molecules have the same sugar-phosphate backbone.

DNA molecules are formed from millions of deoxynucleotides joined through 3′,5′ linkages. We can view a DNA molecule as a backbone of sugar-to-phosphate-to-sugar-to-phosphate linkages. Protruding from the backbone are the nitrogen bases (A, G, C, or T) that are attached to the sugars. As we will see,

It is the order in which the N bases appear on a DNA molecule that supplies the hereditary information.

Figure 24.5*a* shows a segment of a DNA molecule, including the constituent atoms of all its components. Figure 24.5*b* and *c* shows shorthand versions of the same segment of DNA. We will use, most frequently, the skeleton version shown in Figure 24.5*c*.

We have just described the *primary* structure of DNA. In the next section we will find that DNA molecules also possess secondary structure (see Section 23.9). The discovery in 1953 of this secondary structure, the *double helix* of DNA, revolutionized the field of biochemistry.

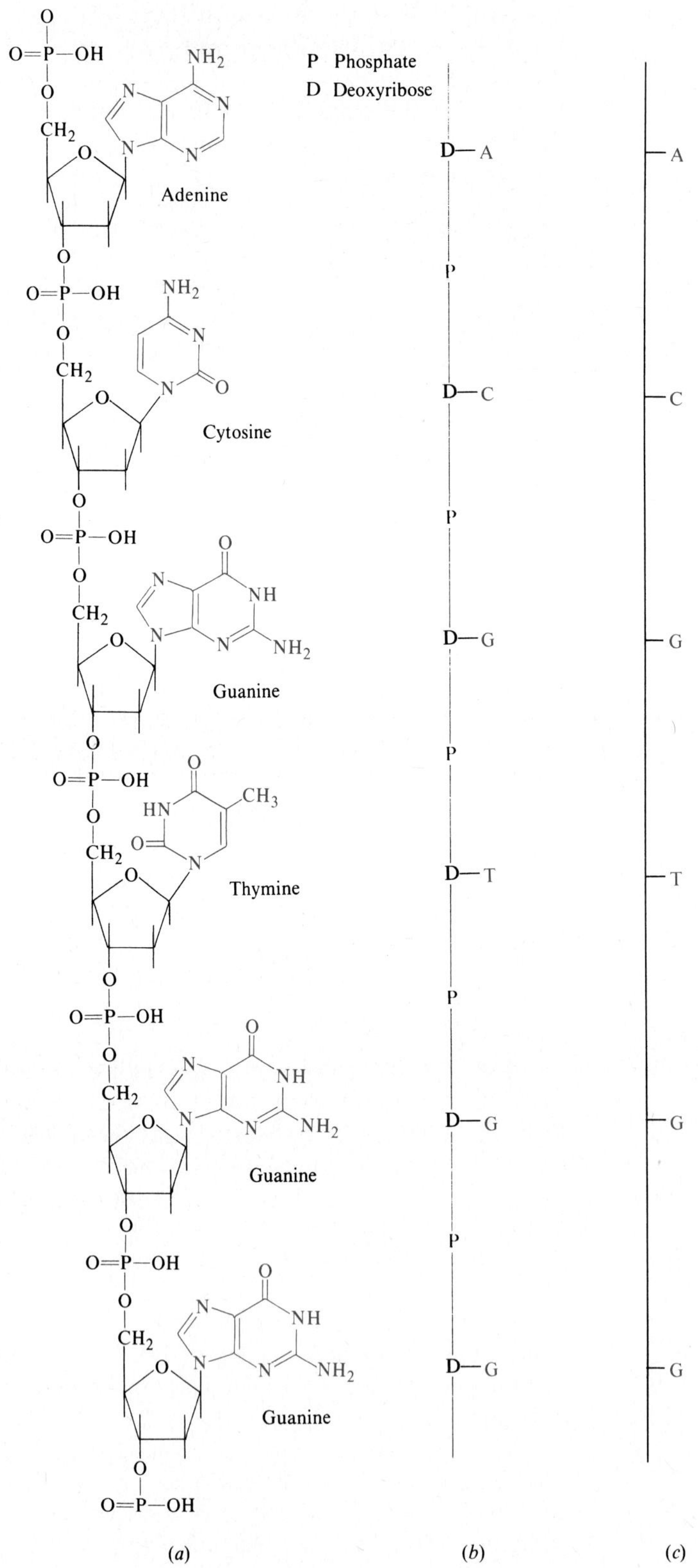

P Phosphate
D Deoxyribose

Adenine

Cytosine

Guanine

Thymine

Guanine

Guanine

D—A
P
D—C
P
D—G
P
D—T
P
D—G
P
D—G

A
C
G
T
G
G

(a) (b) (c)

FIGURE 24.5
Views of the DNA structure.

SAMPLE EXERCISE 24.3

Give a shorthand description of a DNA segment in which the sequence of nitrogen bases is TGC.

Solution:

To form a trinucleotide, we need three sugar (D) units linked by phosphates (P).

—P—D—P—D—P—D—

To the sugars are joined the N bases T, G, and C.

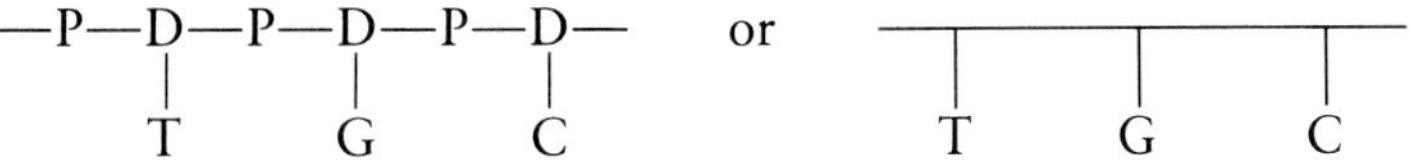

EXERCISE 24.3

What abbreviated formula corresponds to a DNA segment in which the N base sequence is adenine, guanine, guanine, thymine, cytosine, and thymine?

24.5 DNA DOUBLE HELIX

The distances were found by studying the interaction of x-rays with proteins and with DNA.

In Section 23.9 we said that the secondary structure of proteins was determined by analysis of distances between atoms in the protein molecules. To deduce the shape of DNA molecules scientists made use of the distance between its component nucleotides, along with another crucial piece of evidence. Analysis of DNA samples revealed that the ratio of adenine to thymine units in DNA was always close to 1 : 1, as was the ratio of cytosine to guanine. However, there was no constant ratio for any of the other possible pairs of bases, adenine to cytosine, guanine to thymine, etc.

The fact that there is one adenine for every thymine and one cytosine for every guanine can be explained if every A is somehow bonded to a T and every C to a G. Examining the structures of the N bases tells us what kinds of bonds are involved. Looking closely at the cytosine and guanine structures, you see that three hydrogen bonds (Section 4.16) can form between them, as shown below:

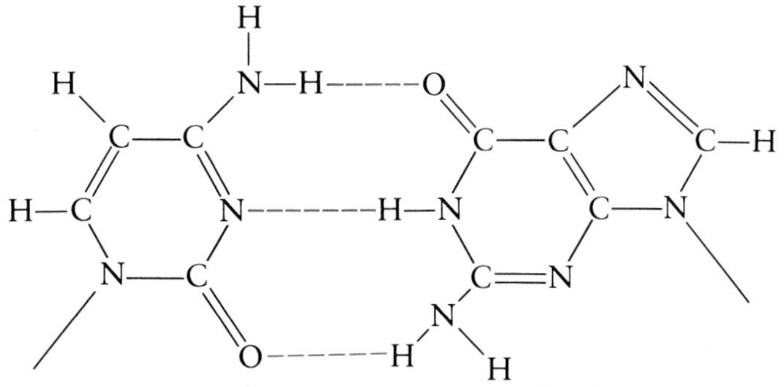

Cytosine Guanine

Likewise, thymine and adenine are attracted to each other by two hydrogen bonds:

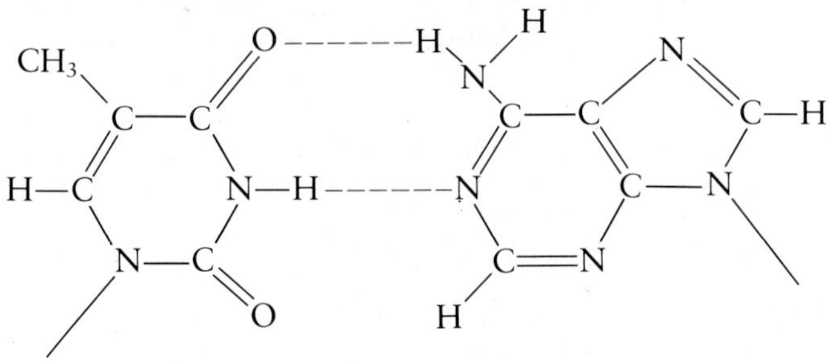

Thymine Adenine

There is no hydrogen bond between the other thymine carbonyl and the H atom adjacent to it because that H atom is bonded to a C atom. Recall that the H atoms involved in H bonding must be bonded to the highly electronegative atoms O, N, or F (not C).

The hydrogen-bonded nitrogen bases, adenine-thymine and guanine-cytosine, are called **base pairs.** It was discovered that

DNA molecules exist as double strands attracted to each other by the hydrogen-bonded base pairs A to T and G to C.

A always forms base pairs with T and C with G.

The strands are said to be **complementary** to each other. Suppose one strand of a DNA molecule has the base sequence ACGTGG. The complementary strand must have a T where there is an A on the original strand, a G where there is a C, and so on.

Original strand: ACGTGG
Complementary strand: TGCACC

This short segment of a DNA molecule is shown in detail in Figure 24.6, where you can see the base pairs. You can also see that the original and complementary strands run in opposite directions. The one on the left (the original strand) is drawn with the C-5′ of each deoxyribose unit pointing upward. On the complementary strand the C-5′ of every deoxyribose unit points downward.

Rosalind Franklin, Maurice Wilkens, and their coworkers supplied the x-ray data.

Crick, Watson, and Wilkens shared the Nobel prize for medicine and physiology in 1962.

For the DNA structure to agree with the interatomic distances obtained from the x-ray data, the base-paired strands had to be twisted to form a **double helix** (see Figure 24.7). The discovery of the double helical structure of DNA at Cambridge University in 1953 earned a Nobel prize for its codiscoverers, Francis Crick and James Watson. What Crick and Watson had feared most was that the DNA structure would turn out to be boring and give no insight into the molecular basis of heredity. On the contrary, the double helical base-paired DNA structure led directly to a theory for the process of gene duplication, as we shall see in the next few sections.

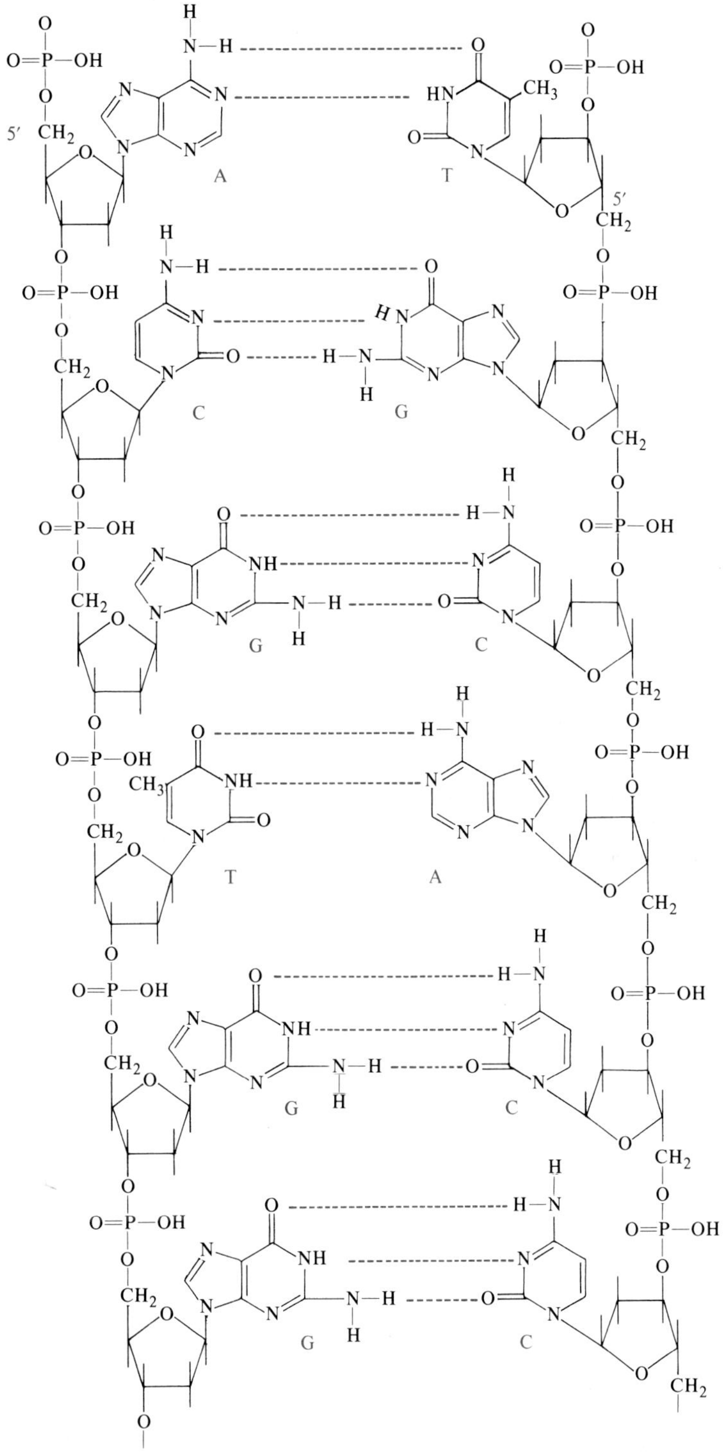

FIGURE 24.6
Base pairs in DNA segment.

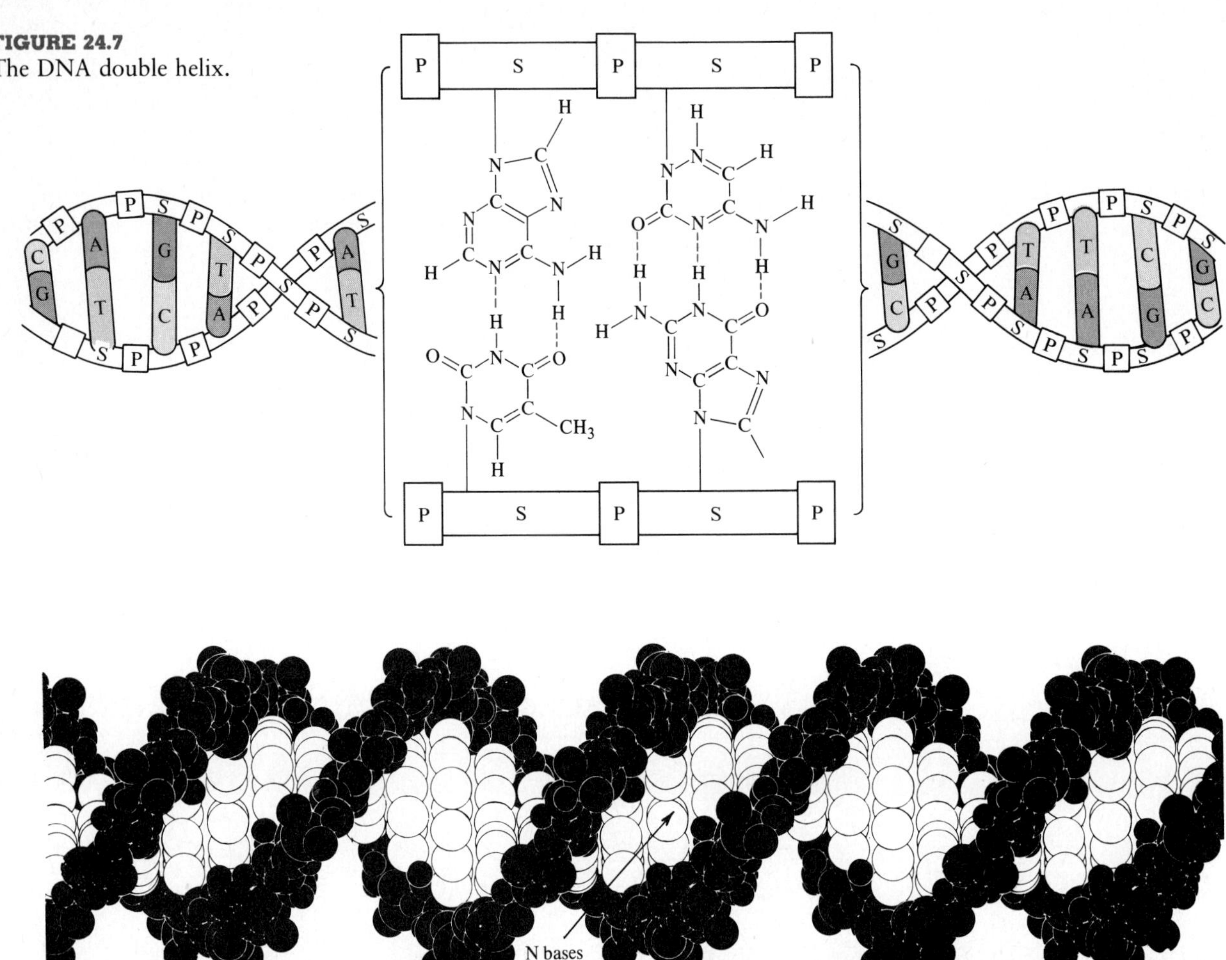

FIGURE 24.7
The DNA double helix.

SAMPLE EXERCISE 24.4

Give the shorthand formula for the segment of a DNA double helix in which the base sequence of one strand is ACT. Include the H bonds in your sketch.

Solution:

First write the given strand, using three sugar units (D) attached to the bases A, C, and T.

```
—D—P—D—P—D—     Original strand
 |     |     |
 A     C     T
```

To show the doubled strands it is most convenient to use a solid line for the sugar phosphate backbone.

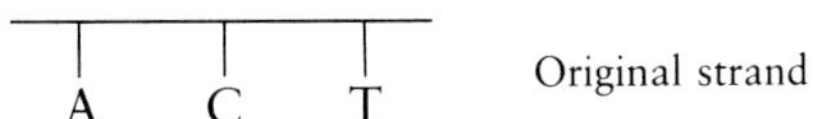

Next add the complementary strand, pairing A and T, and C and G. Place two H bonds between A and T and three between C and G.

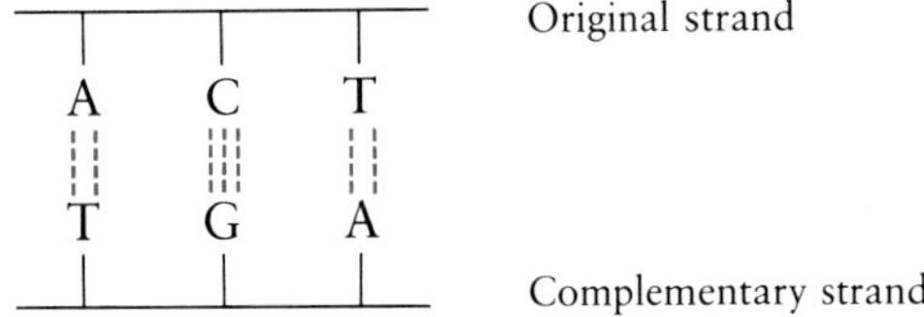

EXERCISE 24.4

Given that the base sequence of a strand of DNA is CAGGGT, what is the base sequence of its complementary strand?

24.6 CHROMOSOMES, GENES, AND DNA

Before we begin our discussion of the functions of DNA, let us first look at the modern description of genes and chromosomes.

Chromosomes

DNA molecules are enormous, with formula weights in the billions.

Each **chromosome** found in the nucleus of a cell is thought to contain one very large DNA molecule; the total length of the DNA molecules in a cell far exceeds the cell dimensions. If stretched out, the DNA molecules packed into the nucleus of a human cell would cover a distance of about 2 *meters*. The number of chromosomes in a nucleus depends on the species in which it is found. Note from Table 24.2 that the fruit fly has just 8 chromosomes (4 pairs) compared with 78 (39 pairs) for the chicken. Some DNA molecules are larger than others. From studies of bacterial DNA molecules it has been found that each millimeter of DNA molecule corresponds to a formula weight of about 2×10^9. From this we can find the approximate formula weight of other DNA molecules which have a known length. For instance, the DNA in the largest fruit fly chromosome is known to be 4 cm (40 mm) in length.

TABLE 24.2

CHROMOSOME NUMBERS IN VARIOUS SPECIES

Species	Number of chromosomes
Chicken	78
Human	46
Rabbit	44
Rat	42
Mouse	40
Frog	26
Corn	20
Peas	14
Fruit fly	8

$$\frac{2 \times 10^9}{\cancel{\text{mm}}} \times 40\,\cancel{\text{mm}} = 80 \times 10^9$$

Thus, a fruit fly DNA molecule has a formula weight of about 80 billion.

Genes

On a single chromosome there may be hundreds or thousands of genes. As mentioned in the introduction, a gene was originally defined as a unit of inheritance that controls the appearance of some trait, such as curliness of hair or color of eyes. A better definition for a **gene** is a segment of DNA that contains the information for the synthesis of a particular protein. In one way or another this accounts for every trait of a living organism. Many structural components of living things are made up of protein and are thus directly controlled by genes. As you saw in Section 23.9, hair *is* protein. One or more genes responsible for the synthesis of hair protein determines whether the hair is curly or straight by directing the detailed structure of hair keratin. Other parts of an organism are not protein but are synthesized in reactions which require proteins as enzyme catalysts. For instance, the pigment that produces eye color is not itself a protein, but the enzyme that catalyzes the biochemical reaction for producing a particular color of eye pigment *is* a protein. The gene directs the synthesis of this enzyme and thus determines eye color.

Directing the synthesis of proteins is one of the *two* functions served by DNA molecules. A DNA molecule also has the ability to make an exact copy of itself.

24.7 DNA AND GENE COPYING (REPLICATION)

From what we have found so far about the structure of DNA, it is possible to explain why daughter cells are identical to original parent cells. First let us see what happens to the chromosomes in a cell when the cell divides, a process known as *mitosis*. Suppose we consider a cell containing four chromosomes (two pairs) in its nucleus, as shown in Figure 24.8*a*. Just before cell division each of the four original chromosomes duplicates itself to make a total of eight (Figure 24.8*b*). As the cell begins its division by elongating itself, the pairs of chromosomes separate, one set staying in the original cell and one set moving into the new daughter cell (Figure 24.8*c*). Thus both cells have an identical set of chromosomes. From the double helical structure of DNA Watson and Crick were able to suggest a molecular explanation for the ability of chromosomes to double themselves.

The codiscoverers of the double helix first proposed the idea that the double-stranded DNA in each original chromosome *unwinds* before the cell divides. This leaves unpaired nitrogen bases on two single strands of DNA. An unpaired base is left free to attract its complementary base, a base which comes from one of

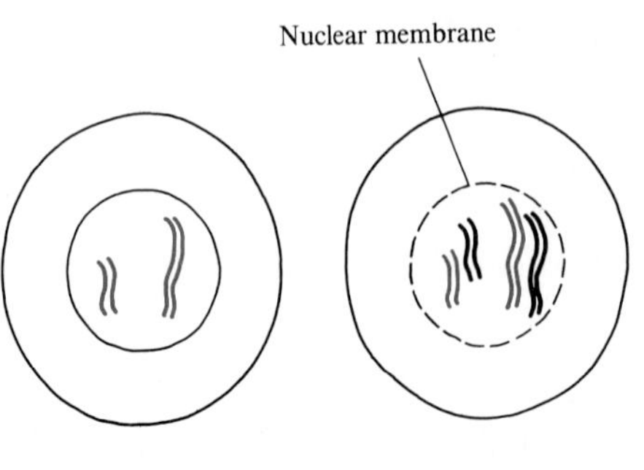

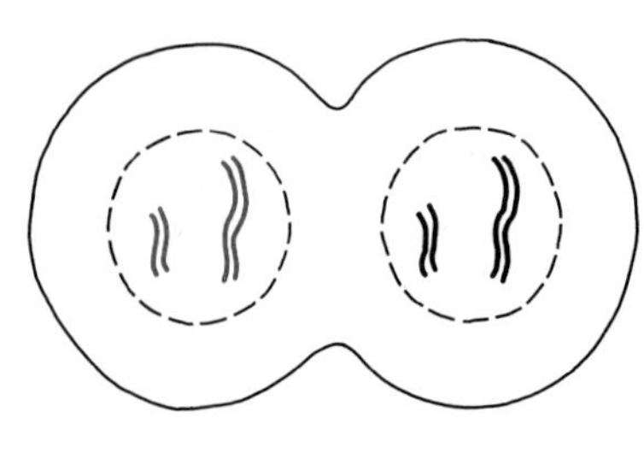

FIGURE 24.8
Mitosis (the initial and final steps). (*a*) Cell with four chromosomes. (*b*) Prior to cell division, the four chromosomes double to become eight chromosomes and the nuclear membrane breaks. (*c*) The cell divides so that each cell has an identical set of chromosomes.

Replicated DNA forms from the combination of nucleotide triphosphates.

four different nucleotide ingredients present in the cell, namely, dATP, dCTP, dTTP, and dGTP. As you can see in Figure 24.9*a*, dATP, dCTP, dTTP, and dGTP refer to deoxynucleoside *tri*phosphates formed by the addition of two more phosphate groups to the monophosphates dAMP, dCMP, dTMP, and dGMP. Each unpaired A bonds to a T (of dTTP), each C to a G (of dGTP), and vice versa in a predictable, accurate fashion. As each nucleotide is attached to the end of the new growing DNA strand, a diphosphate (PP) is released (Figure 24.9*b*). An enzyme called *DNA polymerase* is also needed to link the nucleotides.

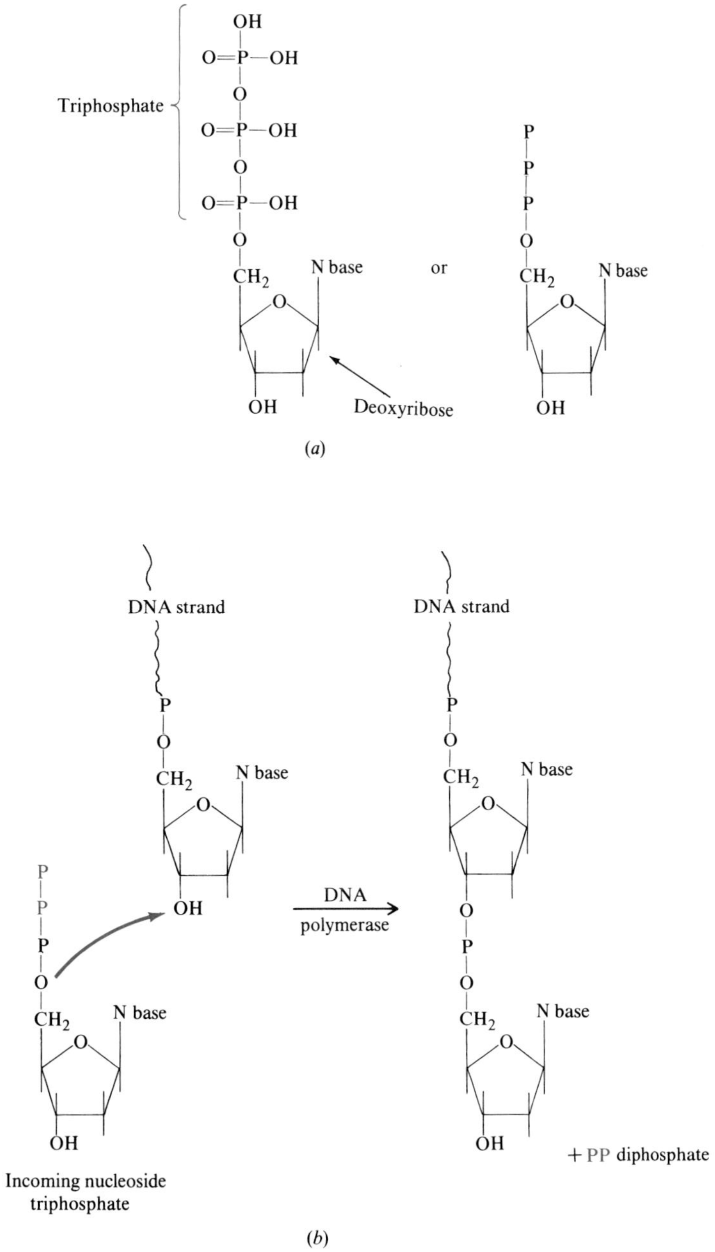

FIGURE 24.9
(*a*) Deoxynucleotide triphosphate. As the incomin triphosphate is added to the growing DNA molecule, a diphosphate (in color) is released.

In this way each unwound single, or *parent,* strand behaves as a *template* for a new complementary strand called a *daughter* strand, as shown in Figure 24.10. The two new daughter strands (in color) rewind around the parent strands to form two new DNA molecules, identical in structure to one another and to the original DNA double strand. Note that each new DNA contains one *replicated* strand and one strand from the original double helix. The behavior of an unraveled DNA strand in serving as a template for a new complementary strand is called **replication.** Now you can see how a chromosome, which *is* a DNA molecule, doubles in preparation for cell division. It is through replication that the characteristics of a parent cell are passed on to its daughter.

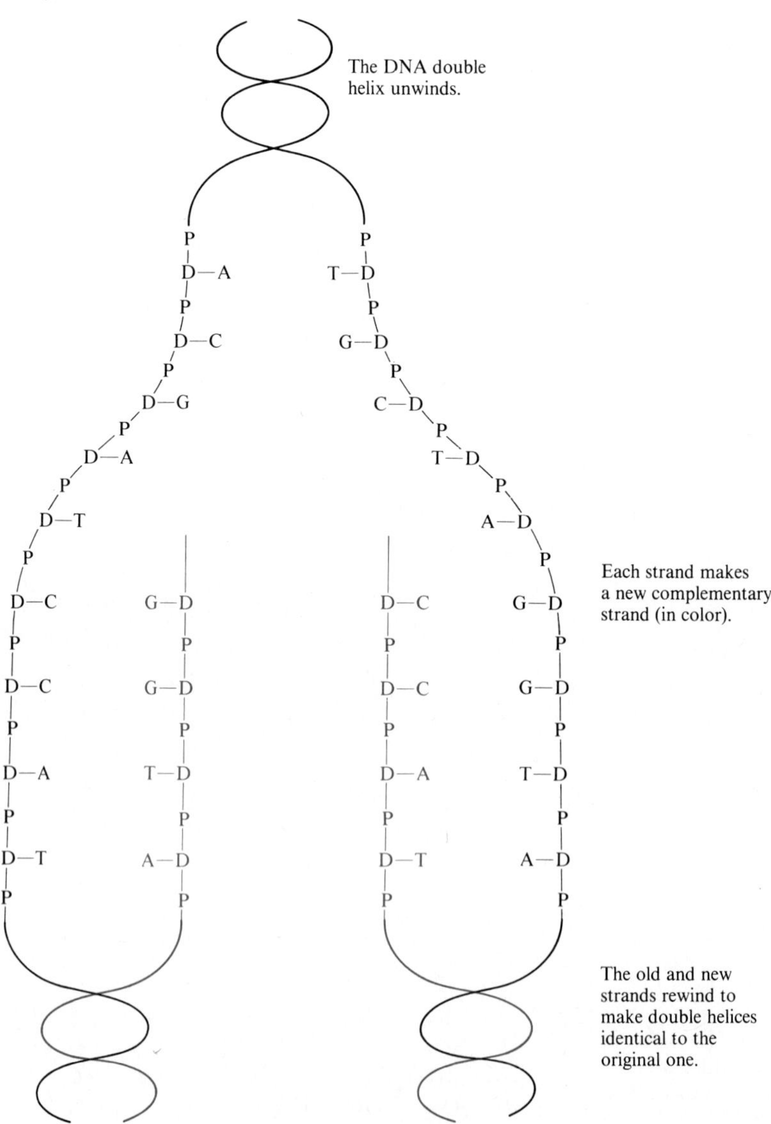

The DNA double helix unwinds.
Each strand makes a new complementary strand (in color).
The old and new strands rewind to make double helices identical to the original one.

FIGURE 24.10
Replication.

24.8 STRUCTURE OF RNA

Now we are ready to consider the other function of DNA, its role as a carrier of the genetic information needed to direct the synthesis of protein molecules. In order to understand how this happens we must first look at the structure of RNA, the other nucleic acid that plays a major part in transmitting hereditary information.

The nucleotides that join together to form ribonucleic acid are AMP, GMP, CMP, and UMP, that is, the ones containing ribose and the nitrogen bases A, G, C, and U (no T) (see Figure 24.11). As in DNA, the nucleotides are joined one to another through 3′,5′ linkages. Figure 24.12 shows a segment of RNA in various degrees of detail. We can represent the same RNA segment by simply giving the nucleotide base sequence, AUGCCU, or by using the abbreviated formula below, where the solid line represents a backbone composed of ribose to phosphate (—P—R—P—R—P—R—P—R—P—R—P—R—).

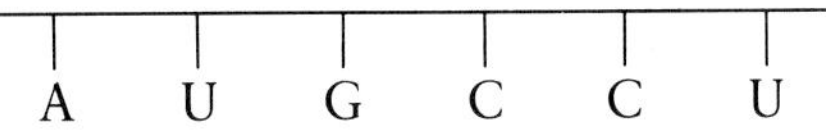

There is usually no 1:1 ratio between U and A or between C and G in RNA molecules, which indicates that RNA molecules tend to exist as single strands.

UMP

GMP

CMP

AMP

FIGURE 24.11
Nucleotide components of RNA.

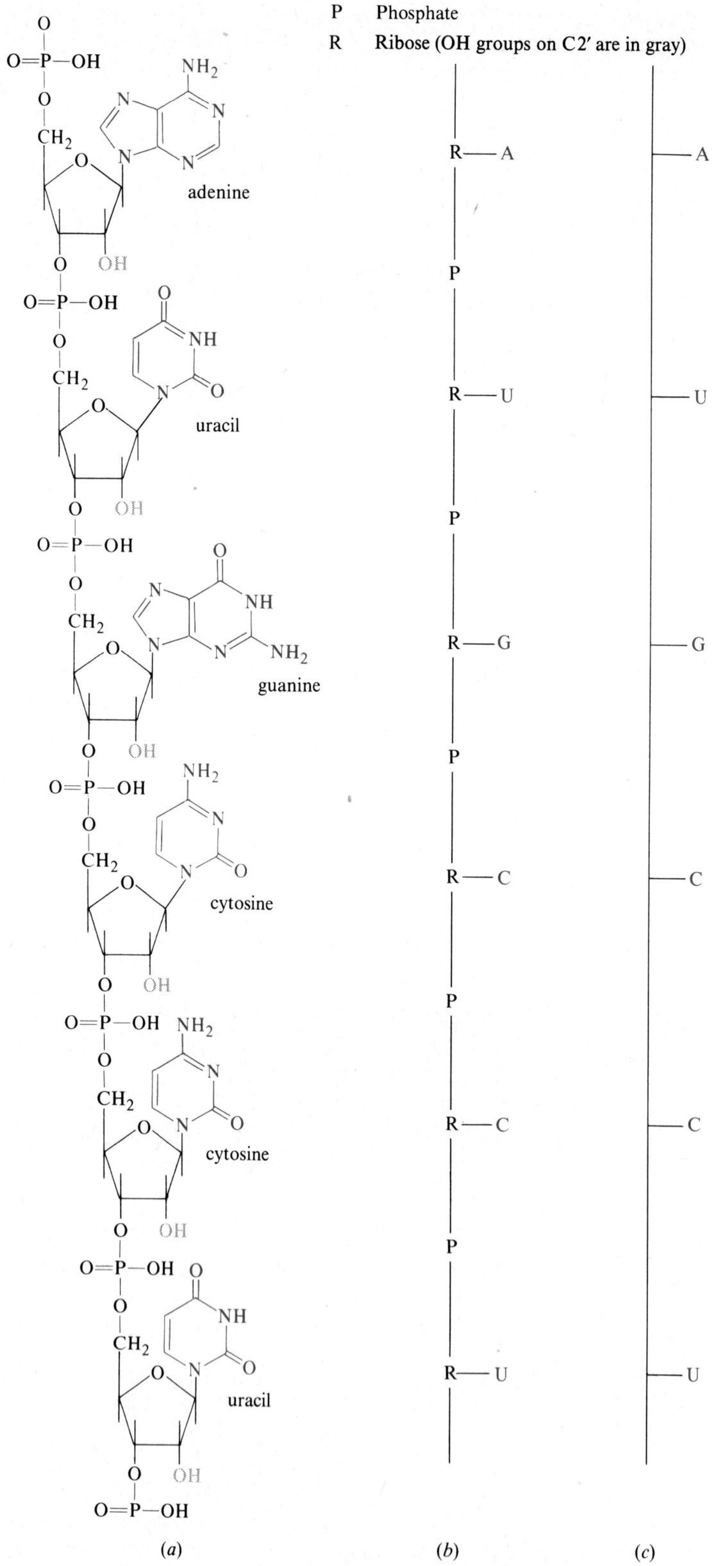

FIGURE 24.12
Views of the RNA structure.

Nucleic acid	DNA	RNA
Sugar	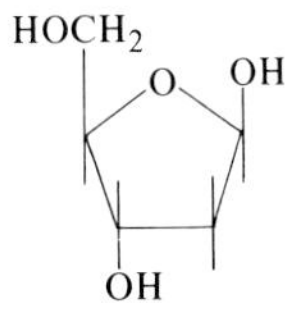 $HOCH_2$, O, OH, OH Deoxyribose	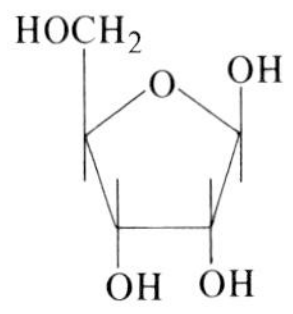 $HOCH_2$, O, OH, OH, OH Ribose
Nitrogen bases	A Adenine C Cytosine G Guanine T Thymine	A Adenine C Cytosine G Guanine U Uracil
Secondary structure	Double-stranded	Usually single-stranded
Location in cell	Nucleus	Nucleus and cytoplasm
Sample segment	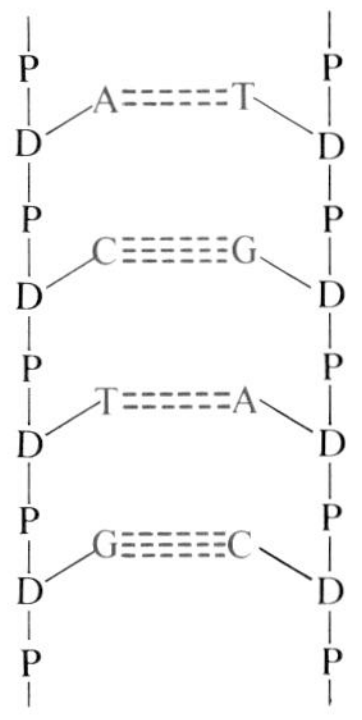 P–D–P–D–P–D–P–D–P paired with P–D–P–D–P–D–P–D–P A====T C====G T====A G====C	 P–R–P–R–P–R–P–R–P R—U R—G R—C R—A

FIGURE 24.13
Comparing RNA and DNA.

For a comparison of the structural features of DNA and RNA see Figure 24.13.

There are several different kinds of RNA molecules, which differ in shapes, formula weights, and function.

Messenger RNA (mBNA)

Molecules of mRNA copy the genetic message of DNA and carry it from the nucleus to the cytoplasm.

You just saw that DNA molecules are found in chromosomes located within the nucleus of the cell. However, protein molecules are not synthesized in cell nuclei but rather in the **ribosomes,** cellular structures located in the fluid portion of the cell called the **cytoplasm** (see Figure 22.15). Some intermediate template is needed to carry the genetic information on DNA to the ribosomes. The "go-between" compounds are **messenger RNA,** or **mRNA,** molecules that copy the genetic *message* contained in DNA molecules and carry it out of the nucleus to the ribosomes, the sites of protein synthesis. The single-stranded mRNA molecules, with formula weights from about 300,000 to 2,000,000, are much smaller than DNA molecules. In the next section we will see how the message they carry is decoded at the ribosome so that the correct protein can be synthesized.

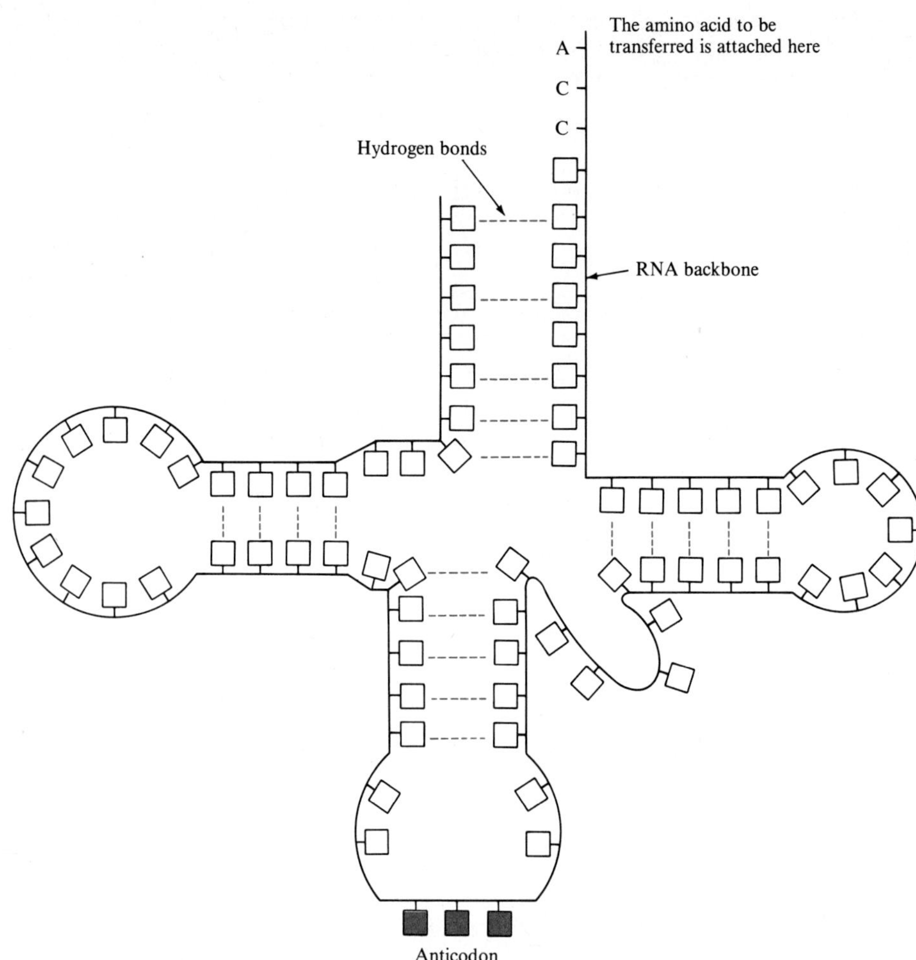

FIGURE 24.14
tRNA. All tRNA molecules contain CCA at one end. Many of the other N bases indicated by squares are hydrogen-bonded to each other. The anticodon is represented by the three bases in color.

Transfer RNA (tRNA)

Molecules of tRNA carry amino acids to the ribosomes, the sites of protein synthesis.

The **transfer RNA,** or **tRNA** molecules, *transfer* amino acids to the ribosomes. The tRNA molecules are the smallest RNA molecules, having formula weights between 25,000 and 40,000 and including about 80 nucleotide units. The molecules of tRNA are single-stranded but are looped into a coiled structure that resembles a cloverleaf (Figure 24.14). The structure is stabilized by the formation of hydrogen bonds between base pairs, as shown in the figure. The amino acid to be transferred is attached to one end of the molecule. In another loop of the tRNA structure you can see a set of three N bases. These bases, called *anticodons,* correspond to particular amino acids in a way that we will discuss in the next section.

Ribosomal RNA (rRNA)

Ribosome is "ribose-containing body," from *ribo-* in RNA and the Greek word *soma,* meaning "body."

Although the **ribosomal RNA,** or **rRNA,** accounts for as much as 80 percent of all the RNA in cells, it has a function which is not entirely understood. The name is derived from ribosome because ribosomes are half rRNA and half protein.

24.9 TRANSCRIPTION: DNA → mRNA

Now we are ready to combine all the structural information about the nucleic acids and see how it is used to direct protein synthesis. You have seen that the genetic information is found in the *sequence of the N bases* on the DNA molecule. However, as mentioned above, the DNA molecule is in the nucleus while the polypeptide chains are assembled at the ribosome. To transmit its message, the DNA molecule creates a messenger RNA molecule, a molecule which can pass through the nuclear membrane (Section 22.10) and thus *can* get to the ribosome "protein factories." The process of creating an mRNA molecule from a DNA molecule is called **transcription,** or the writing of a copy.

Transcribe means "write across."

To transcribe a gene, the DNA segment corresponding to that gene unwinds, exposing two single strands. Only *one* of the two unwound DNA strands represents the base sequence to be put on the mRNA template. That DNA strand synthesizes the mRNA strand by base pairing in the same way that DNA produces a complementary strand in replication. Since there is no thymine in RNA molecules, the adenine base pairs instead with uracil (Figure 24.15). For instance, suppose a segment of one strand of DNA has the base sequence CGTA. It would synthesize a strand of mRNA with the sequence GCAU.

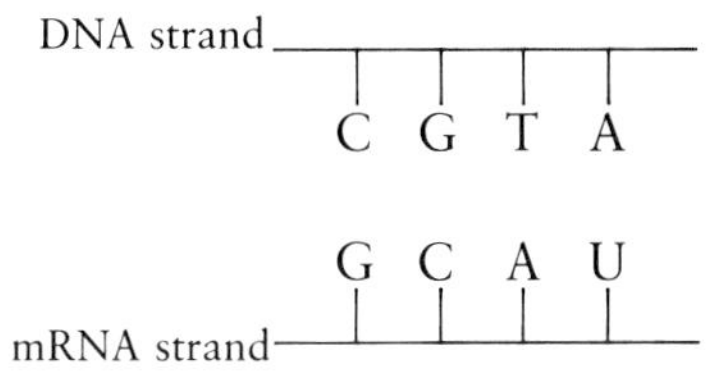

DNA strand
C G T A

G C A U
mRNA strand

Besides the DNA template itself, other ingredients are needed to synthesize the mRNA molecule. Its nucleotide components are derived from four triphosphate nucleotides, ATP, GTP, CTP, and UTP, which are linked together with the assistance of the enzyme *RNA polymerase.*

The newly created mRNA molecule leaves the nucleus and binds to the ribosome, where the information in the N bases it carries must be read and translated by the ribosome. The ribosome acts like a tape player and the mRNA molecule like the tape it plays; but first the code carried in the N-base sequence of mRNA must be broken.

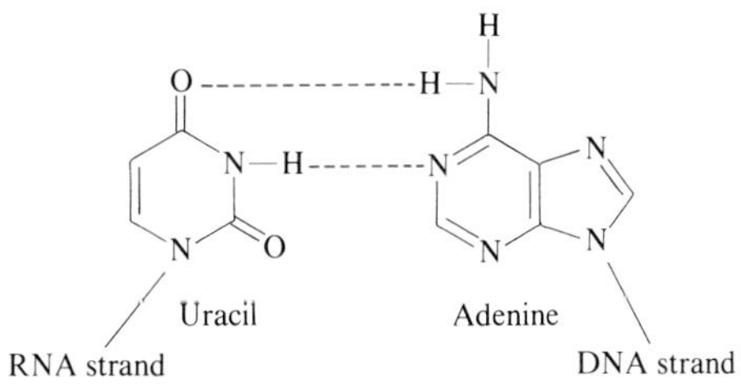

Uracil
Adenine
RNA strand
DNA strand

FIGURE 24.15

SAMPLE EXERCISE 24.5

One segment of a single strand DNA contains the base sequence ACGTTA. What is the base sequence on: (**a**) the complementary strand; (**b**) the mRNA strand it creates.

Solution:

(**a**) The complementary strand is DNA formed by base pairing.

Original DNA strand:	A C G T T A
Complementary DNA strand:	T G C A A T

(**b**) The RNA strand also forms by base pairing, but A pairs with U (not T).

Original DNA strand:	A C G T T A
mRNA strand:	U G C A A U

EXERCISE 24.5

Sketch the strand of DNA that produced the mRNA segment shown below:

24.10 GENETIC CODE; CODONS

We said above that it is the *sequence of N bases on DNA* that contains the information that directs protein synthesis, information that is passed on to mRNA. The genetic code, derived from the base sequence on mRNA, is a series of "words" made up of N-base "letters." There are four different letters possible on an mRNA strand, A, C, G, and U. Each word, called a **codon,** stands for a particular amino acid. The first step in decoding the mRNA message is to determine the length of the codon words.

Suppose we try to use one-letter words. Thus, there would be four possible codons, A, G, C, and U. However, there are twenty common amino acids (see Table 23.1). Four words can represent only four different amino acids, and thus the code must be more complex. Suppose we use two-letter words. How many combinations are possible? There are 16 (4^2) different codons that contain two bases, namely, AA, AU, AG, AC, UA, UU, UC, UG, GA, GU, GG, GC, CA, CU, CG, and CC, but 16 words are still not enough to represent the 20 amino acids in protein molecules. If we use three-letter words there will be 64 (4^3) combinations of the four N bases and more than enough words. In fact, the genetic code is composed of three-letter words.

Each set of three bases, a triplet of bases, on mRNA is a codon which represents one amino acid.

A codon is a sequence of three nitrogen bases that specifies a particular amino acid.

The meaning of each of the 64 codons has been deduced. For instance, the first codon to be unambiguously associated with a particular amino acid (in 1961) was UUU, which translates into phenylalanine, Phe. This was discovered when a synthetic RNA containing U only (polyuridine) caused bacteria to synthesize the polypeptide polyphenylalanine.

UUU codes for phenylalanine, which is $NH_2—CH(CH_2C_6H_5)—C(=O)—OH$

More than one codon can represent a given amino acid, but a given codon cannot represent more than one amino acid.

Table 24.3 lists all 64 codons and corresponding amino acids. Since there are more than 20 words, the code contains some redundancy, meaning that several different codons may represent the same amino acid. You can see that UUU is not the only codon for Phe; the codon UUC also translates into Phe. The codons UAA, UAG, and UGA are signals to terminate polypeptide synthesis. These *chain termination codons* (labeled "stop" in Table 24.3) cannot be translated into amino acids.

TABLE 24.3 **THE mRNA CODONS; GENETIC CODE**

UUU Phe	UCU Ser	UAU Tyr	UGU Cys
UUC	UCC	UAC	UGC
UUA Leu	UCA	UAA (stop)	UGA (stop)
UUG	UCG	UAG (stop)	UGG Trp
CUU Leu	CCU Pro	CAU His	CGU Arg
CUC	CCC	CAC	CGC
CUA	CCA	CAA Gln	CGA
CUG	CCG	CAG	CGG
AUU Ile	ACU Thr	AAU Asn	AGU Ser
AUC	ACC	AAC	AGC
AUA	ACA	AAA Lys	AGA Arg
AUG Met	ACG	AAG	AGG
GUU val	GCU Ala	GAU Asp	GGU Gly
GUC	GCC	GAC	GGC
GUA	GCA	GAA Glu	GGA
GUG	GCG	GAG	GGG

SAMPLE EXERCISE 24.6

The sequence of bases on a DNA template strand is CCT AGT. What dipeptide does this produce?

Solution:

First find out what mRNA strand is produced and then look up the mRNA codons in Table 24.3 to see what amino acids they code for.

DNA:	CCT AGT
mRNA:	GGA UCA
Dipeptide:	Gly—Ser

EXERCISE 24.6

The DNA strand CCG AGT synthesizes the mRNA strand GGC UCA, which also codes for the dipeptide Gly-Ser, the answer to the sample exercise above. List all other possible DNA sequences that could produce Gly—Ser.

24.11 PROTEIN SYNTHESIS; ANTICODONS

You have seen that a polypeptide chain is synthesized at the ribosome from information on mRNA codons. The assembly begins with the amino end of the polypeptide chain and continues until the final carboxyl-end amino acid is put into place to terminate the protein molecule. Let us now take a close look at the whole process starting from the binding of mRNA to the ribosome and finishing with the release of the completed protein from the ribosome. A large number of ingredients is needed. Among them are the 20 amino acids, at least 20 different tRNA molecules to carry the amino acids, and a variety of protein molecules of which some serve as enzymes and others as special *factors* that are needed in protein construction. Below is a simplified description of the complex sequence of events involved in the synthesis of proteins.

mRNA Binds to Ribosome

Ribosomes are known to consist of two sections, one larger than the other, as represented in the enlarged ribosome shown in Figure 24.16. The mRNA molecule threads through the ribosome by fitting into a channel located between the larger and smaller segments. The two areas shown on the larger unit represent two binding sites, the *peptidyl* and *aminoacyl* sites, which we will refer to simply as P and A sites. The amino acids used to build the protein are attached through these sites.

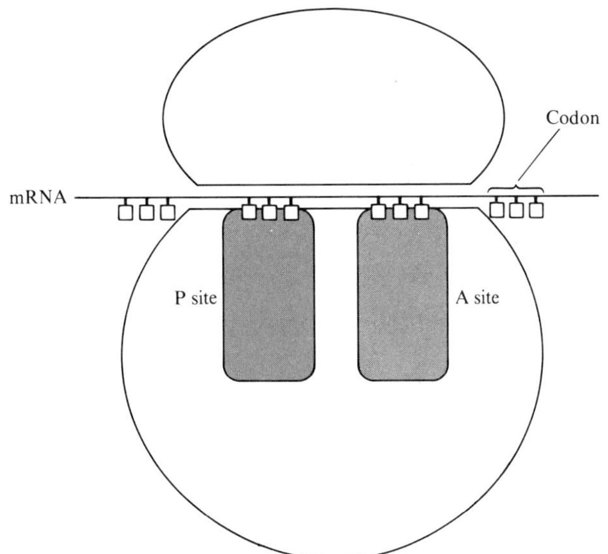

FIGURE 24.16
The mRNA molecule threads through the channel between the larger and smaller subunits of the ribosome.

AUG Initiates the Synthesis

It is known that polypeptide chains begin with the amino acid methionine (Met). Its codon AUG (see Table 24.3), called the *initiation codon,* is said to *initiate* the protein synthesis. To bring the methionine into place the AUG codon on mRNA forms a base pair with the anticodon part of the tRNA molecule which carries methionine. This amino acid–RNA complex is called methionyl tRNA (or Met-tRNA). The anticodon that corresponds to AUG is UAC.

Met codon (on mRNA):	AUG
Met anticodon (on Met-tRNA):	UAC

In Figure 24.17*a* you can see that the Met-tRNA is bound at the P site. Now the ribosome is ready to start translating the mRNA.

Elongation of the Chain

Suppose the next amino acid coded by mRNA is valine. The Val is brought into place by its tRNA and is bound to the A site of the ribosome. This is shown in Figure 24.17*b*, where the codon GUC (for Val) attracts the anticodon CAG of Val-tRNA. A peptide bond forms between the Val and Met, which are now side by side on the ribosome (Figure 24.17*c*). In Figure 24.17*d* the Met-tRNA shifts out of the P site and releases its tRNA, while the Val-tRNA shifts into the P site. The A site is temporarily empty. The Gly-tRNA is now ready to occupy the A site to form the tripeptide Met-Val-Gly. In this way more and more amino acids are brought into place according to the message on mRNA to form the growing polypeptide at a rate of about one amino acid every second. That means that the body is able to synthesize a molecule of hemoglobin with its 574 amino acid residues in about 10 min.

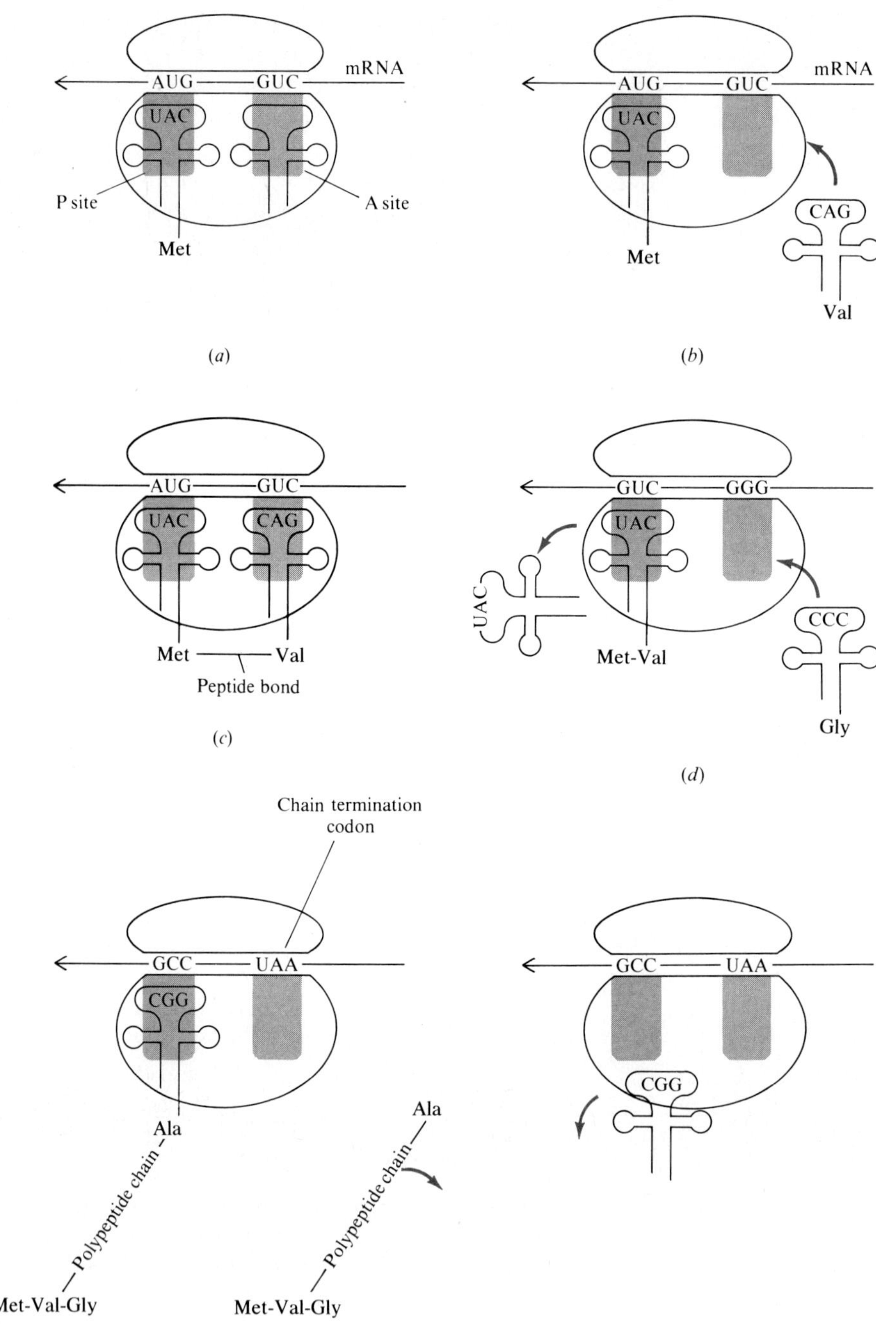

FIGURE 24.17
(*a*) Met-tRNA at the P site.
(*b*) Val-tRNA moves in.
(*c*) A peptide bond forms between Met and Val.
(*d*) Met-tRNA is released, Val-tRNA shifts into P site, and Gly-tRNA moves in.
(*e*) The protein is released.
(*f*) The last tRNA leaves the P site.

Termination of the Chain

Any one of the three chain termination codons (UAA, UAG, and UGA) designated "stop" in Table 24.3 signals the *termination* of a polypeptide chain. When one of these codons arrives at the A site, it ends the synthesis of the protein (Figure 24.17*e*). The protein molecule is released and Ala-tRNA, the last tRNA in our example, leaves the P site (Figure 24.17*f*). A summary of the process of protein synthesis, from translation to release of the polypeptide strand, is shown in Figure 24.18.

Diseases can result from mistakes in protein synthesis.

The complicated scheme by which proteins are manufactured by the body is carried out with such remarkable accuracy that mistakes are rare. However, there are many known diseases in humans (see Table 24.4 for a partial list of these) in which something does go wrong somewhere in the synthesis of a necessary protein enzyme. This can happen through alterations in the chemical struc-

FIGURE 24.18
Protein synthesis.

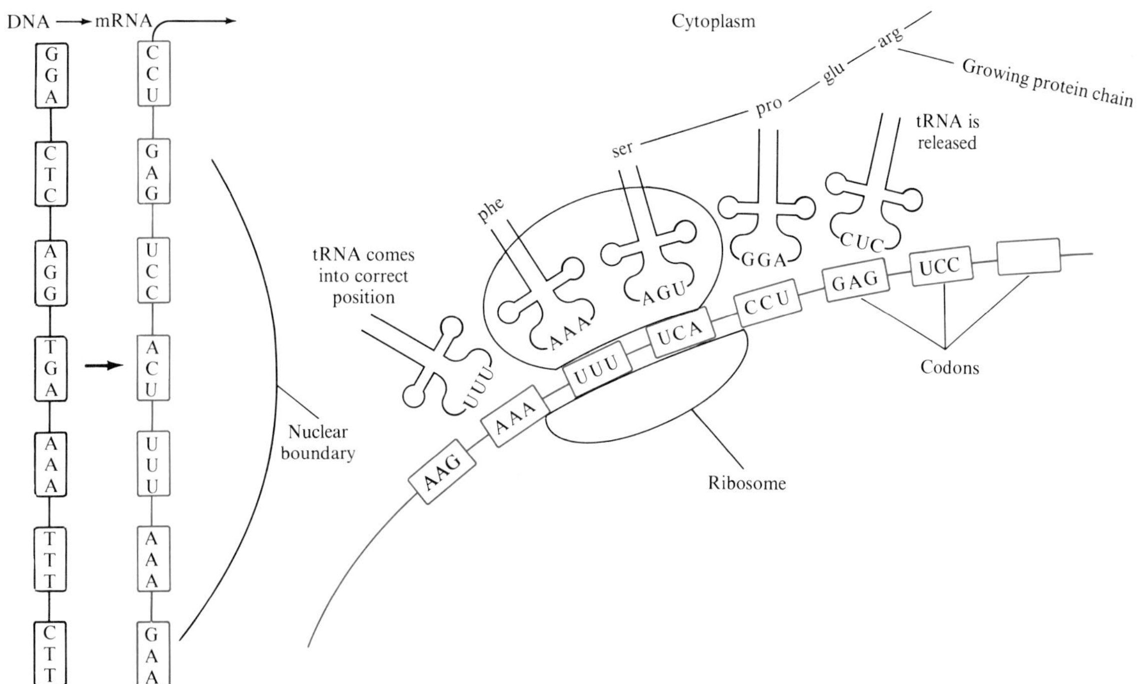

TABLE 24.4 GENETIC DISORDERS

Disease*	Section reference	Disease*	Section reference
Alkaptonuria	28.6	Lactase deficiency	21.9
Andersen's disease	26.9	Limit dextrinosis	26.3
Diabetes (juvenile)	26.10	Maple syrup urine disease	28.6
Fabry's disease	25 (Exercise 25.19)	McArdle's disease	26.3
Fructose intolerance	26.2	Phenylketonuria	28.6
Galactosemia	21.3, 26.2	Sickle cell anemia	24.13
Gaucher's disease	22.6	Tay-Sachs disease	22.6
Homocystinuria	28.8	Wilson's disease	8.13
Hyperammonemia	28.5		

For details about the symptoms of each disease and the defective or missing proteins, refer to the chapter section listed and look for the disease names, which are all printed in boldface.

ture of DNA, which cause the wrong mRNA and hence the wrong protein to be synthesized. In the next section we will investigate some ways in which the DNA structure can be changed.

SAMPLE EXERCISE 24.7

The base order on a strand of DNA is GGCTAT. Give the following:
(**a**) The corresponding mRNA strand
(**b**) The dipeptide that is synthesized
(**c**) The anticodons

Solution:

It is easiest to translate the message if the bases are first grouped into triplets:

DNA: GGC TAT

Now construct the corresponding mRNA:

mRNA: CCG AUA

Consult Table 24.3 to translate the condons CCG and AUA:

Dipeptide: Pro—Ile

Find the anticodons complementary to each coden:

Anticodons: GGC UAU

EXERCISE 24.7

Give the mRNA strand, tripeptide, and anticodons corresponding to the DNA strand TGTCACGGG.

24.12 MUTATIONS

Changes in the base order sequence of DNA, known as **mutations,** change the genetic code information and cannot be repaired. Agents that cause mutations, such as high-energy radiation and certain chemicals, are called **mutagens.** The amino acid sequence of a protein synthesized by mutated DNA will nearly always be changed. The new protein may not function properly. If the protein is to serve as an enzyme, the enzyme may have impaired activity or possibly no activity at all.

Mutations include the addition, deletion, or substitution of one or more bases.

There are many ways in which mutations can occur. One base may be substituted for another, one or more bases may be deleted, or extra bases may be inserted. The result of any of these changes is a change in the codons and hence a change in the amino acid sequence of the protein chain.

Substitution mutations in which one base (or base pair) of DNA is replaced by another are the most common ones. One codon on the mRNA strand produced by this altered DNA will be changed. In many cases the new codon will be for a different amino acid than the original codon. For instance, in the DNA strand shown below let us suppose that the fourth base, an adenine unit, is replaced by a guanine. We can compare the tetrapeptides produced in both cases.

	Unmutated	**Mutated**
Original DNA	TGC ATA GGT CGA AC	TGC GTA GGT CGA AC
mRNA codon	ACG UAU CCA GCU UG	ACG CAU CCA GCU UG
Tetrapeptide	Thr—Tyr—Pro—Ala	Thr—His—Pro—Ala

HbA	HbS
1 val	1 val
his	his
leu	leu
thr	thr
pro	pro
6 glu	6 val
glu	glu
lys	lys
ser	ser
10 ala	10 ala
val	val
thr	thr
ala	ala
leu	leu
trp	trp

FIGURE 24.19
HbA and HbS segments.

The second amino acid in the tetrapeptide, a tyrosine, becomes a histidine as a result of the mutation.

A protein in which only one amino acid is different from what it normally would be may or may not be functional. In Chapter 23 you saw that changing only one amino acid of the hormone oxytocin (a nonapeptide) had an enormous effect on its biological activity. Another well-studied example is the production of abnormal hemoglobin (Section 23.10). In Figure 24.19 you can see that in a segment of normal hemoglobin, called *HbA*, the amino acid in position 6 (part of one of the chains labeled β in Figure 23.17) is glutamic acid, Glu. However, in one form of abnormal hemoglobin known as *HbS*, the Glu is replaced by valine, Val. This mutation is known to result from changing a thymine on DNA to an adenine, thus changing the normal codon GAA (for Glu) to GUA (for val).

	HbA	**HbS**
DNA	CTT	CAT
mRNA	GAA	GUA
Amino acid	Glu	Val

Hemoglobin molecules in persons with sickle cell anemia have a valine where there should be a glutamic acid unit.

The result of this change in only one amino acid residue of the giant hemoglobin molecule (which contains a total of 574 amino acid residues) is severely impaired function of the hemoglobin. The disease ***sickle cell anemia*** is caused by the presence of HbS instead of the normal HbA hemoglobin. Red blood cells containing HbS are sickled in shape, unlike the normal globular disk-shaped cells (see Figure 24.20). These misshapen sickle cells are very poor oxygen carriers. They may tangle with other blood cells to clog small blood vessels and are fragile and easily destroyed.

Individuals who have sickle cell anemia suffer from recurring pain attacks and frequent bacterial infections.

Sickle cell anemia is a genetically transmitted disease. Persons carrying two genes (one from each parent) that produce the abnormal HbS suffer from sickle-cell anemia. Those who have one gene for HbS and one for normal HbA are said

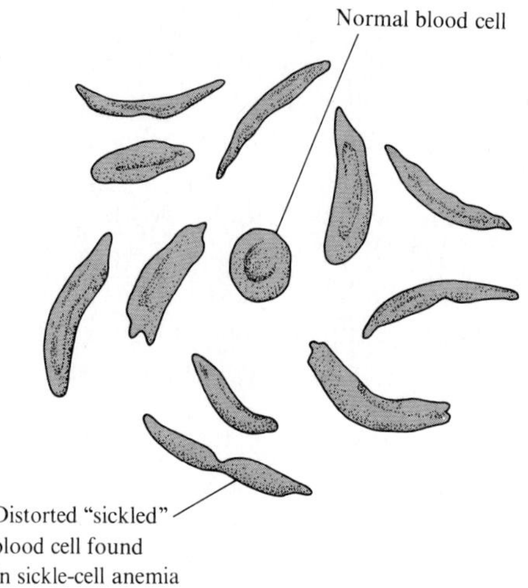

FIGURE 24.20

to be *carriers of the sickle cell trait*. Although their hemoglobin is about 40 percent HbS, carriers do not suffer from the disease. The production of HbS and of the sickled cells it causes is one of many examples in which an altered DNA strand codes for the synthesis of a defective protein. Table 24.4 lists the numerous genetic disorders that are mentioned throughout this text.

As you have seen, the replacement of one amino acid in a protein can be serious, and replacement of any more than one is likely to produce a protein which does not function at all. This is precisely what happens in *deletion* and *insertion* mutations, in which a base is deleted from or a new base inserted, into a DNA strand, respectively. For instance, suppose we delete the fourth base in the same DNA strand we considered above. All bases in the mRNA tape now shift one space to the left; the first codon remains the same, but all the others are entirely different.

	Original DNA	**Mutated DNA**
DNA segment	TGC ATA GGT CGA AC	TGC □TA GGT CGA AC
mRNA Codon	ACG UAU CCA GCU UG	ACG □AU CCA GCU UG or after shifting: ACG AUC CAG CUU G
Tetrapeptide	Thr—Tyr—Pro—Ala	Thr—Ile—Gln—Leu

Note that the new tetrapeptide has three amino acids that are different from those of the original peptide.

SAMPLE EXERCISE 24.8

A segment of mRNA produced by a strand of DNA is UGG CCC GAC CAG UUG UU. For what pentapeptide does this segment code: (**a**) without any mutation; (**b**) if the third base is deleted?

Solution:

Look up the RNA codons in Table 24.3

(a) UGG CCC GAC CAG UUG UU
Trp—Pro—Asp—Gln—Leu

(b) Delete the third base:UG□ CCC GAC CAG UUG UU
Regroup the letters into triplet codons:
UGC CCG ACC AGU UGU U
Cys—Pro—Thr—Ser—Cys

EXERCISE 24.8

Suppose the C in the RNA segment GGC UAU UUG is replaced with an A. How would this change the tripeptide it produces?

24.13 GENETIC ENGINEERING

Plasmid DNA molecules have formula weights of 5 million to 100 million.

Note from Figure 23.6 that human insulin is slightly different from porcine or bovine insulin, the ones that are used to make insulin preparations.

We have seen that the genetic blueprint needed to design a protein is present in the chemical structure of DNA gene molecules. Incredible as it may seem, it is possible to "cut apart" a bacterial DNA molecule and then attach a segment from some foreign DNA molecule onto it. The new DNA molecule made from *combining* the bacterial DNA with the foreign segment DNA is called a **hybrid recombinant DNA.** Like uncombined DNA, the hybrid recombinant DNA molecule can make copies of itself and can direct the synthesis of proteins.

The bacterial DNA used for this purpose is a small, circular DNA molecule called a **plasmid,** which can readily be taken out of bacteria and then reintroduced once the new DNA segment has been added to it. Thus if the foreign DNA joined to the plasmid is the gene segment responsible for the synthesis of human insulin, within its bacterial host the hybrid DNA will begin to synthesize human insulin. Since plasmid DNA replicates frequently, the bacteria can be used as an insulin factory. We are ready now to find out how this remarkable feat of microengineering is actually done. The indispensable tools are enzymes that assist in cutting apart DNA molecules and "pasting" them back together.

Cutting Enzymes

The cutting enzymes are called *restriction endonucleases,* enzymes known to cleave DNA molecules at specific sites. Enzymes such as this were first used to determine the base order sequences in DNA molecules, much as the primary structure of proteins was found by utilizing enzymes known to cut specific peptide bonds (Section 23.7). Restriction endonucleases are used to cut DNA molecules in preparation for joining the segments to DNA segments from other molecules.

One invaluable restriction endonuclease called *EcoRI* is known to cut DNA molecules between G and A bases, provided they are part of the sequence GAATTC. For instance, both strands of the DNA segment below can be cut:

$$\begin{array}{l}\text{—G|AATTC—}\\ \text{—CTTAA|G—}\end{array} \xrightarrow{\text{EcoRI}} \begin{array}{l}\text{—G* + *AATTC}\\ \text{—CTTAA* + *G—}\end{array}$$

The cut ends indicated above by asterisks are called *sticky ends* because they are complementary and can be rejoined.

Suppose we wish to make a recombinant DNA from a plasmid DNA and some foreign DNA. The first step is to treat both DNA molecules with EcoRI to produce identical sticky ends, as shown in Figure 24.21*a* and *b*.

Pasting Enzymes

In the next step the plasmid DNA and the foreign DNA, which have complementary sticky ends, are joined together to produce a hybrid recombinant DNA molecule. Special pasting enzymes called *DNA ligases* are needed for this process. In the presence of a DNA ligase the sticky ends produced upon cutting with EcoRI join to form covalent bonds (see Figure 24.21*c*).

$$\underset{\text{Plasmid DNA}}{\begin{array}{l}\text{—G*}\\ \text{CTTAA*}\end{array}} \begin{array}{c}+\\+\end{array} \underset{\text{Foreign DNA}}{\begin{array}{r}\text{*AATTC—}\\ \text{*G—}\end{array}} \xrightarrow{\text{DNA ligase}} \underset{\text{Hybrid recombinant DNA}}{\begin{array}{l}\text{—GAATTC—}\\ \text{—CTTAAG—}\end{array}}$$

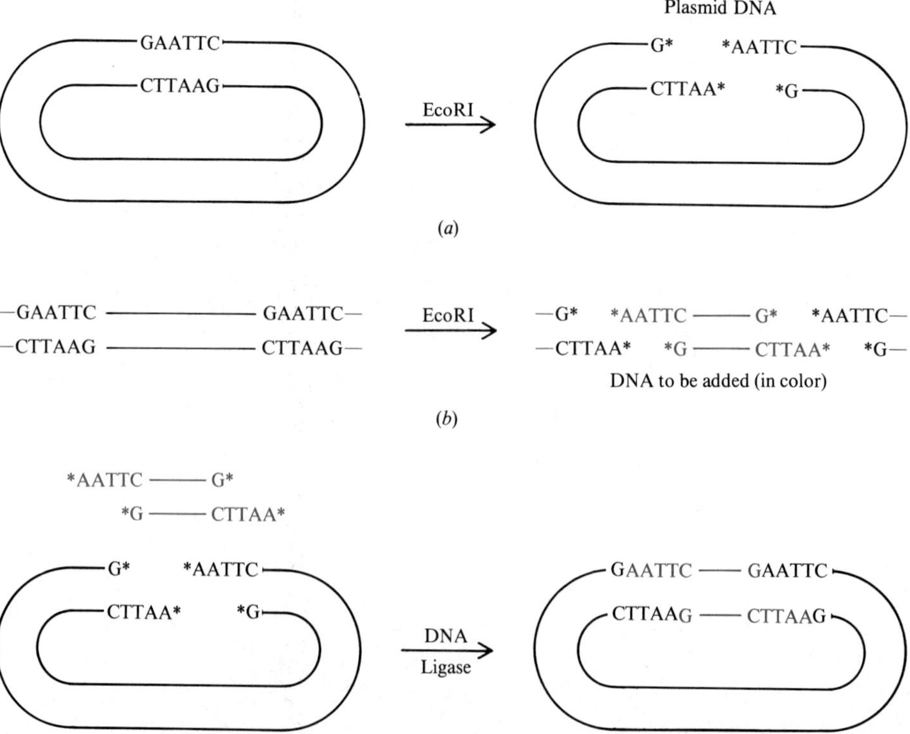

FIGURE 24.21
Gene cloning. (*a*) Cutting the plasmid DNA. (*b*) Cutting the foreign DNA. (*c*) Pasting the plasmid DNA to the foreign DNA.

Cloning

When reintroduced into a bacterial host, the hybrid DNA replicates and produces both the proteins designated by the original plasmid and those directed by the newly added DNA segment. The formation of copies of a foreign gene that is introduced into a host cell is called **gene cloning,** and the foreign gene that is added to the plasmid is said to be *cloned.*

Gene cloning can be used to "farm" proteins such as insulin and interferons.

The practical applications of gene cloning have led to a new field of research called **genetic engineering.** Gene cloning provides a way to synthesize important medical proteins in competition with methods used by pharmaceutical industries. It is possible to turn bacteria into protein factories. For instance, in the previous section you saw that the gene for the synthesis of human insulin can be recombined with a bacterial plasmid and then introduced into a bacterial host for cloning. *Interferons,* proteins which are thought to provide cells with an immunity from viral infections, can also be produced by gene cloning. A virus composed of a nucleic acid core surrounded by a protein coat, as pictured in Figure 24.22, cannot survive by itself and must live inside other cells, which can provide the energy needed to keep them alive. The increased availability of interferons makes it practical to conduct studies about the way in which they inhibit the multiplication of animal viruses.

Another application of hybrid recombinant DNA production is in agriculture. You learned in Chapter 7 that nitrogen fixation is a process by which atmospheric N_2 is converted into useful nitrogen compounds such as proteins (see Section 7.11). Recall that this is accomplished by nitrogen-fixing bacteria present in the roots of legumes, including peas, soybeans, and peanuts. It is possible to program other kinds of plants—corn, for example—to fix nitrogen and thus to produce protein as well. This could be done by removing the appropriate genes from nitrogen-fixing bacteria and then incorporating them into plants by the process of gene cloning. Then plants other than the legumes would also be able to fix nitrogen and thus to provide additional protein to help ease the worldwide shortage of this essential food.

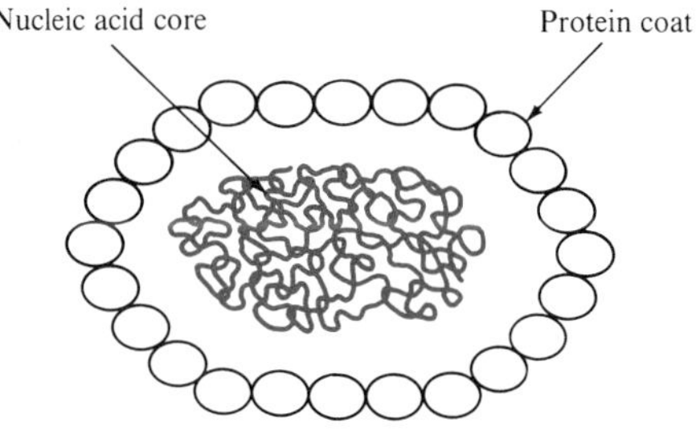

Nucleic acid core

Protein coat

FIGURE 24.22
In these cross sections of typical virus shapes, a protein coat surrounds a nucleic acid core.

SUMMARY

The genetic material of living cells is found in the chromosomes present in their nuclei. Chromosomes are composed of deoxyribonucleic acid (DNA), nucleic acid molecules that are capable of copying themselves and of directing the synthesis of proteins with the assistance of ribonucleic acid (RNA). A gene is a segment of a chromosome that corresponds to a particular protein.

Nucleic acids are polymers of nucleotides. When broken down, a nucleotide produces three components: phosphoric acid, a sugar, and a purine or pyrimidine derivative called a nitrogen base. Nucleosides are nucleotides without the phosphate, that is, only the sugar and nitrogen base. The nucleotides that make up DNA molecules (dAMP, dTMP, dCMP, and dGMP) include the sugar deoxyribose and one of the four nitrogen bases adenine (A), thymine (T), cytosine (C), and guanine (G). The nucleotides are joined to one another through a 3′,5′ linkage which forms between a phosphate group on the C-5′ atom (a deoxyribose C atom) of one nucleotide and the hydroxyl group on the C-3′ atom of the other one. A DNA molecule exists as a double helix in which the two complementary strands are held together by hydrogen bonds that form between the base pairs A and T and C and G. The nucleotide components of RNA (AMP, UMP, CMP, and GMP) include the sugar ribose and the nitrogen bases A, C, G, and U (no T). RNA molecules usually exist as single strands. Messenger RNA, mRNA, transmits the genetic information from DNA in the nucleus to the ribosomes, where proteins are synthesized. Transfer RNA, tRNA, carries amino acids from the cytoplasm to the ribosome, and ribosomal RNA, rRNA, is a major component of the ribosome.

Replication takes place when one DNA molecule makes a copy of itself and thus transmits the characteristics of a parent cell to a daughter cell. Before cell division the DNA partially unwinds to produce two single strands, each of which acts as a template to direct the synthesis of a new complementary strand from nucleotide triphosphates (dATP, dTTP, dGTP, and dCTP) by the process of base pairing.

Genetic information is found in the sequence of nitrogen bases on the DNA molecule. One strand of an unwound DNA double helix directs the synthesis of mRNA by base pairing in transcription. Each triplet of bases on the mRNA is a codon, which represents a particular amino acid (or a "stop" instruction). To synthesize a protein the mRNA binds to the ribosome. Initiation occurs when the P binding site on the ribosome is bound to a tRNA with an anticodon corresponding to the mRNA codon for the initial amino acid (Met). In elongation a second amino acid binds to the A site and a peptide bond forms. The tRNA from the initial amino acid is released and the second tRNA shifts into the P site. Each coded amino acid is introduced in this way as the mRNA codons are translated. In the termination step the completed protein is released. Protein synthesis happens with few mistakes.

Mutations happen when a base is replaced, deleted, or inserted. Deletions and insertions are particularly harmful because they change so many amino acids in the protein that it will almost certainly be nonfunctional.

It is possible to splice together circular DNA molecules from bacterial plasmids with foreign DNA from some other organism. First both DNA's are cut with a restriction endonuclease, an enzyme that cuts DNA at a specific base sequence. The sticky cut ends of the two different DNA molecules can be joined by using a pasting enzyme known as DNA ligase. When this new hybrid recombinant DNA is returned to the bacteria, it replicates itself and directs synthesis of proteins specified by both kinds of DNA. The copying of the foreign DNA segment is called gene cloning. Genetic engineering uses gene cloning to cause bacteria to synthesize valuable proteins.

KEY WORDS

gene
chromosome
deoxyribonucleic acid (DNA)
ribonucleic acid (RNA)
nucleoside
nucleotide
nitrogen base

adenine (A)
thymine (T)
uracil (U)
cytosine (C)
guanine (G)
double helix
base pair

complementary strand
replication
messenger RNA (mRNA)
transfer RNA (tRNA)
ribosome
transcription
genetic code

codon
anticodon
mutation
plasmid
hybrid recombinant DNA
gene cloning
genetic engineering

EXERCISES

24.9 Into what two components can a nucleoside be broken down?

24.10 What is the difference between a nucleoside and a nucleotide?

24.11 Match the correct abbreviation with the correct nucleotide structure: (**a**) AMP; (**b**) dCMP; (**c**) CMP; (**d**) 3′-GMP.

(I)

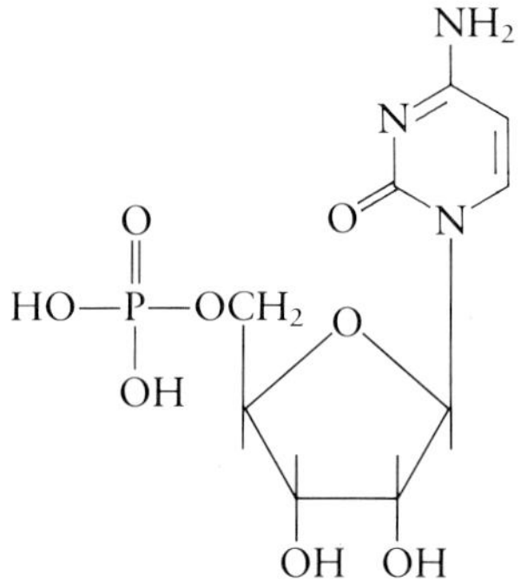

(II)

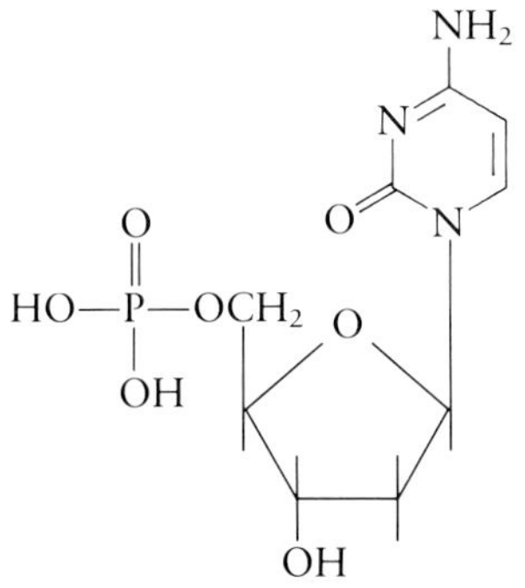

(III)

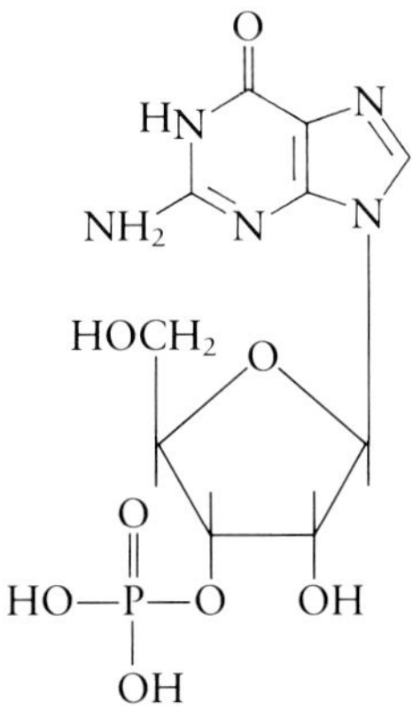

(IV)

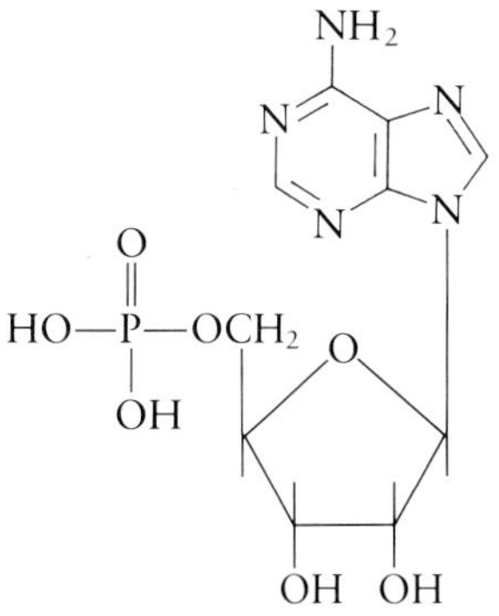

24.12 Is 2′-dAMP a possible nucleotide? Why?

24.13 Describe the linkages that join nucleotides in nucleic acid molecules.

24.14 List the structural differences between RNA and DNA.

24.15 Is the dinucleotide shown below a building block for a DNA molecule or an RNA molecule? What structural features play a part in your decision?

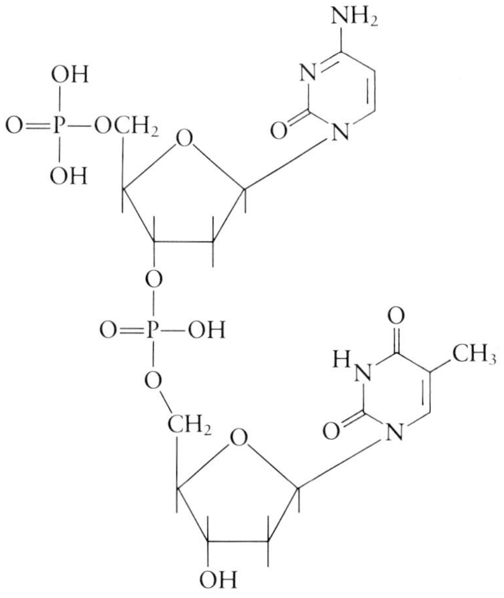

24.16 In DNA molecules the ratio of adenine to thymine and of guanine to cytosine is close to 1:1. Why?

24.17 In RNA the ratio of adenine to uracil and of guanine to cytosine is not usually 1:1. Why not?

24.18 Adenine does not form a base pair with guanine. Why?

24.19 Why do only two H bonds form between A and T (compared with three for C and G)?

24.20 Is the following statement true or false? In DNA molecules the amount of adenine plus thymine (A + T) *divided by* guanine plus cytosine (C + G) is always close to 1. Explain your answer.

24.21 A segment of a DNA molecule has the base sequence ATGAAC. Write a shorthand structure for this segment and for its complementary strand, using the symbols D for deoxyribose and P for phosphate.

24.22 What is meant by *DNA replication?*

24.23 The sketches below represent a parent double helix and its two daughter double helices (newly replicated strands are in color). How many granddaughter double helices are there? Sketch them, choosing a dotted line (or a new color) for the newly replicated granddaughter strands.

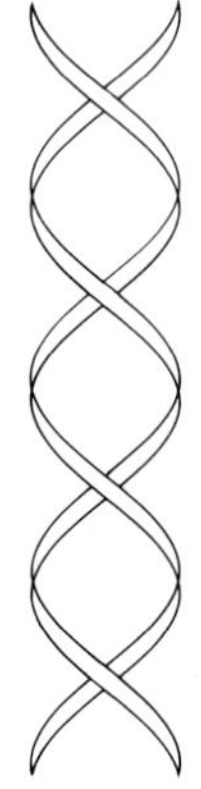

Parent DNA

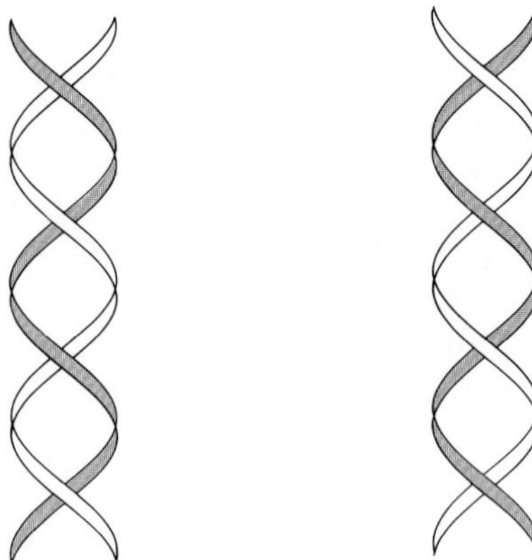

Daughter DNAs

24.24 What is meant by the term *transcription?*

24.25 What are the three different kinds of RNA?

24.26 Why is it that mRNA rather than DNA molecules actually bind to the ribosome at which protein synthesis takes place?

24.27 Originally it was thought that nucleic acids were polytetranucleotides in which a single monomer tetranucleotide was repeated throughout the entire molecule. Could such a nucleic acid molecule contain the information needed to synthesize a protein?

24.28 Why must codons include base triplets (instead of doublets or singlets)?

24.29 Is galactose a protein? How do genes control the development of diseases such as galactosemia (Section 21.3)?

24.30 What codon(s) represent the amino acids shown below?

(a) $NH_2-CH(CH_2-CH_2-C(=O)-NH_2)-C(=O)-OH$

(b) $NH_2-CH(CH_2OH)-C(=O)-OH$

24.31 What is meant by *translation?*

24.32 A DNA segment has the base order AGTCCTGGG.
(a) Give the base order of its complementary strand.
(b) What mRNA molecule would be synthesized by the original segment of DNA?
(c) What tripeptide would it produce?

24.33 What is the difference between a codon and an anticodon?

24.34 What are the possible anticodons on the tRNA molecules that carry the amino acids (a) valine; (b) leucine?

24.35 Why is dangerous to expose chromosomes to x-radiation?

24.36 What is meant by *mutation?*

24.37 The codons CAU UUU correspond to the dipeptide His—Phe. What other mRNA codons translate into the same dipeptide?

24.38 A segment of DNA has the base sequence TCATAGCAAATGTCC.
(a) What mRNA does it synthesize?
(b) For what pentapeptide does this code without any mutation?
(c) For what peptide does this code if the third base is deleted?

24.39 A segment of a DNA molecule has the base sequence ACC GGG CTG AAC AAA TTC GG.
(a) Give the corresponding mRNA segment.
(b) What is the sequence of amino acids in the peptide it would synthesize?
(c) The second base, a cytosine, is replaced by a guanine. What amino acid sequence is present in the peptide synthesized by this new strand?
(d) If the second base were to be deleted by high-energy radiation, what peptide structure would result?

(e) Which peptide would be most likely to be nonfunctional, the one from **c** or the one from **d** above?

24.40 What set of codons could produce the encephalin (Section 23.6) shown below?

$$NH_2\text{—}\underset{\substack{|\\ CH_2\\ |\\ C_6H_4\\ |\\ OH}}{CH}\text{—}\overset{\substack{O\\ \|}}{C}\text{—}NH\text{—}CH_2\text{—}\overset{\substack{O\\ \|}}{C}\text{—}NH\text{—}CH_2\text{—}\overset{\substack{O\\ \|}}{C}\text{—}NH\text{—}\underset{\substack{|\\ CH_2\\ |\\ C_6H_5}}{CH}\text{—}\overset{\substack{O\\ \|}}{C}\text{—}NH\text{—}\underset{\substack{|\\ CH_2\\ |\\ CH_2SCH_3}}{CH}\text{—}\overset{\substack{O\\ \|}}{C}\text{—}OH$$

24.41 List the possible codon changes that could cause the amino acid replacement responsible for converting HbA into HbS, the abnormal hemoglobin that causes sickle cell anemia? (See Section 24.12.)

24.42 About how long would it take the body to translate the mRNA that codes for the insulin molecule (51 amino acid residues)?

24.43 One powerful mutagen is nitrous acid (HNO_2), which removes an amino group from a nitrogen base and replaces it with a keto group. What nitrogen base forms when HNO_2 reacts with cytosine? Could HNO_2 react with thymine in this way?

24.44 What is the difference between a gene and a chromosome?

24.45 Make a sketch of the process of protein synthesis, starting with a strand of DNA. Indicate where in the cell each process is taking place.

24.46 What is meant by: (**a**) hybrid recombinant DNA; (**b**) gene cloning?

24.47 What is a plasmid? Why is it used in gene cloning?

24.48 A DNA segment has the following base sequence: ATATGAATTCAATT. Could this DNA be cut by the enzyme EcoRI? If so, give the fragments which would result from both the given strand and its complementary strand.

24.49 What is an interferon? Explain how a bacterium could be programmed to manufacture interferon.

24.50 Suppose a mammalian DNA molecule contains about 10^8 base pairs. On the assumption that all its genes code for proteins with 300 amino acid residues, state how many genes it contains.

25 BIOENERGETICS, ENZYMES, AND VITAMINS

25.1 INTRODUCTION

So far we have studied the chemical composition of the components of living cells. We are now prepared to consider the transformations that they undergo, in other words, the chemical reactions that are responsible for every activity performed by your body. Each time you move, a chemical reaction causes muscles to contract. Your body constantly synthesizes new compounds for growth and repair of tissues. The food you eat is digested as larger molecules break down into smaller ones. All the reactions involved in these processes that distinguish living things from nonliving things belong to the field of study called **metabolism.**

Catabolic processes degrade biomolecules.

Anabolic processes synthesize biomolecules.

There are two subgroups of metabolic processes. In **catabolism** complex molecules are broken down into simpler molecules, usually with the *release* of energy. The oxidation of ethanol to acetaldehyde, a step in its eventual conversion to CO_2 and H_2O (Section 15.5), and the hydrolysis of carbohydrates, proteins, and fats are all examples of catabolic processes. **Anabolism** refers to the biochemical reactions in which simpler molecules are used to build up complex molecules, reactions that require *input* of energy. For instance, the combination of amino acids to form proteins is an anabolic process.

The chemical *pathways* of metabolism, called **intermediary metabolism,** are the series of chemical reactions required to produce the final product. Most metabolic processes consist of more than one step. The intermediate products of each reaction are called **metabolites;** for instance, the compounds acetaldehyde and acetic acid, the intermediates in the metabolism of ethanol, are metabolites.

In Chapter 10 you were introduced to different types of chemical reactions, the *energy changes* accompanying them, and their *rates.* Here we will expand that discussion to include more about the energies and rates of biochemical reactions. In the remaining chapters of the text we will go on to study specific reactions involved in the metabolism of carbohydrates, lipids, and proteins.

25.2 FREE ENERGY CHANGE: ΔG

Recall that ΔH means change in enthalpy.

For biochemical reactions to support life they must be able to take place without any outside influence, that is, they must be *spontaneous* (Section 10.5). The same criteria used to predict the spontaneity of laboratory reactions also apply to reactions that occur in a living cell. In Chapter 10 you saw that chemical reactions are accompanied by heat changes (measured by ΔH) and that the value of ΔH gives chemists a good indication about whether or not given chemical reactions are spontaneous. We said that reactions that have a negative value of ΔH are *usually* spontaneous, that is, they tend to proceed toward the formation of products. In this chapter we will introduce the quantity called ΔG (*free energy change*), the proper criterion for judging spontaneity of chemical reactions.

The **free energy change** (ΔG) is the energy change that accompanies every chemical reaction. Its value indicates the amount of energy available to do useful work under conditions of constant temperature and pressure. Reactions that have a negative value of ΔG are *always* spontaneous, tend to proceed toward the formation of products, and are called **exergonic** reactions. **Endergonic** reactions have a positive value of ΔG and are *never* spontaneous; when ΔG for a reaction is positive, the process tends to proceed toward reactants rather than products. Reactions in which ΔG is zero are at equilibrium.

When

$\Delta H < 0$, a reaction is *usually* spontaneous

$\Delta H > 0$, a reaction is *usually not* spontaneous

But when

Spontaneous chemical reactions have negative free energy changes.

$\Delta G < 0$, a reaction is *always* spontaneous

$\Delta G > 0$, a reaction is *never* spontaneous

$\Delta G = 0$, a reaction is at *equilibrium.*

The two quantities that contribute to ΔG are ΔH and ΔS.

The capital T in the equation stands for Kelvin temperature.

$$\Delta G = \Delta H - T\,\Delta S$$

We have already discussed ΔH, the heat change that accompanies chemical reactions. From the equation above, you can see that the more negative the value of ΔH, the more negative is ΔG. That is why exothermic reactions ($\Delta H < 0$) tend to be spontaneous. The relationship also shows why chemists cannot use ΔH as the sole criterion for spontaneity. There is another quantity upon which ΔG depends, ΔS, the *change in entropy.*

Entropy (S) is a measure of the randomness or disorder of a system. When $\Delta S > 0$ for a chemical reaction, the entropy increases and the products are more disordered than the reactants. When the entropy decreases in a chemical reaction, $\Delta S < 0$ and the products are more ordered than the reactants. In general, most systems do tend to become more disordered. You have noticed that rooms tend to get messy rather than neat. From $\Delta G = \Delta H - T\,\Delta S$ you can see that increase of entropy (a positive value for ΔS) contributes to spontaneity by making ΔG more negative. However, it is possible for spontaneous reactions to involve a decrease in entropy or to be endothermic, as long as ΔH and ΔS combine to make ΔG negative.

Let us consider the combustion of 4 mol ammonia to produce nitrogen dioxide and water. The free energy change for this reaction is found to be −262 kcal.

The superscript in ΔG° means that the reaction conditions are 25°C, 1 atm, and 1*M* concentration of all components.

$$4NH_3 + 7O_2 \longrightarrow 4NO_2 + 6H_2O \qquad \Delta G^\circ = -262 \text{ kcal}$$

That is, the reaction of ammonia and oxygen to produce nitrogen dioxide and water can proceed spontaneously. The value of ΔG indicates only whether a reaction *can* take place, not how *fast* the reaction goes. In fact, you know that the ammonia in household cleaners does not spontaneously burst into flame when exposed to air—the reaction is much too slow—but when ignited with a small flame or a spark, NH_3 in O_2 will burn and can be used as a fuel.

The ΔG value indicates nothing about the *rate* of a reaction. In fact, some spontaneous reactions are too slow to be observed.

Another example of a spontaneous reaction is the oxidation of glucose to form water and carbon dioxide.

$$C_6H_{12}O_6 + 6O_2 \longrightarrow 6H_2O + 6CO_2 \qquad \Delta G^\circ = -686 \text{ kcal}$$

In the body this conversion occurs not in a single reaction but in dozens of different steps. However, it is not necessary to total the values of ΔG for every one of those steps. In Section 10.5 you saw that the sum of the ΔH values for a multistep process is the same as the value of ΔH for one overall reaction. Likewise, ΔG for the multistep oxidation of glucose in the body is the same as that for the single-step reaction shown above. Because it is associated with such a large negative ΔG, the oxidation of glucose is an important energy-supplying pathway. Glucose and other carbohydrate foods, which themselves are metabolized to form glucose, are called *high-energy substances*. We will see how the energy released by the catabolism of glucose supplies most of the energy for all other biochemical processes in the body. In fact, a general rule of body metabolism is that the catabolic (energy-yielding) pathways supply energy needed for the anabolic (energy-consuming) pathways.

Many biochemical reactions are not spontaneous. Included among these are the energy-consuming reactions required for the buildup of biomolecules in anabolism. For instance, the reaction of carbon dioxide with water to make glucose in photosynthesis is the reverse of the catabolism process shown above and has an equal but positive value for ΔG:

$$6CO_2 + 6H_2O \longrightarrow C_6H_{12}O_6 + 6O_2 \qquad \Delta G = 686 \text{ kcal}$$

In other words, this overall reaction cannot happen without the input of energy, energy which is derived from sunlight.

Without energy-consuming anabolic processes such as the synthesis of protein molecules from amino acids we could not survive. Moreover, some individual steps in catabolic pathways may also be nonspontaneous (even though the overall catabolic pathway is spontaneous). All these reactions must and do take place and therefore have to be driven by some form of energy. In the next section we will look at one specific source of energy that is used to "power" body reactions.

25.3 ATP, A BODY BATTERY

You saw that the monophosphate of adenosine (ribose + adenine + phosphate), AMP, is one of the nucleotide monomers present in ribonucleic acid (Figure 24.11). Then you learned that nucleotide triphosphates such as ATP are the ingredients used to synthesize RNA molecules. Here we find that ATP has *another* vital role in the body. Along with a variety of other phosphate compounds, ATP is used to power biochemical reactions. The energy comes from the breaking of the linkages between the phosphate groups. For instance, the hydrolysis of ATP to produce ADP and a phosphate group (P) involves the breaking of a bond between two phosphates and yields a sizable amount of free energy, −7.4 kcal.

$$\text{ATP} + H_2O \longrightarrow \text{ADP} + \text{P} \qquad \Delta G^\circ = -7.4 \text{ kcal}$$

This reaction is sometimes abbreviated by leaving out the H_2O:

$$\text{ATP} \longrightarrow \text{ADP} + \text{P} \qquad \Delta G^\circ = -7.4 \text{ kcal}$$

High-energy means "energy-yielding."

ATP has two high-energy phosphate bonds, A—P~P~P.

Because it has such a great tendency to undergo hydrolysis to lose a phosphate, ATP is one example of a high-energy phosphate compound. The bonds between the phosphate groups in compounds such as ATP are called high-energy bonds and are often indicated by wavy lines (~) between the phosphates. You can see these linkages in the structures of ATP and creatine phosphate, two high-energy compounds shown in Figure 25.1. The hydrolysis reactions of several important high-energy phosphate compounds are written in color in Table 25.1, where the ΔG values for some biochemical reactions are listed. However, it is the hydrolysis of ATP that is used to drive *most* nonspontaneous biochemical reactions. In fact, it is the ATP produced by catabolic pathways that provides

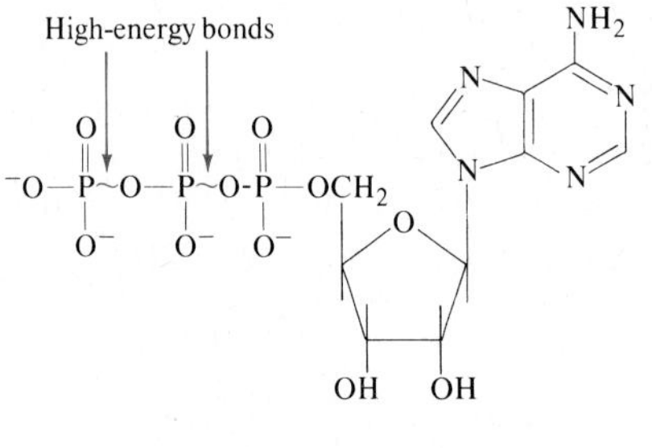

Adenosine triphosphate, ATP
A—P~P~P

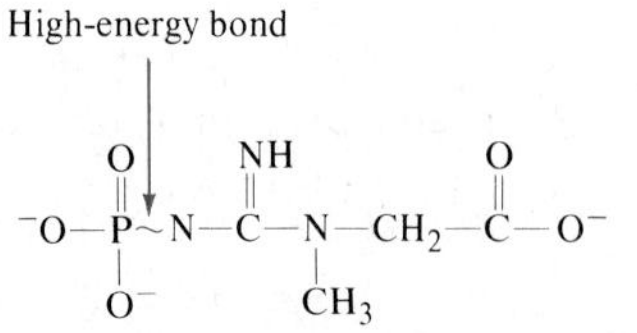

Creatine phosphate, creatine~P

FIGURE 25.1
High-energy phosphate compounds.

TABLE 2.51 **ΔG° VALUES FOR SOME CHEMICAL REACTIONS**

Reaction	ΔG°, kcal/mol ($\Delta G^{\circ\prime}$)
Glucose + $6O_2 \longrightarrow 6CO_2 + 6H_2O$	−686*
$6CO_2 + 6H_2O \longrightarrow$ glucose + $6O_2$	+686*
Glucose-1-P $\longrightarrow$ glucose-6-P	−1.7
Glucose + P $\longrightarrow$ glucose-6-P + H_2O	+4.0
Sucrose + $H_2O \longrightarrow$ glucose + fructose	−6.6
Maltose + $H_2O \longrightarrow$ 2 glucose	−4.0
Glycylglycine + $H_2O \longrightarrow$ 2 glycine	−2.2
AMP + $H_2O \longrightarrow$ adenosine + P	−3.4
†ATP + $H_2O \longrightarrow$ ADP + P	−7.4
†ADP + $H_2O \longrightarrow$ AMP + P	−7.4
†Creatine P + $H_2O \longrightarrow$ creatine + P	−10.3

°′The values of free energy change usually listed in tables, called the standard free energy change or ΔG°, are measured at specified conditions called *standard conditions*, under which the temperature is 25°C, the atmospheric pressure is 1 atm, and the concentration of all reaction components is 1*M*. Tables such as the one above that contain data on free energy changes for biochemical reactions add one more condition, that is, pH = 7, close to physiological pH. Biochemical free energy change values are called $\Delta G^{\circ\prime}$, where the prime (′) indicates that the pH is 7. For convenience we will refer to $\Delta G^{\circ\prime}$ values as ΔG°.

*The ΔG values for any of the reverse reactions listed are equal and opposite in sign, as shown for this pair.

†The reactions shown in color represent the hydrolysis of energy-rich phosphate compounds such as ATP.

energy for the anabolic pathways. This cyclic nature of metabolic processes is illustrated in Figure 25.2, where the degradation of glucose supplies energy via ATP for the attachment of amino acids to tRNA, a step in the biosynthesis of proteins (Section 24.11).

Unfavorable reactions are not spontaneous.

In order to drive a reaction, the hydrolysis of ATP combines with the unfavorable (positive ΔG) reaction to produce a single process, which is spontaneous. These two reactions are said to be **coupled.** Thus, a reaction with a positive ΔG can be coupled with a reaction that has a larger negative ΔG value, thus giving the overall reaction a negative ΔG and making it spontaneous. For instance, suppose a reaction A → B has a ΔG° of 4 kcal and another reaction C → D, has a ΔG° value of −10 kcal. If we add the ΔG°'s, the total is −6 kcal and the overall coupled reaction becomes spontaneous. The reaction C → D is the *driving reaction.*

$A \longrightarrow B$	$\Delta G^\circ = 4$ kcal	not spontaneous
$C \longrightarrow D$	$\Delta G^\circ = -10$ kcal	spontaneous
$A + C \longrightarrow B + D$	$\Delta G^\circ = -6$ kcal	spontaneous

Instead of writing the overall reaction as above, we sometimes separate the reactions using a special notation. The driving reaction may be written underneath the other reaction by using a curved arrow, as shown below.

$$A \longrightarrow B$$
$$C \curvearrowright D \quad \text{driving reaction}$$

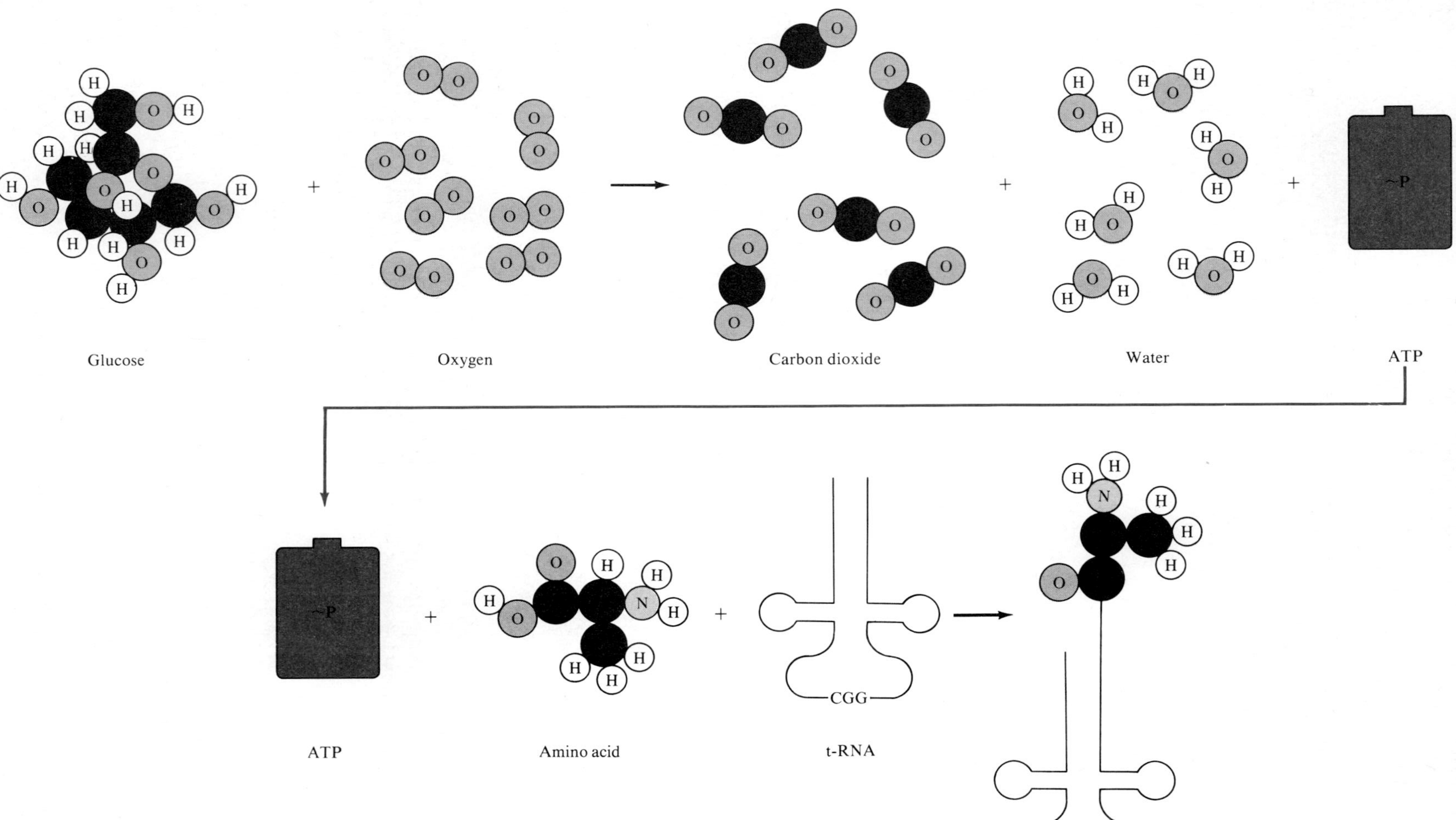

FIGURE 25.2
ATP as a carrier of energy. Part of the energy produced in the catabolism of glucose comes in the form of ATP. The ATP is then available to power the combination of amino acids and tRNA, a step in the anabolic pathway of protein synthesis.

Individual steps in catabolic pathways can be nonspontaneous.

Let us look at one example of a set of coupled reactions. The free energy changes for some biochemical reactions are listed in Table 25.1, where you can see that the formation of glucose-6-phosphate from glucose and phosphate is not spontaneous ($\Delta G° = +4.0$ kcal). This reaction, the first step in the metabolism of glucose, is an example of a nonspontaneous reaction in a catabolic pathway. The overall degradation of glucose provides the body with energy even though some constituent steps require energy to proceed. When the reaction above is coupled to the hydrolysis of ATP ($\Delta G° = -7.4$ kcal), it becomes spontaneous.

$$\text{Glucose} + \text{P} \longrightarrow \text{glucose-6-P} + H_2O \qquad \Delta G° = +4.0 \text{ kcal}$$

$$\text{ATP} \curvearrowright \text{ADP} + \text{P} \qquad \underline{\Delta G° = -7.4 \text{ kcal}}$$

$$\Delta G°_{\text{overall}} = -3.4 \text{ kcal}$$

The total $\Delta G°$ for the coupled reactions is -3.4 kcal, thus making the formation of glucose-6-phosphate spontaneous. This reaction is typical of the role that ATP plays in metabolism.

In each set of coupled reactions there must be some mechanism that causes one reaction to have an influence on the other. In the most common one, shown above in the formation of glucose phosphate, the ATP actually provides the phosphate for the formation of glucose-6-P and the mechanism is shown by simply adding the two reactions:

$$\text{Glucose} + \text{ATP} \longrightarrow \text{glucose-6-P} + \text{ADP} \qquad \Delta G° = -3.4 \text{ kcal}$$

We say that *ATP transfers a phosphate group.* ATP can transfer a phosphate to another compound provided that the ATP has a greater tendency to undergo hydrolysis than the product phosphate. This is true when ΔG for the hydrolysis of ATP is more negative than that for the phosphate produced. In the case above we see from Table 25.1 that the hydrolysis of glucose-6-P has a $\Delta G°$ value of -4.0 kcal/mol compared with -7.4 kcal/mol for ATP. Thus ATP transfers a phosphate to glucose.

SAMPLE EXERCISE 25.1

Is it possible for the hydrolysis of ATP to ADP to power the formation of maltose from glucose?

Solution:

From Table 25.1 we see that the free energy required to form maltose from glucose is $+4.0$ kcal/mol. We couple this reaction with the ATP hydrolysis reaction and then add the corresponding values of $\Delta G°$.

$$2 \text{ glucose} \longrightarrow \text{maltose} + H_2O \qquad \Delta G° = +4 \text{ kcal/mol}$$

$$\text{ATP} + H_2O \longrightarrow \text{ADP} + \text{P} \qquad \Delta G° = -7.4 \text{ kcal/mol}$$

The overall value of $\Delta G°$ is -3.4 kcal. The hydrolysis of ATP could power the formation of maltose.

EXERCISE 25.1

Would it be possible for the hydrolysis of ATP to power the formation of the dipeptide glycylglycine from two glycine molecules?

SAMPLE EXERCISE 25.2

Would it be possible for glucose-6-P to transfer a phosphate group to adenosine as shown below?

$$\text{Glucose-6-P} + \text{adenosine} \longrightarrow \text{glucose} + \text{AMP}$$

Solution:

To find out, we can divide the overall reaction into two steps:

(1) $$\text{Glucose-6-P} + H_2O \longrightarrow \text{glucose} + \text{P}$$

(2) $$\text{Adenosine} + \text{P} \longrightarrow \text{AMP} + H_2O$$

From Table 25.1 we see that $\Delta G°$ for step 1 is -4.0 kcal since it is the reverse of the reaction in the table and $\Delta G°$ for step 2 is $+3.4$ kcal/mol. The overall value of $\Delta G°$ is -0.6 kcal/mol (3.4 − 4).

Thus glucose-6-P can transfer a phosphate group to adenosine. You can arrive at the same conclusion by noting that the $\Delta G°$ value for hydrolysis of glucose-6-P (-4.0 kcal/mol) is more negative than $\Delta G°$ for hydrolysis of AMP (-3.4 kcal/mol).

EXERCISE 25.2

Can ATP transfer a phosphate group to creatine?

You have seen that in order for biological reactions to occur, they must be spontaneous or must be coupled with a reaction that makes them spontaneous. That is not the only criterion they must satisfy to support the processes needed to keep organisms alive. Biochemical reactions must be incredibly fast. In only 1 min a single molecule of the enzyme β-amylase is able to convert over 1 million starch molecules into maltose. In fact

Enzymes catalyze every biochemical reaction.

Enzyme catalysts are needed for every biochemical reaction.

In Chapter 10 you saw that catalysts work by lowering the energy barriers that reactants must climb in order to become products (Section 10.7). Here we will learn more about the action of enzyme catalysts—how they are classified and the compounds that are needed to assist them and the external factors that influence their activity.

25.4 CLASSES OF ENZYMES

Thus far we have encountered many different kinds of reactions that take place in living systems, each of which is catalyzed by some enzyme. Table 25.2 lists the six major classes into which enzymes can fall, depending upon the type of reaction that they catalyze. These broad groups are named by placing the ending *-ase* on a root derived by modifying the name of the reaction type. For instance, **hydrolases** catalyze hydrolysis reactions and **transferases** catalyze reactions in which a functional group is transferred. Within the major classes are subclasses that give some further detail about the kind of reaction. Hydrolase subclasses refer to the different types of compounds which can be hydrolyzed. For instance, *carbohydrases* are enzymes that assist in breaking glycosidic linkages in carbohydrate molecules. Within each subclass there are the specific enzymes that act upon a specific reactant. Lactase, the enzyme that catalyzes the breakdown of lactose into galactose and glucose, is one example of a carbohydrase.

$$\text{Lactose} + H_2O \xrightarrow{\text{lactase}} \text{galactose} + \text{glucose}$$

Kinases are enzymes that transfer phosphates.

Transphosphorylases, usually called **kinases,** are a subclass of transferases that catalyze phosphate group transfer. A specific example is creatine kinase, the enzyme involved in the transfer of a phosphate from creatine phosphate to ADP.

$$\text{ADP} + \text{creatine phosphate} \xrightarrow{\text{creatine kinase}} \text{ATP} + \text{creatine}$$

TABLE 25.2 CLASSES OF ENZYMES

Major enzyme class	Type of reaction	Some subclasses
Oxidoreductases	Redox	Oxidases Dehydrogenases
Transferases	Transfer of functional groups	Transaminases (transfer amino) Kinases (transfer phosphate)
Hydrolyases	Hydrolysis	Carbohydrases (hydrolyze glycosidic linkages) Lipases (hydrolyze esters) Proteinases (hydrolyze peptides)
Lyases	Addition	
Isomerases	Isomerization	Cis-trans isomerase Racemase
Ligases	Bond formation	DNA ligase

Occasionally enzymes are known by trivial names that give no indication about either the reactants or the reaction. Some trivial names that we have encountered are pepsin, trypsin, and chymotrypsin, the proteinases which catalyze the hydrolysis of peptide bonds in proteins (see Section 23.7).

SAMPLE EXERCISE 25.3

What is the major class and subclass of the enzyme involved in the reaction below?

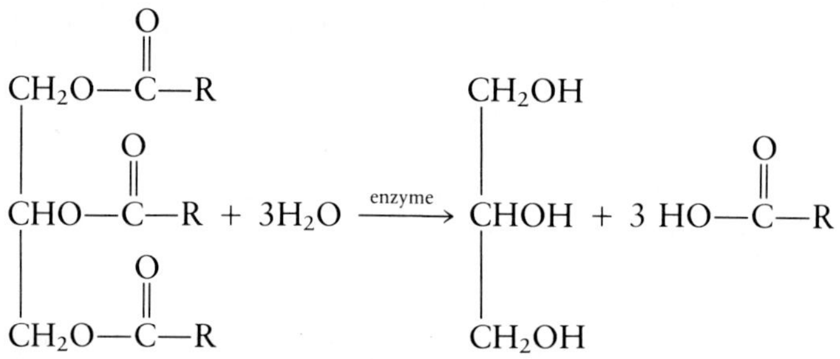

$$\begin{array}{l} CH_2O\!-\!\overset{\overset{\displaystyle O}{\|}}{C}\!-\!R \\ | \\ CHO\!-\!\overset{\overset{\displaystyle O}{\|}}{C}\!-\!R \\ | \\ CH_2O\!-\!\overset{\overset{\displaystyle O}{\|}}{C}\!-\!R \end{array} + 3H_2O \xrightarrow{\text{enzyme}} \begin{array}{l} CH_2OH \\ | \\ CHOH \\ | \\ CH_2OH \end{array} + 3\,HO\!-\!\overset{\overset{\displaystyle O}{\|}}{C}\!-\!R$$

Solution:

The reaction is a hydrolysis and the reactant is a lipid. Hence, this enzyme is a hydrolase (major class) as well as a lipase (subclass).

EXERCISE 25.3

Match the names of the enzymes given with the reactions that they catalyze. (**a**) Aldehyde dehydrogenase; (**b**) arginase; (**c**) arginine kinase; (**d**) sucrase.

(I) [Structure: glucopyranose ring (CH₂OH, O, OH, HO, OH) linked through O to fructofuranose ring (O, CH₂OH, OH, HOCH₂, OH, OH)] $+ H_2O \longrightarrow$ [glucopyranose ring (CH₂OH, O, OH, HO, OH, OH)] $+$ [fructofuranose ring (HO, O, CH₂OH, OH, HOCH₂, OH, OH)]

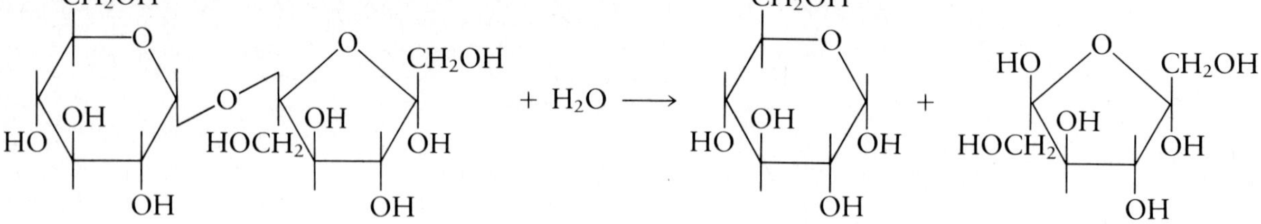

$$\text{(II)}\; NH_2\overset{\overset{\displaystyle NH}{\|}}{C}NHCH_2CH_2CH_2\underset{\underset{\displaystyle NH_2}{|}}{C}H\overset{\overset{\displaystyle O}{\|}}{C}OH + H_2O \longrightarrow NH_2\overset{\overset{\displaystyle O}{\|}}{C}NH_2 + NH_2CH_2CH_2CH_2\underset{\underset{\displaystyle NH_2}{|}}{C}H\overset{\overset{\displaystyle O}{\|}}{C}OH$$

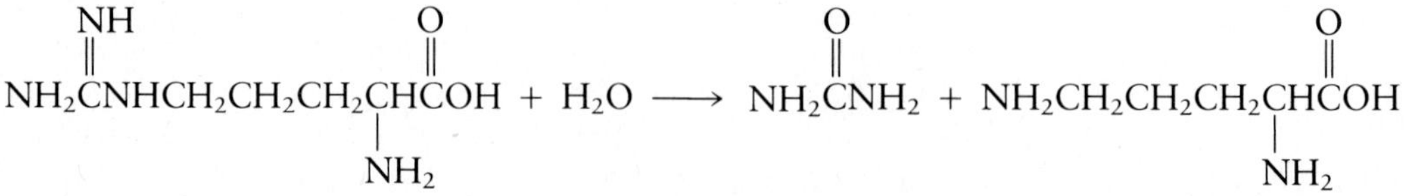

$$\text{(III)}\quad \mathrm{H{-}\overset{\overset{\displaystyle O}{\|}}{C}{-}H} + [\mathrm{O}] \longrightarrow \mathrm{H{-}\overset{\overset{\displaystyle O}{\|}}{C}{-}OH}$$

$$\text{(IV)}\quad \mathrm{HO\underset{\underset{\displaystyle OH}{|}}{\overset{\overset{\displaystyle O}{\|}}{P}}NH\overset{\overset{\displaystyle NH}{\|}}{C}NHCH_2CH_2CH_2\underset{\underset{\displaystyle NH_2}{|}}{C}H\overset{\overset{\displaystyle O}{\|}}{C}OH} + \mathrm{ADP} \longrightarrow \mathrm{NH_2\overset{\overset{\displaystyle NH}{\|}}{C}NHCH_2CH_2CH_2\underset{\underset{\displaystyle NH_2}{|}}{C}H\overset{\overset{\displaystyle O}{\|}}{C}OH} + \mathrm{ATP}$$

25.5 COENZYMES AND VITAMINS

In Greek the prefix *apo* means "away" or "separated" and *holo* means "whole."

In Chapter 23 you saw that enzymes are protein molecules. In many cases the enzyme activity of a protein depends only on its polypeptide structure. Other proteins, known as **apoenzymes,** must be combined with one or more nonprotein components called **cofactors** in order to be active. The apoenzyme together with the cofactor forms a complex called a **holoenzyme.**

$$\underset{\text{Inactive apoenzyme}}{\text{Protein}} + \text{cofactor} \longrightarrow \underset{\text{Active holoenzyme}}{\text{protein-cofactor complex}}$$

Cofactors can be metal ions such as Zn^{2+}, Mg^{2+}, Mn^{2+}, Fe^{2+}, Fe^{3+}, Cu^{+}, Cu^{2+}, K^{+}, and Na^{+}, which are sometimes part of the enzyme formula. For instance, iron is the cofactor in the enzyme catalase, an iron porphyrin (Section 18.9), which catalyzes the breakdown of H_2O_2 in plant and animal cells.

Cofactors can also be organic molecules called **coenzymes.** The building blocks for many coenzymes are vitamins, the organic substances that must be present in trace amounts for cells to function properly. **Vitamins** are required for normal growth and maintenance of humans and must be supplied in the diet since as a rule they are not synthesized in the body.

Vitamins A, D, E, and K are fat-soluble.

Vitamin C and the group of B vitamins are water-soluble.

You have seen that vitamins differ widely in their chemistry and in their functions. In the chapter on lipids (Section 22.9) we discussed the *fat-soluble vitamins,* vitamins A, D, E, and K. Here we will look at the other major subgroups, the *water-soluble vitamins,* including vitamin C and the B family of vitamins. The B vitamins function as coenzymes. In this section we will examine their chemical structures, the enzymes they work with, and the diseases caused by a lack of them. For the dietary sources and RDA (recommended daily allowance) of each B vitamin and a summary of their functions, refer to Table 25.3 and the table on the inside cover as you read the following descriptions. The functional mechanism of the other water-soluble vitamin, ascorbic acid (vitamin C), is not clearly understood.

TABLE 25.3 **BIOCHEMICAL FUNCTION OF THE B VITAMINS**

Vitamin	Coenzyme form	Function
B_1, thiamine	Thiamine pyrophosphate	Transfers aldehyde groups
B_2, riboflavin	FAD and FMN	Accepts two hydrogens
Niacin	NAD^+ and $NADP^+$	Accepts one hydrogen
B_6, pyridoxine	Pyridoxal phosphate	Transfers amino groups
Biotin	Biocytin (biotin + lysine)	Transfers CO_2
Folic acid	Tetrahydrofolic acid (THFA)	Nucleic acid synthesis
B_{12}	Cyanocobalamin	Nucleic acid synthesis
Pantothenic acid	Coenzyme A (CoA)	Transfers acyl groups

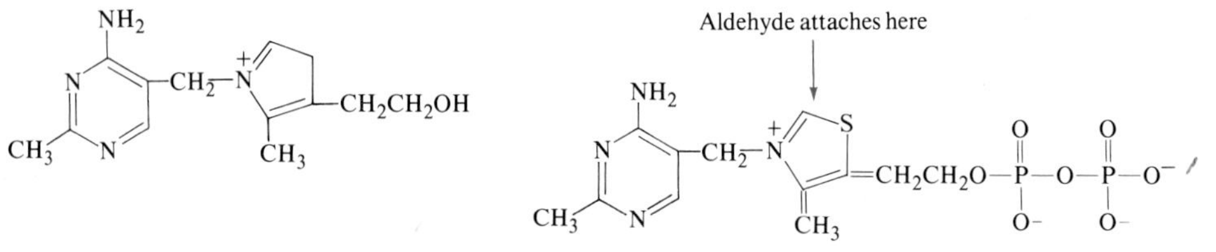

NH2 CH2 CH2CH2OH CH3 CH3 (a)

Aldehyde attaches here NH2 CH2 S CH2CH2O—P—O—P—O⁻ CH3 CH3 (b)

FIGURE 25.3 Thiamin and its coenzyme form. (*a*) Structure of thiamin (vitamin B_1). (*b*) Thiamin pyrophosphate (TPP), coenzyme form of thiamin.

Thiamine, Vitamin B_1

The *thio* root means "sulfur."

The chemical structure of **vitamin B_1** (Figure 25.3*a*) includes a *thio* component, thiazole, and an *amino* component, pyrimidine—hence the name **thiamine.** In most cases the structure of the coenzyme form of a vitamin differs somewhat from the vitamin itself. For thiamine, the coenzyme is actually thiamine pyrophosphate (TPP), shown in Figure 25.3*b*. TPP assists the enzymes involved in the transfer of aldehyde groups in carbohydrate metabolism by "carrying" the aldehyde groups on its thiazole ring (Figure 25.3*b*). A deficiency of thiamine results in the disease called ***beri-beri,*** which causes general weakness followed later by serious cardiac and neurological symptoms.

In Sinhalese *beri-beri* means "I cannot."

Riboflavin, Vitamin B_2

Riboflavin, known as **vitamin B_2,** is contained in the structures of a group of coenzymes known as the **flavoenzymes.** Riboflavin itself contains two components, a *ribose* derivative (see Section 21.3) and a *flavin* heterocyclic nitrogen ring (Figure 25.4*a*). Flavoenzymes are also called *flavonucleotides* because they resemble nucleotides. One of them, called **flavin mononucleotide** (FMN), is actually riboflavin phosphate. As you can see from Figure 25.4*b*, FMN contains the flavin ring (instead of a nitrogen base), the sugar alcohol ribitol (instead of a pentose), and a phosphate. In flavin adenine dinucleotide (FAD) one nucleotide, AMP, is joined to another nucleotide, riboflavin phosphate, through their phosphate groups.

Flavin ring

Ribotol, a Ribose Derivative

(*a*)

FMN (flavinmononucleotide)

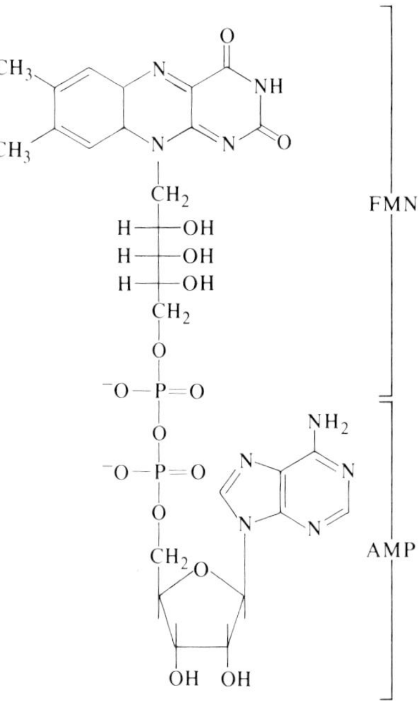

FAD (flavinadeninedinucleotide)

(*b*)

FIGURE 25.4
(*a*) Riboflavin and (*b*) the flavoenzymes (flavonucleotides).

FAD accepts two hydrogens to form $FADH_2$. We can also say that FAD accepts an electron pair (as H:) when it becomes $FADH_2$.

Both FMN and FAD form complexes with enzymes that catalyze oxidation-reduction reactions. The function of the flavoenzymes is to remove two hydrogen atoms from a substrate molecule (RH_2) in the form of H^- (H:) and H^+. The FAD becomes $FADH_2$.

$$\underset{\text{Oxidized form}}{FAD} + RH_2 \longrightarrow \underset{\text{Reduced form}}{FADH_2} + R$$

The hydrogen atoms become part of the flavin rings, as shown in Figure 25.5. When a compound accepts H atoms, it is reduced (Section 16.7). Thus $FADH_2$ is called the *reduced form* of the original flavoenzyme and the coenzyme FAD is said to be in its *oxidized form*.

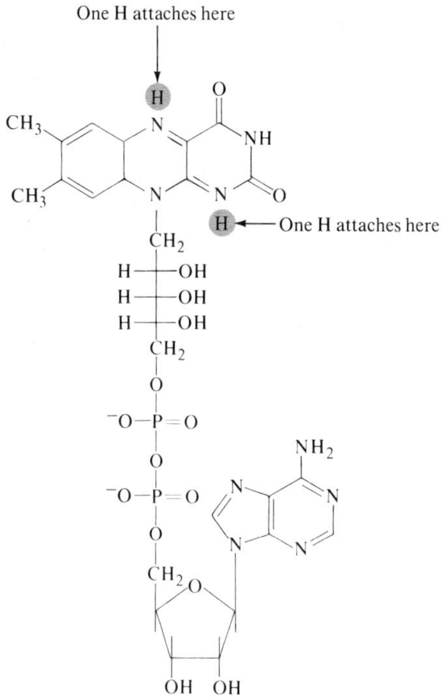

One H attaches here

One H attaches here

FIGURE 25.5
FAD accepts two hydrogens to become $FADH_2$. $FADH_2$ is the reduced form of the coenzyme FAD. The two extra hydrogens are attached to the flavin ring.

The compound riboflavin is a yellow-green substance that was first isolated from milk. Because riboflavin decomposes when exposed to ultraviolet radiation, milk must be stored in opaque cartons.

In many of the reactions involved in *catabolic* pathways, reactant molecules are *oxidized* as part of their eventual breakdown to simpler molecules. You have already seen that the breakdown of alcohol required several oxidation steps (Section 15.5). In the metabolisim chapters coming up we will encounter FAD as a coenzyme for some of the oxidation-reduction reactions that are part of the catabolic pathway in which glucose, fatty acids, and amino acids are degraded to simpler molecules.

Nicotinic Acid, Niacin

The B vitamin **nicotinic acid,** a carboxylic acid derivative of pyridine, is also called **niacin** (Figure 25.6*a*). The amide of nicotinic acid, nicotinamide, is part of two essential coenzymes, **nicotinamide adenine dinucleotide** (NAD^+) and **nicotinamide adenine dinucleotide phosphate** ($NADP^+$). Note from Figure 25.6*b* that the N atom in the pyridine ring of both dinucleotides is positively charged; hence the coenzyme formulas are written as NAD^+ and $NADP^+$.

NAD^+ accepts two hydrogens to form $NADH + H^+$. We also say that NAD accepts an electron pair (from H:) to produce NADH.

Like FAD, these compounds function as coenzymes for a number of oxidoreductases. NAD^+ or $NADP^+$ also removes two hydrogen atoms from a substrate as H^- and H^+. The H^- is accepted by the NAD^+ or $NADP^+$ to produce the reduced form, NADH or NADPH.

$$\text{Oxidized forms}\quad \begin{array}{l} NAD^+ + RH_2 \longrightarrow R + H^+ + NADH \\ NADP^+ + RH_2 \longrightarrow R + H^+ + NADPH \end{array}\quad \text{reduced forms}$$

One of many enzymes linked to the NAD^+ coenzyme is alcohol dehydrogenase,

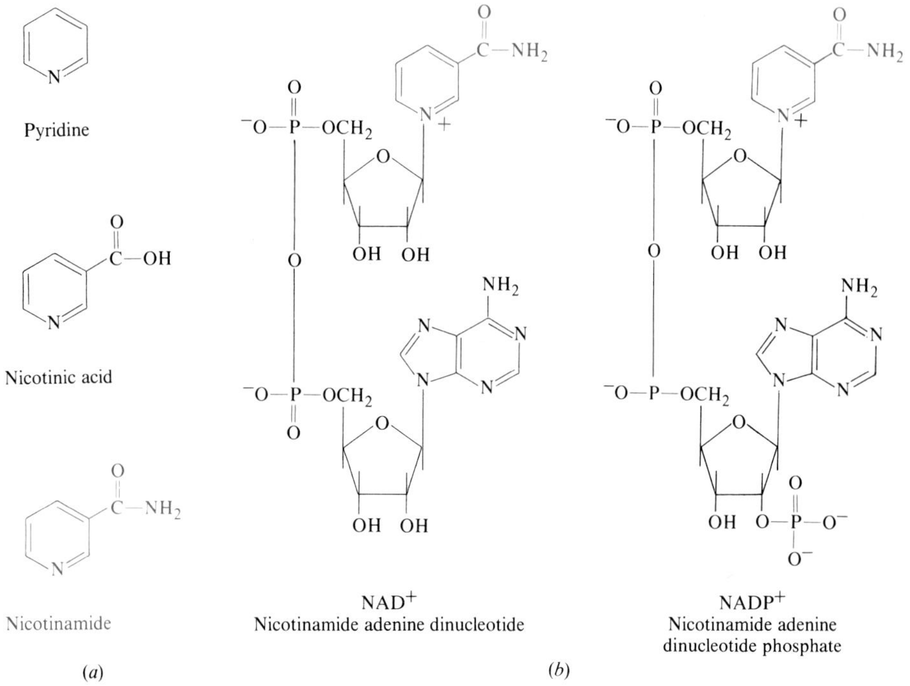

Pyridine

Nicotinic acid

Nicotinamide

(a)

NAD^+
Nicotinamide adenine dinucleotide

$NADP^+$
Nicotinamide adenine dinucleotide phosphate

(b)

FIGURE 25.6
Niacin and conenzyme forms NAD^+ and $NADP^+$.

an enzyme for one of the oxidations in the catabolism of alcohol. In the oxidation reaction in which ethanol is converted to acetaldehyde, shown in Figure 25.7,

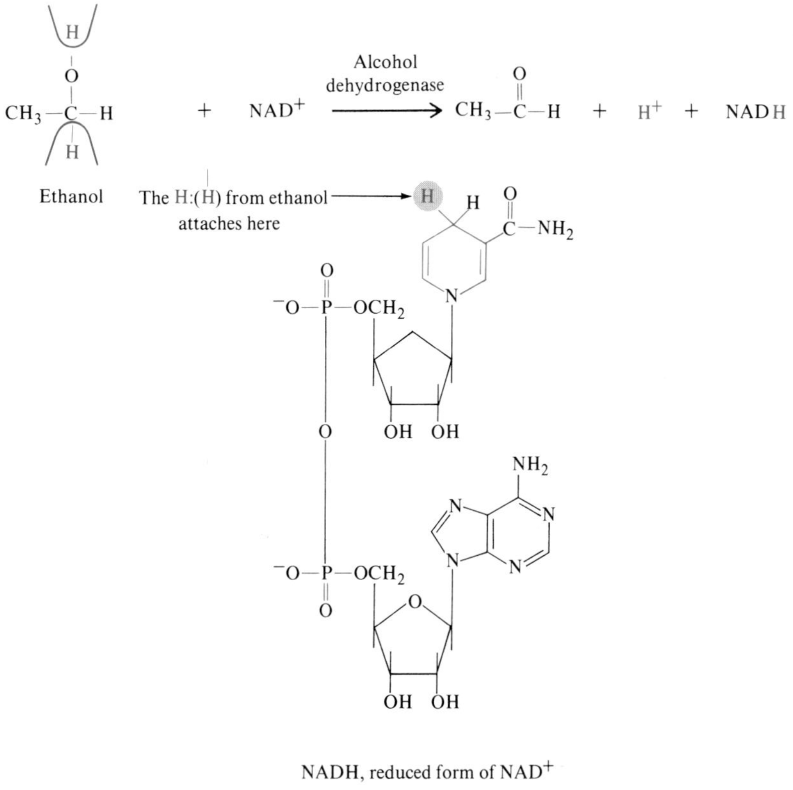

$$CH_3CH_2OH + NAD^+ \xrightarrow{\text{Alcohol dehydrogenase}} CH_3-\overset{O}{\overset{\|}{C}}-H + H^+ + NADH$$

Ethanol

The H:(H) from ethanol attaches here

NADH, reduced form of NAD^+

FIGURE 25.7
NAD^+ removes two hydrogens from ethanol.

note that the pyridine ring (in color) accepts the H^- that is removed from the alcohol.

In Italian *pellagra* means "rough skin."

The body can make nicotinic acid by starting with tryptophan, one of the essential amino acids (Section 23.12), as shown in Figure 25.8. Consequently, diets that are low in protein can result in a deficiency of tryptophan and thus a deficiency of niacin. In humans this deficiency can cause the disease ***pellagra,*** characterized by the three D's, dermatitus, diarrhea, and dementia, and in some cases by a fourth D, death.

Pyridoxine, Vitamin B_6

Aminotransferases catalyze the transfer of amino groups (NH_2) from reactant to product.

Pyridoxine, vitamin B_6, also contains the pyridine nucleus (Figure 25.9*a*). Its derivative pyridoxal phosphate, shown in Figure 25.9*b*, is a coenzyme for enzymes involved in the metabolism of amino acids. Pyridoxal phosphate in combination with aminotransferase enzymes is essential for the conversion of one amino acid to another. For instance, glutamic acid is converted into alanine in the reaction shown in Figure 25.10. Note that an amino group (in color) is transferred from glutamic acid to pyruvic acid (a keto acid), which then becomes alanine. Two other nonessential amino acids synthesized by the body from glutamic acid in this same way are aspartic acid and asparagine. Vitamin B_6 is also involved in the converesion of tryptophan to niacin and so its absence may produce symptoms of pellagra.

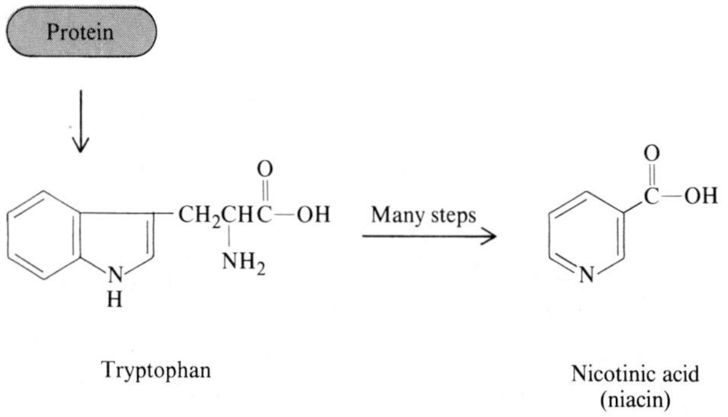

Protein

↓

Tryptophan —Many steps→ Nicotinic acid (niacin)

FIGURE 25.8
Tryptophan → nicotinic acid. About 60 mg of tryptophan is needed to furnish 1-mg niacin by this biosynthetic route.

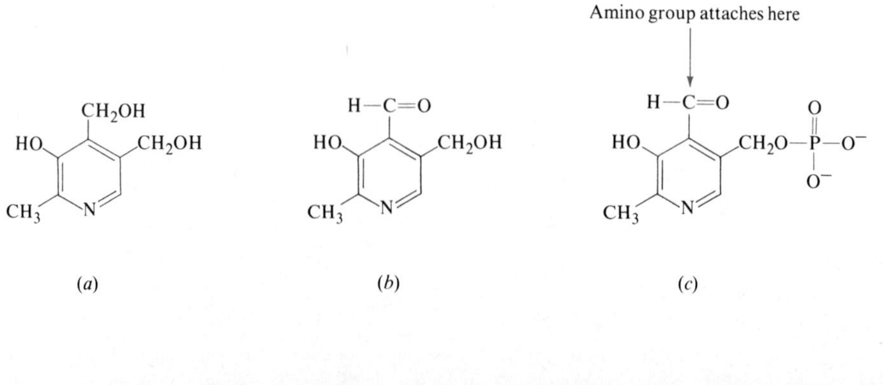

Amino group attaches here

(*a*) (*b*) (*c*)

FIGURE 25.9
Pyridoxine (vitamin B_6) and its coenzyme forms.
(*a*) Pyridoxine, vitamin B_6.
(*b*) Pyridoxal, in which the alcohol group of pyridoxine is replaced by an aldehyde.
(*c*) Pyridoxal phosphate, one coenzyme of vitamin B_6.

FIGURE 25.10
Amino group transfer.

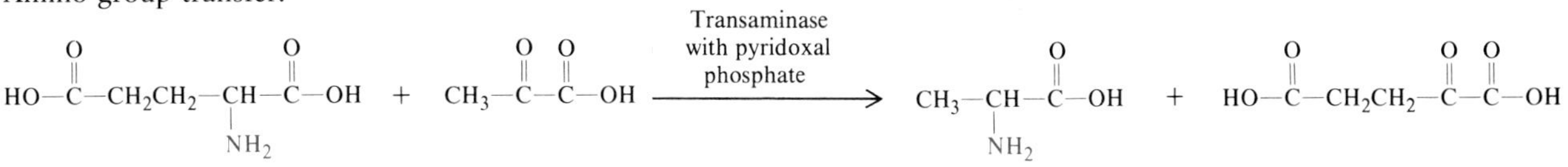

$$HO-\overset{O}{\overset{\|}{C}}-CH_2CH_2-\underset{NH_2}{\underset{|}{CH}}-\overset{O}{\overset{\|}{C}}-OH + CH_3-\overset{O}{\overset{\|}{C}}-\overset{O}{\overset{\|}{C}}-OH \xrightarrow[\text{phosphate}]{\text{Transaminase with pyridoxal}} CH_3-\underset{NH_2}{\underset{|}{CH}}-\overset{O}{\overset{\|}{C}}-OH + HO-\overset{O}{\overset{\|}{C}}-CH_2CH_2-\overset{O}{\overset{\|}{C}}-\overset{O}{\overset{\|}{C}}-OH$$

Glutamic acid Pyruvic acid Alanine α-ketoglutaric acid

Pantothenic Acid

Pantos in Greek means "everywhere."

Pantothenic acid, another B vitamin, present in all plants and animals, contains a unit of β-alanine (Figure 25.11*a*). Pantothenic acid is part of coenzyme A, CoA (Figure 25.11*b*), a molecule that we will have more to say about when we discuss its role in the metabolism of fats and carbohydrates. The A in the name of the coenzyme comes from its function as a carrier of acetyl groups ($\overset{O}{\overset{\|}{C}}CH_3$). From the table on the inside cover you can see that deficiencies of this vitamin are rare in humans.

Biotin

The B vitamin **biotin** (Figure 25.12) serves as a carrier of CO_2. No spontaneous biotin deficiency is observed in humans. Biotin deficiency can be artificially produced

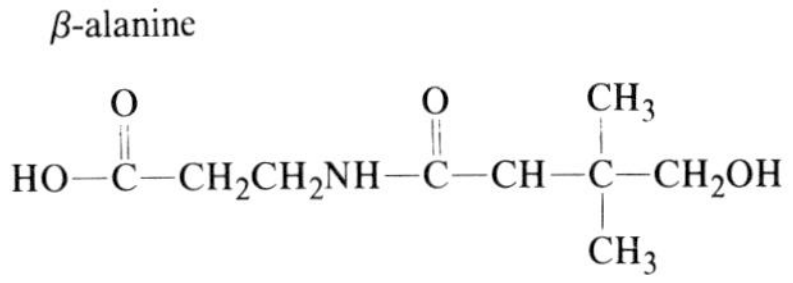

β-alanine

$$HO-\overset{O}{\overset{\|}{C}}-CH_2CH_2NH-\overset{O}{\overset{\|}{C}}-CH-\overset{CH_3}{\overset{|}{\underset{CH_3}{\underset{|}{C}}}}-CH_2OH$$

Pantothenic acid

(*a*)

Acetyl group attaches here

$$HSCH_2CH_2NH-\overset{O}{\overset{\|}{C}}-CH_2CH_2NH-\overset{O}{\overset{\|}{C}}-\underset{OH}{\underset{|}{CH}}-\overset{CH_3}{\overset{|}{\underset{CH_3}{\underset{|}{C}}}}-CH_2O-\overset{O}{\overset{\|}{\underset{O^-}{\underset{|}{P}}}}-O-\overset{O}{\overset{\|}{\underset{O^-}{\underset{|}{P}}}}-O-CH_2\text{(ribose, OH OH; adenine, }NH_2\text{)}$$

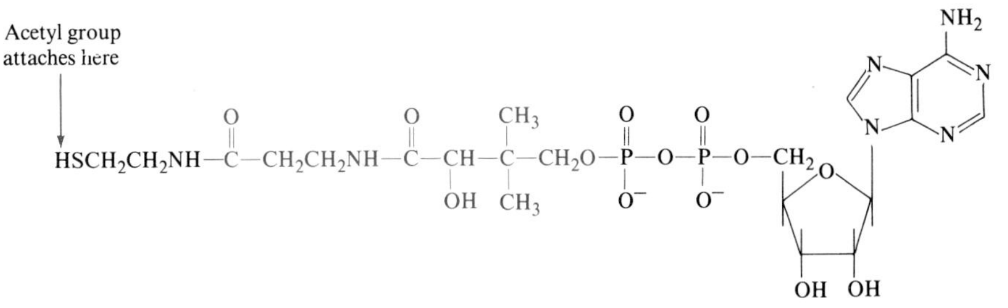

Coenzyme A

(*b*)

FIGURE 25.11
Coenzyme A includes pantothenic acid.

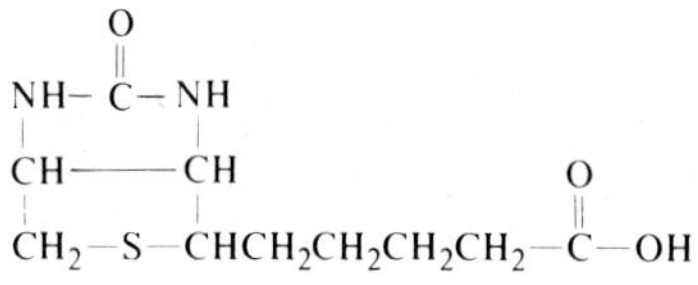

$$\begin{array}{l} \quad\quad O \\ \quad\quad \| \\ NH-C-NH \\ | \quad\quad\quad | \\ CH-\!\!-\!\!-CH \quad\quad\quad\quad\quad\quad\quad\quad\quad O \\ | \quad\quad\quad | \quad\quad\quad\quad\quad\quad\quad\quad\quad\quad \| \\ CH_2-S-CHCH_2CH_2CH_2CH_2-C-OH \end{array}$$

FIGURE 25.12
Biotin.

by feeding large amounts of raw eggs to people (much more than the amount in a few servings of eggnog). A protein in the egg white, avidin, binds to the biotin, causing nausea, muscle pain, and other unpleasant symptoms.

Folic Acid

The name *folic* is derived from the Latin word *folium*, meaning "leaf."

Lack of folic acid causes megaloblastic anemia, in which the erythroblasts that become red blood cells are *very large (megalo)*.

The structure of **folic acid,** found in spinach and other green leaves, is composed of three fragments, an N ring compound called pteridine, glutamic acid, and PABA, para-aminobenzoic acid (Figure 25.13*a*). Its coenzyme form, tetrahydrofolic acid (Figure 25.13*b*), takes part in the synthesis of nitrogen-base components of nucleic acids, including the purines and thymine (Section 24.2). Folic acid need is greatest in tissues that have a high turnover rate, such as bone marrow, because these tissues must constantly produce DNA strands for replication when cells divide (Section 24.7). Folic acid is necessary for proper maturation of red blood cells in the bone marrow, and thus one symptom of folic acid deficiency is ***anemia.*** This is not the same as ***iron deficiency anemia,*** the anemia that is caused by inability of the body to produce enough hemoglobin as a result of inadequate iron in the diet.

Earlier you saw that sulfa drugs kill bacteria by preventing them from making folic acid from PABA (Section 18.7). Humans do not have the ability to convert PABA to folic acid; in humans folic acid is a vitamin which is provided in the diet and is thus not dependent on the availability of PABA.

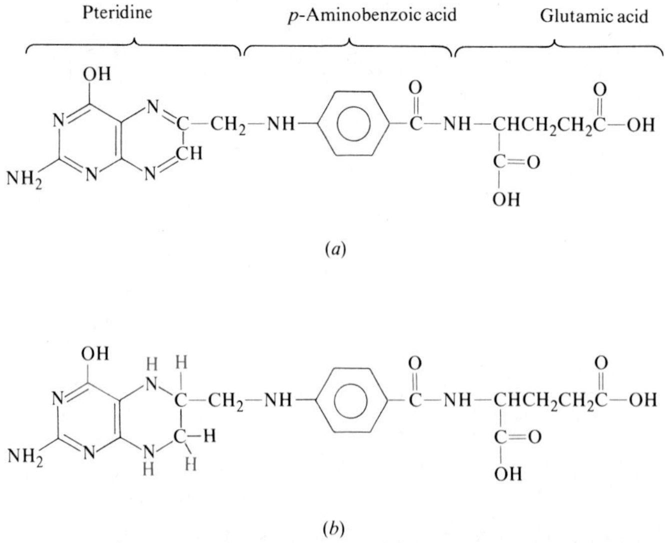

Pteridine | *p*-Aminobenzoic acid | Glutamic acid

(*a*)

(*b*)

FIGURE 25.13
(*a*) Folic acid.
(*b*) Tetrahydrofolic acid, the coenzyme form of folic acid. The four extra H atoms in its structure are shown in color.

Vitamin B_{12}

The formula for vitamin B_{12} is shown in Figure 18.18.

Vitamin B_{12}, also called **cyanocobalamin,** is involved in nucleic acid synthesis and is needed for normal formation of red blood cells. The disease known as ***pernicious anemia,*** the anemia that results from a lack of vitamin B_{12}, is similar to anemia caused by folic acid deficiency. Proper absorption of vitamin B_{12} requires a special protein called the **intrinsic factor,** which combines with the vitamin in the stomach and then transports it to the blood.

The lack of vitamin V_{12} *or* of the intrinsic factor causes pernicious anemia.

To help you answer questions about the pros and cons of vitamin supplements, we have gathered data for you to consider, as we did in Section 22.9 for the fat-soluble vitamins. The amounts of water-soluble vitamins in some vitamin supplements and in some common foods are included in the nutritional data given on the inside cover of the text. Also included is information on the toxic effects of ingesting amounts of these vitamins that far exceed the RDA.

25.6 HOW ENZYMES WORK

Catalysts alter the rates of chemical reactions without being consumed by the reaction. A catalyst cannot cause a reaction to happen that would not happen anyway; that is, a catalyst cannot influence the free energy change for a reaction. Catalysts speed up reactions by providing alternative faster pathways for reactants to become products. In addition to these general features shared by *all* catalysts, enzymes have some special properties that make them unique. For one thing, enzyme-catalyzed reactions are very efficient ones with no side reactions. In many of the laboratory reactions we have discussed there are possible side reactions, often resulting in mixtures of products, some of which may not be desired. This wastefulness does not happen in body reactions.

Enzymes are highly specific catalysts.

But the outstanding feature of enzyme activity is that most enzymes are highly *specific* compared with synthetic catalysts; that is, most enzymes combine with only one substrate or a few closely related substrates. For instance, the only known function of the carbohydrase maltase is to cut the glycosidic linkage in the disaccharide maltose. No other enzyme can substitute for maltase in this reaction.

$$\text{Maltose} + H_2O \xrightarrow{\text{maltase}} 2\ \text{glucose}$$

Other enzymes are less specific in that they are able to catalyze the reactions of a whole class of compounds. One example is carboxypeptidase, a hydrolase that is specific for the peptide bond at the carboxyl end of a peptide but works on all peptides.

$$\cdots\overset{\overset{\displaystyle O}{\|}}{C}\,\Big|\,NH\underset{\underset{\displaystyle R}{|}}{C}H\overset{\overset{\displaystyle O}{\|}}{C}OH + H_2O \xrightarrow{\text{carboxypeptidase}} \cdots\overset{\overset{\displaystyle O}{\|}}{C}{-}OH + NH_2\underset{\underset{\displaystyle R}{|}}{C}H\overset{\overset{\displaystyle O}{\|}}{C}OH$$

We will discuss two theories of enzyme activity that are consistent with the efficiency and specificity of nature's biochemical catalysts.

Enzymes act upon reactant compounds called **substrates.** For instance, lactose is the substrate for the enzyme lactase and creatine phosphate for creatine kinase. According to the theory first proposed by Emil Fischer, a substrate (S) and an enzyme (E) combine to form a complex called an **enzyme-substrate complex** (ES).

$$E + S \longrightarrow ES$$

The complex forms because the enzyme and the substrate have complementary shapes that allow them to bind together. Fischer postulated this from an experiment in which he noticed that an enzyme was able to attack only the D-isomer of a sugar compound. According to Fischer's theory the enzyme and substrate must fit together exactly as a key fits into the lock it opens. This is called the **lock-and-key theory** of enzyme activity, as pictured in Figure 25.14.

Another theory that describes the fitting of enzymes and substrates is known as the **induced-fit theory** of enzyme activity. According to this model the shape of an *unoccupied* enzyme is flexible and thus does not have to be exactly complementary to that of the substrate. When a substrate actually binds to a given enzyme, it is able to force the enzyme into a complementary shape, as shown in Figure 25.15. In this way the substrate *induces* the enzyme to *fit* with it. This does not mean that any substrate can fit with any enzyme; a substrate must still have the appropriate size and shape and functional groups to allow it to bind to a particular enzyme.

Lysozyme has antibacterial properties.

Various forces are responsible for the enzyme-substrate interactions in both the lock and key and induced fit models. In Chapter 23 you saw that enzymes are globular proteins with hydrophilic and hydrophobic regions. The charged side groups that are present in the hydrophilic areas are able to attract substrate molecules through electrostatic forces (positive charges attract negative charges). A negatively (or positively) charged part of the substrate molecule is attracted to a positively (or negatively) charged site on the enzyme. Substrate molecules can also be attracted to enzymes through the forces of hydrogen bonding or through interactions among nonpolar groups of the enzyme and substrate. The region of the enzyme where the attractions between enzyme and substrate take place is called the **active site.** One enzyme for which the structure of the active site is known is lysozyme, the first enzyme to have its molecular structure worked out. Lysozyme attacks bacteria by dissolving a polysaccharide component of their cell walls, a process known as *lysing*. Lysozyme is found in a variety of body fluids (tears, saliva, mucus, and perspiration), where it serves as one of our lines of defense against invading bacteria. In Figure 25.16*a* lysozyme is pictured without its substrate, so you can see its hydrophilic groups arranged to form an active site "crevice" into which the substrate can fit. In Figure 25.16*b* the enzyme-substrate complex is shown with the substrate (a hexasaccharide) in place.

In the ES complex the substrate is more reactive than it would be if uncombined, which lowers the energy of activation for the reaction (see Figure 10.8). Finally, the ES complex comes apart to produce the product (P) and the enzyme, which, unchanged by the reaction, is now ready for another "round."

$$E + S \longrightarrow ES \longrightarrow E + P$$

Substrate
Enzyme
Enzyme-substrate complex

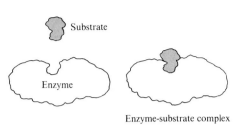

FIGURE 25.14
Lock-and-key theory, whereby the enzyme and substrate fit together exactly.

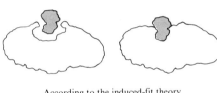

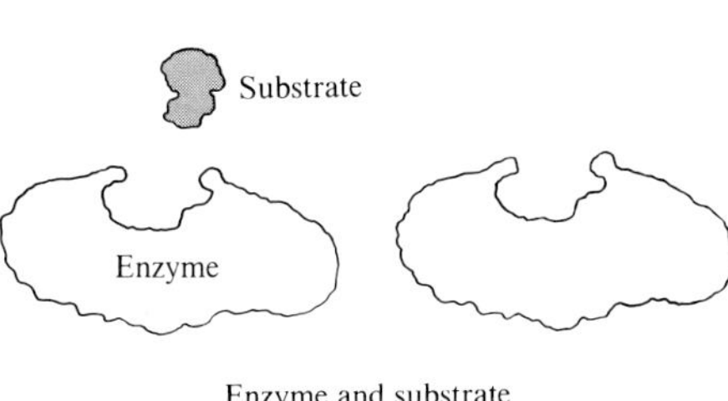
Substrate
Enzyme
Enzyme and substrate
do not fit exactly

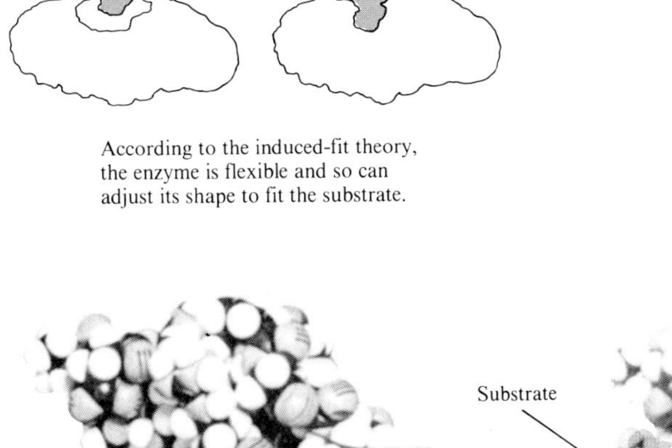
According to the induced-fit theory,
the enzyme is flexible and so can
adjust its shape to fit the substrate.

FIGURE 25.15
Induced-fit theory, in which the enzyme is flexible and so can adjust its shape to fit the substrate.

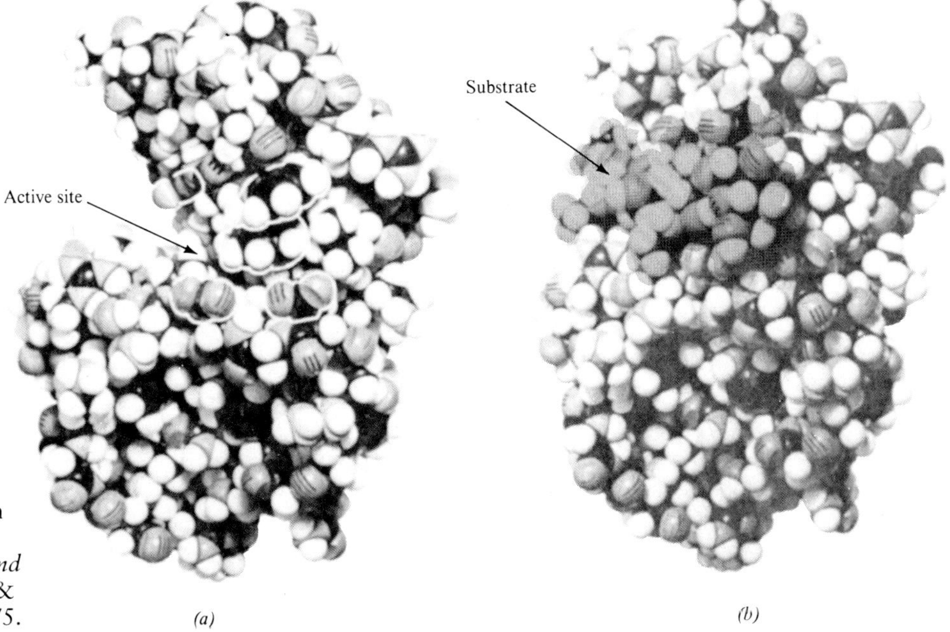
Active site
Substrate
(a)
(b)

FIGURE 25.16
(*a*) Lysozyme. (*b*) Lysozyme and substrate. Adapted from Richard E. Dickerson and Irving Geis, *The Structure and Action of Proteins,* Harper & Row, New York, 1969, p. 75.

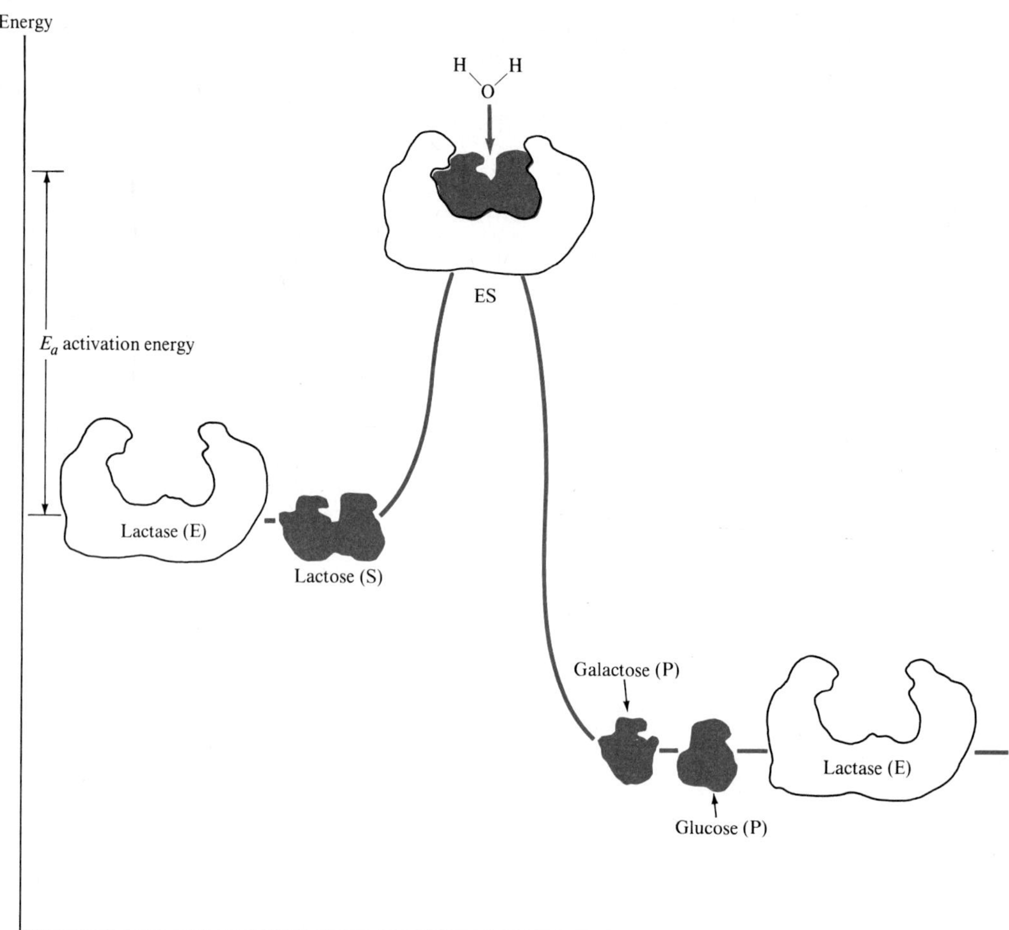

FIGURE 25.17
The activation energy for this reaction would be greater without the enzyme. The lactase (E) bonds to the lactose (S), making it more easily attacked by water.

One overall process from enzyme plus substrate to enzyme plus product is diagrammed in Figure 25.17, where lactose is the substrate and glucose and galactose are the products. When bonded to the enzyme lactase, the disaccharide lactose becomes more susceptible to attack by water.

25.7 INHIBITION OF ENZYMES

Enzymes are proteins and so are vulnerable to the same external factors that influence all proteins. In this section you will see that changes in external factors such as temperature, pH, and the presence of other substances can **inhibit** an enzyme, that is, destroy its activity.

There are two major groups into which enzyme inhibitors can fall, depending upon how they work. **Nonspecific inhibitors** denature *any* enzyme, thus destroying its activity. For instance, very high temperatures and extreme changes in pH are examples of nonspecific inhibition because they inactivate *any* enzyme.

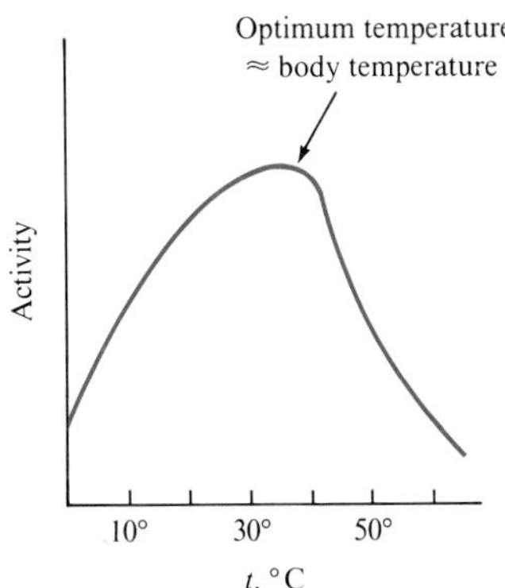

FIGURE 25.18

Temperature

In Section 10.7, where we discussed the effect of temperature on reaction rates, you saw that a 10°C temperature rise generally causes the rate to double. This is also true for enzyme-catalyzed reactions; however, most enzymes, being proteins, are denatured and rendered inactive when heated above 55°C. Most enzymes are active in a temperature range between 10° and 50°C, with optimum activity around 37°C, as you can see in Figure 25.18, where enzyme activity is plotted against temperature.

pH

Trypsin and pepsin are enzymes that cleave peptide bonds in proteins (Table 23.5).

While laboratory reactions often require strong acidic or basic conditions, the same type of reaction can take place readily in the body at the pH of most body fluids, which is just above 7. In fact, for most enzymes, as shown for trypsin in Figure 25.19, activity is greatest around physiological pH (slightly alkaline). An exception is pepsin, which is found in the stomach and must operate effectively under stomach conditions. Note from Figure 25.19 that the activity of pepsin is highest at a pH less than 2, which is the pH of gastric juices.

Specific inhibitors are substances that interfere with the activity of a *particular* enzyme. We will see that this type of enzyme inhibition is the mechanism by

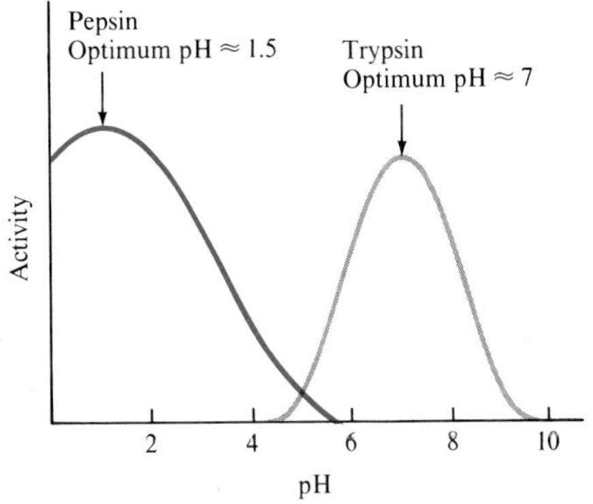

FIGURE 25.19
Pepsin is found in the stomach and trypsin is found in the small intestine.

which many drugs work and also the way in which certain toxic substances produce their effects.

In general, specific inhibitors work by forming *enzyme inhibitor complexes* (EI), thereby interfering with normal formation of enzyme substrate complexes.

$$\mathrm{I + E \rightleftharpoons EI}$$

There are two ways in which this can happen and hence two different types of specific inhibitors: those which have chemical structures similar to the substrate are **competitive inhibitors,** and those which have structures very different from those of the substrate are **noncompetitive inhibitors.**

Competitive Inhibitors

Because they have structures close to that of the substrate molecule, competitive inhibitors are able to bind to the active site of the enzyme, where the substrate would normally bind. Thus competitive inhibitors *compete* with the substrate for a position on the active site of the enzyme. *Both* ES and EI complexes form:

EI complexes are inactive and do not lead to product.

$$\mathrm{E + S + I \rightleftharpoons ES + EI}$$

ES leads to the biological product but EI does not. The greater the concentration of inhibitor I compared with that of substrate S, the greater the amount of EI formed compared with that of ES. More EI means more enzyme inhibition. The effect of an inhibitor can be reversed by increasing the amount of substrate S. The general way in which competitive inhibitors work is illustrated in Figure 25.20.

We encountered one example of competitive inhibition when discussing the activity of the antibacterial sulfanilamide drugs (Section 18.7). You saw that the structure of a sulfanilamide is similar to that of para-aminobenzoic acid (PABA), an intermediate needed to synthesize folic acid, an essential nutrient for bacteria. By competitive inhibition the sulfanilamides bind to the enzyme (E) that would normally attract the PABA, thus preventing the PABA from participating in the folic acid synthesis.

Enzyme inhibitors are used as **cancer chemotherapeutic agents,** that is, drugs that interfere with the growth of cancer cells. One such drug is methotrexate, a derivative of folic acid (see Figure 25.21). The principal action of methotrexate

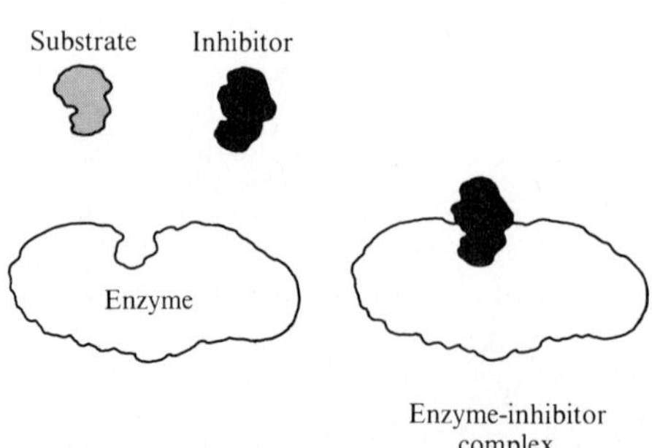

FIGURE 25.20
Competitive inhibition. A competitive inhibitor has a structure similar to that of the substrate and thus occupies the site that normally would enclose the substrate.

FIGURE 25.21
The only difference in the structure of Methotrexate and folic acid is the methyl group shown in color. Methotrexate has an affinity for dihydrofolate reductase that is about 100,000 times greater than that of folic acid.

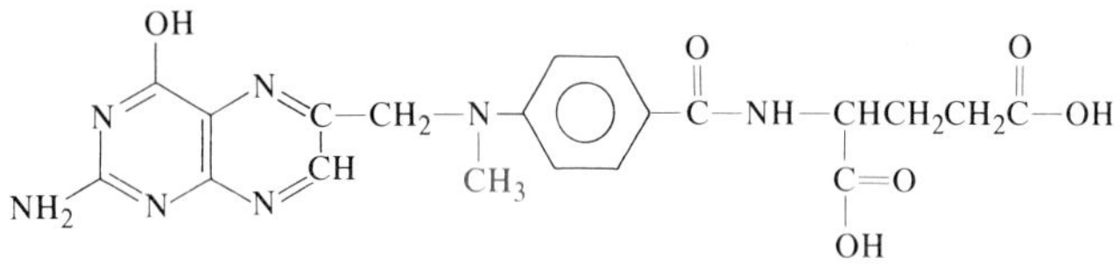

Methotrexate

is to inhibit dihydrofolate reductase, the enzyme that converts folic acid into tetrahydrofolic acid, its active coenzyme form (see discussion of folic acid in Section 25.5).

$$\text{Folic acid} \xrightarrow[\text{reductase}]{\text{dihydrofolate}} \text{tetrahydrofolic acid}$$

Some agents used in chemotherapy are competitive enzyme inhibitors.

Methotrexate has a much higher affinity for the enzyme than does folic acid, its normal substrate. Earlier you saw that tetrahydrofolic acid is needed for the biosynthesis of purines and thymine. By preventing the formation of tetrahydrofolic acid methotrexate reduces the formation of nitrogen bases, depresses DNA synthesis, and thus retards cell growth. Actively proliferating tissues, such as those containing malignant cells, are especially sensitive to the effects of the drug. Thus it is possible to impair malignant tissue without doing irreversible damage to normal tissue. However, to protect normal fast-growing tissues such as bone marrow (where folic acid need is greatest) the dosage of methotrexate must be carefully regulated. Frequent blood cell counts are used to monitor the effects of the drug, with a sudden drop indicating that the drug should be stopped immediately.

Noncompetitive Inhibition

Noncompetitive inhibitors have chemical structures that are very different from those of the substrate. They bind to the enzyme at some point other than the active site, that is, at a point not normally occupied by the substrate. Thus they do not prevent the substrate from binding to the enzyme, as you can see in Figure 25.22. Noncompetitive inhibitors can bind to the enzyme (E) to produce an enzyme-inhibitor (EI) complex *or* to the enzyme substrate (ES) to form an enzyme-substrate-inhibitor (ESI) complex.

$$\text{E} + \text{I} \rightleftharpoons \text{EI}$$

or

$$\text{ES} + \text{I} \rightleftharpoons \text{ESI}$$

Both EI and ESI are inactive, that is, they do not form product.

As_2O_3 is almost tasteless and looks like sugar. Stomach pain and difficulty in swallowing occur about 30 min after intake.

Examples of noncompetitive inhibitors are trivalent arsenic (in As_2O_3 and AsO_2^-, arsenite) and heavy metal ions such as silver, Ag^+, or mercury, Hg^{2+}. These species form inactive EI complexes by reacting with SH groups (outside the active site) that are part of the amino acid cysteine.

$$\underset{\text{Active enzyme (E)}}{\text{E-SH}} + Ag^+ \longrightarrow \underset{\text{Inactive enzyme complex (EI)}}{\text{E-SAg}} + H^+$$

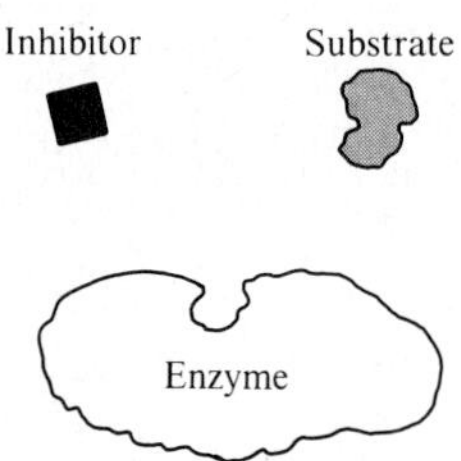

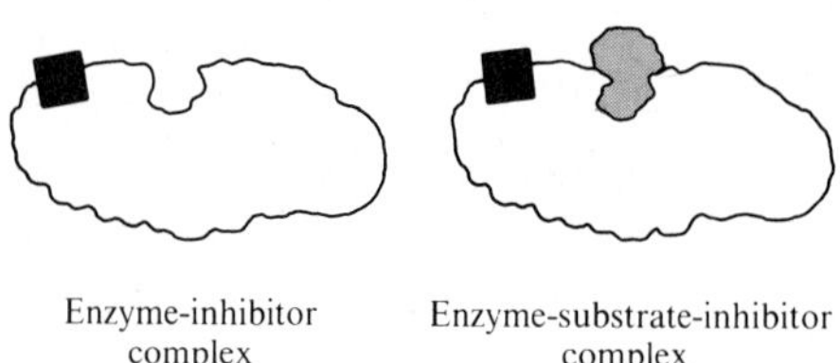

FIGURE 25.22 Noncompetitive inhibition. Noncompetitive inhibitors form inactive EI and ESI complexes.

The arsenite and metal ions inactivate the enzyme by modifying its SH groups, a structural change that alters the three-dimensional conformation of the enzyme. Thus heavy metals and arsenite behave as poisons because they react with SH groups. Recall that the antidotes for heavy metal poisoning (such as dimercaprol) also contain SH groups (Section 8.13) to attract metal ions away from the enzyme.

Another less toxic noncompetitive inhibitor is disulfuram (Antabuse), which inhibits aldehyde dehydrogenase, the enzyme that catalyzes the conversion of acetaldehyde to acetic acid in the metabolism of ethanol.

$$CH_3{-}\overset{\overset{\large O}{\|}}{C}{-}H \xrightarrow[\text{dehydrogenase}]{\text{aldehyde}} CH_3{-}\overset{\overset{\large O}{\|}}{C}{-}OH$$

The buildup of acetaldehyde has unpleasant effects but is not fatal. The structure of the substrate acetaldehyde is nothing at all like that of the inhibitor disulfuram (see Section 15.10 and Figure 15.8).

25.8 ENZYME REGULATION

Enzyme inhibition is not always detrimental. In some cases inhibitors are needed to regulate biochemical reactions. Sometimes the product of a sequence of reactions works as an inhibitor by inactivating an enzyme involved in an earlier step. For instance, let us consider a biochemical process which occurs in a sequence of three steps in which the substrate S is converted to A, which is, in turn, converted to B and finally to the product P:

$$S \xrightarrow{E_1} A \xrightarrow{E_2} B \xrightarrow{E_3} P$$

Suppose the compound P is capable of inhibiting E_1, the enzyme that catalyzes the formation of the intermediate A. In doing this, P slows down the formation of A and regulates its own formation.

Allosteric is derived from *allo*, meaning "other" and *steric*, meaning "space."

The enzyme E_1 in the example above that is inactivated (or stimulated) is called an **allosteric enzyme.** An allosteric enzyme has *two* binding sites. It has an active site, as all enzymes do, which binds to the substrate (S). The second site binds to the product P, called a *modulator* or *effector*. In general, allosteric enzymes are larger and more complex than ordinary enzymes and contain two or more polypeptide chains.

25.9 ZYMOGENS

Zymogens, or proenzymes, are precursors of active enzymes, which must be modified in their primary structure before they can exhibit enzyme activity. The body stores these enzymes in an inactive form so that they will not act on body tissues. For instance, pepsinogen is the zymogen form of pepsin. When pepsinogen is secreted into the stomach, 42 amino acids are cleaved from it, leaving active pepsin. Free pepsin acts as a catalyst to further the breakdown of pepsinogen.

$$\underset{\text{Zymogen}}{\text{Pepsinogen}} \xrightarrow{H^+,\ \text{pepsin}} \underset{\text{Active enzyme}}{\text{pepsin}} + \text{peptide mixture}$$

Prothrombin, the precursor of thrombin, the clotting enzyme (Section 23.9), is another example of a zymogen. Blood vessel injury triggers the release of the thromboplastins, which along with calcium ions are needed to produce thrombin from prothrombin.

$$\underset{\text{Zymogen}}{\text{Prothrombin}} \xrightarrow{\text{thrombo-plastins, } Ca^{2+}} \underset{\text{Active enzyme}}{\text{thrombin}} + \text{peptide}$$

Anticoagulants such as heparin, sodium oxalate, and sodium citrate interfere with the activation of prothrombin.

Anticoagulants work by interfering with the process shown above. The anticoagulant activity of *heparin*, a sulfonated polysaccharide present in the circulating blood (see Figure 25.23), is partly due to its ability to inhibit the formation of thromboplastins. Many anticoagulants work by reacting with Ca^{2+} ions. For instance, when sodium oxalate is added to samples of blood, it reacts to form insoluble calcium oxalate, which precipitates. Oxalates are toxic and are used only for laboratory tests. The nontoxic compound sodium citrate reacts with Ca^{2+} ions, making them unavailable, and is the principal anticoagulant used in blood transfusions.

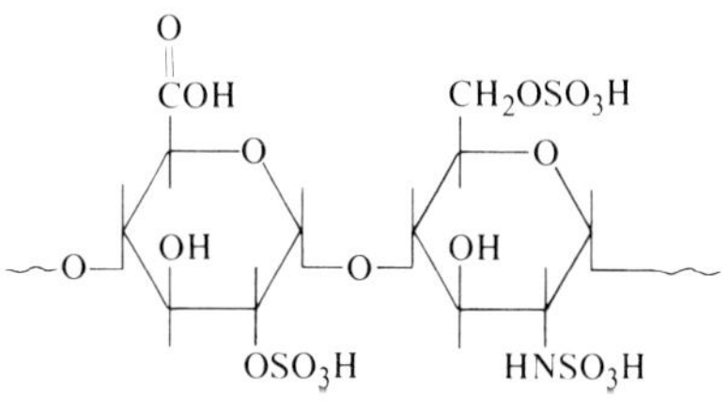

O
COH
CH_2OSO_3H
O
O
OH
OH
O
O
OSO_3H
$HNSO_3H$

FIGURE 25.23 Repeat unit of the anticoagulant heparin

SUMMARY

Metabolism is the study of the reactions that take place in living things. In catabolic pathways complex molecules are broken down into simpler ones. In anabolic pathways energy is consumed in order to construct complex molecules from simpler ones. It is generally true that the catabolic processes provide the energy for the anabolic ones.

Spontaneous chemical reactions tend to proceed toward the formation of products, are energy-yielding (exergonic), and are associated with a negative change in free energy ($\Delta G < 0$). Since $\Delta G = \Delta H - T\,\Delta S$, negative enthalpy changes (heat evolved) and positive entropy changes (increase in disorder) contribute to a negative ΔG. Biochemical reactions that are not spontaneous are driven to form product by coupling with other, spontaneous reactions, so that the overall ΔG is < 0. Driving reactions involve the breaking of high-energy phosphate bonds such as those in ATP, adenosine triphosphate.

Spontaneous reactions are always possible but may be too slow to be of practical use. In the body enzyme catalysts are required for every biochemical reaction. Enzymes are all proteins. Most enzyme names include a root describing the reaction type followed by the ending *-ase*. To be active many enzymes must combine with a cofactor (organic molecule or metal ion) to form an active holoenzyme.

The water-soluble B vitamins are organic molecules serving as building blocks for many cofactors called coenzymes. Vitamin B_1 is thiamine, which forms the coenzyme thiamine pyrophosphate (TPP), involved in aldehyde transfer reactions. Thiamine deficiency causes beri-beri. Riboflavin, or vitamin B_2, is part of the flavoenzymes FMN and FAD, which participate in oxidation-reduction reactions by accepting two hydrogen atoms to become $FMNH_2$ and $FADH_2$. Vitamin B_6 is pyridoxine. Its coenzyme form, pyridoxal phosphate, participates in amino acid metabolism by the transfer of amino groups. Vitamin B_{12}, a porphyrin derivative, forms a coenzyme needed for nitrogen base synthesis. Pernicious anemia results from a deficiency of vitamin B_{12}.

Niacin, a B vitamin, is part of NAD^+ (or $NADP^+$), nucleotides of nicotinamide. When these coenzymes accept two hydrogens in oxidation reactions, they are converted to $NADH + H^+$ (or $NADPH + H^+$). Niacin deficiency results in pellagra. The B vitamin pantothenic acid is part of coenzyme A, which plays a major role in fat and carbohydrate metabolism. Biotin is a B vitamin that is involved in carboxyl group transfer. The vitamin folic acid produces tetrahydrofolic acid, a coenzyme needed for the synthesis of nitrogen bases. Folic acid deficiency produces an anemia similar to that caused by lack of vitamin B_{12}.

Enzyme catalysts are very efficient and highly specific compared with synthetic catalysts. According to one theory the enzyme and substrate fit together like a lock and key. The induced-fit theory proposes that the enzyme can "flex" to accept the substrate. According to either theory the enzyme is attracted to the substrate by electrostatic forces between functional groups in a region of the enzyme known as the active site.

Inhibition of an enzyme destroys its activity. Nonspecific inhibitors such as high temperatures or extreme pH values denature any enzyme. Specific inhibitors deactivate particular enzymes. Competitive inhibitors occupy the active site since their structures are similar to that of the normal substrate. A noncompetitive inhibitor occupies some other site and generally has a very different chemical structure from that of the substrate. Allosteric regulation of enzyme activity takes place when the product (called a modulator) of a series of biochemical reactions inactivates an enzyme, known as an allosteric enzyme, involved in an earlier step. Zymogens, precursors of enzymes, are activated as the need for them arises.

KEY WORDS

metabolism
catabolism
anabolism
free energy change (ΔG)
high-energy phosphate compound
coenzyme
vitamin B_1 (thiamin)
vitamin B_2 (riboflavin)
flavoenzyme
niacin
nicotinamide
NAD^+
$NADP^+$
vitamin B_6 (pyridoxine)
coenzyme A (pantothenic acid)
biotin
folic acid
vitamin B_{12}
enzyme
substrate
lock-and-key theory
induced-fit theory
active site
nonspecific inhibitor
specific inhibitor
competitive inhibitor
noncompetitive inhibitor
allosteric enzyme
zymogen

EXERCISES

25.4 What is the difference between catabolism and anabolism

25.5 Are the following processes classified as catabolic or anabolic?
(a) Amino acids → insulin
(b) Gelatin → amino acids
(c) Nucleotides → DNA
(d) Glucose → glycogen
(e) Carbon dioxide and water → glucose
(f) Triacylglycerol → carbon dioxide and water

25.6 What do chemists mean when they say that the reaction A + B → C is spontaneous.

25.7 What is the ΔG criterion for a spontaneous reaction?

25.8 The free energy change for the conversion of carbon in its diamond form to carbon in its graphite form is negative.

$$\text{C (diamond)} \longrightarrow \text{C (graphite)} \qquad \Delta G < 0$$

Why do you not observe diamonds spontaneously turning into graphite?

25.9 Why is it possible for endothermic (heat-absorbing) reactions to be spontaneous?

25.10 What is meant by a high-energy phosphate compound? Give an example.

25.11 Which of the following reactions could possibly be "powered" by the hydrolysis of ATP to form ADP? (See Table 25.1.)
(a) Glucose + fructose → sucrose + H_2O
(b) Glucose-6-P → glucose-1-P
(c) Creatine + P → creatine-P + H_2O

25.12 Of the reactions in Exercise 25.11, which one(s) could be powered by the hydrolysis of AMP to form adenosine? (See Table 25.1.)

25.13 Is it possible for glucose-6-P to transfer a phosphate to ADP?

25.14 What is meant by a driving reaction? Suppose a process in which A is converted to B is driven by the hydrolysis of ATP. Write the two reactions which describe this, using the special notation for a driving reaction.

25.15 Find the free energy change for the set of coupled reactions shown below. Is the overall process spontaneous? Use Table 25.1.

$$\text{Glu} + \text{Glu} \longrightarrow \text{maltose} + H_2O$$
$$\text{AMP} + H_2O \curvearrowright \text{adenosine} + \text{P}$$

25.16 Can the synthesis of sucrose take place according to this set of coupled reactions?

$$\text{Glucose} + \text{fructose} \longrightarrow \text{sucrose} + H_2O$$
$$\text{Creatine-P} + H_2O \curvearrowright \text{creatine} + \text{P}$$

25.17 To prevent the ATP from diminishing during a muscle contraction, a phosphate compound provides the energy for converting ADP into ATP. Of the following compounds which one could it be: (a) glucose-6-P; (b) AMP; or (c) creatine-P?

25.18 Match the following enzymes with the correct reactions below: (a) isocitrate dehydrogenase; (b) amylase; (c) glycerol kinase.

(I) CH_2OH–CHOH–CH_2OH + ATP ⟶ CH_2OH–CHOH–CH_2O—P + ADP

(II) HO—C(=O)—CH(OH)—CH_2—C(=O)—OH ⟶ HO—C(=O)—C(=O)—CH_2—C(=O)—OH + 2H

(III) Starch + H_2O ⟶ maltose units

25.19 Below is shown the lipid compound that accumulates in ***Fabry's disease,*** a rare disease resulting in death by kidney or heart failure. This lipid normally would be broken down by hydrolysis of the α linkage indicated. Can you make an educated guess about the name of the missing or defective enzyme in persons who are afflicted with Fabry's disease?

25.20 What is wrong with the following statement: The enzyme maltase makes the synthesis of maltose from glucose spontaneous even though ΔG for the reaction is +4 kcal/mol.

25.21 What is meant by a coenzyme?

25.22 Match the conditions below with the correct vitamin deficiency.

(a) Pellagra	(I) Vitamin B_{12}
(b) Pernicious anemia	(II) Vitamin B_1
(c) Beri-beri	(III) Niacin

25.23 A patient suffering from anemia shows no sign of recovery when treated with an adequate iron supplement. Can you think of an explanation for this?

25.24 One consequence of the surgical removal of the stomach is the eventual development of pernicious anemia. Why should this happen?

25.25 What is meant by the oxidized and reduced forms of nicotine adenine dinucleotide and nicotine adenine dinucleotide phosphate? To answer this question provide abbreviations for the formulas of each one.

25.26 Repeat Exercise 25.25 for the flavonucleotides.

25.27 In what ways do synthetic catalysts differ from enzymes?

25.28 Compare the lock-and-key and induced-fit theories of enzyme activity. Include sketches in your answer.

25.29 An enzyme prepared in the laboratory is accidentally allowed to reach the temperature of boiling water. Will it still be active? Why?

25.30 Explain the difference between competitive enzyme inhibition and noncompetitive enzyme inhibition. Give an example of each one.

25.31 What enzyme is inhibited by methotrexate? What compound is not produced as a result of this? How does this prevent cell growth?

25.32 Methotrexate prescriptions can include a supply sufficient for as long as 7 days but no more. Why do you think such care is taken? What test is used to detect methotrexate toxicity?

25.33 In Section 15.10 we discussed the use of ethanol as an antidote for methanol poisoning. Is this an example of: (**a**) nonspecific inhibition; (**b**) competitive inhibition; or (**c**) noncompetitive inhibition?

25.34 Explain why heavy metal ions are toxic.

25.35 According to the reaction scheme shown below, compound IV reduces the formation of compound II.

$$\text{I} \xrightarrow{E_1} \text{II} \xrightarrow{E_2} \text{III} \xrightarrow{E_3} \text{IV}$$

(**a**) Identify the allosteric enzyme.
(**b**) Which compound is the modulator?

25.36 Why do you think allosteric enzymes are larger and more complex than ordinary enzymes?

25.37 What is a zymogen? Give an example.

25.38 How do the anticoagulants sodium oxalate and sodium citrate work? Which one is used for blood transfusions and which is used only in the laboratory? Why?

26 METABOLISM OF CARBOHYDRATES

26.1 INTRODUCTION

In the last chapter you saw that the catabolic breakdown of glucose provides energy in the form of ATP to power other reactions in the body. Here you will learn the details of that complex process, which we simplified by showing one overall reaction in which glucose and oxygen combine to form carbon dioxide and water. In fact, the catabolism of glucose is divided into two major pathways. In the first one, called *glycolysis*, a glucose molecule is split in half. Glycolysis takes place in the absence of oxygen and supplies about 5 percent of the energy we get from carbohydrates. The continuing breakdown of the fragments produced from glucose happens during *respiration*, the catabolic pathway that requires the oxygen in the air you breathe and provides the bulk of the energy derived from carbohydrate foods. Respiration is a common pathway for all foodstuffs, proteins and fats as well as carbohydrates.

We will also give shorter descriptions of two anabolic pathways: *glycogenesis*, the formation of glycogen from glucose; and *gluconeogenesis*, the biosynthesis of glucose. Throughout our discussion of carbohydrate metabolism you can see where each pathway fits into the whole picture by referring to the diagram in Figure 26.1.

Finally, we will see how green plants, by the process of photosynthesis, manufacture carbohydrates, many of which are fit for human consumption.

Let us first see how the carbohydrates we actually eat are digested. By **digestion** we mean the hydrolysis of larger molecules, such as disaccharides and polysaccharides, to smaller components, such as glucose and other monosaccharides that can be absorbed and further metabolized. We always use glucose rather than other monosaccharides as the starting reactant for carbohydrate breakdown because glucose is the main form in which cells utilize carbohydrates.

26.2 DIGESTION OF CARBOHYDRATES

Among the carbohydrates in our diets are the disaccharides sucrose (glucose + fructose) and lactose (galactose + glucose) and the plant starches amylose and

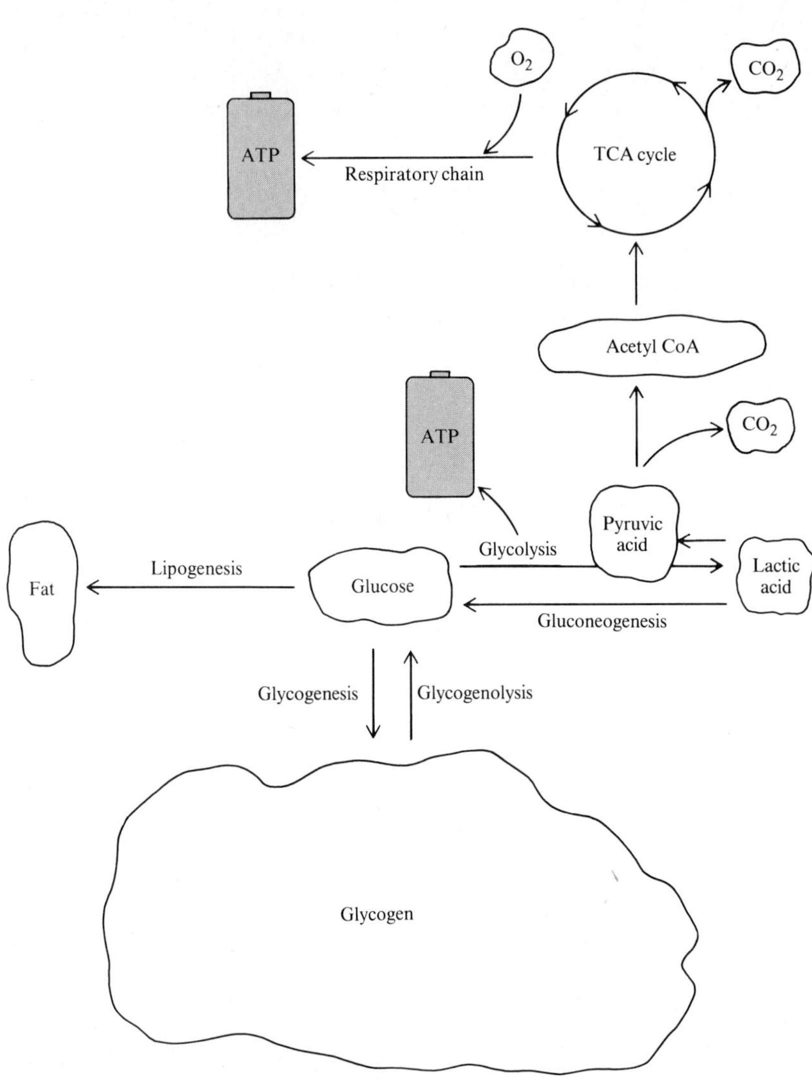

FIGURE 26.1
Carbohydrate metabolic pathways.

amylopectin (polymers of glucose). Let us follow the path of these carbohydrates from the mouth to the stomach to the small intestine, which contains most of the enzymes needed to break them down into monosaccharides (see Figure 26.2).

The HCl in gastric juices kills microorganisms.

Carbohydrate foods are broken down physically when they are chewed in the mouth. For plant starches some chemical breakdown also begins in the saliva where the enzyme salivary α-amylase begins its work. In the stomach carbohydrates are mixed with gastric juice, a highly acidic liquid, which is about 0.02 to 0.05% HCl, with a pH of around 2. Gastric juices also contain inorganic salts; the enzymes pepsin and rennin, which act upon proteins; a weak lipase enzyme, which attacks lipids; and a glycoprotein substance called mucin, which protects the stomach walls from irritants. Because these juices contain no specific enzymes for digestion of carbohydrates, very little breakdown happens there.

A glycoprotein breaks down to produce a carbohydrate and a protein.

The major part of all carbohydrate digestion takes place in the small intestine. The breakdown of starches not already attacked by salivary amylase continues

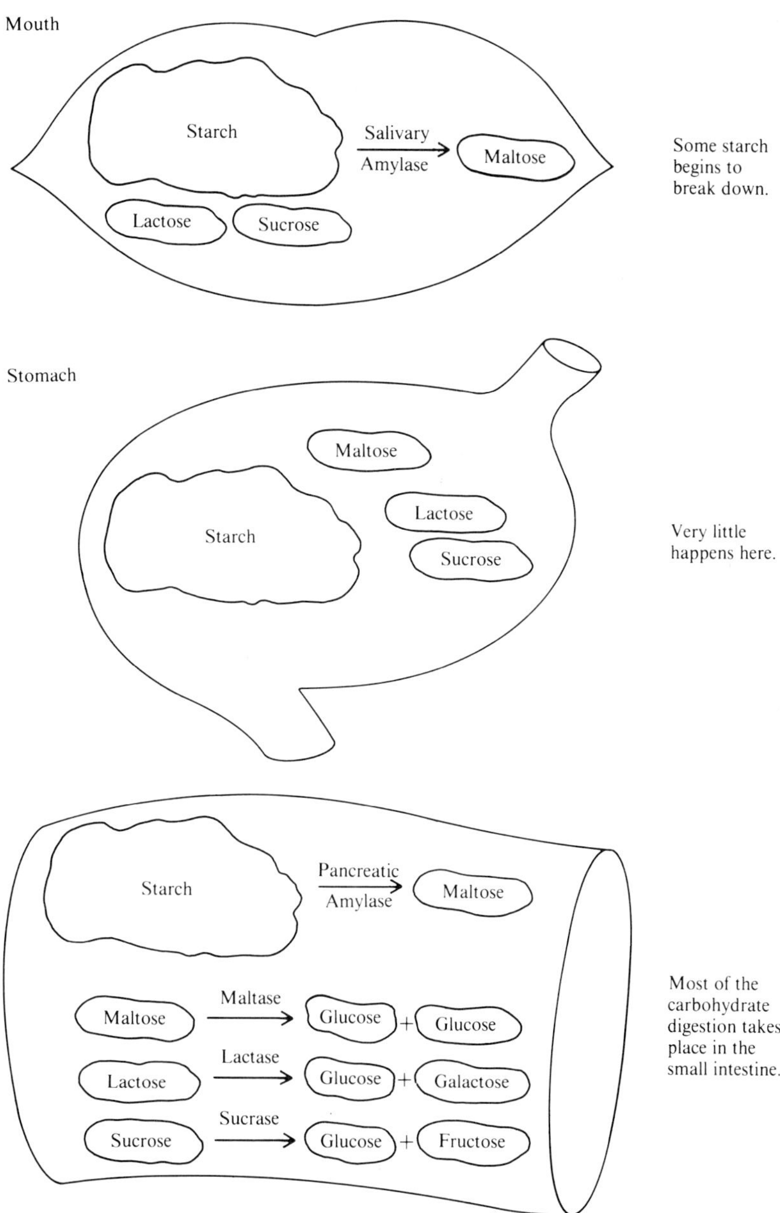

FIGURE 26.2
Digestion of carbohydrates.

by the action of amylase produced in the pancreas. The products of starch breakdown are mainly the disaccharide maltose (glucose + glucose) and glucose.

$$\text{Starch} \xrightarrow{\text{amylase}} \text{maltose} + \text{glucose}$$

The disaccharides, those from the diet and from starch breakdown, are then hydrolyzed by the enzymes sucrase, lactase, and maltase, also present in the small intestine. The products are the constituent monosaccharides.

Recall that a deficiency of lactase leads to lactose intolerance (Section 21.9).

$$\text{Sucrose} \xrightarrow{\text{sucrase}} \text{glucose} + \text{fructose}$$

$$\text{Lactose} \xrightarrow{\text{lactase}} \text{glucose} + \text{galactose}$$

$$\text{Maltose} \xrightarrow{\text{maltase}} \text{glucose} + \text{glucose}$$

Galactosemia occurs once in every 25,000 births.

In this way the three most common products of carbohydrate digestion, glucose, fructose, and galactose, are produced. Galactose is converted into glucose in the liver. Inherited defects in one of the enzymes needed to complete this transformation cause ***galactosemia,*** with symptoms described in Section 21.3. Fructose is not converted directly into glucose but is converted into fructose-1-phosphate, which then splits apart to form smaller molecules which enter the metabolic pathway used to degrade glucose. The two fragments can also recombine to form glucose. The absence of the enzyme needed for the splitting causes ***fructose intolerance,*** a rare disorder characterized by vomiting and sweating.

26.3 GLYCOGENOLYSIS

Glycogen accounts for 2 to 8 percent of mammalian liver and 0.5 to 1 percent of muscle.

Another source of glucose is glycogen, the starch synthesized within animals and stored in the liver and muscle until their bodies need to use it.

Like plant starch, glycogen must first be broken down into glucose or glucose phosphate monomers, a process known as **glycogenolysis**. The first step in the breakdown of glycogen is the removal of one unit of glucose, in the form of glucose-1-P, from the glycogen polymer.

Glycogenolysis comes from glycogen and *lysis,* a Greek word meaning "act of loosening."

$$\underset{\text{Glycogen}}{\left(\text{glucose}\right)_n} + \text{P} \xrightarrow{\text{phosphorylase}} \text{glucose-1-P} + \left(\text{glucose}\right)_{n-1}$$

The glucose-1-P is converted into glucose-6-P, a compound that enters the catabolic pathway. In the liver but *not* in the muscle, glucose can be liberated from glucose-6-P by the action of the enzyme glucose-6-phosphatase (not present in muscle). The freed glucose can now be transported through the bloodstream to a muscle that needs it. Thus, liver glycogen is able to supplement the energy needs of a muscle. However, muscle glycogen cannot supply energy as glucose to another muscle; it must be utilized at the site where it breaks down because it cannot be converted into free glucose. The glucose-1-P it does produce cannot be transported through the blood.

The exercised muscle of a trained athlete contains about two to three times more glycogen than ordinary muscle.

If needed, muscle glycogen can support intense activity for up to 1 h. Athletes involved in endurance events, such as long-distance running or cycling, depend heavily upon muscle glycogen. When their reserves are depleted, it is very difficult to keep moving. Some athletes elect to follow a special diet called "carbohydrate loading" in order to increase their muscle glycogen. The muscle to be loaded is first depleted of glycogen by the combination of exhausting exercise of that muscle and a low carbohydrate diet, and then 3 to 6 days before the event a high-carbohydrate diet is used to supersaturate, that is, to "load," the exercised muscles with glycogen.

Excessive buildup of glycogen in the muscle can lead to muscle weakness and deterioration.

There are things that can go wrong with glycogen breakdown. For instance, the enzyme phosphorylase, needed for the breakdown of glycogen, is defective in some individuals. The result is ***McArdle's disease,*** in which glycogen builds up in muscles, resulting in severe muscle weakness. As you saw in Section 21.10, glycogen molecules are branched. Another enzyme, called the *debranching enzyme,* is needed to sever glucose monomers from the branch points. The absence of the debranching enzyme causes a condition known as ***limit dextrinosis,*** which also results in the accumulation of muscle glycogen. These are two of the many known hereditary disorders of glycogen metabolism, called *glycogen storage* diseases or *glycogenoses,* all of which are fatal or life-shortening.

26.4 GLYCOLYSIS, AN ANAEROBIC PATHWAY

You saw earlier that glucose is produced in the small intestine from the digestion of larger carbohydrate molecules. From the intestinal cells the glucose is carried into the liver through the portal vein. From there the absorbed glucose can take many different paths (Figure 26.3). About two-thirds of the glucose stays in the liver, where most is built into glycogen or fat and a little is oxidized for energy. The remaining free glucose is transported away from the liver to other body cells through the bloodstream. Some of this free glucose is stored as fat (in adipose, or fatty, tissue) or as glycogen (in muscles). In this section we will see what happens to the very large fraction of blood glucose which enters the various body

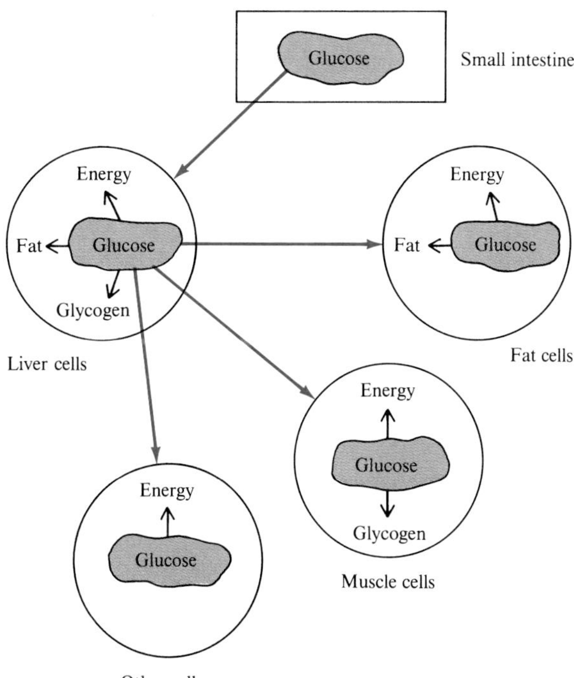

FIGURE 26.3
Glucose is transported from the small intestine to the liver via the hepatic portal vein. The liver stores some of the glucose and passes the rest into the systemic blood where it is distributed to other tissues.

cells, where it is oxidized to provide energy for body activities. Glycolysis, the first pathway in the oxidation of glucose, occurs in a part of the cell called the *cytosol,* the soluble portion of the cytoplasm, where molecular oxygen is not available (see Figure 26.4).

Glycolysis is derived from *glyco* for glucose and *lysis,* (loosening).

During **glycolysis** each glucose molecule is broken down into two molecules of lactic acid while providing energy in the form of two molecules of ATP. The overall process actually takes place in not 1 but 11 steps, each one requiring a different enzyme.

The pathway from glucose to lactic acid can be divided into two stages (Figure 26.5). In the *first stage of glycolysis* the six-carbon skeleton of glucose is cut into two three-carbon fragments. In the *second stage of glycolysis* the aldehyde fragments (glyceraldehyde) are oxidized to produce the carboxylic acid (lactic acid). We will examine the reactants, enzymes, coenzymes, and ATP input needed for many of the component steps. The names only of most of the reactants and products are given in the written text. Their formulas appear in figures streamlined to emphasize the reactive parts of each intermediate. The ATP molecules fed into the pathway and those which come out are highlighted to help you keep track of them so that you can evaluate the net ATP output from glycolysis.

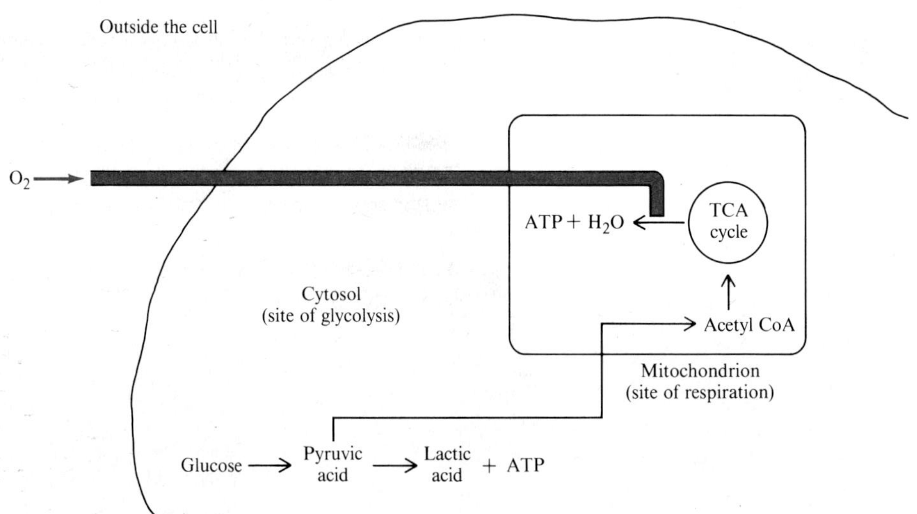

FIGURE 26.4
Oxygen is not available in the cytosol where glycolysis takes place. Oxygen *is* delivered to the mitochondria, where respiration occurs.

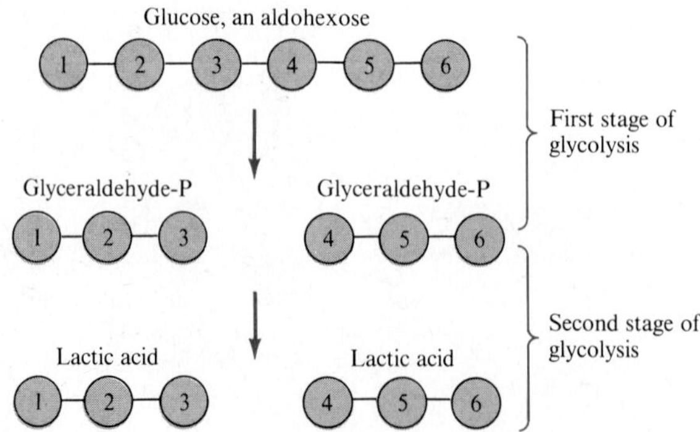

FIGURE 26.5
In the first stage of glycolysis, the glucose splits into two glyceraldehydes. In the second stage, the glyceraldehydes are oxidized to lactic acid.

Color Plate 1
Benedict's test. The addition of Benedict's reagent to the aqueous glucose solutions in each test tube produces colors that indicate the quantity of glucose that is present. From left to right, the test tubes contain 0 percent glucose (pure water), 0.5 percent glucose, 1 percent glucose, and 2 percent glucose. A blood glucose level of 130 mg per 100 ml blood is necessary before traces of glucose appear in the urine. *(Photo by Paul Winkfield.)*

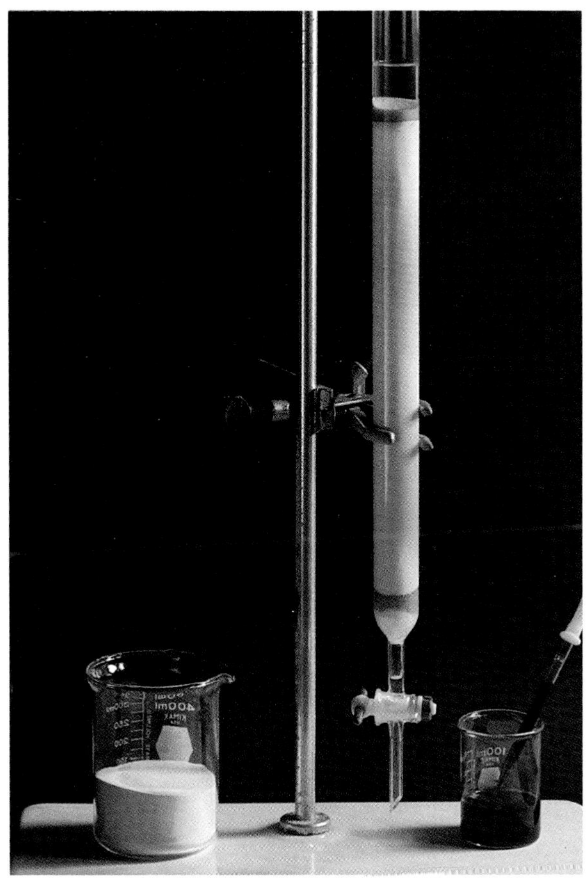

Color Plate 2
Chromatography column. A dye mixture (in the beaker on the right) is placed on a chromatography column, where it is separated into three different colored components. The adsorbing substance is Al_2O_3, the white solid in the beaker on the left. The white material at the very bottom of the column is cotton, which is covered with a layer of brownish sand. Sand is also used to keep the top of the column flat when the solvent is added. *(Photo by Paul Winkfield.)*

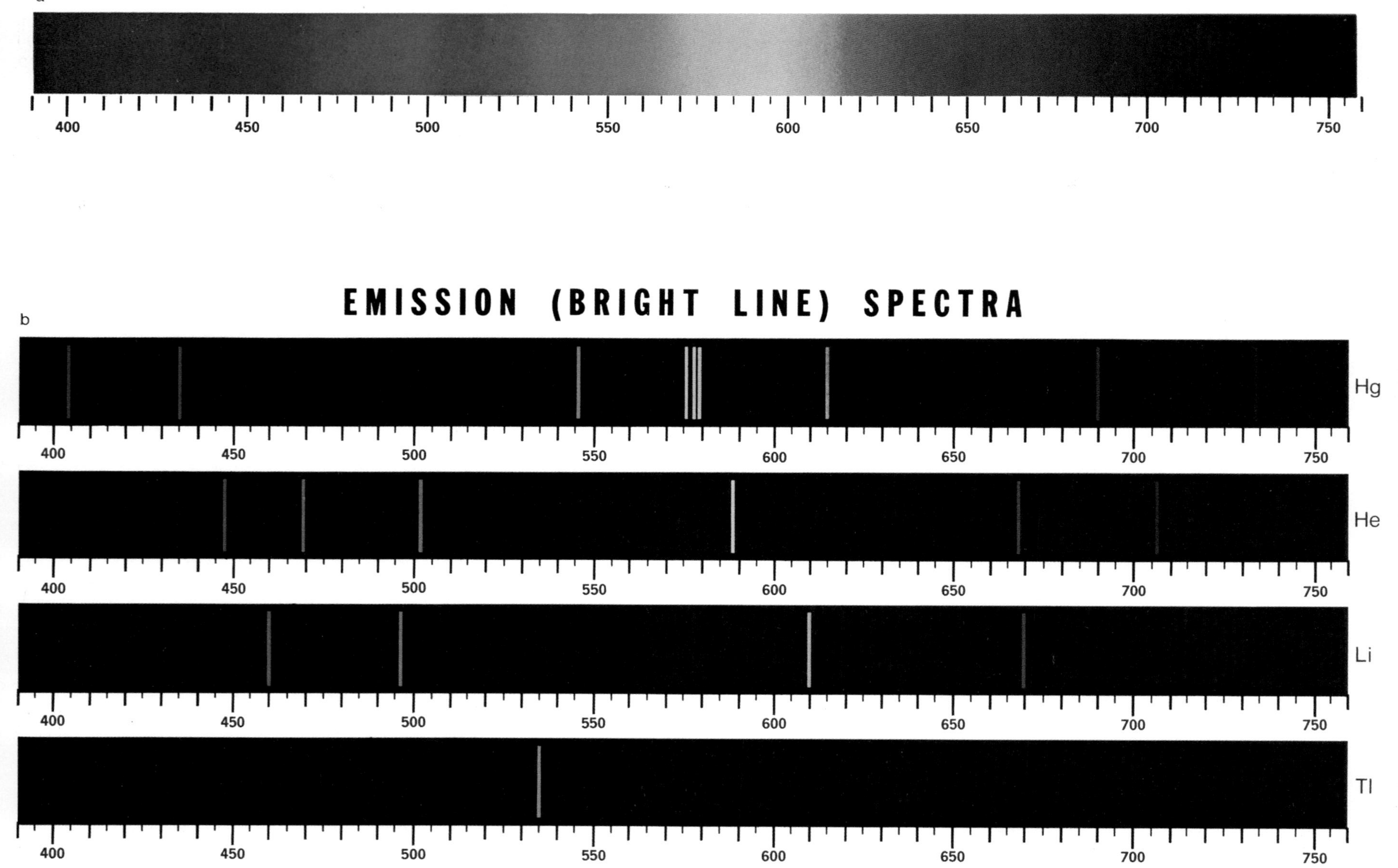
VISIBLE SPECTRUM
a
400
450
500
550
600
650
700
750
EMISSION (BRIGHT LINE) SPECTRA
b
Hg
He
Li
Tl
400
450
500
550
600
650
700
750

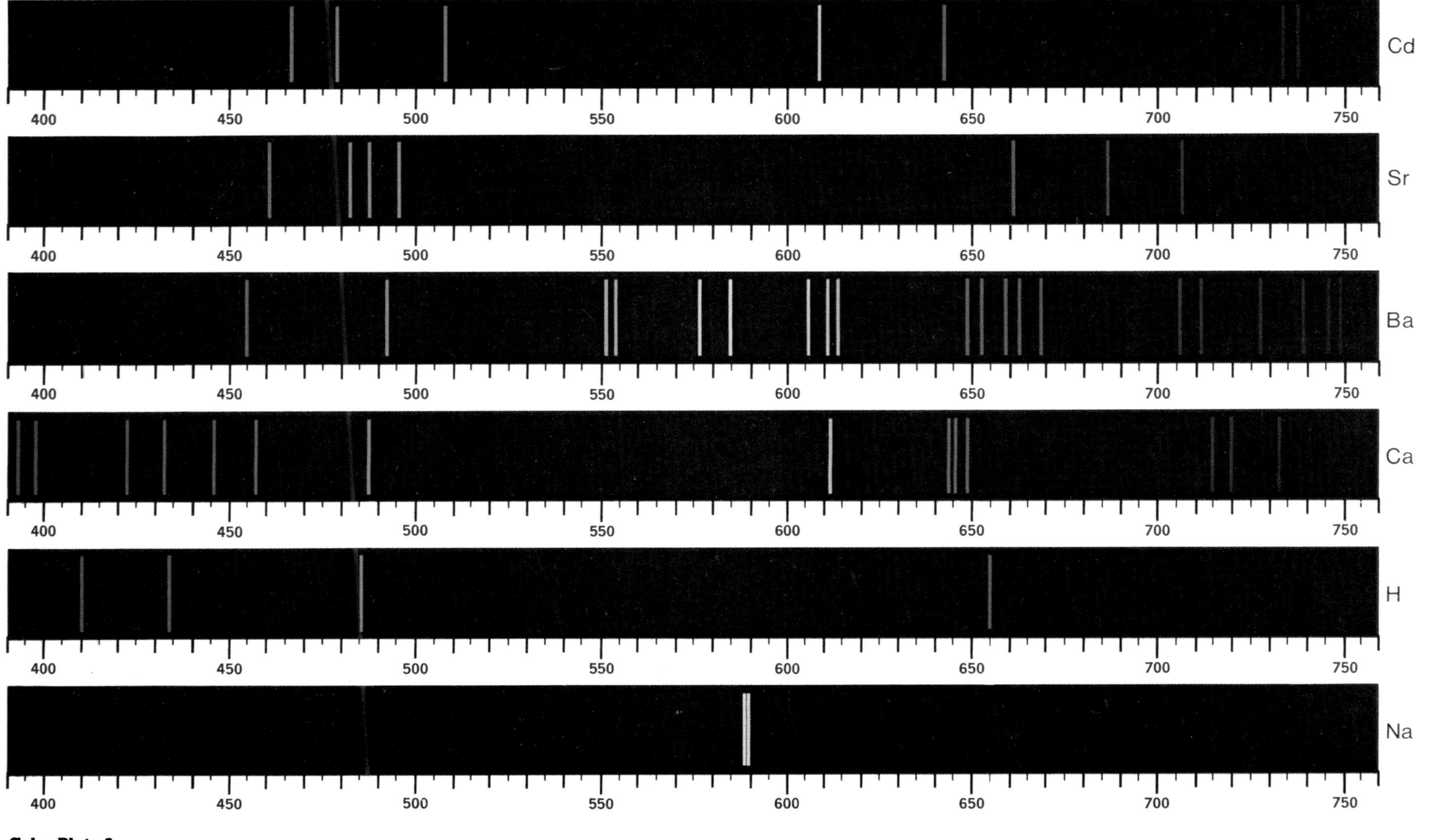

Color Plate 3
(a) Continuous spectrum. The visible light from an ordinary light bulb is continuous. *(b)* Line spectra. The visible light emitted from an element in a flame or a gas discharge tube consists of discrete lines. Since there is a different spectrum for each element, the atomic line spectrum of an element can be used to identify it. *(Wabash Instrument Company.)*

Color Plate 4
Laser surgery. The blue-green argon laser is being used to remove excess tissue from the eye retina of a diabetic patient. *(Sheie Eye Institute, Philadelphia, PA.)*

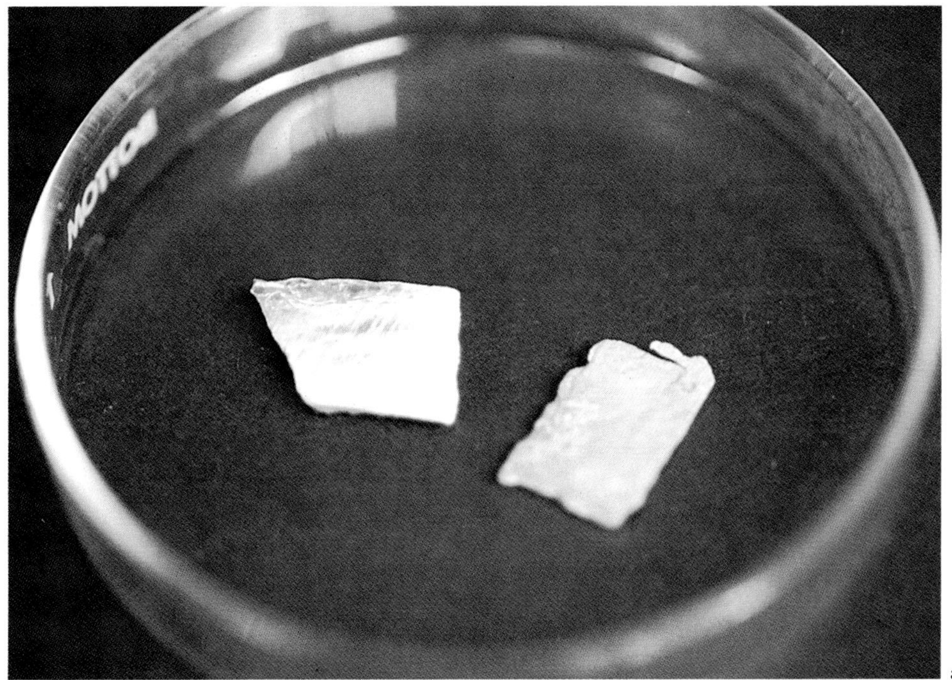

a

Color Plate 5
Alkali metals. *(a)* Alkali metals react with the O_2 in air to form oxides. The freshly cut sodium on the left has a shiny metallic luster. The sample of sodium on the right has been dulled by the formation of a coating of white sodium oxide. *(b)* Alkali metals undergo vigorous reactions with water to produce H_2 gas and a hydroxide. The potassium in the picture reacts so violently with the water that the H_2 produced bursts into flame.
(Photos by Paul Winkfield.)

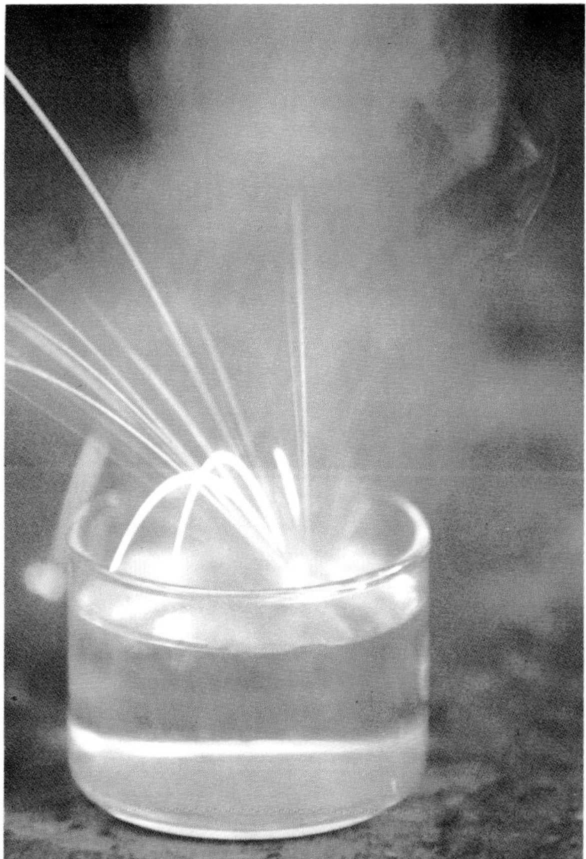

b

Color Plate 6

Emissions from elements. *(a)* A red emission is produced when a strontium salt is placed in a flame. *(b)* The sodium emission on the left comes from a sodium vapor lamp and that on the right from the addition of sodium (in the form of sodium chloride) to a flame. Note that the colors are identical. The sodium vapor lamp is a component of the polarimeter device. *(Photos by Paul Winkfield.)* *(c)* Red fireworks are sometimes colored by the addition of strontium salts to the firework explosive. *(Zambelli Fireworks Manufacturing Company, Inc.)*

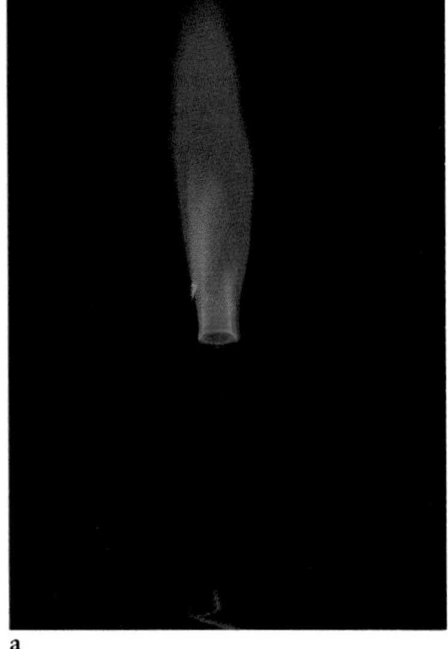

a

b

c

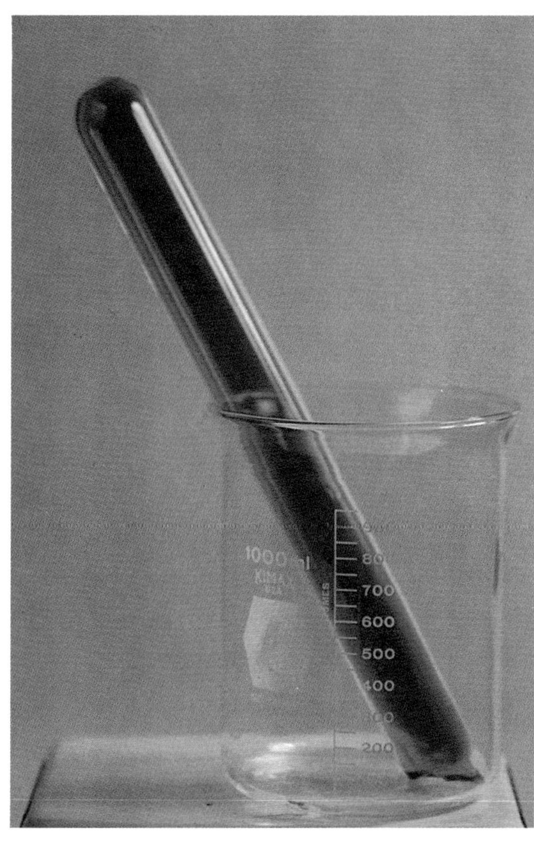

a

Color Plate 7
Nitrogen dioxide. *(a)* The tube is filled with the brownish gas NO_2, the gas responsible for the color of brown smog. NO_2 is in equilibrium with the colorless gas N_2O_4. The photograph was taken at room temperature. *(b)* The tube looks nearly colorless because the equilibrium $N_2O_4 \rightleftharpoons 2NO_2$ shifts to the left upon cooling. *(c)* The tube becomes very dark because the equilibrium shifts to the right upon heating. *(Photo by Paul Winkfield.)*

b

c

Color Plate 8
Growing crystals. The large crystal of copper sulfate (actually $CuSO_4 \cdot 5H_2O$) was grown by suspending a tiny seed crystal into the concentrated copper sulfate solution and allowing the solution to evaporate slowly. *(Photo by Paul Winkfield.)*

Color Plate 9
Sapphires. *(Gem Instruments Corporation.)*

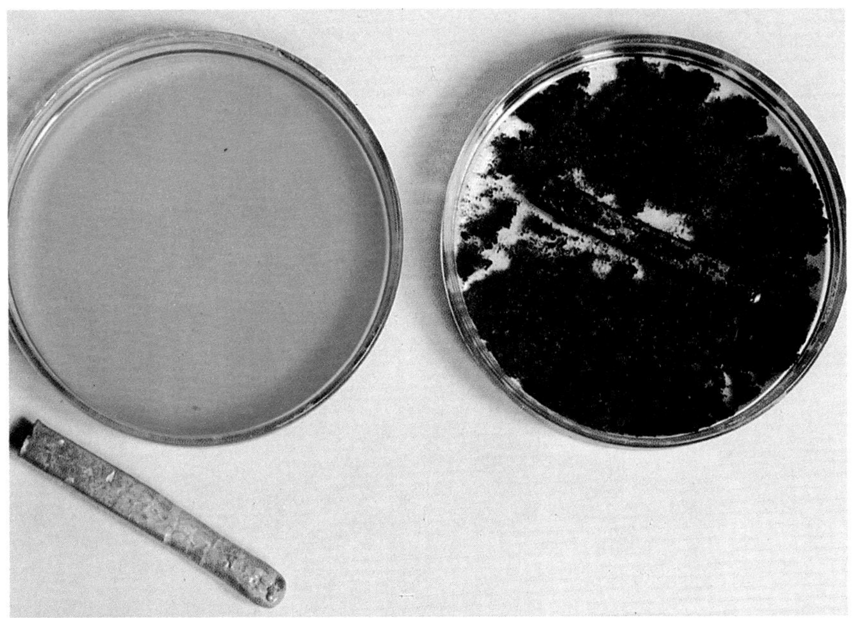

Color Plate 10
Reaction of Zn metal with $CuSO_4$. When the zinc rod is placed in a solution of copper sulfate, the zinc metal dissolves and the reddish colored copper metal is produced. The solution turns colorless, since zinc sulfate is colorless. *(Photo by Paul Winkfield.)*

Color Plate 11
Strips of paper coated with litmus dye turn blue when dipped into the soapy solution in the breaker and pink when dipped into acids such as lemon juice or vinegar (in the Erlenmeyer flask). *(Photo by Paul Winkfield.)*

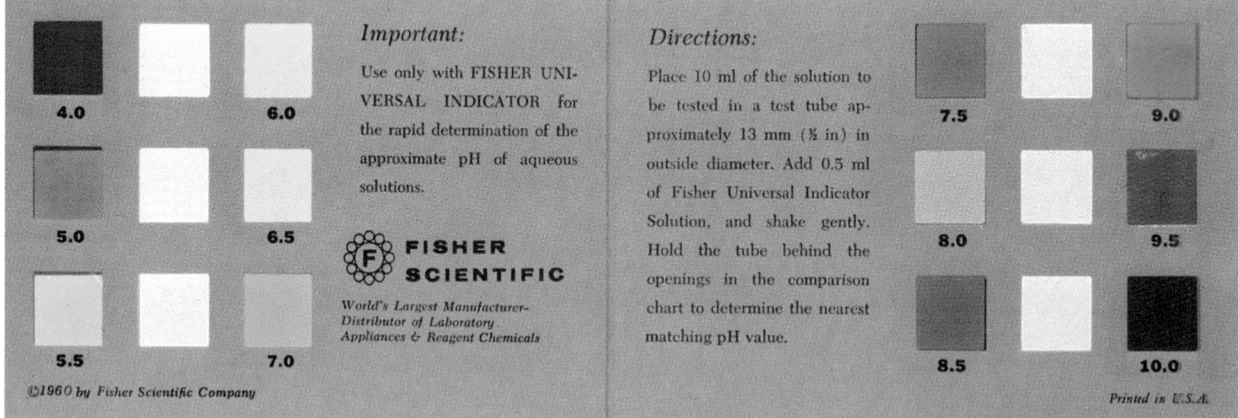
4.0
6.0
5.0
6.5
5.5
7.0
Important:
Use only with FISHER UNIVERSAL INDICATOR for the rapid determination of the approximate pH of aqueous solutions.
FISHER SCIENTIFIC
World's Largest Manufacturer-Distributor of Laboratory Appliances & Reagent Chemicals
©1960 by Fisher Scientific Company
Directions:
Place 10 ml of the solution to be tested in a test tube approximately 13 mm (½ in) in outside diameter. Add 0.5 ml of Fisher Universal Indicator Solution, and shake gently. Hold the tube behind the openings in the comparison chart to determine the nearest matching pH value.
7.5
9.0
8.0
9.5
8.5
10.0
Printed in U.S.A.

a

Color Plate 12
(a) The pH values of solutions can be measured by comparing their colors with those shown on the chart. *(Used with permission of Fisher Scientific; photo by Paul Winkfield.)* *(b)* The beakers from left (red) to right (purple) contain universal indicater mixed with solutions of acetic acid, HAc, ammonium chloride, NH_4Cl, sodium acetate, NaAc, and sodium hydroxide, NaOH. *(c)* The beakers from left (green) to right (orange) contain universal indicator mixed with pure water, water plus 1 ml of 0.1 *M* NaOH, buffer (HAc + NaAc), and buffer plus 1 ml of 0.1*M* NaOH. *(Photos by Paul Winkfield.)*

b

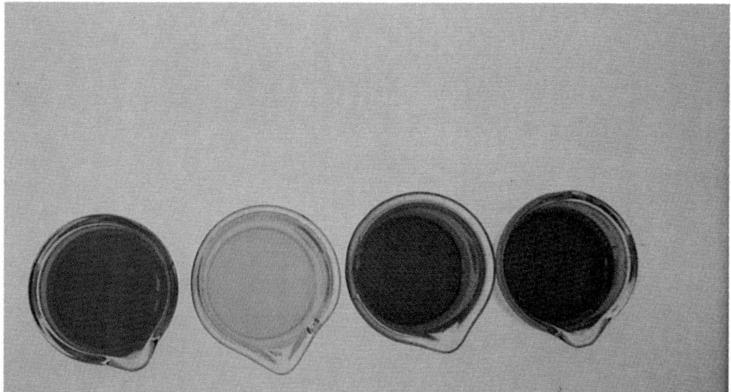

c

Color Plate 13
Acid base titration. Both burets contain NaOH solution that is being added to the HCl samples mixed with a few drops of phenolphthalein indicator. The pale pink color of the solution in the flask on the left is the phenolphthalein endpoint. One extra drop of NaOH solution has been added to produce the deeper pink color of the solution on the right. *(Photo by Paul Winkfield.)*

Color Plate 14
The reagent bottle contains a solution of potassium permanganate. When the $KMnO_4$ solution is added, the alkane in the left Erlenmeyer flask does not react and can be seen as a separate purple layer. When added to the flask on the right, solid MnO_2 forms and the $KMnO_4$ is completely decolorized as a result of the formation of a colorless organic product. *(Photo by Paul Winkfield.)*

Color Plate 15
The Br_2 dissolved in CCl_4 (in the reagent bottle) is rapidly decolorized by the alkene (on the right) but not by the alkane. *(Photo by Paul Winkfield.)*

Color Plate 16
When Br_2 (in CCl_4) is added to benzene, there is no reaction and the red color persists. Compare this with the addition of Br_2 to an alkene and an alkane as shown in Color Plate 15. *(Photo by Paul Winkfield.)*

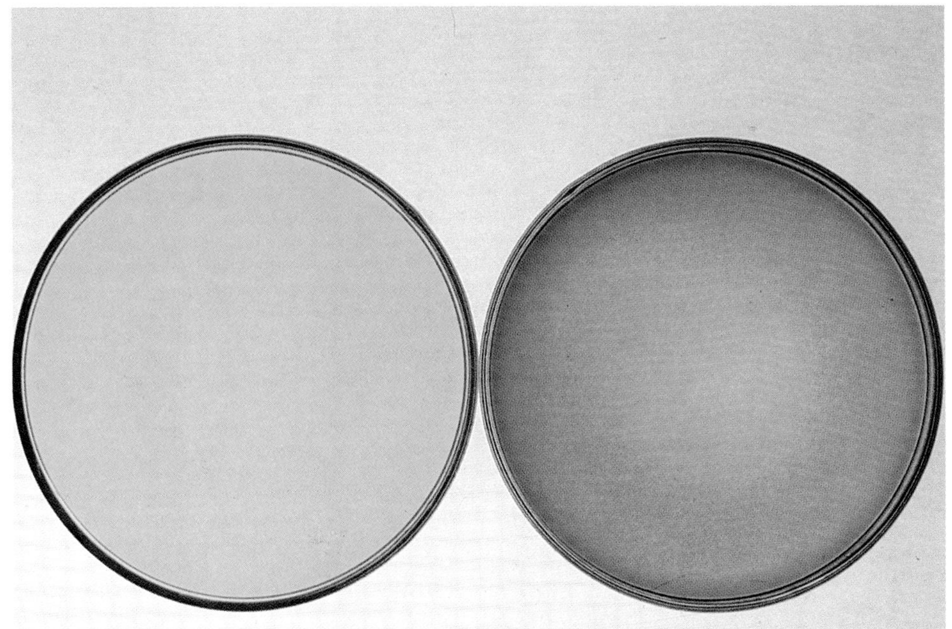

Color Plate 17
Breathalyzer test. The dish on the left contains the orange-yellow standard solution of $K_2Cr_2O_7$ plus H_2SO_4 used in the Breathalyzer machine. The addition of ethanol causes the disappearance of the orange-yellow color as shown on the right where the solution turns color as chromium(III) sulfate forms. *(Photo by Paul Winkfield.)*

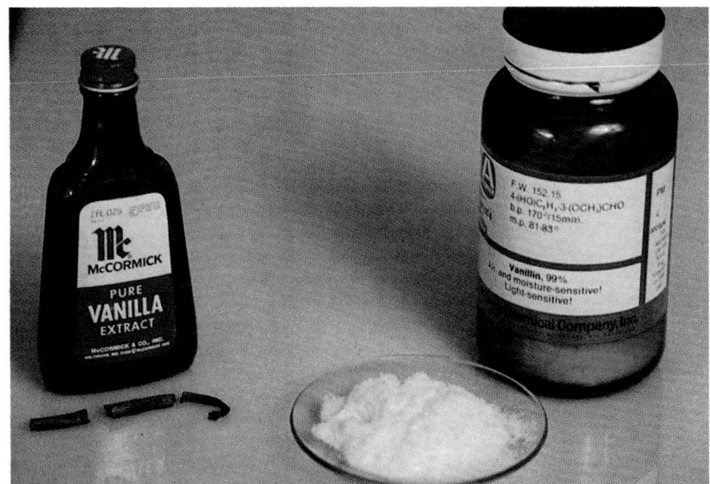

Color Plate 18
The vanilla bean used to prepare vanilla extract contains the aromatic aldehyde, vanillin, the same vanillin present in the chemical reagent bottle. *(Photo by Paul Winkfield.)*

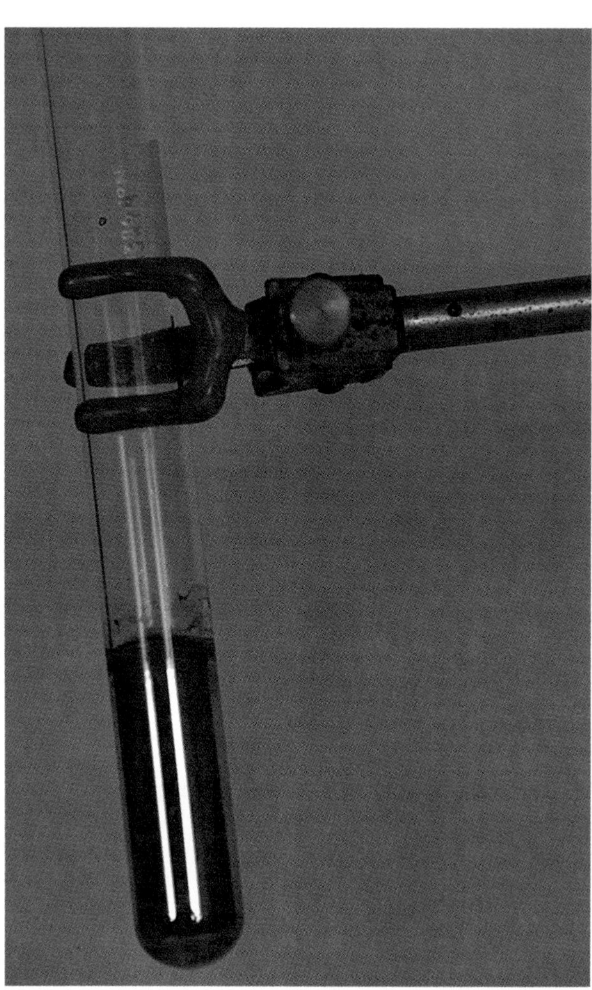

Color Plate 19
Tollen's test. A "silver mirror" forms on the test tube when Tollen's reagent is added to the aldehyde, hexanal ($CH_3CH_2CH_2CH_2CH_2CHO$). *(Photo by Paul Winkfield.)*

Color Plate 20
Crossed polarizers. Each polaroid plastic square (on the left) removes all but one plane of light. When one polarizer is turned 90° and placed on top of the other, no light comes through. *(Photo by Paul Winkfield.)*

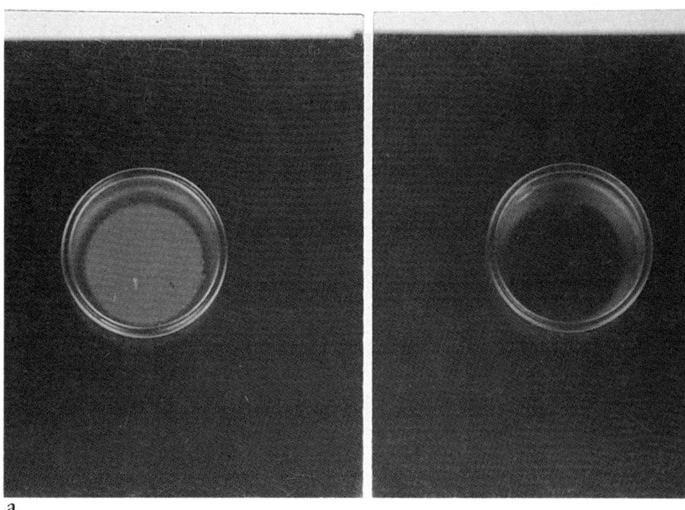

a

Color Plate 21 Rotation of polarized light. *(a)* The vials are placed between two "crossed" polarizers. The vial on the left contains an optically active sample which rotates the polarized light, thereby allowing light to come through the crossed polarizers. The vial on the right contains water which does not rotate polarized light; hence, no light can be seen coming through the crossed polarizers. *(b)* One vial contains the (−) isomer and the other the (+) isomer of an optically active compound. *(c)* The two samples rotate polarized light in opposite directions, so to extinguish the light coming through, one of the top polarizers must be rotated counterclockwise and the other clockwise (through the same angles). *(Photo by Paul Winkfield.)*

b

c

Color Plate 22
Enzyme test for glucose. Dipping glucose oxidase test strips into 5 percent glucose solution (dark blue strip) and 0.1 percent glucose (green strip) causes color changes. The original yellow color of the test strip is unchanged when the strip is dipped into water (on the left) or 5 percent lactose solution (on the right). Benedict's reagent *would* react with the lactose. *(Photo by Paul Winkfield.)*

Color Plate 23
Starch-I_2 complex. The solution in the dropping bottle on the left is tincture of iodine which contains 2% I_2, the silvery violet crystals shown on the watchglass. The middle flask contains a starch solution. Adding a few drops of the I_2 solution to the starch solution results in the typical blue color of the starch-I_2 complex. *(Photo by Paul Winkfield.)*

Recall that kinases catalyze phosphate transfer.

The first step in glycolysis involves the conversion of glucose into glucose-6-P. Recall that this reaction is a nonspontaneous process that requires energy in the form of ATP (Section 25.3). The enzyme is a *hexokinase* because it catalyzes a reaction in which a phosphate is transferred to a hexose (see Section 25.4).

Step 1:

$$\text{Glucose} \xrightarrow{\text{hexokinase}} \text{glucose-6-P}$$
$$\text{ATP} \curvearrowright \text{ADP}$$

We say that ATP molecules are used to *prime* the glycolysis process (which eventually yields more ATP than is put in) in much the same way that water is needed to prime a pump (which eventually supplies a continuing stream of water). Note in Figure 26.6*a* that an ATP molecule is fed into step 1.

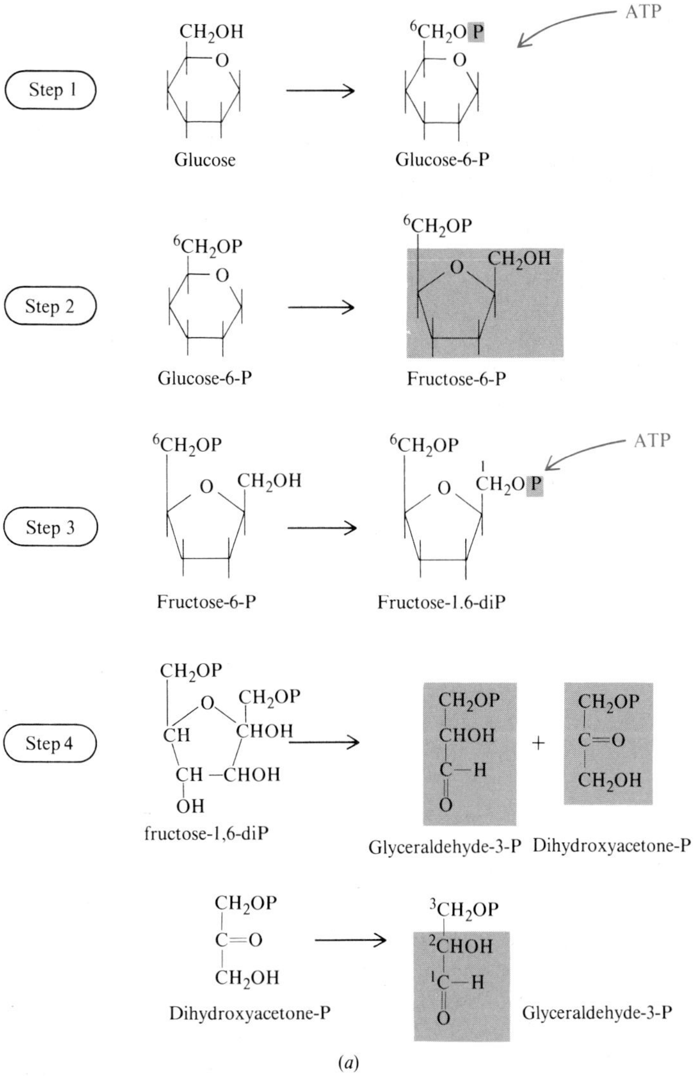

FIGURE 26.6*a*
First stage of glycolysis. The portion of each product molecule that is different from the reactant is indicated by color shading. The colored line drawn through fructose-1,6-diP shows where it splits.

(*a*)

FIGURE 26.6b The second stage of glycolysis. Carboxylic acids are shown in their unionized forms; that is, lactic acid rather than lactate, CH_3CHCOO^- (with OH on the central carbon)

Step 5

$$2NAD^2 + 2\ CH_2OP{-}CHOH{-}C(=O){-}H + 2\ P_i \longrightarrow 2\ CH_2OP{-}CHOH{-}C(=O){-}O{\sim}P + 2NADH + 2H^+$$

Glyceraldehyde-3-P → 3-Phosphoglyceroyl~P

Step 6

$$2\ CH_2OP{-}CHOH{-}C(=O){-}O{\sim}P \longrightarrow 2\ CH_2OP{-}CHOH{-}C(=O){-}OH \quad (\rightarrow 2ATP)$$

3-Phosphoglyceroyl~P → 3-phosphoglyceric acid

Step 7

$$2\ CH_2OP{-}CHOH{-}C(=O){-}OH \longrightarrow 2\ CH_2OH{-}CHOP{-}C(=O){-}OH$$

3-phosphoglyceric acid → 2-phosphoglyceric acid

Step 8

$$2\ CH_2OH{-}CHOP{-}C(=O){-}OH \longrightarrow 2\ CH_2{=}CHO{\sim}P{-}C(=O){-}OH$$

2-phosphoglyceric acid → 2-phosphoenolpyruvic acid

Step 9

$$CH_2{=}CHO{\sim}P{-}C(=O){-}OH \longrightarrow 2\ CH_3{-}C(=O){-}C(=O){-}OH \quad (\rightarrow 2ATP)$$

2-phosphoenolpyruvic acid → pyruvic acid

Step 10

$$2\ CH_3{-}C(=O){-}C(=O){-}OH + 2NADH + 2H^+ \longrightarrow 2\ CH_3{-}CHOH{-}C(=O){-}OH + NAD^+$$

(2NADH + 2H⁺: From step 5)

Pyruvic acid → Lactic acid

In the next step glucose-6-P is converted into fructose-6-P.

Step 2: Glucose-6-P $\xrightarrow{\text{isomerase}}$ fructose-6-P

In the conversion from glucose to fructose the number of atoms and hence the molecular formula does not change; only the way in which the atoms are joined to each other changes. Glucose-6-P and fructose-6-P are structural isomers. Thus the enzyme needed is an isomerase (Table 25.2).

In the third step of glycolysis a second phosphate is added to convert fructose-6-P into fructose-1,6-di-P. Another priming ATP and a hexokinase are needed.

Step 3: Fructose-6-P $\xrightarrow{\text{hexokinase}}$ fructose-1,6-di-P

ATP ⌒→ ADP

Glyceraldehyde is the simplest aldose and dihydroxyacetone is the simplest ketose.

Now the six-carbon reactant is cleaved into the two smaller fragments that will eventually become lactic acid. Fructose-1,6-di-P splits into two molecules, the phosphates of glyceraldehyde and of dihydroxyacetone (Figure 26.6*a*).

Step 4: Fructose-1,6-di-P $\xrightarrow{\text{aldolase}}$ glyceraldehyde-3-P + dihydroxyacetone-P

The dihydroxyacetone then isomerizes to glyceraldehyde-3-P:

Dihydroxyacetone-P $\xrightarrow{\text{isomerase}}$ glyceraldehyde-3-P

This completes the first stage of glycolysis (summarized in the overall equation below), in which glucose has been cleaved into two molecules of glyceraldehyde-3-phosphate. Up to this point two ATP's have been consumed (in steps 1 and 3).

First stage of glycolysis: Glucose $\longrightarrow$ 2 glyceraldehyde-3-P

2ATP ⌒→ 2ADP

As you saw in Section 16.6, aldehydes are readily oxidized to acids.

The two molecules of glyceraldehyde-3-P now begin the *second stage of glycolysis*, in which each will be converted into lactic acid.

In the fifth step of glycolysis the aldehyde group of glyceraldehyde-P is oxidized to a carboxylic *acid* (see Figure 26.6*b*). The dehydrogenase enzyme requires the coenzyme NAD^+, which is converted to NADH, as discussed in Section 25.5. As part of this step an inorganic phosphate (P_i) is also introduced so that the product appears as a phosphate instead of an acid. In Figure 26.6*b* the newly formed phosphate ester linkage is denoted by a wavy line (~), meaning that this is a high-energy phosphate bond, which can produce energy (ATP) when broken.

Step 5: 2 Glyceraldehyde-3-P + $2NAD^+$ + $2P_i$ $\xrightarrow{\text{dehydrogenase}}$
2NADH + **2H**$^+$ + 2 3-phosphoglyceroyl~P

Also note that this step produces 2NADH + $2H^+$ for each molecule of glucose. Each NADH and H^+ contains a *pair of H atoms* (in bold above). Later we will see that these H atom pairs lead to the formation of ATP during respiration, when O_2 is present. We will follow the fate of H atom pairs when we discuss the details of the final stage of respiration.

Now let us return to glycolysis, in which the high-energy phosphate bond breaks, transferring the P from 3-phosphoglyceroyl-P to ADP to produce ATP.

Step 6: 2 3-Phosphoglyceroyl~P + 2ADP $\xrightarrow{\text{kinase}}$ 2 3-phosphoglyceric acid + 2ATP

In the next step the phosphate on the C-3 atom shifts to the C-2 atom (see Figure 26.6*b*). The reactant and product are structural isomers (same molecular formula); hence the enzyme is an isomerase.

Step 7: 2 3-Phosphoglyceric acid $\xrightarrow{\text{isomerase}}$ 2 2-phosphoglyceric acid

In the next two steps (8 and 9), shown in Figure 26.6*b*, the two molecules of 2-phosphoglyceric acid are converted into two molecules of pyruvic acid.

Step 8: 2 2-Phosphoglyceric acid $\xrightarrow{\text{enolase}}$ 2 phosphoenolpyruvic acid + $2H_2O$

Phosphoenolpyruvic acid also has a high-energy phosphate bond (~P), as you can see in Figure 26.6*b*.

Step 9: 2 Phosphoenolpyruvic acid + 2ADP $\xrightarrow{\text{kinase}}$ 2 pyruvic acid + 2ATP

These first nine steps, from glucose to pyruvic acid (instead of lactic acid), are known as the **Embden-Meyerhof pathway**. We can summarize this pathway with the overall reaction below:

$$\text{Glucose} + 2P_i + 2\text{ADP} + 2\text{NAD}^+ \longrightarrow 2 \text{ pyruvic acid} + 2\text{ATP} + 2\text{NADH} + 2H^+$$

Emden-Meyerhof pathway

From this point pyruvic acid may take either of *two* pathways. If aerobic conditions prevail, that is, if a supply of O_2 is present, the pyruvic acid enters respiration, the next pathway we will study.

Under anaerobic conditions the pyruvic acid is converted to lactic acid, the product of glycolysis. This step occurs by using up the 2NADH + $2H^+$ generated in step 5 (shown in gray in Figure 26.6*b*).

Step 10: 2 Pyruvic acid + 2NADH + $2H^+$ $\xrightarrow{\text{dehydrogenase}}$ 2 lactic acid + 2NAD^+

In the final step of the glycolysis pathway pyruvic acid is reduced by NADH as its carbonyl group becomes the hydroxyl group of lactic acid. (Recall from Section 16.7 that carbonyl groups are reduced to hydroxyl groups.)

The overall glycolysis reaction from one molecule of glucose to two molecules of lactic acid can be written:

$$\text{Glucose} + 2P_i + 2\text{ADP} \longrightarrow 2 \text{ lactic acid} + 2\text{ATP}$$

Glycolysis

We see that the glycolysis pathway produces two ATP molecules for every glucose. To confirm this let us count the ATP's fed into the glycolysis pathway and compare them with those that are formed.

Step 1:	1 ATP used up	−1 ATP
Step 3:	1 ATP used up	−1 ATP
Step 6:	2 ATP's formed	+2 ATP's
Step 9:	2 ATP's formed	+2 ATP's
Net ATP's involved in glycolysis:		+2 ATP's

The net production of ATP from glycolysis is 2 ATP's for every glucose.

In the overall catabolism reaction of glucose, 38 net ATP molecules are produced per molecule of glucose. Thus the two ATP's formed as a result of glycolysis represent only a small part of the energy that glucose can supply. The rest is produced when the lactic acid reverts back to pyruvic acid and enters respiration, a pathway for which O_2 is needed. Ancient organisms forced to exist in an atmosphere without oxygen were able to survive on glycolysis alone. As we will see next, there are times when humans must also depend upon glycolysis for emergency energy.

SAMPLE EXERCISE 26.1

The reaction below is the fifth step in glycolysis. What is the coenzyme and what vitamin provides it?

$$\text{Glyceraldehyde-P} + \text{NAD}^+ + \text{P}_i \xrightarrow{\text{dehydrogenase}} \text{NADH} + \text{H}^+ + \text{3-phosphoglyceroyl}\sim\text{P}$$

Solution:

The coenzyme is NAD^+, provided by niacin, a B vitamin.

EXERCISE 26.1

In the fifth step of glycolysis, what is the functional group of the substrate? Of the product? What general type of chemical reaction is this?

26.5 GLYCOLYSIS AND INTENSE EXERCISE

Muscle contraction requires input of ATP, which may be supplied by several possible sources. One is the high-energy phosphate compound creatine~P, which combines with ADP to make ATP; this is the most rapid means of forming ATP in muscle cells.

$$\text{ADP} + \text{P} \longrightarrow \text{ATP}$$
$$\text{Creatine}{\sim}\text{P} \curvearrowright \text{Creatine} + \text{P}$$

However, the available creatine~P is quickly used up and supports muscle activity for only a few seconds. The availability of creatine~P is crucial in events that last about 8 s, such as the 100-m dash, shotput, and javelin throw.

Glycolysis, a fast process, provides emergency energy for muscle cells.

Suppose a maximum muscular effort is needed for as long as 1 min. For regular muscular activity a new supply of ATP could then come from respiration, which provides the bulk of ATP from glucose. However, during intense exercise, when the available ATP is rapidly used up, there is not enough time for adequate oxygen to be delivered to the muscle so that respiration can take place. When ATP from respiration is not available, the cells in muscle tissue must depend upon the ATP evolved in glycolysis as a source of emergency energy. This is practical because glycolysis is *very fast* compared with respiration. In the same time that it takes for respiration to produce 36 molecules of ATP from 1 molecule of glucose, glycolysis can form about 64 molecules of ATP from 32 molecules of glucose. In this way muscle tissue is able to function undamaged without air (anaerobically) for short periods of time. After 1 min of maximal effort in events such as that required for a gymnastic routine, speed skating, or a middle-distance run (400 m), anaerobic metabolism is providing over two-thirds of the energy. After 2 min, this is reduced by half as oxygen becomes available to the muscle cells. Figure 26.7 summarizes the various biochemical pathways that supply ATP for muscle contractions.

"Anaerobic exercise" refers to activities involving short periods of intense muscular exertion.

Muscle cells that depend on glycolysis accumulate lactic acid, which can be detected in the tissues and in the blood or urine. Following a period of extreme muscle exertion the breathing rate is greater than normal. The extra oxygen consumed in this way, called the *oxygen debt,* is needed to metabolize some or all of the excess lactic acid in the blood.

The disadvantage of producing ATP from glycolysis is that relatively large amounts of glucose must be used to expend small amounts of energy. The source of the glucose is stored glycogen, which breaks down as described in Section 26.3.

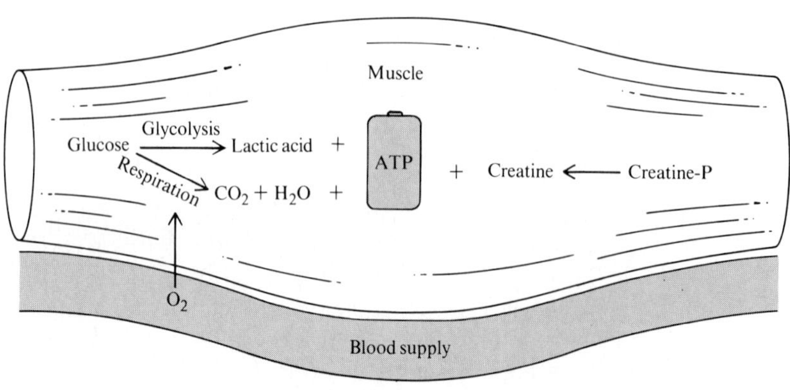

FIGURE 26.7
Glycolysis, respiration, and creatine-P supply ATP for muscle contraction.

26.6 FORMATION OF ACETYL-CoA

You have seen that glycolysis provides only a fraction of the energy available in carbohydrate molecules. The rest comes from respiration, the process by which fuel molecules are ultimately converted to CO_2 and H_2O. The parts of the cell in which respiration takes place are called the **mitochondria,** structures found throughout the cytoplasm of the cell (see Figure 22.15). The mitochondria behave as powerhouses for the cell and contain all the enzymes and coenzymes needed for the various stages of respiration. Figure 26.8 gives an enlarged picture of one mitochondrion, showing how it is divided into compartments by inner membranes.

Carbohydrates, proteins, and fats all lead to acetyl-CoA.

Any type of food molecule can enter the respiration process, including amino acids from proteins and fatty acids from fats, as well as glucose from carbohydrates. They all do so by forming the *same* starting material, **acetyl coenzyme A** (acetyl-CoA) (see Figure 25.11).

glucose amino acids fatty acids
↘ ↓ ↙
acetyl-CoA

Recall that CoA is pantothenic acid, one of the B group of vitamins (Figure 25.11).

Thus acetyl-CoA is the intersection point for all metabolic processes.

Here we will see how pyruvic acid from the Embden-Meyerhof pathway is converted to acetyl-CoA. (The conversion of amino acids and fatty acids is discussed in the remaining two metabolism chapters.)

For pyruvic acid to follow the respiration pathway it must first get to the mitochondria, where the necessary enzymes are located. Once there it is transformed into acetyl-CoA by a complex process, summarized below in a single step.

The coenzyme thiamine pyrophosphate from vitamin B_1 is involved in one of the component steps (Section 25.5).

$$2\text{ Pyruvic acid} + 2NAD^+ + 2CoA \longrightarrow 2\text{ acetyl-CoA} + 2NADH + 2H^+ + 2CO_2$$

Among the products of this conversion are 2NADH and $2H^+$; thus another two H atom pairs are produced (for each glucose molecule), which will be able to

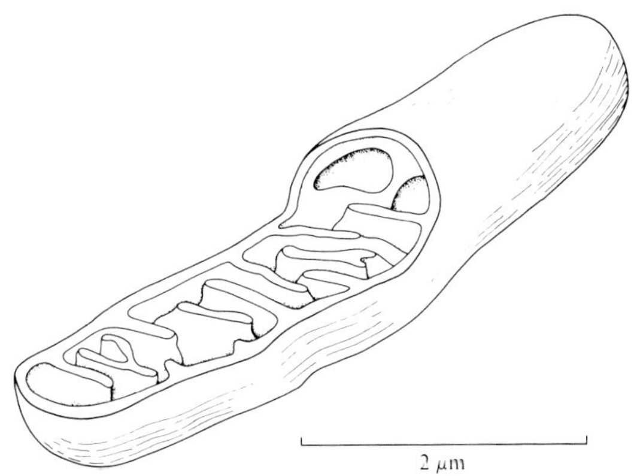

FIGURE 26.8
View of a liver mitochondrion. (*From Albert List, The Flow of Life* Freelance Publishing, 1977.

provide ATP in the final stages of respiration. (Recall that 2NADH plus $2H^+$ are produced in step 5 of glycolysis.)

Exhaled CO_2 is a waste product of glucose metabolism.

Also note that two molecules of CO_2 are released for every two molecules of pyruvic acid that are converted to two acetyl-CoA's. Thus two molecules of CO_2 are evolved for every molecule of glucose. This accounts for two of the six molecules of CO_2 that appear in the overall catabolism of glucose. In Figure 26.1 this CO_2 is shown as a product of the conversion of pyruvic acid to acetyl-CoA. The acetyl-CoA is now ready to enter the first stage of respiration, called the *tricarboxylic acid cycle.*

26.7 TRICARBOXYLIC ACID CYCLE

The first stage of respiration is the **tricarboxylic acid cycle** (TCA cycle), often called the *Krebs cycle* because it was first discovered by H. A. Krebs in 1937. This cyclic pathway is represented by a circle that joins each intermediate, as shown in Figure 26.9. Note that the first intermediate (in the upper-right part of the circle) is citric acid, a compound which contains three carboxylic acid groups and gives the TCA cycle its name. As you read the description of each of the steps, refer to the figure to help you follow the structural changes that take place.

To begin the cycle-acetyl, CoA combines with oxaloacetic acid to form citric acid.

Step 1: Acetyl-CoA + oxaloacetic acid + $H_2O \xrightarrow[\text{synthase}]{\text{citric}}$ citric acid + CoA

The oxaloacetic acid reactant will be regenerated in the final step of the cycle.

The citric acid is dehydrated to form an unsaturated acid called *cis*-aconitic acid; then water adds across the double bond of *cis*-aconitic acid to produce isocitric acid.

Steps 2 and 3: Citric acid $\xrightarrow{\text{hydratase}}$ *cis*-aconitic acid + H_2O

cis-Aconitic acid + $H_2O \xrightarrow{\text{hydratase}}$ isocitric acid

Note that the difference in the structures of citric acid and isocitric acid is in the location of the hydroxyl group (see Figure 26.9).

In the fourth step of the TCA cycle the isocitric acid is oxidized to form oxalosuccinic acid, another tricarboxylic acid. This step is an oxidation reaction in which two H atoms (in color in Figure 26.9) are removed from isocitric acid by NAD^+. The oxalosuccinic acid next loses a molecule of CO_2 to become α-ketoglutaric acid, which has a carbonyl group in the α-position (adjacent to the carboxyl group).

Steps 4 and 5: Isocitric acid + $NAD^+ \xrightarrow{\text{dehydrogenase}}$

oxalosuccinic acid + NADH + H^+

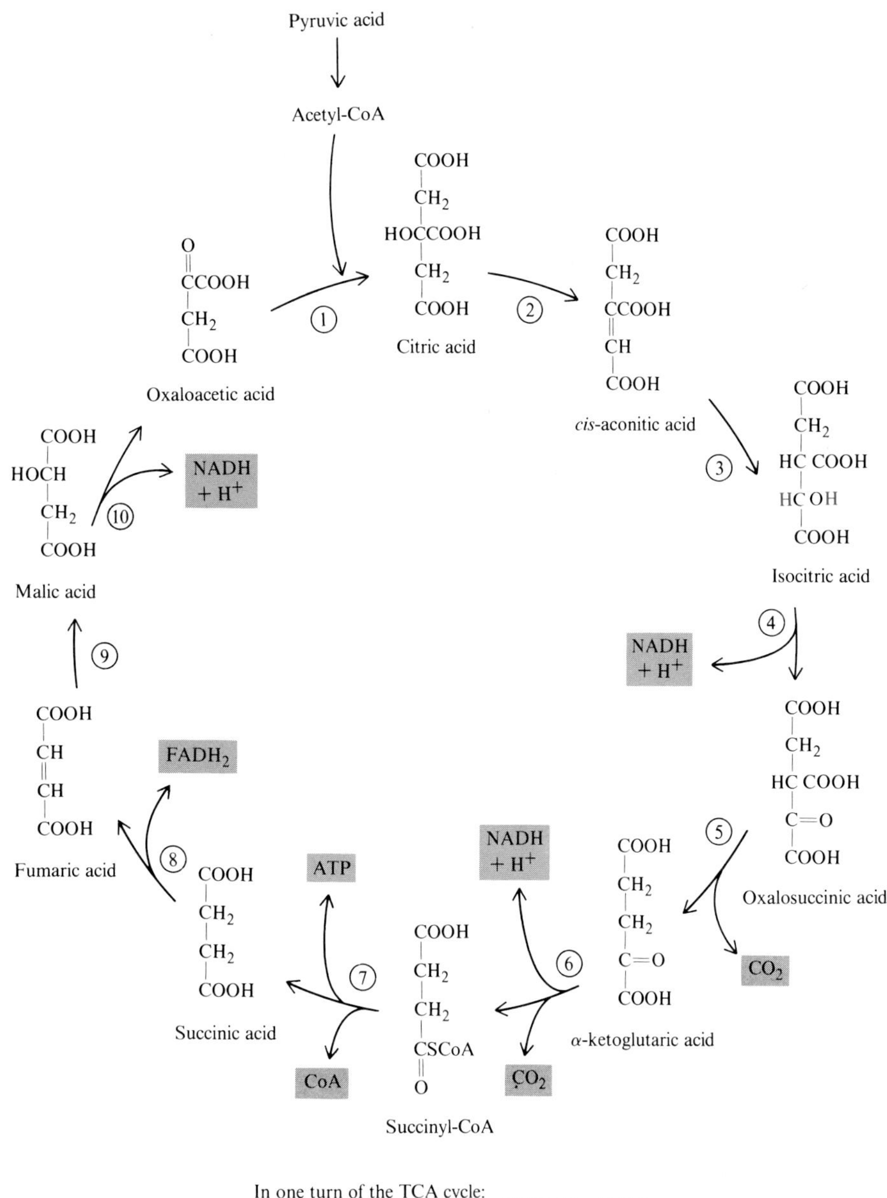

FIGURE 26.9
Tricarboxylic acid cycle.

The H pair stripped away will lead to ATP in the final stage of respiration.

$$\text{Oxalosuccinic acid} \xrightarrow{\text{dehydrogenase}} \alpha\text{-ketoglutaric acid} + CO_2$$

In the sixth step the α-ketoglutaric acid is oxidized to succinic acid, which then combines with acetyl-CoA to form succinyl-CoA. Another molecule of CO_2 is lost in this step and a second H pair is produced.

$$\begin{array}{l} O \\ \| \\ C-OH \\ | \\ CH_2 \\ | \\ CH_2 \\ | \\ C\sim SCoA \\ \| \\ O \end{array}$$

Succinyl-CoA

FIGURE 26.10

Step 6: α-Ketoglutaric acid + NAD^+ + CoA $\xrightarrow{\text{dehydrogenase}}$ succinyl-CoA + CO_2 + NADH + H^+

The succinyl-CoA produced in step 6 has a high-energy sulfur bond (see Figure 26.10); upon its reaction with GDP (guanosine diphosphate), the formation of GTP is powered by the breaking of this high-energy bond.

Step 7: Succinyl-CoA + GDP + P_i $\xrightarrow{\text{succinic synthetase}}$ GTP + succinic acid + CoA

The GTP product is then able to transfer a phosphate to ADP to form ATP.

$$\text{GTP + ADP} \xrightarrow{\text{kinase}} \text{ATP + GDP}$$

Thus step 7 of the TCA cycle generates one ATP molecule.

Next, succinic acid is oxidized to the unsaturated acid fumaric acid. This time it is FAD that accepts a pair of hydrogen atoms.

Step 8: Succinic acid + FAD $\xrightarrow{\text{dehydrogenase}}$ fumaric acid + $FADH_2$

In the ninth step the fumaric acid is hydrated to form malic acid, which has no C to C double bond, as you can see by looking at its structure in Figure 26.9.

Step 9: Fumaric acid + H_2O $\xrightarrow{\text{hydratase}}$ malic acid

In the tenth and final step in the TCA cycle, the malic acid is oxidized by NAD^+ to re-form oxaloacetic acid, the original reactant used in step 1.

Step 10: Malic acid + NAD^+ $\xrightarrow{\text{dehydrogenase}}$ oxaloacetic acid + NADH + H^+

In this last step a fourth H pair is removed. The set of reactions above that comprises the TCA cycle is called one *turn*. We can write one overall reaction to describe a turn:

$$\text{ADP} + P_i + \text{Acetyl-CoA} \longrightarrow 2CO_2 + \text{CoA} + 4\text{H pairs} + \text{ATP}$$

One glucose produces two acetyl-CoA's; thus there are *two* turns around the TCA cycle for every *one* glucose molecule:

$$2\text{ ADP} + 2P_i + 2\text{ Acetyl-CoA} \longrightarrow 4CO_2 + 2\text{CoA} + 8\text{H pairs} + 2\text{ATP}$$

Note that four molecules of carbon dioxide and eight pairs of H atoms are produced, along with energy in the two molecules of ATP. Let us examine the source of each product. The CO_2 is evolved in two different reactions, as you can see in Figure 26.9, where the CO_2's are shown "leaving" the TCA cycle. At this point we have accounted for all the waste carbon dioxide that appears in the overall reaction in which glucose is degraded to $6CO_2$ and $6H_2O$.

Formation of 2 acetyl-CoA:	2 Pyruvic acid produce	$2CO_2$
TCA cycle:	2 Acetyl-CoA produce	$4CO_2$
Total:	1 Glucose produces	$6CO_2$

Including the ATP that is released in the sixth step of the cycle, we have now accounted for four of the ATP molecules produced for each molecule of glucose that is fed into glycolysis and the TCA cycle.

Glycolysis:	1 glucose produces	2ATP
TCA cycle:	2 Acetyl-CoA produce	2ATP
Total:	1 glucose produces	4ATP

Phosphorylation means the formation of a phosphate ester.

The ATP formed *before* the final stage of respiration is said to form as a result of **substrate level phosphorylation.** That is, the phosphate that is added to ADP to create ATP is derived from some intermediate compound, or substrate, in the metabolism pathway. In glycolysis the phosphate comes from phosphenolpyruvic acid and in the TCA cycle from GTP. In Table 26.1, where the source of the ATP produced from glucose catabolism is given, these four ATP's appear in the category called *substrate level.*

The rest of the ATP comes from reactions involving the H atom pairs carried in NADH + H^+ or $FADH_2$. Each H atom pair provides two electrons to be fed into the last stage of respiration, when molecular O_2 is available to accept them. This is where the H_2O product will appear, along with the remaining ATP. The H pairs we have encountered so far have come from glycolysis (step 5), the formation of acetyl-CoA from pyruvic acid, and the TCA cycle:

Glycolysis:	1 glucose produces	2 H pairs
Formation of 2 acetyl-CoA:	2 pyruvic acid produce	2 H pairs
TCA cycle:	2 acetyl-CoA produce	8 H pairs
Total:	1 glucose produces	12 H pairs

In the next section we will see how these 12 H atom pairs participate in energy-releasing reactions.

TABLE 26.1 **TOTAL PRODUCTION OF ATP FROM CATABOLISM OF ONE GLUCOSE MOLECULE**

Stage of catabolism	ATP's from substrate level phosphorylation (without electron transport)	ATP's from oxidative phosphorylation (with electron transport)	Total net ATP
Glucose to pyruvic acid	2	6 (from 2NADH + $2H^+$)	8
Pyruvic acid to acetyl-CoA	0	6 (from 2NADH + 2 $^+$)	6
TCA cycle	2	4 (from $2FADH_2$) and 18 (from 6NADH + $6H^+$)	24
		Grand total	38 ATP

Each $FADH_2$ produces two ATP molecules and each NADH + H^+ produces three ATP molecules.

26.8 FINAL STAGE OF RESPIRATION

One H pair includes H: + H^+.

Associated with each of the H pairs is a pair of electrons. From 12 H atom pairs there are 12 electron pairs. In the final stage of respiration, each pair of electrons is transferred from compound to compound in a process called **electron transport.** The compounds involved in electron transport are **electron carriers.** Since the electron carriers accept electrons, they are all classified as *oxidizing agents.*

Oxidizing agents are electron acceptors.

The electron carrier compounds form a chain, the **respiratory chain,** through which electron pairs are passed from the weakest oxidizing agent at the top to the strongest one at the bottom. The oxidized and reduced forms of the known electron carriers are pictured in Figure 26.11, where you can see that the one at the bottom of the chain, the strongest oxidizing agent in the respiratory chain,

Oxidized forms

Reduced forms

ADP—OCH_2

NAD^+

OH OH

ADP—OCH_2

+ H^+

$NADH + H^+$

CH_3

CH_2

CH_2OP

FMN

$FMNH_2$

CH_3O

Coenzyme Q

$(CH_2CH{=}CCH_2)_{10}H$

Coenzyme Q (reduced)

Protein Fe^{3+}

Fe(III) Protein

Protein Fe^{2+}

Fe(II) Protein

O_2 Oxygen

H O H Water

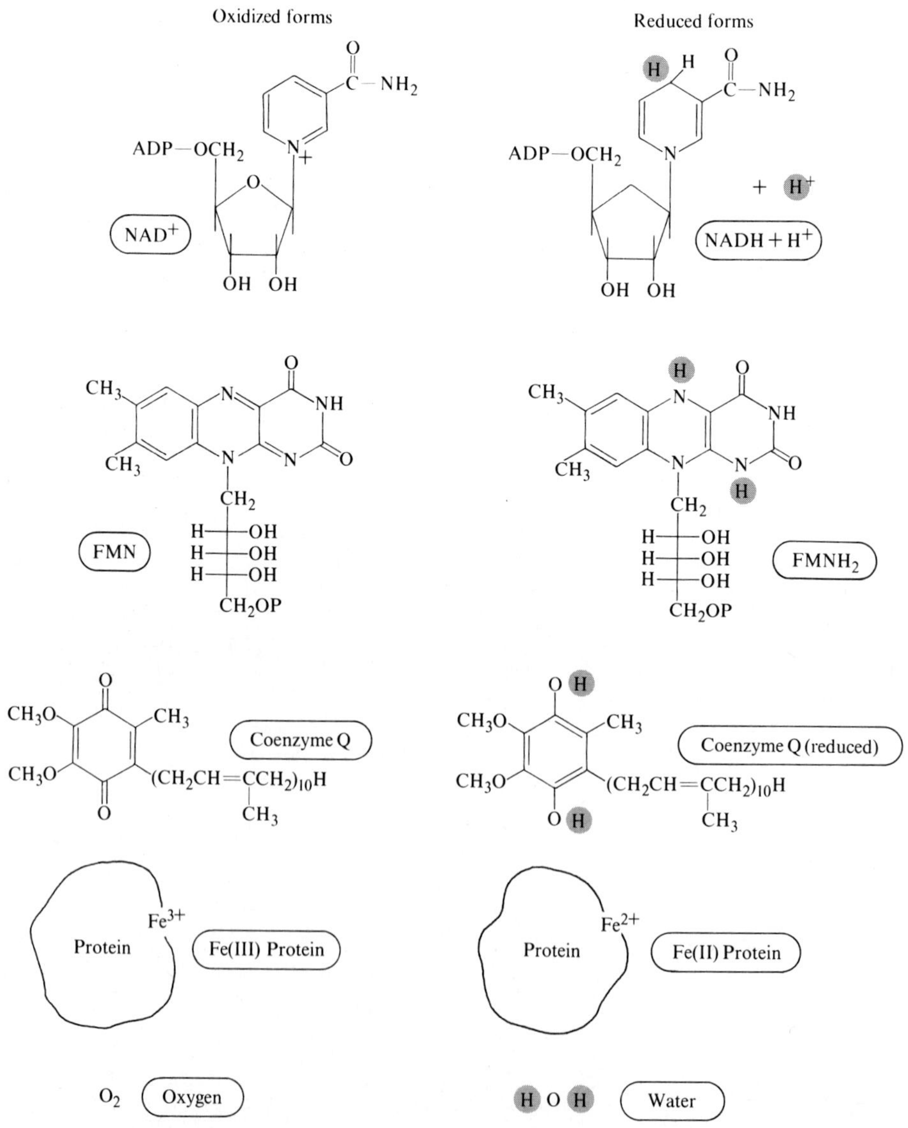

FIGURE 26.11
Electron carriers.

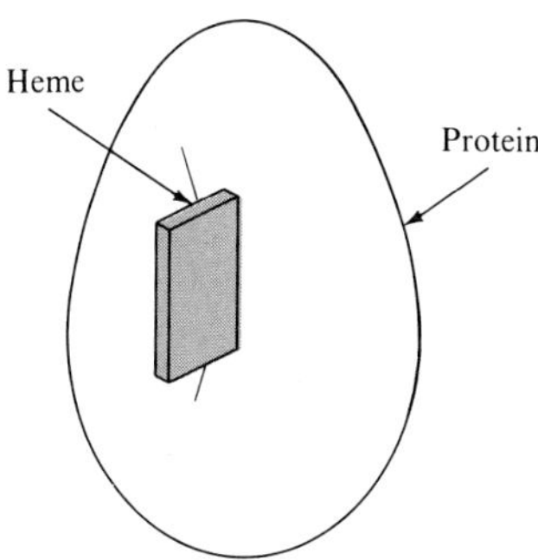

FIGURE 26.12
Cytochrome c structure. The schematic drawing represents the hemeprotein cytochrome c, one of the electron carriers in the respiratory chain. Its structure includes 104 amino acid residues and a heme group.

is molecular oxygen, O_2. Eventually water will form as the H pairs arrive at the end of the chain and combine with oxygen molecules. We have already encountered some members of the respiratory chain, including the coenzymes NAD^+, FAD, and FMN (see Section 25.5). Others include *coenzyme Q* (CoQ), an *iron-sulfur protein* ($S\text{-}Fe^{3+}$), and a set of hemeproteins (Section 23.10) called the *cytochromes* ($cyt\text{-}Fe^{3+}$). The structures of the iron(III) protein carriers are represented by a single abbreviated formula, given in Figure 26.11. The formula of a cytochrome is described in more detail in Figure 26.12. The passage of each electron pair through the respiratory chain produces energy used to make ATP. This process is called **oxidative phosphorylation** because *oxidation* reactions provide the energy for the *phosphorylation* of ADP to ATP.

Let us examine the movement of electron pairs down the first rung of the respiratory ladder. The electron pairs are carried in the form of hydrogens on $NADH + H^+$ or on $FADH_2$. First we see what happens when $NADH + H^+$ enters the respiratory chain. The first carrier listed is FMN, which accepts the H pair and two electrons, as shown below (in color). Note that both electrons come from the hydrogen on NADH, which is removed as H^- (H:). Both hydrogens (as H^+ and H^-) are transferred to FMN to form $FMNH_2$.

$$\text{FMN} + \text{NAD:H} + \text{H}^+ \longrightarrow \text{FMNH}_2 + \text{NAD}^+$$

The $FMNH_2$ transports the electron pair to the next carrier, an iron-sulfur protein, then to CoQ, through the cytochromes, and finally to O_2, as shown in Figure 26.13. Let us look at the final step, in which two Fe^{2+} ions lose two electrons to become two Fe^{3+} ions. Oxygen gains the electrons and combines with H^+ ions to form H_2O:

$$2(\text{cytochrome})\text{Fe}^{2+} + \tfrac{1}{2}\text{O}_2 + 2\text{H}^+ \longrightarrow 2(\text{cytochrome})\text{Fe}^{3+} + \text{H}_2\text{O}$$

This is how each pair of hydrogens removed through the earlier stages of glucose catabolism becomes a water molecule.

Energy to make ATP by oxidative phosphorylation is supplied through electron transport.

In the overall reaction that occurs as the H atom pair from $NADH + H^+$ is transferred from FMN through the electron transport system to O_2, about 53 kcal is released.

$$\text{NADH} + \text{H}^+ + \tfrac{1}{2}\text{O}_2 \longrightarrow \text{NAD}^+ + \text{H}_2\text{O} \qquad \Delta G = -53 \text{ kcal}$$

More than half of that energy (58 percent, or 31 kcal) provides heat needed to maintain a normal body temperature. The remaining 42 percent, or about 22 kcal, can be trapped to power the synthesis of ATP from ADP and phosphate, an endothermic process (see Table 25.1). The phosphate (P) in the equation below comes from *inorganic phosphate* (P_i).

$$\text{ADP} + \text{P}_i \longrightarrow \text{ATP} \qquad \Delta G = +7.4 \text{ kcal}$$

Since each mole of ATP produced requires about 7 kcal of energy input, this

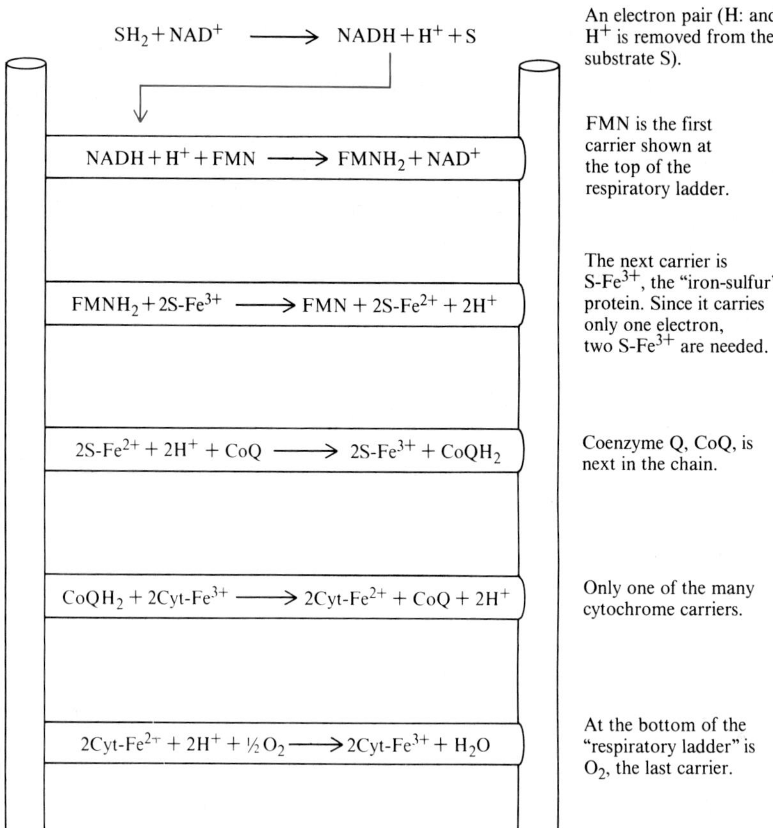

$SH_2 + NAD^+ \longrightarrow NADH + H^+ + S$
An electron pair (H: and H^+ is removed from the substrate S).
$NADH + H^+ + FMN \longrightarrow FMNH_2 + NAD^+$
FMN is the first carrier shown at the top of the respiratory ladder.
$FMNH_2 + 2S\text{-}Fe^{3+} \longrightarrow FMN + 2S\text{-}Fe^{2+} + 2H^+$
The next carrier is $S\text{-}Fe^{3+}$, the "iron-sulfur" protein. Since it carries only one electron, two $S\text{-}Fe^{3+}$ are needed.
$2S\text{-}Fe^{2+} + 2H^+ + CoQ \longrightarrow 2S\text{-}Fe^{3+} + CoQH_2$
Coenzyme Q, CoQ, is next in the chain.
$CoQH_2 + 2Cyt\text{-}Fe^{3+} \longrightarrow 2Cyt\text{-}Fe^{2+} + CoQ + 2H^+$
Only one of the many cytochrome carriers.
$2Cyt\text{-}Fe^{2+} + 2H^+ + \frac{1}{2}O_2 \longrightarrow 2Cyt\text{-}Fe^{3+} + H_2O$
At the bottom of the "respiratory ladder" is O_2, the last carrier.

FIGURE 26.13
One trip down the "respiratory ladder."

means that the 22 kcal remaining is enough to synthesize *three* moles of ATP. The number of ATP's per H pair that can be synthesized by energy from electron transport depends upon where the H atom pair enters the electron transport system and is sometimes less than three. For instance, the H pair that comes from $FADH_2$ skips the first step of electron transfer and thus provides enough energy to produce only two molecules of ATP. (See Table 26.1 for a summary of the source of all 38 ATP's resulting from the catabolism of one molecule of glucose.)

KCN causes respiratory arrest because CN^- ions bind to carriers in the electron transport chain and inhibit electron transfer to O_2.

Experiments have shown that it is possible to inhibit certain electron transport enzymes, thus blocking respiration steps. For instance, cyanide ions (CN^-) inhibit the oxygen utilization of tissues by forming stable complexes with ferric ions of (cytochrome)Fe^{3+} and thus interfering with the transfer of electrons to O_2 (see Figure 26.14*a*). An antidote for cyanide poisoning depends upon the ability of cyanide ions to form even stronger complexes with an iron(III) derivative of hemoglobin (Hb), called *methemoglobin* (metHb), formed by the reaction of sodium nitrite (administered intravenously) with hemoglobin. The (cytochrome)Fe^{3+} is freed to continue in electron transport while the nontoxic cyanide complex of metHb is slowly metabolized (see Figure 26.15*b*).

The ATP released from glucose or other carbohydrates is available to provide energy for muscle contraction, biochemical synthesis (Figure 25.2), and hundreds of other cellular processes. In the next section we will see how the body stores glucose that it does not have an immediate need for.

FIGURE 26.14
Sodium nitrite as an antidote for CN^- poisoning.

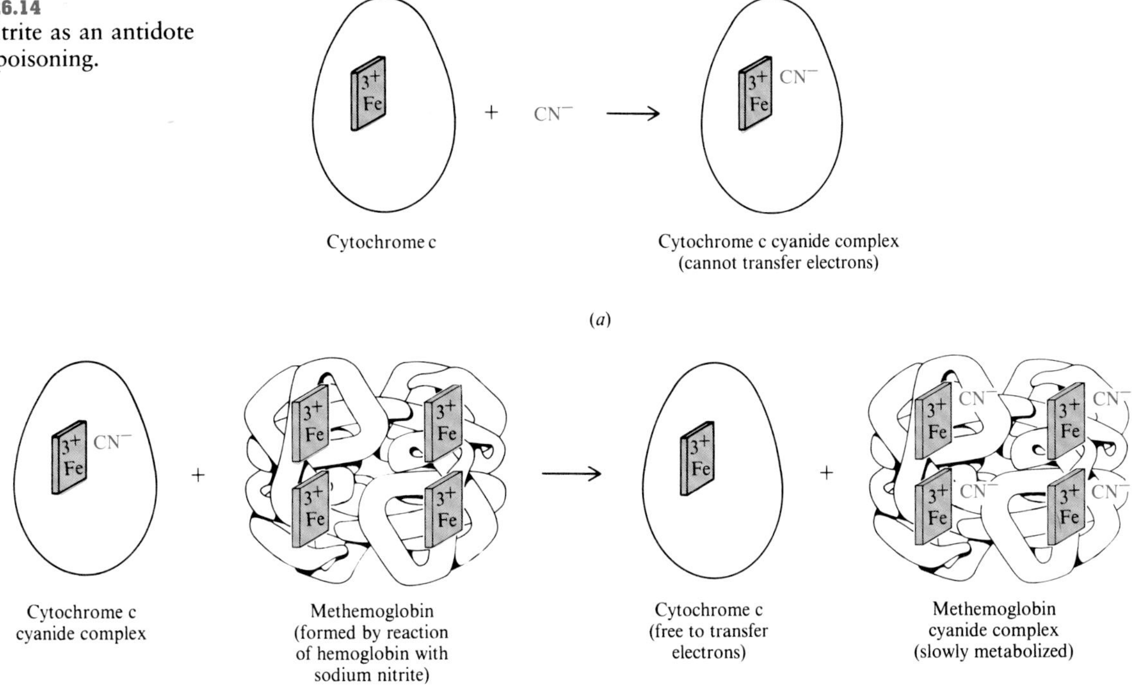

26.9 SYNTHESIS OF GLYCOGEN AND GLUCOSE

Glucose molecules not needed for immediate energy are linked together and stored as glycogen. The process, called **glycogenesis,** is not simply the reverse of glycogenolysis, the pathway discussed earlier in which glycogen breaks down to form glucose (see Figure 26.1).

The first two steps in glycogenesis are the formation of glucose-6-P and its conversion to glucose-1-P. At this point the biosynthesis of glycogen differs from its breakdown. The glucose-1-P is activated by reaction with UTP, a triphosphate of uridine (uracil + ribose), to produce glucose attached to UDP, the corresponding diphosphate (see Figure 26.15).

CH_2OH HO OH OH O—P(=O)(OH)—O—P(=O)(OH)—OCH_2 HN O N OH OH

Glucose

UDP (uridine diphosphate)

FIGURE 26.15
UDP-glucose is a starting material for glycogen synthesis.

$$\text{Glucose-1-P} + \text{UTP} \longrightarrow \text{UDP-glucose} + \text{PP}$$

The UDP-glucose is one ingredient needed for the synthesis of glycogen. The other ingredient is a preexisting carbohydrate molecule called a "*primer.*" Supposing that the priming carbohydrate includes n glucose monomer units, we may write

$$\text{UDP-glucose} + (\text{glucose})_n \xrightarrow{\text{synthetase}} \text{UDP} + (\text{glucose})_{n+1}$$

Glucose monomers are added one at a time to form a growing polysaccharide chain. Finished glycogen molecules have formula weights between 1 million and 2 million.

A *branching enzyme* is also needed to create the branch points, the α-1,6 linkages that are part of normal glycogen structure (Figure 21.13). In the reaction below each G stands for a glucose monomer. The branching enzyme removes the section in color and reattaches it through an α-1,6 linkage.

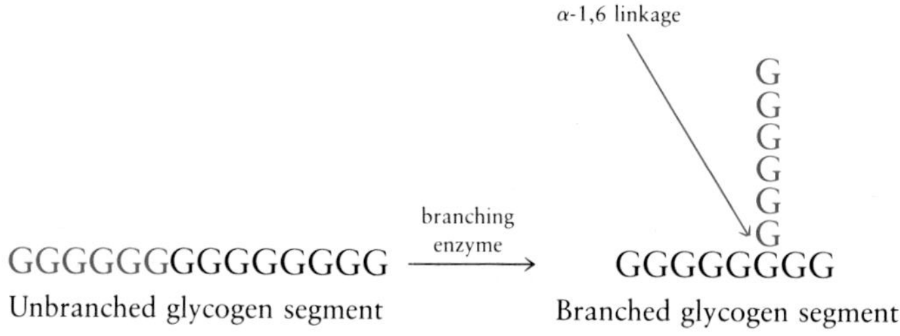

Andersen's disease is one of about a dozen glycogen storage diseases (Section 26.3).

If the branching enzyme happens to be defective, another disorder of carbohydrate metabolism, called ***Andersen's disease,*** occurs because glycogen with unbranched chains cannot be properly utilized by breakdown enzymes.

When the body does not need glucose for energy demands *or* for synthesizing glycogen to replenish storage reserves, the excess glucose is converted into fat by

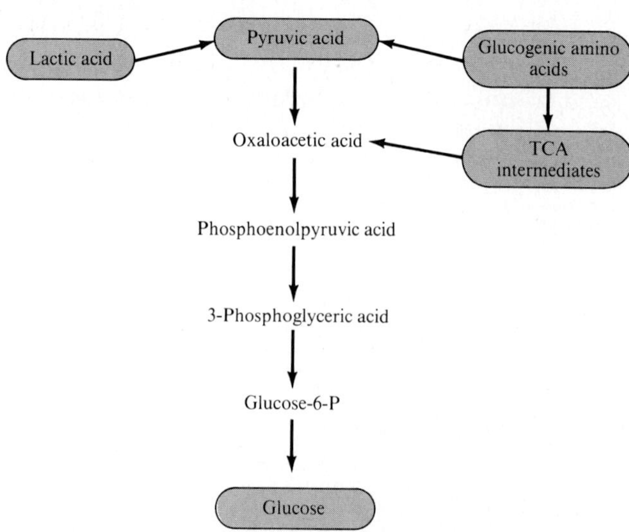

FIGURE 26.16
Gluconeogenesis pathways.

lipogenesis, a process discussed in Chapter 27. The fat produced in this way is stored in tissues located throughout the body.

If there is an insufficient amount of carbohydrate in the diet, the body makes glucose from other noncarbohydrate molecules, a pathway known as **gluconeogenesis** (see Figure 26.1). Our bodies need glucose to supply energy for anaerobic muscle activity, to supply glycerol for fat biosynthesis (from the reduction of dihydroxyacetone, a glycolysis intermediate), and (in nursing mothers) to produce lactose in the mammary glands. In gluco*neo*genesis, *new* glucose is synthesized from pyruvic acid, from lactic acid, from intermediates of the TCA cycle, and from certain amino acids known as *glucogenic* amino acids (see Figure 26.16). Most of the reactions in the gluconeogenesis pathway from pyruvic acid to glucose proceed by reversing the steps in glycolysis, thus utilizing the same enzymes as the glycolysis pathway.

Recall that lactose is glucose plus galactose.

26.10 REGULATION OF BLOOD GLUCOSE

Under normal conditions the level of glucose in the blood is 70 to 90 mg per 100 mL. There are several hormones, including *insulin, glucagon,* and *epinephrine* (adrenalin), that help to regulate blood levels of glucose.

Insulin

Insulin lowers blood glucose level.

The protein insulin (see Figure 23.6) is a hormone that *lowers* blood glucose levels. When the blood glucose rises to too high a level, insulin is secreted by the pancreas, a slender, tapering gland located behind and below the stomach. The pancreas is shown in Figure 26.17, where you can see the large cells that secrete digestive enzymes and the much smaller cells that produce hormones.

There are various mechanisms by which insulin is thought to lower blood glucose levels. Insulin is needed for the transport of glucose through cell membranes, thus allowing it to diffuse into cells, where it can be oxidized to produce energy. Insulin is also believed to activate the enzyme glycogen synthetase, which

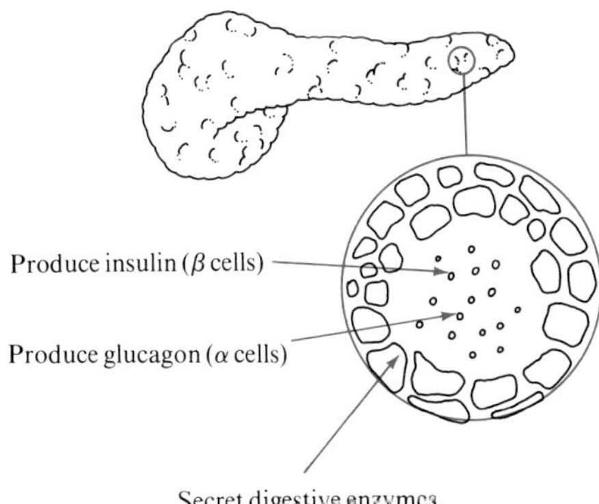

FIGURE 26.17
Pancreas. The cells that produce the hormones are called the "islet cells of Langerhans."

is required for the conversion of glucose to glycogen. The plots in Figure 26.18 show how the levels of insulin and glucose are related. As blood glucose level rises, so does the insulin level in a *normal* person.

Mellitus means "honeyed" in Latin.

"*Glycemia*" means glucose in the blood. *Hyper* is "over" and *hypo* is "under."

The glucose tolerance test (GTT) evaluates the ability of the body to metabolize glucose.

When the pancreas cannot produce enough insulin, the disease called ***diabetes mellitus*** results. One consequence is ***hyperglycemia,*** a condition in which blood glucose rises above normal. The two most frequently encountered symptoms in persons suffering from hyperglycemia are frequent urination and increased thirst. Temporary hyperglycemia occurs in persons who have recently eaten a carbohydrate-rich meal, but blood glucose returns to normal within a few hours. The various levels of hyperglycemia, listed in Table 26.2, are called *fasting* blood glucose levels, levels measured at least 3 h after a meal. When the blood level exceeds about 180 mg, the glucose begins to spill into the urine, producing glucosuria, "sugar in the urine." This is the source of the glucose detected in the Benedict's or enzyme tests, as shown in Color Plates 1 and 22. There are other causes of mild hyperglycemia, but a moderate or marked elevation (300 mg and above) nearly always indicates diabetes mellitus. To make the diagnosis of diabetes mellitus, a *glucose tolerance test* is performed to determine a patient's response to a standard amount of glucose. Blood and urine specimens are examined at

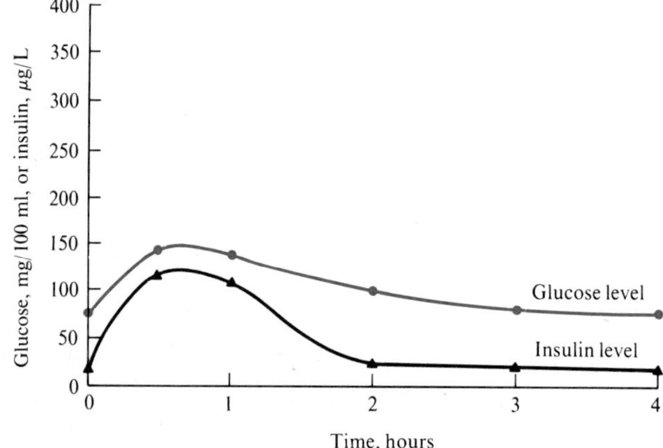

FIGURE 26.18
Blood levels of glucose and insulin following ingestion of 100 g of glucose by a normal individual. The glucose is ingested at time 0. Note that the glucose blood level returns to normal after about 3 h.

TABLE 26.2 BLOOD GLUCOSE LEVELS

Blood glucose, mg/100 mL	**Condition**	**Causes**
80–100	Normal	—
120–130	Mild hyperglycemia	Pancreatic disorders
300–500	Moderate hyperglycemia	Diabetes mellitus
> 500	Marked hyperglycemia	Uncontrolled diabetes mellitus

FIGURE 26.19
Blood levels of glucose following ingestion of 100 g of glucose by two individuals (one normal and one diabetic) undergoing a glucose tolerance test.

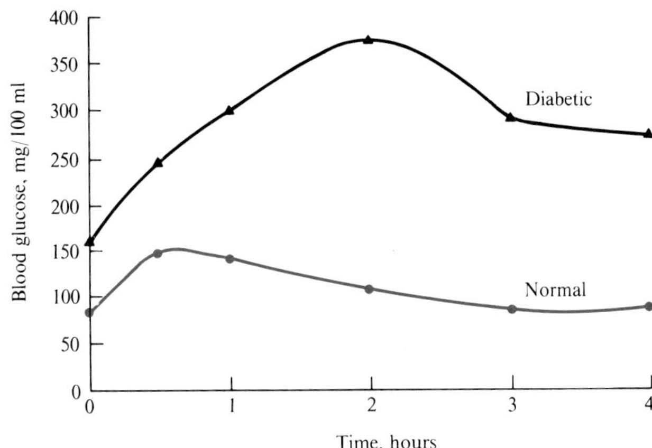

timed intervals from 0.5 to 3 h after glucose intake. The results of a glucose tolerance test are compared for a normal and a diabetic subject in Figure 26.19.

The generous amount of unusable glucose available to the tissues of diabetics has often been described as "starvation in the midst of plenty." To survive, the cells must utilize other foodstuffs, including proteins and fats. However, there is a danger in this. When excessive amounts of fats are oxidized, toxic by-products of fat metabolism can build up. This results in ketosis, a condition in which ketones accumulate in the blood and urine (discussed in detail in Chapter 27).

Diabetes is kept under control, not cured, by administration of the lacking hormone insulin. The insulin, usually derived from cattle, must be injected, because if administered orally it is digested and broken down before it can be utilized. Too much insulin causes the blood glucose level to dip below normal, causing ***hypoglycemia,*** the condition in which the blood glucose level falls below 40 mg per 100 mL blood. Symptoms of hypoglycemia include weakness, hunger, dizziness, sweating, headache, and mental confusion. In extreme cases, brain damage, coma, or death can result. Under certain special conditions, such as starvation or extreme exercise, nondiabetics can also suffer from severe hypoglycemia. For instance, the blood glucose level of a runner who has just completed a marathon (26 miles) can sink so low that intravenous glucose treatment may be needed at the finish line.

The diet of diabetics who are receiving insulin therapy must be carefully regulated. Too much concentrated sugar in any form, including fruit sugars and honey, can cause hyperglycemia. Ingestion of food must be frequent and regularly spaced so that the administered insulin will not cause hypoglycemia. Some diabetic conditions can be controlled by diet alone, particularly the form of diabetes known as ***maturity onset diabetes,*** caused by the inability of older persons to utilize insulin effectively. This condition is aggravated in obese individuals, whose enlarged adipose cells are less responsive to insulin.

Juvenile onset diabetes occurs early in life and is more severe than maturity onset diabetes.

In some cases diabetics can be treated successfully with orally administered drugs that stimulate the release of insulin from the pancreatic cells, including

FIGURE 26.20
Antidiabetic sulfonurea derviatives.

$CH_3-C_6H_4-SO_2-NH-CO-CH_2CH_2CH_2CH_2CH_3$

tolbutamide
Orinase

$CH_3-C_6H_4-SO_2-NH-CO-NHN$ (seven-membered ring)

tolazamide
Tolinase

tolbutamide and tolazamide (see Figure 26.20). These drugs have been shown to have *no* effect in lowering the blood sugar levels of diabetic patients whose pancreatic cells do not *make* insulin, and thus it is incorrect to call them "oral insulin."

Glucagon and Epinephrine

Glucagon and epinephrine raise blood glucose levels.

Glucagon (Figure 26.21), a polypeptide containing 29 amino acids, is secreted by the alpha cells of the pancreas (Figure 26.19). The role of the hormone glucagon is to *increase* the blood glucose level. When blood glucose levels are low glucagon is secreted, stimulating the liver to convert glycogen into glucose. The glucose is then released into the bloodstream.

Epinephrine was discussed in Section 18.2, where you saw that it prepares the body for emergencies by increasing blood pressure and cardiac output. Another function of this hormone is to accelerate the breakdown of glycogen. When liver glycogen breaks down, it produces glucose and thereby *increases* the blood glucose levels. The breakdown of muscle glycogen feeds glucose into the glycolysis cycle, thus providing instant energy for emergencies. Table 26.3 summarizes the actions of the hormones that regulate glucose blood level.

Amino end
1 his
ser
gln
gly
thr
phe
thr
ser
asp
10 tyr
ser
lys
tyr
leu
asp
ser
arg
arg
ala
20 gln
asp
phe
val
gln
trp
leu
met
asn
29 thr

FIGURE 26.21
Bovine glucagon.

TABLE 26.3 HORMONES THAT REGULATE GLUCOSE BLOOD LEVEL

Hormone	Structure	Source	Effect on blood glucose
Insulin	Small protein (51 amino acid residues)	Pancreas	↓
Glucagon	Polypeptide (29 amino acid residues)	Pancreas	↑
Epinephrine (adrenalin)	Phenyethylamine derivative	Adrenal gland	↑

26.11 PHOTOSYNTHESIS; SYNTHESIS OF CARBOHYDRATES

The carbohydrates that we ingest are made by plants from the starting materials CO_2 and H_2O in the anabolic process called **photosynthesis** (see Fig. 21.10). Photosynthesis, the reverse of the catabolism of glucose, is an energy-consuming pathway, which requires energy in the form of sunlight to make it happen. Plants contain chlorophyll pigments, most of which are green, that capture the light of the sun. The structure of chlorophyll is shown in Figure 18.17, where you can see that the porphin ring system (in color) is part of the structure.

Photosynthesis does not occur in one single step. Instead it is a complex set of reactions, using many of the same enzymes and intermediates involved in glucose catabolism.

SUMMARY

Glucose produced from digestion of carbohydrates or from the breakdown of glycogen is absorbed into the bloodstream. A large fraction of blood glucose undergoes glycolysis in the cytosol of the cell, where no oxygen is present. Each glucose molecule is degraded to two lactic acid molecules through a series of reactions, which provides energy in the form of two molecules of ATP. This ATP comes from substrate level phosphorylation, since the P added to ADP is derived from a substrate formed as a glycolysis intermediate. Such anaerobic energy is required for maximal muscular activity, during which there is not enough time for sufficient O_2 to be delivered to the muscle cells.

Under aerobic conditions pyruvic acid enters the respiration pathway rather than forming lactic acid. Respiration takes place in the mitochondria, the "powerhouses" of the cell. Pyruvic acid is first converted into acetyl-CoA, a compound also formed by amino acids and fatty acids and hence known as the intersection point for all metabolic processes. The acetyl-CoA enters the tricarboxylic acid cycle (TCA cycle), where it undergoes a set of reactions known as a turn. Two turns (for one glucose molecule) produce two ATP molecules by substrate level phosphorylation. Each glucose molecule that undergoes glycolysis and the TCA cycle thus provides a total of four ATP's from substrate level phosphorylation—two from glycolysis and two from two turns of the TCA cycle. In addition, a total of 12 H atom pairs are produced for every glucose—two H pairs from glycolysis, two H pairs from the conversion of pyruvic acid to acetyl-CoA, and eight H pairs from two turns of the TCA cycle.

The 12 H atom pairs carry 12 electron pairs. These are transported through the respiratory chain, which is a set of oxidizing agents or electron carrier compounds. In the final step molecular oxygen accepts an electron pair from (cytochrome)Fe^{2+} (the next-to-last carrier). Water forms by combination with oxygen of the H atom pair present as H^+ ions.

The travel of each H pair through the respiratory chain releases energy, which is used to synthesize ATP from ADP and inorganic phosphate, a process called oxidative phosphorylation. For every H pair derived from NADH + H^+, three ATP's form, and from the H pairs carried by $FADH_2$, only two ATP's form. The grand total produced from the complete metabolism of one molecule of glucose is 38 ATP molecules.

The body synthesizes carbohydrates as well as breaking them down: glucose not needed for immediate energy is converted into glycogen, and the body makes its own glucose from noncarbohydrate molecules through gluconeogenesis.

Several hormones regulate blood levels of glucose, which should range from 70 to 90 mg per 100 mL blood. Insulin lowers blood glucose levels. When the body does not provide enough insulin, diabetes mellitus is the result. Untreated diabetics suffer from hyperglycemia, abnormally high blood levels of glucose. Therapy consists of insulin administration. Too much insulin produces hypoglycemia, in which glucose levels dip below normal. The hormones glucagon and adrenalin both act to increase blood glucose.

Plants synthesize carbohydrates through photosynthesis, a complex set of reactions that requires energy from sunlight. The overall reaction is the reverse of the catabolism of glucose in that CO_2 combines with H_2O to produce glucose and O_2.

KEY WORDS

digestion
glycogenolysis
glycolysis
Embden-Meyerhof pathway
mitochondria
acetyl coenzyme A (acetyl-CoA)
tricarboxylic acid cycle (TCA cycle)
substrate level phosphorylation
electron transport
electron carriers
respiratory chain
oxidative phosphorylation
glycogenesis
gluconeogenesis
diabetes mellitus
hyperglycemia
hypoglycemia
photosynthesis

EXERCISES

26.2 Classify each pathway as anabolic or catabolic: (**a**) gluconeogenesis; (**b**) glycolysis; (**c**) Embden-Meyerhof; (**d**) glycogenesis; (**e**) glycogenolysis.

26.3 What are the main sources of carbohydrate in your diet? What compound is used as the starting material for carbohydrate catabolism?

26.4 Describe what happens to the starch you eat: (**a**) in your mouth; (**b**) in your stomach; (**c**) in your small intestine.

26.5 Compare the net production of ATP from glycolysis with that from respiration.

26.6 One of the values below corresponds to the free energy (ΔG) of hydrolysis of phosphoenolpyruvic acid. Which one must it be? Explain how you made your choice. (**a**) 10.0 kcal/mol; (**b**) -3.0 kcal/mol; (**c**) -14.7 kcal/mol.

26.7 What are the sources of ATP utilized by muscle cells?

26.8 Under what circumstances would a muscle cell depend upon glycolysis to supply a large percentage of the energy needed for a contraction?

26.9 After 1 min of which of the following activities would a muscle be receiving about two-thirds of its energy from glycolysis: (**a**) studying chemistry; (**b**) weight lifting; (**c**) jogging?

26.10 What is meant by aerobic exercise? Give some examples.

26.11 What is meant by the statement: Acetyl-CoA is the intersection point for all metabolic processes?

26.12 Thiamine deficiency is common in individuals suffering from ***alcoholism*** who are also nutritionally deprived. Because of this, interference with one of the following metabolic processes leads to acidosis and can be lethal. Which process is it?
(a) Pyruvic acid → lactic acid
(b) Pyruvic acid → acetyl-CoA
(c) Glycogen → glucose

26.13 In what part of the cell does respiration take place? Glycolysis?

26.14 What is meant by substrate level phosphorylation? How many ATP's per molecule of glucose are formed by substrate level phosphorylation?

26.15 Which vitamins are "links" of the respiratory chain?

26.16 What is oxidative phosphorylation? How does it differ from substrate level phosphorylation?

26.17 Which of the intermediates in the TCA cycle are tricarboxylic acids?

26.18 Assuming *no* waste at all, state how many ATP's could be formed from the addition of inorganic phosphate to ADP using the 53 kcal supplied by the passage of an H atom pair (from NADH + H^+) through the respiratory chain? How many ATP's actually are formed? In mammals, what happens to the rest of this energy?

26.19 How does ***diabetes mellitus*** differ from ***diabetes insipidus*** (Section 23.6)? Why are they both called diabetes?

26.20 What is meant by hypoglycemia and hyperglycemia? What are the symptoms of each disorder?

26.21 Why is it essential for a diabetic undergoing insulin treatment to have regularly spaced meals?

26.22 Why is insulin administered by injection rather than orally?

26.23 What simple treatment can be used to counteract the effects of too much insulin in the bloodstream?

26.24 Marathon (26-mile run) runners report that it is very difficult to keep moving at about the twentieth mile of the race, a point known as the "wall." Why should this happen?

26.25 Is it possible for muscle glycogen to eliminate hypoglycemia? Why?

26.26 Suppose the calf muscle becomes exhausted by running. Could this muscle receive a new supply of glycogen from the biceps? Why or why not?

26.27 In which of the following events would carbohydrate loading be useless: (**a**) distance cycling; (**b**) 1-mile run; (**c**) baseball; (**d**) downhill skiing?

26.28 Why is cyanide toxic?

26.29 What is the difference between glycogenesis and gluconeogenesis? Under what conditions do these processes take place?

26.30 Is the product "glucagon for injection" used to counteract severe cases of hyperglycemia or hypoglycemia? Explain.

26.31 Would glucagon treatment be useful in cases of starvation? Why or why not?

27 METABOLISM OF LIPIDS

27.1 INTRODUCTION

A triacylglycerol is made from glycerol and three fatty acid molecules.

In Chapter 22 you were introduced to triacylglycerols, phosphoglycerides, steroids, and a variety of other lipids. The triacylglycerol fats, along with carbohydrates and proteins, are major nutrients, and so are the lipids that will be the subject of nearly all our metabolic discussion. We will also examine the metabolism of one other lipid, cholesterol, because of its relationship to cardiovascular diseases.

In Chapter 26 you found out how glucose derived from carbohydrate foods is broken down to provide energy for body activities, and you saw that excess glucose not needed by the body is stored as glycogen. Triacylglycerol fats perform similar functions, but instead of glycolysis, they are degraded by a pathway called the *fatty acid cycle.* This cycle, like the aerobic degradation of glucose, produces acetyl-CoA, which can then enter into respiration. Any excess acetyl-CoA may be used to rebuild the storage fats by the biosynthetic process called *lipogenesis.* While reading this chapter you will find it helpful to refer to Figure 27.1, which shows how the fatty acid cycle, lipogenesis, and other pathways involved in the metabolism of fats are related to each other.

Through lipogenesis most excess food is converted to fats, which are deposited as adipose tissue. There are two main reasons why the body does not use primarily glycogen for energy storage. First, gram for gram fat can store much more energy than glycogen. We will see that 1 g of fat that undergoes catabolism via the fatty acid cycle and respiration generates more than *twice* as many high-energy phosphate bonds as 1 g of glycogen that goes through glycolysis and respiration. Another advantage that fats have over glycogen for energy storage is their aversion to water, meaning that they can be stored in concentrated droplets with no space wasted by associated water. Because glycogen contains hydroxyl groups, it *is* attracted to water. Thus glycogen deposits are 50 percent water while fat cells are more than 90 percent pure triacylglycerols. To give you an idea of how much more effective fats are than glycogen for energy storage, consider a person weighing 130 lb, with 20 lb of that weight as fat. Suppose the fat were entirely replaced with glycogen. Glycogen deposits storing the same amount of energy would weigh about 100 lb, thus adding 80 lb onto the body weight. That

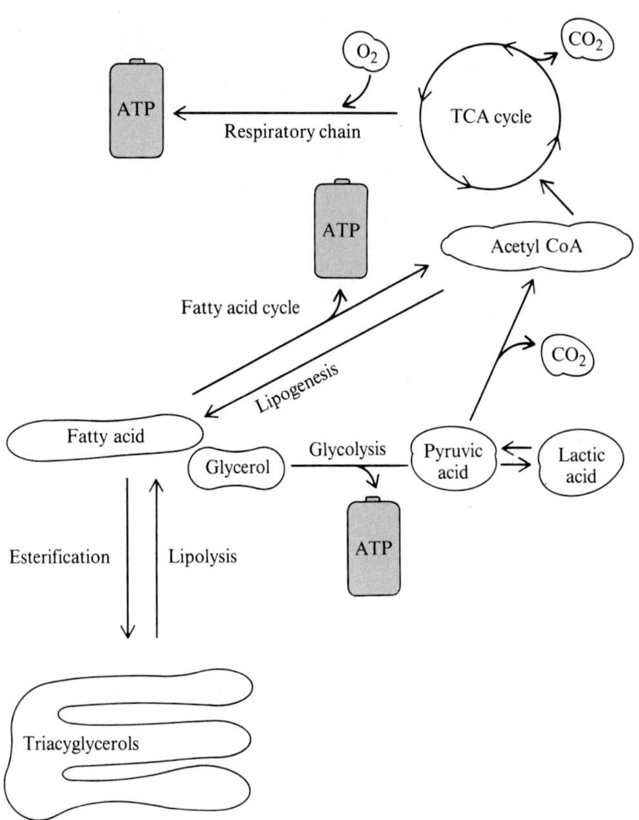

FIGURE 27.1
Triacylglycerol metabolic pathways.

If glycogen were our primary energy storage form, each of us would weigh about 50 percent more.

means that a 130-lb person would have to weigh over 200 lb if nature used glycogen instead of fat as its primary substance for energy storage!

Our study of fat metabolism begins with the initial breakdown of dietary fats and storage fats, which is followed by their transport to the tissues, where metabolism takes place.

27.2 DIGESTION AND ABSORPTION OF FATS

Medium-chain triglycerides (MCT) are used in diets of children with cystic fibrosis, a disease associated with fat malabsorption.

A preliminary step in the digestion of dietary triacylglycerols is **lipolysis,** the hydrolysis of lipids. Lipolysis is catalyzed by the **lipases** (Section 22.4), the enzymes that attack the ester linkages between glycerol and the fatty acids, as shown in Figure 27.2. There are no lipases in the saliva. Although the gastric juices do contain some lipase, nearly all the hydrolysis of ingested fat takes place in the small intestine by the action of *pancreatic lipase* or of *enteric lipase,* secreted by the intestine walls.

The hydrolysis of fat globules is assisted by *bile salts,* which behave like detergents. The bile salts break up the large fat globules so that they can be hydrolyzed more effectively. This occurs because the smaller particles have more

Lipases attack ester linkages.

$$
\begin{array}{ccccc}
CH_2 & — & CH & — & CH_2 \\
| & & | & & | \\
O\swarrow & & O\swarrow & & O\swarrow \\
C{=}O & & C{=}O & & C{=}O \\
| & & | & & | \\
(CH_2)_{14} & & (CH_2)_{14} & & (CH_2)_7 \\
| & & | & & | \\
CH_3 & & CH_3 & & CH \\
 & & & & \| \\
 & & & & CH \\
 & & & & | \\
 & & & & (CH_2)_7 \\
 & & & & | \\
 & & & & CH_3
\end{array}
$$

FIGURE 27.2

surface area to come into contact with more lipase (see Figure 27.3). The bile salts "ferry" the hydrolysis products to the intestinal wall. There the short- and medium-chain fatty acids (less than 10 C atoms) and the glycerol are released directly into the bloodstream (see Figure 27.4). Because they are easily absorbed by the body, **medium-chain triglycerides** (6 to 10 C atoms) are used in the diets of patients with impaired absorption and digestion of fat. Longer-chain fatty acids (more than 10 C atoms) are not sufficiently water-soluble for direct transport and must be moved to the blood in a different way. First they combine with glycerol to re-form the neutral triglyceride (TG) fats in the intestinal wall, from which they are then transported to the lymph system by attaching themselves to a water-soluble protein to form a lipoprotein. The **lipoproteins** appear in the lymph as tiny fat droplets (about 1μm in diameter) called **chylomicrons. The** chylomicrons are transported through the aqueous lymph system to the bloodstream (see Figure 27.4), which delivers them mainly to the liver and adipose tissue but also to the heart, lungs, and other organs. At the tissues the TG's are hydrolyzed again, this time by *lipoprotein lipase.*

So far we have discussed the fate of *dietary* fats. Fats stored in adipose tissue can also be mobilized for catabolism. They are first hydrolyzed by lipases present in the adipose tissue. The glycerol produced goes directly to the bloodstream. The fatty acids are bound to serum albumin present in the blood serum, which then transports them to various body organs. The fatty acids derived from adipose tissue or from dietary fat can then be degraded, as we will describe in the next section, or they can be rebuilt into storage fats.

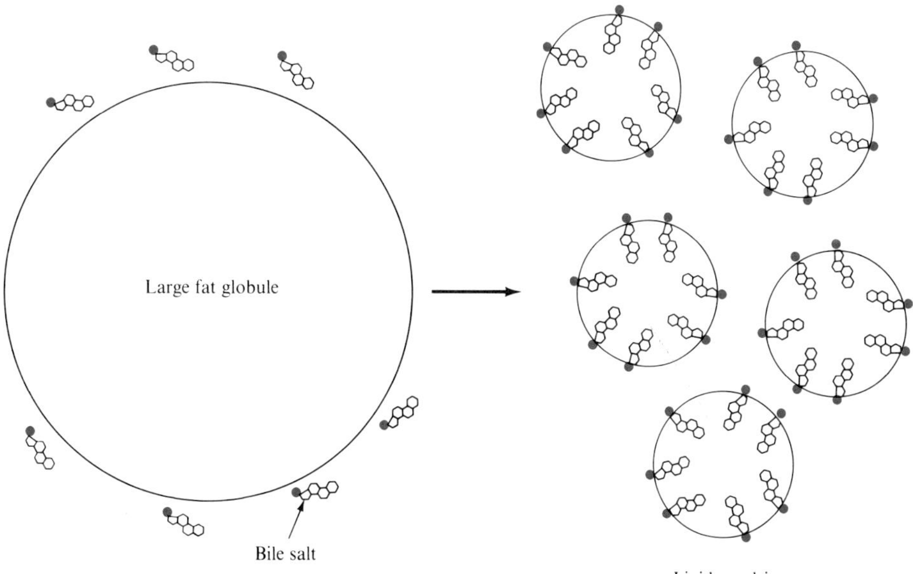

FIGURE 27.3
The polar head of the bile salt (in color) dissolves in water and the nonpolar end in the lipid, thus breaking the large globule into small droplets.

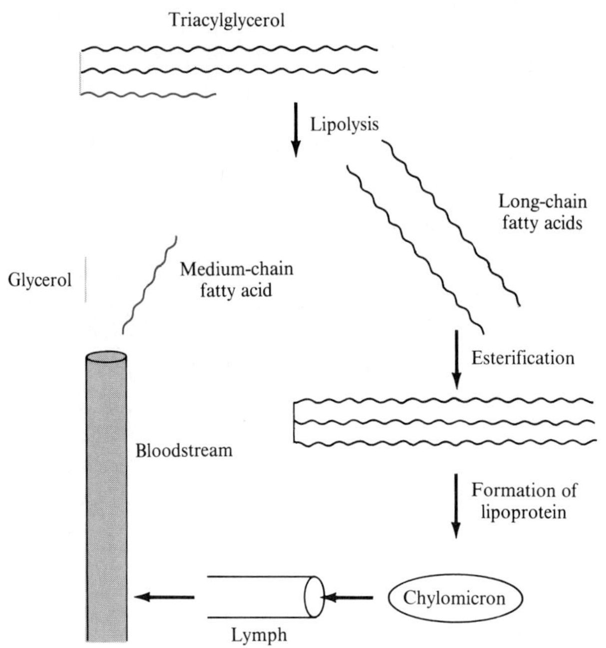
Triacylglycerol
Lipolysis
Long-chain fatty acids
Glycerol
Medium-chain fatty acid
Esterification
Bloodstream
Formation of lipoprotein
Chylomicron
Lymph
Glycerol, medium- and short-chain fatty acids go directly from the intestine to the bloodstream.
Long-chain fatty acids are re-formed into fats. The fats combine with proteins to form lipoproteins. The lipoproteins form chylomicra that are transported through the lymph system to the bloodstream.

FIGURE 27.4
Digestion of fats.

27.3 THE FATTY ACID CYCLE

The glycerol component of a fat is degraded by glycolysis.

Fatty acids, like glucose, are degraded to acetyl-CoA but by a different pathway known as the **fatty acid cycle** (FA cycle), and in the mitochondria rather than in the cytosol, where glycolysis takes place. Fatty acids are broken down two carbon atoms at a time. Each terminal two-carbon segment is converted into one acetyl-CoA through a set of four reactions collectively called one *turn* of the fatty acid cycle. Acetyl-CoA can then enter respiration (or can be used to resynthesize more storage fat).

Let us follow the progress of hexanoic acid through the fatty acid cycle to see how many acetyl-CoA's emerge and how many turns are required. (The two-carbon segments that are being removed are shown in boldface.)

Recall that CoA is derived from pantothenic acid, one of the B vitamins.

First the acid must be activated by reaction with CoA.

$$CH_3CH_2CH_2CH_2CH_2\overset{\overset{\displaystyle O}{\|}}{C}OH + CoA \xrightarrow{\text{synthetase}} CH_3CH_2CH_2CH_2CH_2\overset{\overset{\displaystyle O}{\|}}{C}{-}CoA + H_2O$$

$$ATP \curvearrowright AMP + 2P$$

In the first of the four reactions needed to remove the first two-carbon segment, one FAD accepts two H atoms (in color), leaving an unsaturated fat.

Step 1 $$\mathrm{FAD} + \mathrm{CH_3CH_2CH_2}\overset{\mathrm{H}}{\underset{\mathrm{H}}{\mathrm{C}}}-\overset{\mathrm{H}}{\underset{\mathrm{H}}{\mathrm{C}}}-\overset{\mathrm{O}}{\overset{\|}{\mathrm{C}}}-\mathrm{CoA} \xrightarrow{\text{dehydrogenase}} \mathrm{CH_3CH_2CH_2}\overset{\beta}{\mathrm{CH}}{=}\overset{\alpha}{\mathrm{CH}}\overset{\mathrm{O}}{\overset{\|}{\mathrm{C}}}-\mathrm{CoA} + \mathrm{FADH_2}$$

Next, water adds across the double bond to put a hydroxyl substituent on C-3 (the β carbon atom).

Step 2 $$\mathrm{CH_3CH_2CH_2}\overset{\beta}{\mathrm{CH}}{=}\mathrm{CH}\overset{\mathrm{O}}{\overset{\|}{\mathrm{C}}}-\mathrm{CoA} + \mathrm{H_2O} \xrightarrow{\text{hydrase}} \mathrm{CH_3CH_2CH_2}\underset{\mathrm{OH}}{\overset{\beta}{\mathrm{CH}}}\mathrm{CH_2}\overset{\mathrm{O}}{\overset{\|}{\mathrm{C}}}-\mathrm{CoA}$$

In the third step the β-hydroxyl group is *oxidized* to a carbonyl by NAD^+. Because of this reaction the fatty acid cycle is also known by another name, the *β oxidation of fatty acids.*

Step 3 $$\mathrm{CH_3CH_2CH_2}\overset{\mathrm{OH}}{\overset{|}{\mathrm{C}}}\mathrm{HCH_2}\overset{\mathrm{O}}{\overset{\|}{\mathrm{C}}}-\mathrm{CoA} + \mathrm{NAD^+} \xrightarrow{\text{dehydrogenase}} \mathrm{CH_3CH_2CH_2}\overset{\mathrm{O}}{\overset{\|}{\mathrm{C}}}\mathrm{CH_2}\overset{\mathrm{O}}{\overset{\|}{\mathrm{C}}}-\mathrm{CoA} + \mathrm{NADH} + \mathrm{H^+}$$

Note that the product of this reaction has a carbonyl at the β position.

Butanoic acid, a component of butter, is most often called *butyric* acid, hence the name *butyryl* rather than butanoyl.

In the fourth and final step of the first turn, acetyl-CoA splits off from the β-keto product. A new molecule of CoA attaches to the remaining fragment, butyryl-CoA, which has two less C atoms than the starting material, hexanoyl-CoA (see Figure 27.5).

Step 4 $$\mathrm{CoA} + \mathrm{CH_3CH_2CH_2}\overset{\mathrm{O}}{\overset{\|}{\mathrm{C}}}\mathrm{CH_2}\overset{\mathrm{O}}{\overset{\|}{\mathrm{C}}}-\mathrm{CoA} \xrightarrow{\text{thiolase}} \underset{\text{Butyryl-CoA}}{\mathrm{CH_3CH_2CH_2}\overset{\mathrm{O}}{\overset{\|}{\mathrm{C}}}-\mathrm{CoA}} + \underset{\text{Acetyl-CoA}}{\mathrm{CH_3}\overset{\mathrm{O}}{\overset{\|}{\mathrm{C}}}-\mathrm{CoA}}$$

The acetyl-CoA can enter the TCA cycle (Section 26.7). The butyryl-CoA then goes through another turn of the fatty acid cycle, in which it will be broken down

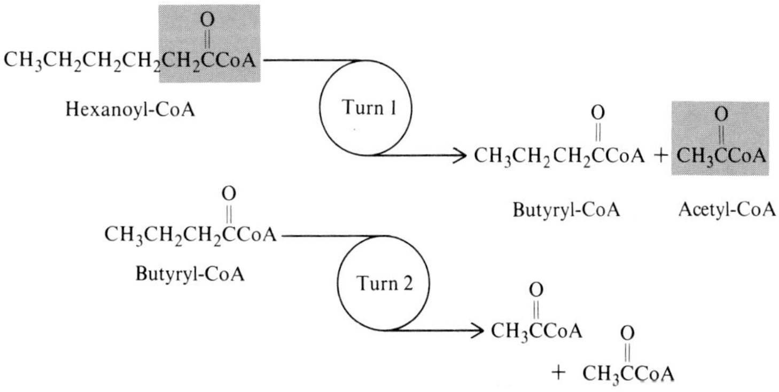

FIGURE 27.5
Fatty acid cycle.

into two more acetyl-CoA molecules. The last turn in the fatty acid cycle for any fatty acid always involves the breakdown of butyryl-CoA and always produces two acetyl-CoA's.

A fatty acid with n C atoms produces $\frac{1}{2}n$ acetyl-CoA's and requires $(\frac{1}{2}n-1)$ turns of the fatty acid cycle.

Above you saw that hexanoic acid went through *two* turns of the fatty acid cycle and produced *three* acetyl-CoA's. In general, a fatty acid must go through a number of turns equal to *one less than half* the number of C atoms in its formula. The total number of acetyl-CoA's produced by a trip through the fatty acid cycle must always be *half* the number of C atoms in the fatty acid formula. Recall that virtually all carboxylic acids in natural fats have an even number of carbon atoms (Section 22.2), because they are built up two carbon atoms at a time, just as they are degraded two C atoms at a time. We have used a saturated fatty acid to illustrate the reactions in the fatty acid cycle, but unsaturated fatty acids follow a similar pathway.

SAMPLE EXERCISE 27.1

For lauric acid (dodecanoic acid) to be degraded through the fatty acid cycle, how many turns are needed and how many acetyl CoA's are produced?

Solution:

Lauric acid is a 12-carbon acid, $CH_3(CH_2)_{10}\overset{\overset{\large O}{\|}}{C}OH$.

$$n = 12$$

$$\text{Number of turns} = \tfrac{1}{2}n - 1 = 6 - 1 = 5$$

$$\text{Number of acetyl CoA's} = 6 \text{ (4 from the first four turns and 2 from the last turn)}$$

EXERCISE 27.1

How many turns through the fatty acid cycle are required to degrade palmitic acid? How many acetyl-CoA's are produced?

27.4 ENERGY FROM FATTY ACID CYCLE AND TCA CYCLE

Fats produce much more energy than do carbohydrates. To prove this we can first see how many ATP's are derived from the complete oxidation (fatty acid cycle plus respiration) of one molecule of palmitic acid, the most common saturated fatty acid present in natural fats.

Each turn of the fatty acid cycle produces five ATP's.

Seven turns through the fatty acid cycle are needed to degrade a 16-carbon acid. Each turn of the fatty acid cycle results in the formation of two H atom pairs, one from NADH + H^+ (step 3) and the other from $FADH_2$ (step 1). The H atom pairs from one turn produce a total of five ATP's, three from NADH + H^+ and two from $FADH_2$ via the respiratory chain (see Section 26.8). To get the net total of ATP's produced from the passage of one palmitic acid (hexadecanoic acid) through the fatty acid cycle, we must also subtract the ATP that was required to activate the original palmitic acid. Recall that the ATP used in this step was converted to AMP rather than ADP; an additional ATP is used to convert the AMP product back into ADP. To account for this we must deduct two ATP's for the activation step.

Activation step	−2 ATP's
Seven turns	+35 ATP's
Total ATP's from FA cycle	33 ATP's

One acetyl-CoA degraded to CO_2 and H_2O provides 12 ATP's.

The eight molecules of acetyl-CoA produced from one palmitic acid molecule go on to produce more ATP's as they undergo respiration (TCA cycle plus respiratory chain). In Table 26.1 you can see that 24 ATP's come from one molecule of glucose (two molecules of acetyl-CoA) in the TCA cycle. The passage of only one acetyl-CoA through the TCA and respiratory cycles leads to the formation of 12 ATP's, 11 from oxidative phosphorylation and 1 from substrate level phosphorylation. Thus the eight acetyl-CoA's produce 96 (8×12) ATP's. The grand total of ATP's from the complete oxidation of palmitic acid is

ATP's from FA cycle:	33
ATP's from TCA cycle:	96
Total ATP's from one palmitic acid:	129

Recall that the total ATP production for one molecule of glucose was only 38. We can show that 1 g of palmitic acid produces more than *twice* as much ATP as 1 g of glucose. To make the calculation we need the formula weights of glucose (180) and palmitic acid (256).

$$\frac{38 \text{ ATP's}}{180 \text{ g glucose}} \approx 0.2 \text{ ATP/g glucose}$$

$$\frac{129 \text{ ATP's}}{256 \text{ g palmitic acid}} \approx 0.5 \text{ ATP/g palmitic acid}$$

We get 9 food calories from 1 g fat compared with only 4 for 1 g carbohydrate.

Thus we see that 1 g of the fatty acid provides about $2\frac{1}{2}$ times as much ATP as 1 g of glucose. That is one important reason why the body uses triacylglycerol molecules to store its energy.

Gram for gram fats provide much more ATP energy than any other kind of food.

We can give a qualitative molecular explanation for the extra ability of fats to produce ATP energy by comparing their formulas. Fats and fatty acids contain a much greater weight percentage of H in their formulas than do carbohydrates. For instance, the weight percentage of H in palmitic acid (formula weight 256) is nearly twice as great as that in glucose (formula weight 180):

$$\text{Palmitic acid } (C_{16}H_{32}O_2): \quad \frac{32}{256} \times 100\% = 12.5\%\ H$$

$$\text{Glucose } (C_6H_{12}O_6): \quad \frac{12}{180} \times 100\% = 6.7\%\ H$$

Therefore, each gram of palmitic acid contains more H atoms than a gram of glucose. Thus palmitic acid provides more H atoms to be stripped away as it is degraded. Recall that those H atoms are picked up by NAD^+ or FAD, which eventually travels through the respiratory chain to provide ATP.

SAMPLE EXERCISE 27.2

Calculate the number of ATP's produced when lauric acid is completely oxidized.

Solution:

From Sample Exercise 27.1 we found that lauric acid goes through five turns of the FA cycle and also produces six acetyl-CoA's. Count the total ATP's from this:

Activation :		−2 ATP's
Five turns :	5 × 5 ATP's =	+25 ATP's
Six acetyl-CoA :	6 × 12 ATP's =	+72 ATP's
Total ATP's from one lauric acid :		95 ATP's

EXERCISE 27.2

The formula weight of lauric acid ($C_{12}H_{24}O_2$) is 200. Calculate the ATP production per gram of lauric acid. How does this compare with that from palmitic acid?

27.5 BIOSYNTHESIS OF FATTY ACIDS

Lipogenesis is from *lipo-* for "lipid" and *genesis* meaning "birth."

The starting material for the biosynthesis of fatty acids, or **lipogenesis,** is acetyl-CoA, which can come from the degradation of *any* food. The fatty acids are built up two C atoms at a time, just as they are degraded two C atoms at a time, but the synthesis takes place in the cytosol of adipose tissue cells, not in the mitochondria, where the fatty acid cycle occurs. Also, a different set of enzymes is required for lipogenesis. In the description below we will point out some of the important features of this complex process.

One ingredient that organisms use to synthesize fatty acids is *malonyl-CoA*. Malonic acid is a dicarboxylic acid with one unit of CH_2 between the two carboxyl groups (see Section 17.3).

$$\underset{\text{Malonic acid}}{HO{-}\overset{\overset{\displaystyle O}{\|}}{C}{-}CH_2{-}\overset{\overset{\displaystyle O}{\|}}{C}{-}OH} \qquad \underset{\text{Malonyl-CoA}}{HO{-}\overset{\overset{\displaystyle O}{\|}}{C}{-}CH_2{-}\overset{\overset{\displaystyle O}{\|}}{C}{-}CoA}$$

Malonyl-CoA is made from acetyl-CoA; a molecule of CO_2 provides the additional C and two O atoms in its formula (in color) according to the reaction below, where you see that one molecule of ATP is consumed. The vitamin biotin, a CO_2 carrier, acts as a coenzyme (see Section 25.5).

$$\underset{\text{Acetyl-CoA}}{CH_3{-}\overset{\overset{\displaystyle O}{\|}}{C}{-}CoA} + CO_2 \xrightarrow[\text{ATP} \to \text{ADP} + \text{P}]{\text{carboxylase}} \underset{\text{Malonyl-CoA}}{HO{-}\overset{\overset{\displaystyle O}{\|}}{C}{-}CH_2{-}\overset{\overset{\displaystyle O}{\|}}{C}{-}CoA}$$

To start the biosynthesis of a fatty acid several other ingredients are needed. Another molecule of acetyl-CoA acts as a *primer*. Then, a protein called the *acyl carrier protein* (ACP) replaces the CoA on both the acetyl-CoA and malonyl-CoA reactants. The synthesis begins when acetyl-ACP adds to malonyl-ACP with the loss of a CO_2 molecule. The product contains four C atoms, two from acetyl and two from malonyl.

$$\underset{\text{Acetyl-ACP}}{CH_3\overset{\overset{\displaystyle O}{\|}}{C}{-}ACP} + \underset{\text{Malonyl-ACP}}{HO\overset{\overset{\displaystyle O}{\|}}{C}CH_2\overset{\overset{\displaystyle O}{\|}}{C}{-}ACP} \xrightarrow{\text{synthase}} \underset{\beta\ \text{Acetoacetyl-ACP}}{CH_3\overset{\overset{\displaystyle O}{\|}}{C}CH_2\overset{\overset{\displaystyle O}{\|}}{C}{-}ACP} + CO_2$$

NADPH + H^+ supplies the hydrogen to reduce C=O to CH_2.

The CO_2 originally added to form malonyl-CoA is the same one lost in the CO_2 by-product. Also the terminal (highest-numbered) C atoms in the fatty acid precursor come from the acetyl reactant. You can see that acetoacetyl-ACP contains two carbonyl groups. The carbonyl at the β position must be reduced by the addition of two H atoms to construct the saturated fatty acid hydrocarbon chain. Two NADPH molecules supply the two H atoms to convert acetoacetyl to butyryl. The equation below describes this overall reduction, which actually takes place in several steps.

$$\underset{\text{Acetoacetyl-ACP}}{CH_3\overset{\overset{\displaystyle O}{\|}}{C}CH_2\overset{\overset{\displaystyle O}{\|}}{C}{-}ACP} + 2NADPH + 2H^+ \xrightarrow{\text{reductase}} \underset{\text{Butyryl-ACP}}{CH_3CH_2CH_2\overset{\overset{\displaystyle O}{\|}}{C}{-}ACP} + 2NADP^+ + 2H_2O$$

If butyric acid were the final product of this synthesis, two acetyl CoA's (one to

Fatty acids are built up two C atoms at a time.

make malonyl and one as a primer), one ATP, and two NADPH would be used up. For longer-chain fatty acids, each additional two-carbon segment requires another acetyl-CoA, another ATP to make malonyl, and another 2NADPH for the reduction. The hydrocarbon chain is built up as successive two-carbon segments (malonyl-CoA) are added to the growing fatty acid chain. This continues until the fatty acid product is palmitic acid, the normal product of lipogenesis in most organisms.

Making a fatty acid with n C atoms uses up $\frac{1}{2}n$ acetyl-CoA's, $(n-2)$ NADPH's, and $(\frac{1}{2}n-1)$ ATP's.

By the time palmitic acid (with its 16 C atoms) is created, a total of 8 acetyl-CoA's, 14 NADPH's, and 7 ATP's have been consumed. Thus we can summarize the overall synthesis of palmitic acid in one equation:

$$\text{8 Acetyl-CoA} + \text{14NADPH} + \text{14H}^+ \xrightarrow[\text{7ATP} \curvearrowright \text{7ADP} + \text{7P}]{} \text{palmitic acid} + \text{8CoA} + \text{14NADP}^+$$

Palmitic acid is not the only fatty acid that occurs in living things. Animals can convert palmitic acid to stearic acid (18 C atoms) and to the unsaturated fatty acids palmitoleic and oleic (see Table 22.2). Plants use oleic acid as the starting materials for linoleic and linolenic acids. Recall that linoleic acid is an essential fatty acid and must be supplied in our diets (Section 22.2).

The lipids present in living things are not present as free fatty acids (FFA). In the next section we will see how fatty acids are converted into triacylglycerols.

SAMPLE EXERCISE 27.3

Write the overall reaction starting with acetyl-CoA for the biosynthesis of lauric acid.

Solution:

Lauric acid has 12 C atoms. Ingredients include:

6 Acetyl-CoA's
5 ATP's (to convert five acetyls to five malonyls)
10 NADPH's (to reduce five of the carbonyls; the sixth carbonyl remains as part of the lauric acid structure)

$$\text{6 Acetyl-CoA} + \text{10 NADPH} + \text{10H}^+ \xrightarrow[\text{5ATP} \curvearrowright \text{5ADP} + \text{5P}]{} \text{lauric acid} + \text{6CoA} + \text{10 NADP}^+$$

EXERCISE 27.3

In the equation below fill in the missing coefficients for the biosynthesis of myristic acid (see Table 22.1).

$$?\text{Acetyl-CoA} + ?\text{NADPH} + ?\text{H}^+ \longrightarrow \text{myristic acid} + ?\text{CoA} + ?\text{NADP}^+$$
$$?\text{ATP} \curvearrowright ?\text{ADP} + ?\text{P}$$

27.6 BIOSYNTHESIS OF TRIACYLGLYCEROLS

Storage fat, or *depot* fat, is composed of triacylglycerols. You just saw how fatty acids are synthesized from acetyl-CoA. The other ingredient, glycerol-P, can be derived from the glycerol that comes from lipolysis. Before being incorporated into a triacylglycerol, the free glycerol is first *activated* by phosphate transfer from ATP.

$$\text{Glycerol} + \text{ATP} \longrightarrow \text{glycerol-P} + \text{ADP}$$

Glycerol-P is also derived from the reduction of dihydroxyacetone-P, an intermediate in the glycolysis pathway (Section 26.4).

$$\text{Dihydroxyacetone-P} + \text{NADH} + \text{H}^+ \longrightarrow \text{glycerol-P} + \text{NAD}^+$$

Biosynthesis of triacylglycerols is called *esterification*.

The pathway by which fatty acids combine with glycerol-P to form triacylglycerol molecules is called **esterification** (see Figure 27.1); one glycerol-P molecule reacts with three acyl-CoA molecules (Figure 27.6). The ester formation, which actually requires several steps, is summarized below in a single equation:

$$3\text{Acyl-CoA} + \text{glycerol-P} \longrightarrow \text{triacylglycerol} + 3\text{CoA} + \text{P}$$

Animal fats are generally mixed, that is, they contain two or more different fatty acid groups (Section 22.3).

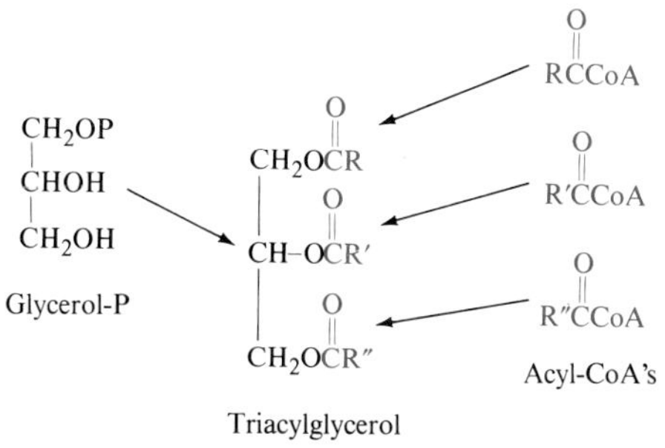

FIGURE 27.6
A triacylglycerol is derived from the combination of glycerol-P with three acyl-CoAs.

27.7 METABOLISM OF CHOLESTEROL

Cholesterol has been discussed in Section 22.8.

The accumulation of cholesterol and other lipids on the walls on the arteries (Figure 27.7) causes ***atherosclerosis,*** the underlying cause of cardiovascular diseases such as ***coronary heart disease*** and ***stroke.*** Because of this the metabolism of cholesterol has received much attention. Here we will see how the body deals with dietary cholesterol and how it synthesizes endogenous cholesterol.

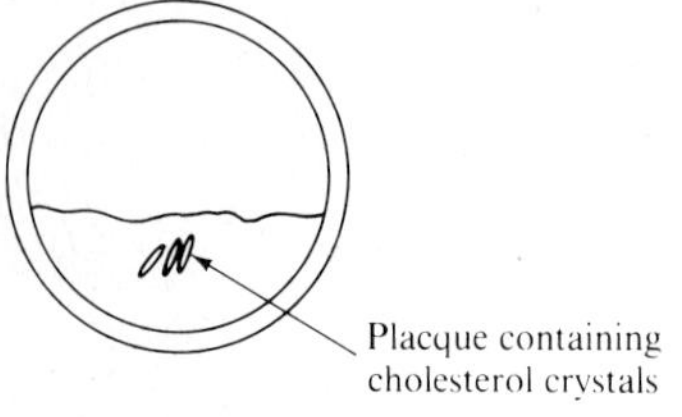

FIGURE 27.7
Cross section of an artery showing cholesterol containing deposits called plaques nearly filling the space within the blood vessel.

Dietary Cholesterol

Cholesterol is a product of animal metabolism and thus is found only in foods derived from animals. From the table on the inside cover, which lists the cholesterol content of a number of common foods, you can see that egg yolks are a particularly rich source.

Most of the cholesterol in humans comes from biosynthesis rather than from diet.

An average diet provides about 300 mg a day, compared with the 1000 mg a day that is synthesized within the body.

Unlike carbohydrates and triacylglycerol fats, cholesterol is not completely degraded; *the tissues cannot break down the steroid ring system.* In fact, the end products of cholesterol metabolism are *bile acids,* compounds synthesized from cholesterol in the liver which still contain the steroid nucleus (Section 22.8). The bile acids are present in bile as sodium or potassium salts, which have both polar and nonpolar character, allowing them to serve as detergents capable of emulsifying lipid deposits (Figure 27.3) and carrying them through the aqueous body fluids, as mentioned earlier.

Gallstones are mostly cholesterol.

Along with free cholesterol, bile salts form a major component of the greenish-yellow bile fluid secreted from the liver into the small intestine. The bile is stored in the gallbladder, an organ located on the underside of the liver. In patients with ***gallstones,*** the bile fluid contains too much cholesterol to remain dissolved in the bile salt micelles; the cholesterol then precipitates and begins to form "stones."

Hypercholesterolemia is associated with atherosclerosis.

Some bile is present in the feces, a major pathway for the elimination of cholesterol. Bile acids are synthesized in the liver at a rate just sufficient to replace those lost in the feces, that is, from 200 to 500 mg/day. Patients with familial ***hypercholesterolemia,*** an excess of blood cholesterol, eliminate bile acids at an abnormally slow rate.

Biosynthesis of Cholesterol

Cholesterol is synthesized primarily in the cells of the liver, starting from acetyl-CoA. We will eliminate the details of the 25-step synthesis in which acetyl-CoA first forms squalene, an intermediate that eventually becomes cholesterol.

$$\text{Acetyl-CoA} \longrightarrow \text{squalene} \longrightarrow \text{cholesterol}$$

In Figure 27.8 the structure of squalene is drawn in such a way that its conversion to cholesterol can easily be visualized.

Squalene → Cholesterol

FIGURE 27.8

27.8 BLOOD LIPIDS

Normal human blood contains a total of 500 mg lipid per 100 mL blood, divided into triacylglycerols, cholesterol, and phosphoglycerides, as shown in Figure 27.9. The blood lipids that circulate in the plasma are there in the form of lipoproteins (Section 27.2). Because of their water-soluble protein component, lipoproteins are able to carry water-insoluble lipids through the blood. Lipoproteins in the blood can be separated by electrophoretic techniques (Section 23.4) and classified according to density, which results in the types listed in Table 27.1. Note that chylomicrons, the lowest-density lipoproteins are nearly all triacylglycerol (TG), while the high-density lipoproteins (HDL) have very little TG and much more protein.

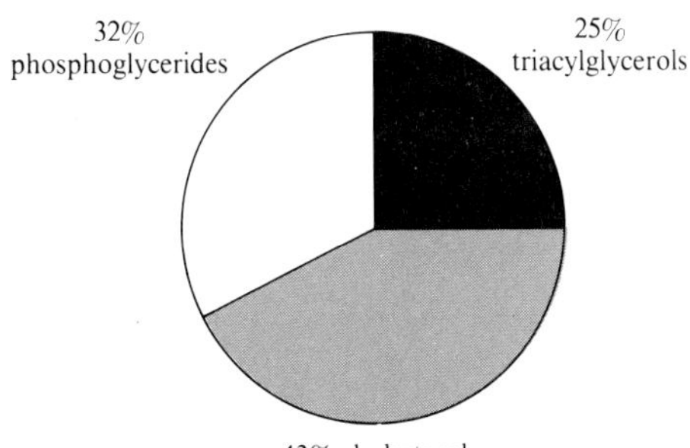

FIGURE 27.9
Major lipid components in a typical sample of normal human blood plasma.

TABLE 27.1 **CLASSES OF LIPOPROTEINS**

Class	Abbreviation	Density, g/ml	TG, %	CH, %	PG, %	PRO, %
Chylomicrons		< 0.95	83	8	7	2
Very low density	VLDL	0.95–1.006	51	22	18	9
Low density	LDL	1.006–1.063	11	46	22	21
High density	HDL	1.063–1.210	8	30	29	33
Very high density	VHDL	> 1.210	5	17	21	57

TG = triacylglycerol, CH = cholesterol, PG = phosphoglyceride, PRO = protein

Note that LDL are very rich in cholesterol.

Blood lipid tests measure the amount of LDL and HDL present.

Patients with advanced atherosclerosis very often have elevated blood cholesterol levels. They also have an abnormally high amount of low-density lipoproteins (LDL) compared with HDL. Because of this, the relationship between dietary lipids and blood lipids is being extensively studied.

27.9 KETONE BODIES AND KETOSIS

You have seen that the metabolism of fats produces acetyl-CoA from the passage of fatty acids through the fatty acid cycle. It is possible for the amount of acetyl-CoA formed from fatty acids to exceed the ability of the tricarboxylic acid cycle to degrade it. This is a situation that arises in untreated diabetics because their bodies cannot degrade carbohydrates and are thus forced to metabolize unusually large amounts of fats. The excess acetyl-CoA reacts to form three different products—acetoacetic acid, β-hydroxybutyric acid, and acetone, collectively known as **ketone bodies.**

Note that one of the "ketone" bodies, β-hydroxybutyric acid, is a carboxylic acid, not a ketone.

$$CH_3\overset{\overset{\large O}{\|}}{C}CH_2\overset{\overset{\large O}{\|}}{C}OH \quad \text{Acetoacetic acid}$$

$$CH_3\underset{\underset{\large OH}{|}}{C}HCH_2\overset{\overset{\large O}{\|}}{C}OH \quad \beta\text{-Hydroxybutyric acid}$$

$$CH_3\overset{\overset{\large O}{\|}}{C}CH_3 \quad \text{Acetone}$$

Acetoacetic acid is formed from the combination of two acetyl-CoA's according to the overall reaction shown below.

$$\underset{\text{Acetyl-CoA}}{2\ CH_3\overset{\overset{\large O}{\|}}{C}{-}CoA} + H_2O \longrightarrow \underset{\text{Acetoacetic acid}}{CH_3\overset{\overset{\large O}{\|}}{C}CH_2\overset{\overset{\large O}{\|}}{C}OH} + 2CoA$$

From acetoacetic acid come the other ketone bodies. The loss of a molecule of CO_2 leads to acetone.

$$\underset{\text{Acetoacetic acid}}{CH_3\overset{\overset{\large O}{\|}}{C}CH_2\overset{\overset{\large O}{\|}}{C}OH} \longrightarrow \underset{\text{Acetone}}{CH_3\overset{\overset{\large O}{\|}}{C}CH_3} + CO_2$$

Reduction of acetoacetic acid converts its carbonyl to the hydroxyl group of β-hydroxybutyric acid.

TABLE 27.2 **TOTAL KETONE BODIES**

Blood level:	< 3 mg/100 mL
Urine level:	20–80 mg daily

$$\underset{\text{Acetoacetic acid}}{CH_3\overset{O}{\overset{\|}{C}}CH_2\overset{O}{\overset{\|}{C}}OH} + NADH + H^+ \longrightarrow \underset{\beta\text{-Hydroxybutyric acid}}{CH_3\overset{OH}{\overset{|}{C}}HCH_2\overset{O}{\overset{\|}{C}}OH} + NAD$$

There are always some ketone bodies in the bloodstream and in the urine. The normal levels are given in Table 27.2.

In diabetics the level of ketone bodies in the urine is greater than 50 mg per 100 mL.

Ketonemia and ***ketonuria*** describe abnormally high concentrations of ketone bodies in the blood and in the urine, respectively. Individuals who are fasting, starving, or suffering from untreated diabetes mellitus accumulate ketone bodies. The condition that is present when excess ketone bodies are produced is known as ***ketosis,*** a disorder with severe consequences. Note that two of the ketone bodies, acetoacetic acid and β-hydroxybutyric acid, are acids. The presence of abnormally high amounts of these acids in the bloodstream causes metabolic acidosis (Section 11.14). The excess acetoacetic and β-hydroxybutyric acids are neutralized by reaction with bicarbonate, HCO_3^-, leading to a decrease in blood pH (see Table 11.8). The form of acidosis brought on by the presence of excess ketone bodies is known as ***ketoacidosis.***

Ketoacidosis causes weakness, headache, thirst, and, in extreme cases of untreated diabetes, diabetic coma.

Another problem that arises in ketosis is general dehydration brought on because the kidneys eliminate acidic ketone bodies in the form of their salts. Thus Na^+ ions are excreted in the urine, which in turn leads to a loss of body fluid as the body eliminates water in order to increase its electrolyte concentration.

Since acetone is volatile (bp 56°C), it can be excreted through the lungs. Thus the breath of individuals suffering from ketosis may smell like acetone.

SUMMARY

The body uses triacylglycerol fats rather than glycogen to store energy because fats provide more energy per gram and can be stored without associated water.

Fats undergo lipolysis, catalyzed by lipases found in the small intestine. Short- and medium-chain fatty acids and glycerol are absorbed directly into the bloodstream. Longer-chain fatty acids are re-formed into fats, which are transported through the bloodstream as lipoproteins called chylomicrons. These fats are hydrolyzed back to fatty acids and glycerol at the tissues, where they are metabolized.

Fatty acids are degraded, two C atoms at a time, by the fatty acid cycle. Each set of four reactions in this pathway is known as a turn. A fatty acid molecule with n C atoms goes through $(\frac{1}{2}\,n-1)$ turns and yields $\frac{1}{2}\,n$ acetyl-CoA molecules as the final product of the cycle. Five ATP molecules are produced from each turn of the fatty acid cycle plus an additional 12 ATP's for every acetyl-CoA product that is degraded through the TCA cycle. In this way fats provide more than twice as much energy as carbohydrates.

The biosynthesis of fats is called lipogenesis, a pathway in which fatty acids are constructed two C atoms at a time. The necessary ingredients for making a fat with n C atoms include $\frac{1}{2}\,n$ acetyl-CoA's, $(n-2)$ NADPH's, and $(\frac{1}{2}\,n-1)$ ATP's. The free fatty acids so produced are esterified by reaction with glycerol phosphate to form the triacylglycerols that make up storage fat.

The body synthesizes cholesterol from acetyl-CoA in amounts about three times that present in an average diet. The steroid ring system of cholesterol cannot be completely degraded by body tissues. The end products of cholesterol metabolism are bile acids, which are converted to bile salts, used to emulsify lipid deposits.

Blood lipids include cholesterol, triacylglycerols, and phosphoglycerides. The relationship between blood cholesterol levels, blood lipid levels, and dietary lipids is of great interest because of the connection between blood lipids and cardiovascular disease.

Excessive metabolism of fats produces more acetyl-CoA than the TCA cycle can degrade. The extra acetyl-CoA leads to the ketone bodies, acetoacetic acid, acetone, and β-hydroxybutyric acid. Abnormally large amounts of ketone bodies are accumulated by diabetics and others whose bodies must metabolize unusually large amounts of fat. The result is ketosis, a dangerous condition that leads to metabolic acidosis.

KEY WORDS

lipolysis	lipoprotein	lipogenesis	ketosis
lipase	chylomicron	esterification	ketoacidosis
medium-chain triglyceride	fatty acid cycle	ketone bodies	

EXERCISES

27.4 Give two reasons why triacylglycerols rather than glycogen are used as the body's energy reservoir.

27.5 Classify the following pathways as anabolic or catabolic: (**a**) lipogenesis; (**b**) fatty acid cycle; (**c**) lipolysis; (**d**) esterification.

27.6 What is the difference in the methods by which butyric acid and palmitic acid are transported from the small intestine to various body tissues?

27.7 What is the advantage of using medium-chain triacylglycerols in the diets of patients with impaired fat digestion and absorption?

27.8 What essential nutrient would have to be supplied in diets that contain medium-chain triglycerides as the only source of fatty acids?

27.9 For the fatty acid cycle give the: (**a**) starting material; (**b**) product; (**c**) portion of the cell in which it occurs.

27.10 Why is the fatty acid cycle also known as a β oxidation pathway? Use formulas in your explanation.

27.11 What is meant by a *turn* of the fatty acid cycle?

27.12 How many turns are required and how many acetyl-CoA's are produced from the degradation in the fatty acid cycle of: (**a**) butyric acid and (**b**) octanoic acid?

27.13 Calculate the number of ATP's produced when decanoic acid is degraded through:
(**a**) The fatty acid cycle only (two ATP's assumed to be consumed for initial activation)
(**b**) Respiration only
(**c**) The fatty acid cycle and respiration

27.14 Calculate the number of ATP's produced per gram of decanoic acid. How does this compare with that produced from palmitic acid?

27.15 Repeat Exercises 27.13 and 27.14 for myristic acid (tetradecanoic acid).

27.16 How is the vitamin biotin involved in fatty acid synthesis?

27.17 Why is it that most natural fats have an even number of C atoms?

27.18 The biosynthesis of a fatty acid involves NADPH + H^+. Is this an oxidizing agent or a reducing agent? What functional group does it react with? What vitamin provides this coenzyme?

27.19 For the biosynthesis of one molecule of decanoic acid, give the required number of: (**a**) acetyl-CoA's; (**b**) ATP's; (**c**) NADPH + H^+ units.

27.20 In the equation below fill in the missing coefficients for the biosynthesis of each of the following fatty acids: (**a**) butyric; (**b**) octanoic; (**c**) decanoic.

$$\text{?Acetyl-CoA} + \text{?NADPH} + \text{?H}^+ \longrightarrow \textbf{fatty acid} + \text{?CoA} + \text{?NADP}^+$$
$$\text{?ATP} \curvearrowright \text{?ADP} + \text{?P}$$

27.21 Explain how a person can get "fat" by eating a diet containing a minimal amount of fat.

27.22 Of the total amount of cholesterol in your body, approximately what percentage is derived from (**a**) your diet; (**b**) biosynthesis?

27.23 Explain what is incorrect about the following statement: A 100-g sample of safflower oil has a much lower cholesterol content and caloric value than a corresponding 100-g sample of butter.

27.24 Why isn't cholesterol completely degraded to acetyl-CoA as other foodstuffs are?

27.25 How does the body eliminate cholesterol?

27.26 What is the starting material for the biosynthesis of cholesterol?

27.27 Why is there such great interest in the connection between dietary lipids and blood lipid levels?

27.28 What is meant by LDL's and HDL's? Compare their (**a**) densities; (**b**) lipid composition; (**c**) relationship to heart disease.

27.29 Which of the "ketone" bodies are actually ketones?

27.30 How are ketone bodies formed? Under what circumstances do they accumulate? Why are they harmful?

27.31 Freshly voided urine samples must be used to test for acetone. What property of acetone makes this necessary?

27.32 What is the danger in following a weight reduction diet that includes little or no carbohydrate?

27.33 Under what conditions would the breath of a diabetic have the odor of acetone?

28 METABOLISM OF PROTEINS

28.1 INTRODUCTION

In Chapters 26 and 27 you saw that the body stores excess fatty acids as triacylglycerols and unneeded glucose as glycogen. In this respect the metabolism of proteins, the third major group of nutrients, differs markedly from that of fats and carbohydrates—*there is no equivalent storage form for excess amino acids.* Although they are composed of amino acids, proteins are used not for storage but for crucial operational and functional purposes. Only in dire situations in which it faces starvation does the body use its protein molecules for fuel.

Recall from Figure 23.1 that 15 percent of body weight is protein.

However, that does not mean that proteins never change. Even in healthy individuals about 1 to 2 percent of the body's proteins are degraded into their component amino acids each day. Of the 9.1 kg (20 lb) of protein carried by a person weighing 59 kg (130 lb), approximately 130 g (0.3 lb) breaks down daily. More than three-quarters of the free amino acids released in this way are rebuilt into new proteins. The rest, which amount to about 30 g per day, are further metabolized and thus lost by the normal body. Between 30 and 60 g of dietary protein is needed to replenish this lost protein.

If the diet contains more protein than needed for protein biosynthesis, amino acids will be converted to glucose (gluconeogenesis) or metabolized to produce energy. The catabolic pathway of amino acids results in the loss of their α-amino groups, which are eventually released as waste ammonia (NH_3), which goes through the *urea cycle* and is eliminated in the urine. The carbon atom skeletons that remain are degraded to some intermediate in one of the pathways used for metabolism of carbohydrates or fats. Proteins catabolized in this way represent an expensive source of energy, since fats and carbohydrates can provide as much or more energy at a much lower cost.

We have already touched on several aspects of the metabolism of proteins. A large section of our discussion of the nucleic acids dealt with the anabolism of protein molecules on nucleic acid templates (Section 24.11). Here we will study the anabolic pathways by which the body synthesizes some of the amino acid building blocks. In Chapter 23 you saw how proteins are hydrolyzed into their component amino acids by the action of the protease enzymes (Section 23.7). To begin our discussion of protein metabolism, we will fill in the details of that digestive process and then follow the route of the amino acids to the sites at which they are catabolized. Figures 28.1 and 28.2 will help you follow the major pathways involved in the metabolism of the amino acids.

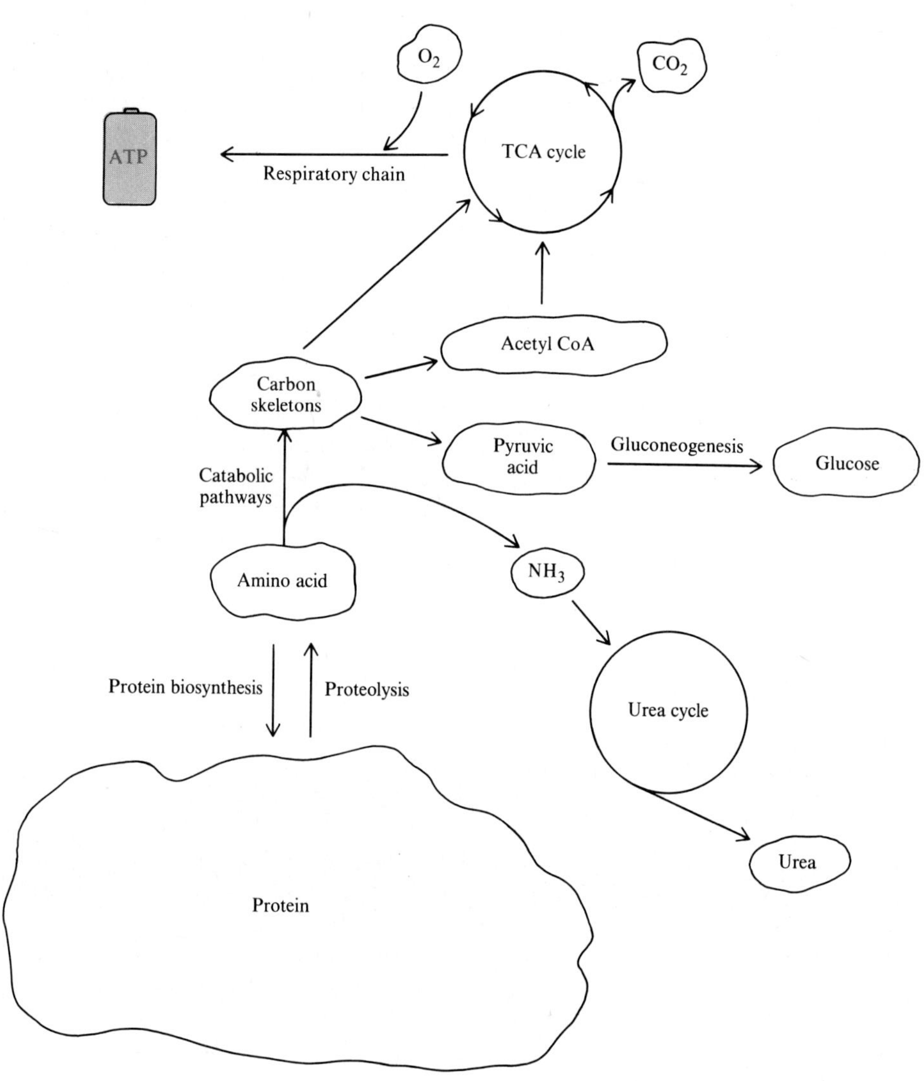

FIGURE 28.1
Protein metabolic pathways.

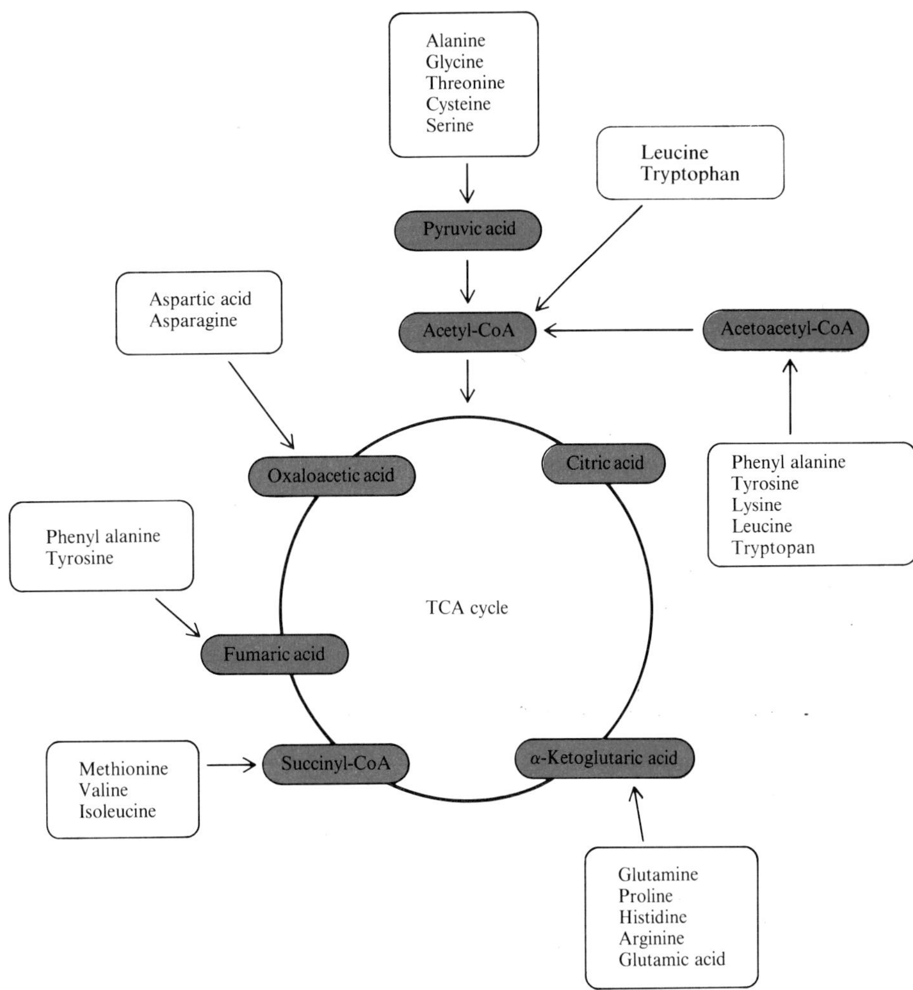

FIGURE 28.2
Catabolism of amino acid carbon skeletons. Some amino acids appear in more than one box, since they lead to more than one intermediate.

28.2 DIGESTION AND ABSORPTION OF PROTEINS

Protein digestion begins in the stomach.

Rennin is an important enzyme in infants, whose main source of protein is milk.

The hydrolysis of proteins is called **proteolysis** (see Figure 28.1). So far, the other foodstuffs we have discussed have undergone most of their initial degradation in the small intestine. The proteinase, or *protease,* enzymes that are needed to break peptide bonds are present both in the stomach and in the small intestine. Proteins start to break down in the stomach by the action of *pepsin,* an enzyme that is activated at pH values between 2 and 3 and has optimum activity between pH 1.5 and 2 (see Figure 25.19, where the activity of pepsin is plotted as a function of pH). Another enzyme present in the gastric juices of infants is *rennin,* the enzyme that causes milk to coagulate by denaturing casein. Rennin is especially important in infant stomachs, where the pH is not sufficiently acidic for pepsin to exhibit maximum action. The rennin slows the passage of the milk through the infant's stomach, thus giving the pepsin time to work.

Pepsin cannot liberate free amino acids since it acts only on certain types of peptide bonds (see Table 23.5) and since foods pass through the stomach too quickly. Instead, the action of pepsin produces smaller polypeptides called *proteoses* and *peptones.*

In Greek the word *chymos* means "juice."

In the small intestine protein hydrolysis is completed.

The fluid that leaves the stomach, called **chyme,** passes into the small intestine, where further digestion takes place by the action of the pancreatic enzymes *trypsin* and *chymotrypsin.* Trypsin cleaves peptide bonds in basic amino acids and chymotrypsin cleaves them in uncharged amino acids (see Table 23.5 for their major sites of action). One other enzyme secreted by the pancreas is *carboxypeptidase,* which splits a single amino acid off the carboxyl end of a peptide chain by attacking a peptide linkage adjacent to a terminal amino acid. Other digestive enzymes are secreted by intestinal juices. In the small intestine hydrolysis of the remaining peptides continues as *aminopeptidases* liberate the amino end residues and *dipeptidases* break dipeptide linkages. By the time the intestinal wall is reached, the proteins are completely hydrolyzed to amino acids, which then pass directly into the bloodstream. Figure 28.3 illustrates the initial digestion of proteins. For a summary of the digestion of all three major food groups see Table 28.1, which

TABLE 28.1 DIGESTIVE ENZYMES

Substrate	Enzyme	Major products	Site of action	Body fluid
		Carbohydrates		
Starch	Salivary amylase	Maltose	Mouth	Saliva
	Pancreatic amylase	Maltose	Small intestine	Pancreatic fluid
Sucrose	Sucrase	Fructose + glucose	Small intestine	Pancreatic fluid
Maltose	Maltase	2 Glucose	Small intestine	Pancreatic fluid
Lactose	Lactase	Galactose + glucose	Small intestine	Pancreatic fluid
		Lipids		
Fats	Lipase	Glycerol + fatty acids	Small intestine Stomach	Pancreatic fluid Gastric juice
		Proteins		
Protein	Pepsin	Proteoses Peptones	Stomach	Gastric juice
Protein Proteoses Peptones	Chymotrypsin and trypsin	Proteoses Peptones Smaller peptides Amino acids	Small intestine	Pancreatic fluid
Proteoses Peptones	Carboxypeptidase	Smaller peptides Amino acids	Small intestine	Pancreatic fluid
Proteoses Peptones	Aminopeptidase	Smaller peptides Amino acids	Small intestine	Pancreatic fluid
Dipeptides	Dipeptidase	Amino acids	Small intestine	Pancreatic fluid

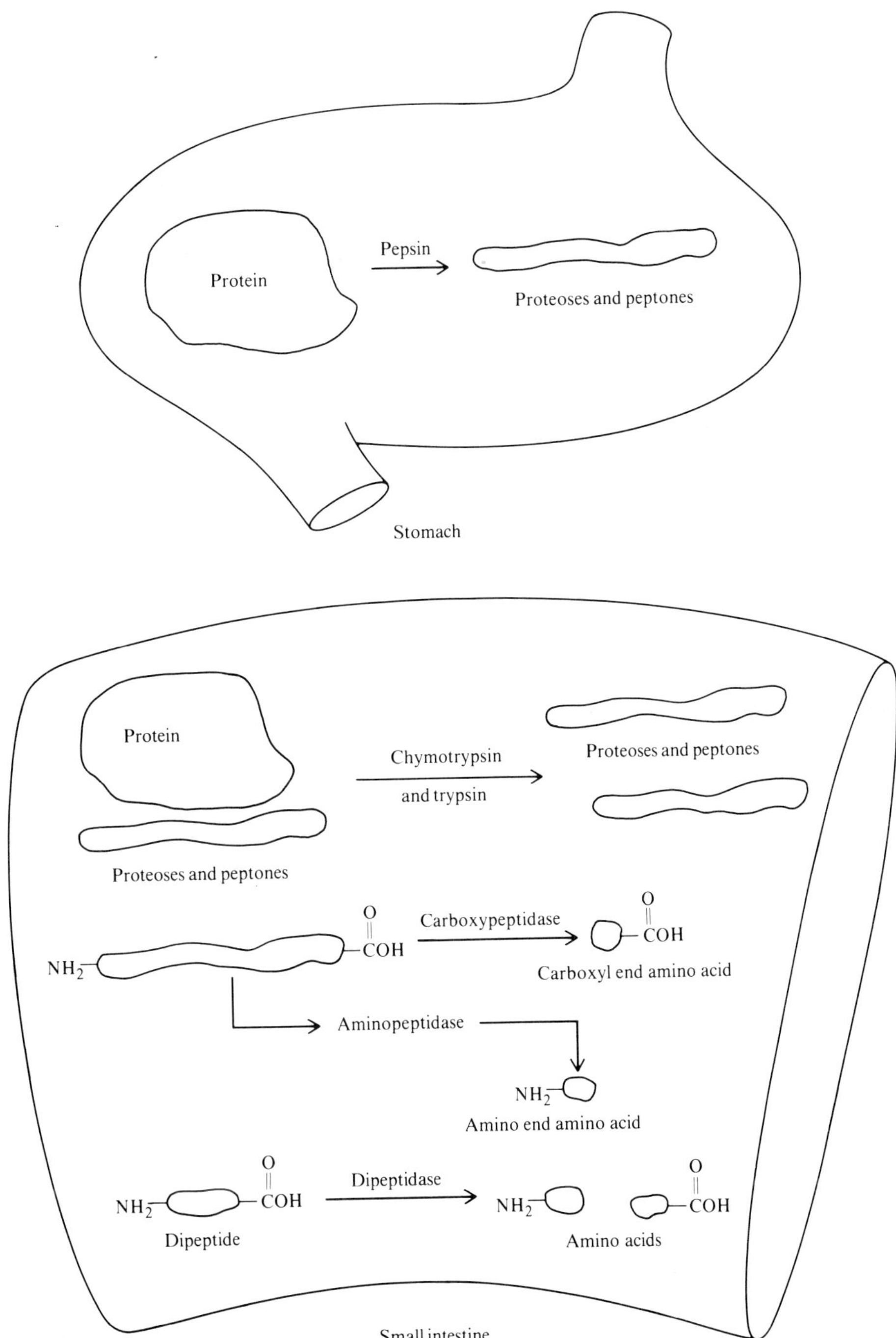

FIGURE 28.3
Digestion of proteins.

shows the necessary hydrolytic enzymes, their body fluid sources, the substrates they act upon, the major products they produce, and their sites of action in the digestive tract.

The free amino acids not needed for protein biosynthesis are further metabolized in the liver, where most amino acid catabolism takes place. In the next sections we will look at a few types of reactions involved in the catabolism of amino acids.

28.3 TRANSAMINATION

In transamination reactions amino acids transfer their amino groups to keto acids.

An early step in the catabolism of most amino acids (often the first one) is the removal of their amino groups. This usually involves **transamination,** a reaction in which an NH_2 group from one α-amino acid is transferred to a keto acid to form a new α-amino acid (Figure 25.10). The necessary enzymes are transaminases and the coenzyme is pyridoxal phosphate, a derivative of vitamin B_6 (see Section 25.5).

Transamination reactions, in which an amino acid with a side chain R′ reacts with a general α-keto acid, occur as follows:

$$\underset{\text{Amino acid}_1}{\mathrm{R'CH(NH_2)COOH}} + \underset{\alpha\text{-Ketoacid}_1}{\mathrm{RCOCOOH}} \xrightarrow{\text{transaminase}} \underset{\alpha\text{-Ketoacid}_2}{\mathrm{R'COCOOH}} + \underset{\text{Amino acid}_2}{\mathrm{RCH(NH_2)COOH}}$$

In most transamination reactions that are part of a catabolic pathway the keto acid_1 reactant is specifically *α-ketoglutaric acid.*

$$\underset{\alpha\text{-Ketoglutaric acid}}{\mathrm{HOOCCH_2CH_2COCOOH}}$$

Transaminations involving α-ketoglutaric acid lead to glutamic acid (R is CH_2CH_2COOH). For instance, one step in the degradation of alanine (R is CH_3) is the transfer of its amino group to α-ketoglutaric acid to produce glutamic acid.

$$\underset{\text{Alanine}}{\mathrm{CH_3CH(NH_2)COOH}} + \underset{\alpha\text{-Ketoglutaric acid}}{\mathrm{HOOCCH_2CH_2COCOOH}} \xrightarrow{\text{transaminase}} \underset{\text{Pyruvic acid}}{\mathrm{CH_3COCOOH}} + \underset{\text{Glutamic acid}}{\mathrm{HOOCCH_2CH_2CH(NH_2)COOH}}$$

Note that the new α-keto acid (keto acid_2) is pyruvic acid. For each different starting amino acid there will be a corresponding new α-keto acid; but as long as the original α-keto acid is α-ketoglutaric acid, the new amino acid will always be glutamic acid. The degradation of glutamic acid is discussed in the next section.

Transamination reactions are involved *both* in catabolism and in biosynthesis of amino acids. In the reverse of the reaction above, glutamic acid reacts with pyruvic acid to form alanine, one of the nonessential amino acids (Section 23.12). We will have more to say about the biosynthesis of nonessential amino acids in the last section of this chapter.

SAMPLE EXERCISE 28.1

Write the reaction in which cysteine undergoes transamination with α-ketoglutaric acid.

Solution:

One product is glutamic acid. The other is a mercapto (—SH) derivative of the α-keto acid, pyruvic acid (mercaptans are discussed in Section 18.11).

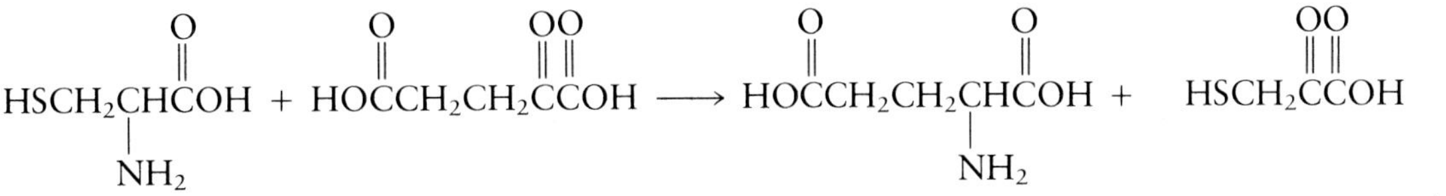

$$\underset{\text{Cysteine}}{HSCH_2\underset{\underset{NH_2}{|}}{C}H\overset{\overset{O}{\|}}{C}OH} + \underset{\alpha\text{-Ketoglutaric acid}}{HO\overset{\overset{O}{\|}}{C}CH_2CH_2\overset{\overset{O}{\|}}{C}\overset{\overset{O}{\|}}{C}OH} \longrightarrow \underset{\text{Glutamic acid}}{HO\overset{\overset{O}{\|}}{C}CH_2CH_2\underset{\underset{NH_2}{|}}{C}H\overset{\overset{O}{\|}}{C}OH} + \underset{\beta\text{-Mercaptopyruvic acid}}{HSCH_2\overset{\overset{O}{\|}}{C}\overset{\overset{O}{\|}}{C}OH}$$

EXERCISE 28.1

Suppose a transamination reaction produces oxaloacetic acid and glutamic acid as the products. What were the original α-keto acid and amino acid?

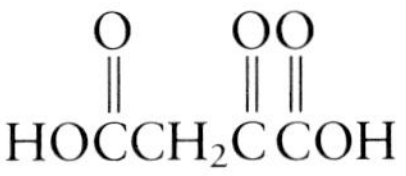

$$HO\overset{\overset{O}{\|}}{C}CH_2\overset{\overset{O}{\|}}{C}\overset{\overset{O}{\|}}{C}OH \quad \text{Oxaloacetic acid}$$

Hepatitis (from *hepat-* for "liver") is inflammation of the liver.

Jaundice, a yellowish pigmentation of skin, tissues, and body fluids, is derived from the French word *jaune*, meaning "yellow."

Transaminase elevations are associated with liver and heart diseases.

Blood serum levels of transaminase enzymes, which catalyze the reactions above, are used in diagnostic tests for liver or heart damage. In disease conditions transaminases are found in abnormally high concentrations in the blood because they are liberated by the damaged or destroyed cells. The enzyme *alanine transaminase* (ALT) is found primarily in the liver. When the liver is secreting more ALT into the blood than it should be, this is a sign that the liver is not functioning properly. Blood ALT determinations can be used to diagnose ***hepatitis***, ***jaundice***, and other liver disorders listed in Table 28.2. Hepatic disease can be differentiated from cardiac disease by comparing levels of both ALT and another transaminase enzyme, *aspartate transaminase* (AST), which is present both in the liver *and* in the heart muscle. A *marked* elevation of AST is detected in ***myocardial infarction***, a reduction of blood flow through the coronary arteries leading to a decrease of O_2 and nutrient substances to the heart and eventually to the death of heart tissue

TABLE 28.2 DISEASE DIAGNOSIS FROM BLOOD LEVELS OF ALT AND AST

Disease	AST* (in heart and liver)	ALT* (in liver)	Description of disease
Viral hepatitis†	Marked	Very marked	Hepatitis (inflammation of the liver) caused by a virus
Obstructive jaundice	Marked	Moderate	Jaundice due to interference with outflow of bile
Cholangiolitic hepatitis	Moderate	Marked	Hepatitis caused by obstruction of bile channels in the liver
Toxic hepatitis	Marked	Very marked	Hepatitis caused by the action of toxic substances
Infectious mononucleosis	Marked	Very marked	Disorder marked by abnormal lymphocytes (white blood cells with a round, centrally located nucleus)
Myocardial infarction	Marked	Slight	Death of heart muscle tissue due to lack of blood flow

*AST was formerly called GOT (glutamic acid oxaloacetic acid transaminase) and ALT was called GPT (glutamic acid pyruvic acid transaminase).

†There are several types of viral hepatitis, including hepatitis A (formerly called infectious hepatitis), caused by the hepatitis A virus, and hepatitis B (formerly called serum hepatitis), caused by the hepatitis B virus.

cells. When this happens, AST leaks out of the heart muscle into the bloodstream. Thus if AST is elevated and ALT is not, myocardial damage is suspected (see Table 28.2).

28.4 OXIDATIVE DEAMINATION

Many amino acids undergo transamination as the first step in their catabolism. This is followed by **oxidative deamination**, in which the amino acid is converted to a keto acid and ammonia. First the amino acid is *oxidized* by NAD^+ and then it is *deaminated* (loses its amino group) by reaction with water, as shown in the overall reaction below. The ammonia product appears as ammonium ion, NH_4^+.

$$\underset{\text{Amino acid}}{R{-}\underset{\displaystyle NH_2}{\underset{|}{CH}}{-}\overset{\displaystyle O}{\overset{\|}{C}}{-}OH} + NAD^+ + H_2O \xrightarrow{\text{dehydrogenase}} \underset{\text{Keto acid}}{R{-}\overset{\displaystyle O}{\overset{\|}{\mathbf{C}}}{-}\overset{\displaystyle O}{\overset{\|}{C}}{-}OH} + NADH + NH_4^+$$

You can see that the C (in boldface) that carried the amino group is now part of a carbonyl group. The keto acids produced by oxidative deamination can enter carbohydrate or ketone body metabolic pathways.

Glutamic acid, a product of nearly all transaminations (Section 28.3), undergoes oxidative deamination much faster than the other amino acids and thus provides a major way for the conversion of amino groups to ammonia.

$$\underset{\text{Glutamic acid}}{HO\overset{O}{\overset{\|}{C}}CH_2CH_2\underset{NH_2}{\underset{|}{C}}H\overset{O}{\overset{\|}{C}}OH} + NAD^+ + H_2O \xrightarrow{\text{dehydrogenase}} \underset{\alpha\text{-Ketoglutaric acid}}{HO\overset{O}{\overset{\|}{C}}CH_2CH_2\overset{O}{\overset{\|}{C}}\overset{O}{\overset{\|}{C}}OH} + NADH + NH_4^+$$

We say "ammonia" although the ammonia appears as NH_4^+, the ammonium ion.

In the next section we will see how the body disposes of ammonia, the toxic product of oxidative deaminations.

SAMPLE EXERCISE 28.2

Write the reaction for the oxidative deamination of alanine and name the keto acid product.

Solution:

$$\underset{\text{Alanine}}{CH_3\underset{NH_2}{\underset{|}{C}}H\overset{O}{\overset{\|}{C}}OH} + NAD^+ + H_2O \longrightarrow \underset{\text{Pyruvic acid}}{CH_3\overset{O}{\overset{\|}{C}}\overset{O}{\overset{\|}{C}}OH} + NADH + NH_4^+$$

EXERCISE 28.2

Write the oxidative deamination reaction for aspartic acid and name the keto acid that forms.

28.5 UREA CYCLE

Some aquatic animals release NH_3 directly into the surrounding water.

Ammonia is produced in the tissues as a product of oxidative deamination and also by the action of intestinal bacteria. Some of the ammonia is needed for biosynthesis. Since excess ammonia is toxic to the central nervous system, the body eliminates it by converting it to **urea**, a nontoxic, water-soluble compound.

$$NH_2-\overset{O}{\overset{\|}{C}}-NH_2 \quad \text{Urea}$$

Urea is the principal nitrogen-containing compound in urine. In fact, between 80 and 90 percent of the N eliminated in the urine appears as urea, which is synthesized in the liver, released into the blood, and then removed by the kidney. The biosynthesis of urea in the liver utilizes a complex series of steps, a pathway called the **urea cycle**, in which the starting materials are ammonia (as NH_4^+) and CO_2 and the product is urea. Recall that urea was the first organic compound ever made in the laboratory from inorganic starting materials (Section 12.1).

The urea cycle is also called the *ornithine cycle.*

Note that urea contains two N atoms. One is derived from NH_4^+ and the other from aspartic acid, an amino acid which appears as an intermediate in the urea cycle, as shown in Figure 28.4. In addition to NH_4^+, CO_2, and aspartic acid, three ATP's are consumed through each *turn* of the urea cycle. The reason that this pathway is called a *cycle* is that *ornithine,* an amino acid reactant in the second step, is ultimately regenerated in the final step.

Hyperammonemia is derived from *hyper-*, "over," *ammon-* "ammonia," and *-emia* "in the blood."

Defects in one of the enzymes involved in the first two steps of the urea cycle lead to ammonia intoxication, or ***hyperammonemia***, a condition that first causes vomiting and lethargy and eventually progresses to ataxia (lack of coordination), slurred speech, and mental retardation. Liver disorders or inadequate blood circulation to the liver can both result in elevated blood levels of ammonia. Treatment for hyperammonemia is designed to reduce ammonia production by use of a low-protein diet and antibiotics that destroy ammonia-producing intestinal bacteria.

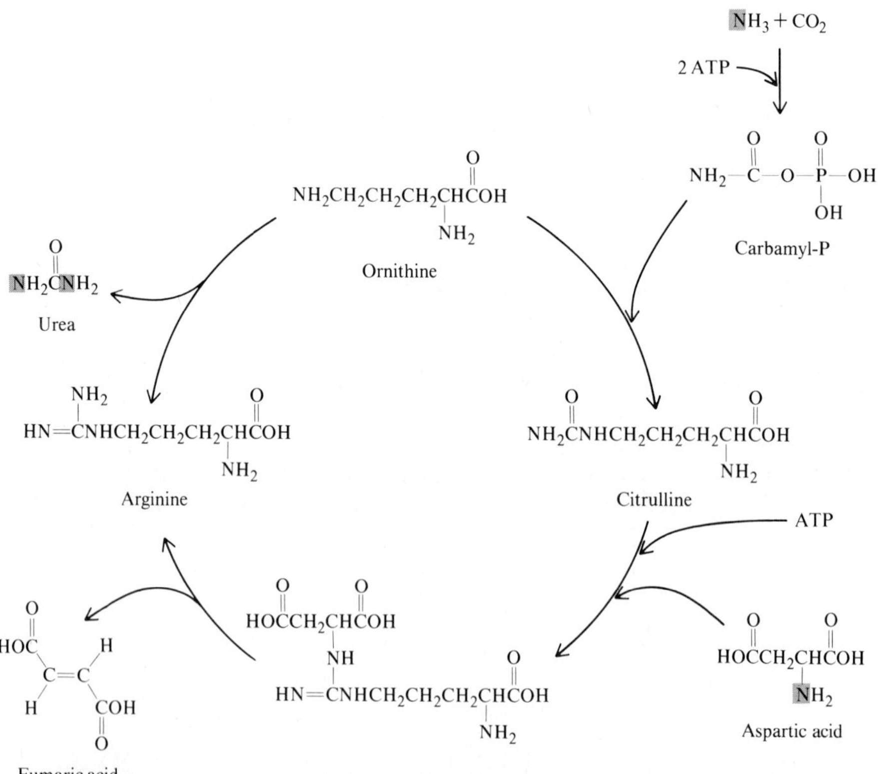

FIGURE 28.4
Urea cycle. The urea cycle converts ammonia to urea. The N atoms that become part of urea are shown in color. All intermediates are shown in their un-ionized forms.

28.6 CATABOLISM OF AMINO ACIDS

The C skeletons of amino acids enter fat or carbohydrate metabolic pathways.

Above we said that an early step in the catabolism of amino acids is the loss of the amino group, leaving a carbon atom skeleton. Since the body no longer recognizes that these carbon skeletons belonged previously to amino acids, they are further metabolized by entering some other metabolic pathway. Most of the 20 common amino acids are converted to carbon compounds that are part of the TCA cycle. From there the intermediates can be degraded further or can be used to produce building blocks for biosynthesis.

Each of the 20 common amino acids follows a somewhat different catabolic pathway leading to one of seven metabolic intermediates. These include pyruvic acid, acetoacetyl-CoA, acetyl-CoA, and the four TCA intermediates, succinyl-CoA, oxaloacetic acid, α-ketoglutaric acid, and fumaric acid. Figure 28.3 indicates which of the 20 common amino acids lead to which of the seven compounds above. Many of the pathways involved in these transformations include steps associated with inherited metabolic disorders.

Phenylketonuria

One step in the degradation of phenylalanine is associated with the metabolic disorder ***phenylketonuria*** (PKU). In genetically normal individuals, phenylalanine is converted to tyrosine by an enzyme called *phenylalanine-4-monooxygenase.* Unfortunately, in about 1 out of every 10,000 human beings this enzyme is absent. Thus the phenylalanine must seek some other pathway to degrade itself. The alternative pathway involves the transamination reaction shown below:

$$\underset{\text{Phenylalanine}}{C_6H_5\text{—}CH_2\underset{\substack{|\\NH_2}}{C}H\overset{\substack{O\\\|}}{C}OH} + \underset{\alpha\text{-Ketoglutaric acid}}{HO\overset{\substack{O\\\|}}{C}CH_2CH_2\overset{\substack{O\\\|}}{C}\overset{\substack{O\\\|}}{C}OH} \longrightarrow \underset{\text{Phenylpyruvic acid}}{C_6H_5\text{—}CH_2\overset{\substack{O\\\|}}{C}\overset{\substack{O\\\|}}{C}OH} + \underset{\text{Glutamic acid}}{HO\overset{\substack{O\\\|}}{C}CH_2CH_2\underset{\substack{|\\NH_2}}{C}H\overset{\substack{O\\\|}}{C}OH}$$

Individuals without the enzyme that transforms phenylalanine to tyrosine accumulate phenylpyruvic acid, a *phenyl ketone.*

The blood test used to detect PKU is called the Guthrie test.

The phenylpyruvic acid accumulates in the blood and is excreted in the urine. Excess circulating phenylpyruvic acid in young children causes mental retardation by damaging brain development. Fortunately the disease is readily diagnosed in the newborn by noting elevated levels of phenylalanine in blood taken from the heel of the infant a few days after birth. The effects of PKU can be avoided entirely by restricting phenylalanine in the diet, particularly before the age of 6. Table 28.3 gives the total protein and phenylalanine content of some common foods. After the age of 8, when 90 percent of the brain growth has already occurred, the diet can be somewhat relaxed.

Alkaptonuria

Alkaptonuria is caused by a defect in tyrosine metabolism.

Under normal circumstances the phenylalanine is converted to tyrosine, which is then degraded to acetoacetyl-CoA. Another metabolic disorder called ***alkapton-***

TABLE 28.3 **PHENYLALANINE (Phe) CONTENT OF FOODS**

Food	Serving	Mass, g	Protein, g	Phe, mg	Phe, % of total protein
Milk	1 cup	244	9	415	4.6
Chicken	3 oz	85	20	1180	5.9
Cheese	1 oz	28	7	378	5.4
Egg	1	50	6	370	6.2
Bread, white	1 slice	23	2	99	5.0
Orange juice	1 cup	248	1.7	80	5.0
Green beans	½ cup	62	1	24	3.0
Carrots	½ cup	72	0.8	24	3.0
Apple	1	150	0.3	7	2.3

The daily phenylalanine requirement for a child afflicted with PKU is about 20 mg per kilogram of body weight.

In Greek *melas* means "black."

uria occurs when the enzyme *homogenistic acid-1,2-dioxygenase* is defective and thus cannot degrade homogenistic acid, an intermediate in tyrosine metabolism. Homogenistic acid excreted in the urine is easily observed when the urine is made alkaline because it reacts with air to form the black pigment *melanin.* Cartilage and other connective tissues in older alkaptonuric individuals may also be abnormally dark. There is no specific treatment for this rare disease, which tends to lead to ***osteoarthritis***, characterized by degeneration of the joints.

Maple Syrup Urine Disease

In maple syrup urine disease, keto acids of the branched-chain amino acids cannot be decarboxylated owing to the lack of an enzyme.

One step in the catabolism of isoleucine and valine is the decarboxylation of their α-ketoacids, which requires the enzyme *α-ketoisovaleric acid dehydrogenase.* In about 1 out of 200,000 persons this enzyme is defective, leading to the excretion of ketoacids into the urine. Because the ketoacids impart an odor to the urine that resembles maple syrup, the disease is known as ***maple syrup urine disease***, a condition known to cause mental retardation.

28.7 DECARBOXYLATION OF AMINO ACIDS

We have found that most amino acids transfer their amino groups to α-ketoglutaric acid to form glutamic acid (transamination) and that the amino group of glutamic acid can then be removed (deamination).

Decarboxylation of amino acids produces CO_2 and amines.

In addition to the reactions above, a few amino acids, including histidine, tyrosine, phenylalanine, and tryptophan, can undergo *decarboxylation,* that is loss of CO_2. The following reaction describes a general amino acid decarboxylation in which the product is an amine.

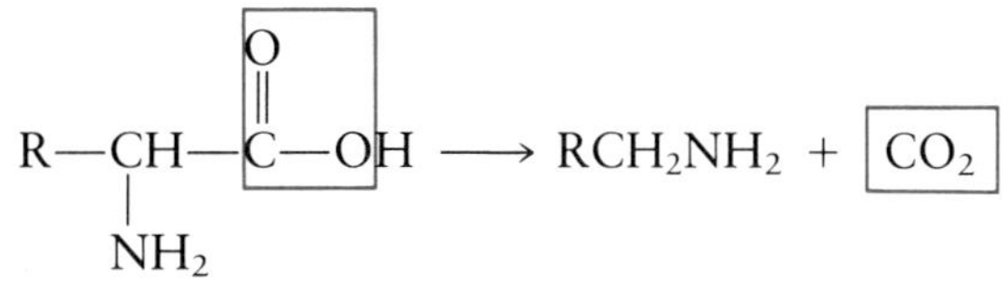

$$R-\underset{NH_2}{CH}-\boxed{\overset{O}{\overset{\|}{C}}-O}H \longrightarrow RCH_2NH_2 + \boxed{CO_2}$$

Amino acid — Amine

Let us consider the biological function of some of the amines that are produced in this way.

A vasodilator enlarges blood vessels.

The product of the decarboxylation of histidine is **histamine,** a vasodilator that is released in tissues as a part of allergic reactions.

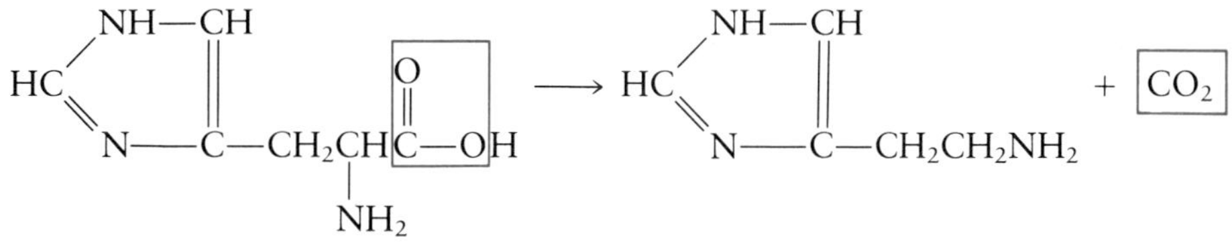

Histidine $\longrightarrow$ Histamine + $\boxed{CO_2}$

(Histidine: HC(NH—CH)=N—C—$CH_2\underset{NH_2}{CH}\boxed{\overset{O}{\overset{\|}{C}}-O}H$; Histamine: HC(NH—CH)=N—C—$CH_2CH_2NH_2$)

Antihistamines are drugs that block the effect of histamine.

Histamine has a number of pharmacological actions, including the stimulation of nerve endings and dilatation of skin vessels, which results in pain and itching. **Antihistamines** are drugs used to counteract the effect of histamine. Looking at the formulas for some of those shown in Figure 28.5, you can see that they bear some structural similarity to histamine and they all contain a C—C—N chain. In fact, the antihistamines behave as *competitive inhibitors,* that is, drug compounds that occupy receptor sites at which a substance such as histamine would normally produce its action. The antihistamine, which produces no action of its own, prevents histamines from working by occupying their receptor sites, known as *H_1 sites.* Drugs that act in this way are known as **antagonists,** that is, drug compounds that oppose the effect of some other substance.

The amino acids arginine, lysine, tyrosine, and histidine are decarboxylated by the action of bacterial decarboxylase enzymes found in intestinal bacteria. The RCH_2NH_2 products are known as *ptomaines* and were previously thought to be responsible for food poisoning. Some ptomaines *can* be very dangerous if allowed to accumulate in the body because they are *pressor amines,* that is, they cause an increase in blood pressure. For instance, *tyramine,* the product of the decarboxylation of tyrosine, is a very potent pressor amine.

FIGURE 28.5

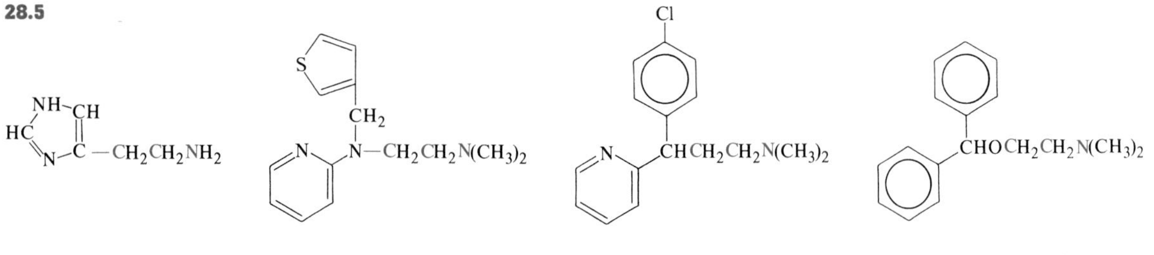

NH—CH, HC, N—C—$CH_2CH_2NH_2$

Histamine

S, CH_2, N, N—$CH_2CH_2N(CH_3)_2$

Methapyrilene

Cl, N, $CHCH_2CH_2N(CH_3)_2$

Chlorpheniramine

$CHOCH_2CH_2N(CH_3)_2$

Diphenhydramine

Excessive histamine released into the body produces toxic effects.

Antihistamines have a N to C to C chain (in color) as does histamine. The antihistamines shown are ingredients in many common cold and allergy remedies.

$$HO-C_6H_4-CH_2CH(NH_2)\boxed{C(=O)-OH} \longrightarrow HO-C_6H_4-CH_2CH_2NH_2 + \boxed{CO_2}$$

Tyrosine Tyramine

Foods containing tyramine must be avoided by persons taking MAOI drugs (Section 18.6).

The enzyme that is needed to continue the metabolism of tyramine is monamine oxidase (MAO), the same enzyme that oxidizes the biogenic amines such as norepinephrine (Section 18.6). Anyone taking a medication that inhibits MAO, known as a monamine oxidase inhibitor, MAOI, must be very careful not to ingest foods that may contain tyramine. Tyramine appears in foods that are aged or fermented, such as aged cheeses, pickled herring, chianti wine, sherry, beer, and yeast extracts, all of which can cause serious, even fatal, hypertensive crises in persons taking MAOI medications.

SAMPLE EXERCISE 28.3

The decarboxylation of lysine produces cadaverine, a foul-smelling compound produced from the bacterial decomposition of proteins. Write the reaction for the formation of cadaverine. What is the systematic name for cadaverine? (See Section 18.2.)

Solution:

$$NH_2CH_2CH_2CH_2CH_2CH(NH_2)\overset{O}{\overset{\|}{C}}OH \longrightarrow NH_2CH_2CH_2CH_2CH_2CH_2NH_2 + CO_2$$

Lysine Cadaverine

The products are cadaverine and carbon dioxide. Cadaverine is also called 1,5-diaminopentane.

EXERCISE 28.3

The organic product of the decarboxylation of an amino acid is ethyl amine. What was the amino acid?

28.8 BIOSYNTHESIS OF NONESSENTIAL AMINO ACIDS

In the preceding sections you saw how the amino acids are catabolized. Now we will see how they are built up. The *essential* amino acids (tryptophan, leucine, isoleucine, valine, lysine, threonine, methionine, phenylalanine, arginine, and his-

The body makes nonessential amino acids from metabolic intermediates, other nonessential amino acids, and essential amino acids.

tidine) cannot be made in the body. The body can synthesize the remaining amino acids (glutamic acid, glutamine, aspartic acid, asparagine, proline, alanine, glycine, serine, tyrosine, and cysteine), the *nonessential* ones that need not be supplied in the diet. The starting materials are metabolic intermediates, other nonessential amino acids, and in some cases essential amino acids (see Table 28.4). You will find that the synthetic pathways are relatively short. In some cases they are the reverse of catabolic pathways; that is, they require the same enzymes—for example, those that catalyze transamination. In most cases the anabolic and catabolic pathways are not the same.

The starting material for many of the nonessential amino acids is *glutamic acid,* which is produced by reduction and amination of α-ketoglutaric acid.

$$\alpha\text{-Ketoglutaric acid} + \text{NADPH} + \text{NH}_4^+ \longrightarrow \text{glutamic acid} + \text{NADP}^+ + \text{H}_2\text{O}$$

Note that this reaction is the reverse of the oxidative deamination reaction in which glutamic acid is converted to α-ketoglutaric acid and ammonia.

Addition of NH_3 to glutamic acid gives *glutamine* in a reaction that consumes ATP:

$$\text{NH}_3 + \text{glutamic acid} \xrightarrow[\text{ATP} \rightarrow \text{ADP} + \text{P}]{} \text{glutamine} + \text{H}_2\text{O}$$

Alanine and *aspartic acid* arise from the transfer of an amino group from glutamic acid to pyruvic acid and oxaloacetic acid, respectively.

$$\text{Glutamic acid} + \text{pyruvic acid} \longrightarrow \text{alanine} + \alpha\text{-ketoglutaric acid}$$

$$\text{Glutamic acid} + \text{oxaloacetic acid} \longrightarrow \text{aspartic acid} + \alpha\text{-ketoglutaric acid}$$

From aspartic acid comes *asparagine* by a reaction similar to the one in which glutamic acid gives glutamine.

TABLE 28.4 STARTING MATERIALS FOR BIOSYNTHESIS OF NONESSENTIAL AMINO ACIDS

Amino acid	Starting material(s)
Glutamic acid	α-Ketoglutaric acid (TCA)
Glutamine	Glutamic acid, ammonia
Alanine	Glutamic acid, pyruvic acid (glycolysis)
Aspartic acid	Glutamic acid, oxaloacetic acid (TCA)
Asparagine	Aspartic acid, ammonia
Serine	3-Phosphoglyceric acid (glycolysis)
Glycine	CO_2, NH_3
Cysteine	Methionine, serine
Proline	Glutamic acid
Tyrosine	Phosphoenolpyruvic acid (glycolysis), erythrose-4-phosphoric acid (a sugar phosphate)

$$NH_3 + \text{aspartic acid} \longrightarrow \text{asparagine} + H_2O$$
$$\text{ATP} \curvearrowright \text{ADP} + \text{P}$$

Proline is another amino acid that forms from glutamic acid. *Serine* is derived from 3-phosphoglyceric acid, a glycolysis intermediate (Section 26.4). *Glycine* synthesis happens in several ways, including a sequence requiring CO_2 and NH_3.

Methionine-restricted diets are used in the treatment of homocystinuria.

Cysteine is made by utilizing sulfur provided by methionine and transferred to the carbon skeleton of serine. Keep in mind that methionine *is* essential because the body *cannot* make it from any available materials. Cysteine *is not* essential since the body *can* make it. A disease called ***homocystinuria*** arises from accumulation of *homocysteine,* the amino acid intermediate shown below, which is involved in the biosynthetic pathway for cysteine.

$$HSCH_2CH_2\underset{\underset{NH_2}{|}}{C}H\overset{\overset{O}{\|}}{C}OH \quad \text{Homocysteine}$$

The body synthesizes *tyrosine* from the essential amino acid phenylalanine. Phenylalanine *is* essential because it *cannot* be made by starting with tyrosine or any other available materials.

SUMMARY

Unlike glycogen and fat, proteins are used by the body for functional and operational purposes, not for storage. Excess amino acids not needed to synthesize proteins are built into glucose or are metabolized to produce energy.

Proteolysis, the hydrolysis of proteins, takes place both in the stomach and in the small intestine by the action of protease enzymes.

The first step in the catabolism of most amino acids is transamination, in which an amino group is transferred to an α-keto acid. The keto acid involved is nearly always α-ketoglutaric acid, which leads to formation of glutamic acid and another α-keto acid. The new α-keto acids so produced are further metabolized by being converted into intermediates that are part of some other metabolic pathway, such as glycolysis or the TCA cycle. The glutamic acid loses its amino group by oxidative deamination, in which the products are ammonia and α-ketoglutaric acid, an intermediate in the TCA cycle. Ammonia, a toxic compound, is removed from the body in the form of urea, a nontoxic compound produced by the urea cycle.

A few amino acids can also undergo decarboxylation (loss of CO_2) to produce amines that have a variety of biological functions. The histamine that causes some of the unpleasant symptoms of allergic reactions comes from decarboxylation of histidine.

Nonessential amino acids, the ones that need not be supplied in the diet, are synthesized in the body. The starting materials include intermediates from another metabolic pathway, other nonessential amino acids, or, in some cases, an essential amino acid.

There are a number of genetic disorders associated with the metabolism of amino acids. The most common one is phenylketonuria, caused by a defect in the enzyme that normally degrades phenylalanine to tyrosine.

KEY WORDS

proteolysis
protease
transamination
transaminase
oxidative deamination
urea
urea cycle
phenylketonuria
decarboxylation
histamine
antihistamine
antagonist

EXERCISES

28.4 In what outstanding way does protein metabolism differ from the metabolism of fats or carbohydrates?

28.5 What is meant by proteolysis?

28.6 Where is the enzyme rennin found? Why is this enzyme so important for infants?

28.7 Explain the difference between transamination and deamination.

28.8 Give the reaction in which valine transfers its amino group to α-ketoglutaric acid.

28.9 Suppose the product keto acid of a transamination is pyruvic acid. What was the original amino acid?

28.10 Why is α-ketoglutaric acid a reactant in many metabolic transamination reactions?

28.11 If the products of a transamination reaction are glutamic acid and the keto acid shown below, what were the reactants?

$$\begin{array}{c} \qquad\qquad\quad O\;O \\ \qquad\qquad\quad \| \;\; \| \\ CH_3CHCH_2CCOH \\ | \qquad\qquad \\ CH_3 \qquad\qquad \end{array}$$

28.12 What enzymes are represented by the abbreviations AST and ALT? How would you use blood levels of AST and ALT to diagnose myocardial infarction?

28.13 Write the reaction for the oxidative deamination of valine.

28.14 Why must the body get rid of excess ammonia?

28.15 Give the formulas for the two inorganic starting materials of the urea cycle. What is the organic product?

28.16 What properties of urea make it a suitable form for the disposal of excess ammonia?

28.17 Tryptophan is decarboxylated by intestinal bacteria to form tryptamine, a compound that is absorbed into the bloodstream and eliminated in the urine. Write the reaction for this.

28.18 Bacterial enzymes can decarboxylate ornithine, an intermediate in the urea cycle, to form putrescine, a compound derived from decomposing protein. Write the reaction that produces putrescine. Name this compound as a diamine.

28.19 The antidepressant drug Nardil is a potent MAOI. Patients receiving Nardil are warned not to eat high-protein food (such as meat) that has been aged to improve its flavor. Explain this warning. What other foods must also be avoided?

28.20 How do antihistamine drugs work?

28.21 Why is there a "Warning: Phenylketonurics" message printed on packages of the artificial sweetener aspartame (see Figure 21.4 for the formula)?

28.22 What is the treatment for PKU?

28.23 Using Table 28.3, make a *rough* estimate of the amount of phenylalanine obtained each day by a 3-year-old child who consumes 35 g of protein daily (recommended daily intake for a 2- to 3-year-old). How does this compare with the daily allowance of phenylalanine for a 30-lb child with PKU?

28.24 The infant formula preparation called "phenyl-free" contains no phenylalanine at all. Is it possible for an infant suffering from PKU to thrive on a diet that includes phenyl-free only? Why?

28.25 Why is a low-methionine diet used to treat patients with homocystinuria?

28.26 What are the starting materials used by the body to make nonessential amino acids?

28.27 What enzyme is missing in individuals with maple syrup urine disease? What general type of reaction is catalyzed by the enzyme? What amino acids must be restricted in the diet of a person with this condition?

APPENDIX

A. SCIENTIFIC NOTATION

Scientific notation is also called exponential notation.

Many of the numbers that are encountered in the study of chemistry are so much larger or smaller than 1 that it is inconvenient to express them in decimal notation. Instead we often express these numbers in terms of *scientific notation.* A number expressed in scientific notation is written in two parts: one part is a number between 1 and 10, and the other part is the number 10 raised to a *power* called an *exponent.* To write numbers in scientific notation we begin by writing the powers of 10 in exponential form.

Powers of 10

For numbers greater than 1, the exponent of a power of 10 is positive. Suppose the exponent is the positive integer a. The value of 10^a is the number obtained by multiplying 10 by itself a times. For instance, suppose the value of a is 6:

$$10^6 = 10 \times 10 \times 10 \times 10 \times 10 \times 10 = 1{,}000{,}000 \text{ (1 million)}$$

We say that 1 million is 10 raised to the sixth power. Note that the number of zeros in 1,000,000 is the same as the value of the exponent used to put it into exponential form:

$$\overset{6}{\downarrow}\quad 10^6 = \underbrace{1{,}000{,}000}_{\text{6 zeros}}$$

For exponential numbers that are less than 1 the exponent is negative. The value of 10^{-a} is the number obtained by dividing 1 by 10 a times. For instance, suppose the exponent is -6:

$$10^{-6} = \frac{1}{10 \times 10 \times 10 \times 10 \times 10 \times 10} = 0.000001 \text{ (one-millionth)}$$

POWERS OF TEN

Numbers > 1		Numbers < 1	
Exponential form	**Number**	**Exponentional form**	**Number**
10^{10}	10,000,000,000	10^{-10}	0.0000000001
10^{9}	1,000,000,000	10^{-9}	0.000000001
10^{8}	100,000,000	10^{-8}	0.00000001
10^{7}	10,000,000	10^{-7}	0.0000001
10^{6}	1,000,000	10^{-6}	0.000001
10^{5}	100,000	10^{-5}	0.00001
10^{4}	10,000	10^{-4}	0.0001
10^{3}	1000	10^{-3}	0.001
10^{2}	100	10^{-2}	0.01
10^{1}	10	10^{-1}	0.1

The exponential number $10^0 = 1$.

This time note that the absolute value of *a* is the same as the number of decimal places in the number that it represents:

$$10^{-6} = \underbrace{0.000001}_{\text{6 decimal places}}$$

Table A.1 gives the values of 10 raised to powers from −10 to 10. In chemical discussions we will often use numbers such as 10^{23} and 10^{-23}.

SAMPLE EXERCISE A.1

Write the numbers represented by 10^{23} and 10^{-23}.

Solution:

$$10^{23} = 1\underbrace{00000000000000000000000}_{\text{23 zeros}}$$

$$10^{-23} = 0.\underbrace{00000000000000000000001}_{\text{23 decimal places}}$$

EXERCISE A-1

Write the numbers represented by 10^{12} and 10^{-12}.

Scientific Notation

The scientific notation form of a number greater than 1 is expressed as a number (n) between 1 and 10 multiplied by 10 raised to the appropriate power a:

$$n \times 10^a$$

To convert a number that is greater than 1 to exponential notation you can rewrite the number so that it consists of a number n (between 1 and 10) times a multiple of 10, then choose the proper exponent by counting zeros in the multiple of 10. For instance, to write 3,000,000 in scientific notation:

$$3{,}000{,}000 = 3 \times \underbrace{1{,}000{,}000}_{6\text{ zeros}} = 3 \times 10^{\overset{6}{\downarrow}6}$$

Or you may find it easier to put a decimal point at the end of the number and move it to the left to produce n. The number of places the decimal point is moved is the same as the exponent.

$$3{,}000{,}000. = 3 \times 10^6$$

6 places to the left

To convert 3800 to scientific notation,

$$3800 = 3.8 \times \underbrace{1000}_{3\text{ zeros}} = 3.8 \times 10^3$$

or

$$3800. = 3.8 \times 10^3$$

3 places to the left

The exponential form of a number less than 1 is expressed as a number n multiplied by 10 raised to the appropriate negative power $-a$:

$$n \times 10^{-a}$$

To convert a number that is less than 1 to scientific notation rewrite the number so that it is the form of a number between 1 and 10 multiplied by a decimal fraction of 10 and choose the proper exponent by counting decimal places in the fraction of 10. Alternatively, count the number of places that you must shift the decimal point to the right to produce *n*. For instance, to write the numbers below in scientific notation,

$$0.0003 = 3 \times \underbrace{0.0001}_{\text{4 decimal places}} = 3 \times 10^{-4}$$

or

$$0.0003 = 3 \times 10^{-4}$$

4 places to the right

$$0.0158 = 1.58 \times \underbrace{0.01}_{\text{2 decimal places}} = 1.58 \times 10^{-2}$$

or

$$0.0158 = 1.58 \times 10^{-2}$$

2 places to the right

SAMPLE EXERCISE A.2

Express the following numbers in terms of exponential notation: (**a**) 400,000,000; (**b**) 0.000000071

Solution:

(**a**)

$$400{,}000{,}000 = 4 \times \underbrace{100{,}000{,}000}_{\text{8 zeros}} = 4 \times 10^{8}$$

or by moving the decimal point,

$$400{,}000{,}000. = 4 \times 10^{8}$$

8 places to the left

(**b**)

$$0.0000071 = 7.1 \times \underbrace{0.000001}_{\text{6 decimal places}} = 4 \times 10^{-6}$$

$$0.0000071 = 7.1 \times 10^{-6}$$

6 places to the right

EXERCISE A-2

Express the numbers below in terms of exponential notation:

(a) 5,000,000,000
(b) 0.025
(c) 670,000,000,000,000,000,000,000,000,000
(d) 0.0000000000000000000085

Multiplication and Division

When performing arithmetic operations on very large or small numbers, it is helpful first to express them in scientific notation. To multiply or divide two exponential numbers, follow the rules below:

To multiply numbers expressed in scientific notation add their exponents.

$$10^a \times 10^b = 10^{a+b}$$

To divide two exponential numbers *subtract* their exponents.

$$\frac{10^a}{10^b} = 10^{a-b}$$

For instance, to multiply 3000 by 20,000 first convert to scientific notation.

$$3000 = 3 \times 10^3$$

$$20{,}000 = 2 \times 10^4$$

The product is

$$3 \times 10^3 \times 2 \times 10^4$$

We can rearrange the numbers, putting the exponential ones together:

$$3 \times 2 \times 10^3 \times 10^4 = 6 \times 10^7$$

To divide 600,000,000 by 300 express both numbers in scientific notation:

$$600{,}000{,}000 = 6 \times 10^8$$

$$300 = 3 \times 10^2$$

$$\frac{6 \times 10^8}{3 \times 10^2} = 2 \times 10^{8-2} = 2 \times 10^6$$

And to divide 90,000 by 0.003:

$$90000 = 9 \times 10^4$$

$$0.003 = 3 \times 10^{-3}$$

$$\frac{9 \times 10^4}{3 \times 10^{-3}} = 3 \times 10^{4-(-3)} = 3 \times 10^7$$

SAMPLE EXERCISE A.3

Perform the following arithmetic operations: (**a**) 2,000,000 × 350; (**b**) 62,000,000/0.00031

Solution:

(**a**)

$$2{,}000{,}000 = 2 \times 10^6$$

$$350 = 3.5 \times 10^2$$

and

$$2 \times 10^6 \times 3.5 \times 10^2 = 2 \times 3.5 \times 10^6 \times 10^2$$

$$= 7 \times 10^8$$

(**b**)

$$62{,}000{,}000 = 6.2 \times 10^7$$

$$0.00031 = 3.1 \times 10^{-4}$$

$$\frac{6.2 \times 10^7}{3.1 \times 10^{-4}} = 2 \times 10^{7-(-4)}$$

$$= 2 \times 10^{11}$$

EXERCISE A.3

Perform the following operations:

(**a**) 2000 × 3,000,000,000
(**b**) 84,000/420
(**c**) 6,000,000,000,000,000 × 1,000,000
(**d**) 9600/0.00000032
(**e**) 0.000008/4000

Occasionally you may need to rewrite an exponential number so that it fits the scientific notation form in which a number between 1 and 10 is multiplied by the exponential term. For instance, suppose you wish to express the number 35×10^5 in scientific notation. Dividing 35 by 10 gives 3.5, the number between 1 and 10. To avoid altering the value of the entire expression we must also multiply by 10. Dividing a number by 10, then multiplying it by 10 is equivalent to multiplying by 10/10, or 1. Its quantity remains the same; only the form changes.

$$35 \times 10^5 \times \frac{10}{10} = \frac{35}{10} \times 10^5 \times 10$$
$$= 3.5 \times 10^{5+1}$$
$$= 3.5 \times 10^6$$

Thus 35×10^5 can also be written 3.5×10^6. With practice you will be able to perform conversions like this in your mind. However, be careful! It is common (even for skilled mathematicians) to decrease the exponent when it should be increased, and vice versa.

SAMPLE EXERCISE A.4

Express the number 0.25×10^{-8} in standard scientific notation form.

Solution:

Multiplying 0.25 by 10 gives 2.5, a number between 1 and 10.

$$0.25 \times 10^{-8} \times \frac{10}{10} = 0.25 \times 10 \times \frac{10^{-8}}{10}$$
$$= 2.5 \times 10^{-9}$$

EXERCISE A.4

Rewrite the numbers below to fit standard scientific notation form: (**a**) 0.16×10^7; (**b**) 30×10^{-23}

B. SIGNIFICANT FIGURES

Significant figures include all digits which can be measured accurately plus the first uncertain digit. By applying the rules below you can identify the significant figures in the numerical part of a measured quantity.

Rule 1. All nonzero digits *are* significant. In the examples shown below all significant figures are shown in bold print.

244 **567.9** **2.14162553**

Rule 2. All zeros in between two significant digits *are* significant.

109 20.09 3000.75

Rule 3. Zeros used to fix a decimal place *are not* significant. These zeros appear as the leftmost digit(s) of a number.

0.789 0.098 0.000003

Rule 4. A zero to the right of a decimal point *is* significant, provided that there is at least one nonzero digit to the left of that zero.

2.00 9.560 450.0

Rule 5. Zeros to the right of the last nonzero digit in a number which has no decimal point *may* or *may not* be significant:

200	460000	10
??	????	?

It is generally correct to assume that such zeros are *not* significant unless there is information about the nature of the measurement.

Rule 6. In scientific notation all digits in the coefficient number (n) *are* significant:

2.5×10^{7} 6.02×10^{23} 3.00×10^{-15}

In fact, the best way to remove ambiguity about significant figures is to express numbers in scientific notation, where zeros are not needed to indicate multiples or fractions of 10.

Rule 7. Quantities that are defined exactly have an *unlimited* number of significant figures.

The number of inches in a foot is *exactly* 12, the number of seconds in a minute is *exactly* 60, and the number of people in a group of 10 people is *exactly* 10.

SAMPLE EXERCISE B.1

Indicate the significant zeros in the following numbers: (**a**) 307; (**b**) 0.0806; (**c**) 2.540; (**d**) 4500; (**e**) 4.500×10^{3}; (**f**) a dozen

Solution:

(**a**) 307 (see rule 2).
(**b**) 0.0806 (see rule 2 and rule 3).
(**c**) 2.540 (see rule 4).
(**d**) 4500 or 4500 or 4500 (see rule 5). The zeros may or may not be significant.

(e) 4.500×10^3 (see rule 6). Note that the use of scientific notation removes the ambiguity found in the form used in **d**.
(f) A dozen means 12 *exactly* (see rule 7).

EXERCISE B.1

Identify the significant zeros in the following numbers: (**a**) 1809 (**b**) 0.0010005 (**c**) 3.000×10^6 (**d**) 6000 (**e**) 4.30

Multiplication and Division

Retain only the number of significant figures present in the number with the *lowest* number of significant figures. The rules for dropping insignificant digits, that is, for **rounding off,** are given below.

1. When the first nonsignificant digit (underlined in the examples below) is less than 5, drop it. Replace this and *all* other nonsignificant digits with zeros.

   172.2 becomes 170

2. When the first nonsignificant digit is more than 5, round *up*.

   1467 becomes 1470

3. When the first nonsignificant digit is 5 followed by any digit that is nonzero, round up.

   88.56 becomes 89   655,020 becomes 660,000

4. When the first nonsignificant digit is 5 followed by no other digits or by zeros only, round off to make an *even* number

   13500 becomes 14000   265 becomes 260

If you use this system consistently, it is likely that for a large group of results you will be rounding up about half the time and keeping the last significant digit the same about half the time.

Suppose you wish to multiply **82** by **2.1**. Both **82** and **2.1** include only two significant figures, and thus you must round off the calculated answer, *172.2*, which contains four significant figures, to produce a number with only two significant figures.

172.2 becomes 170

and we write that

$$82 \times 2.1 = 170$$

Including insignificant digits in a calculated answer is incorrect.

It is not "more correct" to include all the digits calculated! It is incorrect, since it attaches significance to digits that are not really meaningful.

When you multiply **45.675** × **23.0**, the answer must include three significant figures (from **23.0**). The calculated answer is **105**0.525, which becomes **105**0:

$$45.675 \times 23.0 = 1050$$

Dividing **49.5** by **18** gives a number with two significant figures (from **18**) when the calculated answer, **2.7**5, is rounded off (according to rounding-off rule 4).

$$\frac{49.5}{18} = 2.8$$

SAMPLE EXERCISE B.2

Perform the following multiplication and division, retaining the correct number of significant figures in your answer: (**a**) 1.057 × 3.2 × 783; (**b**) 156/32.10.

Solution:

(a) 1.057 × 3.2 × 783
The number 3.2 has the least number of significant figures, two. The calculated result, **26**48.4192, must be rounded to 2600.

$$1.057 \times 3.2 \times 783 = 2600$$

(b) 156/32.10
In this example the number of significant figures in the answer, **4.85**98, must be three, the same number as in **156**.

$$\frac{156}{32.10} = \mathbf{4.86}$$

EXERCISE B.2

Retain the correct number of significant figures in your answers to the following: (a) 3.65 × 3.654 × 1.3; (**b**) 0.150 × 6732; (**c**) $\frac{93.5}{2.5}$; (**d**) $\frac{0.502 \times 68.4}{1.325}$

Addition and Subtraction

When adding and subtracting numbers derived from measured quantities, the last digit in the answer must be significant for all numbers added. Use rounding-off rules to achieve this. In the answer all significant figures are in boldface and the first nonsignificant digit (the one used in applying the rounding rules) is underlined.

$$\begin{array}{rrl} & 235.0 & \\ & 48 & \\ & \underline{4699.585} & \\ \text{Calculated sum} = & 4982.\underline{5}85 & \quad \text{becomes } 4983 \end{array}$$

Note that the *number* of significant digits in the answer can be greater than the number in any one quantity. The answer (4983) in the example above has four significant digits and one of the quantities added (48) has only two.

SAMPLE EXERCISE B.3

Perform the following operations, retaining only significant figures in your answer: (**a**) 32 + 16.0 + 1.01; (**b**) 7.65 − 1.2

Solution:

(**a**) Only the ones digit is significant in all three numbers.

$$\begin{array}{rl} 32 & \\ 16.0 & \\ \underline{+\ \ 1.01} & \\ 49.\underline{0}1 & \quad \text{becomes } 49 \end{array}$$

(**b**) In this example the tenths digit is the last significant one in 1.2.

$$\begin{array}{rl} 7.65 & \\ \underline{-1.2\ \ } & \\ 6.3\underline{5} & \quad \text{becomes } 6.4 \end{array}$$

EXERCISE B.3

Perform the following additions and subtractions, and round off the answers to the right number of significant figures:

(**a**) 24.0 + 6.0 + 27; (**b**) 567.35 − 0.2; (**c**) 18765.3 + 43.997 + 0.006.

C. ALGEBRAIC MANIPULATIONS

The rules of algebra given below are the ones that you will need to solve problems in this text. For a more complete discussion refer to a beginning algebra textbook.

Rule 1. Both sides of an equation $a = b$ may be divided by the same quantity q, provided that q is not equal to zero.

$$a = b$$

$$\frac{a}{q} = \frac{b}{q}$$

Rule 2. Both sides of an equation $a = b$ may be multiplied by the same quantity q, provided that q is not equal to zero.

$$a = b$$

$$q \times a = q \times b$$

Rule 3. The same quantity q may be added to (or subtracted from) both sides of an equation.

$$a = b$$

$$a + q = b + q$$

and

$$a - q = b - q$$

Rule 4. Both sides of an equation may be squared or cubed.

$$a = b$$

$$a^2 = b^2$$

$$a^3 = b^3$$

Rule 5. The square or cube of a product ab is found by squaring or cubing each quantity in it.

$$(ab)^2 = a^2b^2$$

$$(ab)^3 = a^3b^3$$

Now we will apply the rules above to solve for given quantities. For instance, suppose you are asked to solve for P, given the equation $8P = 24$:

$$8P = 24$$

Divide both sides of the equation by 8.

$$\frac{\cancel{8}P}{\cancel{8}} = \frac{24}{8}$$

$$P = 3$$

Given the equation $P \times V = n \times R \times T$ or $PV = nRT$, solve for n. $PV = nRT$ can be rewritten as $nRT = PV$. Now apply rule 1 twice, dividing by R and by T:

$$\frac{n\cancel{RT}}{\cancel{RT}} = \frac{PV}{RT}$$

$$n = \frac{PV}{RT}$$

Suppose you wish to solve for the quantity P in the following equation:

$$2P + 7 = 10$$

First subtract 7 from both sides of the equation:

$$2P + 7 - 7 = 10 - 7$$

or

$$2P = 3$$

Then divide both sides of the equation by 2:

$$\frac{\cancel{2}P}{\cancel{2}} = \frac{3}{2}$$

$$P = 3/2, \text{ or } 1.5$$

To find D^2 if you are given $D = 2r$, square both sides of the equation. To square the quantity $2r$, apply rules 4 and 5:

$$D^2 = (2r)^2 = 2^2r^2$$
$$= 4r^2$$

SAMPLE EXERCISE C.1

Solve for the quantity in boldface in each example below:

(a) $\frac{\mathbf{V_1}}{T_1} = \frac{V_2}{T_2}$ (b) $6\mathbf{V} - 273 = T$ (c) $\frac{V_1}{T_1} = \frac{V_2}{\mathbf{T_2}}$

Solution:

(a) Multiplying both sides of the equation by T_1 gives an expression for V_1:

$$\frac{T_1 \times V_1}{T_1} = \frac{T_1 \times V_2}{T_2}$$

The T_1's on the left side cancel and

$$V_1 = \frac{T_1 \times V_2}{T_2}$$

(b) In this example begin by adding 273 to both sides of the equation.

$$6V_1 - 273 + 273 = T + 273$$

leaving

$$6V_1 = T + 273$$

Now divide both sides of the equation by 6:

$$\frac{\not{6}V_1}{\not{6}} = \frac{T + 273}{6}$$

$$V_1 = \frac{T + 273}{6}$$

(c) This time begin by multiplying both sides of the equation by T_2.

$$\frac{T_2 \times V_1}{T_1} = \frac{\not{T_2} \times V_2}{\not{T_2}}$$

giving

$$\frac{T_2 \times V_1}{T_1} = V_2$$

Now multiply by T_1 and divide by V_1, leaving the expression for T_2:

$$\frac{\not{T_1} \times T_2 \times \not{V_1}}{\not{T_1} \times \not{V_1}} = \frac{T_1 \times V_2}{V_1}$$

$$T_2 = \frac{T_1 \times V_2}{V_1}$$

EXERCISE C.1

Solve for the variable in boldface in each of the equations below:

(a) $3\mathbf{M} = P$ (b) $PV = n\mathbf{R}T$ (c) $\mathbf{P} + 8 = 3V$ (d) $\frac{P_1}{\mathbf{T_1}} = \frac{P_2}{T_2}$

GLOSSARY

Absolute zero The lowest possible temperature; 0 K or $-273°C$

Acetal Organic compound formed by the reaction of an alcohol (ROH) with a hemiacetal and having the general formula (see also Hemiacetal)

$$\begin{array}{c} OR \\ | \\ R'—C—H \\ | \\ OR'' \end{array}$$

Acetyl coenzyme A (acetyl-CoA) Acetyl derivative of coenzyme A; the intersection point for all metabolic processes (see also CoA)

Achiral compound Compound that can be superimposed upon its mirror image

Acid Species that donates a proton (see also Brönsted-Lowry theory)

Acid anhydride Carboxylic acid derivative in which a molecule of water is removed from two molecules of carboxylic acid and having the general formula

$$\begin{array}{c} O \quad\quad\; O \\ \| \quad\quad\;\; \| \\ R—C—O—C—R \end{array}$$

Acidic solution Aqueous solution in which $[H_3O^+] > [OH^-]$, $[H_3O^+] > 10^{-7}$, and $pH < 7$

Acidosis Condition in which blood pH dips below 7.36

Activation energy (E_a) The minimum amount of energy that reactants must have so that a reaction can take place

Active site Region of an enzyme where the enzyme substrate interactions take place

Acyl chloride Carboxylic acid derivative having the general formula

$$\begin{array}{c} O \\ \| \\ R—C—Cl \end{array}$$

Addition polymer Polymer that forms from the addition of double-bonded monomers to each other

Addition reaction Reaction in which two reactants combine to form one product

Adenine (A) Nitrogen base derived from purine and found in both RNA and DNA

Adenosine diphosphate (ADP) Product of ATP hydrolysis

Adenosine monophosphate (AMP) Product of the hydrolysis of ATP or ADP

Adenosine triphosphate (ATP) High-energy phosphate compound consisting of ribose, adenine, and three phosphate groups

Adrenergic drug Drug that evokes a response similar to that of norepinephrine; phenylethylamine derivative

Aerobic In the presence of air

Alcohol Oxygen-containing organic compound with the general formula ROH

Aldehyde Oxygen-containing organic compound with the general formula

$$\begin{array}{c} O \\ \| \\ R—C—H \end{array}$$

Aldose Monosaccharide containing an aldehyde functional group

Aliphatic compounds Open-chain compounds and their corresponding ring compounds

Alkali metals Elements in group IA of the periodic table

Alkaline See Basic

Alkaline earth metals Elements in group IIA of the periodic table

Alkalosis Condition in which blood pH rises above 7.44

Alkane Hydrocarbon which includes only C to C single bonds and has the general formula C_nH_{2n+2}

Alkene Hydrocarbon which includes a C to C double bond and has the general formula C_nH_{2n}

Alkoxide ion Anion (RO^-) produced when an alcohol donates a proton to water, $ROH + H_2O \rightleftharpoons RO^- + H_3O^+$

Alkoxy group Substituent ($-OR$) produced by removal of the hydroxyl H of an alcohol

Alkyl Hydrocarbon group derived by removal of a hydrogen atom from an alkane

Alkylammonium ion Derivatives of the ammonium ion, NH_4^+, in which an alkyl group replaces a hydrogen, such as RNH_3^+

Alkyne Hydrocarbon which includes a C to C triple bond and has the general formula C_nH_{2n-2}

Allosteric enzyme Enzyme with two binding sites, of which one binds to a substrate and the other binds to an inhibitor (or a stimulator)

Alpha particle (α) Particle with a nuclear charge of $+2$ and a mass of 4 amu, ${}^4_2\alpha$; helium nucleus

Alpha rays Radiation consisting of α particles

Amide Acid derivative with the general formula $\mathrm{R{-}\overset{\overset{O}{\|}}{C}{-}NH_2}$ (for a carboxylic acid)

Amine Organic derivative of ammonia in which one or more NH_3 hydrogen atoms are replaced by alkyl groups to form RNH_2, R_2NH, or R_3N

Amine hydrochloride Alkylammonium chloride, RNH_3Cl, written $RNH_2{\cdot}HCl$

α-Amino acid Carboxylic acid with an amino group on C-2, the α carbon atom

Amphoteric Exhibiting the properties of both acids and bases

Amylopectin Starch component consisting of a branched polymer of D-glucose

Amylose Starch component consisting of a linear polymer of D-glucose

Anabolism Biochemical reactions in which simpler molecules are used to build up complex molecules

Anaerobic In the absence of air

Angle strain Difference between the bond angle in a cycloalkane and 109.5°, the tetrahedral angle

Anion Negatively charged ion

Anomeric carbon Carbon atom originally part of the carbonyl group of a monosaccharide, C-1 of aldoses and C-2 of ketoses

Anomers Pair of cyclic sugars that differ only in their orientations about the anomeric C atom

Antagonist Drug compound that opposes the effect of another substance

Anticodon Triplet of bases on a tRNA molecule that attracts a codon on mRNA

Antihistamine Drug used to counteract the effect of histamine (see also Histamine)

Antioxidant Easily oxidized substance used to protect other substances from oxidizing agents

Arene Hydrocarbon with both aliphatic and aromatic components

Aromatic compound Compound containing the benzene ( ) structure or having chemical properties similar to those of benzene compounds

Aromatic substitution Reaction in which a ring H atom of benzene is substituted by another atom or group

Artificial transmutation Bombardment of target isotopes with "bullet" particles to produce new isotopes

Asymmetric C atom Carbon atom bonded to four different groups; chiral center

Atmosphere (atm) Pressure unit approximately equal to the pressure exerted by air around sea level; 1 atm = 760 mmHg

Atom Indivisible (by chemical reaction), discrete particle, of which all matter is composed

Atomic mass unit (amu) 1 amu = 1.66×10^{-24} g

Atomic number (*Z*) The number of protons in the nucleus of an atom; ordering number of an element in the periodic table

Atomic orbital Electronic energy level in the modern Schrödinger atom

Atomic spectrum Recording of the wavelengths of light emitted or absorbed by an atom and characteristic for each element

Atomic weight The mass of an average atom of an element compared with the mass of an atom of C-12, which has an atomic weight of exactly 12

Avogadro's number 6.02×10^{23}; the number of units in a mole

Background radiation Radiation from cosmic rays or naturally occurring radioisotopes

Balancing (equations) Adjustment of the coefficients of each species in a chemical equation to equate the number of atoms on both sides of the equation

Barbiturate Central nervous system depressant derived from the N heterocyclic compound, barbituric acid

Basal metabolic rate (BMR) The amount of energy which must be expended to just maintain the body

Base Species that accepts a proton (see Brönsted-Lowry theory)

Base pair Hydrogen-bonded pairs of nitrogen bases; guanine with cytosine (G to C), adenine with thymine (A to T), or adenine with uracil (A to U)

Basic solution Aqueous solution in which $[OH^-] > [H_3O^+]$, $[OH^-] > 10^{-7}$ and pH > 7; alkaline

Battery Device that uses an oxidation reduction reaction to generate electricity; voltaic cell

Benedict's test Test for the presence of glucose (and other reducing sugars) in urine based upon the reduction of glucose by Cu^{2+} ion

Benzene Liquid hydrocarbon (C_6H_6) with a stable ring structure (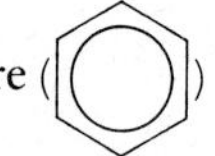) that is present in most aromatic compounds (see also Aromatic compound)

Beta particle (β or β^-) Particle identical to an electron, $_{-1}^{\ 0}\beta$

β-Pleated sheet Secondary structure of proteins in which one polypeptide segment forms hydrogen bonds to a neighboring segment

Beta rays Radiation consisting of β particles

Bilayer Cell membrane structure formed by a double layer of lipid molecules

Biologic value (BV) Rating given to a protein that reflects the essential amino acid content of a protein

Biotin B vitamin that forms a coenzyme involved in transfer of carboxyl groups

Boiling point (bp) Temperature at which the vapor pressure of a liquid is equal to the external atmospheric pressure (see also normal boiling point)

Boiling point elevation (ΔT_b) Difference between the boiling point of a solution and the boiling point of the pure solvent

Bomb calorimeter Device used to determine the amount of heat produced by reaction of a substance with O_2; used to find caloric value of food samples

Bond energy Energy required to break a chemical bond between atoms

Boyle's law Gas law stating that at constant temperature the volume of a fixed sample of gas is inversely proportional to the pressure; *PV* is constant; or $P_1V_1 = P_2V_2$

Branched chain C to C chain in which at least one C atom is branched off a continuous C to C chain,

—C—C—C—C—
      |
      C

Brönsted-Lowry theory Acid-base theory in which an acid is defined as a proton donor and a base as a proton acceptor

Buffer Solution that resists changes in pH; prepared from a weak acid and its salt or from a weak base and its salt

Carbohydrates Compounds that are polyhydroxy aldehydes or ketones or can be broken down to produce them; sugars, starch, and cellulose
Carbonyl group Carbon double-bonded to oxygen, C=O
Carboxyl group Functional group of a carboxylic acid, $-\overset{\overset{\displaystyle O}{\|}}{C}-OH$ or $-COOH$
Carboxylate anion $R\overset{\overset{\displaystyle O}{\|}}{C}O^-$ anion, produced when a carboxylic acid donates a proton to water, $RCOOH + H_2O \rightleftharpoons RCOO^- + H_3O^+$
Carboxylic acid Organic compound with the general formula $R-\overset{\overset{\displaystyle O}{\|}}{C}-OH$ or RCOOH
Carcinogen Cancer-causing substance
Catabolism Biochemical breakdown of complex molecules into simpler molecules
Catalyst Substance that changes the rate of a reaction but is not altered by the reaction
Cation Positively charged ion
Cationic detergent Quaternary ammonium salt containing a long-chain hydrocarbon group (see also Detergent)
Cellulose Polysaccharide in which glucose monomers are joined by β-1,4-glycosidic linkages
Celsius scale Temperature scale in which the freezing point of water is 0°C and the boiling point of water is 100°C
Cephalin Ethanolamine phosphoglyceride found in brain tissue
Ceramide Fatty acid amide of sphingosine present in sphingolipids and glycolipids
Cerebroside Glycolipid found in brain tissue
Chain reaction Reaction in which a product initiates a new reaction; often used to describe fission reactions (see also Nuclear fission)
Charles' law Gas law stating that at constant pressure the volume of a fixed sample of gas is directly proportional to its (kelvin) temperature T; V/T = constant and $V_1/T_1 = V_2/T_2$
Chemical bond Attractive force which joins atoms
Chemical change Change that occurs when the atoms of a substance rearrange by breaking and forming of bonds
Chemical conversion factor Conversion factor based upon chemical definitions, such as the mass of a mole or equivalent quantities involved in a given chemical reaction (see also Conversion factor)
Chemical energy Energy change which accompanies a chemical reaction
Chemical equilibrium Reversible reaction in which the rate of a forward reaction is the same as that of the reverse reaction, indicated by double arrows: reactants $\rightleftharpoons$ products
Chemical property Property of a substance that describes its ability to undergo a chemical change
Chemical reaction Chemical changes described by chemical equations: reactants $\rightarrow$ products
Chiral center Carbon atom attached to four different groups; asymmetric carbon atom
Chiral compound Compound that cannot be superimposed upon its mirror image
Cholesterol Sterol important in animal metabolism and found in nerve tissue, blood, and bile (see also Steroid)
Chromatography Separation technique that depends upon the different abilities of each component of a mixture to adhere to a given substance
Chromosome Very large DNA molecule found in the cell nucleus and differing in number for each species
Chylomicron Tiny fat droplet present in the lymph and blood
Chyme Fluid that passes into the small intestine from the stomach and contains partially digested foods
Cis (*cis*-) Term (and prefix) used to refer to the geometric isomer of an alkene XYC=CYX in which the X's are on the same side of the double bond,

```
X       X
 \     /
  C=C
 /     \
Y       Y
```

Codon Triplet of N bases on mRNA that represents an amino acid or chain termination
Coenzyme Cofactor that is an organic compound
Coenzyme A (CoA) Pantothenic acid, a B vitamin that transfers acyl groups (see also Acetyl-CoA)
Cofactor Nonprotein that must be combined with a protein in order to convert it into an active enzyme
Collagen Protein component of connective tissues and the most abundant protein in the body
Colligative property Property of a solution that depends upon the concentration of solute particles, including freezing point depression, boiling point elevation, osmotic pressure, and vapor pressure lowering
Colloid Homogeneous mixture containing particles ranging in size from 10 to 100 nm
Combination reaction Linking of two reactants to make a single product, as in $A + B \rightarrow AB$
Combined gas law Combination of Boyle's and Charles' laws, which states that for a fixed sample of gas, PV/T is constant; $P_1V_1/T_1 = P_2V_2/T_2$
Competitive inhibitor Enzyme inhibitor with a structure similar to that of the substrate, allowing it to bind to the active site of the enzyme
Complementary strands The strands of a DNA double helix that are attracted to each other by hydrogen-bonded base pairs
Compound Pure substance containing atoms of more than one element
Condensation polymer Polymer that is made by a condensation reaction in which monomer molecules combine to split out a small molecule
Condensation reaction Reaction in which two reactant molecules combine to form one product molecule, along with a small molecule, usually H_2O or HCl
Conjugate acid New acid formed when a base accepts a proton
Conjugate base New base formed when an acid donates a proton
Conjugate pair Reactant acid and its conjugate base or reacting base and its conjugate acid according to Brönsted-Lowry proton transfer theory
Conversion factor Equation that re-

lates two different units for a given physical quantity (e.g., 1 ft = 12 in)

Covalent bond Bond, formed generally between two nonmetallic atoms, in which one or more electron pairs are shared

Covalent compound Compound containing discrete molecules in which atoms are joined by covalent bonds

Covalent crystal Crystal in which nonmetallic atoms are all bonded to each other, leaving no discrete molecules, as in gemstones

Curie (Ci) Radioactivity unit that measures activity; 1 Ci = amount of radioactive substance that undergoes 3.7×10^{10} disintegrations per second

Cyclic sugar Hemiacetal or hemiketal form of a monosaccharide

Cycloalkane Hydrocarbon containing a single-bonded C to C ring and having the general formula C_nH_{2n}

Cycloalkene Hydrocarbon ring compound containing one or more C to C double bonds in the ring

Cytosine (C) Nitrogen base derived from pyrimidine and found both in RNA and DNA

D-L system System for specifying the absolute configuration of optical isomers by comparing them with D- and L-glyceraldehyde

Dalton's atomic theory Theory including the concept that elements are composed of a single kind of indestructible atom and that compounds form from simple and fixed combinations of atoms

Dalton's law of partial pressures Gas law stating that the total pressure (P_T) of a mixture of gases is the sum of the partial pressures of each component gas; $P_T = p_1 + p_2 + p_3 + \cdots$

Daughter isotope New isotope that forms as a result of a transmutation

Decomposition reaction Breakdown of a reactant into two or more products, as in $AB \rightarrow A + B$

Dehydration reaction Reaction in which a reactant is converted to a product with loss of a molecule of water

Dehydrogenation Reaction in which the reactant loses hydrogen

Denaturation Alteration in the secondary or tertiary structure of a protein that produces a dramatic change in its properties

Density Mass per unit volume

Deoxyribonucleic acid (DNA) Polynucleotide that contains the hereditary information and consists of the four monomer nucleotides dAMP, dTMP, dCMP, and dGMP and the sugar deoxyribose

Deoxyribose Aldopentose in which an OH group of ribose is replaced with a hydrogen atom

Detergent Compound with both polar and nonpolar character that is capable of forming micelles (see also Micelle)

Dextrorotatory (+) Rotating the plane of polarized light in the clockwise direction

Diabetes mellitus Disorder, caused by a deficiency of insulin, in which blood sugar rises far above normal (see also Insulin)

Dialysis Process of separating substances from a solution by taking advantage of their differing abilities to pass through a porous membrane; basis of the artificial kidney machine

Diastereoisomers Optical isomers of a compound which are not mirror images of each other

Dicarboxylic acid Compound containing two carboxyl groups

Diene Hydrocarbon containing two C to C double bonds

Diffusion of gases Process by which gases mix as a result of random motion (see also Graham's law)

Digestion Hydrolysis of larger food molecules to form smaller components, as in starch → glucose

Dipeptide Two amino acids joined by a peptide linkage

Disaccharide Sugar that forms when two monosaccharides are joined by a glycosidic linkage (see also Glycosidic linkage)

Displacement reaction Reaction in which a reactant replaces an element in another reactant, as in $A + BC \rightarrow AB + C$

Distillation Separation technique in which a liquid mixture is first vaporized, then condensed in such a way that each component with a different boiling point is removed separately

Disulfide Compound with the structure R—S—S—R′

Disulfide linkage —S—S— group such as that formed from the combination of two cysteine amino acid residues

Double bond Covalent bond formed by the sharing of two electron pairs and indicated by two dashes between bonded atoms (C═C, C═O)

Double displacement reaction Reaction in which both reactants exchange atoms or groups with each other, as in $AB + CD \rightarrow AD + CB$

Double helix Secondary structure of DNA in which two base-paired strands are twisted to form a helix

Electrolyte Ionic compound that is soluble in water and forms solutions capable of conducting electricity

Electron (*e*) Subatomic particle which has a mass of 9.110×10^{-28} g(1/1836 amu), a charge of -1.60×10^{-19} (-1), and is located outside the nucleus of an atom

Electron capture (EC) Nuclear decay mode in which the parent isotope captures an orbiting electron

Electron carrier Oxidizing agent involved in the transport of electron pairs in the final stage of respiration

Electron dot structure Structures in which a covalent bond is represented by a pair of dots; Lewis structure

Electronegativity Number that indicates the degree of attraction an atom has for bonding electrons

Electronic configuration Atomic orbitals occupied by the electrons of an atom

Electron transport Transfer of electron pairs from compound to compound in the final stage of respiration

Electrophoresis Method used to separate mixtures of amino acids or proteins

Element One of the 106 pure substance all of whose atoms have the same number of protons in their nuclei

Embden-Meyerhoff pathway Anaerobic metabolic pathway in which glucose is converted to pyruvic acid

Empirical formula Formula which gives the simplest whole number ratio of atoms in a molecule

Enantiomers A chiral molecule and its mirror image

Encephalin Pentapeptide that has a narcotic analgesic effect

Endergonic Energy-absorbing; $\Delta G > 0$

Endorphins Polypeptides from which

encephalins are derived; endogenous morphines

Endothermic reaction Reaction that absorbs heat and for which $\Delta H > 0$

Energy Ability to do work, expressed in joules (J) or calories (cal); 1 cal = 4.184 J

Enthalpy change (ΔH) Heat change that accompanies a process such as a chemical reaction

Enzyme Protein that behaves as a biochemical catalyst

Equilibrium constant (K_{eq}) Quantity, constant at a given temperature, defined as the product of molar concentrations of products divided by that for reactants; for the reaction $aA + bB \rightleftharpoons cC$,

$$K_{eq} = \frac{[C]^c}{[A]^a[B]^b}$$

Essential amino acid (EAA) Amino acid component of protein that is not synthesized in the body and must be supplied in the diet

Essential fatty acid (EFA) Fatty acid that cannot be synthesized in the body and must be supplied in the diet

Ester Acid derivative formed by the reaction of an alcohol (ROH) and an acid and having the general formula

$$R'—\overset{\overset{\displaystyle O}{\|}}{C}—OR$$

when the acid is carboxylic

Esterification Ester formation; pathway by which fatty acids combine with glycerol-P to form triacylglycerols

Ether Oxygen-containing organic compound with the general formula R—O—R′

Evaporation Conversion of a liquid into a gas (vapor) by escape of energetic surface molecules

Exergonic Energy-releasing; $\Delta G < 0$ (compare Endergonic)

Exothermic reaction Reaction that evolves heat and for which $\Delta H < 0$

Family Vertical column of the periodic table, also called a group

Fat See Triacylglycerol

Fat-soluble vitamins Vitamins A, D, E, and K

Fatty acid (FA) Carboxylic acid in which the R group is long and unbranched (see also Carboxylic acid)

Fatty acid cycle (FA cycle) Pathway by which fatty acids are degraded to acetyl-CoA

Fibrin Insoluble fibrous protein that causes the formation of blood clots

Fibrinogen Water-soluble fibrous protein found in blood

Fibrous proteins Proteins in which polypeptide chains form long fibers; proteins that make up the structural components of the body

Fischer projection Formula used to represent optical isomers, in which the intersection of a vertical and horizontal line represents a chiral C atom

Flavin adenine dinucleotide (FAD) Flavoenzyme that accepts two hydrogens from a substrate: $FAD + SH_2 \rightarrow FADH_2 + S$

Flavoenzyme Coenzymes containing riboflavin, including the flavonucleotides FAD and FMN (see also vitamin B_1 and FAD)

Fluid mosaic model Model of cell membrane in which proteins are embedded in a lipid bilayer

Folic acid B vitamin that is part of tetrahydrofolic acid, a coenzyme involved in nucleic acid synthesis

Formula Combination of element symbols and subscripts used to represent a chemical species

Formula weight Sum of the atomic weights of all the atoms in a formula; molecular weight

Fossil fuels Coal, natural gas, and petroleum

Free aldehyde Aldehyde group of an aldose that is available to react with oxidizing agents

Free energy change (ΔG) Criterion for reaction spontaneity; spontaneous, $\Delta G < 0$, nonspontaneous $\Delta G > 0$, equilibrium $\Delta G = 0$ (see Spontaneous reaction)

Freezing point depression (ΔT_f) Difference between the freezing point of a pure solvent and a solution

Free radical Very reactive species containing one unpaired electron, such as phenoxy, $C_6H_5—O\cdot$

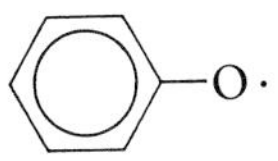

Fructose Ketohexose; fruit sugar or levulose; a component of sucrose

Functional group Atom or group of atoms which determines the properties of an organic compound

Furanose Cyclic form of a sugar containing five-membered furanlike rings

Fused-ring aromatic Compound that forms when two or more aromatic rings are joined through two or more C atoms, as in 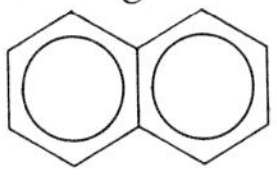 (naphthalene)

Galactose Aldohexose; component of lactose

Galactosemia Disorder in which the enzyme needed to degrade galactose is lacking

Gamma rays (γ) Massless and chargeless radiation ($^0_0\gamma$) emanating from a radioactive atom; electromagnetic radiation similar to x-rays

Ganglioside Ceramide attached to a complex sugar

Gas Physical state of a substance in which it takes both the shape and the volume of its container

Gas pressure Force per unit area exerted by a gas; most often expressed in terms of the height of a liquid column that the gas is able to support

Gene Segment of DNA that contains the information for the synthesis of a particular protein

Gene cloning Formation of copies of a foreign gene introduced into a host cell

General anesthetic Agent that produces loss of sensation with loss of consciousness

Genetic code Set of 64 codons each of which specifies an amino acid or chain termination

Genetic engineering Use of gene cloning to synthesize proteins

Geometric isomers Compounds which have the same molecular formula and the same structural formula but a different arrangement of their atoms in space (see also Cis and Trans)

Glass transition temperature (T_g) Temperature at which a polymer begins to soften

Globular protein Water-soluble proteins in which polypeptide chains are folded into spherical shapes, including enzymes and other operational molecules

Glucagon Polypeptide hormone that increases blood glucose by stimulating the conversion of glycogen to glucose

Gluconeogenesis Biosynthesis of glucose from noncarbohydrate molecules

Glucose Aldohexose; blood sugar; component of starch, cellulose, sucrose, and lactose

Glycogen Highly branched polysaccharide consisting of D-glucose monomers; animal starch

Glycogenesis Formation of glycogen from glucose

Glycogenolysis Breakdown of glycogen to form glucose

Glycolipid Ceramide attached to a simple sugar

Glycolysis Anaerobic pathway in which glucose is converted to lactic acid

Glycoside Acetal of a sugar

Glycosidic linkage Reaction involving the hydroxyl on the anomeric C atom of a sugar and the hydroxyl group of an alcohol or of another sugar; linkage that joins monosaccharides in disaccharides and polysaccharides

Graham's law Gas law stating that the higher the molecular weight of a gas (M), the slower its rate of diffusion (D), according to the relationship $\frac{D_1}{D_2} = \sqrt{\frac{M_2}{M_1}}$

Gram equivalent weight (eq) For acids or bases, the number of grams of acid (or base) donating (or accepting) one mole of protons; equivalent

Group Vertical column of the periodic table, also called a family

Guanine (G) Nitrogen base derived from purine and found both in RNA and DNA

Half-life ($t_{1/2}$) Length of time necessary for one-half of a given mass of radioactive isotope to decay to its disintegration product

Halogen Element in group VIIA, salt former

Halogenated alkane Alkane in which one or more H atoms are substituted by halogen atoms

α-Helix Secondary structure of proteins in which the polypeptide chain spirals in a clockwise direction

Hemeprotein Protein that includes the iron porphyrin structure, heme

Hemiacetal Organic compound formed by the addition of an alcohol to an aldehyde ($R'—\overset{O}{\overset{\|}{C}}—H$) and having the general formula

$$R'—\underset{OR}{\underset{|}{\overset{OH}{\overset{|}{C}}}}—H$$

Hemiketal Organic compound formed by the addition of an alcohol to a ketone ($R'—\overset{O}{\overset{\|}{C}}—R''$) and having the general formula

$$R'—\underset{OR}{\underset{|}{\overset{OH}{\overset{|}{C}}}}—R''$$

Hemoglobin Hemeprotein in the blood responsible for the transport of O_2 from the lungs

High-energy bond Bond that releases a relatively large amount of energy when broken; indicated by a wavy line, as in ~P, a high-energy phosphate bond

High-energy compounds Compounds such as ATP that contain high-energy bonds and are used to supply energy for biochemical reactions

Histamine Compound derived from the amino acid histidine and released in tissues as part of allergic reactions

Homologous series Series of organic compounds in which adjacent members differ by one repeating $—CH_2—$ unit

Hybridization Mixing of two or more atomic orbitals to form new hybrid atomic orbitals

Hybrid recombinant DNA DNA molecule made by combining bacterial plasmid DNA with foreign DNA

Hydration Addition of water across a double bond to form an alcohol

Hydrocarbon Organic compound containing the elements H and C only

Hydrogen bond Intermolecular attractive force between a highly electronegative atom (F, O, N) of one molecule and the H atom attached to such an electronegative atom in a neighboring molecule; often indicated by dots or dashes, as in H—F·······H—F

Hydrogenation Conversion of a double bond to a single bond by the addition of hydrogen

Hydrolysis reaction Type of reaction in which water reacts with a compound to break it down into its original components

Hydrometer Weighted glass tube that floats in a liquid and is used to measure its specific gravity

Hydrophilic Attracted to an aqueous environment; "water-loving"

Hydrophobic Attracted to nonpolar groups; "water-hating"

Hydroxyl group Functional group of alcohols, —OH

Hyperglycemia Condition in which blood glucose level is above normal

Hypertonic solution Solution with a higher solute concentration (in osmolarity) than normal tissue fluid

Hypoglycemia Condition in which blood glucose level is below normal

Hypotonic solution Solution with a lower solute concentration (in osmolarity) than normal tissue fluid

Ideal gas Gas that obeys the ideal gas law

Ideal gas constant (R) $R = 0.0821$ L·atm/mol·K = 62.4 L·mmHg/mol·K

Ideal gas law Gas law stating that $PV = nRT$

Indicator Acidic or basic substance that changes color in a given pH range, used to measure acidity and to determine the endpoint of a titration

Induced-fit theory Theory of enzyme activity in which the substrate induces the flexible enzyme to fit with it

Insulin Protein hormone released by the pancreas that acts to lower the blood glucose level

Iodine number Number of grams of iodine absorbed by 100 g fat in the addition of I_2 (or ICl or IBr) across C=C bonds

Ionic bond Electrostatic attraction between an anion and a cation

Ionic compound Compound in which ionic bonds join cations and anions and which contains no discrete molecules

Ionic crystal Crystal formed by ionic compounds in which lattice positions are occupied by cations and anions

Irreversible reaction Reaction that does not proceed in the reverse direction and for which the extent of reaction is 100 percent

Isoalkane Methylalkane in which the methyl group is attached to the next-to-last C atom

Isoelectric point (pI) pH at which a given amino acid or protein has no net electric charge and fails to move in an electric field

Isotonic solution Solution with the same solute concentration (in osmolarity) as normal tissue fluid

Isotopes Atoms of the same element (same atomic number Z) which contain different numbers of neutrons in their nuclei (different mass numbers A)

IUPAC system Definitive set of nomenclature rules for organic compounds; International Union of Pure and Applied Chemistry

Kelvin scale: Temperature scale, sometimes called the absolute temperature scale since absolute zero is zero kelvin (0 K)

α-Keratin Protein in skin, wool, and hair with α-helical secondary structure

Ketal Organic compound formed by the reaction of an alcohol (ROH) with a hemiketal and having the general formula

```
        OR
        |
  R'—C—R"
        |
        OR
```

Ketoacidosis Acidosis brought on by the presence of excess ketone bodies

Ketone Oxygen-containing organic compound with the general formula

```
    O
    ||
R—C—R'
```

Ketone bodies Acetone, β-hydroxybutyric acid, and acetoacetic acid

Ketose Monosaccharide containing a ketone functional group

Ketosis Condition resulting from the presence of excess ketone bodies (see Ketoacidosis)

Kilogram (kg) Base unit of mass in the SI system; 1 kg = 1000 g = 2.2 lb

Kinetic-molecular theory Theory upon which the ideal gas laws are based, including the idea that gas molecules are in constant motion and are so far apart that there are no forces of attraction among them

Kinetics Study of the rates of chemical reactions

Lactose Disaccharide consisting of galactose and glucose; milk sugar

Lactose intolerance Disorder in which the enzyme lactase is deficient, preventing proper lactose metabolism; lactase deficiency syndrome

Laser Concentrated source of light energy in which the radiation includes a narrow band of wavelengths; in surgery, used to cut tissues

Law of conservation of energy Energy is neither created nor destroyed but may be changed in form

Law of conservation of matter Matter is neither created nor destroyed but may be changed in form

Law of constant composition Chemical compounds always break down to produce a constant percentage of each element present

Law of multiple proportions When two elements (say A and B) form more than one compound, the weight of A divided by the weight of B in each compound must be multiples of each other

Le Chatelier's principle Whenever a stress is placed on an equilibrium system, the system will shift in order to relieve the stress

Lecithin Choline phosphoglyceride found in cell membranes

Levorotatory (−) Rotating the plane of polarized light in the counterclockwise direction

Lipase Enzyme that catalyzes hydrolysis of lipids by attacking ester linkages between fatty acids and glycerol

Lipid Compound in living tissue that is soluble in nonpolar solvents

Lipogenesis Biosynthesis of fatty acids from acetyl-CoA

Lipolysis Breakdown of lipids by hydrolysis

Lipoprotein Protein attached to a fat

Liquid Physical state of a substance in which it takes the shape but not the volume of its container

Liter (L) Volume unit; 1 L = 1000 mL = 1 dm^3 = 1000 cm^3

Local anesthetic Compound (usually an amine) that temporarily blocks nerve conduction

Lock-and-key theory Enzyme activity theory stating that the enzyme and substrate fit together like a lock and key

Macroscopic Large enough to be observed with the eye

Markovnikov's rule Rule stating that in the addition of H-containing compounds across a double bond, the H adds to the double-bonded C that already contains the most H atoms

Mass Measure of a body's resistance to motion (inertia)

Mass number (A) Sum of the number of protons and neutrons in the nucleus of an atom and indicated by a superscript at upper left of the element symbol (^{A}E)

Mass percent composition Percentage of each element present in a compound (also called weight percent composition)

Matter Anything that has mass and occupies space

Medium-chain triglyceride (MCT) Triacylglycerol fats in which the fatty acid chains are 6 to 10 C atoms in length

Melting point (mp) Temperature at which a solid becomes a liquid

Mercaptan Sulfur alcohol, RSH with the hydroxyl oxygen atom of the alcohol replaced by a sulfur atom); thiol

Meso isomer Stereoisomer that can be superimposed upon its mirror image and is not optically active

Messenger RNA (mRNA) RNA molecules that copy the genetic message of DNA and carry it to the ribosomes

Meta (*m*-) Term describing a 1,3-disubstituted benzene (and prefix replacing 1,3- in the name)

Metabolism Chemical reactions in living things

Metabolite Product of metabolic change

Meter (m) Base unit of length in the SI system; 1 m = 1000 mm = 100 cm = 0.001 km

Micelle Spherical structure such as that formed by soap or detergent molecules in which their hydrocarbon tails are oriented toward each other and their polar ends are dissolved in the surrounding water

Microscopic Invisible to the naked eye

Milliliter (ml) Volume unit; 1 ml = 1/1000 L = 1 cm^3

Mineral Element other than C, H, O, N needed by humans; may be Ca, P, Mg, Fe, Cu, Zn, or I

Mitochondrion Site of respiration found within the cytoplasm of the cell

Mixture Combination of substances that can be separated from each other without breaking any chemical bonds

Molality (*m*) Concentration unit, moles of solute per kilogram of solvent

Molarity (*M* or []) Most common concentration unit used by chemists, moles of solute per liter of solution

Mole (mol) Amount of substance containing 6.02×10^{23} units and having a mass in grams which is numerically equal to its formula weight

Molecular crystal Crystal formed by a covalent compound in which lattice positions are occupied by molecules

Molecular formula Formula which gives the actual number of each kind of atom in one molecule of the compound

Molecular geometry Three-dimensional description of a molecule in which correct bond angles are shown

Molecular orbital Orbital formed by the combination of two atomic orbitals

Molecule Collection of two or more atoms joined by chemical bonds

Monomer Small molecule that links with others to form a giant polymer molecule

Monosaccharide Carbohydrate that cannot be broken down into smaller carbohydrates

Multiple bond Covalent bond that includes more than one shared electron pair

Mutarotation Change in the rotation angle of polarized light when a pair of anomers is mixed

Mutation Change in the base order sequence of DNA that changes the genetic code information

NAD^+ Nicotinamide adenine dinucleotide, a coenzyme derived from niacin, which takes part in oxidation-reduction reactions by removing hydrogen atoms from substrates: $NAD^+ + SH_2 \rightarrow NADH^+ + H^+ + S$

$NADP^+$ Nicotinamide adenine dinucleotide phosphate, a coenzyme derived from niacin, which functions like NAD^+

Narcotic analgesic Substance that kills pain and causes central nervous system depression

Neutralization Reaction of an acid with a base

Neutral solution Aqueous solution in which $[H_3O^+] = [OH^-]$, $[H_3O^+] = 10^{-7}$, and pH = 7

Neutron (*n*) Subatomic particle with a mass of 1.675×10^{-24} g (about 1 amu) and a charge of zero; found in the nucleus of the atom

Niacin Nicotinic acid, a B vitamin required to prevent pellagra (see also NAD^+ and $NADP^+$)

Nicotinamide Amide of nicotinic acid that forms the coenzymes NAD^+ and $NADP^+$

Nitrile Organic compound containing the cyano group (—C≡N, or —CN) and having the general formula RCN

Nitrogen bases Heterocyclic N compounds, including the purine derivatives adenine and guanine and the pyrimidine derivatives cytosine, thymine, and uracil

Nitrogen fixation Conversion of atmospheric nitrogen (N_2) to useful nitrogen compounds

Nitrogen heterocyclic Cyclic compound in which one or more ring atoms are nitrogens

Noble gas Element in group 0 of periodic table

Noncompetitive inhibitor Enzyme inhibitor with a structure very different from that of the substrate

Nonpolar bond Covalent bond in which electrons are equally shared by both atoms

Nonpolar molecule Molecule in which all bonds are nonpolar or in which polarities of any polar bonds cancel each other

Nonreducing sugar Sugar (such as sucrose) that is not oxidized by Benedict's solution (see also Reducing sugar)

Nonspecific inhibitor Agent that inhibits enzymes by denaturing them

Normal (*n*-) Term (and prefix) used to indicate straight-chain alkanes in the common naming system

Normal boiling point Boiling point measured at an external pressure of 760 mmHg (see also Boiling point)

Normality (*N*) Concentration unit, equivalents per liter of solution (see also Gram equivalent weight)

Nuclear fission Splitting of an atom producing two smaller atoms, two or three neutrons, and a tremendous amount of energy

Nuclear fusion Joining of smaller nuclei to form larger nuclei, accompanied by emission of enormous energy

Nuclear medicine Use of radioactive isotopes to diagnose and treat patients

Nucleoside Sugar combined with a nitrogen base

Nucleotide Monomer unit of nucleic acids, consisting of sugar, nitrogen base, and phosphoric acid components

Nucleus The tiny volume of the atom, in which the protons and neutrons are found, that includes more than 99.95 percent of the atomic mass

Nylon Polyamide made from the reaction of a diamine with a diacid

Octet rule Rule stating that each atom in a covalent bond must be surrounded by eight electrons (or by two electrons in case of hydrogen)

Open-chain sugar Noncyclic form of monosaccharides

Optical isomers Compounds that are nonsuperimposable mirror images of each other

Organic chemistry The chemistry of carbon compounds

Ortho (*o*-) Term describing a 1,2-disubstituted benzene (and prefix replacing 1,2- in the name)

Osmolarity Concentration unit related to molarity (*M*): osmolarity = $i \times$ molarity, where i = number of ions produced per unit of solute

Osmosis Movement of solvent from a less concentrated solution through a semipermeable membrane into a more concentrated solution

Osmotic pressure (Π) Pressure that must be applied to a solution to stop the flow of solvent through a semipermeable membrane; $\Pi V = nRT$

Oxidation number Number assigned

to an atom in order to keep track of electrons transferred in a reaction
Oxidation-reduction reaction Reaction in which there is a net transfer of electrons; also called redox reaction
Oxidative deamination Reaction in which an amino acid loses its amino group to produce ammonia and a keto acid
Oxidative phosphorylation Addition of inorganic phosphate to ADP to form ATP, with energy provided by oxidation reactions of the respiratory chain
Oxidizing agent Substance that gains electrons in a chemical reaction
Oxytocin Nonapeptide hormone, which regulates uterine contractions and lactation

Para (p-) Term describing a 1,4-disubstituted benzene (and prefix replacing 1,4- in the name)
Parent isotope The original isotope in a transmutation
Partial pressure Pressure that a gas in a gaseous mixture would exert if that gas occupied the container by itself
Pendant group Substituent attached to the main chain of a polymer molecule
Peptide linkage Amide linkage that joins two amino acids, $\text{—}\overset{\text{O}}{\overset{\|}{\text{C}}}\text{—NH—}$
Period Horizontal row of the periodic table
Periodic table Table of elements arranged according to increasing atomic number
Peroxide (organic) Relatively unstable oxygen-containing organic compound with the general formula R—O—O—R
pH Convenient way to express acidity; $pH = -\log [H_3O^+]$
Phenols Derivatives of phenol (hydroxybenzene)
Phenyl (ϕ or Ph) Name of the substituent formed by removal of an H atom from benzene
Phenylketonuria (PKU) Disorder caused by the lack of the enzyme that catalyzes conversion of phenylalanine to tyrosine
Phosphoglyceride Lipid compound that includes a glycerol backbone attached to two fatty acids and to one phosphoric acid esterified with an alcohol
Photon Packet of light energy
Photosynthesis Process by which plants use CO_2, H_2O, and energy from sunlight to produce glucose; reverse of the catabolism of glucose
Physical change Change that occurs without the breaking or forming of chemical bonds
Physical property Property of a substance that can be observed without causing it to undergo a chemical reaction
Physical state The state of matter of a substance, i.e., solid, liquid or gas
Pi bond (π) Molecular orbital formed from the side-by-side overlap of two p atomic orbitals
Plane-polarized light Light consisting of waves all aligned in a single plane
Plasma membrane Wall about 6 to 10 nm thick that surrounds the protoplasm in a cell
Plasmid Circular DNA molecule that can readily be removed from a bacterium and reintroduced into it; used for making hybrid recombinant DNA
Polar covalent bond Covalent bond in which electrons are not equally shared by both atoms
Polar molecule Molecule containing polar bonds whose polarities do not cancel
Polyatomic ion Ion containing more than one kind of atom
Polyester Polymer made by reaction of a diol with a diacid
Polyhydric alcohol Alcohol containing more than one hydroxyl group
Polymer Giant molecule made up of smaller molecules called monomers
Polypeptide Molecule consisting of α-amino acid units joined by peptide linkages
Polysaccharide Polymer, such as starch and cellulose, that consists of monosaccharide monomers
Porphyrin Nitrogen heterocyclic compound present in naturally occurring compounds such as chlorophyll, heme, and vitamin B_{12}
Positron (β^+) Particle with the mass of an electron and a +1 charge
Precipitate Insoluble compound that forms in a reaction taking place in solution
Primary alcohol Alcohol in which the hydroxyl group is bonded to a C atom which itself is bonded to only one other C atom
Primary amine Amine in which one ammonia H atom is replaced by a hydrocarbon group, RNH_2
Primary structure (of proteins) Sequence of amino acids in a protein molecule
Principal quantum number Integer (1, 2, 3, 4 . . .) used to label a principal energy level of electrons in an atom
Product New substance produced as a result of a chemical reaction
Prostaglandins Lipid compounds that have hormonal activity and are thought to cause pain
Protease Enzyme that catalyzes protein hydrolysis
Protein Polypeptide containing more than about 40 amino acids
Proteolysis Breakdown of proteins by hydrolysis
Proton (p) Subatomic particle with a mass of 1.673×10^{-24} g (about 1 amu) and a charge of $+1.60 \times 10^{-19}$ C (+1), which is found in the nucleus of the atom
Pyranose Cyclic sugar with six-membered pyranlike ring
Pyrolysis Breakdown of a large alkane into a mixture of smaller hydrocarbons by heating under high pressure; cracking reaction

Qualitative Involving the presence or absence of a substance
Quantitative Involving a measured amount of a substance
Quaternary ammonium salt Salt in which the cation NR_4^+ includes a nitrogen atom bonded to four alkyl groups
Quaternary structure (of proteins) Aggregation of more than one polypeptide chain to form a protein molecule, as in hemoglobin

Racemic mixture (DL) or (±) 50-50 mixture of two enantiomers; racemate
Rad Absorbed dose of radiation accompanied by the liberation of 10^{-5} J per gram of absorbing material
Radioactive series Sequence of spontaneous decay processes which eventually leads to a stable nonradioactive isotope
Radioisotopes Atoms containing unstable nuclei which undergo spon-

taneous and continuous emission of particles

Rancidification Oxidation of an unsaturated fat, producing compounds with unpleasant odors and tastes

Reactant Original substance involved in a chemical reaction

Reaction mechanism The way in which bonds between atoms in reactants are modified to form new bonds between product atoms

Real gas Gas that does not obey the ideal gas law

Receptor site Site that must interact with certain drugs, such as narcotic analgesics, to produce an effect

Reducing agent Substance that loses electrons in a chemical reaction

Reducing sugar Sugar that can be oxidized by Benedict's solution, including all monosaccharides

Relative humidity Actual amount of water in air divided by the maximum possible amount (generally expressed as a percentage)

Rem Dose of radiation absorbed by tissue exposed to 1 roentgen of γ-radiation; roentgen equivalent man

Repeating unit Unit of a polymer that is repeated throughout the polymer chain

Replication Behavior of an unraveled DNA strand in serving as a template for a new complementary strand

Representative element Element with highest-energy electrons in *s* or *p* orbitals, found in the A groups of the periodic table

Resonance structures Two or more structures used to represent a single compound and separated from each other by a double-headed arrow $\leftrightarrow$

Respiratory chain Series of electron carriers involved in the final stage of respiration

Reversible reaction Reaction that proceeds in both the forward and reverse directions; extent of reaction <100 percent

Riboflavin Ribose derivative bonded to a flavin ring; vitamin B_2 (see also flavoenzyme and FAD)

Ribonucleic acid (RNA) Nucleic acid consisting of the four monomer component nucleotides AMP, UMP, CMP, and GMP and the sugar ribose

Ribose Aldopentose found in RNA

Ribosome Site of protein synthesis consisting half of ribosomal RNA and half of protein

Roentgen (R) Quantity of γ- or x-radiation that produces 2.08×10^9 ion pairs in 1 cm^3 air; a measure of exposure to γ- or x-radiation

Rotation angle (α) Angle through which an optically active sample rotates plane-polarized light

Saponification Base-catalyzed hydrolysis of an ester

Saturated fat Fat containing approximately equal amounts of saturated and unsaturated fatty acids

Saturated hydrocarbon Hydrocarbon with no multiple bonds

Scan Recorded observation showing the distribution of radioisotopes within the body

Scientific method Use of experimental observations to develop theories

Secondary alcohol Alcohol in which the hydroxyl group is bonded to a carbon atom which itself is bonded to two other C atoms

Secondary amine Amine in which two ammonia H atoms are replaced by hydrocarbon groups, RNHR′

Secondary structure (of proteins) Shapes, such the α-helix and β-pleated sheet, that are adopted by a protein as a result of hydrogen bonding within polypeptide chains

Semipermeable membrane Membrane that allows small solvent molecules such as water to pass but not larger solute molecules or ions

SI base units Set of units for seven independent physical quantities from which units for all other physical quantities can be derived

SI derived units Units derived from SI base units by multiplication or division

Significant figures Those figures in a number that are correct, that is, the results of a measurement

SI (unit system) International System of Units, consisting of SI units and SI prefixes

Silicone rubber Strong and chemically inert polymer made by linking silicon-containing polymer chains together

Siloxane The —O—Si—O—Si— backbone of a silicone polymer

Single bond Covalent bond in which one electron pair is shared; indicated by a dash, as in the formula for water H—O—H

Soap Na or K salt of long-chain carboxylic acid, having both polar and nonpolar character and able to form micelles (see also Micelle)

Solid Physical state of a substance in which it takes neither the shape nor the volume of its container

Solubility The maximum amount of a given solute that can be dissolved in a particular solvent to make a solution

Solute The dispersed medium and usually the less-abundant component of a solution

Solution Homogeneous mixture containing particles that range in size between 0.1 and 10 nm

Solvent The dispersing medium and usually the component of a solution that is most abundant

Specific gravity Density of a substance divided by the density of water in the same units

Specific heat Amount of heat needed to raise the temperature of 1 g of a substance by 1°C; specific heat of water = 1 cal/(g)(°C) = 4.18 J/(g)(°C)

Specific inhibitor Substance that interferes with the activity of a particular enzyme

Specific rotation ([α]) Rotation angle measured at a specified concentration, temperature, light source, and sample cell length (see also Rotation angle)

Sphingolipid Lipid containing the ceramide structure (sphingosine + fatty acid)

Sphingosine Backbone molecule present in sphingolipids

Spontaneous reaction Reaction that tends to proceed in the forward direction

Spontaneous transmutation Nuclear decay process in which a parent isotope spontaneously emits radiation to form a new daughter isotope

***sp* Hybrid orbital** Hybrid atomic orbital produced by the mixing of one *s* orbital and one *p* orbital

sp^2 Hybrid orbital Hybrid atomic orbital produced by the mixing of one *s* orbital and two *p* orbitals

sp^3 Hybrid orbital Hybrid atomic orbital produced by the mixing of one *s* orbital and three *p* orbitals

Stability zone Range of *N*/*Z* ratios for which isotopes could be stable

Starch Polysaccharide formed by α-glycosidic linkages between glucose monomers

Stereoisomers Compounds which differ only in their spatial arrangements, including geometric isomers and optical isomers

Steroid Derivative of a specific hydrocarbon ring system including three six-membered rings and one five-membered ring

Stoichiometry Measurement of quantities involved in chemical reactions

Straight chain C to C chain in which all C atoms are bonded together in a single continuous chain with no branching

Strong acid Acid that is 100 percent ionized

Strong base Base that is 100 percent ionized

Structural formula Formula that indicates how atoms in a molecule are bonded to one another

Structural isomers Two or more compounds which have the same molecular formulas but different arrangements of atoms (different structural formulas)

Subatomic particle Particle such as the electron, proton, and neutron, which are smaller than the smallest atom

Sublimation Conversion of a solid directly to a gas (vapor) when energetic solid molecules escape from the solid phase to the gaseous phase

Substituted amide Amide in which one or both amide H atoms are replaced by hydrocarbon groups, as in $R{-}C(=O){-}NHR'$ and $R{-}C(=O){-}NR'R''$

Substitution reaction Reaction in which a hydrogen atom in an organic molecule is replaced with some other atom or group of atoms

Substrate (S) Biochemical reactant compound

Substrate level phosphorylation Formation of ATP from ADP by addition of a phosphate provided by a substrate in a metabolic pathway

Sucrose Disaccharide consisting of fructose and glucose; table sugar

Sulfa drug Antibacterial drug derived from sulfanilamide, $NH_2{-}C_6H_4{-}SO_2NH_2$

Sulfide (organic) Sulfur ether, $R{-}S{-}R'$

Sulfonic acid Sulfur-containing organic acid with the general formula RSO_3H

Sulfoxide Organic sulfur compound with the general formula $R{-}S(=O){-}R'$

Surface tension Resistance of a liquid surface to being broken

Terpene Naturally occurring compound that includes isoprene ($CH_2{=}C(CH_3){-}CH{=}CH_2$) fragments; type of lipid

Tertiary alcohol Alcohol in which the hydroxyl group is bonded to a carbon atom which itself is bonded to three other C atoms

Tertiary amine Amine in which three ammonia H atoms are replaced by hydrocarbon groups, $R{-}N(R''){-}R'$

Tertiary structure (of proteins) Bending and folding of protein molecules due to interactions among R side groups

Tetrahedron Solid figure with four faces; tetrahedral angle $\approx 109°$

Thermochemistry Study of the heat changes that accompany chemical reactions

Thiamine Vitamin B_1, a compound that leads to the coenzyme thiamine pyrophosphate and is required to prevent beri-beri

Thiol Sulfur alcohol, RSH (with the hydroxyl oxygen atom of the alcohol replaced by a sulfur atom); mercaptan

Thymine (T) Nitrogen base derived from pyrimidine and found in DNA

Titration Method used to find the concentration of a substance in solution by its reaction with a solution of known concentration

Tollens' test Test for an aldehyde by reducing Ag^+ to Ag, which appears as a silver mirror; silver mirror test

Torr Pressure unit; 1 torr = 1 mmHg; 760 torr = 1 atm

Trans (*trans-*) Term (and prefix) used to refer to the geometric isomer of an alkene, XYC═CYX in which the X's are on the opposite sides of the double bond, $(Y)(X)C{=}C(X)(Y)$

Transaminase Enzyme that catalyzes transamination reactions and is used to detect liver and heart disorders

Transamination Reaction in which an NH_2 group from one amino acid is transferred to a keto acid to form a new amino acid

Transcription The process of creating mRNA from DNA

Transfer RNA (tRNA) Coiled RNA molecule that transfers amino acids to the ribosomes

Transistor Device made of a semiconductor that is used to direct electron flow

Transition element Element in which highest-energy electrons are in *d* orbitals; in B groups of the periodic table

Transuranium element Element with atomic number > 92

Triacylglycerol Molecule consisting of glycerol esterified with three fatty acids; triglyceride or fat

Tricarboxylic acid Compound containing three carboxyl groups, such as citric acid

Tricarboxylic acid cycle (TCA cycle) The first stage of respiration, in which acetyl-CoA is converted to CO_2, hydrogen pairs, and CoA; Krebs cycle

Triple bond Covalent bond in which three electron pairs are shared; indicated by three dashes between the bonded atoms, as in C≡C and C≡N

Triple helix Protein secondary structure in which three polypeptide chains are wrapped around each other

Uncertainty The smallest division that can be measured on a particular device

Unsaturated fat Fat containing more than 80 percent unsaturated fatty acids, as compared with saturated fatty acids

Unsaturated hydrocarbon Hydrocarbon containing one or more multiple bond(s)

Uracil (U) Nitrogen base derived from pyrimidine and found in RNA

Urea The compound $NH_2{-}C(=O){-}NH_2$ (see also Urea cycle)

Urea cycle Pathway by which toxic ammonia is converted to nontoxic urea, a compound that is eliminated in the urine

Valence electrons Bonding electrons, usually the electrons in the highest energy level of an atom
Vapor Gaseous phase of a substance that is a liquid or a solid under ordinary conditions
Vapor pressure Pressure exerted by gas molecules produced by evaporation of a liquid
Vasopressin Nonapeptide hormone that regulates water balance in the body
Viscosity Resistance of fluids to flow
Vitamin A Retinol, a fat-soluble vitamin involved in the visual cycle
Vitamin B_1 See Thiamine
Vitamin B_2 See Riboflavin
Vitamin B_6 Pyridoxine, a water-soluble vitamin involved in the transfer of amino groups
Vitamin B_{12} Cobalt porphyrin derivative required for normal production of red blood cells and prevention of pernicious anemia
Vitamin C Ascorbic acid; needed to prevent scurvy
Vitamin D Fat-soluble vitamin derived from cholesterol, which is needed for proper Ca and P metabolism and prevention of rickets
Vitamin E α-Tocopherol, a fat-soluble vitamin derived from phenol, which acts as an antioxidant
Vitamin K Fat-soluble vitamin derived from quinone that plays a role in blood clotting

Water-soluble vitamin The B group of vitamins and vitamin C, all of which are soluble in water
Wax (lipid) Ester formed from long-chain fatty acids and high-molecular-weight alcohols
Wax (paraffin) High-molecular-weight alkane mixture
Weak acid Acid that is much less than 100 percent ionized
Weak base Base that is much less than 100 percent ionized
Wedge and dash structure (—C—) Formula used to represent structures of optical isomers, in which wedges indicate groups coming out of the plane of the paper and dashes those extending behind it
Weight Amount of matter that depends upon the gravitational force at the place of measurement; weight = mass × gravitational acceleration (see also Mass)
Weight percent Concentration unit %

$$w/w = \frac{\text{weight solute}}{\text{weight solution}} \times 100\%$$

x-Radiation Electromagnetic radiation of wavelength about 1 nm

Zwitterion Ion containing both a positive and a negative charge, such as that formed from an amino acid, $RCHCOO^-$ (with $^+NH_3$ on the C); dipolar ion
Zymogen Inactive enzyme that is activated by the loss of a segment of its polypeptide chain

ANSWERS

The following are answers to all in-chapter exercises and only odd-numbered end-of-chapter exercises.

CHAPTER 1

1.1 0.03 pg, no
1.2 8 g/cm^3; it is not silver.
1.3 0.35 lb.
1.4 6.00 μg/ml blood.
1.5 0.8 m^2.
1.6 1.3 g/cm^3. No, the gem is not a diamond.
1.7 930 ml.
1.9 (*a*) mm; (*b*) μg; (*c*) cmol; (*d*) dg; (*e*) ns.
1.11 A 1-g mass is too small to be reproduced accurately.
1.13 No. The ångstrom unit = 10^{-10} m.
1.15 10^{-18}.
1.17 1μ = 1 μm; 1 mμ = 1 nm.
1.19 (*a*) 25°C; (*b*) 39.4°C; (*c*) −40°C; this is the temperature at which °F = °C.
1.21 (*a*) 10 g/cm^3, specific gravity = 10; (*b*) 1.59 g/cm^3, specific gravity = 1.59; (*c*) 8 g/cm^3, specific gravity = 8.
1.23 10^{-3} $cm^3/\mu L$.
1.25 Density = 19.3 g/cm^3; yes
1.27 Density = 2 g/cm^3; therefore it is not a ruby.
1.29 A urinometer is a special type of hydrometer.
1.31 91 cm^3 acetone and 316 cm^3 isopropyl alcohol.
1.33 Yes, copper which has a density of 9.0 g/ml.
1.35 *a* and *d*
1.37 (*a*) 52.2 kg; (*b*) 907.44 kg (to five significant figures; since 1 ton is defined to be exactly 2000 lb, we can use as many significant figures as we like); (*c*) 3.4 kg.
1.39 1 dram = 3.89 g.
1.41 (*a*) 0.106 oz. (*b*) The volume of the diamond lies between the values 0.86 cm^3 and 1.0 cm^3.
1.43 1.1 g/cm^3. Yes, the density of salt water is greater than that of pure water, which has a density of 1 g/cm^3.

1.45 d = 10^{-1} and thus 1 dL = 0.1 L; 1 dL < 1 L, and 1 dL > ml
1.47 Compare the densities of the liquids by weighing each sample. Since their volumes are identical, the one that weighs the most has the highest density and must be chloroform (Table 1.5). The one that weighs the least is corn oil and the middle one is glycerol.
1.49 Body surface area = 0.84 m^2 and dose = 120 mg.
1.51 465 ml/day.
1.53 220 g.
1.55 Mercury has an unusually high density (13.6 g/cm^3); 9.19 cm^3.
1.57 Yes, 1 lb of glycerol has a volume of 0.76 pint.

CHAPTER 2

2.1 50°F = 10°C, melting point = 16.6°C, solid.
2.2 No. Chromatography does not cause a chemical change.
2.3 0.22-g carbon dioxide forms.
2.4 8.95 kcal = 8.95 Cal.
2.5 Copper and silver (lowest specific heats). Copper is the most practical, because silver is expensive.
2.6 10,700 kJ = 2560 Cal.
2.7 (*a*) x-rays have lowest wavelength, highest frequency and most energy per photon.
2.9 (*a*) Physical only; (*b*) physical only; (*c*) chemical only; (*d*) physical only; (*e*) physical and chemical.
2.11 (*b*) Salt water is a mixture (water is a compound).
2.13 (*a*) Tristearin; (*b*) butane; no.
2.15 No, rust is a compound.
2.17 Cyclohexane and benzene; chromatography.
2.19 Ice in water.
2.21 18,000 g; law of conservation of matter.
2.23 (*c*) Insulin. (The others are all mixtures.)
2.25 48,000 cal; 48 kcal = 48 Cal; 201,000 J.
2.27 1434 cal.
2.29 58 J = 14 cal.
2.31 Specific heat = 0.21 cal/g°C; aluminum.
2.33 0.67 J/g°C; More heat is required to heat the wood (specific heat = 1.8 J/g°C).
2.35 (*a*) E is directly proportional to frequency ν; (*b*) E is inversely proportional to wavelength λ.
2.37 UV photons are highly energetic and thus capable of causing damage to tissue.
2.39 (*a*) 36 kcal/(m^2)(h); (*b*) 1400 kcal/day and 5800 kJ/day; (*c*) The calculated value of 5600 kJ is close to 5800 kJ, the experimental value.

CHAPTER 3

3.1 I_2.
3.2 K, potassium.
3.3 U-235: 92 protons, 92 electrons, 143 neutrons.
U-238: 92 protons, 92 electrons, 146 neutrons.
3.4 Helium, He (atomic weight = 4.0).
3.5 63.5.

3.6 151.9.

3.7 K) $1s^22s^22p^63s^23p^64s^1$.

3.8 ns^2.

3.9 *a* with 2, *b* with 3, *c* with 1.

3.11 (*a*) iron; (*b*) sodium; (*c*) sulfur; (*d*) carbon; (*e*) potassium; (*f*) technetium; (*g*) lead.

3.13 (*a*) 2 lithium, 1 sulfur; (*b*) 3 barium, 2 phosphorus, 8 oxygen; (*c*) 2 nitrogen, 4 hydrogen, 2 oxygen; (*d*) 2 carbon, 4 hydrogen, 2 oxygen; (*e*) 1 sodium, 1 uranium, 8 oxygen, 6 carbon, 9 hydrogen; (*f*) 3 calcium, 2 arsenic; (*g*) 1 nickel, 2 iodine, 6 oxygen

3.15 +3 unit charges or 4.8×10^{-19} C.

3.17 (*a*) 6; (*b*) 13; (*c*) 82; (*d*) 92; (*e*) 19.

3.19 (*a*) 2*p*, 2*e*, 2*n*; (*b*) 11*p*, 11*e*, 11*n*; (*c*) 38*p*, 38*e*, 52*n*; (*d*) 6*p*, 6*e*, 8*n*; (*e*) 82*p*, 82*e*, 124*n*

3.21 (*a*) No; (*b*) yes; (*c*) yes.

3.23 Because natural carbon contains 1.11% C-13.

3.25 12.01.

3.27 8.3. It makes the atomic weight of the lightest element H close to 1.

3.29 (*a*) 253.8; (*b*) 48.0; (*c*) 256.5.

3.31 See Table 3.6.

3.33 (*a*) 2 (*b*) 0 (*c*) 1

3.35 (*a*) spherical-shaped; (*b*) dumbell-shaped.

3.37 (*a*) ns^2np^1; (*b*) $ns^2np_x{}^1np_y{}^1$ (*c*) $ns^2np_x{}^1np_y{}^1np_z{}^1$; (*d*) $ns^2np_x{}^2np_y{}^1np_z{}^1$.

3.39 The repeating of chemical properties of elements with a regular change in their atomic number such as the similarity of an element to another element eight atomic number units away (for elements 3–18).

3.41 Mercury and neon have emission spectra composed of discrete lines of color; light from the sun or a lamp includes a continuous "rainbow" of colors

3.43 Calcium found in bones and teeth.

3.45 Atomic spectrum of lead.

CHAPTER 4

4.1 Ca: $1s^22s^22p^63s^23p^64s^2$.
Ca^{2+}: $1s^22s^22p^63s^23p^6$, calcium ion.
S: $1s^22s^22p^63s^23p^4$.
S^{2-}: $1s^22s^22p^63s^23p^6$, sulfide ion; Ar: $1s^22s^22p^63s^23p^6$.

4.2 CaS, calcium sulfide.

4.3 $Mg(OH)_2$.

4.4 H:C̈l: (Lewis structure: H shares a pair with Cl, which carries three lone pairs)

4.5 Lewis structure of $SiBr_4$: Si in the center, bonded by shared pairs to four Br atoms, each Br with three lone pairs:
```
      :Br:
:Br : Si : Br:
      :Br:
```

4.6 :N:::N:

4.7 Tetrahedral.

4.8 (*a*) With 2; (*b*) with 3; (*c*) with 1.

4.9 Ionic compounds have higher melting points and higher electric conductivity than covalent compounds.

4.11 K^+: $1s^22s^22p^63s^23p^6$, potassium ion, Ar.
Ca^{2+}: $1s^22s^22p^63s^23p^6$, calcium ion, Ar.
S^{2-}: $1s^22s^22p^63s^23p^6$, sulfide, Ar.

4.13 Cu^+

4.15 (*a*) $BaCl_2$; (*b*) Na_2O; (*c*) KI; (*d*) AlF_3; (*e*) $RaCl_2$; (*f*) Na_2S.
4.17 (*a*) $CaCO_3$; (*b*) Na_3PO_4; (*c*) $CaSO_4$; (*d*) $CaSO_3$; (*e*) Na_2SO_3; (*f*) $AgNO_3$.
4.19 (*a*) Sodium hypochlorite; (*b*) sodium chlorite; (*c*) sodium chlorate; (*d*) sodium perchlorate; (*e*) sodium hypoiodite; (*f*) sodium iodite; (*g*) sodium iodate; (*h*) sodium periodate.
4.21 (*a*) potassium iodide; (*b*) lithium oxide; (*c*) strontium iodide; (*d*) iron(II) bromide or ferrous bromide; (*e*) iron(III)bromide or ferric bromide; (*f*) cesium chloride; (*g*) sodium sulfide; (*h*) copper(I) oxide or cuprous oxide.
4.23 Gold(III) chloride, auric chloride.
4.25 (*a*) 5; (*b*) 7; (*c*) 6; (*d*) 6.
4.27 (*a*) Hydrogen iodide; (*b*) dichlorine or chlorine; (*c*) hydrogen selenide; (*d*) carbon tetrabromide; (*e*) phosphorus triiodide.

4.29
```
  ˙O˙
   ::
 H:C:H
```

4.31 Sodium chloride, NaCl — Sulfur dichloride, SCl_2
Calcium fluoride, CaF_2 — Ammonia, NH_3
Potassium sulfate, K_2SO_4 — Water, H_2O
Magnesium oxide, MgO — Carbon tetrachloride, CCl_4
Radium bromide, $RaBr_2$ — Phosphorus triiodide, PI_3
Barium nitrate, $Ba(NO_3)_2$ — Arsenic tribromide, $AsBr_3$
4.33 Ionic compounds exist in giant crystal lattices in which no one cation belongs to any particular anion.

4.35
```
  F   F
   . .
 F:S:F
   ..
```

No, there are 10 electrons around S.

4.37 *b*, because it includes a triple bond.
4.39 *b* and *c*
4.41 As an iodide compound (such as sodium iodide or potassium iodide).
4.43 *b*
4.45 *b*, higher molecular weight.
4.47 Predicts molecular formulas of many existing compounds, existence of multiple bonds and molecular shapes (molecular geometry).
4.49 Ferrous wheel

CHAPTER 5

5.1 23.0 g.
5.2 0.387 g.
5.3 0.0024 mol or 2.4×10^{-3} mol.
5.4 1.13×10^{23}.
5.5 2.00×10^{-23} g.
5.6 0.813 mol or 8.13×10^{-3} mol.
5.7 40.0% C, 6.7% H, and 53.3% O.
5.8 *a* and 3, *b* and 2, *c* and 1.
5.9 $C_9H_{18}O$.
5.10 CH_3O.
5.11 $C_{16}H_{32}O_2 + 24O_2 \longrightarrow 16CO_2 + 16H_2O$.
5.12 470 g N_2.
5.13 21.0 g N_2.

5.15 (*a*) 12.0 g; (*b*) 254 g; (*c*) 32.0 g; (*d*) 48.0 g; (*e*) 42.5 g; (*f*) 602 g; (*g*) 296 g; (*h*) 180 g.
5.17 0.0180 g.
5.19 7.77 mol.
5.21 1.91×10^{16}.
5.23 (*a*) 1.37×10^{24}; (*b*) 4.24×10^{23}; (*c*) 1.76×10^{23}.
5.25 (*a*) 2.82×10^{-23} g; (*b*) 3.27×10^{-22} g.
5.27 (*a*) 1; (*b*) 1; (*c*) 6; (*d*) 6; (*e*) 1; (*f*) 2.
5.29 0.00590 mol $AgNO_3$, 5.5 mol H_2O.
5.31 (*a*) 0.015 mol KCl; (*b*) 0.00401 mol $KHCO_3$; (*c*) 5.0×10^{-4} mol K_2CO_3; total mol K = 0.020.
5.33 84.5 mol Fe.
5.35 (*a*) 32.0 g; (*b*) 5.32×10^{-23} g; (*c*) 3.12 mol; (*d*) 12.0×10^{23} atoms; (*e*) 6.02×10^{23} molecules.
5.37 (*a*) %C = 27.3, %O = 72.7; (*b*) %N = 43.8, %H = 6.2%, %O = 50.0%; (*c*) %Fe = 27.9, %S = 24.1, %O = 48.0; (*d*) %Na = 57.5, %O = 40.0%, %H = 2.5%.
5.39 62.4% C.
5.41 $C_6H_4Cl_2$.
5.43 (*a*) CH_3; (*b*) C_2H_6.
5.45 (*a*) $2Na + 2H_2O \longrightarrow 2NaOH + H_2$.
(*b*) $2Al + 3Br_2 \longrightarrow 2AlBr_3$.
(*c*) $H_2SO_4 + 2KOH \longrightarrow 2H_2O + K_2SO_4$.
(*d*) $2C_4H_{10} + 13O_2 \longrightarrow 8CO_2 + 10H_2O$.
(*e*) $C_{12}H_{24}O_2 + 17O_2 \longrightarrow 12CO_2 + 12H_2O$
5.47 (*a*) $NaHCO_3 + HCl \longrightarrow NaCl + H_2O + CO_2$.
(*b*) 3.00 mol; (*c*) 0.500 mol; (*d*) 1.67 mol; (*e*) 5.29 g.
5.49 (*a*) $CaCl_2 + Na_2CO_3 \longrightarrow CaCO_3 + 2NaCl$. (*b*) 320 g.
5.51 (*a*) $2H_2O_2 \longrightarrow 2H_2O + O_2$. (*b*) $\frac{1}{2}$ mol. (*c*) 1.41 g.

CHAPTER 6

6.1 (*a*) N/Z = 1, yes; (*b*) Z > 83, no; (*c*) N/Z < 1, no.
6.2 $^{63}_{28}Ni \longrightarrow {}^{63}_{29}Cu + {}^{0}_{-1}\beta$.
6.3 Positron, $^{0}_{1}\beta$.
6.4 $\frac{1}{8}$.
6.5 Gamma, $^{0}_{0}\gamma$.
6.7 (*a*) Ni-62; (*b*) Pb-206; (*c*) Si-28; (*d*) Mg-26; (*e*) F-18; (*f*) Mo-93.
6.9 $\alpha < \beta < \gamma$.
6.11 (*a*) Ra-226; (*b*) In-121; (*c*) Sr-83; (*d*) In-117m; (*e*) K-38; (*f*) Ne-19.
6.13 (*a*) $^{123}_{53}I + {}^{0}_{-1}e \longrightarrow {}^{123}_{52}Te$ (*b*) $^{113m}_{49}In \longrightarrow {}^{113}_{49}In + \gamma$ (*c*) $^{32}_{15}P \longrightarrow {}^{32}_{16}S + {}^{0}_{-1}\beta$.
6.15 (*a*) 28; (*b*) 2.5; (*c*) 5.
6.17 $\frac{1}{32}$.
6.19 11,400 years.
6.21 (*a*) In-113 (In-113m); (*b*) Tc-99 (Tc-99m).
6.23 Fe-60; since it has a longer half-life, a greater mass is needed to produce 3.7×10^{10} disintegrations in a second.
6.25 rem = rad × RBE (relative biological effect).
6.27 In artificial transmutation, the parent isotope is bombarded with particles to produce a daughter isotope; in spontaneous transmutation nuclei of the parent isotope decay spontaneously to form daughter isotopes.
6.29 Natural; otherwise the processes would not be very practical. 100% of P is P-31, 4.2% of S is S-34, and 10% of Co is Co-59.

6.31 (*a*) $^4_2\alpha$; (*b*) ^1_1p; (*c*) ^1_0n.
6.33 Relatively short $t_{\frac{1}{2}}$, γ emitter (see Section 6.13).
6.35 I-137 has a half-life of only 22 s.
6.37 $^{128}_{53}I + {}^{0}_{-1}e \longrightarrow {}^{128}_{52}Te$.
6.39 90 mrem (maximum) compared with about 100 mrem from background.
6.41 Tag the O atoms in the acid and see if they appear in the water product. (Or tag the O atoms in the alcohol and see where they appear.)
6.43 Obtaining the high temperatures needed to initiate the fusion reaction.
6.45 Kr-90.
6.47 Bones and teeth.
6.49 Cold spot.
6.51 They accumulate in the milk supply.
6.53 Uncharged neutrons are not repelled by nuclei.
6.55 Discovery of nuclear fission and of radioactivity.

CHAPTER 7

7.1 (*a*) 1.00 atm; (*b*) 762 torr.
7.2 It is halved.
7.3 It increases by 323/298 = 1.08.
7.4 0.602 L.
7.5 563 mmHg.
7.6 76.4 L.
7.7 No (69.9 mmHg is needed).
7.8 10 mol; no, since the T and V are the same for both gases.
7.9 22.0%.
7.11 72.6 kg.
7.13 (*a*) 1520 mmHg; (*b*) 762 mmHg; (*c*) 35.9 mmHg; (*d*) 300 mmHg; (*e*) 0.76 mmHg; (*f*) 0.0075 mmHg; (*g*) 750 mmHg; (*h*) 750 mmHg.
7.15 (*a*) 62.4; (*b*) 62.4.
7.17 25 cm^3.
7.19 13.0 L.
7.21 44.8 L.
7.23 9700 mmHg.
7.25 646 mmHg; halothane, cyclopropane, ether.
7.27 (*c*) higher pressure and lower temperature bring molecules closer together.
7.29 (*a*) $2C_4H_{10} + 13O_2 \longrightarrow 8CO_2 + 10H_2O$.
(*b*) $2C_4H_{10} + 9O_2 \longrightarrow 8CO + 10H_2O$.
7.31 Winter, because more hydrocarbon fuels are burned, thus producing more CO_2 product.
7.33 $ZnS + O_2 \longrightarrow Zn + SO_2$; 224 L.

CHAPTER 8

8.1 Yes.
8.3 (*a*) Vapor; (*b*) gas; (*c*) vapor; (*d*) vapor; (*e*) gas; (*f*) gas.
8.5 At high altitudes atmospheric pressure is reduced, water boils at a lower temperature, and cooking times must be increased.

8.7 The vapor pressure of mercury at room temperature is very low.

8.9 Boiling points are much more sensitive to external pressure than are melting points.

8.11 (*b*) BP ethanol = 78.5 and BP ether = 34.5 (BP carbon tetrachloride = 76.5).

8.13 Blood viscosity and blood pressure would both increase.

8.15 Has a high boiling point and expands when frozen; hydrogen-bonding between water molecules causes most of the unusual properties of water.

8.17 *a, c, d, f*.

8.19

```
     H
     |
  H—C—S
     |    \Cu
  H—C—S/
     |
  H—C—O—H
     |
     H
```

8.21 By binding it to a chelating agent.

8.23 Al_2O_3, aluminum oxide; rubies contain Cr impurities while sapphires contain both Fe and Ti.

8.25 Individuals with Wilson's disease cannot metabolize copper.

8.27 A compound (such as EDTA or demercaprol) that binds to a metal ion.

8.29 Very young children may eat inedible material such as paint chips containing lead. Blood samples are analyzed for lead by use of atomic spectroscopy.

8.31 The alkali metals react readily with H_2O and O_2.

8.33 Calcium is involved in bone and teeth development, blood clotting, muscle contraction, and nerve conduction.

CHAPTER 9

9.1 Unsaturated.

9.2 24 ml.

9.3 1.49 g.

9.4 5×10^{-4} mol.

9.5 1.04 m which is close to the molar concentration, 1.00 M.

9.6 9.1% NaCl.

9.7 15 ml.

9.8 100.14°C.

9.9 0.15 mol.

9.10 Hypotonic.

9.11

	Solvent	Solute
(*a*)	H_2O	NaCl
(*b*)	H_2O	CO_2
(*c*)	H_2O	Ethanol
(*d*)	Ag	Cu
(*e*)	He	O_2

9.13 (*a*) Unsaturated; (*b*) supersaturated; (*c*) unsaturated; (*d*) unsaturated; (*e*) unsaturated; (*f*) supersaturated.

9.15 Formation of two layers, since CCl_4 is nonpolar and $HOCH_2CH_2OH$ is polar.

9.17 (*a*) 0.556 m; (*b*) 1.0 m; (*c*) 0.556 m.

9.19 (*a*) 2M; (*b*) 1M; (*c*) 0.90M.

9.21 26.5% NaCl and 73.5% H_2O.

9.23 (*a*) 29.2 g NaOH; (*b*) 7.45 g KCl; (*c*) 17.6 g NaCl; (*d*) 36 g glucose.

9.25 *b*

9.27 See Figure 9.7.

9.29 (*a*) 0.250 atm; (*b*) 0.500 atm.

9.31 i × molarity.

9.33 The osmolarity of the solution is the same as that of the body fluid.

9.35 $T_f = -0.074°C$ and $T_b = 100.021°C$.

9.37 Water will flow out of swollen gums to the surrounding salt water.

9.39 Gases always dissolve to form true solutions.

9.41 Electrolytes can pass through capillary walls but not through semipermeable membranes.

9.43 To remove the waste material from the patient's blood and to maintain normal electrolyte concentration.

CHAPTER 10

10.1 $Na_2SO_4(aq) + Pb(NO_3)_2(aq) \longrightarrow 2NaCl(aq) + PbSO_4(s)$

10.2 (*a*) 0; (*b*) +4; (*c*) +2.

10.3 The oxidation number of C in C_2H_2 is −1 and changes to +4 in CO_2.

10.4 The oxidation number of mercury changes from Hg^{2+} to Hg^0; and the oxidation number of zinc changes from Zn^0 to Zn^{2+}, meaning that electrons have been transferred.

10.5 Calculated value: Protein 24 cal + fat 54 cal = 78 Cal.
Tabulated value: 80 Cal

10.6 $K_{eq} = \dfrac{[HI]^2}{[H_2][I_2]}$ toward product, HI, since K > 1.

10.7 Color gets darker.

10.9 $Ba(NO_3)_2(aq) + Na_2SO_4(aq) \longrightarrow \underline{BaSO_4} + 2NaNO_3(aq)$.

10.11 Redox reactions involve electron transfer.

10.13

	Reducing agent	Oxidizing agent
(*a*)	Mg	O_2
(*b*)	Mg	Cl_2
(*c*)	Sn	F_2
(*d*)	H_2	ZnO

10.15 ΔH depends on the initial reactant(s) and final product(s) and not on the reaction pathway.

10.17

	Calculated value	Tabulated value
(*a*)	233 cal	245 cal
(*b*)	100 cal	95 cal
(*c*)	54 cal	50 cal
(*d*)	120 cal	120 cal

10.19 On the microscopic (invisible) level there is change; however, it is not visible to the eye.

10.21 Energy barrier that must be climbed for reactants to become products; E_a catalyzed reaction $< E_a$ for uncatalyzed reaction.

10.23 Equilibrium systems shift to relieve stresses put upon them.

10.25 2, lowering the temperature shifts the reaction to the left to the reactants; a catalyst does not shift the equilibrium.

10.27 A catalyst changes the rate of both the forward and reverse reactions but does not shift the equilibrium.

10.29 A reaction that tends to proceed in the forward direction, that is, from reactants to products.

10.31 19; toward product.

CHAPTER 11

11.1 $\underset{\text{acid}}{HNO_3} + \underset{\text{base}}{H_2O} \longrightarrow \underset{\text{conj acid}}{H_3O^+} + \underset{\text{conj base}}{NO_3^-}$

11.2 Reaction 1.

11.3 $HClO + H_2O \rightleftharpoons H_3O^+ + ClO^-$

$$K_a = \frac{[H_3O^+][ClO^-]}{[HClO]}$$

11.4 Acidic, 2×10^{-7}.

11.5 2.3.

11.6 0.82.

11.7 13.7.

11.8 1.7.

11.9 56 (KOH) and 32.7 (H_3PO_4).

11.10 0.05M, 1.3.

11.11 4.74.

11.13 (*a*) $Zn + 2HCl \longrightarrow ZnCl_2 + H_2$.
(*b*) $H_2SO_4 + K_2CO_3 \longrightarrow H_2CO_3 + K_2SO_4$.
(*c*) $3KOH + FeCl_3 \longrightarrow Fe(OH)_3 + 3KCl$.

11.15 (*a*) $HBr + H_2O \longrightarrow \underset{\text{conj acid}}{H_3O^+} + \underset{\text{conj base}}{Br^-}$ conj pairs: HBr/Br^-, H_2O/H_3O^+.

(*b*) $NH_4^+ + H_2O \rightleftharpoons \underset{\text{conj base}}{NH_3} + \underset{\text{conj acid}}{H_3O^+}$ conj pairs: NH_4^+/NH_3, H_2O/H_3O^+.

(*c*) $CH_3NH_2 + H_2O \rightleftharpoons \underset{\text{conj acid}}{CH_3NH_3^+} + \underset{\text{conj base}}{OH^-}$ conj pairs: $CH_3NH_2/CH_3NH_3^+$, $H_2O,/OH^-$

11.17 $CH_3CH_2CH_2COOH + H_2O \rightleftharpoons CH_3CH_2CH_2COO^- + H_3O^+$.

$$K_a = \frac{[CH_3CH_2CH_2COO^-][H_3O^+]}{[CH_3CH_2CH_2COOH]}$$

11.19 (*a*) 1; (*b*) 4; (*c*) 4; (*d*) −1; (*e*) −2; (*f*) 2.3; (*g*) 3.48; (*h*) −1.15; (*i*) −6.1; (*j*) −0.3; (*k*) −8.5; (*l*) 0.3.

11.21 Pears < apples < lemons.

11.23 3×10^{-6}

11.25 (*a*) 10^{-12}; (*b*) 10^{-10}.

11.27 pH = 12, $[H^+] = 10^{-12}$.

11.29 *c*

11.31 At the equivalence point the reaction is complete; at the end point the indicator changes color

11.33 $[H^+] = 0.020$, pH = 1.7.

11.35 HBr, 81 g; NaOH, 40 g.
H_2SO_4 49 g, KOH, 56.
HCl 36.5 g, $Ca(OH)_2$, 37.

11.37 $[H^+] = 0.05$, pH = 1.3.

11.39 NaCN or KCN.

11.41 (*a*) $KOH + HAc \longrightarrow KAc + H_2O$.
(*b*) $HBr + Ac^- \longrightarrow HAc + Br^-$.

11.43 The NH_4^+ ion is a proton donor.

11.45 $HCO_3^- + HCl \longrightarrow H_2CO_3 + Cl^-$.
$H_2CO_3 + NaOH \longrightarrow NaHCO_3 + H_2O$.

11.47 Acidosis blood pH < 7.36; alkalosis blood pH > 7.44.

11.49 Increased elimination of CO_2 leads to decrease in H_2CO_3 to replenish CO_2, and thus alkalosis.

11.51 (*a*) pH = 6.5 (yes, acidosis); (*b*) pH = 7.5 (yes, alkalosis); (*c*) pH = 7.2 (no).

11.53 0.892 N, 3.75 g.

11.55 NH_4Cl.

CHAPTER 12

12.1 31.

12.2
```
  H H H H
H:C:C:C:C:H
  H H H H
```

12.3 Molecular formula = C_8H_{18}.
```
          H
          |
       H—C—H
          |
     H    |    H    H
     |    |    |    |
H—  C—C——C——C—C—H
     |    |    |    |
     H    |    H    |    H
          |         |
       H—C—H  H—C—H
          |         |
          H         H
```

12.4 *c*, *d*.

12.5 (1) hexane; (2) 2-methylpentane; (3) 3-methylpentane; (4) 2,3-dimethylbutane; (5) 2,2-dimethylbutane.

12.6 2,2,4-trimethylpentane, octane isomer.

12.7 5-*t*-butylnonane.

12.8
```
            CH3
            |
CH3CH2—C—CH2CHCH2CH2CH3
            |         |
            CH3       CH3
```

12.9 2-methylhexane or isoheptane.

12.10 $2C_4H_{10} + 13O_2 \longrightarrow 8CO_2 + 10H_2O$.

12.11 $CH_3CH_3 + Cl_2 \longrightarrow CH_3CH_2Cl + HCl$.

12.12 ethyl chloride or chloroethane.

12.13
```
      CH2
     /   \
  CH2     CH2
   |       |
  CH2     CH2
     \   /
       C
     /   \
  CH3     CH3
```
1,1-dimethylcyclohexane

12.15 (*a*) C_2H_6; (*b*) C_4H_{10}; (*c*) C_5H_{12}; (*d*) C_8H_{18}.

12.17 (*a*) $C_{33}H_{68}$; (*b*) $C_{35}H_{72}$; (*c*) $C_{37}H_{76}$.

12.19
```
  H H H H          H H H
H:C:C:C:C:H      H:C:C:C:H
  H H H H          H ·· H
                   H:C:H
                     H
```

12.21 (*a*) 2-methylbutane; (*b*) 2,2-dimethylhexane.

12.23
```
CH3CH2CH2CH2CH2CH2CH3 (1) heptane (n-heptane)

CH3CHCH2CH2CH2CH3 (2) 2-methylhexane (isoheptane)
   |
   CH3

CH3CH2CHCH2CH2CH3 (3) 3-methylhexane
        |
        CH3

CH3CHCHCH2CH3 (4) 2,3-dimethylpentane
   |  |
 H3C  CH3
```

$$\begin{array}{l} CH_3\underset{\displaystyle CH_3}{\underset{|}{C}}HCH_2\underset{\displaystyle CH_3}{\underset{|}{C}}HCH_3 \end{array}$$ (5) 2,4-dimethylpentane

$$CH_3-\overset{\displaystyle CH_3}{\overset{|}{\underset{\displaystyle CH_3}{\underset{|}{C}}}}-CH_2CH_2CH_3$$ (6) 2,2-dimethylpentane

$$CH_3-\overset{\displaystyle CH_3}{\overset{|}{\underset{\displaystyle CH_3}{\underset{|}{C}}}}-\underset{\displaystyle CH_3}{\underset{|}{C}}HCH_3$$ (7) 2,2,3-trimethylbutane

12.25 (*a*) 2,2,4-trimethylhexane; (*b*) 3-methyl-5-ethyloctane; (*c*) 3-methylpentane; (*d*) 4-isopropylheptane.

12.27 (*a*) $CH_3\underset{\displaystyle CH_3}{\underset{|}{C}}HCH_3$ (*b*) $CH_3CH_2CH_2CH_2CH_2CH_2CH_2CH_3$

(*c*) $CH_3\underset{\displaystyle CH_3}{\underset{|}{C}}HCH_2\underset{\underset{\displaystyle CH_3}{\underset{|}{CH_2}}}{\underset{|}{C}}HCH_2CH_2CH_2CH_2CH_3$

(*d*) $CH_3-\overset{\displaystyle CH_3}{\overset{|}{\underset{\displaystyle CH_3}{\underset{|}{C}}}}-CH_2CH_2\underset{\displaystyle CH_3}{\underset{|}{C}}HCH_2CH_3$

12.29 2-methylbutane.

12.31 (*a*) H_2O; (*b*) hexane.

12.33 No; isooctane is $CH_3CH_2CH_2CH_2CH_2\underset{\displaystyle CH_3}{\underset{|}{C}}HCH_3$, 2-methylheptane.

12.35 (*a*) $2C_2H_6 + 7O_2 \longrightarrow 4CO_2 + 6H_2O$.
(*b*) $C_5H_{12} + 11O_2 \longrightarrow 5CO_2 + 6H_2O$.
(*c*) $C_6H_{12} + 12O_2 \longrightarrow 6CO_2 + 6H_2O$.

12.37 (*a*) $CH_4 + Br_2 \longrightarrow CH_3Br + HBr$
bromomethane (methyl bromide)
(*b*) $CH_4 + 2Br_2 \longrightarrow CH_2Br_2 + 2HBr$
dibromomethane (methylene bromide)
(*c*) $CH_4 + 3Br_2 \longrightarrow CHBr_3 + 3HBr$
tribromomethane (bromoform)
(*d*) $CH_4 + 4Br_2 \longrightarrow CBr_4 + 4HBr$
carbon tetrabromide

12.39 Halothane and halopropane are not flammable.

12.41 Triiodomethane and iodoform; no, because I_2 is not reactive enough.

12.43 (*a*)

$$\begin{array}{c} CH_2 \\ / \quad \backslash \\ CH_2-CH_2 \end{array}$$

(*b*)

$$\begin{array}{c} CH_2 \\ / \quad \backslash \\ CH_2 \quad CH_2 \\ | \qquad | \\ CH_2 \quad CH_2 \\ \backslash \quad / \\ CH_2 \end{array}$$

12.45 (*a*) 1,2,3-trimethylcyclohexane; (*b*) 1,1-dimethylcyclobutane; (*c*) 1,3-diethylcyclopentane.

12.47 Dichlorodifluoromethane.

12.49 *b*

12.51 No; cyclohexane is twisted into a chair (or boat) form in which bond angles are tetrahedral.

CHAPTER 13

13.1 Decene.

13.2 $CH_3CH{=}CHCH_2CHCH_3$

$CH_3 \quad CH_3$

The bold faced C has five bonds.

13.3 *b,c,e,f.*

13.4 1-pentene(1); 2-pentene(2); 3-methyl-1-butene(3); 2-methyl-1-butene(4); 2-methyl-2-butene(5).

13.5 3,5-dimethyl-2-heptene.

13.6

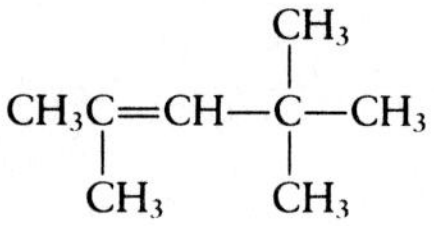

13.7

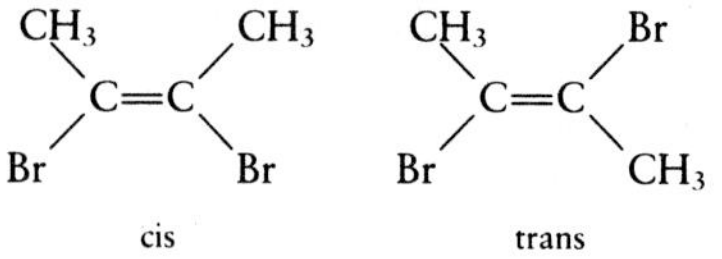

13.8 3-hexene, yes.

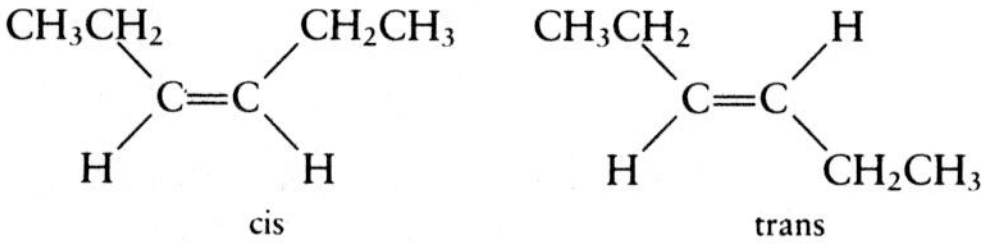

2-methyl-2-pentene, no.

13.9 $CH_3CH_2CH{=}CH_2 + Br_2 \longrightarrow CH_3CH_2CHCH_2Br.$

Br

13.10 $CH_3CH_2CH{=}CHCH_3 + HI \longrightarrow CH_3CH_2CH_2CHCH_3$

I

and

$CH_3CH_2CH{=}CHCH_3 + HI \longrightarrow CH_3CH_2CHCH_2CH_3.$

I

Carbon atoms in double bond both contain 1 H atom.

13.11 $CH_3CH{=}CHCH_3 + HOH \longrightarrow CH_3CH_2CHCH_3$: no.

OH

13.12 5-methyl-3-octyne.

13.13 $CH_3CH{=}CH_2$ propene; $CH_3CH_2CH_3$ propane.

13.15 Saturated compounds contain no multiple bonds; unsaturated compounds do contain multiple bonds.

13.17 $C_{10}H_{18}$, alkyne.

13.19 $\pi < \sigma$.

13.21 (*a*) $CH_2{=}CHF$; (*b*) $CH_2{=}CHCH_2CH_2CH_3$;
(*c*) $ClCHCH{=}CCH_3$; (*d*) $CH_3{-}C{\equiv}C{-}CH_2CH_3$.

$Cl \quad CH_3$

13.23 (*a*) ethyne (acetylene); (*b*) 3-chloro-5-methyl-1-hexene; (*c*) 2-methyl-4-bromo-2-pentene; (*d*) 4-methyl-2-hexene; (*e*) 2-pentyne; (*f*) 6,6-dimethyl-2-heptene.

13.25 *d* and *f*.

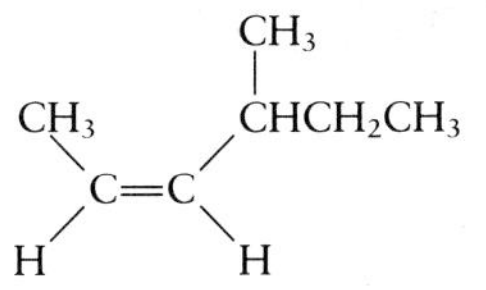

```
        CH3                        CH3
        |                          |
CH3     CHCH2CH3         H         CHCH2CH3
   \   /                   \      /
    C=C                     C=C
   /   \                   /   \
H       H              CH3      H
     cis                    trans

      CH3                               CH3
      |                                 |
CH3—C—CH2CH2        CH3       CH3—C—CH2CH2        H
      |      \      /               |      \      /
      CH3     C=C                   CH3     C=C
             /   \                         /   \
            H     H                       H     CH3
              cis                            trans
```

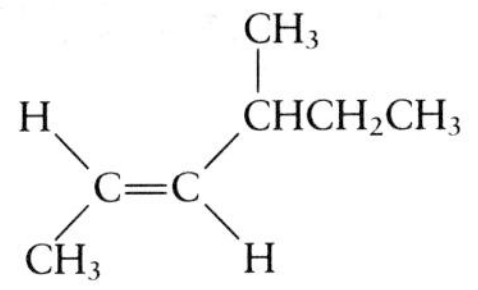

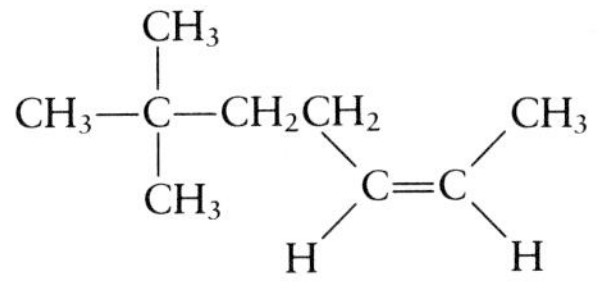

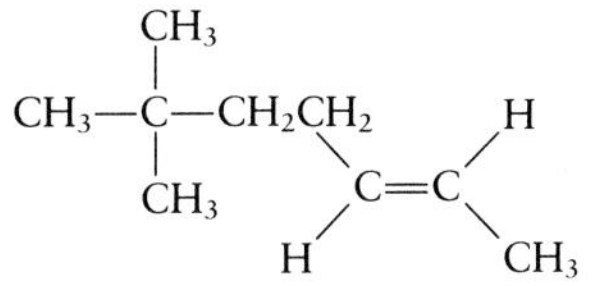

13.27 (*a*) $CH_3CH{=}CHCH_2CH_2CH_3$; (*b*) $CH_3—C{\equiv}C—CH_2CH_2CH_3$

(*c*) Br—C=CH—CH_3 (Br on the first C)

```
Br—C=CH—CH3
   |
   Br
```

(*d*) Br—CH=C—CH_3 (Br on the second C)

```
Br—CH=C—CH3
       |
       Br
```

(*e*)

```
                      CH3
                      |
CH3CH2CH=CH—C—CHCH2CH3
                      |   |
                      CH3CH3
```

(*f*) I—C≡C—I (*g*) $CH_2{=}CHCH_3$

(*h*)

```
CH=CH
|    |
CH2—CH2
```

(*i*) $CH_2{=}CH—CH{=}CH—CH_3$

13.29 (*a*) $CH_2{\equiv}C—CH_3$ (C with five bonds).

(*b*)

```
CH2=CHCH2CH2CH3   (C with five bonds).
    |
    CH3
```

(*c*) $CH_3C{=}CHCH_2CH_2CH_3$ (C with three bonds).

(*d*)

```
CH3CH2C≡CCH2CH2CH3   (C with five bonds).
        |
        Cl
```

13.31

```
F       F
 \     /
  C=C
 /     \
F       F
```

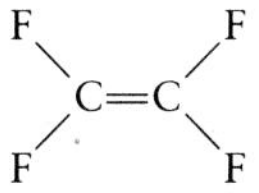

13.33 Alkanes are less reactive; pyrolysis (cracking) reactions.

13.35 (*a*) CH_3CH_3 ethane.

(*b*)

```
ClCH2CHCH2CH3   1,2-dichlorobutane.
     |
     Cl
```

(*c*) CH_3CH_2OH ethyl alcohol (ethanol).

(*d*)

```
CH3CH2CHCH3   2-iodobutane.
       |
       I
```

(*e*) [cyclopentane ring with Br on two adjacent carbons] 1,2-dibromocyclopentane

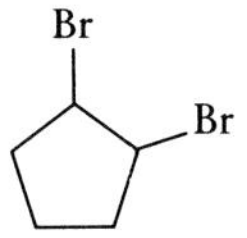

13.37

```
CH3CH=CH2 + KMnO4 + H2O ⟶ CH2CHCH3 + KOH + MnO2
                            |   |
                            OH  OH
                    purple ⟶ colorless
```

13.39 The addition of water to propene, a method for preparing isopropyl alcohol, gives mostly isopropyl alcohol (rather than propyl alcohol) because the reaction follows Markovnikov's Rule.

13.41 $CH_2{=}CHCH_3 + Cl_2 \longrightarrow Cl{-}CH_2\underset{\displaystyle Cl}{\underset{|}{C}}HCH_3$ 1,2-dichloropropane

13.43
$$3C + CaO \rightarrow CaC_2 + CO$$
$$CaC_2 + 2H_2O \rightarrow HC{\equiv}CH + Ca(OH)_2$$
$$HC{\equiv}CH + 2H_2 \rightarrow CH_3CH_3$$

13.45 butene, C_4H_8

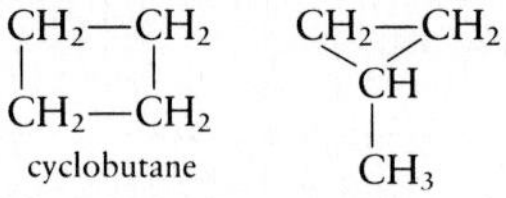

$CH_2{-}CH_2$ / $CH_2{-}CH_2$ (ring): cyclobutane

$CH_2{-}CH_2$ / CH (three-membered ring) with CH_3: methylcyclopropane

13.47 0.5 μg (one β-carotene → two vitamin A).

CHAPTER 14

14.1 *p*-aminobenzoic acid.

14.2 (benzene ring with OH, Cl, NH_2, and Cl substituents)

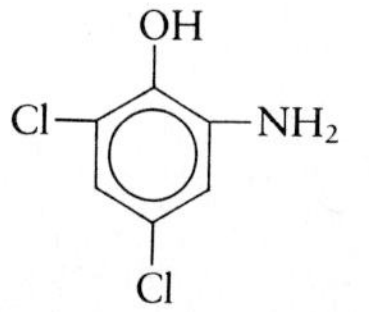

14.3 1-phenylpropane.

14.4 $C_6H_5Cl + Cl_2 \longrightarrow C_6H_4Cl_2$ (o-dichlorobenzene) $+ HCl$

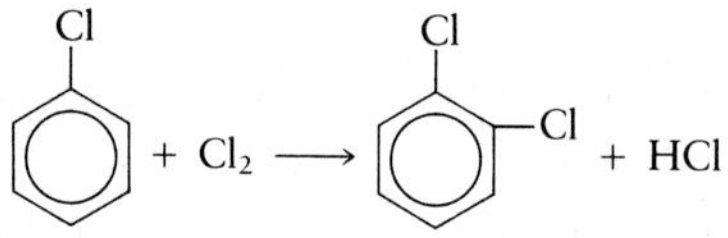

14.5 $C_{17}H_{14}$; yes.

14.7 (*a*) C_6H_{12}, cyclohexane; (*b*) C_6H_{10}, cyclohexene; (*c*) C_6H_6, benzene.

14.9 (*a*) 1,2-dibromobenzene or *o*-dibromobenzene; (*b*) chlorobenzene; (*c*) 1,3-diiodobenzene or *m*-diiodobenzene; (*d*) 1,4-difluorobenzene or *p*-difluorobenzene.

14.11 (*a*) 1,2,3,5-tetrachlorobenzene; (*b*) 1,3,5-tribromobenzene.

14.13 *o*-hydroxybenzoic acid or 2-hydroxybenzoic acid.

14.15 Paradox and orthodox.

14.17 (*a*) phenylmethane; (*b*) 1-phenyl-2-methylpropane; (*c*) phenylethane.

14.19 The double arrow $\rightleftharpoons$ is used to describe a reversible chemical reaction. The double-headed arrow $\leftrightarrow$ is not used to describe a chemical reaction. It is placed between resonance structures, none of which actually exist.

14.21 (*a*) Toluene has only 1 substituent; (*b*) the lower set of numbers 1,2 should be used; (*c*) the lower set of numbers 1,3,5 should be used; (*d*) the lower set of numbers 1,2,4 should be used.

14.23 No reaction.

14.25 (*a*) Br_2; (*b*) H_2SO_4.

14.27 N, $C_6H_5{-}NH{-}\overset{\displaystyle S}{\overset{\|}{C}}{-}NH_2$

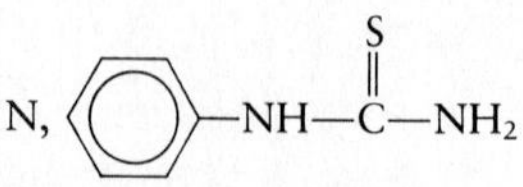

14.29 Phenylethene or vinylbenzene.

14.31 Benzoic acid.

14.33 $C_{19}H_{14}$; yes because it contains a "bay area".

14.35 PBB (polybrominatedbiphenyl).

CHAPTER 15

15.1 (*a*) 3-methyl-1-pentanol; (*b*) 6-methyl-3-octanol.

15.2 2-isopropyl-5-methylphenol.

15.3

$$CH_3CH_2CH_2\text{—}\overset{\displaystyle CH_3\atop|}{\underset{|\atop \displaystyle OH}{C}}\text{—}CH_3$$ tertiary

15.4

$$CH_3\underset{|\atop \displaystyle CH_3}{C}H\text{—}\overset{\displaystyle O\atop \|}{C}\text{—}H$$

15.5 (*a*) $CH_3CH_2CH{=}CH_2$; (*b*) $CH_3CH_2CH_2CH_2\text{—}0\text{—}CH_2CH_2CH_2CH_3$.

15.6 $CH_3\underset{|\atop \displaystyle CH_3}{C}H\text{—}O\text{—}\underset{|\atop \displaystyle CH_3}{C}HCH_3$

15.7 No; the formula would be HOH, water.

15.9 (*a*) 1-propanol; (*b*) 2-propanol or isopropyl alcohol; (*c*) 3-pentanol; (*d*) 3-methyl-2-butanol.

15.11 (*a*) Primary; (*b*) secondary; (*c*) secondary; (*d*) secondary. (*a*) Primary; (*b*) primary; (*c*) primary; (*d*) tertiary.

15.13 OH

OH

$CH_2CH_2CH_2CH_2CH_2CH_3$

15.15 The C to C double bonds of the substituents are in different positions.

15.17

$CH_3CH_2CH_2CH_2OH$	1-butanol	primary
$CH_3CH_2\underset{|\atop \displaystyle CH_3}{C}HOH$	2-butanol	secondary
$CH_3\underset{|\atop \displaystyle CH_3}{C}HCH_2OH$	2-methyl-1-propanol	primary
$CH_3\text{—}\overset{\displaystyle CH_3\atop|}{\underset{|\atop \displaystyle CH_3}{C}}\text{—}OH$	2-methyl-2-propanol or *t*-butyl alcohol	tertiary

15.19 Alcohols with fewer than 5 C atoms are water-soluble.

15.21 Hexahydroxyhexane.

15.23 (1) $CH_3\text{—}O\text{—}CH_2CH_2CH_2CH_3$

(2) $CH_3\text{—}O\text{—}\underset{|\atop \displaystyle CH_3}{C}HCH_2CH_3$

(3) $CH_3\text{—}O\text{—}CH_2\underset{|\atop \displaystyle CH_3}{C}HCH_3$

(4) $CH_3CH_2\text{—}O\text{—}CH_2CH_2CH_3$

(5) $CH_3CH_2\text{—}O\text{—}\underset{|\atop \displaystyle CH_3}{C}HCH_3$

(6) $CH_3\text{—}O\text{—}\overset{\displaystyle CH_3\atop|}{\underset{|\atop \displaystyle CH_3}{C}}\text{—}CH_3$

15.25 (*a*) butylethylether; (*b*) ethylisopropylether; (*c*) methylphenylether or anisole; (*d*) butylphenylether.

15.27 (*a*) BHT, butylated hydroxytoluene; BHA, butylated hydroxyanisole; (*b*) Phenols are very easily oxidized.

15.29

(*a*) $CH_3CH_2OH + [O] \longrightarrow CH_3{-}\overset{\overset{\displaystyle O}{\|}}{C}{-}H + H_2O.$

(*b*) $CH_3{-}\overset{\overset{\displaystyle O}{\|}}{C}{-}H + [O] \longrightarrow CH_3{-}\overset{\overset{\displaystyle O}{\|}}{C}{-}OH.$

(*c*) $CH_3OH + [O] \longrightarrow H{-}\overset{\overset{\displaystyle O}{\|}}{C}{-}H + H_2O.$

(*d*) $H{-}\overset{\overset{\displaystyle O}{\|}}{C}{-}H + [O] \longrightarrow H{-}\overset{\overset{\displaystyle O}{\|}}{C}{-}OH.$

15.31 Methanol produces the toxic metabolites, formaldehyde, and formic acid. Ethanol binds to alcohol dehydrogenase, the same enzyme needed to oxidize methanol, thus preventing the metabolism of methanol and the formation of the toxic metabolites.

15.33 Peroxide.

15.35

(*a*) $CH_3CH_2OH \xrightarrow[\Delta]{H_2SO_4} CH_2{=}CH_2 + H_2O.$

(*b*) $CH_3OH \xrightarrow[\Delta]{H_2SO_4} CH_3{-}0{-}CH_3 + H_2O.$

15.37 Alcohols participate in intermolecular hydrogen bonding because they contain an O-H bond in their formulas. Ethers do not have O-H bonds.

15.39 Divinylether; no, this is a highly flammable compound.

15.41 Ether, no because it is halogenated.

15.43 Nitrous oxide is not very potent.

15.45 Octanol (8 C atoms) is not very soluble in water (Table 15.3).

CHAPTER 16

16.1 2,2,2-trichloroethanal or trichloroacetaldehyde

16.2

$CH_3{-}\overset{\overset{\displaystyle O}{\|}}{C}{-}CH_2CH_2CH_2CH_2CH_2CH_2CH_2CH_2CH_3$ 2-undecanone.

16.3 Yes

16.4

$CH_3CH_2CH_2{-}\overset{\overset{\displaystyle O}{\|}}{C}{-}H$ butanal.

16.5

$CH_3CH_2{-}\underset{\underset{\displaystyle CH_3}{|}}{\overset{\overset{\displaystyle OH}{|}}{C}}{-}CH_3$

16.7 (*a*) methanal; (*b*) 2-methylpropanal; (*c*) ethanal; (*d*) heptanal.

16.9 (*a*) formaldehyde; (*b*) α-methylpropionaldehyde; (*c*) acetaldehyde.

16.11 Valeric acid.

16.13 *p*-methoxybenzaldehyde.

16.15

(*a*) $CH_3\underset{\underset{\displaystyle Cl}{|}}{C}H\overset{\overset{\displaystyle O}{\|}}{C}{-}H$ (*b*) $CH_3CH_2\underset{\underset{\displaystyle Cl}{|}}{C}H\overset{\overset{\displaystyle O}{\|}}{C}{-}H$ (*c*) $CH_3\underset{\underset{\displaystyle CH_3}{|}}{C}H\ \underset{\underset{\displaystyle Cl}{|}}{C}HCH_2\overset{\overset{\displaystyle O}{\|}}{C}{-}H$

16.17 (*a*) 2-butanone or methylethylketone; (*b*) diphenylketone; (*c*) 2-heptanone or methylpentylketone; (*d*) ethylpropylketone or 3-hexanone; (*e*) 2-chloro-3-pentanone.

16.19 (a) $ClCH_2\overset{O}{\overset{\|}{C}}CH_2CH_2CH_3$ (b) $CH_3CH_2\overset{O}{\overset{\|}{C}}-C_6H_5$

16.21 $CH_3CH_2CH_2\overset{O}{\overset{\|}{C}}-C_6H_5$ phenylpropylketone.

16.23 $CH_3\overset{O}{\overset{\|}{C}}CH_2CH_2CH_2CH_2CH_2CH_3$ 2-octanone

$CH_3CH_2\overset{O}{\overset{\|}{C}}CH_2CH_2CH_2CH_2CH_3$ 3-octanone

$CH_3CH_2CH_2\overset{O}{\overset{\|}{C}}CH_2CH_2CH_2CH_3$ 4-octanone

16.25 There are two electron pairs involved in both alkene double bonds and carbonyls; the alkene double bond is nonpolar and the carbonyl group is polar.

16.27 *b* (an aldehyde).

16.29 *a* and 3 Pentanol exhibits hydrogen-bonding
b and 2 Diethylketone is polar, but does not exhibit hydrogen bonding
c and 1 Hexane is nonpolar

16.31 Octanal; no, aromatic aldehydes do not react with Benedict's or Fehling's solutions.

16.33

$$CH_3CH_2CH_2CH_2\overset{O}{\overset{\|}{C}}-H + H_2 \xrightarrow{Ni} CH_3CH_2CH_2CH_2CH_2OH$$

$$CH_3CH_2CH_2\overset{O}{\overset{\|}{C}}CH_3 + H_2 \xrightarrow{Ni} CH_3CH_2CH_2\overset{OH}{\overset{|}{C}}HCH_3$$

16.35

$$CH_3-\overset{O}{\overset{\|}{C}}-H + HOCH_2CH_3 \longrightarrow CH_3-\underset{OCH_2CH_3}{\underset{|}{\overset{OH}{\overset{|}{C}}}}-H$$

$$CH_3-\underset{OCH_2CH_3}{\underset{|}{\overset{OH}{\overset{|}{C}}}}-H + HOCH_2CH_3 \longrightarrow CH_3-\underset{OCH_2CH_3}{\underset{|}{\overset{OCH_2CH_3}{\overset{|}{C}}}}-H + H_2O$$

16.37 *a* and 1, *b* and 3, *c* and 2, *d* and 4.

16.39 It is stable and is used as a sedative.

16.41 No

16.43 Formaldehyde reacts with itself to form a polymer.

CHAPTER 17

17.1 2-aminoethanoic acid and α-aminoacetic acid.

17.2

$$\underset{\text{pentanoic acid}}{CH_3CH_2CH_2CH_2\overset{O}{\overset{\|}{C}}OH} + H_2O \rightleftharpoons \underset{\text{pentanoate ion}}{CH_3CH_2CH_2CH_2\overset{O}{\overset{\|}{C}}O^-} + H_3O^+$$

17.3

$$C_6H_5-\overset{O}{\overset{\|}{C}}OH + NaOH \longrightarrow C_6H_5-\overset{O}{\overset{\|}{C}}ONa + H_2O$$

17.4 $CH_3CH_2CH_2CH_2CH_2CH_2CH_2CH_2CH_2CH_2CH_2CH_2-C_6H_4-\overset{\overset{\displaystyle O}{\|}}{\underset{\underset{\displaystyle O}{\|}}{S}}-ONa$

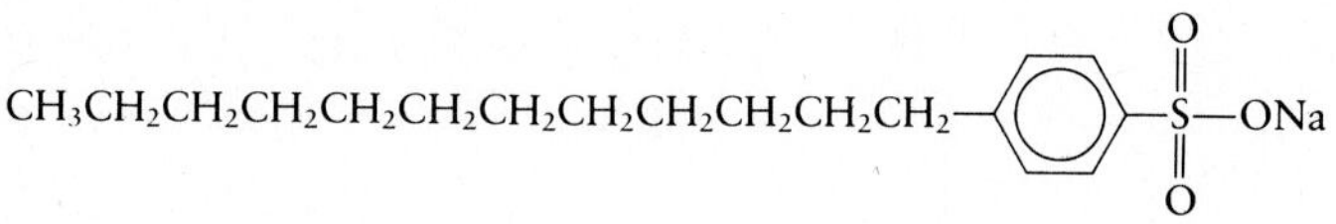

17.5 $CH_3CH_2CH_2\overset{\overset{\displaystyle O}{\|}}{C}OH + HOCH_2CH_3 \xrightarrow{H^+} CH_3CH_2CH_2\overset{\overset{\displaystyle O}{\|}}{C}OCH_2CH_3 + H_2O$

ethylbutanoate (ethylbutyrate)

17.6 $CH_3(CH_2)_{16}\overset{\overset{\displaystyle O}{\|}}{C}OCH_2CH_3$.

17.7 $CH_3CH_2CH_2\overset{\overset{\displaystyle O}{\|}}{C}NH_2 + H_2O \xrightarrow{H^+} CH_3CH_2CH_2\overset{\overset{\displaystyle O}{\|}}{C}OH + NH_4^+$.

17.8 $CH_3CH_2CH_2CH_2\overset{\overset{\displaystyle O}{\|}}{C}-Cl$ and $HOCH_2CH_3$.

17.9 $R-\overset{\overset{\displaystyle O}{\|}}{C}-OH$, R can be hydrocarbon or H.

17.11 (*a*) 4,4-dichloroheptanoic acid; (*b*) 2-methyl-3-bromopropanoic acid; (*c*) *o*-methylbenzoic acid or 2-methylbenzoic acid; (*d*) ethanedioic acid or (oxalic acid).

17.13 (*a*) 2-aminopropanoic acid, α-aminopropionic acid

(*b*) 2-amino-3-methylbutanoic acid, α-amino-β-methylbutyric acid

(*c*) 2-amino-3-hydroxypropanoic acid, α-amino-β-hydroxypropionic acid

(*d*) 2-amino-3-phenylpropanoic acid, α-amino-β-phenylpropionic acid They all have an amino group on C-2, the α C.

17.15 (*a*) $CH_3\underset{\underset{\displaystyle Cl}{|}}{C}HCH_2\overset{\overset{\displaystyle O}{\|}}{C}OH$ (*b*) $CH_3CH_2\underset{\underset{\displaystyle OH}{|}}{C}HCH_2\overset{\overset{\displaystyle O}{\|}}{C}OH$

(*c*) $HO\overset{\overset{\displaystyle O}{\|}}{C}CH_2CH_2CH_2CH_2\overset{\overset{\displaystyle O}{\|}}{C}OH$ (*d*) $CH_3(CH_2)_{12}\overset{\overset{\displaystyle O}{\|}}{C}OH$

17.17 $CH_3CH_2-C\begin{smallmatrix}\diagup\!\!\!\!\diagup O\cdots HO \diagdown \\ \diagdown OH\cdots O \diagup\!\!\!\!\diagup\end{smallmatrix}C-CH_2CH_3$

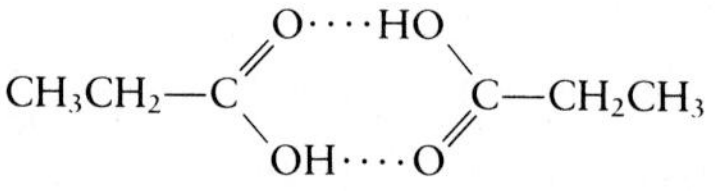

17.19 $CH_3CH_2\overset{\overset{\displaystyle O}{\|}}{C}OH + NaOH \longrightarrow CH_3CH_2\overset{\overset{\displaystyle O}{\|}}{C}ONa + H_2O$

17.21 $CH_3CH{=}CHCH{=}CH\overset{\overset{\displaystyle O}{\|}}{C}OH + KOH \longrightarrow CH_3CH{=}CHCH{=}CH\overset{\overset{\displaystyle O}{\|}}{C}OK + H_2O$

17.23 $(CH_2{=}CH(CH_2)_8\overset{\overset{\displaystyle O}{\|}}{C}O)_2Ca$, calcium undecylenate

17.25 Calcium, iron and magnesium salts of soaps (carboxylic acid derivatives) are not water-soluble. Calcium, iron, and magnesium salts of detergents (including sulfonic acid derivatives) are water-soluble.

17.27 Alkylbenzenesulfonate (a detergent); *b* and *d*.

17.29 (*a*) methyl propanoate; (*b*) methyl heptanoate; (*c*) isopropyl ethanoate or isopropyl acetate; (*d*) propyl methanoate or propyl formate; (*e*) octyl propanoate; (*f*) ethylbenzoate; (*g*) ethyl salicylate.

17.31 $CH_3(CH_2)_{12}\overset{\overset{\displaystyle O}{\|}}{C}O\underset{\underset{\displaystyle CH_3}{|}}{C}HCH_3$

17.33 (*a*) butanamide; (*b*) dodecanamide or lauramide.

17.35 $R-\overset{O}{\overset{\|}{C}}-Cl$; acyl halides are more reactive than carboxylic acids

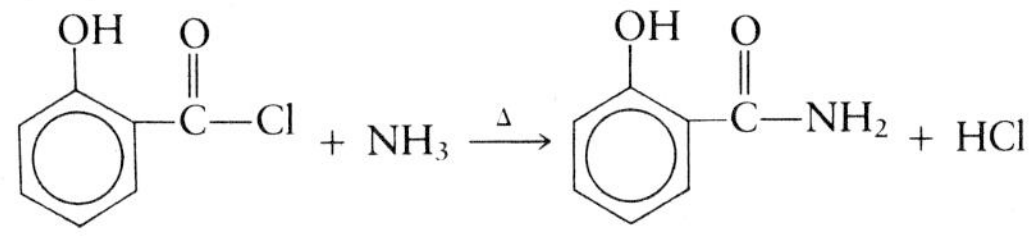

$$C_6H_4(OH)\overset{O}{\overset{\|}{C}}-Cl + NH_3 \xrightarrow{\Delta} C_6H_4(OH)\overset{O}{\overset{\|}{C}}-NH_2 + HCl$$

17.37 (*a*) $CH_3O\overset{O}{\overset{\|}{C}}CH_2CH_2CH_3$ (*b*) $CH_3\underset{CH_3}{\underset{|}{C}}HOH$ and $CH_3CH_2\overset{O}{\overset{\|}{C}}OH$

(*c*) KOH (*d*) $CH_3CH_2CH_2CH_2CH_2\overset{O}{\overset{\|}{C}}NH_2 + H_2O$

(*e*) HCl (*f*) $CH_3CH_2\overset{O}{\overset{\|}{C}}ONa + CH_3CH_2OH$

(*g*) $H-\overset{O}{\overset{\|}{C}}-OH$

17.39 Acyl chloride, benzoyl chloride.

17.41 (*a*) Salicylic acid damages tissues; (*b*) Acetyl chloride is too difficult to handle.

17.43 Esterifications are equilibrium reactions; and according to LeChatlier's principle, removal of a product in an equilibrium reaction drives the reaction to produce more product.

CHAPTER 18

18.1 1-amino-2-phenylethane.

18.2 $HO-C_6H_3(HO)-CH_2CH_2NH_2 + HCl \longrightarrow HO-C_6H_3(HO)-CH_2CH_2NH_2\cdot HCl$

or $HO-C_6H_3(HO)-CH_2CH_2NH_3Cl$

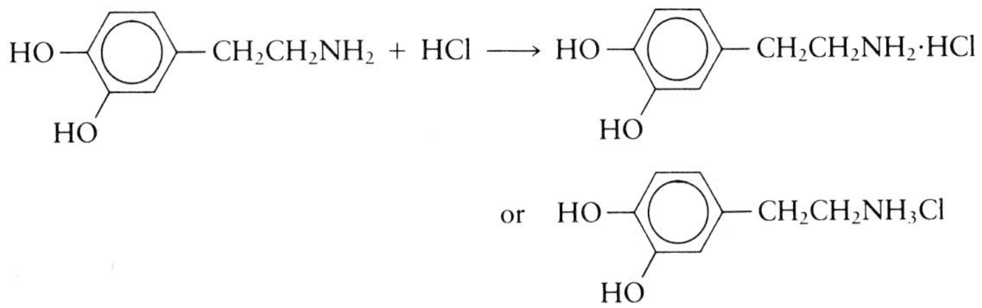

18.3 N,N-diethylethanamide or N,N-diethylacetamide.

$CH_3CH_2NHCH_2CH_3$ and $CH_3\overset{O}{\overset{\|}{C}}OH$

18.4 Benzenenitrile or cyanobenzene.

18.5 (*a*) ethylamine; (*b*) 2-aminobutane; (*c*) *p*-chloroaniline; (*d*) ethylphenylamine.

18.7 18.5: (*a*) primary; (*b*) primary; (*c*) primary; (*d*) secondary.
18.6: (*a*) secondary; (*b*) tertiary; (*c*) tertiary; (*d*) primary; (*e*) primary.

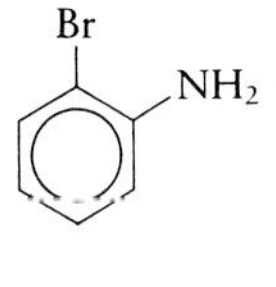

18.9 (*a*) $CH_3\underset{CH_3}{\underset{|}{C}}HNH_2$ primary (*b*) $C_6H_4(Br)NH_2$ (Br, NH_2 on benzene ring) primary (*c*) $CH_3CH_2CH_2CH_2CH_2NCH_3$ (with CH_3 on N) tertiary

(*d*) $CH_3CH_2NHCH_2CH_2CH_3$ secondary

(*e*) $CH_3CHCHCH_3$ (with H_2N and CH_3 substituents) primary

(*f*) C_6H_5–NCH_3 (with CH_3 on N) tertiary

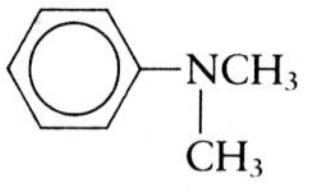

(*g*) $CH_3(CH_2)_9NH_2$ primary

(*h*) 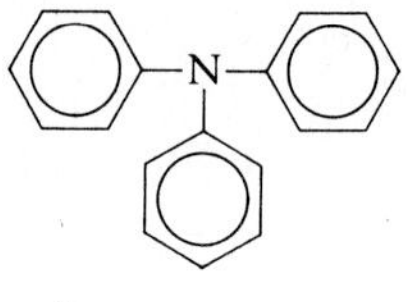 $(C_6H_5)_3N$ tertiary

(*i*) $NH_2CH_2CH_2CH_2NH_2$ primary

18.11 Amino and carboxyl groups; carboxyl; 2-amino-4-methylpentanoic acid

18.13 Amine hydrochloride: $RNH_2{\cdot}HCl$ or RNH_3Cl; free base amine: RNH_2.

18.15 $CH_3CH_2CH_2CH_2NH_2 + HCl \longrightarrow CH_3CH_2CH_2CH_2NH_2{\cdot}HCl$
or $\underbrace{CH_3CH_2CH_2CH_2NH_3^+}_{\text{cation}}\underbrace{Cl^-}_{\text{anion}}$

18.17 C_6H_5–$CHCHNH_2$ (with HO and CH_3 substituents) + HCl ⟶ C_6H_5–$CHCHNH_2{\cdot}HCl$ (with HO and CH_3 substituents)

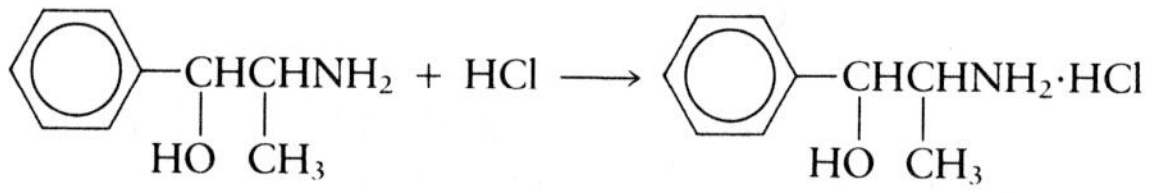

18.19 (*a*) N-methylpropanamide; (*b*) N-methyl-N-propylformamide; (*c*) N,N-dimethylbenzamide.

18.21

$$CH_3CH_2\overset{O}{\overset{\|}{C}}OH + CH_3NH_2 \xrightarrow{\Delta} CH_3CH_2\overset{O}{\overset{\|}{C}}NHCH_3 + H_2O$$

Use CH_3NHCH_3 instead of CH_3NH_2.

18.23 Derivatives of sulfanilamide (Section 18.7). They prevent the formation of folic acid, an essential nutrient for bacteria.

18.25 Quaternary ammonium compound; tetraethylammonium bromide.

18.27 $CH_3CH_2NH_2 + H_2O \rightleftharpoons CH_3CH_2NH_3^+ + OH^-$.

18.29 The infected gums were acidic, thus preventing the formation of free base procaine, the form in which it can cross lipid membranes and produce an effect.

18.31 Lemon juice contains citric acid, a tricarboxylic acid that can neutralize amines present in stale fish.

CHAPTER 19

19.1 $n\ (H)(H)C{=}C(H)(CH_2CH_2CH_3) \longrightarrow \!\!+\!\!C(H)(H){-}C(H)(CH_2CH_2CH_3)\!\!+_n$

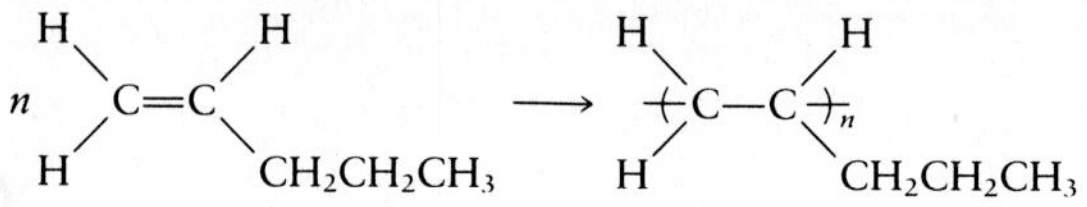

$—CH_2CH_2CH_3$

19.2 $\mathrm{H_2C{=}CCl_2}$ (H and H on one carbon, Cl and Cl on the other: C=C)

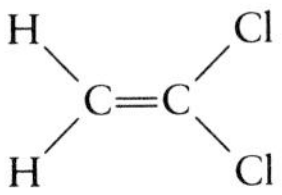

19.3 $\mathrm{NH_2CH_2CH_2CH_2\overset{O}{\overset{\|}{C}}{-}OH}$.

19.5 *a*

19.7 *c*, because the formula weight of the repeating unit is 42 and the polymer must have a molecular weight of about 10,000.

19.9 (*a*) $\mathrm{+CH_2CF_2+_n}$ poly-1,1-difluorethene or polyvinylidene fluoride.
(*b*) $\mathrm{+CH_2CH+_n}$ poly-1-heptene, with $\mathrm{CH_2CH_2CH_2CH_2CH_3}$ on the CH

19.11 Poly-1-octene $\mathrm{CH_2{=}CHCH_2CH_2CH_2CH_2CH_2CH_3}$.

19.13 Polyvinyl alcohol.

19.15 $\mathrm{NH_2CH_2CH_2CH_2CH_2CH_2CH_2NH_2}$ 1,6-diaminohexane

19.17 $\mathrm{HO\overset{O}{\overset{\|}{C}}CH_2CH_2CH_2CH_2CH_2CH_2CH_2CH_2\overset{O}{\overset{\|}{C}}OH}$ decanedioic acid

$\mathrm{NH_2CH_2CH_2CH_2CH_2CH_2CH_2NH_2}$ and $\mathrm{Cl\overset{O}{\overset{\|}{C}}CH_2CH_2CH_2CH_2\overset{O}{\overset{\|}{C}}Cl}$; HCl

19.19 $\mathrm{HO{-}Si{-}OH}$, with $\mathrm{CH_3}$ above Si and a benzene ring below Si

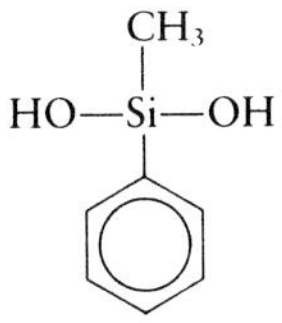

19.21 $\mathrm{NH_2(CH_2)_{10}\overset{O}{\overset{\|}{C}}{-}OH}$

19.23 Cross-linked silicone polymer; silicon rubber is inert.

CHAPTER 20

20.1 Achiral

20.2 Benzene ring–$\mathrm{CH_2\mathbf{C}NH_2}$, with H above the C and $\mathrm{CH_3}$ below it

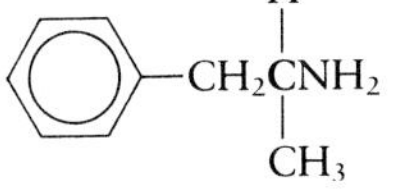

The C in bold is bonded to 4 different groups.

20.3 Four projections, each with COOH at top and $\mathrm{CH_3}$ at bottom:
H····C····$\mathrm{NH_2}$ $\mathrm{NH_2}$····C····H H—+—$\mathrm{NH_2}$ $\mathrm{NH_2}$—+—H

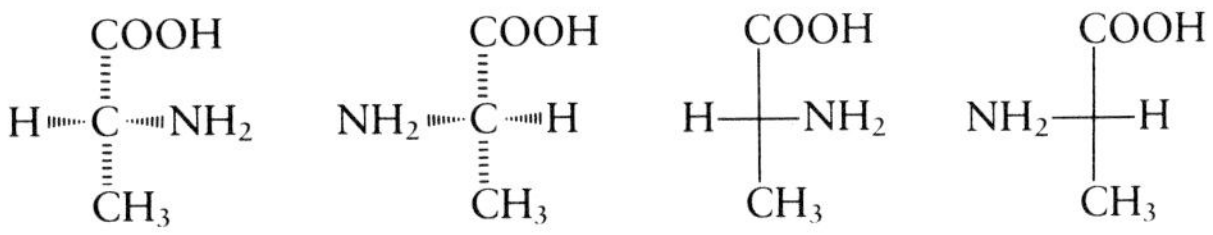

20.4 Fischer projections, each with COOH at top, then $\mathrm{CHCH_3}$, then $\mathrm{CH_3}$ at bottom:
D-valine: H—+—$\mathrm{NH_2}$
L-valine: $\mathrm{NH_2}$—+—H

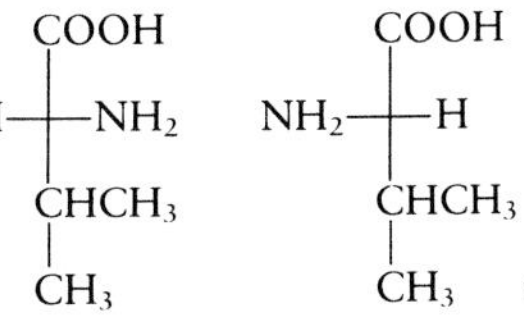

20.5

CH_2OH	CH_2OH	CH_2OH	CH_2OH
C=O	C=O	C=O	C=O
H—OH	HO—H	H—OH	HO—H
H—OH	HO—H	HO—H	H—OH
CH_2OH	CH_2OH	CH_2OH	CH_2OH
D-ribulose	L-ribulose	L-xylulose	D-xylulose

Enantiomers: D- and L-ribulose; D and L-xylulose.
Diastereoisomers: D-ribulose and D- or L-xylulose; L-ribulose and D- or L-xylulose.

20.7 *b*.
20.9 *b, d, e, g, h*.

20.11 H, NH_2, or $\overset{\overset{\displaystyle O}{\|}}{C}$—OH.

20.13 $CH_3\underset{Br}{\overset{H}{C^*}}CH_2CH_2CH_2CH_3$; H, CH_3, Br, $CH_2CH_2CH_2CH_3$.

CH_3	CH_3
H—Br	Br—H
CH_2	CH_2
CH_2	CH_2
CH_2	CH_2
CH_3	CH_3

20.15 Levorotatory (−) means rotation in a counterclockwise direction and dextrorotatory (+) means rotation in a clockwise direction.
20.17 No, the D and L do not refer to rotation directions.
20.19 No.
20.21 $[\alpha]_D = +15.9°$; boiling point = 118°C.
20.23 (*a*) 2 and 3, 1 and 4; (*b*) 1 and 2, 1 and 3, 2 and 4, 3 and 4; (*c*) 2 and 4 are D-isomers, 1 and 3 are L-isomers.
20.25 A racemic mixture consists of two compounds, a pair of enantiomers. A meso compound is a single compound.
20.27 (-)-amphetamine is not very potent.

20.29 (*a*) 4.
(*b*)

OH	OH	OH	OH
C=O	C=O	C=O	C=O
H—NH_2	NH_2—H	H—NH_2	NH_2—H
CH_2	CH_2	CH_2	CH_2
CH_2	CH_2	CH_2	CH_2
H—OH	HO—H	H—OH	HO—H
CH_2NH_2	CH_2NH_2	CH_2NH_2	CH_2NH_2

(*c*) D-isomer; L-isomer; D-isomer; L-isomer.

20.31 $CH_3CH_2C(=O)—O—C^*(C_6H_5)(CH_2C_6H_5)—CH(CH_3)CH_2N(CH_3)CH_3$, methadone.

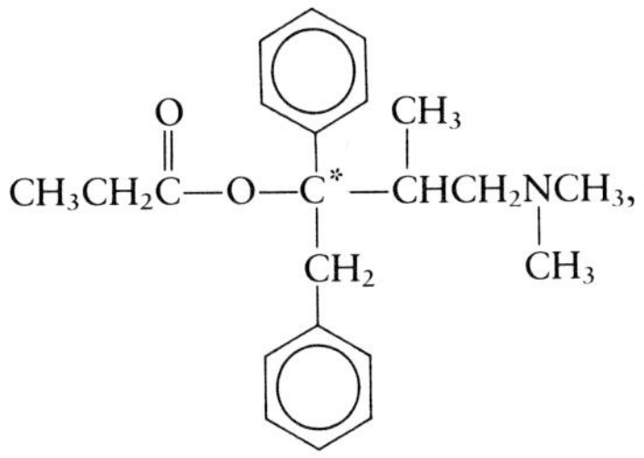

CHAPTER 21

21.1 Ketooctose.

21.2 $CH_2OH—C{=}O—H^*COH—H^*COH—CH_2OH$

CH₂OH	CH₂OH	CH₂OH	CH₂OH
C=O	C=O	C=O	C=O
H—OH	H—OH	HO—H	HO—H
H—OH	HO—H	HO—H	H—OH
CH₂OH	CH₂OH	CH₂OH	CH₂OH

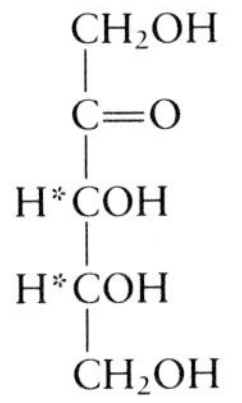

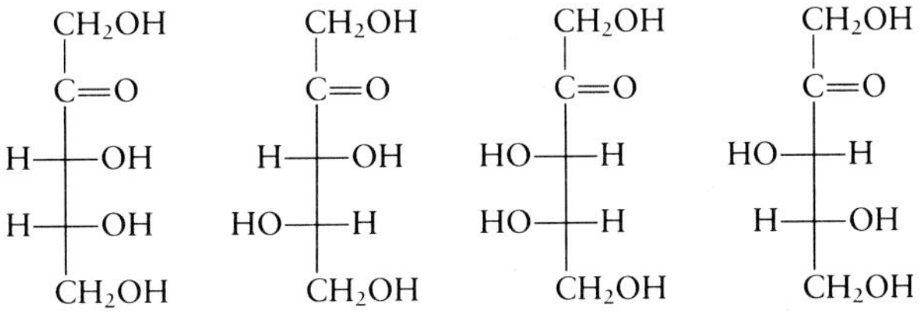

21.3 2-deoxyribofuranose, because the cyclic form of 2-deoxyribose includes a five-membered ring.

21.4 Structure I is β-D-fructose and structure II α-D-fructose.

21.5 $HOCH_2—C—OH$; HO—H; H—OH; H— (ring O); CH_2OH α-D-fructose

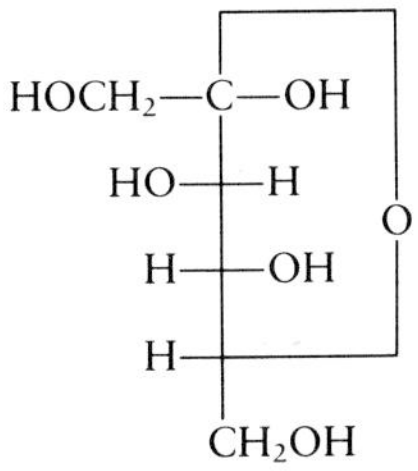

21.6 CH_2OH, O, OCH_2CH_3, OH OH $+ H_2O$

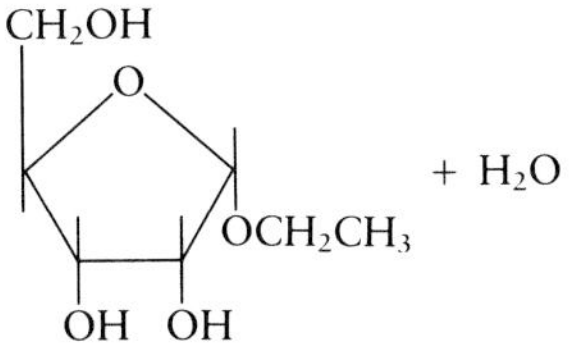

α-D-ethylriboside (α-D-ethylribofuranoside)

21.7 A nonreducing sugar, since the anomeric carbons from both glucose units are involved in the linkage.

21.9 (*a*) $2^3 = 8$; (*b*) $2^6 = 64$; (*c*) $2^2 = 4$; (*d*) $2^2 = 4$.

21.11

$$\text{Aldoheptose, } \mathrm{HOCH_2\underset{OH}{CH}\,\underset{OH}{CH}\,\underset{OH}{CH}\,\underset{OH}{CH}\,\underset{OH}{CH}\overset{O}{\overset{\|}{C}}H},\ 2^5 = 32.$$

$$\text{Ketoheptose, } \mathrm{HOCH_2\underset{OH}{CH}\,\underset{OH}{CH}\,\underset{OH}{CH}\,\underset{OH}{CH}\overset{O}{\overset{\|}{C}}CH_2OH},\ 2^4 = 16.$$

Aldoses have twice as many stereoisomers as ketoses with the same number of C atoms.

21.13 (*a*) ketohexose; L-sorbose.

21.15

```
      H
      |
      C=O
      |
   H——+——OH
      |
  HO——+——H
      |
  HO——+——H
      |
   H——+——OH
      |
      CH2OH
```

21.17 As in cyclopentane and cyclohexane, the bond angles are close to the tetrahedral angle.

21.19 *a*, *b*, *d*, *e*.

21.21

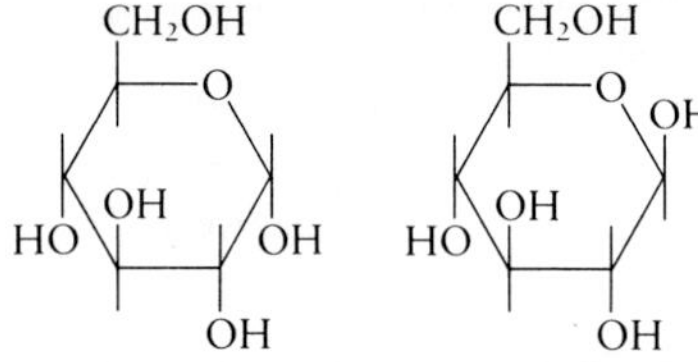

α-D-glucopuranose β-D-glucopyranose

21.23 (*a*) glucose; (*b*) β-1,6; (*c*) yes.

21.25 (*a*) Trisaccharide; (*b*) galactose, glucose, and fructose; (*c*) nonreducing sugar, since all the anomeric carbons are involved in the linkages joining the three monosaccharides.

21.27 A deficiency of the enzyme lactase, needed to break down lactose; lactose-containing foods such as dairy products.

21.29 Lactase-deficiency syndrome is most common among persons of African and Far Eastern origin, who are thus unable to digest the milk sugar present in dairy products.

21.31 H_2O_2 and gluconic acid.

21.33 (*a*) positive; (*b*) negative. See Color Plate 22.

21.35 Methanol and α-D-ribose (α-D-ribofuranose).

21.37 *c*, *d*, *e*, *f*, *g*.

21.39 No, because as in cellulose, the glucose units of cellobiose are joined by β-linkages.

21.41 No, because the glycosidic linkage involves the anomeric carbons of both glucose and fructose, meaning that neither ring can open up.

21.43 *b*.

21.45 Test the urine for the presence of galactose, a reducing sugar that would react with Benedict's solution but not with the glucose oxidase enzyme test strips. Explain that milk sugar contains galactose, meaning that all dairy foods must be avoided as well as foods containing free galactose such as peas and organ meats.

CHAPTER 22

22.1

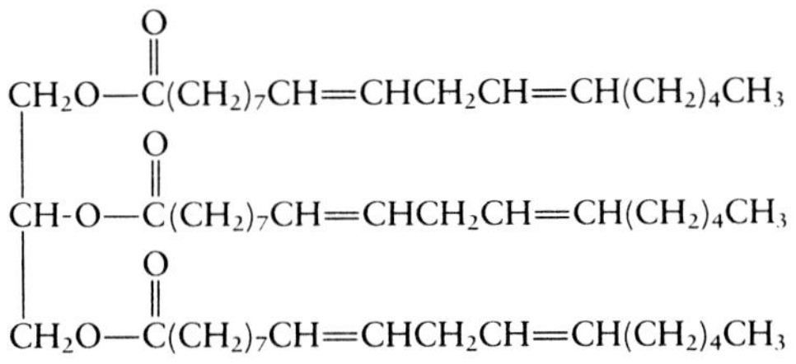

$$\begin{array}{l}
CH_2O-\overset{O}{\overset{\|}{C}}(CH_2)_7CH=CHCH_2CH=CH(CH_2)_4CH_3 \\
| \\
CH\text{-}O-\overset{O}{\overset{\|}{C}}(CH_2)_7CH=CHCH_2CH=CH(CH_2)_4CH_3 \\
| \\
CH_2O-\overset{O}{\overset{\|}{C}}(CH_2)_7CH=CHCH_2CH=CH(CH_2)_4CH_3
\end{array}$$

22.2

$$\begin{array}{l}
CH_2O-\overset{O}{\overset{\|}{C}}(CH_2)_7\underset{Br}{\underset{|}{C}}H\underset{Br}{\underset{|}{C}}HCH_2\underset{Br}{\underset{|}{C}}H\underset{Br}{\underset{|}{C}}H(CH_2)_4CH_3 \\
| \\
CH\text{-}O-\overset{O}{\overset{\|}{C}}(CH_2)_7\underset{Br}{\underset{|}{C}}H\underset{Br}{\underset{|}{C}}HCH_2\underset{Br}{\underset{|}{C}}H\underset{Br}{\underset{|}{C}}H(CH_2)_4CH_3 \\
| \\
CH_2O-\overset{O}{\overset{\|}{C}}(CH_2)_{14}CH_3
\end{array}$$

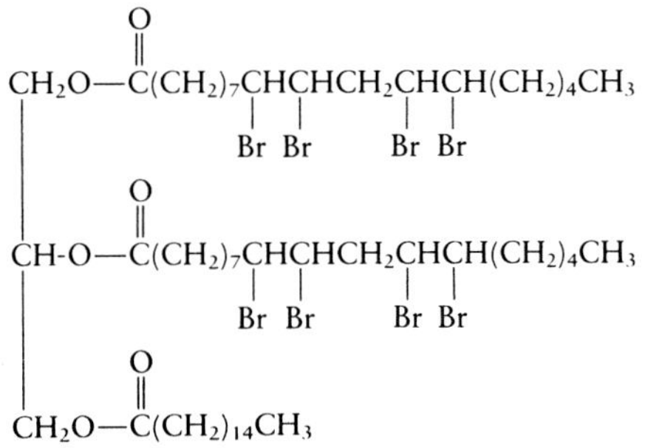

22.3 Linoleic acid and palmitic acid.
22.4 Glycolipid.
22.5 They are soluble in nonpolar solvents.
22.7 *c*, *e*, and *f* are lipids; *c* is a wax, *e* is a triacylglycerol fat, and *f* is a steroid; *a* is a ketotriose, dihydroxyacetone; *b* is a ketoheptose; *d* is glycerol.
22.9 (*a*) myrystic, stearic, oleic.

(*b*)

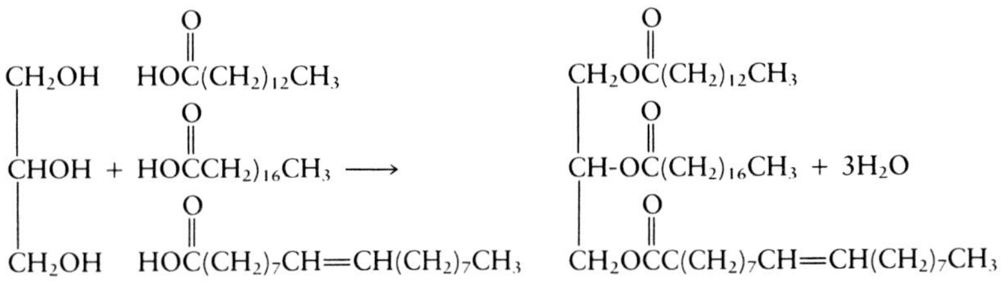

$$\begin{array}{llll}
CH_2OH & HO\overset{O}{\overset{\|}{C}}(CH_2)_{12}CH_3 & & CH_2O\overset{O}{\overset{\|}{C}}(CH_2)_{12}CH_3 \\
| & & & | \\
CHOH\ + & HO\overset{O}{\overset{\|}{C}}CH_2)_{16}CH_3 & \longrightarrow & CH\text{-}O\overset{O}{\overset{\|}{C}}(CH_2)_{16}CH_3\ +\ 3H_2O \\
| & & & | \\
CH_2OH & HO\overset{O}{\overset{\|}{C}}(CH_2)_7CH=CH(CH_2)_7CH_3 & & CH_2O\overset{O}{\overset{\|}{C}}C(CH_2)_7CH=CH(CH_2)_7CH_3
\end{array}$$

22.11 (*a*) $3H_2$; (*b*) palmitic acid; (*c*) linoleic acid.
22.13 Soybean oil because it contains 50 to 59% of the doubly unsaturated linoleic acid.

22.15

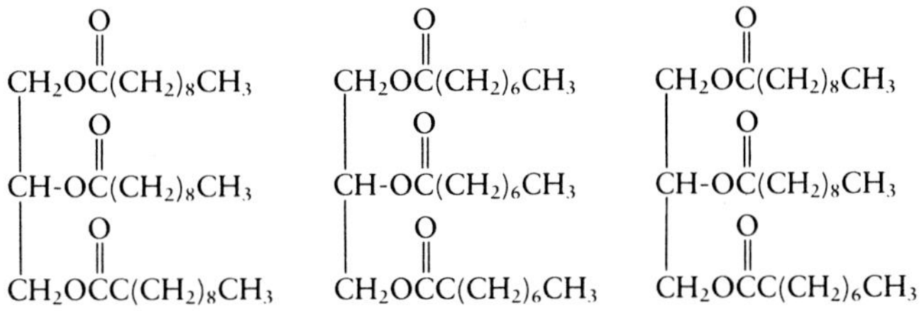

$$\begin{array}{lll}
CH_2O\overset{O}{\overset{\|}{C}}(CH_2)_8CH_3 & CH_2O\overset{O}{\overset{\|}{C}}(CH_2)_6CH_3 & CH_2O\overset{O}{\overset{\|}{C}}(CH_2)_8CH_3 \\
| & | & | \\
CH\text{-}O\overset{O}{\overset{\|}{C}}(CH_2)_8CH_3 & CH\text{-}O\overset{O}{\overset{\|}{C}}(CH_2)_6CH_3 & CH\text{-}O\overset{O}{\overset{\|}{C}}(CH_2)_8CH_3 \\
| & | & | \\
CH_2O\overset{O}{\overset{\|}{C}}C(CH_2)_8CH_3 & CH_2O\overset{O}{\overset{\|}{C}}C(CH_2)_6CH_3 & CH_2O\overset{O}{\overset{\|}{C}}C(CH_2)_6CH_3
\end{array}$$

$$\begin{array}{lll}
CH_2OC(=O)(CH_2)_8CH_3 & CH_2OC(=O)(CH_2)_8CH_3 & CH_2OC(=O)(CH_2)_6CH_3 \\
| & | & | \\
CH\text{-}OC(=O)(CH_2)_6CH_3 & CH\text{-}OC(=O)(CH_2)_6CH_3 & CH\text{-}OC(=O)(CH_2)_8CH_3 \\
| & | & | \\
CH_2OC(=O)C(CH_2)_6CH_3 & CH_2OC(=O)C(CH_2)_8CH_3 & CH_2OC(=O)C(CH_2)_6CH_3
\end{array}$$

22.17 Soybean oil.

22.19 95, peanut oil and 36 butter; the higher the iodine number, the greater the number of g I_2 absorbed by double bonds and the more unsaturated the fatty acids in the fat.

22.21 Reaction of oxidizing agents such as O_2 with unsaturated fatty acids in fat; addition of antioxidants such as the phenol derivatives BHA and BHT.

22.23 Arachidonic acid.

22.25 *b, d, f.*

22.27 Glycolipid, glucose.

22.29 *c*

22.31 (*a*) Steroid; (*b*) $C_{18}H_{24}O_2$.

22.33 Small water molecules can pass through the "pores," which are about 0.8 nm in diameter.

22.35 (*b*)

$$\begin{array}{lll}
CH_2OC(=O)R & CH_2OC(=O)R & R = \text{fatty acid chain} \\
| & | & \\
CH\text{-}OC(=O)OH & CH\text{-}OC(=O)R & \\
| & | & \\
CH_2OC(=O)OH & CH_2OC(=O)OH & \\
\text{monoglyceride} & \text{diglyceride} &
\end{array}$$

(*c*) emulsifier; (*d*) so that they will be solid.

22.37 Exposure to sunlight and from food sources such as fish liver oils or fortified milk.

22.39 They contain carotene, a precursor of vitamin A.

22.41 1 quart.

CHAPTER 23

23.1 $CH_3CH(CH_3)CH_2CH(NH_2)COOH$

2-amino-4-methylpentanoic acid, leucine

23.2 *b.*

23.3

Phenylalanine, $C_6H_5\text{—}CH_2CH(^+NH_3)C(=O)\text{—}O^-$

23.4

$$NH_2CH(CH_2C_6H_5)C(=O)\text{—}\boxed{OH + H}\text{—}N(H)CH(CH_2COOH)C(=O)OH \longrightarrow NH_2CH(CH_2C_6H_5)C(=O)\text{—}NHCH(CH_2COOH)C(=O)OH + H_2O$$

phe—asp

23.5 (*a*) 2 ala + 2 gly + glu + lys + arg (trp is usually destroyed and gln is converted to glu); (*b*) ala-ala-trp-gly-lys + gly-gln-arg.

23.6 Hydrogen bonding between hydroxyl groups.

23.7

(*a*) $HOCH(CH_3)CH(NH_2)C(=O)OH$, threonine

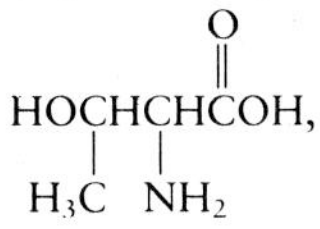

(*b*) $CH_3SCH_2CH_2CH(NH_2)C(=O)OH$, methionine

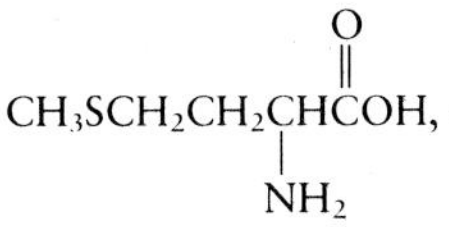

23.9 Glycine; there is no asymmetric C atom.

23.11 No, because it is a D-isomer (D-glutamic acid).

23.13

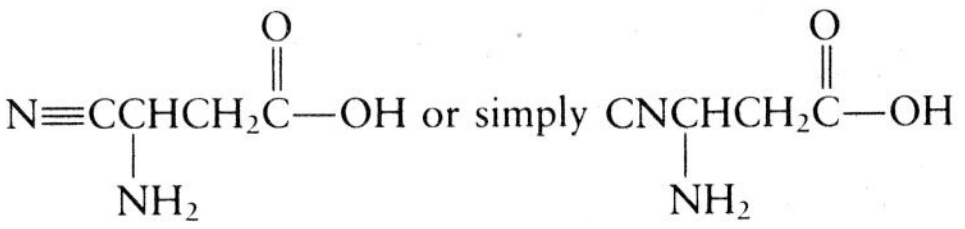

$N{\equiv}CCH(NH_2)CH_2C(=O){-}OH$ or simply $CNCH(NH_2)CH_2C(=O){-}OH$

23.15

$NH_2CH((CH_2)_4NH_2)C(=O){-}[OH + H]{-}NHCH((CH_2)_4NH_2)C(=O)OH \longrightarrow NH_2CH((CH_2)_4NH_2)C(=O)NH\ CH((CH_2)_4NH_2)C(=O)OH + H_2O$

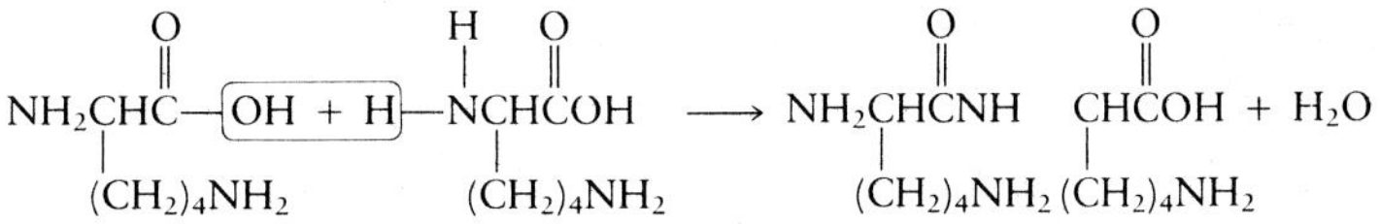

lysyllysine or lys—lys

23.17

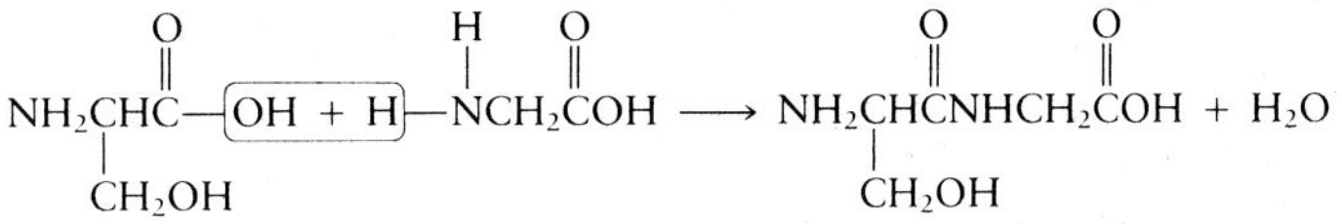

$NH_2CH(CH_2OH)C(=O){-}[OH + H]{-}NHCH_2C(=O)OH \longrightarrow NH_2CH(CH_2OH)C(=O)NHCH_2C(=O)OH + H_2O$

ser—gly

$NH_2CH_2C(=O){-}[OH + H]{-}NHCH(CH_2OH)C(=O)OH \longrightarrow NH_2CH_2C(=O)NHCH(CH_2OH)C(=O)OH + H_2O$

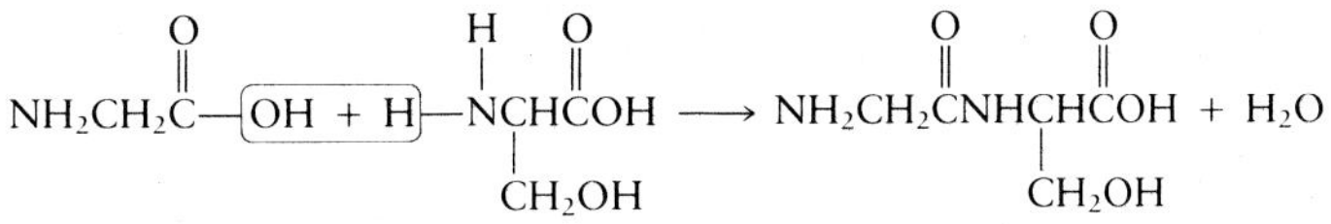

gly—ser

23.19 ser-leu-val, ser-val-leu; leu-ser-val, leu-val-ser; val-ser-leu, val-leu-ser.

23.21 (1) $CH_3CH(CH_3)CH(NH_2)C(=O)O^-$ (2) $CH_3CH(CH_3)CH(^+NH_3)C(=O)OH$ (3) $CH_3CH(CH_3)CH(^+NH_3)C(=O)O^-$

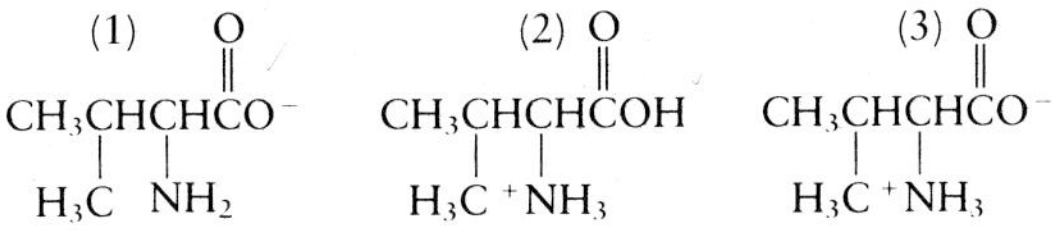

Structure (3) is present in neutral solution.

23.23

Threonine, $HOCH(CH_3)CH(^+NH_3)C(=O)O^-$

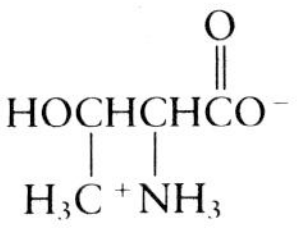

23.25 (*a*) 2ala + gly + lys + asp + glu; (*b*) phe + arg + thr + leu + ile.

23.27 All peptide linkages would be broken; trp would probably be destroyed, and the glutamine (gln) would appear as glutamic acid (glu).

23.29 ile-glu-phe, ile-phe-glu, glu-ile-phe, glu-phe-ile; phe-glu-ile, phe-ile-glu; phe-glu-ile, phe-ile-glu are still possible.

23.31

$$\begin{array}{l} \quad\quad\quad\ \ O \quad\quad\quad\quad\quad\ O \\ \quad\quad\quad\ \ \| \quad\quad\quad\quad\quad\ \| \\ NH_2CH_2C{-}N{-}CH{-}C{-}OH \\ \quad\quad\quad\ \ CH_2 \quad\ CH_2 \\ \quad\quad\quad\quad\ \ CH_2 \end{array}$$

gly—pro

There is no H atom on the amide N.

$$\begin{array}{l} \quad\quad\quad\quad\quad\ O \quad\quad\quad\quad\quad\quad\ O \\ \quad\quad\quad\quad\quad\ \| \quad\quad\quad\quad\quad\quad\ \| \\ NH{-}CH{-}C{-}\mathbf{NH}{-}CH_2C{-}OH \\ CH_2 \quad CH_2 \\ \quad\ CH_2 \end{array}$$

pro—gly

There is an H atom (in bold print) on the amide N.

23.33 Hydrogen bonds form between surrounding water molecules and the hydrophilic side chains on the spherical surfaces of globular proteins.

23.35 Hair contains much more cysteine than does silk.

23.37 See Table 23.7.

23.39 The ionic bonds between the side groups lysine and glutamic acid on neighboring helices of α-keratin are weakened in the presence of water.

23.41 Triple helix; components of connective tissues.

23.43 It helps to degrade the large amount of collagen present in less tender cuts of meat.

23.45 Protein 2 is egg white; lysine.

23.47 Fibrinogen is water-soluble. Fibrinogen is converted to insoluble fibrin which causes the blood to clot.

23.49 No; they are both deficient in lysine.

CHAPTER 24

24.1 Guanine and ribose.

24.2 (*a*) Uracil; (*b*) ribose; (*c*) 5′; (*d*) RNA.

24.3

$$\begin{array}{l} {-}P{-}D{-}P{-}D{-}P{-}D{-}P{-}D{-}P{-}D{-}P{-}D{-} \\ \quad\ \ |\quad\quad\ |\quad\quad\ |\quad\quad\ |\quad\quad\ |\quad\quad\ | \\ \quad\ \ A\quad\quad G\quad\quad G\quad\quad T\quad\quad C\quad\quad T \end{array}$$

or

$$\begin{array}{cccccc} \hline | & | & | & | & | & | \\ A & G & G & T & C & T \end{array}$$

24.4 GTCCCA.

24.5 CCATAG.

24.6

CCA AGA, CCA AGG, CCA AGC, CCA TCA, CCA TCG
CCT AGA, CCT AGG, CCT AGC, CCT TCA, CCT TCG
CCC AGA, CCC AGG, CCC AGC, CCC TCA, CCC TCG
CCG AGA, CCG AGG, CCG AGC, CCG TCA, CCG TCG
CCA AGT, CCC AGT, CCT AGT

24.7 mRNA, ACA GUG CCC; tripeptide, thr-val-pro; anticodons, UGU CAC GGG.

24.8 The same tripeptide would be produced since GGC and GGA both code for glycine.

24.9 Sugar and nitrogen base.

24.11 *a* and IV, *b* and II, *c* and I, *d* and III.

24.13 3′,5′ linkage that forms between the phosphate group of one nucleotide and the hydroxyl group on C 3′ of another.

24.15 DNA; the sugar is deoxyribose and one of the N bases is thymine which appears in DNA and not in RNA.

24.17 RNA exists in single strands and thus there are no base pairs.

24.19 The third available H atom on A is bonded to carbon rather than oxygen or nitrogen.

24.21

```
—D—P—D—P—D—P—D—P—D—P—D—     original strand
 |     |     |     |     |     |
 A     T     G     A     A     C
 ::    ::    :::   ::    ::    :::
 T     A     C     T     T     G
 |     |     |     |     |     |
—D—P—D—P—D—P—D—P—D—P—D—     complementary strand
```

24.23 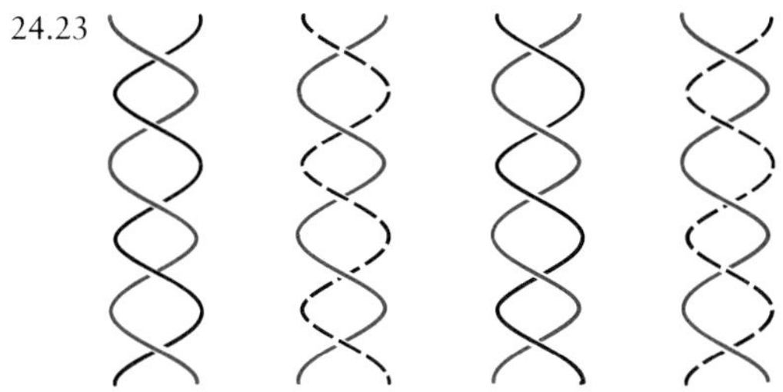

24.25 mRNA, rRNA, tRNA.

24.27 No.

24.29 No. Genes direct the synthesis of protein enzymes such as the one needed to degrade galactose.

24.31 The conversion of a sequence of N bases on mRNA to a sequence of amino acids.

24.33 A codon is a triplet of N bases on a mRNA strand. An anticodon is a triplet of N bases on one end of a tRNA molecule.

24.35 X-radiation can alter the structure of DNA, causing mutations.

24.37 CAU UUC, CAC UUU, CAC UUC.

24.39 (*a*) UGG CCC GAC UUG UUU AAG CC; (*b*) trp-pro-asp-leu-phe-lys; (*c*) ser-pro-asp-leu-phe-lys; (*d*) regrouped mRNA UGC CCG ACU UGU UUA AGC C would produce cys-pro-thr-cys-leu-ser; (*e*) *d*.

24.41 glu(GAA) $\longrightarrow$ val (GUA or GUU or GUC or GUG).

24.43 Uracil; no, since thymine has no amino substituent.

24.45 (See Figure 24.18, where the process of protein synthesis is summarized.)

24.47 A small circular DNA molecule. Plasmids can be readily removed from bacteria, modified, and put back into bacteria.

24.49 A protein thought to provide cells with an immunity from viral infections. The gene for the synthesis of an interferon can be combined with a bacterial plasmid and then introduced into the bacteria host for cloning.

CHAPTER 25

25.1

$$\text{2Glycine} \longrightarrow \text{gly-gly} \qquad \Delta G = 2.2 \text{ kcal}$$

$$\text{ATP} + H_2O \longrightarrow \text{ADP} + \text{P} \qquad \Delta G = -7.4 \text{ kcal}$$

ΔG overall $= -5.2$ kcal, yes.

25.2 No, since ΔG^0 for hydrolysis of creatine-P (-10.3 kcal/mol) has a larger negative value than that for the hydrolysis of ATP (-7.4 kcal/mol).

25.3 *a* and III, *b* and II, *c* and IV, *d* and I.

25.5 Catabolic: *b*, *f*; anabolic: *a*, *c*, *d*, *e*.

25.7 When $\Delta G < 0$, the reaction tends to proceed from reactants to products.

25.9 ΔG depends upon ΔS (entropy change) as well as ΔH.
25.11 *a* and *b*.
25.13 No.
25.15 +0.6 kcal, no.
25.17 *c*.
25.19 α-galactosidase is one name for this enzyme (which you probably guessed to be α-galactase).
25.21 Organic compounds that must be combined with proteins to form active enzymes.
25.23 The anemia may be caused by folic acid or vitamin B_{12} deficiency instead of iron deficiency.
25.25 NAD^+ (oxidized form) NADH (reduced form); $NADP^+$ (oxidized form) NADPH (reduced form).
25.27 Enzymes are highly specific and very efficient.
25.29 No, because most proteins are denatured and rendered inactive at temperatures above 55°C.
25.31 Dihydrofolate reductase; tetrahydrofolic acid; by reducing the formation of nitrogen bases needed to form the DNA needed for cell growth.
25.33 *b*.
25.35 (*a*) E_1; (*b*) IV.
25.37 Precursors of active enzymes; pepsinogen is the zymogen form of pepsin

CHAPTER 26

26.1 Aldehyde, carboxylic acid, oxidation.
26.3 Sucrose, lactose, and starch. Glucose is the main form in which cells utilize carbohydrates.
26.5 Much less (2 ATP compared with 38 ATP from complete oxidation of one glucose molecule).
26.7 Creatine~P, glycolysis, respiration.
26.9 *b*.
26.11 All foods enter respiration by first forming acetyl-CoA.
26.13 Respiration, mitochondria,; glycolysis, cytosol.
26.15 Niacin and riboflavin (vitamin B_2).
26.17 Citric acid, *cis*-aconitic acid, isocitric acid, oxalosuccinic acid.
26.19 Diabetes mellitus results from a lack of the hormone insulin and diabetes insipidus from a lack of antidiuretic hormone; both involve excessive output of urine, hence the name diabetes.
26.21 So that insulin level will not become too high, thereby causing hypoglycemia.
26.23 Eating a candy bar.
26.25 No, muscle glycogen produces glucose-1-P, which cannot be transported through the blood.
26.27 *b*, *c*, and *d*.
26.29 Glycogenesis: glucose $\longrightarrow$ glycogen; takes place when glucose is not needed for immediate energy. Gluconeogenesis: noncarbohydrate molecules $\longrightarrow$ glucose; takes place when there is not enough carbohydrate in the diet.
26.31 No, because glucagon raises blood glucose levels by stimulating the liver to product glucose from glycogen; in starvation there would be no glycogen reserve.

CHAPTER 27

27.1 7, 8.
27.2 0.48 ATP/g lauric acid (0.50 ATP/g palmitic acid).
27.3 $$7\text{Acetyl-CoA} + 12\ \text{NADPH} + 12\ \text{H}^+ \longrightarrow \text{myristic acid} + 7\text{CoA} + 12\text{NADP}^+$$
$$6\text{ATP} \curvearrowright 6\text{ADP} + 6\text{P}$$

27.5 Anabolic: *a, d;* catabolic: *b, c.*

27.7 They are absorbed directly into the blood stream.

27.9 (*a*) fatty acid; (*b*) acetyl-CoA; (*c*) mitochondria.

27.11 The four reactions by which the terminal two carbon segment of a fatty acid is converted to acetyl-CoA.

27.13 (*a*) 18; (*b*) 60; (*c*) 78.

27.15 (*a*) 28; (*b*) 84; (*c*) 112. 112 ATP/228g = 0.49 ATP/g myristic acid compared with 0.50 ATP/g palmitic acid.

27.17 Fatty acids are built up two C atoms at a time.

27.19 (*a*) 5; (*b*) 4; (*c*) 8.

27.21 All foods are converted to acetyl-CoA, which may then be used to synthesize fat.

27.23 The caloric value of all fats, animal or vegetable, is approximately the same.

27.25 By the formation of bile salts which are eliminated in the feces.

27.27 High cholesterol levels and abnormally high amounts of low-density lipoproteins are often found in the blood of patients with advanced atherosclerosis.

27.29 Acetone and acetoacetic acid.

27.31 Acetone is very volatile (boiling point = 56°C) and can readily evaporate from urine samples that are allowed to stand.

27.33 Ketosis.

CHAPTER 28

28.1 α-ketoglutaric acid and aspartic acid.

28.2

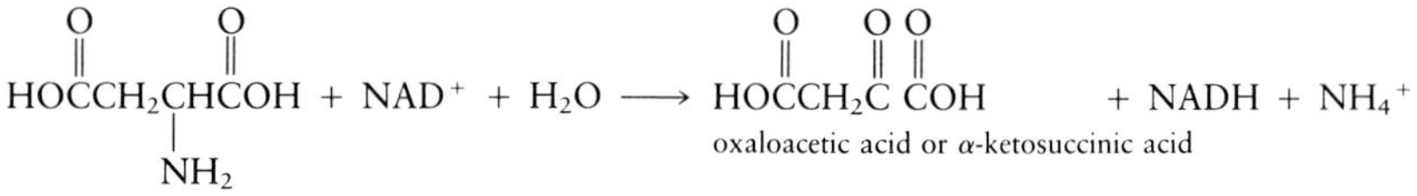

$$HO\overset{O}{\overset{\|}{C}}CH_2\underset{\underset{NH_2}{|}}{C}H\overset{O}{\overset{\|}{C}}OH + NAD^+ + H_2O \longrightarrow \underset{\text{oxaloacetic acid or } \alpha\text{-ketosuccinic acid}}{HO\overset{O}{\overset{\|}{C}}CH_2\overset{O}{\overset{\|}{C}}\overset{O}{\overset{\|}{C}}OH} + NADH + NH_4^+$$

28.3

$$\underset{\text{alanine}}{CH_3\underset{\underset{NH_2}{|}}{C}H\overset{O}{\overset{\|}{C}}OH} \longrightarrow CH_3CH_2NH_2 + CO_2$$

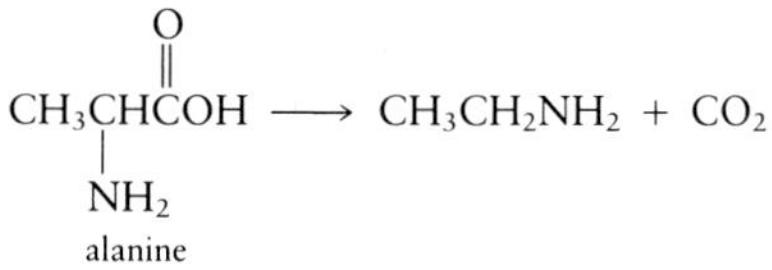

28.5 Hydrolysis of proteins.

28.7 Transamination: the transfer of an amino group from an amino acid to a ketoacid to form a new amino acid and a new ketoacid. Deamination: the conversion of an amino acid to a keto acid and ammonia.

28.9 Alanine.

28.11

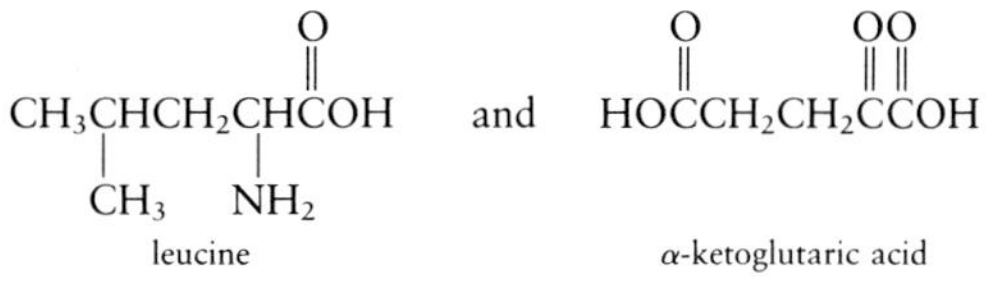

$$\underset{\text{leucine}}{CH_3\underset{\underset{CH_3}{|}}{C}HCH_2\underset{\underset{NH_2}{|}}{C}H\overset{O}{\overset{\|}{C}}OH} \quad \text{and} \quad \underset{\alpha\text{-ketoglutaric acid}}{HO\overset{O}{\overset{\|}{C}}CH_2CH_2\overset{O}{\overset{\|}{C}}\overset{O}{\overset{\|}{C}}OH}$$

28.13

$$CH_3\underset{\underset{H_3C}{|}}{C}H\underset{\underset{NH_2}{|}}{C}H\overset{O}{\overset{\|}{C}}OH + NAD^+ + H_2O \longrightarrow CH_3\underset{\underset{CH_3}{|}}{C}H\overset{O}{\overset{\|}{C}}\overset{O}{\overset{\|}{C}}OH + NADH + NH_4^+$$

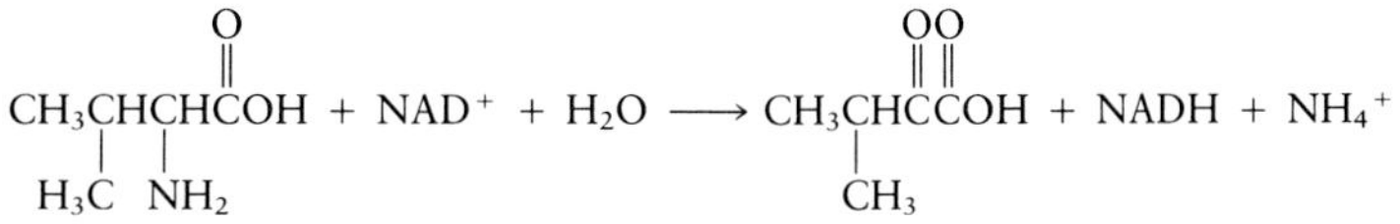

28.15 NH_4^+ and CO_2; urea, $NH_2\overset{O}{\overset{\|}{C}}NH_2$.

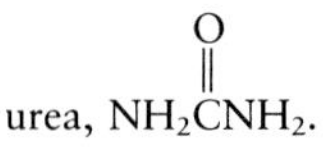

28.17

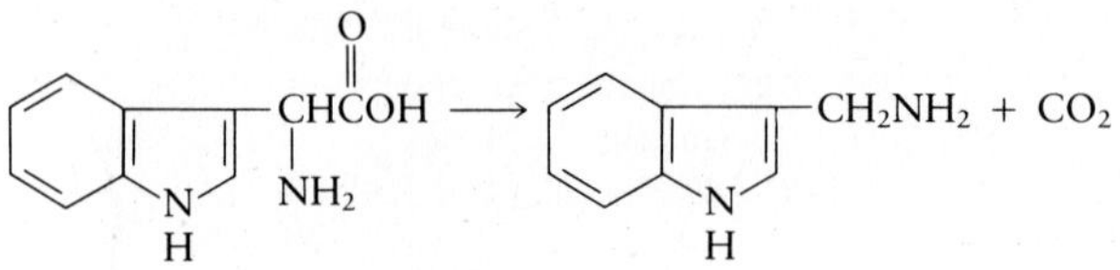

$$\text{(indol-3-yl)}\!-\!\underset{\displaystyle NH_2}{\underset{|}{C}}H\overset{\displaystyle O}{\overset{\|}{C}}OH \longrightarrow \text{(indol-3-yl)}\!-\!CH_2NH_2 + CO_2$$

28.19 Aged meat contains tyramine which elevates blood pressure and requires MAO to be degraded; any aged or fermented food.

28.21 Aspartame is the methyl ester of a dipeptide formed from phenylalanine and aspartic acid.

28.23 About 0.05×35 g $\approx$ 1.8 g phenylalanine consumed (assuming that protein is about 5% phenylalanine); only 0.27 g phenylalanine allowed.

28.25 Synthesis of homocysteine requires sulfur provided by methionine.

28.27 α-ketoisovaleric acid dehydrogenase; decarboxylation of α-keto acids, isoleucine and valine.

APPENDIX

A.1 10^{12}; 10^{-12}.

A.2 (*a*) 5×10^9; (*b*) 2.5×10^{-2}; (*c*) 6.7×10^{29}; (*d*) 8.5×10^{-19}.

A.3 (*a*) 6×10^{12}; (*b*) 2×10^2; (*c*) 6×10^{21}; (*d*) 3×10^{10}; (*e*) 2×10^{-9}.

A.4 (*a*) 1.6×10^6; (*b*) 3.0×10^{-22}.

B.1 (*a*) 1809; (*b*) 0.0010005; (*c*) 3.000×10^6; (*d*) 6000; (*e*) 4.30
???

B.2 (*a*) 17; (*b*) 1010; (*c*) 37; (*d*) 25.9

B.3 (*a*) 57; (*b*) 567.2; (*c*) 18,809.3

C.1 (*a*) $M = P/3$; (*b*) $PV/nT = R$; (*c*) $P = 3V - 8$; (*d*) $T_1 = \dfrac{T_2 \times P_1}{P_2}$

INDEX